Prepare for Exams with Lehmann's
New Interactive Video Lecture Series

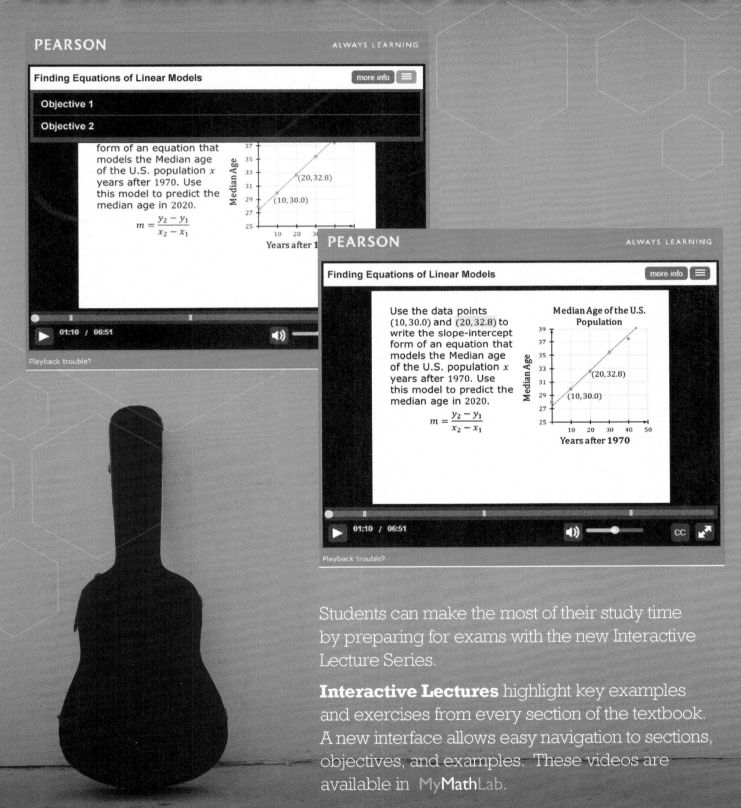

Students can make the most of their study time by preparing for exams with the new Interactive Lecture Series.

Interactive Lectures highlight key examples and exercises from every section of the textbook. A new interface allows easy navigation to sections, objectives, and examples. These videos are available in MyMathLab.

Jay Says...

Before writing my algebra series, it was apparent that my students couldn't relate to the applications in the course; they would repeatedly ask, "What is this good for?" To try to bridge that gap, I wrote some labs, which helped my students collect data, find models via curve fitting, and use the models to make estimates and predictions. My students really loved working with the current, compelling, and authentic data and experiencing how mathematics truly is useful.

My students' response was so strong that I decided to write an algebra series. Little did I know that, to realize this goal, I'd need to embark on a 15-year challenging journey, but the rewards of hearing such excitement from students and faculty across the country have made it all worthwhile! I'm proud to have played even a small role in raising people's respect and enthusiasm for mathematics.

I've tried to honor my inspiration: By working with authentic data, students can experience the power of mathematics. A random-sample study at my college suggests that I'm achieving this goal. The study concludes that students who used my series were more likely to feel that mathematics would be useful in their lives $(p = 0.0061)$ as well as in their careers $(p = 0.024)$.

In addition to curve fitting, my approach includes other types of meaningful modeling, directed-discovery explorations, conceptual questions, and, of course, a large bank of skill problems. The curve-fitting applications serve as a portal for students to see the usefulness of mathematics so that they become fully engaged in the class. Once involved, they're more receptive to all aspects of the course.

Jay Lehmann

Intermediate Algebra

Functions and Authentic Applications

Custom Edition for El Camino College
Math 73/80

Taken from:
Intermediate Algebra: Functions and Authentic Applications, Fifth Edition
by Jay Lehmann

Cover Art: Courtesy of Artville/Getty Images.

Taken from:

Intermediate Algebra: Functions and Authentic Applications, Fifth Edition
by Jay Lehmann
Copyright © 2015, 2011, 2008 by Pearson Education, Inc.
Boston, Massachusetts 02116

This special edition published in cooperation with Pearson Learning Solutions.

Pearson Learning Solutions, 501 Boylston Street, Suite 900, Boston, MA 02116
A Pearson Education Company
www.pearsoned.com

Printed in the United States of America

3 4 5 6 7 8 9 10 V0UD 18 17 16 15 14

000200010271884328

MS

ISBN 10: 1-269-87436-5
ISBN 13: 978-1-269-87436-6

Contents

PREFACE   ix
TO THE STUDENT   xv
ACKNOWLEDGMENTS   xvii
INDEX OF APPLICATIONS   xix

Prices of Air Jordans (pp. 1–2)

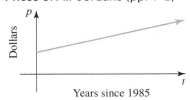

1 LINEAR EQUATIONS AND LINEAR FUNCTIONS   1

1.1   Using Qualitative Graphs to Describe Situations   1
1.2   Graphing Linear Equations   7
1.3   Slope of a Line   17
1.4   Meaning of Slope for Equations, Graphs, and Tables   26
1.5   Finding Linear Equations   35
1.6   Functions   43
CHAPTER SUMMARY   53
Key Points of Chapter 1   53
Chapter 1 Review Exercises   55
Chapter 1 Test   56

Percentages of American Adults Who Smoke (pp. 72–73)

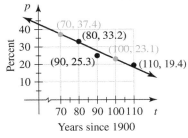

2 MODELING WITH LINEAR FUNCTIONS   58

2.1   Using Lines to Model Data   58
2.2   Finding Equations of Linear Models   69
2.3   Function Notation and Making Predictions   78
2.4   Slope Is a Rate of Change   92
Taking It to the Lab: Climate Change Lab • Used Car Lab • Golf Ball Lab • Walking Student Lab • Linear Model Lab: Topic of Your Choice   104
CHAPTER SUMMARY   110
Key Points of Chapter 2   110
Chapter 2 Review Exercises   112
Chapter 2 Test   113

U.S. Life Expectancies of Women and Men (pp. 115–116)

Year of Birth	Women (years)	Men (years)
1980	77.4	70.0
1985	78.2	71.1
1990	78.8	71.8
1995	78.9	72.5
2000	79.5	74.1
2005	79.9	74.9
2009	81.3	76.2

3 SYSTEMS OF LINEAR EQUATIONS   115

3.1   Using Graphs and Tables to Solve Systems   115
3.2   Using Substitution and Elimination to Solve Systems   125
3.3   Using Systems to Model Data   136
3.4   Value, Interest, and Mixture Problems   143
3.5   Using Linear Inequalities in One Variable to Make Predictions   155
3.6   Linear Inequalities in Two Variables; Systems of Linear Inequalities   167
Taking It to the Lab: Climate Change Lab • Sports Lab • Truck Lab   175
CHAPTER SUMMARY   177

Key Points of Chapter 3   177

Chapter 3 Review Exercises   180

Chapter 3 Test   182

Cumulative Review of Chapters 1–3   183

Average Ticket Prices to Major League Baseball Games (p. 213)

Year	Average Ticket Price (dollars)
1950	1.54
1960	1.96
1970	2.72
1980	4.45
1991	8.84
2000	16.22
2011	26.91

Safe Exposure Times to Music at Rock Concerts (p. 287)

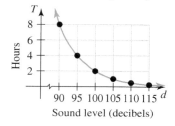

4 EXPONENTIAL FUNCTIONS   186

4.1   Properties of Exponents   186

4.2   Rational Exponents   199

4.3   Graphing Exponential Functions   206

4.4   Finding Equations of Exponential Functions   216

4.5   Using Exponential Functions to Model Data   224

Taking It to the Lab: Stringed Instrument Lab • Cooling Water Lab • Exponential Lab: Topic of Your Choice   237

CHAPTER SUMMARY   239

Key Points of Chapter 4   239

Chapter 4 Review Exercises   241

Chapter 4 Test   243

5 LOGARITHMIC FUNCTIONS   244

5.1   Composite Functions   244

5.2   Inverse Functions   255

5.3   Logarithmic Functions   267

5.4   Properties of Logarithms   274

5.5   Using the Power Property with Exponential Models to Make Predictions   282

5.6   More Properties of Logarithms   292

5.7   Natural Logarithms   299

Taking It to the Lab: China and India Populations Lab • Folding Paper Lab • Exponential/Logarithmic Lab: Topic of Your Choice   306

CHAPTER SUMMARY   307

Key Points of Chapter 5   307

Chapter 5 Review Exercises   310

Chapter 5 Test   312

Cumulative Review of Chapters 1–5   313

New-Home Sales Rates in July (p. 380)

Year	Sales Rate (thousands of homes per year)
2005	1348
2006	1030
2007	800
2008	479
2009	402
2010	289
2011	300
2012	381

6 POLYNOMIAL FUNCTIONS   316

6.1   Adding and Subtracting Polynomial Expressions and Functions   316

6.2   Multiplying Polynomial Expressions and Functions   327

6.3   Dividing Polynomials: Long Division and Synthetic Division   338

6.4   Factoring Trinomials of the Form $x^2 + bx + c$; Factoring Out the GCF   346

6.5   Factoring Polynomials   355

6.6   Factoring Special Binomials; A Factoring Strategy   362

6.7   Using Factoring to Solve Polynomial Equations   368

Taking It to the Lab: Climate Change Lab • Projectile Lab   382

CHAPTER SUMMARY   384

Key Points of Chapter 6   384
Chapter 6 Review Exercises   387
Chapter 6 Test   388

Bottled-Water Consumption
(p. 438)

Year	Bottled-Water Consumption (billions of gallons)
1990	2.2
1995	3.1
2000	4.7
2005	7.5
2009	10.6

7   QUADRATIC FUNCTIONS   390

7.1   Graphing Quadratic Functions in Vertex Form   390
7.2   Graphing Quadratic Functions in Standard Form   401
7.3   Using the Square Root Property to Solve Quadratic Equations   413
7.4   Solving Quadratic Equations by Completing the Square   425
7.5   Using the Quadratic Formula to Solve Quadratic Equations   431
7.6   Solving Systems of Linear Equations in Three Variables; Finding Quadratic Functions   442
7.7   Finding Quadratic Models   450
7.8   Modeling with Quadratic Functions   457
        Taking It to the Lab: Climate Change Lab • Projectile Lab • Projectile Lab (Using a CBR or CBL) • Water Flow Lab • Quadratic Lab: Topic of Your Choice   467
        CHAPTER SUMMARY   470
        Key Points of Chapter 7   470
        Chapter 7 Review Exercises   474
        Chapter 7 Test   476
        Cumulative Review of Chapters 1–7   477

Numbers of Internet Users
in the United States
(pp. 486–487)

Year	Number of Internet Users (millions)
2006	204
2007	212
2008	220
2009	228
2010	240

8   RATIONAL FUNCTIONS   479

8.1   Finding the Domains of Rational Functions and Simplifying Rational Expressions   479
8.2   Multiplying and Dividing Rational Expressions; Converting Units   491
8.3   Adding and Subtracting Rational Expressions   499
8.4   Simplifying Complex Rational Expressions   510
8.5   Solving Rational Equations   518
8.6   Modeling with Rational Functions   526
8.7   Variation   539
        Taking It to the Lab: Climate Change Lab • Illumination Lab • Boyle's Law Lab   553
        CHAPTER SUMMARY   555
        Key Points of Chapter 8   555
        Chapter 8 Review Exercises   558
        Chapter 8 Test   559

Percentages of Births "Despite
Contraception" (p. 610)

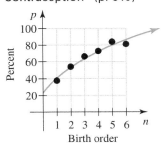

Birth order

9   RADICAL FUNCTIONS   561

9.1   Simplifying Radical Expressions   561
9.2   Adding, Subtracting, and Multiplying Radical Expressions   571
9.3   Rationalizing Denominators and Simplifying Quotients of Radical Expressions   579
9.4   Graphing and Combining Square Root Functions   586
9.5   Solving Radical Equations   593
9.6   Modeling with Square Root Functions   602
        Taking It to the Lab: Pendulum Lab   611

CHAPTER SUMMARY   612
Key Points of Chapter 9   612
Chapter 9 Review Exercises   614
Chapter 9 Test   615

Rates for Math Tutoring
(p. 619)

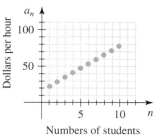

10   SEQUENCES AND SERIES   617

10.1   Arithmetic Sequences   617
10.2   Geometric Sequences   624
10.3   Arithmetic Series   630
10.4   Geometric Series   635
       Taking It to the Lab: Bouncing Ball Lab • Stacked Cups Lab   640
       CHAPTER SUMMARY   642
       Key Points of Chapter 10   642
       Chapter 10 Review Exercises   643
       Chapter 10 Test   644
       Cumulative Review of Chapters 1–10   644

Intercepts of an Ellipse
(pp. 669–670)

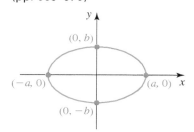

11   ADDITIONAL TOPICS   647

11.1   Absolute Value: Equations and Inequalities   647
       Key Points of Section 11.1   653
11.2   Performing Operations with Complex Numbers   655
       Key Points of Section 11.2   659
11.3   Pythagorean Theorem, Distance Formula, and Circles   660
       Key Points of Section 11.3   664
11.4   Ellipses and Hyperbolas   667
       Key Points of Section 11.4   673
11.5   Solving Nonlinear Systems of Equations   675
       Key Points of Section 11.5   679

Coordinate System (p. 681)

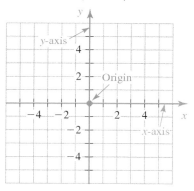

A   REVIEWING PREREQUISITE MATERIAL   681

A.1   Plotting Points   681
A.2   Identifying Types of Numbers   681
A.3   Absolute Value   682
A.4   Performing Operations with Real Numbers   683
A.5   Exponents   684
A.6   Order of Operations   684
A.7   Constants, Variables, Expressions, and Equations   685
A.8   Distributive Law   685
A.9   Combining Like Terms   685
A.10   Solving Linear Equations in One Variable   686
A.11   Solving Equations in Two or More Variables   688
A.12   Equivalent Expressions and Equivalent Equations   689

Tracing a Curve

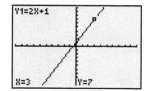

B   USING A TI-83 OR TI-84 GRAPHING CALCULATOR   *available online only*

B.1   Turning a Graphing Calculator On or Off
B.2   Making the Screen Lighter or Darker

B.3   Entering an Equation

B.4   Graphing an Equation

B.5   Tracing a Curve without a Scattergram

B.6   Zooming

B.7   Setting the Window Format

B.8   Plotting Points in a Scattergram

B.9   Tracing a Scattergram

B.10   Graphing Equations with a Scattergram

B.11   Tracing a Curve with a Scattergram

B.12   Turning a Plotter On or Off

B.13   Creating a Table

B.14   Creating a Table for Two Equations

B.15   Using "Ask" in a Table

B.16   Finding the Regression Curve for Some Data

B.17   Plotting Points in Two Scattergrams

B.18   Finding the Intersection Point(s) of Two Curves

B.19   Finding the Minimum Point(s) or Maximum Point(s) of a Curve

B.20   Storing a Value

B.21   Finding Any x-Intercepts of a Curve

B.22   Turning an Equation On or Off

B.23   Finding Coordinates of Points

B.24   Graphing Equations with Axes "Turned Off"

B.25   Entering an Equation by Using Y_n References

B.26   Responding to Error Messages

ANSWERS TO ODD-NUMBERED EXERCISES   690
INDEX   I-1

Preface

These words seem to suggest that poet and editor James Russell Lowell (1819–1891) took Intermediate Algebra. How many times have your students asked, "What is it good for?" After years of responding "You'll find out in the next course," I began an ongoing quest to develop a more satisfying and substantial response to my students' query.

Curve-Fitting Approach Although there are many ways to center an Intermediate Algebra course around authentic applications, I chose a curve-fitting approach for several reasons. A curve-fitting approach

- allows great flexibility in choosing interesting, authentic, current situations to model.
- emphasizes concepts related to functions in a natural, substantial way.
- deepens students' understanding of functions, because it requires students to describe functions graphically, numerically, symbolically, and verbally.
- unifies the many diverse topics of a typical Intermediate Algebra course.

  To fit a curve, students learn the following four-step modeling process:

1. Examine the data set to determine which type of model, if any, to use.
2. Find an equation of the model.
3. Verify that the model fits the data.
4. Use the model to make estimates and predictions.

This four-step process weaves together topics that are crucial to the course. Students must notice numerical patterns from data displayed in tables, recognize graphical patterns in scattergrams, find equations of functions, graph and evaluate functions, and solve equations.

Not only does curve fitting foster cohesiveness within chapters, but it also creates a parallel theme for each chapter that introduces and discusses a new function. This structure enhances students' abilities to observe similarities and differences among fundamental functions such as linear functions, exponential functions, and quadratic functions. The coverage of exponential functions directly follows that of linear functions so students can see the dual nature of these two functions (by comparing the slope addition property with the base multiplier property). In addition, logarithms can then be studied relatively early in the course, when students have plenty of energy to learn about an unfamiliar function.

Some students find it hard to stay interested, because they've "seen it all before" in Elementary Algebra. To address this issue, content that will be new to most students is presented in Sections 1.1, 1.4, and 1.6, as well as in most of Chapters 2–11. Section 1.1 sets the tone that this course will be different, interesting, alive, and relevant, inviting students' creativity into the classroom.

Throughout the text, the authentic applications serve as a portal for students to see the usefulness of mathematics so they become fully engaged in the class. Once involved, students are more receptive to all aspects of the course.

NEW TO THE FIFTH EDITION

Students will benefit from the following changes to the fifth edition of *Intermediate Algebra: Functions and Authentic Applications*:

- Section 5.1 on composite functions has been added.
- The text now has a section on dividing by monomials, dividing polynomials by using long division, and dividing polynomials by using synthetic division (Section 6.3).
- 27 labs have been added, including 8 Climate Change labs.
- The text now includes an additional 113 conceptual exercises.
- A subsection on converting units has been inserted in Section 10.2.
- 144 data sets in examples and exercises have been replaced with more compelling and current topics.
- 148 data sets in examples and exercises have been augmented to include values for recent years.
- Examples on solving general (literal) equations have been added to Sections 1.2, 1.4, 4.4, 5.4, 7.3, and 9.5.
- Grids have been added to most graphs of models so students can better line up inputs and outputs.
- New Interactive Video Lecture Series are available in MyMathLab.
- The quantity and quality of video lectures in MyMathLab have been increased.

CONTINUED FROM THE FOURTH EDITION

Modeling Exercises To give this fifth edition a current and lively feel, the vast majority of the hundreds of modeling exercises in the text have been updated or replaced. Most of the application exercises contain tables of data, but some describe data in paragraph form to give students practice in picking out relevant information and defining variables. Both types of applications are excellent preparation for subsequent courses (especially Statistics).

Functions This key concept is introduced early (Section 1.6) and is emphasized throughout the book, providing students with a solid foundation for subsequent courses such as Trigonometry, College Algebra, and Precalculus.

Group Explorations Almost all sections of this text contain one or two explorations that support student investigation of a concept. Instructors can use explorations as collaborative activities during class time or as part of homework assignments. Some explorations lead students to think about concepts introduced in the current section. Other, "Looking Ahead" explorations are directed-discovery activities that introduce key concepts to be discussed in the section that follows. The explorations empower students to become active explorers of mathematics and can open the door to the wonder and beauty of the subject.

Taking It to the Lab Sections Laboratory assignments have been included at the end of most chapters, to increase students' understanding of concepts and the scientific method. These labs reinforce the idea that mathematics is useful. They are also an excellent avenue for more in-depth writing assignments.

Some of the labs are about climate change and have been written at a higher reading level than the rest of the text in order to give students a sense of what it is like to perform research. Students will find that by carefully reading (and possibly rereading) the background information, they can comprehend the information and apply concepts they have learned in the course to make estimates and predictions about this compelling, current, and authentic situation.

Balanced Extensive Homework Sections   Most exercise sets contain a large number of modeling, skill, and conceptual exercises to allow professors maximum flexibility in setting assignments.

Related Review   These exercises (in every section of Chapters 4–11) relate current concepts to previously learned concepts. Such exercises assist students in seeing the "big picture" of the course.

Expressions, Equations, Functions, and Graphs   These exercises (in every section of Chapters 4–11) help students gain a solid understanding of those core concepts, including how to distinguish among them.

Technology   The text assumes students have access to technology such as the TI-83 or TI-84 graphing calculator. Technology of this sort allows students to create scattergrams and check the fit of a model quickly and accurately. It also empowers students to verify their results from Homework exercises and efficiently explore mathematical concepts in the Group Explorations.

The text supports instructors in holding students accountable for all aspects of the course without the aid of technology, including finding equations of models. (Regression equations are included in the Answers section, because it can be difficult or impossible to anticipate which points a student will choose in trying to find a reasonable equation.)

Appendix B: Using a TI-83 or TI-84 Graphing Calculator   Appendix B contains step-by-step instructions for using the TI-83 and TI-84 graphing calculators. A subset of this appendix can serve as a tutorial early in the course. In addition, when the text requires a new calculator skill, students are referred to the appropriate section in Appendix B, available online in MyMathLab and at http://www.pearsonhighered.com/mathstatsresources/.

Exposition   If students can't make sense of the prose, it doesn't matter how precise it is. One of my top goals is to write descriptions that are straightforward, accessible, clear, and rigorous.

Tips for Success   Many sections close with tips that are intended to help students succeed in the course. A complete listing of these tips is included in the Index.

Additional Topics Chapter   Topics typically taught in an Intermediate Algebra course that cannot be connected with a curve-fitting approach at the appropriate level are assembled in Chapter 11. Each section contains a Section Quiz feature. The union of these quizzes can be used as a set of review exercises for Chapter 11. Instructors who wish to "cut and paste" sections from that chapter into earlier chapters can append these quizzes to the appropriate Chapter Review exercises.

Appendix A: Reviewing Prerequisite Material   Appendix A can be used to remind students of important topics typically addressed in an Elementary Algebra course. Examples and exercises are included in each section.

RESOURCES FOR INSTRUCTORS

Instructor's Resource Manual   This manual contains suggestions for pacing the course and creating homework assignments. It discusses how to incorporate technology and how to structure lab and project assignments. The manual also contains section-by-section suggestions for presenting lectures and for undertaking the explorations in the text.

Instructor's Solutions Manual This manual includes complete solutions to the even-numbered exercises in the homework sections of the text.

MyMathLab® Online Course (access code required) MyMathLab from Pearson is the world's leading online resource in mathematics, integrating interactive homework, assessment, and media in a flexible, easy to use format.

MyMathLab delivers **proven results** in helping individual students succeed.

- MyMathLab has a consistently positive impact on the quality of learning in higher education math instruction. MyMathLab can be successfully implemented in any environment–lab-based, hybrid, fully online, traditional–and demonstrates the quantifiable difference that integrated usage has on student retention, subsequent success, and overall achievement.

- MyMathLab's comprehensive online gradebook automatically tracks your students' results on tests, quizzes, homework, and in the study plan. You can use the gradebook to quickly intervene if your students have trouble, or to provide positive feedback on a job well done. The data within MyMathLab is easily exported to a variety of spreadsheet programs, such as Microsoft Excel. You can determine which points of data you want to export, and then analyze the results to determine success.

MyMathLab provides **engaging experiences** that personalize, stimulate, and measure learning for each student.

- **Exercises:** The homework and practice exercises in MyMathLab are correlated to the exercises in the textbook, and they regenerate algorithmically to give students unlimited opportunity for practice and mastery. The software offers immediate, helpful feedback when students enter incorrect answers.

- **Multimedia Learning Aids:** Exercises include guided solutions, sample problems, animations, videos, and eText access for extra help at point-of-use.

- **Expert Tutoring:** Although many students describe the whole of MyMathLab as "like having your own personal tutor," students using MyMathLab do have access to live tutoring from Pearson, from qualified math and statistics instructors.

And, MyMathLab comes from an **experienced partner** with educational expertise and an eye on the future.

- Knowing that you are using a Pearson product means knowing that you are using quality content. That means that our eTexts are accurate and our assessment tools work. It means we are committed to making MyMathLab as accessible as possible.

- Whether you are just getting started with MyMathLab, or have a question along the way, we're here to help you learn about our technologies and how to incorporate them into your course.

To learn more about how MyMathLab combines proven learning applications with powerful assessment, visit www.mymathlab.com or contact your Pearson representative.

New Ready to Go courses provide students with all the same great MyMathLab features, but make it easier for instructors to get started. Both the Standard and Ready To Go courses include pre-made homework and quizzes, which are pre-assigned in the Ready To Go course to make creating a course even easier.

TestGen TestGen enables instructors to build, edit, print, and administer tests by using a computerized bank of questions developed to cover all the objectives of the text. TestGen is algorithmically based, allowing instructors to create multiple, but equivalent, versions of the same question or test with the click of a button. Instructors can also modify test bank questions or add new questions. Tests can be printed or administered online. The software and testbank are available for download from Pearson Education's online catalogue.

PowerPoint Lecture Slides (download only)   Available through www.pearsonhighered. com or inside your MyMathLab course, these fully editable lecture slides include definitions, key concepts, and examples for use in a lecture setting and are available for each section of the text.

RESOURCES FOR STUDENTS

New Interactive Video Lecture Series   This series has been completely revised to provide students with extra help for each section of the textbook. The Lecture Series includes:

- Interactive Lectures that highlight key examples and exercises for every section of the textbook.
- A new interface that allows easy navigation to sections, objectives, and examples.

These lectures are available in MyMathLab.

Student's Solutions Manual   This manual contains the complete solutions to the odd-numbered exercises in the Homework sections of the text.

GETTING IN TOUCH

I would love to hear from you and would greatly appreciate receiving your comments regarding this text. If you have any questions, please ask them, and I will respond.

Thank you for your interest in preserving the rose.

Jay Lehmann

MathNerdJay@aol.com

To the Student

You are about to embark on an exciting journey. In this course, you will learn not only more about algebra but also how to apply algebra to describe and make predictions about authentic situations. This text contains data that describe hundreds of situations. Most of the data have been collected from recent newspapers and Internet postings, so the information is current and of interest to the general public. I hope that includes you.

Working with authentic data will make mathematics more meaningful. While working with data about authentic situations, you will learn the meaning of mathematical concepts. As a result, the concepts will be easier to learn, because they will be connected to familiar contexts. And you will see that almost any situation can be viewed mathematically. That vision will help you understand the situation and make estimates and/or predictions.

Many of the problems you will explore in this course involve data collected in a scientific experiment, survey, or census. The practical way to deal with such data sets is to use technology. So, a graphing calculator or computer system is required.

Applying mathematics to authentic situations is a lifelong skill. In addition to working with data sets in this text, your instructor may assign some of the labs. Here you will collect data through experiment or research. This will give you a more complete picture of how you can use the approaches presented in this text in everyday life and possibly in your lifelong careers.

Hands-on explorations are rewarding and fun. This text contains explorations with step-by-step instructions that will lead you to *discover* concepts, rather than hear or read about them. Because discovering a concept is exciting, it is more likely to leave a lasting impression on you. Also, as you progress through the explorations, your ability to make intuitive leaps will improve, as will your confidence in doing mathematics. Over the years, students have remarked to me time and time again that they never dreamed that learning math could be so much fun.

Jay has a wide variety of interests. He is pictured here playing with his rock band, The Procrastinistas. (Photo courtesy of Rick Gilbert)

This text contains special features to help you succeed. Many sections contain a Tips for success feature. These tips are meant to inspire you to try new strategies to help you succeed in this course and future courses. Some tips might remind you of strategies that you have used successfully in the past but have forgotten. If you browse through all of the tips early in the course, you can take advantage of as many of them as you wish. Then, as you progress through the text, you'll be reminded of your favorite strategies. A complete listing of Tips for Success is included in the Subject Index.

Other special features that are designed to support you in the course include Warnings, which can help you avoid common misunderstandings; Key Points summaries, which can help you review and retain concepts and skills addressed in the chapter you have just read; Related Review exercises, which can help you understand current concepts in the context of previously learned concepts; and Expressions, Equations, Functions, and Graphs exercises, which can help you understand and distinguish among these four core concepts.

I have also included a review of key concepts from Elementary Algebra in Appendix A. Before or shortly after the course begins, consider reading this appendix and completing the exercises. If you need more review, refer to an Elementary Algebra text or ask your instructor or a tutor.

Feel free to contact me. It is my pleasure to read and respond to e-mails from students who are using my text. If you have any questions or comments about the text, feel free to contact me, through e-mail or the website www.pearsonhighered.com/lehmannseries.

Jay Lehmann
MathNerdJay@aol.com

Acknowledgments

Writing a modeling text is an endurance run I couldn't have completed without the dedicated assistance of many people. First, I'm greatly indebted to Keri, my wife, who yet again served as an irreplaceable sounding board for the multitude of decisions that went into creating this book. In particular, I credit her internal divining rod in selecting captivating data from a mound of data sets I've collected.

I've received much support from the following professors: Ken Brown, Gary Church, Jon Freedman, Eric Freidenreich, Jenny Freidenreich, Cheryl Gregory, Rick Hough, Evan Innerst, and Tadashi Tsuchida. Over the years, they've given much sound advice in responding to my countless e-mail inquiries.

And thanks to Rick Gilbert for the awesome photograph in the "To the Student" section of the author performing with his band, The Procrastinistas, at the Hotel Utah in San Francisco.

I acknowledge several people at Pearson Education. I'm very grateful to Editor-in-Chief Michael Hirsch, who has shared in my vision for this text and has made significant investments to make that vision happen. The book has been greatly enhanced through the support of Senior Acquisitions Editor Dawn Giovanniello, who has made a multitude of contributions, including assembling an incredible team to develop and produce this text. The team includes Senior Content Editor Lauren Morse, who handled countless tasks to support me in preparing the manuscript for production, leading to a significantly better book.

Heartfelt thanks goes to Integra's Associate Managing Editor Allison Campbell, who orchestrated the many aspects of production.

I thank these reviewers, whose thoughtful, detailed comments helped me sculpt this text into its current form:

Ken Anderson, *Chemeketa Community College*
Gwen Autin, *Southeastern Louisiana University*
Sam Bazzi, *Henry Ford Community College*
Joel Berman, *Valencia Community College—East*
Nancy Brien, *Middle Tennessee State University*
Barbara Burke, *Hawaii Pacific University*
Paula Castagna, *Fresno City College*
Jeff Cohen, *El Camino College*
Joseph DeGuzman, *Norco College*
William P. Fox, *Francis Marion University*
Cathy Gardner, *Grand Valley State University*
James Gray, *Tacoma Community College*
Kathryn M. Gundersen, *Three Rivers Community College*
Stephanie Haynes, *Davis & Elkins College*
Rick Hough, *Skyline College*
Denise Hum, *Cañada College*
Evan Innerst, *Cañada College*
Judy Kasabian, *El Camino College*
Julianne M. Labbiento, *Lehigh Carbon Community College*
Diane Mathios, *De Anza College*
Jane E. Mays, *Grand Valley State University*
Scott McDaniel, *Middle Tennessee State University*
Tim Merzenich, *Chemeketa Community College*
C.R. Messer, *American River College*
Jason L. Miner, *Santa Barbara City College*
Nolan Mitchell, *Chemeketa Community College*

Camille Moreno, *Cosumnes River College*
Charlie Naffziger, *Central Oregon Community College*
Donna Marie Norman, *Jefferson Community College*
Denise Nunley, *Glendale Community College*
Ernest Palmer, *Grand Valley State University*
Jody Rooney, *Jackson Community College*
James Ryan, *State Center Community College District, Clovis*
Ingrid Scott, *Montgomery College*
John Szeto, *Southeastern Louisiana University*
Janet Teeguarden, *Ivy Tech Community College*
Lorna TenEyck, *Chemeketa Community College*
Ollie Vignes, *Southeastern Louisiana University*
Lisa Winch, *Kalamazoo Valley Community College*

Index of Applications

A

acoustics
decibel levels, 287
fret position on bass guitar, 237
guitar string vibration, 549, 550
hearing loss and, 287
loudness, 272–73
tuning fork frequency, 560

aeronautics
calcium loss in weightless environment, 287
weight of astronaut, 545–46, 549

agriculture
farmers markets, 114
gross domestic product ranks, 382–83
vs. gross national product, 235
opium cultivations, 389
value of farmland, 336

air travel
airline fuel prices, 454
airline revenue from fees, 591, 601
Alaska Air Group profits, 68–69
altitude of plane after takeoff, 6
Americans flying to Europe, 93
bird strikes, number of, 69–70
charter flight, 461–62, 466
climbing steepness, 24
coach and first-class ticket pricing, 153
distance traveled by airplane, 86, 103
domestic commercial airline boardings, 89
laser incidents, 304–5
to Mars, 287
near collisions on runways, 227
unruly airline passengers, 74
weight of astronaut, 545–46, 549

archaeology
dating of mummy, 291
dating wood tool, 291
mummified bull, 313

art
painting frame, 381, 389

astronomy
period of planet, 578

B

biology
bacterial growth, 287
calcium loses in weightless environment, 287
half-life of substances in bloodstream, 290–91, 517
nerve conduction in muscles, 549

business
advertising
budget, 552
cost of, 4
creativity, 549
Internet, 143, 380
revenue from, 380
sales and, 4
television, 186
Apple stores, number of, 70–72
automobile consumers, 6
board member compensation, 568, 599
bond rating of, 379
brewery openings, 101
company value, 86
costs
to of advertising, 4
of CD production, 527–28, 534
of employee, 85
of manufacturing, 560
days sales of inventory (DSI), 185
depreciation of cars, 142
drug testing, 6
employment
Twitter, 288
working women, 396
female bosses, 91
Ford's U.S. market shares, 143
fraud complaints by consumers, 243
gift cards, 289
health care benefits, 525
market share of eBooks, 230
market shares of cholesterol drugs, 165
market shares of manufacturing output, 326, 460, 462
mileage rates for, 113
music store, 144–45
net incomes of oil companies, 608–9
oil production, 102
paid vacation days and holidays, 453
prices
of Air Jordans, 1–2
of airline fuel, 454
of pizzas, 551
for tickets, 145–47, 152–53
profit
of Alaska Air Group, 68–69
rate of change, 95–96, 250–51
rental by
of conference room, 559
of trucks, 155, 162–63, 164, 177, 314
retail sales, 100, 236
revenues
from adult mattresses, 423
from airline fees, 591, 601
from album sales, 152, 252
of Amazon, 198
annual, 103
from boats and accessories, 440
from books, CDs, and DVDs, 183
from breathalyzers, 287
from cell phone ringtones, ringbacks, and videos, 423
from couch sales, 252
of IKEA, 73–74
of Kodak, 91
of Lipitor and Nexium, 99
of Microsoft, 457–58
from music downloads, 165, 253, 489
from portable media and MP3 players, 611
of recorded music, 1, 49, 165
of restaurants, 374–75
from textbooks, 535
of Whole Foods Market, 315
salaries
annual increases, 33, 42
of college presidents, 112
of major league baseball players, 1, 244, 289
of professors, 81–82, 101, 336–37
vs. time at company, 33, 42
sales
advertising budget and, 4
annual, 242
of books, 183, 230, 231, 535
of CDs, 527–28, 534
of electronic cigarettes, 287
of Encyclopedia Britannica, 232
of energy drinks, 101
of guitar strings, 144–45
of The Kills albums, 252
of Lipitor and Nexium, 99
of men's skin care products, 100
of new homes, 440
of paper shredders, 99
of portable MP3 players, 611
of Radiohead CDs, 4
retail, 100, 236
of smartphones, 97–98
of tickets, 145–47, 152–53, 183
of vehicles, 534
shredder models, 99
Starbucks stores, 232–33
TiVo® subscribers, 231
unions, 379–80, 478
weekly income, 85

C

chemistry
half-life, 231–32, 235, 242, 290–91, 312, 313
radiation, 549
solutions
acid, 149–50, 154
alcohol, 150–51, 154
antifreeze, 154, 183
pH of, 273

communications. *See also* computers and computing
cell phone bill, 316, 336
cell phone ringtones, ringbacks, and videos, revenue from, 423
e-mail messages sent worldwide daily, 259
e-mails received *vs.* time to read, 55
fixed lines *vs.* cell-phone subscriptions, 123, 140, 181
long-distance calling, 101
rumor spreading, 230, 287
smartphone sales, 97–98
texting multiple times per day, 62–64
Twitter employees, 288

computers and computing
Apple stores, number of, 70–72
ATMs, 387–88
BlackBerry subscribers, 303
broadband cable and DSL subscribers, 530–31
digital data storage, 456
e-mails received *vs.* time to read, 55
Google, 230
households with Internet access *vs.* broadband, 123, 140
households with personal computers, 264
Internet advertisers, 143, 380
Internet news sources, 475–76
Internet users, 67, 486–87, 522–23
Pandora Radio, 230
personal information into a pop-up, 476
personal profile page, 68
prank e-mail, 236
spam e-mails, 561, 591, 600–601
wireless Internet users, 232
at work, 458–60
world Internet population, 336
Zimride users, 242

construction
of fencing, 407–9, 411, 412, 466, 475
LEED-certified green buildings, 244, 288

consumer behavior
fraud complaints, 243

contests. *See* games and contests

crime. *See also* law and law enforcement
crime indexes, 77
economy and, 77
ex-convicts re-arrested, 609–10
executions from the death penalty, 99
paper shredder models, 99

D

demographics. *See also* population
adopted children separated from foster parents, 609
births
despite contraception, 610
outside marriage, 75, 88, 252, 264
U.S. population foreign born, 6
deaths
from heart disease, 389
infant mortality, 283–84
from lightning, 234–35
number of cremations, 264–65
from police action in South Africa, 410
foreign born living in California, 455–56, 465
foreign children adopted by American families, 184–85, 288, 419
height
of boy at certain age, 616
of person at certain age, 6
of woman, 498
immigrants living in United States, 398
life expectancy
at birth, 75, 89
of females at birth and age 20, 171–73
by gender, 115–16, 137, 165
of males at birth and age 20, 174
living alone, 536
marriages
married couples, 123
median ages at first, 465
median ages of men's first, 2
support of gay, 67
median heights of boys, 616

distance. *See also* height; length
braking, 326
descent of hot-air balloon, 16, 33, 86
driving time, 6, 16, 33, 531–33, 537, 559, 560
from home, 56
to horizon, 584
of lightning, 549
reaction, 326
skidding, 570
stopping, 325–26, 549
between student and wall, 109
vs. time, 94–95, 103, 114, 549
traveled by airplane, 86, 103

E

economics
bills paid by checks *vs.* online payments, 122–23
crime and economy, 77
federal debt, 234, 423
GNP, 235, 382–83
households with outstanding student debt, 410, 463
inflation, 291–92

percentages of Americans living below the poverty level, 68
percentages of Americans who own car, 6
transaction demand, 548–49
unemployment rate, 100

education
age *vs.* mental functioning test scores, 141
AP tests administered, 204–5
bachelor's degrees, 536–37
charges for supplies and field trips, 533, 601
compensation of college presidents, 253
cost of, 549
dentistry degrees earned by women, 66
early decision, 289–90
enrollment at college
by gender, 322–23
in intermediate algebra, 76–77, 90–91
Iraqi student, 287
men *vs.* all students, 489, 525
private, for-profit, 232
rate of, 33–34
textbook revenues, 535
graduation party, 466
high school reunion costs, 534
history test scores, 91
households with outstanding student debt, 410, 463
interest rates for subsidized student loans, 65
math tutor charges, 607
men's colleges, 232
minority college students, 456
National Assessment of Educational Progress test, 91
new-textbook sales, 231
No Child Left Behind Act, 91
number of colleges, 535–36
public school per-student expenditures, 91
salaries of professors, 81–82, 101, 112–13, 336–37
satellite college, 152
student fees, 100
student loans defaulted on, 84
student-to-faculty ratios, 411
textbook revenues, 535
tuition
costs, 549
and fees at Lehigh Carbou Community College, 100
at Princeton Day School, 601
at Princeton University, 313
at Triton College, 100

electricity
current, 549
natural gas *vs.* coal, 143

electronics
cigarettes, 287
households with VCRs, 379
intensity of TV signal, 550

energy
coal exports, United States, 379

electricity, natural gas *vs.* coal, 143
from ethanol plants, 114, 211, 287
from fossil fuels, 105–6
nuclear power plant capacities, 204
oil production, 102
solar panels manufactured/installed, 455, 464–65
solar power installed in United States, 204
wind, 466

entertainment. *See also* leisure and recreation; music
adults who watch cable television, 604–5, 606
Broadway show attendance, 380
cable channels per household, 231
cable television *vs.* major networks, 143
gambling, online *vs.* casino, 141
Halloween party attendance, 233
high school reunion costs, 534
households with VCRs, 379
monthly bills for pay-TV, 608
movie attendance, 265
online video *vs.* online radio, 164–65
television price, 74
television ratings of World Series and of prime-time shows, 181
ticket prices, 145–47, 152–53
TiVo® subscribers, 231
World Series of Poker, 287

environment
carbon dioxide emissions, 105–7, 175–76, 382–83, 467–68, 553
Chernobyl nuclear accident, 226
clarity of Lake Tahoe, 182–83
Crater Lake formation, 285
LEED-certified green buildings, 244, 288
recycling, 101
timber harvests, 287
U.S. natural catastrophes, 231

F

finance. *See also* business; investments
average annual expenditures, 410–11
bank tellers and ATMs, 387–88
bills paid by checks *vs.* online payments, 122–23
car values, 42, 138–39, 142, 164
charges for supplies and field trips, 533, 601
company value, 86
costs
of car repairs *vs.* age, 6
of conference room rental, 559
to manufacture bikes, 560

mean, per person, 534
of pencils, 5
of school photos, 552
of state corrections, 333–34
credit card debt, 615
credit scores, 265
depreciation of cars, 142
dollar conversions, 252
federal debt, 234, 423
income
annual and federal taxes paid, 6, 252
household, 534–35
personal, 113, 143
personal, spent on food, 102
weekly, 85
inflation, 291–92
interest
compounded annually, 147–49, 153–54, 225, 231, 242, 311
from investment, 147, 182, 185, 282–83, 286–87, 478
for subsidized student loans, 65
interest-bearing accounts, 148–49, 153–54, 231, 236
online bill paying, 100
prices
of airline fuel, 454
of athletic shoes, 1–2
of gasoline, 479, 535
of gold bar, 56
of ounce of gold, 242, 454
of pizzas, 551
of ski rental packages, 75, 89
of television, 74
of tickets, 145–47, 152–53
retail sales, 100, 236
retirement, saving for, 100
revenue
from album sales, 152, 252
from books, CDs, and DVDs, 183
from cell phone ringtones, ringbacks, and videos, 423
from couch sales, 252
from music downloads *vs.* audio CD sales, 165
from portable media and MP3 players, 611
from recorded music, 1, 49, 489
of restaurants, 374–75
from U.S. adult mattresses, 423
salaries
of major league baseball players, 1, 244, 289
of professors, 81–82
vs. time at company, 33, 42
tax on cigarettes, 440
tax returns filed electronically, 66

food and nutrition
Barbara's Puffins Cinnamon Cereal, 498
bottled water consumption, 438, 529

food and nutrition (*continued*)
brewery openings, 101
buying Milky Way bars, 101
chicken and red meat
consumption, 122, 140,
325, 559
cup of coffee cost, 139
DairyCo milk, 498
disposable personal incomes
spent on, 102
farmers markets, 114
french fries consumed, 252
ice cream consumption
rate, 91–92
making lasagna, 6
McDonald's restaurants, 610
milk consumption, 141, 165,
325, 537
Nutrisystem *vs.* Weight
Watchers costs, 142–43
peach, bacteria on, 287
pickles and IQ, 230
pizza cost, 103–4, 551
pizza weight, 551
sodium in chili, 560
soft drinks consumption, 141,
325
spaghetti sauce, 498
tomato juice and hair loss, 287
forestry
deforestation *vs.* species in
existence, 6
leaves on trees, 243, 311
timber harvests, 287

G

games and contests
darts, 6
poker, 287
gardens
dimensions of, 375–76, 380
fencing around, 407–9, 411,
412, 475
mulching, 375–76, 380
sod coverage, 380
geology
continental ice sheet, 291
Outer Continental Shelf
(OCS), 102
tsunamis, 570, 609
volcanic eruption, 285
geometry
angle of hands on clock, 6
area of circle, 6
diameter of balloon, 6
rectangle dimensions, 375–76,
380–81, 388, 389, 411–12,
466, 475, 552
sphere volume, 549
government
Americans for Prosperity, 305
classified federal documents, 74
defense spending, 98, 398
FBI background checks, 310
federal debt, 234, 284–85, 423
federal tax code, 91
First Amendment rights,
113–14

first-class mail volumes, 89, 101
Food Stamp Program, 488–89
Internal Revenue Service
(IRS) standard mileage
rate, 113
laws enacted by Congress, 100
National Assessment of
Educational Progress
test, 91
No Child Left Behind Act, 91
number of filibusters, 464
soldiers unavailable for
combat, 74

H

health
births despite contraception,
610
blood donations to American
Red Cross, 91
Children's Health Insurance
Program (CHIP), 91
cholesterol drugs, 165
community centers, 560
diabetes, 75–76, 91, 253
electronic cigarette sales, 287
flu epidemic, 230
Gold's Gym payment
options, 143
health care coverage, 560
hearing loss, 287
heart attack risk, 233–34
heart disease deaths, 389
high cholesterol, 450–51
HIV cases, 478
insurance costs, 525
lightning deaths, 234–35
Lipitor and Nexium sales, 99
national spending on, 311
obese adults, 398
opioid addiction, 478
polio cases, 288
pregnancy rates, 398
private health insurance
spending, 232
seniors with severe memory
impairment, 289
shingles, 538
smoking, 6, 72–73, 83, 101, 164,
454
synthetic narcotic prescriptions,
388
tuberculosis cases in the
U.S., 315
weight-loss program
promotions, 142–43
height
apparent, 550–51
of balloon, 86
of baseball hit, 410, 441, 475,
476
boys median, 616
of cable, 305
of German stein, 498
of golf ball after dropping, 539,
546
nerve conduction, 549
of person at certain age, 6

of racquetball after dropping,
550
of sheer cliff, 549
of softball tossed vertically,
468–69
of stone thrown from cliff, 410
of stone thrown in air, 441
of tennis ball, 6, 463, 541
of water in cylinder, 469–70
of woman, 498

I

insurance
health, costs, 525
life, 233, 290
private health, 232
investments. *See also* finance
bond rating, 379
compounded annually, 225, 242,
282–83, 286–87
doubling of, 231
households owning stocks,
608
interest from, 147, 153–54, 182,
185, 231, 311, 478
retirement, saving for, 100

L

law and law enforcement. *See*
also crime
costs of state corrections,
333–34
deaths from police action in
South Africa, 410
enacted by Congress, 100
ex-convicts re-arrested, 609–10
executions from the death
penalty, 99
prisoner turnover, 525
women police officers, 440
leisure and recreation. *See also*
entertainment
amusement park costs, 104
audio podcast, listening to, 101
beach house rental, 490
boating fatalities, 411
Broadway show attendance,
380
bus charters, 465, 533
Halloween party, 233
high school reunion costs, 534
little league participants, 74
paid vacation days and
holidays, 453
party boat, 466, 476
passports, Americans with, 74
playing darts, 6
ski run steepness, 24, 57
theater ticket prices, 139,
152–53, 182, 315
theme and amusement park
cost, 104
ticket prices for Walt Disney
Resort, 101, 312
vacations in July, 454–55
visitors to Grand Canyon,
58–61, 64–65
water leaking into boat, 558

length
recommended ski, 174–75
of rubber band, 311–12
of striped bass, 74

M

media
adults who watch cable
television, 604–5, 606
monthly bills for pay-TV, 608
newspapers
circulations, 141–42
morning and evening, 536
purchases of, 411
trust in, 99
news sources, 475–76
Super Bowl television
advertising, 3, 186, 236
TiVo® subscribers, 231
medicine
cancer treatment, 232
cholesterol drugs, 165
heart attack risk, 233–34
laser eye surgery, 6
Lipitor and Nexium sales, 99
opioid addiction, 478
polio cases, 288
private health insurance
spending, 232
radiation treatment, 549
shingles, 538
synthetic narcotic prescriptions,
388
thallium-201 injection, 232
meteorology
atmospheric pressures, 101,
102–3
lightning deaths, 234–35
military
defense spending, 98
Department of Defense
spendings, 398
female troops in Iraq and
Afghanistan, 608
multiple tours of duty in Iraq
and Afghanistan, 475
soldiers unavailable for
combat, 74
miscellaneous
adoptions, 184–85, 288
Americans who are very happy,
390, 423
ball bearing radii and masses,
559
folded paper thickness, 307
ISO paper-size system, 584–85
mountain bike manufacturing
costs, 560
pen and notebook costs, 139
rubber band length *vs.* weight
relationship, 311–12
rug dimensions, 380
specialty bicycle stores, 452
Valentine's Day celebration,
464
words typed, 552
mixtures
acid solutions, 149–50, 154

alcohol solutions, 150–51, 154
antifreeze solution, 154, 183
motor vehicles. *See also*
    transportation; travel
    bicyclists hit and killed by, 185
    buying Honda Accord with
        cash, 142
    car values, 42, 138–39, 142, 164
    depreciation of cars, 142
    ethanol production for, 287
    Ford's U.S. market shares, 143
    fuel consumption, 479, 535
    fuel efficiency of domestic/
        imported cars, 141
    gasoline consumption, 33,
        96–97, 100–101, 112, 479
    gasoline mileage, 252, 498
    gasoline prices, 479, 535
    gasoline sale, 498
    gasoline taxes, 90, 253–54
    General Motors U.S. market
        shares, 143
    Honda Civic CX purchases, 6
    light-duty vehicle sales, 113
    light trucks and passenger cars,
        ages of, 478
    resale value, 108
    sales of, 534
    skidding distance, 570
    teenagers with driver's
        licenses, 114
    temperatures inside, 569
    truck rentals, 155, 162–63, 164,
        181, 314
    Yellow Cab rates in Cincin-
        nati, 101
music
    album sales, 152, 252
    audio podcast, 101
    CD production, 527–28, 534
    CD sales *vs.* advertising dollars
        spent, 4
    fret position of bass guitar, 237
    guitar string sales, 144–45
    online radio *vs.* online video,
        164–65
    Pandora Radio, 230
    piano, 213–14
    revenue from downloaded, 489
    revenue from portable media
        and MP3 players, 611
    revenue of recorded, 1, 49,
        165, 489

N
nutrition. *See* food and nutrition

P
physics
    balloon air pressure, 6
    bounce heights, 6, 108–9, 539,
        541, 546, 550
    dropped objects, 6, 108–9, 609
    escape velocity, 585
    falling objects, 584, 609
    flow rate, 577

force, 549
frequency, 213–14, 550
illumination from light bulb,
    551, 553–54
intensity of radiation, 549
intensity of signal, 550
pendulum motion, 551, 611–12
pressure-volume relationship,
    544, 547, 554
projectile motion, 383, 468–69
tension, 549
vertical throwing speed, 383
vibration, 549, 550
volume of air in lungs, 6
weight, 545–46
politics. *See also* government
    vote-counting systems, 465
    voter-eligible Latinos, 489, 524
    voters who voted, 601
population. *See also*
    demographics
    bacterial, 287
    of bald eagle, 197–98
    of China and India, 306–7
    of city, 103
    of deer, 5
    foreign born, 6, 456, 465
    foreign children adopted by
        American families, 184–85,
        288
    vs. gross national product, 235
    growth in United States, 234
    immigrant, 398
    of Nevada, 102, 264
    of Pittsburgh, 99
    of U.S., 106, 107, 382, 455, 464
    world, 101–2, 106, 229, 232,
        288–89, 382
    world Internet, 336
publishing
    Encyclopedia Britannica sales,
        232
    textbook sales, 535
pyrotechnics
    fireworks, 407

R
ranching
    fencing around ranch, 411, 466
rate
    of filling swimming pool, 5
    of gas consumption, 6
    of pumping out flooded
        basement, 91
    unemployment, 100
real estate
    home prices, 182
    home prices, Phoenix,
        Arizona, 93
    householders who own a
        home, 463
    Manhattan land ownership,
        533–34
    Manhattan two/four-bedroom
        house prices, 100
    new-home sales rates, 380, 440
    painting a house, 6

unoccupied homes, 242
value of farmland, 336
recreation. *See* leisure and
    recreation

S
seismology
    Richter numbers, 270–71, 272
    tsunamis, 570, 609
speed
    driving, 498, 537
    driving time, 6, 16, 33, 531–33,
        537, 559, 560
    land speed records, 538
    of runner, 6
    of speedboat, 6
    of tsunami, 570, 609
    typing, 552
    vertical throwing, 383
    wind, 569–70
sports
    baseball
        fans in America, 58, 75, 88
        home runs, 464
        little league participants, 74
        salaries in, 1, 244, 289
        ticket prices, 213
        viewers of All-Star Game,
            228–29
        World Series television
            ratings, 181
    football
        field, 307, 495
        Super Bowl advertising, 3,
            186, 236
    ironman competition, 378–79
    NCAA basketball
        ad spending, 114
    Olympics
        speed skating, 122, 140
    running
        200-meter run, 185
        400-meter run, 76, 101, 115,
            137–38, 176
        1500-meter run, 142
        New York City Marathon,
            315
        runner's stride rate, 76
    skiing
        prices of rental packages,
            75, 89
        recommended ski lengths,
            174–75
        steepness of ski run, 24, 57
    soccer, 558
    swimming, 549
surveillance
    red-light cameras, 610–11
surveys
    Americans satisfied with
        U.S., 68

T
temperature
    at beach, 6
    boiling point and elevation, 67

boiling points of water, 249–50
cooling time, 237–38, 303
cricket chirps and, 90, 101, 253
of cup of coffee, 3–4, 305
of cup of tea, 305
of Earth, 104–5, 107
in enclosed vehicle, 569
Fahrenheit *vs.* Celsius, 90, 101,
    249–50, 253, 255
heat index, 103
of oven to cook potato, 5
scales for measuring, 90, 101
at specific location at specific
    time, 6
windchills and, 69, 174
tests and testing
    AP tests administered, 204–5
    drug tests on employees, 6
    time to grade, 5
transportation. *See also* motor
    vehicles
    collisions at highway-railroad
        crossings, 66–67
    steepness of two roads, 17–18,
        24
    Yellow Cab rates in Cincin-
        nati, 101
travel. *See also* air travel; motor
    vehicles; transportation
    distance covered at constant
        speed, 100, 103, 104, 490,
        549
    driving time, 6, 16, 33, 531–33,
        537, 559, 560
    passports, Americans with, 74
    ski rental package prices, 75, 89
    speed of car, 6, 498, 537, 560
    speed of speedboat, 6
    trips per year, 99

W
weather
    heat index, 103
    lightning deaths, 234–35
    rainfall, 5
    snow melt, 558
    windchill, 69, 174
    wind intensities, 569–70
weight
    of bar of soap, 291
    and distance from Earth,
        545–46, 549
    of gold bar *vs.* value, 56
    of Mako sharks, 441
    of Pacific albacore tuna, 74
    of spaghetti *vs.* radius of plate, 6
work
    coal miners employed, 466–67
    computer use on job, 458–60
    drug tests on employees, 6
    female workers who prefer
        female boss, 91
    labor union strength, 379–80
    unemployment rate, 100
    union membership, 478
    volunteer, 455, 463
    women ages 25–54, 396

Linear Equations and Linear Functions

Have you bought any recorded music in the past month? The revenue of recorded music including digital music has decreased greatly in the past five years (see Table 1). In an Exploration in Section 1.6, you will estimate the revenue in 2012.

In this course, we will use mathematics to describe many authentic situations, such as the music data. We will use these descriptions to make estimates and predictions, as in estimating the revenue of recorded music in 2012. Later, you will estimate by how much the number of Internet users is increasing per year, you will predict baseball players' minimum salary in 2018, and you will estimate at what age 65% of Americans believe same-sex couples should be recognized by the law as valid.

Table 1 Annual Revenues of Recorded Music	
Year	Annual Revenue (billions of dollars)
2005	12.3
2006	11.8
2007	10.4
2008	8.8
2009	7.7
2010	6.9

Source: *Recording Industry Association of America*

A major objective of this text is to help you view the world in a mathematical manner. That viewpoint will allow you to recognize important patterns—patterns that will enable you to make estimates and predictions like the ones just mentioned.

In this chapter, we will discuss how to describe a line by using a *graph,* an *equation,* and a *table*. We will also discuss how to describe the steepness of a line. Finally, we will work with an important group of lines represented by *linear functions*. We will lay the groundwork so that in Chapter 2 we can use lines to describe authentic situations.

▼ 1.1 Using Qualitative Graphs to Describe Situations

Objectives

» Use qualitative graphs to describe situations.

» Identify independent variables and dependent variables.

» Know the meaning of an *intercept* of a curve.

» Identify increasing curves and decreasing curves.

» Describe a concept or procedure.

In this section, we will use qualitative graphs to describe authentic situations. A **qualitative graph** is a graph without scaling (tick marks and their numbers) on the axes.

Reading Qualitative Graphs

How can we use a qualitative graph to describe an authentic situation?

▶ Example 1   Reading a Qualitative Graph

Since 1985, Michael Jordan has endorsed a successful line of shoes, called Air Jordan®. Let p be the retail price (in dollars) of Air Jordans and t be the number of years since 1985. (For example, $t = 1$ represents the year 1986.) The qualitative graph displayed in Fig. 1 describes the prices of the shoes. What does the graph tell us?

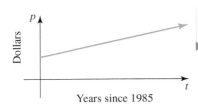

Figure 1 Retail price of Air Jordan shoes

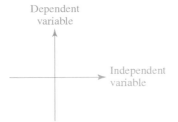

Figure 2 Match the vertical axis with the dependent variable and the horizontal axis with the independent variable

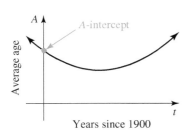

Figure 3 The average age when men first marry

Solution

The graph (or curve) tells us that the retail price of Air Jordans has increased steadily.

A curve is said to be *linear* if it forms a straight line. The curve in Fig. 1 is linear.

Independent and Dependent Variables

The retail price p of Air Jordans depends on the year. Due to inflation and to increasing popularity of the shoes, the price increases over time. Because p depends on t, we call p the *dependent variable*.

The year does *not* depend on the shoe's price. Raising or lowering the price has no effect on the passage of time. Time is independent of the price. Since t is independent of p, we call t the *independent variable*.

▶ **Definition** Independent and dependent variables

Assume that an authentic situation can be described by using the variables t and p and that p depends on t:

• We call t the **independent variable.**
• We call p the **dependent variable.**

▶ **Example 2** Identifying Independent and Dependent Variables

For each situation, identify the independent variable and the dependent variable:

1. You are waiting in line to go to a concert. Let T be the number of minutes you must wait, and let N be the number of people ahead of you when you first get in line.
2. Let n be the number of times a person can lift dumbbells that weigh w pounds.

Solution

1. The more people ahead of you when you first get in line, the more time you must wait. The wait time, T, depends on the number of people ahead of you, N. Thus, T is the dependent variable and N is the independent variable. (The number of people in line does *not* depend on your wait time.)
2. The heavier the dumbbells, the fewer times the person can lift them. The number of times the person can lift the dumbbells, n, depends on the dumbbells' weight, w. Thus, n is the dependent variable and w is the independent variable. (The weight of the dumbbells does *not* depend on the number of times the person can lift them.)

For graphs, we describe the values of the independent variable along the horizontal axis and the values of the dependent variable along the vertical axis (see Fig. 2). For example, in Fig. 1, we describe the values of the independent variable t along the horizontal axis and we describe the values of the dependent variable p along the vertical axis.

▶ **Example 3** Reading a Qualitative Graph

Let A be the average age (in years) when men first marry, and let t be the number of years since 1900. In Fig. 3, the graph describes the relationship between the variables t and A. What does the graph tell us?

Solution

The graph tells us that the average age when men first marry decreased each year for a while and then increased each year after that.

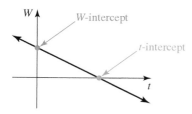

Figure 4 Intercepts of a line

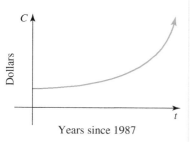

Figure 5 Cost of Super Bowl ads

We say the curve sketched in Fig. 3 is a *parabola*.

In Fig. 3, note that the curve and the *A*-axis intersect. The point of intersection is an *A-intercept*. An **intercept** of a curve is any point where the curve and an axis (or axes) intersect. Two more examples of intercepts are shown in Fig. 4 for a linear curve.

Sketching Qualitative Graphs

In Examples 4–6, we sketch qualitative graphs that describe given situations.

▶ **Example 4**   Sketching a Qualitative Graph

Let *C* be the cost (in dollars) of a 30-second ad during the Super Bowl at *t* years since 1987. For most years, the annual increase in cost is more than the previous annual increase in cost. Sketch a qualitative graph that describes the relationship between *C* and *t*.

Solution

Since the cost of an ad varies according to the year, *C* is the dependent variable and *t* is the independent variable (see Fig. 5). Because ads were not free in 1987 ($t = 0$), the *C*-intercept is above the origin. The costs are increasing, so we sketch a curve that goes upward from left to right. Since most increases are more than the previous increase, the curve should "bend" upward from left to right.

▶

Some *exponential* curves have shapes similar to the shape of the curve sketched in Fig. 5.

If a curve goes upward from left to right, we say the curve is **increasing** (see Fig. 6). For example, the cost curve in Fig. 5 is increasing. If a curve goes downward from left to right, we say the curve is **decreasing** (see Fig. 7).

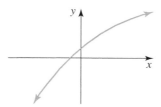

Figure 6 Increasing curve

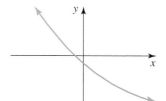

Figure 7 Decreasing curve

In this chapter and future chapters, we will discuss the curves mentioned in this section more thoroughly and use them to make predictions—linear curves in this chapter and Chapter 2, exponential curves in Chapters 4 and 5, and quadratic curves in Chapters 6 and 7. In Chapter 3, you will make predictions with two linear curves.

▶ **Example 5**   Sketching a Qualitative Graph

Hot coffee is poured into a cup at room temperature. Let *F* be the temperature (in degrees Fahrenheit) of the coffee at *t* minutes since the coffee was poured. Sketch a qualitative graph that describes the relationship between the variables *t* and *F*.

Solution

Note that *F* depends on *t*, so we let the vertical axis be the *F*-axis and the horizontal axis be the *t*-axis (see Fig. 8). Since the coffee cools with time, the curve should be decreasing. Further, the curve should show that the drop in temperature during any minute is less than the drop in temperature in the previous minute. (Why?)

The coffee's temperature will not go below room temperature, so the curve should eventually level off.

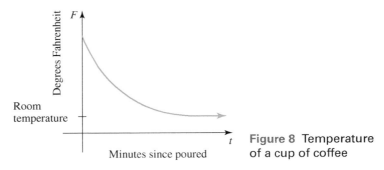

Figure 8 Temperature of a cup of coffee

In Examples 4 and 5, the independent variable represents time. Let's explore a situation in which the independent variable stands for something else.

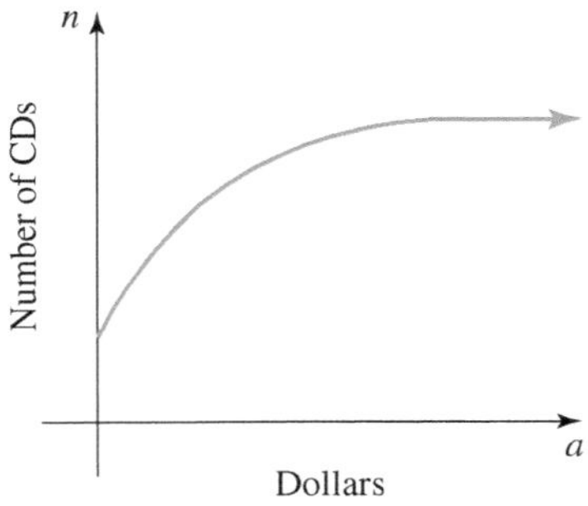

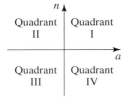

Figure 9 Spending on advertising and CDs sold

▶ **Example 6**   Sketching a Qualitative Graph

Suppose the latest Radiohead CD is about to be released. Let n be the number of CDs that will be sold if a dollars are spent on advertising. Sketch a qualitative graph that describes the relationship between the variables a and n.

Solution

The number of CDs sold is in part determined by the amount of money spent on advertising, so n is on the vertical axis and a is on the horizontal axis (see Fig. 9). Because both n and a must be nonnegative (why?), the qualitative curve is in *quadrant I* (and one point of it is on the n-axis). The four quadrants are shown in Fig. 10.

Even if no money is spent on advertising, some CDs will be sold. So the n-intercept should be above the origin. The more money spent on advertising, the greater the sales, so the curve should be increasing. There are only so many people, however, who would buy the CD no matter how much advertising is done, so the curve should level off. ▶

Figure 10 The four quadrants

Describing a Concept or Procedure

In some homework exercises, you will describe in general a concept or procedure.

Guidelines on Writing a Good Response

- Create an example that illustrates the concept or outlines the procedure. Looking at examples or exercises may jump-start you into creating your own example.
- Using complete sentences and correct terminology, describe the key ideas or steps for your example. You can review the text for ideas, but write your description in your own words.
- Describe also the concept or the procedure in general, without referring to your example. It may help to reflect on several examples and what they all have in common.
- In some cases, it will be helpful to point out the similarities and the differences between the concept or the procedure you are describing and other concepts or procedures.
- Describe the benefits of knowing the concept or the procedure.
- If you have described the steps in a procedure, explain why it's permissible to follow these steps.
- Clarify any common misunderstandings about the concept, or discuss how to avoid making common mistakes when following the procedure.

▶ **Example 7**   Responding to a General Question about a Concept

Describe the meaning of *independent variable* and *dependent variable*.

Solution

Assume that an authentic situation can be described by using the variables t and a and that a depends on t. Then t is the independent variable and a is the dependent variable.

For example, let a be the amount of money (in dollars) that a person is paid for working t hours at a gasoline station. Then t is the independent variable and a is the dependent variable, because the person's pay depends on the number of hours worked.

For graphs, we use the horizontal axis to describe values of the independent variable and the vertical axis to describe values of the dependent variable.

Group Exploration

Sketching a qualitative graph

A bathtub is filled with water, and then the plug is pulled out. Let V be the volume of water (in gallons) in the tub at t seconds after the plug is pulled out.

1. Which variable is the dependent variable? the independent variable? Explain.

2. Sketch a qualitative graph that describes the relationship between V and t. Explain.

Taking It One Step Further

3. Carefully describe an experiment you could run to verify the shape of your curve from Problem 2. In particular, explain how you could measure the volume of water at various times. Ask your instructor if you should run such an experiment.

Homework 1.1

For extra help ▶ **MyMathLab®**   Watch the videos in MyMathLab   Download the MyDashboard App

1. The deer population in a forest is described during the years between 2010 and the present. Let p be the deer population in the forest and t be the number of years since 2010. Match each graph in Fig. 11 with each scenario. The population
   a. decreased steadily.
   b. increased steadily.
   c. remained steady.
   d. decreased for a while and then increased.

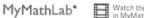 

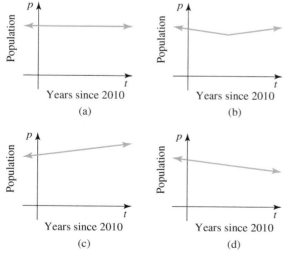

Figure 11 Exercise 1

2. Let A be the amount of rain (in inches) that has fallen in t hours. Match each graph in Fig. 12 with each scenario. The rain fell
   a. harder and harder.

   b. softly and then stopped. After a while, it began raining hard.
   c. hard and then stopped. After a while, it began raining softly.
   d. more and more softly.

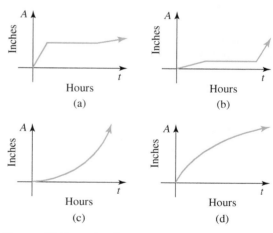

Figure 12 Exercise 2

For Exercises 3–12, identify the independent variable and the dependent variable.

3. Let T be the time (in minutes) it takes to grade N tests.

4. Let c be the total cost (in dollars) of n pencils.

5. Let F be the temperature (in degrees Fahrenheit) of an oven, and let T be the number of minutes it takes to cook a potato in the oven.

6. Let r be the rate (in gallons per hour) at which water is added to a swimming pool, and let t be the number of hours it takes to fill the pool.

7. Let L be the length (in miles) of a running course, and let T be the number of minutes it takes a person to run the course.

8. Let a be the age (in years) of a car, and let c be the annual cost of repairs (in dollars) for the car.

9. Let P be the percentage of Americans who own a car and whose income is I dollars.

10. Let n be the number of people at a beach when the temperature is F degrees Fahrenheit.

11. Let r be the radius (in inches) of a plate, and let n be the number of ounces of spaghetti the plate can hold.

12. Let I be a person's annual income (in dollars), and let T be the federal taxes (in dollars) the person must pay.

For Exercises 13–36, sketch a graph that shows the relationship between the variables defined. Explain why your graph makes sense. Various "correct" graphs are possible.

13. Let F be the temperature (in degrees Fahrenheit) at a specific outdoor location at t hours after 6 A.M. on a specific day. (So, $t = 0$ represents 6 A.M.)

14. A person went for a run. After a while, she stopped to rest. She then walked home. Let s be her speed (in feet per second) at t minutes after she began her run.

15. An airplane flew from New York to Chicago. Let h be the plane's altitude (in feet) at t seconds after takeoff.

16. Let h be the height (in feet) of a tennis ball at t seconds after it was dropped. (Allow for bounces.)

17. The number of people undergoing laser eye surgery has increased since 2010. Let n be the number of people who have undergone laser eye surgery during the year that is t years since 2010.

18. The percentage of smokers in the United States has declined steadily since 2010. Let P be the percentage of smokers in the United States at t years since 2010.

19. The percentage of major firms that perform drug tests on employees and/or job applicants increased from 1987 to 1996 and decreased thereafter. Let p be the percentage of firms that perform drug tests at t years since 1987.

20. The percentage of the U.S. population that is foreign born decreased from 1950 to 1970 and increased thereafter. Let p be the percentage of the U.S. population that is foreign born at t years since 1950.

21. A commuter left home, drove toward her workplace, got gas, then continued driving to work. Let g be the amount of gas (in gallons) in the gas tank at t minutes after she left home.

22. At noon, a person began to breathe in. Let V be the volume of air (in liters) in this person's lungs at t seconds after noon.

23. Let h be the height (in feet) of a specific person at age a years.

24. Let A be the angle (in degrees) between the hour hand and the minute hand of a clock at t minutes from midnight.

25. Let d be the diameter (in inches) of a balloon after a person has blown into it n times.

26. Let n be the number of species in existence, and let d be the total amount of deforestation (in thousands of acres).

27. Let T be the time (in minutes) it takes to drive from home to school if there are an average of n cars per mile on the route.

28. Let s be the maximum speed (in miles per hour) that a specific speedboat can travel when going
   a. downstream on a river with a current of c miles per hour.
   b. upstream on a river with a current of c miles per hour.

29. Let S be the speed of a car (in miles per hour) driven on a level road when the end of the accelerator has been d inches from the floor of the car for several minutes.

30. Let p be the percentage of times a person who is playing darts at d feet from the target hits the bull's-eye.

31. Let T be the number of minutes it takes a person to make lasagna, and let n be the number of times the person has made it before.

32. Let T be the number of hours it takes a painting crew to paint a house, and let N be the number of people in the crew.

33. Let n be the number of people in the United States who would be willing to purchase a new Honda Civic® CX at a price of p dollars.

34. A person plans to drive from Rockville, Maryland, to Raleigh, North Carolina. Let T be the driving time (in hours) if the person drives at S miles per hour.

35. Let A be the area (in square feet) of a circle with radius r feet.

36. Air is blown into a balloon. The balloon is then tied so that no air can enter or leave it. If the balloon is squeezed, the air pressure inside increases. Let P be the air pressure (in pounds per square inch) inside the balloon when the balloon's volume is V cubic inches.

Concepts

37. Sketch a decreasing curve that has exactly one intercept.

38. What is the greatest number of intercepts an increasing curve can have?

39. Write a scenario to match each graph in Fig. 13. Refer to the variables x and y in your description.

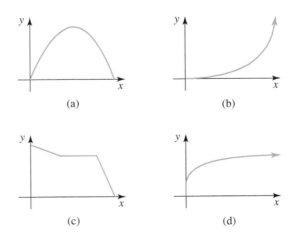

(a) (b) (c) (d)

Figure 13 Exercise 39

40. Explain how to sketch a qualitative graph that describes a given situation. (See page 4 for guidelines on writing a good response.)

1.2 Graphing Linear Equations

Objectives

» Know the meaning of *solution, satisfy*, and *solution set*.

» Know the meaning of the *graph* of an equation.

» Know which equations have graphs that are lines.

» Sketch graphs of linear equations.

» Find intercepts of graphs of linear equations.

» Sketch graphs of vertical and horizontal lines.

In Section 1.1, we worked with many types of curves. For the rest of this chapter, we will focus on lines and various ways to represent them. When we are *not* describing an authentic situation, we will use the variables x and y to describe a line (or any other type of curve). We will treat x as the independent variable and y as the dependent variable.

Definition of Solution, Satisfy, and Solution Set

Consider the equation $y = 3x - 1$. Let's find y when $x = 2$:

$$y = 3x - 1 \qquad \textit{Original equation}$$
$$y = 3(2) - 1 \qquad \textit{Substitute 2 for x.}$$
$$= 6 - 1 \qquad \textit{Multiply before subtracting (see Section A.6).}$$
$$= 5 \qquad \textit{Subtract.}$$

So, $y = 5$ when $x = 2$, which we can represent by using the ordered pair $(2, 5)$. For an **ordered pair** (a, b), we write the value of the independent variable in the first (left) position and the value of the dependent variable in the second (right) position. The numbers a and b are called **coordinates.** For $(2, 5)$, the *x-coordinate* is 2 and the *y-coordinate* is 5.

The equation $y = 3x - 1$ becomes a true statement when we substitute 2 for x and 5 for y:

$$y = 3x - 1 \qquad \textit{Original equation}$$
$$5 \overset{?}{=} 3(2) - 1 \qquad \textit{Substitute 2 for x and 5 for y.}$$
$$5 \overset{?}{=} 5 \qquad \textit{Simplify.}$$
$$\text{true}$$

We say that $(2, 5)$ is a *solution* of the equation $y = 3x - 1$ and that $(2, 5)$ *satisfies* the equation $y = 3x - 1$.

A set is a container. Much like a garbage can contains garbage, a *solution set* contains solutions.

> **Definition** *Solution, satisfy,* and *solution set* of an equation in two variables
>
> An ordered pair (a, b) is a **solution** of an equation in x and y if the equation becomes a true statement when a is substituted for x and b is substituted for y. We say that (a, b) **satisfies** the equation.
>
> The **solution set** of an equation is the set of all solutions of the equation.

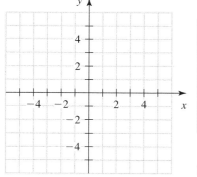

Figure 14 A coordinate system

A **coordinate system** is shown in Fig. 14. We can describe solutions of an equation by plotting points. For a review of plotting points, see Section A.1.

> **Example 1**   Graphing an Equation

Find five solutions of the equation $y = -2x + 1$, and plot them.

Solution

To find solutions, we are free to choose *any* values we'd like to substitute for x, but it's a good idea to pick integers close to or equal to 0 so the solutions are easy to plot. For example, here we substitute 0, 1, and 2 for x:

$$
\begin{array}{lll}
y = -2(0) + 1 & y = -2(1) + 1 & y = -2(2) + 1 \\
\quad = 0 + 1 & \quad = -2 + 1 & \quad = -4 + 1 \\
\quad = 1 & \quad = -1 & \quad = -3 \\
\text{Solution: } (0, 1) & \text{Solution: } (1, -1) & \text{Solution: } (2, -3)
\end{array}
$$

Table 2 Solutions of
$y = -2x + 1$

x	y
-2	5
-1	3
0	1
1	-1
2	-3

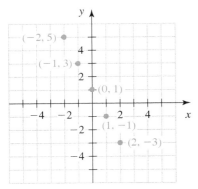

Figure 15 Five solutions of
$y = -2x + 1$

For a review of performing operations with real numbers, see Section A.4.

Next, we substitute -2 and -1 for x:

$$y = -2(-2) + 1 \qquad\qquad y = -2(-1) + 1$$
$$y = 4 + 1 \qquad\qquad\qquad y = 2 + 1$$
$$y = 5 \qquad\qquad\qquad\qquad y = 3$$
$$\text{Solution: } (-2, 5) \qquad\qquad \text{Solution: } (-1, 3)$$

We organize our findings in Table 2 and plot these five solutions in Fig. 15.

Notice that a line contains the five points that we found in Example 1 (see Fig. 16). It turns out that every point on the line represents a solution of the equation $y = -2x + 1$. For example, the point $(3, -5)$ lies on the line (see Fig. 17) and the ordered pair $(3, -5)$ satisfies the equation $y = -2x + 1$. (Try it.)

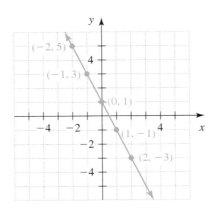

Figure 16 The line contains the points found in Example 1

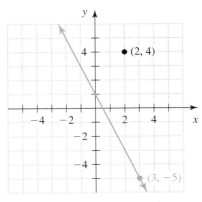

Figure 17 The point $(3, -5)$ lies on the line, but $(2, 4)$ does not

It also turns out that points that do not lie on the line represent ordered pairs that do not satisfy the equation. For example, the point $(2, 4)$ does not lie on the line (see Fig. 17), and the ordered pair $(2, 4)$ does not satisfy the equation $y = -2x + 1$:

$$y = -2x + 1 \qquad \textit{Original equation}$$
$$4 \stackrel{?}{=} -2(2) + 1 \qquad \textit{Substitute 2 for x and 4 for y.}$$
$$4 \stackrel{?}{=} -4 + 1 \qquad \textit{Multiply.}$$
$$4 \stackrel{?}{=} -3 \qquad \textit{Add.}$$
$$\text{false}$$

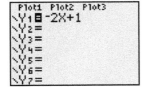

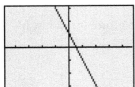

Figure 18 Use ZDecimal
to verify our graph

We refer to the line in Fig. 16 as the *graph* of the equation $y = -2x + 1$.

We can use ZDecimal on a graphing calculator to verify our graph (see Fig. 18). To enter $y = -2x + 1$, press $\boxed{(-)}\,2\,\boxed{X, T, \Theta, n}\,\boxed{+}\,\textbf{1}$. The key $\boxed{-}$ is used for subtraction, and the key $\boxed{(-)}$ is used for negative numbers as well as for taking opposites. For graphing calculator instructions, see Appendix B.3, B.4, and B.6.*

▶ Definition   **Graph**

The **graph** of an equation in two variables is the set of points that correspond to all solutions of the equation.

The graph of an equation in two variables is a visual description of the solutions of the equation. Every point on the graph represents a solution of the equation. Every point *not* on the graph represents an ordered pair that is *not* a solution.

*Appendix B is available online in MyMathLab and at http://www.pearsonhighered.com/mathstatsresources/

Graphs of Linear Equations

We saw that the graph of the equation $y = -2x + 1$ is a line. Notice that the equation $y = -2x + 1$ has the form $y = mx + b$ (where $m = -2$ and $b = 1$).

> **Graphs of Equations That Can Be Put into $y = mx + b$ Form**
>
> If an equation can be put into the form
>
> $$y = mx + b$$
>
> where m and b are constants, then the graph of the equation is a line.

For example, the graphs of the equations

$$y = 3x - 7, \quad y = -\frac{5}{7}x - 2, \quad y = x + 9, \quad y = -2x, \quad \text{and} \quad y = 4$$

are lines. The equation $y = -2x$ is of the form $y = mx + b$, because we can write it as $y = -2x + 0$ (so, $m = -2$ and $b = 0$). The equation $y = 4$ is also of the form $y = mx + b$, because we can write it as $y = 0x + 4$ (so, $m = 0$ and $b = 4$).

> **Example 2** Graphing a Linear Equation

Sketch the graph of $4y - 8x + 12 = 0$.

Solution

First, we solve for y (for a review of solving equations in two or more variables, see Section A.11):

$$4y - 8x + 12 = 0 \qquad \textit{Original equation}$$
$$4y - 8x + 12 + 8x = 0 + 8x \qquad \textit{Add 8x to both sides.}$$
$$4y + 12 = 8x \qquad \textit{Combine like terms (see Section A.9).}$$
$$4y + 12 - 12 = 8x - 12 \qquad \textit{Subtract 12 from both sides.}$$
$$4y = 8x - 12 \qquad \textit{Simplify.}$$
$$\frac{4y}{4} = \frac{8x}{4} - \frac{12}{4} \qquad \textit{Divide both sides by 4.}$$
$$y = 2x - 3 \qquad \textit{Simplify.}$$

Table 3 Solutions of $y = 2x - 3$

x	y
0	$2(0) - 3 = -3$
1	$2(1) - 3 = -1$
2	$2(2) - 3 = 1$

Since the equation $y = 2x - 3$ is of the form $y = mx + b$, we know the graph of the equation is a line. Although we can sketch a line from as few as two points, we plot a third point as a check. If the third point is not in line with the other two, then we know we have computed or plotted at least one of the solutions incorrectly.

To begin, we calculate three solutions of $y = 2x - 3$ in Table 3. We use 0, 1, and 2 as values of x because they correspond to points that are easy to plot. Then we plot the three points and sketch the line through them (see Fig. 19).

We can use ZStandard followed by ZSquare on a graphing calculator to view the graph as a partial check. This check will not reveal whether we isolated y correctly, because we entered $y = 2x - 3$ rather than the *original* equation $4y - 8x + 12 = 0$ (see Fig. 20). For graphing calculator instructions, see Appendix B.3, B.4, and B.6.

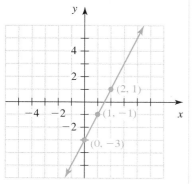

Figure 19 Graph of $y = 2x - 3$ ▶

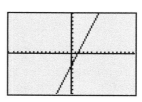

Figure 20 Graph of $y = 2x - 3$

Table 4 Solution of $y = -x + 2$

x	y
0	$-(0) + 2 = 2$
1	$-(1) + 2 = 1$
2	$-(2) + 2 = 0$

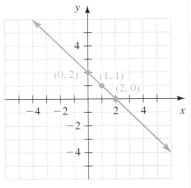

Figure 21 Graph of $y = -x + 2$

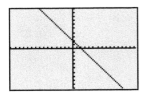

Figure 22 Graph of $y = -x + 2$

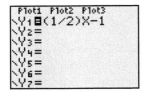

Figure 24 Verify the graph of $y = \dfrac{1}{2}x - 1$

▶ **Example 3**   Using the Distributive Law to Help Graph a Linear Equation

Sketch the graph of $3(2y - 5) = 2x - 3 - 8x$.

Solution

First, we use the distributive law on the left-hand side of the equation and combine like terms on the right-hand side:

$$3(2y - 5) = 2x - 3 - 8x \qquad \text{\textit{Original equation}}$$

$$6y - 15 = -6x - 3 \qquad \begin{array}{l}\textit{Distributive law; combine like terms}\\ \textit{(see Sections A.8 and A.9).}\end{array}$$

$$6y - 15 + 15 = -6x - 3 + 15 \qquad \textit{Add 15 to both sides.}$$

$$6y = -6x + 12 \qquad \textit{Simplify.}$$

$$\frac{6y}{6} = \frac{-6x}{6} + \frac{12}{6} \qquad \textit{Divide both sides by 6.}$$

$$y = -x + 2 \qquad \textit{Simplify.}$$

Next, we calculate three solutions of $y = -x + 2$ in Table 4. Then we plot the solutions listed in Table 4 and sketch the line that contains them (see Fig. 21).

We can use ZStandard followed by ZSquare to view the graph of $y = -x + 2$ as a partial check (see Fig. 22).

▶ **Example 4**   Graphing an Equation That Contains Fractions

Sketch the graph of $y = \dfrac{1}{2}x - 1$.

Solution

Note that $\dfrac{1}{2}$ times an even number is an integer. So, in Table 5, we use even-numbered values of x to avoid fractional values of y. Then we plot the solutions shown in Table 5 and sketch the line that contains the points (see Fig. 23).

Table 5 Solutions of $y = \dfrac{1}{2}x - 1$

x	y
0	$\dfrac{1}{2}(0) - 1 = -1$
2	$\dfrac{1}{2}(2) - 1 = 0$
4	$\dfrac{1}{2}(4) - 1 = 1$

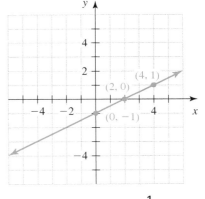

Figure 23 Graph of $y = \dfrac{1}{2}x - 1$

We can use ZDecimal to verify the graph (see Fig. 24).

Finding Intercepts of a Graph

Sometimes we find the intercepts of the graph of an equation to help us sketch the graph of the equation. Since an x-intercept is on the x-axis, we know its y-coordinate is 0 (see Fig. 25). Since a y-intercept is on the y-axis, we know its x-coordinate is 0.

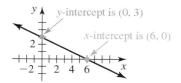

Figure 25 Intercepts of a line

Intercepts of the Graph of an Equation

For an equation containing the variables x and y,

- To find the x-coordinate of each x-intercept, substitute 0 for y and solve for x.
- To find the y-coordinate of each y-intercept, substitute 0 for x and solve for y.

In Example 5, we will find the intercepts of the graph of the equation $y = -2x + 4$ to help us graph that equation. Since the graph of $y = -2x + 4$ is a line, we say "the line $y = -2x + 4$" as shorthand for "the graph of the equation $y = -2x + 4$."

▶ Example 5   Using Intercepts to Sketch a Graph

1. Find the x-intercept of $y = -2x + 4$.
2. Find the y-intercept of $y = -2x + 4$.
3. Sketch the graph of $y = -2x + 4$.

Solution

1. To find the x-intercept, we substitute 0 for y and solve for x (for a review of solving linear equations in one variable, see Section A.10):

$$
\begin{aligned}
y &= -2x + 4 && \text{\textit{Original equation}}\\
0 &= -2x + 4 && \text{\textit{Substitute 0 for y.}}\\
0 + 2x &= -2x + 4 + 2x && \text{\textit{Add 2x to both sides.}}\\
2x &= 4 && \text{\textit{Simplify.}}\\
x &= 2 && \text{\textit{Divide both sides by 2.}}
\end{aligned}
$$

The x-intercept is $(2, 0)$.

2. To find the y-intercept, we substitute 0 for x and solve for y:

$$y = -2(0) + 4 = 4$$

The y-intercept is $(0, 4)$.

3. We list an additional solution of $y = -2x + 4$ in Table 6 and sketch the graph in Fig. 26.

    We use ZStandard followed by ZSquare to verify our graph (see Fig. 27). Then we use "zero" to verify the x-intercept (see Fig. 28) and TRACE to verify the y-intercept (see Fig. 29). For graphing calculator instructions, see Appendix B.5 and B.21.

Table 6 Solutions of $y = -2x + 4$

x	y
0	4
1	2
2	0

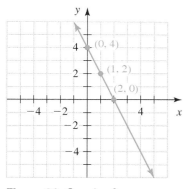

Figure 26 Graph of $y = -2x + 4$

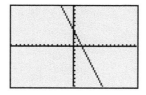

Figure 27 Verify the graph of $y = -2x + 4$

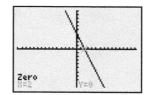

Figure 28 Verify the x-intercept

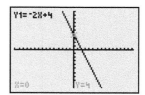

Figure 29 Verify the y-intercept

▶ Example 6   Finding Intercepts of a General Linear Equation

Assume the graph of $a(y - bx) = c$ has an x-intercept and a y-intercept.

1. Find the x-intercept.
2. Find the y-intercept.

Solution

1. To find the x-intercept, we substitute 0 for y and solve for x:

$$a(y - bx) = c \qquad \textit{Original equation}$$
$$a(0 - bx) = c \qquad \textit{Substitute 0 for y.}$$
$$-abx = c \qquad \textit{Simplify.}$$
$$\frac{-abx}{-ab} = \frac{c}{-ab} \qquad \textit{Divide both sides by } -ab.$$
$$x = -\frac{c}{ab} \qquad \textit{Simplify.}$$

The x-intercept is $\left(-\dfrac{c}{ab}, 0\right)$.

2. To find the y-intercept, we substitute 0 for x and solve for y:

$$a(y - bx) = c \qquad \textit{Original equation}$$
$$a(y - b \cdot 0) = c \qquad \textit{Substitute 0 for x.}$$
$$ay = c \qquad \textit{Simplify.}$$
$$\frac{ay}{a} = \frac{c}{a} \qquad \textit{Divide both sides by a.}$$
$$y = \frac{c}{a} \qquad \textit{Simplify.}$$

The y-intercept is $\left(0, \dfrac{c}{a}\right)$.

Vertical and Horizontal Lines

Which types of equations have graphs that are vertical or horizontal lines? We will begin to explore them in Example 7.

▶ **Example 7**   Graphing a Vertical Line

Sketch the graph of $x = 3$.

Solution

Note that the values of x must be 3, but y can have any value. Some solutions of $x = 3$ are listed in Table 7. We see in Fig. 30 that the graph of $x = 3$ is a vertical line.

Table 7 Solutions of $x = 3$

x	y
3	-2
3	-1
3	0
3	1
3	2
3	4.5

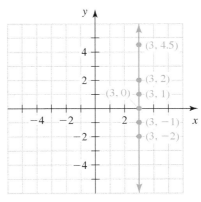

Figure 30 Graph of $x = 3$

Table 8 Solutions of $y = -5$

x	y
−2	−5
−1	−5
0	−5
1	−5
2	−5
3.5	−5

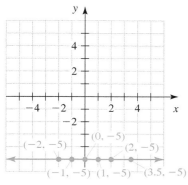

Figure 31 Graph of $y = -5$

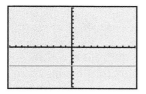

Figure 32 Verify the graph of $y = -5$

In Example 7, we saw that the graph of the equation $x = 3$ is a vertical line. Any equation that can be put into the form $x = a$, where a is a constant, has a vertical line as its graph.

We cannot use a graphing calculator to graph an equation such as $x = 3$. We can only enter equations of the form $y = A$, where A is a constant or an expression in terms of x.

▶ **Example 8** Graphing a Horizontal Line

Sketch the graph of $y = -5$.

Solution

The value of y must be -5, but x can have any value. Some solutions of $y = -5$ are listed in Table 8. We see in Fig. 31 that the graph of $y = -5$ is a horizontal line.

We can use ZStandard to verify the graph (see Fig. 32).

In Example 8, we saw that the graph of the equation $y = -5$ is a horizontal line. Any equation that can be put into the form $y = b$, where b is a constant, has a horizontal line as its graph.

Equations of Vertical and Horizontal Lines

If a and b are constants, then

- An equation that can be put into the form $x = a$ has a vertical line as its graph (see Fig. 33).
- An equation that can be put into the form $y = b$ has a horizontal line as its graph (see Fig. 34).

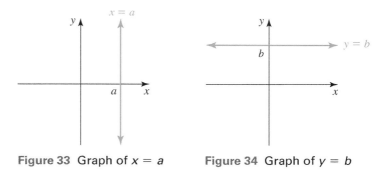

Figure 33 Graph of $x = a$ **Figure 34** Graph of $y = b$

For example, the graphs of the equations $x = 4$ and $x = -7$ are vertical lines. The graphs of the equations $y = 6$ and $y = -2$ are horizontal lines.

Linear Equations in Two Variables

If an equation can be put into the form

$$y = mx + b \qquad \text{or} \qquad x = a$$

where m, a, and b are constants, then the graph of the equation is a line. We call such an equation a **linear equation in two variables.**

Any equation that can be put into the form $x = a$ has a vertical line as its graph. Any equation that can be put into the form $y = mx + b$ has a nonvertical line as its graph.

Group Exploration

Looking ahead: Graphical significance of m and b

1. Use ZDecimal to graph these equations of the form $y = mx$ in order, and describe what you observe:

$$y = 0.3x, \quad y = 0.7x, \quad y = x,$$
$$y = 2x, \quad \text{and} \quad y = 3x.$$

Do the same with the equations

$$y = -0.3x, \quad y = -0.7x, \quad y = -x,$$
$$y = -2x, \quad \text{and} \quad y = -3x.$$

2. Use ZDecimal to graph these equations of the form $y = 2x + b$ in order, and describe what you observe:

$$y = 2x - 2, \quad y = 2x - 1, \quad y = 2x,$$
$$y = 2x + 1, \quad \text{and} \quad y = 2x + 2.$$

3. So far, you have graphed equations of the forms $y = mx$ (where $b = 0$) and $y = 2x + b$ (where $m = 2$). Now graph more equations of the form $y = mx + b$

until you are confident you know the graphical significance of m and b for any values of m and b.

4. Make a guess about the graph of $y = mx + b$ in each situation. Test each guess by checking whether it is true for values of m and b other than the ones you have worked with so far.
   a. m is zero
   b. m is positive
   c. m is negative
   d. m is a large positive number
   e. m is a positive number near 0
   f. m is a negative number near 0
   g. $m < -10$ (for example, $m = -20$)
   h. b is equal to 5
   i. b is equal to -3
   j. b is equal to 0

▶ Tips for Success   **Study Time**

For each hour of class time, study for at least two hours outside class. If your math background is weak, you may need to spend more time studying.

One way to study is to do what you are doing now: Read the text. Class time is a great opportunity to be introduced to new concepts and to see how they fit together with previously learned ones. However, there is usually not enough time to address details as well as a textbook can. In this way, a textbook can serve as a supplement to what you learn in class.

Homework 1.2

For extra help ▶ MyMathLab®   Watch the videos in MyMathLab   Download the MyDashboard App

*Graph the equation by hand. Verify your graph by using ZStandard followed by ZSquare on a graphing calculator. [**Graphing Calculator:** See Appendix B.3, B.4, and B.6. Also, recall that the key $\boxed{-}$ is used for subtraction and that the key $\boxed{(-)}$ is used for negative numbers as well as for taking opposites.]*

1. $y = 4x + 3$
2. $y = 3x + 2$
3. $y = 3x - 10$
4. $y = 2x - 6$
5. $y = -2x + 3$
6. $y = -3x + 7$
7. $y = -3x - 1$
8. $y = -4x - 2$
9. $y = 2x$
10. $y = 4x$
11. $y = -3x$
12. $y = -2x$
13. $y = -x$
14. $y = x$
15. $9x - 3y = 0$
16. $0 = 4y - 20x$
17. $3y - 6x = 12$
18. $10x - 5y = 20$
19. $8x - 2y - 10 = 0$
20. $30x + 6y - 12 = 0$
21. $2y - 6x - 14 = -4$
22. $3y + 3x - 2 = 7$

23. $8y - 7x + 3 = -4x + 5y - 9$
24. $6y - 4x - 1 = 7y - 2x - 4$
25. $-3(y - 5) = 2(3x - 6)$
26. $2(y - 3) = 4(x + 1)$
27. $6x - 3(2y - 3) = y - 2(4x - 1)$
28. $5x - 2(3y - 1) = -2y - 3(x - 2)$
29. $y = \dfrac{1}{3}x$
30. $y = -\dfrac{1}{2}x$
31. $y = \dfrac{3}{4}x - 2$
32. $y = \dfrac{2}{5}x - 1$
33. $y = -\dfrac{1}{2}x + 1$
34. $y = -\dfrac{2}{3}x + 2$

35. **a.** Use a graphing calculator to graph each equation.
   i. $y = 2$
   ii. $y = -2$
   iii. $y = 5.4896$
   b. Describe the graph of $y = b$, where b is a constant.

36. a. Graph each equation by hand.
    i. $x = 4$
    ii. $x = -5$
    iii. $x = 2.5$
  b. Describe the graph of $x = a$, where a is a constant.

Graph the equation by hand.

37. $x = 6$ **38.** $x = 3$ **39.** $y = -4$

40. $y = -3$ **41.** $y = 0$ **42.** $x = 0$

*Use ZDecimal on a graphing calculator to graph the equations that follow. Use TRACE to find the coordinates of a point on the graph. Then verify that the ordered pair for that point satisfies the equation. [**Graphing Calculator:** See Appendix B.6 and B.5.]*

43. $y = -3x + 1$ **44.** $2x - 3y = 6$

45. $0.83x = 4.98y - 2$

46. a. Use a graphing calculator to draw the graph of the line $y = -2.43x + 1.89$.
  b. Use ZDecimal followed by TRACE to help you create a table of ordered-pair solutions of the equation. Include at least five ordered pairs.

Solve the equation. (To review solving equations in one variable, see Section A.10.)

47. $x - 1 + 2x = 3x - 9x + 17$

48. $3 - 5x - 2 = 4x + 9 - 7x$

49. $-2(3w + 5) = 3w - 4$

50. $4(2t - 1) = -5t + 7$

51. $4 - 6(2 - 3x) = 2x - (4 - 5x)$

52. $7 - 2(5 - 4x) = 3x - (8 - 3x)$

53. $4(r - 2) - 3(r - 1) = 2(r + 6)$

54. $-4(a + 6) + 5(a - 3) = 3(a - 1)$

55. $\frac{1}{2}x + \frac{1}{3} = \frac{5}{2}$

56. $\frac{1}{3}x - \frac{1}{4} = \frac{2}{3}$

57. $-\frac{5}{6}b + \frac{3}{4} = \frac{1}{2}b - \frac{2}{3}$

58. $-\frac{3}{4}w - \frac{5}{8} = \frac{3}{2}w + \frac{1}{4}$

Solve the equation. Round your result to the second decimal place.

59. $2.75x - 3.95 = -6.21x + 74.92$

60. $-6.54x + 87.35 = -4.66x - 99.03$

Solve for the specified variable. (To review solving equations in two or more variables, see Section A.11.)

61. $P = 2L + 2W$, for L **62.** $c = 3(x + y)$, for x

63. $ax + by = c$, for y **64.** $\frac{x}{a} + \frac{y}{a} = 1$, for y

Find all x-intercepts and y-intercepts.

65. $y = 2x + 10$ **66.** $y = -3x - 12$

67. $2x + 3y = 12$ **68.** $5x - 4y = 20$

69. $y = 3x$ **70.** $y = -2x$

71. $y = 3$ **72.** $x = -2$

Assuming the graph of the equation has an x-intercept and a y-intercept, find both intercepts.

73. $y = mx + b$ **74.** $ax + by = c$

75. $a(bx + y) = c$ **76.** $a(x - by) = c$

77. $ax = b(cy - d)$ **78.** $ay = b(c + dx)$

79. $\frac{x}{a} + \frac{y}{b} = 1$ **80.** $\frac{y - b}{m} = x$

81. The graph of an equation is sketched in Fig. 35. Describe five ordered-pair solutions of this equation by using a table.

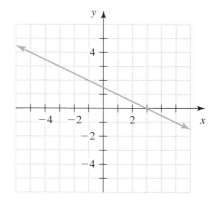

Figure 35 Exercise 81

82. The graph of an equation is sketched in Fig. 36. Describe five ordered-pair solutions of this equation by using a table.

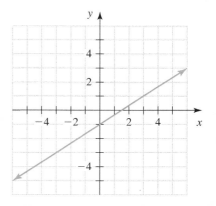

Figure 36 Exercise 82

83. Find an equation of the line sketched in Fig. 37.

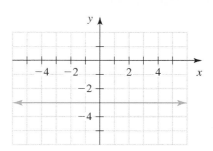

Figure 37 Exercise 83

84. Find an equation of the line sketched in Fig. 38.

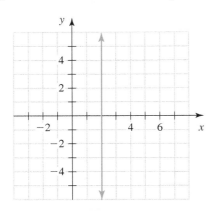

Figure 38 Exercise 84

For Exercises 85–94, refer to Fig. 39.

85. Estimate y when $x = 4$.   **86.** Estimate y when $x = 0$.

87. Estimate y when $x = -7$.   **88.** Estimate y when $x = -3$.

89. Estimate x when $y = 4$.   **90.** Estimate x when $y = 5$.

91. Estimate x when $y = 0$.   **92.** Estimate x when $y = -2$.

93. Estimate x when $y = -1.5$.   **94.** Estimate x when $y = 0.5$.

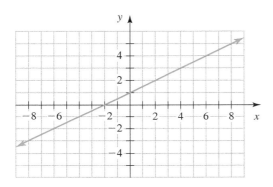

Figure 39 Exercises 85–94

95. A person lowers his hot-air balloon by gradually releasing air from it. Let x be the number of minutes he has been releasing air from the balloon, and let y be the altitude of the balloon (in feet). Assume the relationship between x and y is described by the equation $y = -200x + 800$.
  a. Graph $y = -200x + 800$ by hand.
  b. Find the y-intercept of the graph of $y = -200x + 800$. What does it mean in this situation?
  c. Find the x-intercept of the graph of $y = -200x + 800$. What does it mean in this situation?

96. A person fills up her car's gas tank and then drives for a long time. Let x be the driving time (in hours) since she fueled up, and let y be the number of gallons of gas in the car's gas tank. Assume the relationship between x and y is described by the equation $y = -2x + 10$.
  a. Graph $y = -2x + 10$ by hand.
  b. Find the y-intercept of the graph of $y = -2x + 10$. What does it mean in this situation?
  c. Find the x-intercept of the graph of $y = -2x + 10$. What does it mean in this situation?

Concepts

97. Use a graphing calculator to sketch the graphs of equations of the form $y = mx + b$.
  a. Graph $y = -4.1x + 8.7$. Is the graph a line? (Here, $m = -4.1$ and $b = 8.7$.)
  b. Graph $y = 6$. Is the graph a line? (Here, $m = 0$ and $b = 6$.)
  c. Create and graph at least two more equations of the form $y = mx + b$. Are the graphs lines?

98. A student says the graph of $y + x^2 = 5x + x^2 + 1$ is not a line, since the equation of a line does not have an x^2 term in it. Is the student correct? Explain.

99. The graph of the equation $y = 2x + b$ contains the point $(7, 5)$. What is the constant b?

100. The graph of the equation $y = mx + 3$ contains the point $(2, 11)$. What is the constant m?

101. The graph of an equation is sketched in Fig. 40. Which of the points A, B, C, D, E, and F represent ordered pairs that satisfy the equation?

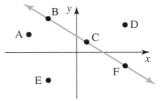

Figure 40 Exercise 101

102. The graphs of $y = ax + b$ and $y = cx + d$ are sketched in Fig. 41. For each part, decide which one or more of the points A, B, C, D, E, and F represent ordered pairs that
  a. satisfy the equation $y = ax + b$.
  b. satisfy the equation $y = cx + d$.
  c. satisfy both equations.
  d. do not satisfy either equation.

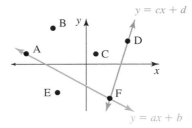

Figure 41 Exercise 102

103. Find the ordered pair or pairs that satisfy both of the equations that follow. Explain. [**Hint:** Graph the equations on the same coordinate system.]

$$y = 2x + 1 \qquad y = -3x + 6$$

104. Explain why the y-coordinate of an x-intercept is 0. Explain why the x-coordinate of a y-intercept is 0.

105. Let a be a constant. Explain why the graph of $x = a$ is a vertical line.

106. Does every line have an x-intercept? If yes, explain why. If no, give an equation of a line that doesn't have one.

107. Describe how to sketch a graph of a linear equation in two variables. Also, describe the meaning of a graph.

▼ 1.3 Slope of a Line

Objectives

» Compare the steepness of two objects.

» Know the meaning of, and how to calculate, the *slope* of a nonvertical line.

» Know the sign of the slope of an increasing or a decreasing line.

» Know the slopes of horizontal lines and vertical lines.

» Know the relationship between slopes of parallel lines.

» Know the relationship between slopes of perpendicular lines.

In this section, we will discuss how to measure the steepness of an object such as a ladder, road, or ski slope. Then we will focus on measuring the steepness of a nonvertical line.

Comparing the Steepness of Two Objects

How do we measure steepness? In this section, we will discuss the *slope* of a line. This important concept has numerous applications in engineering, medicine, surveying, physics, economics, mathematics, and many other fields.

Consider the sketch of two ladders leaning against a building in Fig. 42. Which ladder is steeper?

Ladder B is steeper than ladder A, even though both ladders reach a point at the same height on the building. To measure the steepness of each ladder, we compare the *vertical* distance from the base of the building to the ladder's top with the *horizontal* distance from the ladder's foot to the building. We calculate the ratio of vertical distance to horizontal distance for ladder A:

$$\text{Ladder A:} \quad \frac{\text{vertical distance}}{\text{horizontal distance}} = \frac{8 \text{ feet}}{4 \text{ feet}} = \frac{2}{1}$$

For ladder A, the vertical distance is 2 times the horizontal distance.

Next, we calculate the ratio of vertical distance to horizontal distance for ladder B:

$$\text{Ladder B:} \quad \frac{\text{vertical distance}}{\text{horizontal distance}} = \frac{8 \text{ feet}}{2 \text{ feet}} = \frac{4}{1}$$

For ladder B, the vertical distance is 4 times the horizontal distance.

These calculations confirm that ladder B is steeper than ladder A in Fig. 42.

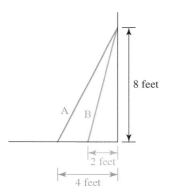

Figure 42 Ladder A and ladder B leaning against a building

> ### Comparing the Steepness of Two Objects
>
> To compare the steepness of two objects such as two ramps, two roofs, or two ski slopes, compute the ratio
> $$\frac{\text{vertical distance}}{\text{horizontal distance}}$$
> for each object. The object with the larger ratio is the steeper object.

▶ Example 1   Comparing the Steepness of Two Roads

Road A climbs steadily for 135 feet over a horizontal distance of 3900 feet. Road B climbs steadily for 120 feet over a horizontal distance of 3175 feet. Which road is steeper? Explain.

Solution

Figure 43 shows sketches of the two roads, but the horizontal distances and vertical distances are not drawn to scale.

Road A | Road B

Figure 43 Roads A and B

Here, we calculate the approximate ratio of the vertical distance to the horizontal distance for each road:

$$\text{Road A:} = \frac{\text{vertical distance}}{\text{horizontal distance}} = \frac{135 \text{ feet}}{3900 \text{ feet}} \approx \frac{0.035}{1}$$

$$\text{Road B:} = \frac{\text{vertical distance}}{\text{horizontal distance}} = \frac{120 \text{ feet}}{3175 \text{ feet}} \approx \frac{0.038}{1}$$

Road B is a little steeper than road A, because road B's ratio of vertical distance to horizontal distance is greater than road A's.

The **grade** of a road is the ratio of the vertical distance to the horizontal distance, written as a percentage. To write a decimal number as a percentage, we move the decimal point two places to the right and insert the percent symbol. In Example 1, the grade of road A is about 3.5% and the grade of road B is about 3.8%.

Finding a Line's Slope

How do we calculate the steepness of a nonvertical line if we are given two points on the line? Let's use the subscript 1 to label x_1 and y_1 as the coordinates of the first point, (x_1, y_1). Likewise, we label x_2 and y_2 as the coordinates of the second point, (x_2, y_2). The horizontal change between point (x_1, y_1) and point (x_2, y_2), called the *run*, is the difference $x_2 - x_1$. The vertical change between these points, called the *rise*, is the difference $y_2 - y_1$ (see Fig. 44). The *slope* of the line is the ratio of the rise to the run. We use the letter m to represent the slope.

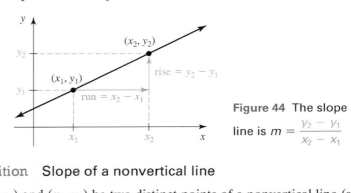

Figure 44 The slope of the line is $m = \dfrac{y_2 - y_1}{x_2 - x_1}$

▶ Definition   Slope of a nonvertical line

Let (x_1, y_1) and (x_2, y_2) be two distinct points of a nonvertical line (see Fig. 44). The **slope** of the line is

$$m = \frac{\text{vertical change}}{\text{horizontal change}} = \frac{\text{rise}}{\text{run}} = \frac{y_2 - y_1}{x_2 - x_1}$$

In words, the slope of a nonvertical line is equal to the ratio of the rise to the run (in going from one point on the line to another point on the line).

A **formula** is an equation that contains two or more variables. We will refer to the equation $m = \dfrac{y_2 - y_1}{x_2 - x_1}$ as the **slope formula**.

Here, we list, in verbal and graphical forms, the directions (right, left, up, or down) associated with the signs of rises and runs:

Sign of rise or run	Direction (verbal)	Direction (graphical)
run is positive	goes to the right	
run is negative	goes to the left	
rise is positive	goes up	
rise is negative	goes down	

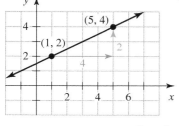

Figure 45 The slope is $\dfrac{2}{4} = \dfrac{1}{2}$

▶ **Example 2** Finding the Slope of a Line

Find the slope of the line that contains the points $(1, 2)$ and $(5, 4)$.

Solution

Using the slope formula, where $(x_1, y_1) = (1, 2)$ and $(x_2, y_2) = (5, 4)$, we have

$$m = \frac{4 - 2}{5 - 1} = \frac{2}{4} = \frac{1}{2}$$

By plotting the points, we find that if the run is 4, then the rise is 2 (see Fig. 45). So, the slope is $m = \dfrac{\text{rise}}{\text{run}} = \dfrac{2}{4} = \dfrac{1}{2}$, which is our result from using the slope formula.

In Example 2, we calculated the slope of a line for $(x_1, y_1) = (1, 2)$ and $(x_2, y_2) = (5, 4)$. Here, we switch the roles of the two points to find the slope when $(x_1, y_1) = (5, 4)$ and $(x_2, y_2) = (1, 2)$ instead:

$$m = \frac{y_2 - y_1}{x_2 - x_1} = \frac{2 - 4}{1 - 5} = \frac{-2}{-4} = \frac{1}{2}$$

The result is the same as our result in Example 2. In general, when we use the slope formula with two points on a line, it doesn't matter which point we choose to be (x_1, y_1) and which we choose to be (x_2, y_2).

WARNING It is a common error to substitute into the slope formula incorrectly. Carefully consider why the middle and right-hand formulas are incorrect:

Correct	**Incorrect**	**Incorrect**
$m = \dfrac{y_2 - y_1}{x_2 - x_1}$	$m = \dfrac{y_2 - y_1}{x_1 - x_2}$	$\dfrac{x_2 - x_1}{y_2 - y_1}$

▶ **Example 3** Finding the Slope of a Line

Find the slope of the line that contains the points $(2, 3)$ and $(5, 1)$.

Solution

$$m = \frac{1 - 3}{5 - 2} = \frac{-2}{3} = -\frac{2}{3}$$

By plotting the points, we find that if the run is 3, then the rise is -2 (see Fig. 46). So, the slope is $\dfrac{-2}{3} = -\dfrac{2}{3}$, which is our result from using the slope formula.

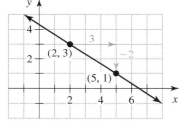

Figure 46 The slope is $\dfrac{-2}{3} = -\dfrac{2}{3}$

Increasing and Decreasing Lines

Consider the increasing line in Fig. 47. Our work with the signs of the rise and run shows that the slope of the line is positive.

Now consider the decreasing line in Fig. 48. Our work with the signs of the rise and run shows that the slope of the line is negative.

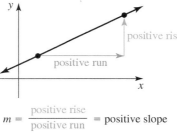

$$m = \frac{\text{positive rise}}{\text{positive run}} = \text{positive slope}$$

Figure 47 An increasing line has positive slope

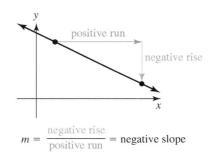

$$m = \frac{\text{negative rise}}{\text{positive run}} = \text{negative slope}$$

Figure 48 A decreasing line has negative slope

> **Slopes of Increasing and Decreasing Lines**

- An increasing line has positive slope (see Fig. 47).
- A decreasing line has negative slope (see Fig. 48).

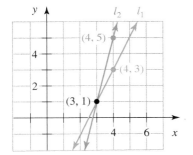

Figure 49 Find the slopes of the two lines

▶ **Example 4** Finding the Slope of a Line

Find the slope of the line that contains the points $(-9, -4)$ and $(12, -8)$.

Solution

$$m = \frac{-8 - (-4)}{12 - (-9)} = \frac{-8 + 4}{12 + 9} = \frac{-4}{21} = -\frac{4}{21}$$

Since the slope is negative, the line is decreasing.

◀

▶ **Example 5** Comparing the Slopes of Two Lines

Find the slopes of the two lines sketched in Fig. 49. Which line has the greater slope? Explain why this makes sense in terms of the steepness of a line.

Solution

For line l_1 in Fig. 50, if the run is 1, the rise is 2. We calculate the slope of line l_1:

$$\text{Slope of line } l_1 = \frac{\text{rise}}{\text{run}} = \frac{2}{1} = 2$$

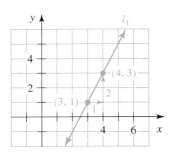

Figure 50 Line with lesser slope

For line l_2 in Fig. 51, if the run is 1, the rise is 4. We calculate the slope of line l_2:

$$\text{Slope of line } l_2 = \frac{\text{rise}}{\text{run}} = \frac{4}{1} = 4$$

Note that the slope of line l_2 is greater than the slope of line l_1, which is what we would expect because line l_2 looks steeper than line l_1.

◀

In general, **for two nonparallel increasing lines, the steeper line has the greater slope.**

Horizontal and Vertical Lines

What is the slope of a horizontal line or vertical line? We will explore this question in Examples 6 and 7.

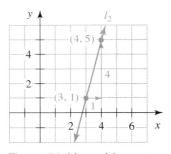

Figure 51 Line with greater slope

▶ **Example 6** Investigating the Slope of a Horizontal Line

Find the slope of the line that contains the points $(2, 3)$ and $(6, 3)$.

Solution

We plot the points $(2, 3)$ and $(6, 3)$ and sketch the line that contains the points (see Fig. 52).

The slope formula gives

$$m = \frac{3 - 3}{6 - 2} = \frac{0}{4} = 0$$

So, the slope of the horizontal line is zero. It makes sense that the horizontal line has slope equal to zero, because such a line has "no steepness."

◀

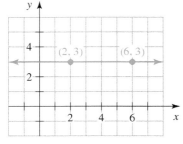

Figure 52 The horizontal line has slope equal to zero

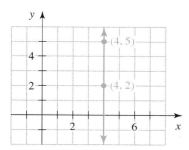

Figure 53 The vertical line has undefined slope

▶ **Example 7** Investigating the Slope of a Vertical Line

Find the slope of the line that contains the points $(4, 2)$ and $(4, 5)$.

Solution

We plot the points $(4, 2)$ and $(4, 5)$ and sketch the line that contains the points (see Fig. 53). The slope formula gives

$$m = \frac{5 - 2}{4 - 4} = \frac{3}{0}$$

Since division by zero is undefined, the slope of the vertical line is *undefined*.

▶ **Slopes of Horizontal and Vertical Lines**

- A horizontal line has slope equal to zero (see Fig. 54).
- A vertical line has undefined slope (see Fig. 55).

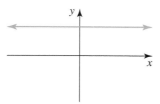

Figure 54 A horizontal line has slope equal to zero

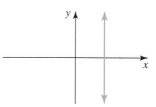

Figure 55 A vertical line has undefined slope

Parallel and Perpendicular Lines

Two lines are called **parallel** if they do not intersect (see Fig. 56). In Example 8, we compare the slopes of two parallel lines.

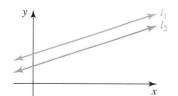

Figure 56 Two parallel lines

▶ **Example 8** Finding Slopes of Parallel Lines

Find the slopes of the parallel lines l_1 and l_2 sketched in Fig. 57.

Solution

For both lines, if the run is 3, the rise is 1 (see Fig. 58). So, the slope of both lines is

$$m = \frac{\text{rise}}{\text{run}} = \frac{1}{3}$$

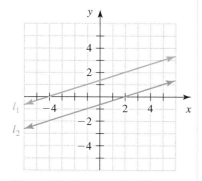

Figure 57 Two parallel lines

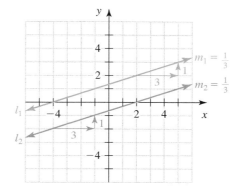

Figure 58 Calculate the slopes of the parallel lines

It makes sense that nonvertical parallel lines have equal slope, since parallel lines have the same steepness.

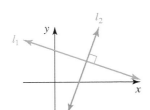

Figure 59 Two perpendicular lines

Slopes of Parallel Lines

If lines l_1 and l_2 are nonvertical parallel lines on the same coordinate system, then the slopes of the lines are equal:

$$m_1 = m_2$$

Also, if two distinct lines have equal slope, then the lines are parallel.

Two lines are called **perpendicular** if they intersect at a 90° angle (see Fig. 59). In Example 9, we compare the slopes of two perpendicular lines.

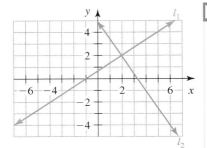

Figure 60 Two perpendicular lines

▶ **Example 9**   Finding Slopes of Perpendicular Lines

Find the slopes of the perpendicular lines l_1 and l_2 in Fig. 60.

Solution

From Fig. 61, we see that the slope of line l_1 is $m_1 = \dfrac{2}{3}$ and that the slope of line l_2 is

$$m_1 = \frac{-3}{2} = -\frac{3}{2}.$$

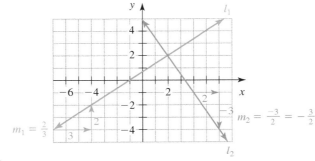

Figure 61 Calculate the slopes of the perpendicular lines

In Example 9, the slope $-\dfrac{3}{2}$ is the opposite of the reciprocal of the slope $\dfrac{2}{3}$.

Slopes of Perpendicular Lines

If lines l_1 and l_2 are nonvertical perpendicular lines, then the slope of one line is the opposite of the reciprocal of the slope of the other line:

$$m_2 = -\frac{1}{m_1}$$

Also, if the slope of one line is the opposite of the reciprocal of another line's slope, then the lines are perpendicular.

▶ **Example 10**   Finding Slopes of Parallel and Perpendicular Lines

A line l_1 has slope $\dfrac{3}{7}$.

1. If line l_2 is parallel to line l_1, find the slope of line l_2.
2. If line l_3 is perpendicular to line l_1, find the slope of line l_3.

Solution

1. The slopes of lines l_2 and l_1 are equal, so line l_2 has slope $\dfrac{3}{7}$.

2. The slope of line l_3 is the opposite of the reciprocal of $\dfrac{3}{7}$, or $-\dfrac{7}{3}$.

Group Exploration

For a line, rise over run is constant

1. A line is sketched in Fig. 62. Plot the points $(-2, -5)$, $(1, 1)$, and $(3, 5)$. (Plotted correctly, these points will lie on the line.)

2. Using the points $(-2, -5)$ and $(1, 1)$, find the slope of the line.

3. Using the points $(1, 1)$ and $(3, 5)$, find the slope of the line.

4. Using the points $(-2, -5)$ and $(3, 5)$, find the slope of the line.

5. Using two other points of your choice, find the slope of the line.

6. What do you notice about the slopes you have calculated? Does it matter which two points on a line are used to find the slope of the line?

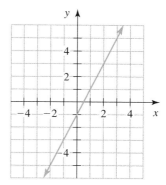

Figure 62 Use different pairs of points to calculate the slope

Group Exploration

Looking ahead: Slope addition property

1. Complete Table 9.

Table 9 Solutions of Three Equations

$y = 2x + 1$		$y = 3x - 5$		$y = -2x + 6$	
x	y	x	y	x	y
0		0		0	
1		1		1	
2		2		2	
3		3		3	
4		4		4	

2. In Table 9, the x-coordinates increase by 1 each time. For each equation, what do you notice about the y-coordinates? Compare what you notice with the coefficient of x in each equation.

3. Describe what the pattern from Problem 2 would be in general for any equation of the form $y = mx + b$.

4. Create an equation of the form $y = mx + b$, and check whether it behaves as you described in Problem 3.

5. Substitute 1 for x in the equation $y = mx + b$. Then substitute 2 for x. Then substitute 3. Explain why these results suggest that your description in Problem 3 is correct.

▶ **Tips for Success** **Use Your Instructor's Office Hours**

Helping students during office hours is part of an instructor's job. Your instructor wants you to succeed and hopes you take advantage of all opportunities to learn.

Come prepared to office visits. For example, if you are having trouble with a concept, attempt some related exercises and bring your work so your instructor can see where you are having difficulty. If you miss a class, to get the most out of the visit, read the material first, borrow class notes, and try completing assigned exercises before visiting your instructor.

Homework 1.3

For extra help ▶ MyMathLab®   Watch the videos in MyMathLab   Download the MyDashboard App

1. A portion of road A climbs steadily for 120 feet over a horizontal distance of 4000 feet. A portion of road B climbs steadily for 160 feet over a horizontal distance of 6500 feet. Which road is steeper? Explain.

2. Airplane A climbs steadily for 2500 feet over a horizontal distance of 8000 feet. Airplane B climbs steadily for 3100 feet over a horizontal distance of 9500 feet. Which plane is climbing more steeply? Explain.

3. Ski run A declines steadily for 90 yards over a horizontal distance of 300 yards. Ski run B declines steadily for 125 yards over a horizontal distance of 450 yards. Which run is steeper? Explain.

4. A ski run declines steadily from the top of a mountain to a chairlift. Then the run continues to decline with a different constant steepness, to end at a restaurant on the mountain. The horizontal distance for the entire run is 1300 yards over a vertical decline of 415 yards. The horizontal distance from the top of the mountain to the chairlift is 400 yards over a vertical decline of 100 yards. Find (the absolute value of) the "slopes" of each part of the run.

Find the slope of the line passing through the given points. State whether the line is increasing, decreasing, horizontal, or vertical.

5. $(2, 3)$ and $(5, 9)$

6. $(1, 8)$ and $(5, 4)$

7. $(-5, 7)$ and $(1, 3)$

8. $(2, 6)$ and $(8, -2)$

9. $(-4, 10)$ and $(2, -2)$

10. $(-3, 6)$ and $(1, -10)$

11. $(1, -2)$ and $(7, -4)$

12. $(2, -3)$ and $(6, -9)$

13. $(-5, -8)$ and $(4, -2)$

14. $(-1, -12)$ and $(7, -2)$

15. $(-4, -9)$ and $(-2, -1)$

16. $(-1, -6)$ and $(-2, -5)$

17. $(0, 0)$ and $(1, 1)$

18. $(0, 0)$ and $(100, 100)$

19. $(2, 6)$ and $(7, 6)$

20. $(-3, -1)$ and $(5, -1)$

21. $(-6, -2)$ and $(-6, 5)$

22. $(4, -1)$ and $(4, 8)$

23. $(5, 0)$ and $(0, -2)$

24. $(-6, 0)$ and $(0, -3)$

Find the slope of the line passing through the given points. Round your result to the second decimal place. State whether the line is increasing, decreasing, horizontal, or vertical.

25. $(1.2, 5.4)$ and $(3.9, 2.6)$

26. $(-3.9, 2.2)$ and $(-5.1, -7.4)$

27. $(8.94, -17.94)$ and $(21.13, -2.34)$

28. $(-25.41, 82.78)$ and $(-11.26, -66.66)$

29. Find the slope of the line sketched in Fig. 63.

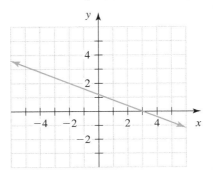

Figure 63 Exercise 29

30. Find the slope of the line sketched in Fig. 64.

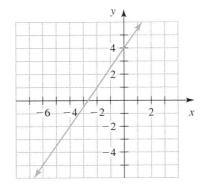

Figure 64 Exercise 30

For Exercises 31–40, using the indicated slopes of lines l_1 and l_2, determine whether the lines are parallel, perpendicular, or neither. Assume the lines are not the same.

31. $m_1 = 2, m_2 = 2$

32. $m_1 = 5, m_2 = 5$

33. $m_1 = 6, m_2 = -6$

34. $m_1 = 1, m_2 = -1$

35. $m_1 = \frac{2}{7}, m_2 = -\frac{7}{2}$

36. $m_1 = -\frac{3}{5}, m_2 = \frac{5}{3}$

37. $m_1 = \frac{7}{4}, m_2 = \frac{4}{7}$

38. $m_1 = \frac{5}{8}, m_2 = \frac{5}{8}$

39. $m_1 = 0, m_2$ is undefined

40. m_1 and m_2 are undefined

41. Are the lines sketched in Fig. 65 perpendicular? Explain.

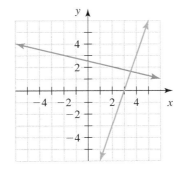

Figure 65 Exercise 41

42. Are the lines sketched in Fig. 66 parallel? Explain.

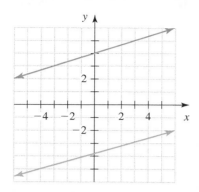

Figure 66 Exercise 42

Sketch a line that has the indicated slope.

43. $m = \dfrac{2}{5}$

44. $m = \dfrac{4}{3}$

45. $m = -\dfrac{4}{3}$ $\left[\textbf{Hint: } -\dfrac{4}{3} = \dfrac{-4}{3}\right]$

46. $m = -\dfrac{2}{3}$

47. $m = 3$ $\left[\textbf{Hint: } 3 = \dfrac{3}{1}\right]$

48. $m = -2$ **49.** $m = 0$ **50.** m is undefined

Concepts

51. For each line sketched in Fig. 67, determine whether the line's slope is positive, negative, zero, or undefined.

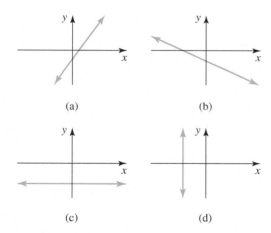

(a)   (b)

(c)   (d)

Figure 67 Exercise 51

52. Draw a line that passes through the origin $(0, 0)$ and has slope $\dfrac{-2}{6}$. Then draw a line that passes through the origin and has slope $\dfrac{1}{-3}$. Explain why it makes sense that the lines are the same.

53. Sketch a line with slope 2 and another line with slope 3. Which line is steeper?

54. Sketch a line with slope 2 and another line with slope -2. Which line is steeper?

Sketch a line that meets the description. Find the slope of that line.

55. An increasing line that is nearly horizontal

56. A decreasing line that is nearly horizontal

57. A decreasing line that is nearly vertical

58. An increasing line that is nearly vertical

For Exercises 59–62, sketch a line that meets the given description.

59. The slope is a large positive number.

60. The slope is a positive number near zero.

61. The slope is a negative number near zero.

62. The slope is less than -5.

63. A student tries to find the slope of the line that contains the points $(2, 5)$ and $(4, 8)$ as follows:

$$\frac{4 - 2}{8 - 5} = \frac{2}{3}$$

Describe any errors. Then find the slope correctly.

64. A student tries to find the slope of the line that contains the points $(7, 1)$ and $(2, 9)$ as follows:

$$\frac{9 - 1}{7 - 2} = \frac{8}{5}$$

Describe any errors. Then find the slope correctly.

65. A line contains the points $(2, 7)$ and $(3, 10)$. Find three more points that lie on the line.

66. A line contains the points $(-6, -4)$ and $(-3, 1)$. Find three more points that lie on the line.

67. a. Carefully graph the given equation by hand. Then find the slope of the line by using the ratio $\dfrac{\text{rise}}{\text{run}}$.

    i. $y = 2x + 1$ **ii.** $y = 3x - 5$ **iii.** $y = -2x + 6$

   b. Compare the slope of each line with the coefficient of x in the corresponding equation.

68. a. Use the expression $\dfrac{y_2 - y_1}{x_2 - x_1}$ to find the slope of the line that contains the points $(x_1, y_1) = (2, 3)$ and $(x_2, y_2) = (7, 5)$.

   b. Use the expression $\dfrac{y_1 - y_2}{x_1 - x_2}$ to find the slope of the line that contains the points $(x_1, y_1) = (2, 3)$ and $(x_2, y_2) = (7, 5)$.

   c. Compare your results from parts (a) and (b).

   d. Show that $\dfrac{y_2 - y_1}{x_2 - x_1} = \dfrac{y_1 - y_2}{x_1 - x_2}$, where (x_1, y_1) and (x_2, y_2) are two distinct points of a nonvertical line. [**Hint:** $a - b = -(b - a)$]

   e. When using two given points on a line to calculate the slope of the line, does it matter which point we choose to be first, (x_1, y_1), and which second, (x_2, y_2)? Explain.

69. Explore the relationship among three lines that pass through the origin $(0, 0)$, where the slope of one of the lines is the reciprocal of the slope of one of the other lines.

   a. By hand, carefully sketch the lines that pass through the origin $(0, 0)$ and that have slopes 5, 1, and $\dfrac{1}{5}$.

b. Sketch the lines that pass through the origin $(0, 0)$ and that have slopes $\frac{2}{5}$, 1, and $\frac{5}{2}$.

c. Sketch the lines that pass through the origin $(0, 0)$ and that have slopes $\frac{3}{4}$, 1, and $\frac{4}{3}$.

d. What pattern do you notice from your graphs in parts (a)–(c)?

e. A line with slope m is sketched in Fig. 68. Sketch a line with slope $\frac{1}{m}$ that passes through the origin $(0, 0)$. Assume both axes are scaled the same.

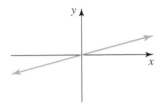

Figure 68 Exercise 69e

70. a. A square has vertices at $(3, 1)$ and $(3, 7)$. How many possible positions are there for the other two vertices? Find the coordinates for each possibility.

b. A parallelogram has vertices at $(-7, -2)$, $(3, 1)$, and $(-4, 2)$. How many possible positions are there for the fourth vertex? Find the coordinates for each possibility. [**Hint:** Try drawing different line segments between the given vertices.]

71. Suppose that a line with slope $-\frac{2}{3}$ contains a point P. A point Q lies three units to the right and two units down from point P. A point S lies three units to the left and two units up from point P. Does the line contain point Q? point S? Explain.

72. Draw a sketch of a road with a grade of 5%.

73. Explain why a decreasing line has negative slope.

74. Describe the meaning of the slope of a line. Sketch various types of lines and give the slope for each line. For each sketch, explain why the slope assignment makes sense. For example, you could sketch a horizontal line, state that the slope is zero, and explain why it makes sense that the slope of a horizontal line is zero in terms of rise and run.

1.4 Meaning of Slope for Equations, Graphs, and Tables

Objectives

» Find the slope and y-intercept of a nonvertical line from an equation in *slope–intercept form*.

» Know the *vertical change property*.

» Use slope and y-intercept to sketch the graph of an equation of the form $y = mx + b$.

» Know the *slope addition property*.

In this section, we will discuss what *slope* means with regards to equations, graphs, and tables. We will also use these meanings to graph a linear equation with defined slope.

Finding Slope from a Linear Equation

How can we use an equation of a nonvertical line to find the line's slope?

▶ **Example 1**   Finding the Slope of a Line

Find the slope of the line $y = 2x + 1$.

Solution

We use $x = 0, 1, 2, 3$ in Table 10 to list solutions, and we sketch the graph of the equation in Fig. 69.

If the run is 1, the rise is 2 (see Fig. 69). So, the slope is

$$m = \frac{\text{rise}}{\text{run}} = \frac{2}{1} = 2$$

Table 10 Solutions of $y = 2x + 1$

x	y
0	1
1	3
2	5
3	7

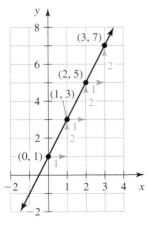

Figure 69 Graph of $y = 2x + 1$

From Example 1, we can make three observations about the slope of the nonvertical line $y = 2x + 1$:

1. The coefficient of x is 2, which is the slope.
2. If the run is 1, then the rise is 2 (the slope). See Fig. 69.
3. As the value of x increases by 1, the value of y increases by 2 (the slope). See Table 10.

Table 11 Solutions of $y = -3x + 8$

x	y
0	8
1	5
2	2
3	−1

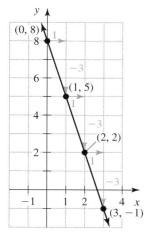

Figure 70 Graph of $y = -3x + 8$

▶ **Example 2** Finding the Slope of a Line

Find the slope of the line $y = -3x + 8$.

Solution

Some solutions are listed in Table 11, and a graph is sketched in Fig. 70.

$$\text{The slope is } m = \frac{\text{rise}}{\text{run}} = \frac{-3}{1} = -3.$$

▶

From Example 2, we can make three observations about the slope of the nonvertical line $y = -3x + 8$:

1. The coefficient of x is -3, which is the slope.
2. If the run is 1, then the rise is -3 (the slope). See Fig. 70.
3. As the value of x increases by 1, the value of y changes by -3 (the slope). See Table 11.

Our first observations made after both Examples 1 and 2 suggest a general property about slope.

▶ **Finding the Slope from a Linear Equation of the Form $y = mx + b$**

For a linear equation of the form $y = mx + b$, m is the slope of the line.

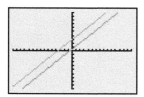

Figure 71 Graphs of the two parallel lines

▶ **Example 3** Identifying Parallel or Perpendicular Lines

Are the lines $y = \dfrac{5}{6}x + 3$ and $12y - 10x = 5$ parallel, perpendicular, or neither?

Solution

For the line $y = \dfrac{5}{6}x + 3$, the slope is $\dfrac{5}{6}$. For $12y - 10x = 5$, the slope is *not* -10. To find the slope, we begin by solving the equation $12y - 10x = 5$ for y:

$$12y - 10x = 5 \qquad \text{\textit{Original equation}}$$
$$12y - 10x + 10x = 5 + 10x \qquad \text{\textit{Add 10x to both sides.}}$$
$$12y = 10x + 5 \qquad \text{\textit{Combine like terms; rearrange terms.}}$$
$$\frac{12y}{12} = \frac{10}{12}x + \frac{5}{12} \qquad \text{\textit{Divide both sides by 12.}}$$
$$y = \frac{5}{6}x + \frac{5}{12} \qquad \text{\textit{Simplify.}}$$

For $y = \dfrac{5}{6}x + \dfrac{5}{12}$, the slope is $\dfrac{5}{6}$, the same as the slope of the line $y = \dfrac{5}{6}x + 3$. Therefore, the two lines are parallel. We use ZStandard followed by ZSquare to draw the lines on the same coordinate system (see Fig. 71).

▶

Vertical Change Property

Our second observations made after both Examples 1 and 2 suggest a general property of a line $y = mx + b$.

▶ **Vertical Change Property**

For a line $y = mx + b$, if the run is 1, then the rise is the slope m. (See Figs. 72 and 73.)

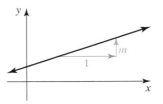

Figure 72 Vertical change property for positive slope

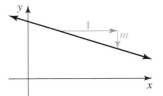

Figure 73 Vertical change property for negative slope

Finding the y-Intercept from a Linear Equation

When we sketch graphs of equations of the form $y = mx + b$, it is helpful to know the y-intercept. Substituting 0 for x in the equation $y = mx + b$ gives

$$y = m(0) + b = b$$

which shows that the y-intercept is $(0, b)$.

▶ **Finding the y-Intercept from a Linear Equation of the Form $y = mx + b$**

For a linear equation of the form $y = mx + b$, the y-intercept is $(0, b)$.

For instance, in Example 1, the line $y = 2x + 1$ has y-intercept $(0, 1)$. In Example 2, the line $y = -3x + 8$ has y-intercept $(0, 8)$. We say both equations are in slope–intercept form.

▶ **Definition   Slope–intercept form**

If an equation is of the form $y = mx + b$, we say it is in **slope–intercept form.**

Graphing Linear Equations

In Example 4, we will graph an equation in slope–intercept form.

▶ **Example 4**   Using Slope to Graph a Linear Equation

Sketch the graph of $y = 3x - 1$.

Solution

Note that the y-intercept is $(0, -1)$ and that the slope is $3 = \dfrac{3}{1} = \dfrac{\text{rise}}{\text{run}}$. To graph,

1. Plot the y-intercept, $(0, -1)$.
2. From $(0, -1)$, look 1 unit to the right and 3 units up to plot a second point, which we see by inspection is $(1, 2)$. See Fig. 74.
3. Sketch the line that contains these two points (see Fig. 75).

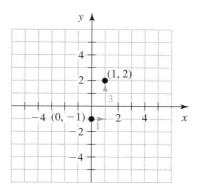

Figure 74 Plot $(0, -1)$. Then look 1 unit to the right and 3 units up, which gives $(1, 2)$

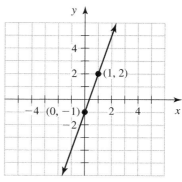

Figure 75 Sketch the line containing $(0, -1)$ and $(1, 2)$

We use ZDecimal to verify our graph (see Fig. 76).

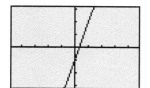

Figure 76 Use ZDecimal to verify our graph

> **Using Slope to Graph a Linear Equation of the Form $y = mx + b$**
>
> To sketch the graph of a linear equation of the form $y = mx + b$,
> 1. Plot the y-intercept $(0, b)$.
> 2. Use $m = \dfrac{\text{rise}}{\text{run}}$ to plot a second point. For example, if $m = -\dfrac{2}{5} = \dfrac{-2}{5}$, then look 5 units to the right (from the y-intercept) and 2 units down to plot another point.
> 3. Sketch the line that passes through the two plotted points.

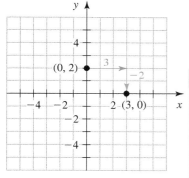

Figure 77 Plot $(0, 2)$. Then look 3 units to the right and 2 units down, which gives $(3, 0)$

> **Example 5** Using Slope to Graph a Linear Equation

Sketch the graph of $2x + 3y = 6$.

Solution

First, we write the equation in slope–intercept form:

$$2x + 3y = 6 \qquad \textit{Original equation}$$
$$2x + 3y - 2x = 6 - 2x \qquad \textit{Subtract 2x from both sides.}$$
$$3y = -2x + 6 \qquad \textit{Combine like terms; rearrange terms.}$$
$$\frac{3y}{3} = \frac{-2x}{3} + \frac{6}{3} \qquad \textit{Divide both sides by 3.}$$
$$y = -\frac{2}{3}x + 2 \qquad \textit{Simplify; } \frac{-a}{b} = -\frac{a}{b}$$

The y-intercept is $(0, 2)$, and the slope is $-\dfrac{2}{3} = \dfrac{-2}{3} = \dfrac{\text{rise}}{\text{run}}$. To graph,

1. Plot the y-intercept, $(0, 2)$.
2. From $(0, 2)$, look 3 units to the right and 2 units down to plot a second point, which we see by inspection is $(3, 0)$. See Fig. 77.
3. Then sketch the line that contains these two points (see Fig. 78).

    We can verify our result by checking that both $(0, 2)$ and $(3, 0)$ are solutions of $2x + 3y = 6$.

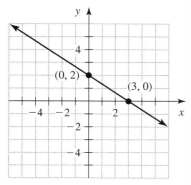

Figure 78 Sketch the line containing $(0, 2)$ and $(3, 0)$

Before we can use the *y*-intercept and the slope to graph a linear equation, we must solve for *y* to put the equation into the form $y = mx + b$.

WARNING   It is a common error to think the slope of the graph of an equation such as $2x + 3y = 6$ is 2, because 2 is the coefficient of *x*. We must first solve for *y* (and get the equation $y = -\frac{2}{3}x + 2$) to determine the slope, which is $-\frac{2}{3}$ (see Example 5).

▶ **Example 6**   Working with a General Linear Equation

1. Determine the slope and the *y*-intercept of the graph of $ax + by = c$, where *a*, *b*, and *c* are constants and *b* is nonzero.
2. Find the slope and the *y*-intercept of the graph of $3x + 7y = 5$.

Solution

1.
$$ax + by = c \qquad \textit{Original equation}$$
$$ax + by - ax = c - ax \qquad \textit{Subtract ax from both sides.}$$
$$by = -ax + c \qquad \textit{Combine like terms; rearrange terms.}$$
$$\frac{by}{b} = \frac{-ax}{b} + \frac{c}{b} \qquad \textit{Divide both sides by b.}$$
$$y = -\frac{a}{b}x + \frac{c}{b} \qquad \textit{Simplify; } \frac{-a}{b} = -\frac{a}{b}$$

The slope is $-\frac{a}{b}$, and the *y*-intercept is $\left(0, \frac{c}{b}\right)$.

2. We substitute 3 for *a*, 7 for *b*, and 5 for *c* in our results from Problem 1 to find that the slope is $-\frac{3}{7}$ and the *y*-intercept is $\left(0, \frac{5}{7}\right)$.

▶

▶ **Example 7**   Working with a General Linear Equation

Determine the slope and *y*-intercept of the graph of $a(y + c) = x$, where *a* and *c* are constants and *a* is nonzero.

Solution
$$a(y + c) = x \qquad \textit{Original equation}$$
$$\frac{a(y + c)}{a} = \frac{x}{a} \qquad \textit{Divide both sides by a.}$$
$$y + c = \frac{x}{a} \qquad \textit{Simplify.}$$
$$y + c - c = \frac{x}{a} - c \qquad \textit{Subtract c from both sides.}$$
$$y = \frac{1}{a}x - c \qquad \textit{Combine like terms: } \frac{x}{a} = \frac{1}{a} \cdot \frac{x}{1} = \frac{1}{a}x$$

The slope is $\frac{1}{a}$, and the *y*-intercept is $(0, -c)$.

▶

Slope Addition Property

Our third observations made after both Examples 1 and 2 suggest a general property of a table of solutions of an equation of the form $y = mx + b$.

> ### Slope Addition Property
>
> For a linear equation of the form $y = mx + b$, if the value of the independent variable increases by 1, then the value of the dependent variable changes by the slope m.

For example, consider the equation $y = -5x + 4$. We know that as the value of x increases by 1, the value of y changes by -5.

▶ **Example 8**   Identifying Possible Linear Equations

Four sets of points are described in Table 12. For each set, decide whether there is a line that passes through every point. If so, find the slope of that line. If not, decide whether there is a line that comes close to every point.

Table 12 Four Sets of Points

Set 1		Set 2		Set 3		Set 4	
x	y	x	y	x	y	x	y
1	23	4	12	0	3	50	8
2	20	5	17	1	6	51	8
3	17	6	22	2	12	52	8
4	14	7	27	3	24	53	8
5	11	8	32	4	48	54	8

Solution

1. For set 1, when the value of x increases by 1, the value of y changes by -3. So, a line with slope -3 passes through every point.
2. For set 2, when the value of x increases by 1, the value of y changes by 5. Therefore, a line with slope 5 passes through every point.
3. For set 3, when the value of x increases by 1, the value of y does not change by the same value. So, a line does not pass through every point. Further, a line does not come close to every point, because the value of y changes by such different amounts each time the value of x increases by 1.
4. For set 4, when the value of x increases by 1, the value of y changes by 0. Therefore, a line with slope 0 (the horizontal line $y = 8$) passes through every point.

▶

Group Exploration

Drawing lines with various slopes

1. On a graphing calculator, graph a group of lines (a *family of lines*) to make a starburst like the one in Fig. 79. List the equations of your lines.

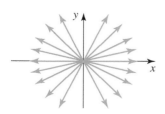

Figure 79 A starburst

2. On a graphing calculator, graph a family of lines to make a starburst like the one in Fig. 80. List the equations of your lines.

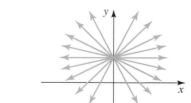

Figure 80 Another starburst

3. Summarize what you have learned about slope from this exploration, this section, and Section 1.3.

 Group Exploration

Looking ahead: Finding an equation of a line

Some solutions of four linear equations are provided in Table 13. Find an equation of each of the four lines.

Table 13 Solutions of Four Linear Equations

Equation 1		Equation 2		Equation 3		Equation 4	
x	y	x	y	x	y	x	y
0	5	3	10	2	7	1	17
1	8	4	8	4	12	3	13
2	11	5	6	6	17	5	9
3	14	6	4	8	22	7	5

 Homework 1.4

For extra help ▶ **MyMathLab®**   Watch the videos in MyMathLab   Download the MyDashboard App

Determine the slope and y-intercept of the graph of the linear equation. Use the slope and y-intercept to graph the equation by hand. Verify your graph by using ZStandard followed by ZSquare on a graphing calculator.

1. $y = 6x + 1$
2. $y = 3x + 6$
3. $y = -2x + 7$
4. $y = -3x + 5$
5. $y = \frac{5}{4}x - 2$
6. $y = \frac{1}{2}x - 8$
7. $y = -\frac{3}{7}x + 2$
8. $y = -\frac{4}{3}x + 1$
9. $y = -\frac{5}{3}x - 1$
10. $y = -\frac{2}{5}x - 3$
11. $y + x = 5$
12. $2x + y = -1$
13. $-7x + 2y = 10$
14. $3y - 5x = 6$
15. $3(x - 2y) = 9$
16. $2(y - 3x) = 8$
17. $2x - 3y + 9 = 12$
18. $-5x - 15y + 23 = 3$
19. $4x - 5y + 3 = 2x - 2y - 3$
20. $3y - 6x + 2 = 7y - x - 6$
21. $1 - 3(y - 2x) = 7 + 3(x - 3y)$
22. $8 - 2(y - 3x) = 2 + 4(x - 2y)$
23. $y = 4x$
24. $y = -7x$
25. $y = -1.5x + 3$
26. $y = 0.25x - 2$
27. $y = x$
28. $y = -x$
29. $y = 4$
30. $y = 0$
31. $y + 2 = 0$
32. $y - 3 = 0$

Determine the slope and y-intercept of the graph of the given equation, where a, b, c, and d are nonzero constants.

33. $ax - by = c$
34. $ax + by + c = 0$
35. $ay = b(x - d)$
36. $ay = b(x + d)$
37. $a(y + b) = x$
38. $a(y - b) = x$

39. $a(x - y) = d$
40. $a(x + y) = d$
41. $\frac{x}{a} + \frac{y}{a} = 1$
42. $\frac{y + b}{a} = x$

43. Four sets of points are described in Table 14. For each set, decide whether there is a line that passes through every point. If so, find the slope of that line. If not, decide whether there is a line that comes close to every point.

Table 14 Four Sets of Points

Set 1		Set 2		Set 3		Set 4	
x	y	x	y	x	y	x	y
1	6	1	5.9	1	3	50	90
2	106	2	5.6	11	8	51	80
3	205	3	5.3	13	13	52	70
4	305	4	5.0	20	18	53	60
5	406	5	4.7	40	23	54	50
6	505	6	4.4	90	28	55	40

44. Four sets of points are described in Table 15. For each set, decide whether there is a line that passes through every point. If so, find the slope of that line. If not, decide whether there is a line that comes close to every point.

Table 15 Four Sets of Points

Set 1		Set 2		Set 3		Set 4	
x	y	x	y	x	y	x	y
0	50	3	2	1	8	5	1
1	47	5	5	2	8	5	9
2	44	7	8	3	8	5	10
3	41	9	11	4	8	5	40
4	38	11	14	5	8	5	46
5	35	13	17	6	8	5	99

45. Some values of four linear equations are provided in Table 16. Complete the table.

Table 16 Values of Four Linear Equations

Equation 1		Equation 2		Equation 3		Equation 4	
x	y	x	y	x	y	x	y
1	12	23	69	1		30	15
2	15	24	53	2		31	
3		25		3	35	32	
4		26		4		33	
5		27		5		34	
6		28		6	17	35	60

46. Some values of four linear equations are provided in Table 17. Complete the table.

Table 17 Values of Four Linear Equations

Equation 1		Equation 2		Equation 3		Equation 4	
x	y	x	y	x	y	x	y
0	16	0		1	36	10	80
1	23	1		2		11	
2		2		3		12	
3		3	6	4		13	
4		4		5		14	70
5		5	14	6	16	15	

Determine whether the given pair of lines is parallel, perpendicular, or neither. Explain.

47. $y = 4x + 7$ and $y = 4x - 3$

48. $y = 7x - 2$ and $y = -7x - 5$

49. $y = \dfrac{3}{8}x + 1$ and $y = \dfrac{8}{3}x + 4$

50. $y = -\dfrac{5}{2}x$ and $y = \dfrac{2}{5}x - 3$

51. $2x + 3y = 6$ and $4x + 6y = 7$

52. $4x + y = 6$ and $x - 4y = 5$

53. $5x - 3y = 1$ and $3x + 5y = -2$

54. $8x - 4y = 1$ and $x + 2y = 6$

55. $x = -3$ and $x = 1$ **56.** $y = 5$ and $y = -2$

57. $x = 0$ and $y = 0$ **58.** $x = -2$ and $y = -4$

59. Let x be the driving time (in hours) since a person has fueled up his car, and let y be the number of gallons of gas in the car's gas tank. Assume the equation $y = -3x + 18$ describes the relationship between x and y.
a. Complete Table 18.

Table 18 Amounts of Gas in a Car's Gas Tank

Driving Time (hours) x	Amount of Gas (gallons) y
0	
1	
2	
3	
4	
5	
6	

b. By how much is the amount of gas decreasing each hour? Compare your result with the slope of the graph of $y = -3x + 18$. Discuss your observation in terms of the slope addition property.
c. If the person is driving at about 60 mph, what is the gas mileage of the car? [**Hint:** *Gas mileage* is the number of miles the car can travel on 1 gallon of gas.]

60. A person lowers her hot-air balloon by gradually releasing air from it. Let x be the number of minutes she has been releasing air from the balloon, and let y be the altitude (in feet) of the balloon. Assume the equation $y = -400x + 2400$ describes the relationship between x and y.
a. Complete Table 19.

Table 19 Altitudes of a Balloon

Time (minutes) x	Altitude (feet) y
0	
1	
2	
3	
4	
5	
6	

b. By how much is the altitude of the hot-air balloon decreasing each minute? Compare your result with the slope of the graph of $y = -400x + 2400$. Discuss your observation in terms of the slope addition property.

61. Let y be a person's salary (in thousands of dollars) after she has worked x years at a company. Assume the equation $y = 2x + 26$ describes the relationship between x and y.
a. Complete Table 20.

Table 20 Salaries

Time at Company (years) x	Salary (thousands of dollars) y
0	
1	
2	
3	
4	

b. By how much does the person's salary increase each year? Compare your result with the slope of the graph of $y = 2x + 26$. Discuss your observation in terms of the slope addition property.

62. Let y be a college's enrollment (in thousands of students), and let x be the number of years the college has been open. Assume the equation $y = 0.5x + 6$ describes the relationship between x and y.

a. Complete Table 21.

Table 21 Enrollments

Number of Years College Has Been Open x	Enrollment (thousand of students) y
0	
1	
2	
3	
4	

b. By how much does the college's enrollment increase each year? Compare your result with the slope of the graph of $y = 0.5x + 6$. Discuss your observation in terms of the slope addition property.

Concepts

63. Graphs of four equations are shown in Fig. 81. State whether m and b are positive, negative, zero, or undefined for the $y = mx + b$ form of each equation.

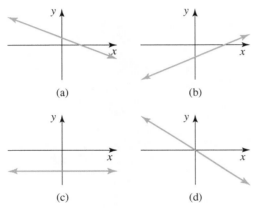

(a)   (b)

(c)   (d)

Figure 81 Exercise 63

64. On a graphing calculator, graph five equations whose graphs are five parallel lines like those in Fig. 82. List your equations.

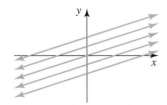

Figure 82 A family of parallel lines for Exercise 64

65. Find an equation of the line sketched in Fig. 83.

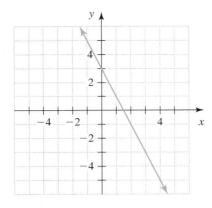

Figure 83 Exercise 65

66. Find an equation of the line sketched in Fig. 84.

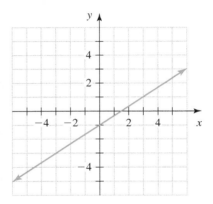

Figure 84 Exercise 66

For Exercises 67–70, write an equation of

67. an increasing line that is nearly horizontal with y-intercept above the origin.

68. an increasing line that is nearly vertical with y-intercept below the origin.

69. a decreasing line that is nearly vertical with y-intercept below the origin.

70. a decreasing line that is nearly horizontal with y-intercept above the origin.

71. a. Use a graphing calculator to graph the line $y = x$ by using the ZDecimal window settings displayed in Fig. 85. [***Graphing Calculator:*** *See Appendix B.7.*]

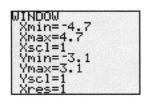

Figure 85 Window for Exercise 71a

b. Graph $y = x$ by using the window settings displayed in Fig. 86.

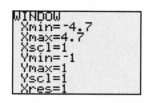

Figure 86 Window for Exercise 71b

c. Graph $y = x$ by using the window settings displayed in Fig. 87.

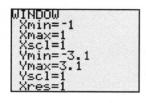

Figure 87 Window for Exercise 71c

d. Compare the results of parts (a) and (b). Explain the different views of $y = x$. Do the same for parts (a) and (c).

e. Can you make the graph of $y = x$ appear to be a decreasing line by adjusting the window settings? Can you make the graph of $y = x$ cross the y-axis at a point other than $(0, 0)$ (the origin) by changing the window settings? Describe all possible appearances of the graph of $y = x$ obtained by using various window settings.

72. a. Use a graphing calculator to graph $y = 0.0005x + 0.003$. You might observe that no graph appears to be drawn on your calculator screen. This does not mean that the calculator is broken! To locate the line, think about its slope and y-intercept. Then use TRACE to confirm your suspicion. Try changing your window settings so you can see the graph clearly. Record a window setting that allows the graph to be seen.

b. Use a graphing calculator to graph $y = -3x + 20{,}000$. Record a window setting that allows you to see the graph.

c. Use a graphing calculator to graph $y = 4000x - 0.04$. Record a window setting that allows you to see the graph.

73. A line passes through the point $(0, -3)$ and has slope 2. What is an equation of the line?

74. A line passes through the point $(0, 4)$ and has slope -5. What is an equation of the line?

75. A line passes through the point $(3, 8)$ and has slope 5.
a. Sketch the line by hand.
b. Find an equation of the line. [**Hint:** Use part (a) to find b for $y = mx + b$.]

c. Use a graphing calculator to verify that your equation is correct.

76. A line passes through the point $(-2, 7)$ and has slope -6.
a. Sketch the line by hand.
b. Find an equation of the line. [**Hint:** Use part (a) to find b for $y = mx + b$.]
c. Use a graphing calculator to verify that your equation is correct.

77. A line passes through the point $(2, 6)$ and has slope $-\dfrac{3}{8}$.
a. Sketch the line by hand.
b. Estimate an equation of the line.
c. Use a graphing calculator to verify that your equation is correct.

78. A line passes through the point $(-3, 2)$ and has slope $\dfrac{1}{4}$.
a. Sketch the line by hand.
b. Estimate an equation of the line.
c. Use a graphing calculator to verify that your equation is correct.

79. a. Find the slope of each line: $y = 2$, $y = -5$, and $y = 3.72$.
b. Find the slope of the graph of any linear equation of the form $y = k$.

80. a. Find the slope of each line: $x = 3$, $x = -6$, and $x = -7.9$.
b. Find the slope of the graph of any equation of the form $x = k$.

81. A student says the line $2x + 3y = 6$ has slope 2 because the coefficient of x is 2. Is the student correct? Explain.

82. A student says the line $y = 3x - 5$ has slope $3x$. Is the student correct? Explain.

83. Explain why the graph of an equation of the form $y = mx + b$ has y-intercept $(0, b)$.

84. Create an equation of the form $y = mx + b$. Find two points on the graph of your equation by substituting two values for x. Use the two points to calculate the slope of the line and compare the result with your chosen value of m.

85. Explain why the slope addition property makes sense. Include a table of ordered pairs for a linear equation. (See page 4 for guidelines on writing a good response.)

86. The graph of a linear equation can be sketched by
• plotting points,
• using the slope and the y-intercept (sometimes), and
• using the x-intercept and the y-intercept (sometimes).

Discuss how to use each method to sketch the graph of a linear equation. For each method, describe the types of equations, if any, for which you would sketch graphs by that method. (See page 4 for guidelines on writing a good response.)

▼ 1.5 Finding Linear Equations

Objectives

» Use the slope–intercept form to find an equation of a line.

» Use the *point–slope form* to find an equation of a line.

In this section, we will discuss two methods of finding an equation of a line: slope–intercept form, which we worked with in Section 1.4, and another form of an equation of a line, called *point–slope form*.

Method 1: Using Slope–Intercept Form

In Example 1, we will use the concept that a point that lies on a line satisfies an equation of the line.

▶ **Example 1**   Using Slope and a Point to Find an Equation of a Line

Find an equation of the line that has slope $m = 3$ and contains the point $(2, 5)$.

Solution

Recall from Section 1.4 that the equation for a nonvertical line can be put into the form $y = mx + b$. Since $m = 3$, we have

$$y = 3x + b$$

To find b, recall from Section 1.2 that every point on the graph of an equation represents a solution of that equation. In particular, the ordered pair $(2, 5)$ should satisfy the equation $y = 3x + b$:

$$5 = 3(2) + b \qquad \text{Substitute 2 for x and 5 for y.}$$
$$5 = 6 + b \qquad \text{Multiply.}$$
$$5 - 6 = 6 + b - 6 \qquad \text{Subtract 6 from both sides.}$$
$$-1 = b \qquad \text{Simplify.}$$

Now we substitute -1 for b in $y = 3x + b$:

$$y = 3x - 1$$

Figure 88 Check that the line contains $(2, 5)$

We can use TRACE on a graphing calculator to verify that the graph of $y = 3x - 1$ contains the point $(2, 5)$. See Fig. 88. For graphing calculator instructions, see Appendix B.5.

▶

In Example 1, we used a point and the slope of a line to find an equation of the line. We can also use two points to find an equation of a line.

▶ **Example 2**   Using Two Points to Find an Equation of a Line

Find an equation of the line that contains the points $(-2, 6)$ and $(3, -4)$.

Solution

First, we find the slope of the line:

$$m = \frac{-4 - 6}{3 - (-2)} = \frac{-10}{3 + 2} = \frac{-10}{5} = -2$$

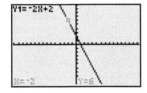

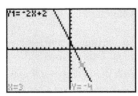

Figure 89 Check that the line contains both $(-2, 6)$ and $(3, -4)$

Thus, we have $y = -2x + b$. Since the line contains the point $(3, -4)$, we substitute 3 for x and -4 for y:

$$-4 = -2(3) + b \qquad \text{Substitute 3 for x and} -4 \text{ for y.}$$
$$-4 = -6 + b \qquad \text{Multiply.}$$
$$-4 + 6 = -6 + b + 6 \qquad \text{Add 6 to both sides.}$$
$$2 = b \qquad \text{Simplify.}$$

So, the equation is $y = -2x + 2$. We can use a graphing calculator to check that the graph of $y = -2x + 2$ contains both $(-2, 6)$ and $(3, -4)$. See Fig. 89.

▶

> ▶ **Finding a Linear Equation That Contains Two Given Points**
>
> To find an equation of the line that passes through two given points whose x-coordinates are different,
>
> 1. Use the slope formula, $m = \dfrac{y_2 - y_1}{x_2 - x_1}$, to find the slope of the line.
> 2. Substitute the m value you found in step 1 into the equation $y = mx + b$.
> 3. Substitute the coordinates of one of the given points into the equation you found in step 2, and solve for b.

4. Substitute the m value you found in step 1 and the b value you found in step 3 into the equation $y = mx + b$.

5. Use a graphing calculator to check that the graph of your equation contains the two given points.

In Example 3, we find an equation of a line whose slope is a fraction.

▶ **Example 3**   Using Two Points to Find an Equation of a Line

Find an equation of the line that passes through the points $(-3, -5)$ and $(2, -1)$.

Solution

First, we find the slope of the line:

$$m = \frac{-1 - (-5)}{2 - (-3)} = \frac{-1 + 5}{2 + 3} = \frac{4}{5}$$

Thus, we have $y = \frac{4}{5}x + b$. Since the line contains the point $(2, -1)$, we substitute 2 for x and -1 for y:

$$-1 = \frac{4}{5}(2) + b \qquad \text{\textit{Substitute 2 for x and} -1 \textit{for y.}}$$

$$-1 = \frac{8}{5} + b \qquad \frac{4}{5}(2) = \frac{4}{5}\left(\frac{2}{1}\right) = \frac{8}{5}$$

$$5 \cdot (-1) = 5 \cdot \frac{8}{5} + 5 \cdot b \qquad \text{\textit{Multiply both sides by 5.}}$$

$$-5 = 8 + 5b \qquad 5 \cdot \frac{8}{5} = \frac{5}{1}\cdot\frac{8}{5} = \frac{8}{1} = 8$$

$$-13 = 5b \qquad \text{\textit{Subtract 8 from both sides.}}$$

$$-\frac{13}{5} = b \qquad \text{\textit{Divide both sides by 5;}} \; \frac{-13}{5} = -\frac{13}{5}$$

So, the equation is $y = \frac{4}{5}x - \frac{13}{5}$. We can use a graphing calculator to check that the graph of $y = \frac{4}{5}x - \frac{13}{5}$ contains both $(-3, -5)$ and $(2, -1)$. See Fig. 90.

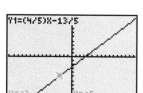
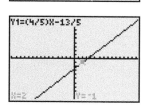

Figure 90 Check that the line contains both $(-3, -5)$ and $(2, -1)$

In Chapter 2, we will discuss how to find an approximate equation of a line to describe an authentic situation. Example 4 will help prepare us for that task.

▶ **Example 4**   Finding an Approximate Equation of a Line

Find an approximate equation of the line that contains the points $(-6.81, 7.17)$ and $(-2.47, 4.65)$. Round the slope and the constant term to two decimal places.

Solution

First, we find the slope of the line:

$$m = \frac{4.65 - 7.17}{-2.47 - (-6.81)} = \frac{-2.52}{4.34} \approx -0.58$$

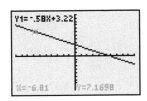

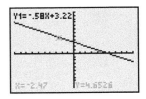

Figure 91 Check that the line comes very close to $(-6.81, 7.17)$ and $(-2.47, 4.65)$

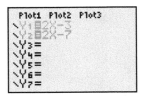

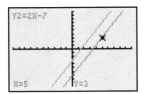

Figure 92 Check that the line contains $(5, 3)$ and is parallel to $y = 2x - 3$

So, we have $y = -0.58x + b$ Since the line contains the point $(-6.81, 7.17)$, we substitute -6.81 for x and 7.17 for y:

$$7.17 = -0.58(-6.81) + b \qquad \text{Substitute } -6.81 \text{ for } x \text{ and } 7.17 \text{ for } y.$$
$$7.17 = 3.9498 + b \qquad \text{Multiply.}$$
$$7.17 - 3.9498 = 3.9498 + b - 3.9498 \qquad \text{Subtract } 3.9498 \text{ from both sides.}$$
$$3.22 \approx b \qquad \text{Combine like terms.}$$

The approximate equation is $y = -0.58x + 3.22$.

We use a graphing calculator to check that the line $y = -0.58x + 3.22$ comes very close to the points $(-6.81, 7.17)$ and $(-2.47, 4.65)$. See Fig. 91.

The line $y = -0.58x + 3.22$ does not contain the points $(-6.81, 7.17)$ and $(-2.47, 4.65)$, because we rounded the slope and the constant term to the second decimal place. However, the line does comes very close to these points. When finding an approximate equation, we will usually round numbers such as the slope or the constant term to the second decimal place.

In Example 5, we will find an equation of a line that contains a given point and is parallel to a given line. Recall from Section 1.3 that nonvertical parallel lines have equal slopes.

▶ **Example 5**   Finding an Equation of a Line Parallel to a Given Line

Find an equation of a line l that contains the point $(5, 3)$ and is parallel to the line $y = 2x - 3$.

Solution

For the line $y = 2x - 3$, the slope is 2. So, the slope of parallel line l is also 2. An equation of line l is $y = 2x + b$. To find b, we substitute the coordinates of $(5, 3)$ into the equation $y = 2x + b$:

$$3 = 2(5) + b \qquad \text{Substitute 5 for } x \text{ and 3 for } y.$$
$$-7 = b \qquad \text{Multiply; subtract 10 from both sides.}$$

An equation of l is $y = 2x - 7$. We use a graphing calculator to verify our equation (see Fig. 92).

Recall from Section 1.3 that if two nonvertical lines are perpendicular, then the slope of one line is the opposite of the reciprocal of the slope of the other line.

▶ **Example 6**   Finding an Equation of a Line Perpendicular to a Given Line

Find an equation of the line l that contains the point $(6, -7)$ and is parallel to the line $-2x + 5y = 10$.

Solution

First, we isolate y in the equation $-2x + 5y = 10$:

$$-2x + 5y = 10 \qquad \text{Original equation: line perpendicular to line } l$$
$$-2x + 5y + 2x = 10 + 2x \qquad \text{Add 2x to both sides.}$$
$$5y = 2x + 10 \qquad \text{Simplify.}$$
$$\frac{5y}{5} = \frac{2x}{5} + \frac{10}{5} \qquad \text{Divide both sides by 5.}$$
$$y = \frac{2}{5}x + 2 \qquad \text{Simplify.}$$

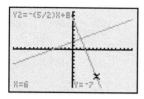

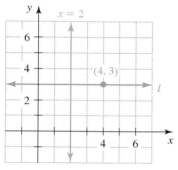

Figure 93 Check that the line contains $(6, -7)$ and is perpendicular to $-2x + 5y = 10$

For the line $y = \dfrac{2}{5}x + 2$, the slope is $m = \dfrac{2}{5}$. The slope of the line l must be the opposite of the reciprocal of $\dfrac{2}{5}$, or $-\dfrac{5}{2}$. An equation of l is $y = -\dfrac{5}{2}x + b$. To find b, we substitute the coordinates of the given point $(6, -7)$ into $y = -\dfrac{5}{2}x + b$:

$$-7 = -\frac{5}{2}(6) + b \quad \text{\small Substitute 6 for } x \text{ and } -7 \text{ for } y.$$

$$-7 = -15 + b \qquad -\frac{5}{2}(6) = -\frac{5}{2}\left(\frac{6}{1}\right) = -\frac{5 \cdot 2 \cdot 3}{2} = -\frac{15}{1} = -15$$

$$8 = b \qquad\qquad\quad \text{\small Add 15 to both sides.}$$

An equation of l is $y = -\dfrac{5}{2}x + 8$. We use ZStandard followed by ZSquare to verify our work (see Fig. 93).

In Example 7, we will use a graphical approach to find the equation of a line.

▶ **Example 7**   Finding an Equation of a Line Perpendicular to a Given Line

Find an equation of the line l that contains $(4, 3)$ and is perpendicular to the line $x = 2$.

Figure 94 Find an equation of the line l

Solution

The graph of $x = 2$ is a vertical line (see Fig. 94). A line perpendicular to it must be horizontal, so there is an equation of l of the form $y = b$. To find b, we substitute the y-coordinate of the given point $(4, 3)$ into $y = b$ and get $3 = b$. So, an equation of l is $y = 3$.

Method 2: Using Point–Slope Form

We can find an equation of a line by another method. Suppose a nonvertical line has slope m and contains the point (x_1, y_1). Then, if (x, y) represents a different point on the line, the slope of the line is

$$\frac{y - y_1}{x - x_1} = m$$

Multiplying both sides of the equation by $x - x_1$ gives

$$\frac{y - y_1}{x - x_1} \cdot (x - x_1) = m(x - x_1)$$

$$y - y_1 = m(x - x_1)$$

We say this linear equation is in **point–slope form.**[*]

> ▶ **Point–Slope Form**
>
> If a nonvertical line has slope m and contains the point (x_1, y_1), then an equation of the line is
>
> $$y - y_1 = m(x - x_1)$$

_____

[*]Although we assumed that (x, y) is different from (x_1, y_1), note that (x_1, y_1) is a solution of the equation $y - y_1 = m(x - x_1)$: $y_1 - y_1 = m(x_1 - x_1)$, or $0 = 0$, a true statement.

▶ **Example 8**   Using Point–Slope Form to Find an Equation of a Line

A line has slope $m = 2$ and contains the point $(3, -8)$. Find an equation of the line.

Solution

Substituting $x_1 = 3$, $y_1 = -8$, and $m = 2$ in the equation $y - y_1 = m(x - x_1)$ gives

$$y - (-8) = 2(x - 3) \qquad \text{\textit{Substitute 3 for } } x_1, -8 \text{ \textit{for} } y_1, \text{\textit{ and 2 for} } m.$$
$$y + 8 = 2x - 6 \qquad \text{\textit{Simplify; distributive law}}$$
$$y + 8 - 8 = 2x - 6 - 8 \qquad \text{\textit{Subtract 8 from both sides.}}$$
$$y = 2x - 14 \qquad \text{\textit{Simplify.}}$$

We can use a graphing calculator to check that the graph of $y = 2x - 14$ contains the point $(3, -8)$.

▶

▶ **Example 9**   Using Point–Slope Form to Find an Equation of a Line

Use the point–slope form to find an equation of the line that contains the points $(-5, 2)$ and $(3, -1)$. Then write the equation in slope–intercept form.

Solution

We begin by finding the slope of the line:

$$m = \frac{-1 - 2}{3 - (-5)} = \frac{-3}{8} = -\frac{3}{8}$$

Then we substitute $x_1 = 3$, $y_1 = -1$, and $m = -\frac{3}{8}$ in the equation $y - y_1 = m(x - x_1)$:

$$y - (-1) = -\frac{3}{8}(x - 3) \qquad \text{\textit{Substitute } } x_1 = 3, y_1 = -1, \text{\textit{and} } m = -\frac{3}{8}.$$

$$y + 1 = -\frac{3}{8}x + \frac{9}{8} \qquad \text{\textit{Simplify; distributive law}}$$

$$y + 1 - 1 = -\frac{3}{8}x + \frac{9}{8} - 1 \qquad \text{\textit{Subtract 1 from both sides.}}$$

$$y = -\frac{3}{8}x + \frac{1}{8} \qquad \text{\textit{Simplify; } } \frac{9}{8} - 1 = \frac{9}{8} - \frac{8}{8} = \frac{1}{8}$$

▶

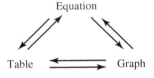

Equation

Table ⟷ Graph

Figure 95 Six paths among equations, tables, and graphs

So far, we have worked with equations, graphs, and tables. In Section 1.2, we sketched a graph by going from an equation to a table and then to a graph. In Section 1.4, we sketched a graph by going directly from an equation to a graph. In Exercises 71–74 at the end of this section, you will find an equation of a line by going from its graph to an equation. Many times throughout the rest of the course, we will use combinations of the six paths indicated in Fig. 95.

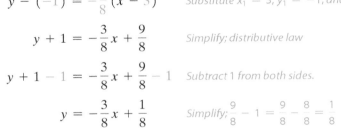

Group Exploration

Deciding which points to use to find an equation of a line

1. a. Use the method shown in Example 2 to find an equation of the line that contains the points $(1, 2)$ and $(3, 8)$.

b. In part (a), you used either point $(1, 2)$ or point $(3, 8)$ to find the constant b for the equation $y = 3x + b$. Now use the other point to find b.

c. Does it matter which point is used to find the constant b? Explain.

2. Imagine any line that is not parallel to either axis. Choose four points on the line. Name the points A, B, C, and D.

a. Use points A and B to find an equation of the line. Write your equation in slope–intercept form.

b. Use points C and D to find an equation of the line. Write your equation in slope–intercept form.

c. Are the equations you found in parts (a) and (b) the same? Explain.

▶ Tips for Success   **Affirmations**

Do you ever tell yourself (or others) that you are not good at math? This is called *negative self-talk*. The more you talk that way, the more likely your subconscious will believe it—and you *will* do poorly in math.

You can counteract years of negative self-talk by telling yourself with conviction that you are good at math. It might seem strange to state that something is true that hasn't happened yet, but it works! Such statements are called *affirmations*.

There are four guiding principles for getting the most out of affirmations:

1. Say affirmations that imply the desired event is currently happening. For example, say "I am good at algebra," not "I will be good at algebra."

2. Say that you are making progress toward the desired result. For example, say "I am good at algebra, and I continue to improve at it."

3. Say affirmations in the positive rather than in the negative. For example, say "I attend each class," not "I don't cut classes."

4. Say affirmations with conviction.

If you would like to learn more about affirmations, the book *Creative Visualization* (Bantam Books, 1985), by Shakti Gawain, is an excellent resource.

Homework 1.5

For extra help ▶ **MyMathLab®**   ▦ Watch the videos in MyMathLab   ● Download the MyDashboard App

Find an equation of the line that has the given slope and contains the given point. Use a graphing calculator to verify that the graph of your equation passes through the given point. Determine whether your line is increasing, decreasing, horizontal, or vertical, and check that the sign of m agrees with your determination.

1. $m = 3, (5, 2)$
2. $m = 2, (3, 1)$
3. $m = -2, (3, -9)$
4. $m = -4, (-2, -8)$
5. $m = \frac{3}{5}, (20, 7)$
6. $m = \frac{2}{3}, (6, 1)$
7. $m = -\frac{1}{6}, (2, -3)$
8. $m = -\frac{1}{4}, (-2, 5)$
9. $m = -\frac{5}{2}, (-3, -4)$
10. $m = -\frac{3}{4}, (-5, -2)$
11. $m = 0, (1, 2)$
12. $m = 0, (-3, -4)$
13. m is undefined, $(3, 7)$
14. m is undefined, $(-5, 1)$

Find an approximate equation of the line that has the given slope and contains the given point. Round the constant term to two decimal places. Use a graphing calculator to verify your result.

15. $m = 1.6, (2.1, 3.8)$
16. $m = -2.7, (6.2, -4.9)$
17. $m = -3.24, (-5.28, 1.93)$
18. $m = 1.94, (-2.53, -3.77)$

Find an equation of the line that passes through the two given points. Use a graphing calculator to verify your result.

19. $(2, 3)$ and $(4, 5)$
20. $(3, 5)$ and $(7, 1)$
21. $(-2, 6)$ and $(3, -4)$
22. $(-1, 3)$ and $(2, -9)$
23. $(-8, -6)$ and $(-4, -14)$
24. $(-4, -1)$ and $(-2, -7)$
25. $(0, 0)$ and $(1, 1)$
26. $(0, 8)$ and $(4, 5)$

27. $(2, 1)$ and $(7, 5)$
28. $(3, 2)$ and $(5, 9)$
29. $(-4, 2)$ and $(2, -5)$
30. $(2, -1)$ and $(5, -3)$
31. $(-5, -7)$ and $(-3, -2)$
32. $(-5, -3)$ and $(-2, -4)$
33. $(2, 5)$ and $(4, 5)$
34. $(-5, -2)$ and $(1, -2)$
35. $(-3, -4)$ and $(-3, 6)$
36. $(4, -7)$ and $(4, -3)$

Find an approximate equation of the line that passes through the two given points. Round the slope and the constant term to two decimal places. Use a graphing calculator to verify your result.

37. $(-5.1, -3.9)$ and $(7.4, 2.2)$
38. $(-9.4, 7.1)$ and $(3.9, -2.3)$
39. $(-5.97, -6.24)$ and $(-1.25, -4.05)$
40. $(-7.13, -2.21)$ and $(-4.99, -7.78)$

Find an equation of the line that contains the given point and is parallel to the given line. Use a graphing calculator to verify your result.

41. $(4, 5), y = 3x + 1$
42. $(1, 4), y = 4x - 6$
43. $(-3, 8), y = -2x + 7$
44. $(2, -3), y = -x + 2$
45. $(4, 1), y = \frac{1}{2}x - 3$
46. $(6, -3), y = -\frac{2}{3}x - 1$
47. $(3, 4), 3x - 4y = 12$
48. $(4, -1), 5x + 2y = 10$
49. $(-3, -2), 6y - x = -7$
50. $(-1, -4), 3y + 5x = -11$
51. $(2, 3), y = 6$
52. $(3, -1), y = -4$
53. $(-5, 4), x = 2$
54. $(-2, -5), x = 1$

Find an equation of the line that contains the given point and is perpendicular to the given line. Use ZStandard followed by ZSquare with a graphing calculator to verify your result.

55. $(3, 8), y = 2x + 5$

56. $(2, 1), y = 5x - 4$

57. $(-1, 7), y = -3x + 7$

58. $(-3, -2), y = -6x - 13$

59. $(2, 7), y = -\dfrac{2}{5}x = 3$

60. $(1, -2), y = \dfrac{1}{3}x - 4$

61. $(10, 3), 4x - 5y = 7$

62. $(6, -1), 5x + 2y = -9$

63. $(-3, -1), -2x + 3y = 5$

64. $(-1, 2), -3x - 4y = 12$

65. $(2, 3), x = 5$

66. $(-4, -2), x = -1$

67. $(2, 8), y = -3$

68. $(1, -1), y = 7$

69. Let y be the value (in thousands of dollars) of a car when it is x years old. Some pairs of values of x and y are listed in Table 22.

Table 22 Values of a Car

Age (years) x	Value (thousands of dollars) y
0	19
1	17
2	15
3	13
4	11

Find an equation that describes the relationship between x and y.

70. Let y be a person's salary (in thousands of dollars) after he has worked at a company for x years. Some pairs of values of x and y are listed in Table 23.

Table 23 Salaries

Time at Company (years) x	Salary (thousands of dollars) y
0	25
1	28
2	31
3	34
4	37
5	40

Find an equation that describes the relationship between x and y.

Concepts

71. Find an equation of the line sketched in Fig. 96. Check your equation with a graphing calculator.

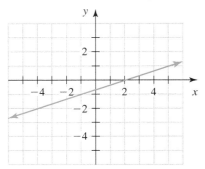

Figure 96 Exercise 71

72. Find an equation of the line sketched in Fig. 97. Check your equation with a graphing calculator.

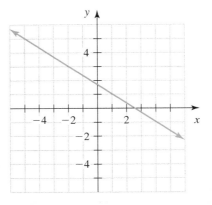

Figure 97 Exercise 72

73. Find an equation of the line sketched in Fig. 98. Check your equation with a graphing calculator.

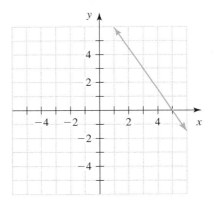

Figure 98 Exercise 73

74. Find an equation of the line sketched in Fig. 99. Check your equation with a graphing calculator.

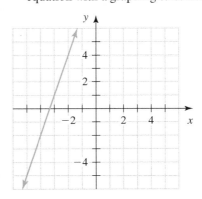

Figure 99 Exercise 74

75. Decide whether a line can have the indicated number of x-intercepts. If it is possible, find an equation of such a line. If it is not possible, explain why.
   a. No x-intercepts
   b. Exactly one x-intercept
   c. Exactly two x-intercepts
   d. An infinite number of x-intercepts

76. Decide whether a line can have the indicated number of y-intercepts. If it is possible, find an equation of such a line. If it is not possible, explain why.
   a. No y-intercepts
   b. Exactly one y-intercept

c. Exactly two y-intercepts

d. An infinite number of y-intercepts

77. Is there a line that contains all of the given points? If so, find an equation of it. If not, find an equation of a line that contains most of the given points.

$$(-4, 15), (-1, 9), (3, 1), (4, -1), (9, -11)$$

78. Is there a line that contains all of the given points? If so, find an equation of it. If not, find an equation of a line that contains most of the given points.

$$(-3, 7), (-1, 5), (1, 1), (3, -3), (4, -5)$$

79. Create a table of seven pairs of values of x and y for which
a. each point lies on the line $y = 3x - 6$.
b. each point lies close to, but not on, the line $y = 3x - 6$.
c. the points do not lie close to the line $y = 3x - 6$, but all of them lie close to another line. In addition to creating the table, provide an equation of the other line.

80. Suppose a set of points all lie 0.5 unit above the line $y = -4x + 3$. Find an equation of the line that passes through the points of the set.

81. a. Find an equation of a line with slope -4.

b. Find an equation of a line with y-intercept $\left(0, \dfrac{3}{7}\right)$. Verify your result with a graphing calculator.

c. Find an equation of a line that contains the point $(-2, 8)$. Verify your result with a graphing calculator.

d. Determine whether there is a line that has slope -4, has y-intercept $\left(0, \dfrac{3}{7}\right)$, and contains the point $(-2, 8)$. Explain.

82. Find equations of two perpendicular lines that intersect at the point $(3, 1)$.

83. Find equations of three lines that contain the point $(3, -2)$.

84. Suppose you are trying to find an equation of the line that contains two given points and you find the slope is undefined. What type of line is it? Explain.

85. A student thinks if a line has slope 2 and contains the point $(3, 5)$, then the equation of the line is $y = 2x + 5$, because the slope is 2 (the coefficient of x) and the y-coordinate of $(3, 5)$ is 5 (the constant term). What would you tell the student?

86. A student tries to find an equation of the line that contains the points $(1, 5)$ and $(3, 9)$. The student believes an equation of the line is $y = 4x + 1$. The student then checks whether $(1, 5)$ satisfies $y = 4x + 1$:

$$y = 4x + 1$$
$$5 \stackrel{?}{=} 4(1) + 1$$
$$5 \stackrel{?}{=} 5$$
$$\text{true}$$

The student concludes that $y = 4x + 1$ is an equation of the line. Find any errors. Then find an equation correctly.

87. Describe how to find an equation of a line that contains two given points. How can you verify that the graph of the equation contains the two points?

1.6 Functions

Objectives

» Know the meanings of *relation, domain, range,* and *function.*

» Identify functions by using the *vertical line test.*

» Know the definition of a *linear function.*

» Know the Rule of Four for functions.

» Use the graph of a function to find the function's domain and range.

Table 24 A Relationship Described by a Table

x	y
3	2
4	1
5	3
5	4

Throughout this chapter, we have described relationships between two variables. In this section, we will discuss how to describe some of these relationships by using an extremely important concept called a *function.*

Relation, Domain, Range, and Function

In this chapter, we have used graphs, tables, and equations to describe the relationship between two variables. For example, Table 24 describes a relationship between the variables x and y. This relationship is also described graphically in Fig. 100.

We call the set of ordered pairs listed in Table 24 a *relation.* This relation consists of the ordered pairs $(3, 2)$, $(4, 1)$, $(5, 3)$, and $(5, 4)$. The *domain* of the relation is the set of all values of x (the independent variable)—in this case, 3, 4, and 5. The *range* of the relation is the set of all values of y (the dependent variable)—here, 1, 2, 3, and 4.

▶ **Definition   Relation, domain, and range**

A **relation** is a set of ordered pairs. The **domain** of a relation is the set of all values of the independent variable, and the **range** of a relation is the set of all values of the dependent variable.

We can think of a relation as a machine in which values of x are "inputs" and values of y are "outputs." In general, each member of the domain is an **input,** and each member of the range is an **output.**

For the relation described in Table 24, we can think of the values of x as being sent to the values of y (see Fig. 101).

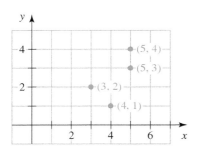

Figure 100 The relationship of Table 24 described by a graph

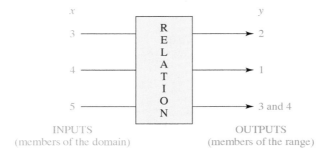

Figure 101 Think of a relation as an input–output machine

Note that the input $x = 5$ is sent to *two* outputs: $y = 3$ and $y = 4$. In a special type of relation called a *function,* each input is sent to exactly *one* output. The relation described in Table 24 is not a function.

▶ Definition   Function

A **function** is a relation in which each input leads to exactly one output.

The equation $y = x + 2$ describes a relation consisting of an infinite number of ordered pairs. We will determine whether the relation is a function in Example 1.

▶ Example 1   Deciding whether an Equation Describes a Function

Is the relation $y = x + 2$ a function? Find the domain and range of the relation.

Solution

Let's consider some input–output pairs (in Fig. 102).

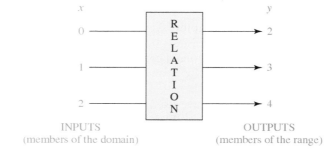

Figure 102 The "increasing by 2" relation: $y = x + 2$

Each input leads to just *one* output—namely, the input increased by 2—so the relation $y = x + 2$ is a function.

The domain of the relation $y = x + 2$ is the set of all real numbers, since we can add 2 to *any* real number. The range of $y = x + 2$ is also the set of real numbers, since any real number is the output of the number that is 2 units less than it.

▶ Example 2   Deciding whether an Equation Describes a Function

Is the relation $y = \pm x$ a function?

Solution

If $x = 1$, then $y = \pm 1$. So, the input $x = 1$ leads to *two* outputs: $y = -1$ and $y = 1$. Therefore, the relation $y = \pm x$ is not a function.

▶ Example 3   Deciding whether an Equation Describes a Function

Is the relation $y^2 = x$ a function?

Solution

Let's consider the input $x = 4$. We substitute 4 for x and solve for y:

$$y^2 = 4 \qquad \textit{Substitute 4 for x.}$$
$$y = -2 \quad \text{or} \quad y = 2 \qquad (-2)^2 = 4, 2^2 = 4$$

The input $x = 4$ leads to *two* outputs: $y = -2$ and $y = 2$. So, the relation $y^2 = x$ is not a function.

▶

Table 25 Input–Output Pairs of a Relation

x (input)	y (output)
0	2
1	3
1	5
2	7
3	10

▶ Example 4   Deciding whether a Table Describes a Function

Is the relation described by Table 25 a function?

Solution

The input $x = 1$ leads to *two* outputs: $y = 3$ and $y = 5$. So, the relation is not a function.

▶

▶ Example 5   Deciding whether a Graph Describes a Function

Is the relation described by the graph in Fig. 103 a function?

Solution

The input $x = 3$ leads to *two* outputs: $y = -4$ and $y = 4$ (see Fig. 104). So, the relation is not a function.

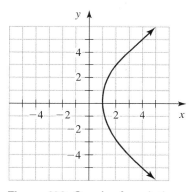

Figure 103 Graph of a relation

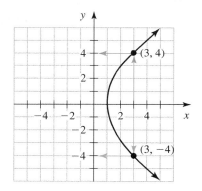

Figure 104 The input $x = 3$ gives two outputs: $y = -4$ and $y = 4$

▶

Vertical Line Test

Notice that the relation described in Example 5 is not a function because some vertical lines would intersect the graph more than once.

▶ Vertical Line Test

A relation is a function if and only if each vertical line intersects the graph of the relation at no more than one point. We call this requirement the **vertical line test.**

▶ **Example 6** Deciding whether a Graph Describes a Function

Determine whether the graph represents a function.

1.

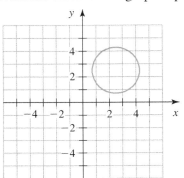

2.

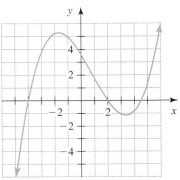

Solution

1. Since the vertical line sketched in Fig. 105 intersects the circle more than once, the relation is not a function.
2. Each vertical line sketched in Fig. 106 intersects the curve at one point. In fact, *any* vertical line would intersect this curve at just one point. So, the relation is a function.

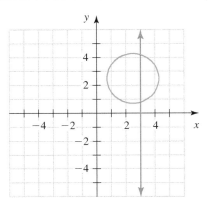

Figure 105 The circle does not describe a function

Figure 106 The curve describes a function

▶

▶ **Example 7** Deciding whether an Equation Describes a Function

Is the relation $y = 2x + 1$ a function?

Solution

We begin by sketching the graph of $y = 2x + 1$ in Fig. 107. Note that each vertical line would intersect the line $y = 2x + 1$ at just one point. So, the relation $y = 2x + 1$ is a function.

▶

Linear Functions

In Example 7, we saw that the line $y = 2x + 1$ is a function. In fact, any nonvertical line is a function, since it passes the vertical line test.

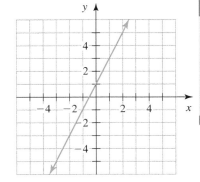

Figure 107 Graph of $y = 2x + 1$

▶ **Definition** Linear function

A **linear function** is a relation whose equation can be put into the form

$$y = mx + b$$

where m and b are constants.

In this chapter, we have made many observations about linear equations. Since a linear function can be described by a linear equation, these observations tell us about linear functions. Let's summarize what we know about a linear function $y = mx + b$:

1. The graph of the function is a nonvertical line.
2. The constant m is the slope of the line, a measure of the line's steepness.
3. If $m > 0$, the graph of the function is an increasing line.
4. If $m < 0$, the graph of the function is a decreasing line.
5. If $m = 0$, the graph of the function is a horizontal line.
6. If an input increases by 1, then the corresponding output changes by the slope m.
7. If the run is 1, the rise is the slope m.
8. The y-intercept of the line is $(0, b)$.

Finally, since a linear equation of the form $y = mx + b$ is a *function,* we know each input leads to exactly one output.

When the graph of a function is increasing, we say the function is **increasing** (see Fig. 108). When the graph of a function is decreasing, we say the function is **decreasing** (see Fig. 109).

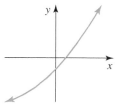

Figure 108 An increasing function

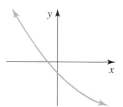

Figure 109 A decreasing function

For example, the linear function $y = 4x - 7$ is increasing, because the graph is an increasing line ($m = 4 > 0$). The linear function $y = -3x + 6$ is decreasing, because the graph is a decreasing line ($m = -3 < 0$).

Rule of Four for Functions

We can describe functions in four ways. For instance, in Example 7, we described the function $y = 2x + 1$ by using (1) the equation and (2) a graph (see Fig. 107). We can also describe some of the input–output pairs for the same function by using (3) a table (see Table 26). Finally, we can describe the function (4) verbally: In this case, for each input–output pair, the output is 1 more than twice the input.

Table 26 Input–Output Pairs for $y = 2x + 1$

x	y
0	1
1	3
2	5
3	7
4	9

> **Rule of Four for Functions**
>
> We can describe some or all of the input–output pairs of a function by means of
>
> 1. an equation,
> 2. a graph,
> 3. a table, or
> 4. words.
>
> These four ways to describe input–output pairs of a function are known as the **Rule of Four** for functions.

▶ **Example 8** Describing a Function by Using the Rule of Four

1. Is the relation $y = -2x - 1$ a function?
2. List some input–output pairs of $y = -2x - 1$ by using a table.
3. Describe the input–output pairs of $y = -2x - 1$ by using a graph.
4. Describe the input–output pairs of $y = -2x - 1$ by using words.

Table 27 Input–Output Pairs of $y = -2x - 1$

x	y
−2	$-2(-2) - 1 = 3$
−1	$-2(-1) - 1 = 1$
0	$-2(0) - 1 = -1$
1	$-2(1) - 1 = -3$
2	$-2(2) - 1 = -5$

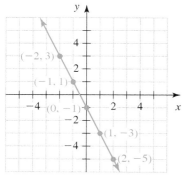

Figure 110 Graph of $y = -2x - 1$

Solution

1. Since $y = -2x - 1$ is of the form $y = mx + b$, it is a (linear) function.
2. We list five input–output pairs in Table 27.
3. We graph $y = -2x - 1$ in Fig. 110.
4. For each input–output pair, the output is 1 less than -2 times the input.

Using a Graph to Find the Domain and Range of a Function

To describe the domain or range of a function, it is sometimes helpful to use the *inequality symbols* $\leq$ and $\geq$. The symbol $\leq$ means "is less than or equal to"; the symbol $\geq$ means "is greater than or equal to." For example, the inequality $x \leq 4$ means all values of x are less than or equal to 4. And the inequality $y \geq 7$ means all values of y are greater than or equal to 7.

The inequality $5 \leq x$ means 5 is *less* than or equal to all values of x. Notice that it is more natural to say all values of x are *greater* than or equal to 5, which is true.

The inequality $2 \leq x \leq 6$ means $2 \leq x$ *and* $x \leq 6$: All values of x are *both* greater than or equal to 2 *and* less than or equal to 6. In other words, all values of x are between 2 and 6, inclusive.

▶ **Example 9**   Finding the Domain and Range

Use the graph of the function to determine the function's domain and range.

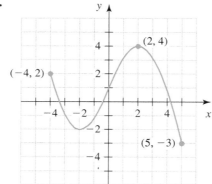

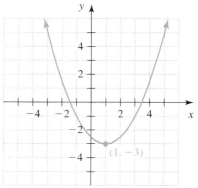

Solution

1. The domain is the set of all x-coordinates of points in the graph. Since there are no breaks in the graph, and since the leftmost point is $(-4, 2)$ and the rightmost point is $(5, -3)$, the domain is $-4 \leq x \leq 5$.

   The range is the set of all y-coordinates of points in the graph. Since the lowest point is $(5, -3)$ and the highest point is $(2, 4)$, the range is $-3 \leq y \leq 4$.

2. The graph extends to the left and right indefinitely without breaks, so every real number is an x-coordinate of some point in the graph. The domain is the set of all real numbers.

   The output -3 is the smallest number in the range, because $(1, -3)$ is the lowest point in the graph. The graph also extends upward indefinitely without breaks, so every number larger than -3 is also in the range. The range is $y \geq -3$.

◣◤ Group Exploration
Vertical line test

1. Consider the relation described by Table 28. Is the relation a function? Explain. Now plot the points on a coordinate system. What do you notice about them?

2. Consider the relation described by Table 29. Is the relation a function? Explain. Now plot the points on a coordinate system. What do you notice about them?

Table 28 A Relation Described by a Table

x	y
2	1
2	5
2	7

Table 29 A Relation Described by a Table

x	y
4	2
4	3
4	6

3. Describe the graph of a relation that is not a function.

4. Determine whether each graph in Fig. 111 is the graph of a function. Explain.

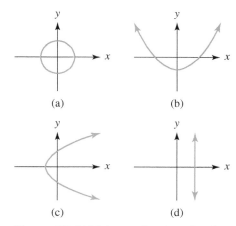

Figure 111 Which graphs describe functions?

Group Exploration

Looking ahead: Linear modeling

The annual revenue of recorded music including digital music has decreased since 2005 (see Table 30).

Table 30 Annual Revenue of Recorded Music

Year	Annual Revenue (billions of dollars)
2005	12.3
2006	11.8
2007	10.4
2008	8.8
2009	7.7
2010	6.9

Source: *Recording Industry Association of America*

1. Let R be the annual revenue (in billions of dollars) of recorded music, and let t be the number of years since 2005. For example, $t = 1$ represents 2006, because 2006 is 1 year since 2005. So, the 2006 revenue of $11.8 billion is represented by $t = 1$ and $R = 11.8$. The information in Table 30 can be summarized with a table of values for t and R. Create such a table by filling in the missing entries in Table 31.

Table 31 Values of t and R for the Music Data

Number of Years since 2005 t	Annual Revenue (billions of dollars) R
0	12.3
1	11.8
2	
3	
	7.7
	6.9

2. Plot the points (t, R) that you listed in Table 31 on a coordinate system like the one in Fig. 112.

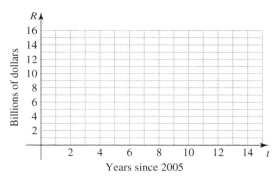

Figure 112 Plot the data points

3. When examining your graph, what do you notice about the arrangement of your plotted points?

4. Sketch a line that comes close to the six data points.

5. Use the line to estimate the revenue in 2012.

6. Use the line to predict when the annual revenue will be $2 billion.

7. Find the t-intercept of the line. What does the t-intercept mean in this situation? Will this prediction happen for certain? Explain.

8. Give some possible reasons why the revenue decreased so much from 2005 to 2010.

▶ Tips for Success   **Practice Exams**

When studying for an exam (or a quiz), try creating your own exam to take for practice. Select several homework exercises from each section on which you will be tested. Choose a variety of exercises that address concepts your instructor has emphasized. Include many exercises that are moderately difficult and some that are challenging. Completing such a practice test will help you reflect on important concepts and pin down what types of problems you need to study more.

Work on the practice exam for a predetermined time. Doing so will help you get used to a timed exam, build your confidence, and lower your anxiety for the real exam.

If you are studying with another student, each of you can create a test and then take each other's test. Or create a test together and each take it separately.

Homework 1.6

For extra help ▶ **MyMathLab®**   ▣ Watch the videos in MyMathLab   ◉ Download the MyDashboard App

1. Some ordered pairs of four relations are listed in Table 32. Which of these relations could be functions? Explain.

Table 32 Which Relations Might Be Functions? (Exercise 1)

Relation 1		Relation 2		Relation 3		Relation 4	
x	y	x	y	x	y	x	y
1	1	3	27	0	4	5	10
2	3	4	24	1	4	6	20
3	5	5	21	2	4	7	30
3	7	6	18	3	4	8	40
4	9	7	15	4	4	8	50

2. Some ordered pairs of four relations are listed in Table 33.

Table 33 Which Relations Might Be Functions? (Exercise 2)

Relation 1		Relation 2		Relation 3		Relation 4	
x	y	x	y	x	y	x	y
1	3	5	27	0	50	3	11
2	4	5	24	1	45	4	13
3	5	5	21	2	40	5	17
3	6	5	18	3	35	6	25
4	7	5	15	4	30	7	40

    a. Which of the relations could be functions? Explain.
    b. Which could be linear functions? Explain.

3. For a certain relation, an input leads to two different outputs. Could the relation be a function? Explain.

4. For a certain relation, two different inputs lead to the same output. Could the relation be a function? Explain.

5. A relation's graph contains the points $(2, 3)$ and $(5, 3)$. Could the relation be a function? Explain.

6. A relation's graph contains the points $(4, 5)$ and $(4, 9)$. Could the relation be a function? Explain.

Determine whether the graph represents a function. Explain.

7.

8.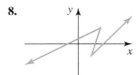

9.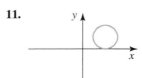

10.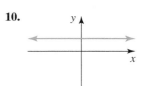

11.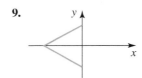

12.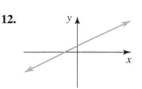

13.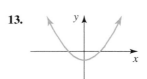

14.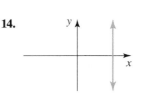

Determine whether the relation is a function. Explain.

15. $y = 5x - 1$

16. $y = -3x + 8$

17. $2x - 5y = 10$

18. $4x + 3y = 24$

19. $y = 4$

20. $y = -1$

21. $x = -3$

22. $x = 0$

23. $7x - 2y = 21 + 3(y - 5x)$

24. $2x + 5y = 9 - 4(x + 2y)$

25. Is a nonvertical line the graph of a function? Explain.

26. Is a vertical line the graph of a function? Explain.

27. Is a circle the graph of a function? Explain.

28. Is a semicircle that is the "upper half" of a circle the graph of function? Explain.

29. Recall that we can describe some or all of the input–output pairs of a function by means of an equation, a graph, a table, or words.

    a. Describe five input–output pairs of $y = 3x - 2$ by using a table.

    b. Describe the input–output pairs of $y = 3x - 2$ by using a graph.

    c. Describe the input–output pairs of $y = 3x - 2$ by using words.

30. Recall that we can describe some or all of the input–output pairs of a function by means of an equation, a graph, a table, or words.

    a. Describe five input–output pairs of $y = \frac{1}{2}x + 2$ by using a table.

    b. Describe the input–output pairs of $y = \frac{1}{2}x + 2$ by using a graph.

    c. Describe the input–output pairs of $y = \frac{1}{2}x + 2$ by using words.

For Exercises 31–42, use the graph of the function to determine the function's domain and range.

31.

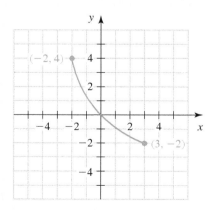

32.

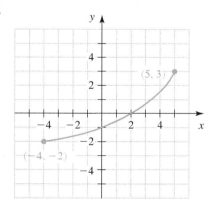

33.

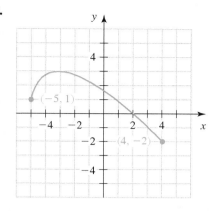

34.

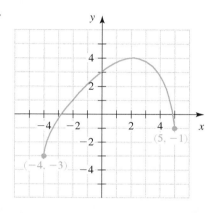

35.

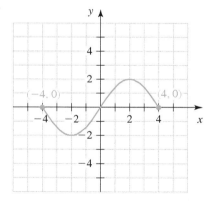

36.

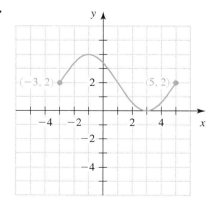

37.

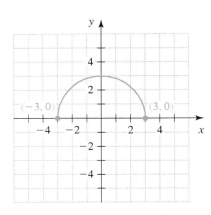

38.

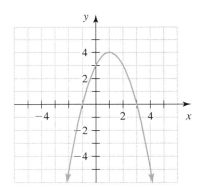

39.

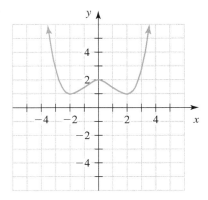

40.

41.

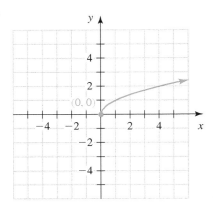

42.

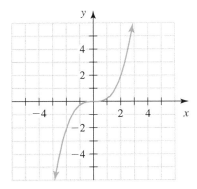

Decide whether the relation is a function. Explain.

43. $y = \sqrt{x}$ [**Hint:** Sketch a graph.]

44. $y = x^4$ [**Hint:** Sketch a graph.]

45. $y^4 = x$ [**Hint:** Substitute 16 for x; then solve for y.]

46. $y^3 = x$ [**Hint:** Substitute 0, 1, and 8 for x, and solve for y after each substitution.]

Concepts

47. Describe the input–output pairs of a function (different from those in this section) by using an equation, a graph, and words. Describe also five input–output pairs of the function by using a table. Explain why your relation is a function.

48. Sketch the graph of a relation (different from those in this section) that is not a function. Next, create a table that lists five ordered pairs of the relation. Explain why your relation is not a function.

49. Sketch the graph of a relation for which the input $x = 2$ gives exactly two outputs and the input $x = 6$ gives exactly one output. Is the relation a function? Explain.

50. Sketch the graph of a relation for which the input $x = -4$ gives exactly three outputs and the input $x = 5$ gives exactly one output. Is the relation a function? Explain.

51. Sketch the graph of a function whose domain is $-3 \le x \le 5$ and whose range is $-2 \le y \le 4$.

52. Sketch the graph of a function whose domain is $-2 \le x \le 4$ and whose range is $-1 \le y \le 5$.

53. Sketch the graph of a function whose domain is the set of all real numbers and whose range is $y \ge 2$.

54. Sketch the graph of a function whose domain is the set of all real numbers and whose range is $y \leq 3$.

55. Which types of lines are linear functions? Explain why other lines are not functions.

56. Explain why the vertical line test works.

57. A student tries to determine whether the relation $y = x^2$ is a function. She finds that both inputs $x = -3$ and $x = 3$ give the same output, $y = 9$. The student concludes the relation is not a function. Is her conclusion correct? Explain.

58. Explain how you can determine whether a relation is a function.

Chapter Summary

Key Points of Chapter 1

Section 1.1   Using Qualitative Graphs to Describe Situations

Qualitative graph	A **qualitative graph** is a graph without scaling on the axes.
Independent and dependent variables	Assume that an authentic situation can be described by using the variables t and p and that p depends on t: • We call t the **independent variable.** • We call p the **dependent variable.**
Axes of a graph	For graphs, we describe the values of the independent variable along the horizontal axis and the values of the dependent variable along the vertical axis.
Intercept	An **intercept** of a curve is any point where the curve and an axis (or axes) intersect.
Increasing curve	If a curve goes upward from left to right, the curve is an **increasing curve.**
Decreasing curve	If a curve goes downward from left to right, the curve is a **decreasing curve.**

Section 1.2   Graphing Linear Equations

Solution, satisfy, and solution set of a linear equation in two variables	An ordered pair (a, b) is a **solution** of an equation in terms of x and y if the equation becomes a true statement when a is substituted for x and b is substituted for y. We say (a, b) **satisfies** the equation. The **solution set** of an equation is the set of all solutions of the equation.
Graph	The **graph** of an equation in two variables is the set of points that correspond to all solutions of the equation.
Intercepts of the graph of an equation	For an equation containing the variables x and y, • To find the x-coordinate of each x-intercept, substitute 0 for y and solve for x. • To find the y-coordinate of each y-intercept, substitute 0 for x and solve for y.
Equations of vertical and horizontal lines	If a and b are constants, then • An equation that can be put into the form $x = a$ has a vertical line as its graph. • An equation that can be put into the form $y = b$ has a horizontal line as its graph.
Linear equations in two variables	If an equation can be put into the form $y = mx + b$ or $x = a$, where m, a, and b are constants, then the graph of the equation is a line. We call such an equation a **linear equation in two variables.**

Section 1.3   Slope of a Line

Comparing the steepness of two objects	To compare the steepness of two objects, compute the ratio $$\frac{\text{vertical distance}}{\text{horizontal distance}}$$ for each object. The object with the larger ratio is the steeper object.
Slope of a nonvertical line	Let (x_1, y_1) and (x_2, y_2) be two distinct points of a nonvertical line. The **slope** of the line is

$$m = \frac{\text{vertical change}}{\text{horizontal change}} = \frac{\text{rise}}{\text{run}} = \frac{y_2 - y_1}{x_2 - x_1}$$

Section 1.3   Slope of a Line (*Continued*)

Slopes of increasing and decreasing lines	An increasing line has positive slope. A decreasing line has negative slope.
Comparing the steepness of two lines	For two nonparallel increasing lines, the steeper line has the greater slope.
Slopes of horizontal and vertical lines	A horizontal line has slope equal to zero. A vertical line has undefined slope.
Slopes of parallel lines	If lines l_1 and l_2 are nonvertical parallel lines on the same coordinate system, then the slopes of the lines are equal: $m_1 = m_2$. Also, if two distinct lines have equal slope, then the lines are parallel.
Slopes of perpendicular lines	If lines l_1 and l_2 are nonvertical perpendicular lines, then the slope of one line is the opposite of the reciprocal of the slope of the other line: $m_2 = -\dfrac{1}{m_1}$. Also, if the slope of one line is the opposite of the reciprocal of another line's slope, then the lines are perpendicular.

Section 1.4   Meaning of Slope for Equations, Graphs, and Tables

Finding the slope and y-intercept from a linear equation of the form $y = mx + b$; slope–intercept form	For a linear equation of the form $y = mx + b$, m is the slope of the line and the y-intercept is $(0, b)$. We say the equation is in **slope–intercept form.**
Vertical change property	For a line $y = mx + b$, if the run is 1, then the rise is the slope m.
Using slope to graph a linear equation of the form $y = mx + b$	To sketch the graph of a linear equation of the form $y = mx + b$, **1.** Plot the y-intercept $(0, b)$. **2.** Use $m = \dfrac{\text{rise}}{\text{run}}$ to plot a second point. **3.** Sketch the line that passes through the two plotted points.
Solve for y first	Before we can use the y-intercept and the slope to graph a linear equation, we must solve for y to put the equation into the form $y = mx + b$.
Slope addition property	For a linear equation of the form $y = mx + b$, if the value of the independent variable increases by 1, then the value of the dependent variable changes by the slope m.

Section 1.5   Finding Linear Equations

Finding an equation of a line that contains two given points	To find an equation of the line that passes through two given points whose x-coordinates are different, **1.** Use the slope formula, $m = \dfrac{y_2 - y_1}{x_2 - x_1}$, to find the slope of the line. **2.** Substitute the m value you found in step 1 into the equation $y = mx + b$. **3.** Substitute the coordinates of one of the given points into the equation you found in step 2, and solve for b. **4.** Substitute the m value you found in step 1 and the b value you found in step 3 into the equation $y = mx + b$. **5.** Use a graphing calculator to check that the graph of your equation contains the two given points.
Point–slope form	If a nonvertical line has slope m and contains the point (x_1, y_1), then an equation of the line is $y - y_1 = m(x - x_1)$. We say such an equation is in **point–slope form.**

Section 1.6   Functions

Relation, domain, and range	A **relation** is a set of ordered pairs. The **domain** of a relation is the set of all values of the independent variable, and the **range** of the relation is the set of all values of the dependent variable.
Input and output	Each member of the domain is an **input,** and each member of the range is an **output.**
Function	A **function** is a relation in which each input leads to exactly one output.

Section 1.6   Functions (*Continued*)

Vertical line test	A relation is a function if and only if each vertical line intersects the graph of the relation at no more than one point.
Linear function	A **linear function** is a relation whose equation can be put into the form $y = mx + b$, where m and b are constants.
Rule of Four for functions	We can describe some or all of the input–output pairs of a function by means of (1) an equation, (2) a graph, (3) a table, or (4) words. These four ways to describe input–output pairs of a function are known as the **Rule of Four** for functions.

Chapter 1 Review Exercises

1. Let n be the number of e-mails that a person receives, and let t be the total amount of time (in minutes) it takes to read and reply to them. Identify the independent variable and the dependent variable.

Sketch a qualitative graph that shows the relationship between the variables defined in each exercise. Justify your sketch.

2. Let L be the length (in inches) of a candle at t minutes after it is lit.

3. Let T be the number of seconds it takes to cook a marshmallow that is d inches from a campfire.

For Exercises 4 and 5, solve.

4. $3(2x - 4) - 2 = 5x - (3 - 4x)$

5. $\dfrac{2}{3}w - \dfrac{1}{2} = \dfrac{5}{6}w + \dfrac{4}{3}$

6. Solve the equation $a(x - c) = d$ for x.

7. Find the x-intercept and y-intercept of the graph of the equation $3x - 5y = 17$.

8. Find the x-intercept and y-intercept of the graph of $ax + b = cy$.

For Exercises 9–12, refer to Fig. 113.

9. Estimate y when $x = 5$.
10. Estimate y when $x = 0$.
11. Estimate x when $y = 2$.
12. Estimate x when $y = 0$.

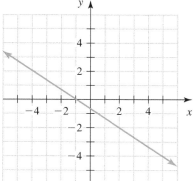

Figure 113 Exercises 9–12

For Exercises 13–15, find the slope of the line that passes through the given points. State whether the line is increasing, decreasing, horizontal, or vertical.

13. $(-3, -2)$ and $(2, -5)$
14. $(-9, -7)$ and $(-1, -3)$
15. $(4, -1)$ and $(4, 3)$

16. Find the slope of the line that passes through the points $(-5.27, 2.99)$ and $(3.54, -8.48)$. Round your result to the second decimal place. State whether the line is increasing, decreasing, horizontal, or vertical.

For Exercises 17–22, graph the equation by hand.

17. $y = -3x + 10$
18. $y + 2x = 0$
19. $y = 7$
20. $3x - 2y = 12$
21. $-3(y + 2) = 2x + 9$
22. $3x - 2(2y - 1) = 8x - 3(x + 2)$
23. Determine the slope and y-intercept of the graph of $a(x - y) = c$.

Determine whether the given lines are parallel, perpendicular, or neither. Explain.

24. $2x + 5y = 7$ and $y = \dfrac{2}{5}x + 7$
25. $3x - 8y = 7$ and $-6x + 16y = 5$

Find an equation of the line that has the given slope and contains the given point.

26. $m = -4, (-3, 7)$
27. $m = -\dfrac{2}{3}, (5, -4)$

For Exercises 28–30, find an equation of the line that passes through the given points.

28. $(-3, -2)$ and $(2, 6)$
29. $(-4, 6)$ and $(2, -2)$
30. $(3, -2)$ and $(3, 5)$
31. Find an approximate equation of the line that passes through the points $(-3.62, -8.79)$ and $(2.51, -6.38)$. Round the slope and the constant term to two decimal places.
32. Find equations of each line sketched in Fig. 114.

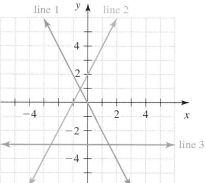

Figure 114 Exercise 32

33. Some values of a linear equation are provided in Table 34. Complete the table.

Table 34 Values of a Linear Equation (Exercise 33)

x	y
2	20
3	
4	
5	
6	4
7	

34. Graphs of the functions $y = 0.5x + 6$ and $y = -1.5x + 3$ are shown in Fig. 115. Find an equation of line 1, also sketched in Fig. 115. Assume line 1 and the line $y = 0.5x + 6$ are parallel.

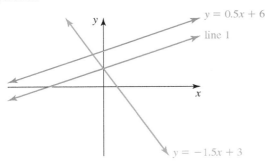

Figure 115 Exercise 34

35. The graphs of $y = ax + b$ and $y = cx + d$ are sketched in Fig. 116.

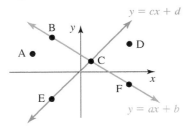

Figure 116 Exercise 35

For each part, decide which one or more of the points A, B, C, D, E, and F represent ordered pairs that
a. satisfy the equation $y = ax + b$.
b. satisfy the equation $y = cx + d$.
c. satisfy both equations.
d. do not satisfy either equation.

36. Find an equation of the line that contains the point $(-2, 5)$ and is parallel to the line $3x - y = 6$.

37. Decide whether a line can have an infinite number of x-intercepts. If it can, find an equation of such a line. If it cannot, explain why.

38. Some ordered pairs for four relations are listed in Table 35. Which of these relations could be functions? Explain.

Table 35 Which Relations Might Be Functions? (Exercise 38)

Relation 1		Relation 2		Relation 3		Relation 4	
x	y	x	y	x	y	x	y
1	12	3	27	0	7	2	1
2	15	4	24	1	7	2	2
3	18	4	21	2	7	2	3
4	21	5	18	3	7	2	4
5	24	6	15	4	7	2	5

39. Determine whether the graph in Fig. 117 represents a function. Explain.

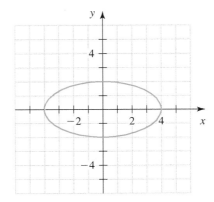

Figure 117 Exercise 39

For Exercises 40–42, determine whether each relation is a function. Explain.

40. $5x - 6y = 3$ **41.** $x = 9$ **42.** $y^2 = x$

43. Use the graph of the function in Fig. 118 to determine the function's domain and range.

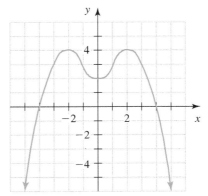

Figure 118 Exercise 43

Chapter 1 Test

1. Let w be the weight (in pounds) of a gold bar, and let v be its value (in dollars). Identify the independent variable and the dependent variable.

2. A student eats breakfast at home. She then begins walking to school. After a while, she jogs. After jogging for some time, she runs the rest of the way at a faster pace. Let d be how far she is from home (in yards) at t minutes since she started eating breakfast. Sketch a qualitative graph that describes the relationship between t and d.

3. Write a scenario to match the graph in Fig. 119. Refer to the variables x and y in your description.

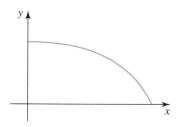

Figure 119 Exercise 3

4. Solve the equation $5 - 3(4x - 2) = 8 - (7x + 1)$.

5. Find equations of each of the three lines sketched in Fig. 120.

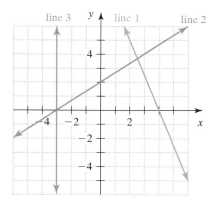

Figure 120 Exercise 5

6. Graphs of the equations $y = mx + b$ and $y = kx + c$ are sketched in Fig. 121.

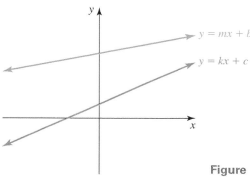

Figure 121 Exercise 6

   a. Which is greater, m or k? Explain.
   b. Which is greater, b or c? Explain.

7. Ski run A declines steadily for 85 yards over a horizontal distance of 270 yards. Ski run B declines steadily for 140 yards over a horizontal distance of 475 yards. Which run is steeper? Explain.

8. Some values of a linear equation are provided in Table 36. Complete the table.

Table 36 Values of a Linear Equation (Exercise 8)

x	y
4	
5	
6	33
7	
8	
9	45

For Exercises 9 and 10, graph the equation by hand.

9. $y = -\dfrac{1}{5}x + 4$

10. $2(2x - y) = 2x + 9 + y$

11. Find the slope of the line that contains the points $(-3, 2)$ and $(5, -8)$.

12. A line contains the points $(2, 8)$ and $(5, 6)$. Find three more points that lie on the line.

13. Find an equation of the line with slope $-\dfrac{3}{7}$ that contains the point $(-2, 5)$.

14. Find an equation of the line that contains the points $(-3, 7)$ and $(2, -5)$.

15. Is there a line that contains all of the given points? If so, find an equation of the line. If not, find an equation that contains most of the points.

$$(-2, 5), (0, 2), (2, -3), (3, -5), (5, -9)$$

16. Find the equation of a line that contains the point $(4, -1)$ and is perpendicular to the line $3x - 5y = 20$.

17. Find the x-intercept and y-intercept of the graph of the equation $2y + 5 = 4(x - 1) + 3$.

18. Recall that we can describe some or all of the input–output pairs of a function by means of an equation, a graph, a table, or words.
   a. Describe five input–output pairs of $y = 2x - 4$ by using a table.
   b. Describe the input–output pairs of $y = 2x - 4$ by using a graph.
   c. Describe the input–output pairs of $y = 2x - 4$ by using words.

19. Sketch the graph of a relation that is *not* a function. Explain.

20. Determine whether the relation described by $y = \pm\sqrt{x}$ is a function. Explain.

21. Determine whether the relation described by $y = -2x + 5$ is a function. Explain.

22. Use the graph of the relation in Fig. 122 to determine the relation's domain and range. Determine whether the relation is a function.

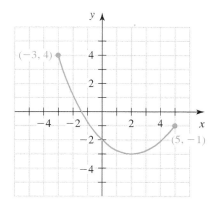

Figure 122 Exercise 22

2 Modeling with Linear Functions

Are you a baseball fan? Baseball has been dubbed "America's favorite pastime." However, the popularity of baseball is waning. Table 1 shows, for various years, the percentage of Americans who are baseball fans. In Exercise 77 of Homework 2.3, you will predict when only 28% of Americans will be baseball fans.

In Section 1.1, we used qualitative graphs to describe situations. In this chapter, we will discuss how to use linear functions to describe authentic situations. We will use graphs and equations of these functions to make estimates and predictions, such as predicting the percentage of dentistry degrees that will be earned by women in 2018. We will also discuss the meaning of the slope of the graph of a linear function used to describe an authentic situation.

Table 1 Percentages of Americans Who Are Baseball Fans

Year	Percent
1999	54
2001	51
2003	50
2005	48
2007	44
2008	43

Source: *The Gallup Organization*

▼2.1 Using Lines to Model Data

Objectives

» Know the meaning of *scattergram, approximately linearly related, model,* and *linear model.*

» Use a linear model to make estimates and predictions.

» Find intercepts of a linear model.

» Know the meaning of *interpolate, extrapolate,* and *model breakdown.*

In this section, we use graphs of linear functions to make estimates and predictions about authentic situations.

Scattergrams

We begin by creating a special type of graph called a *scattergram.*

▶ **Example 1**   Using a Graph to Describe an Authentic Situation

The Grand Canyon is a beautiful landmark, yet the difficulty of finding a parking spot can detract from visitors' enjoyment. The numbers of Grand Canyon visitors are listed in Table 2 for various years. Describe the data with a graph.

Solution

Let v be the number (in millions) of visitors in the year that is t years since 1960. For example, $t = 10$ represents 1970, since 1970 is 10 years after 1960. Then we can describe the data with a table of values for t and v (see Table 3).

Recall from Section 1.2 that, for an ordered pair (a, b), we write the value of the independent variable in the first (left) position and the value of the dependent variable in the second (right) position. Since v depends on t, we write ordered pairs in the form (t, v). For example, the ordered pair $(10, 2.3)$ indicates that when $t = 10$, $v = 2.3$—or that in 1970 there were 2.3 million visitors.

Year	Number of Visitors (millions)
1960	1.2
1970	2.3
1980	2.6
1990	3.8
2000	4.8
2010	4.4

Table 2 Visitors to the Grand Canyon

Source: *National Park Service*

Number of Years since 1960 t	Number of Visitors (millions) v
0	1.2
10	2.3
20	2.6
30	3.8
40	4.8
50	4.4

Table 3 Visitors to the Grand Canyon

Next, we plot the (t, v) data points shown in Fig. 1. Recall from Section 1.1 that the values of the independent variable are described by the horizontal axis and the values of the dependent variable are described by the vertical axis. So, we let the horizontal axis be the t-axis and the vertical axis be the v-axis. We write the units "Years since 1960" and "Millions of visitors" on the appropriate axes.

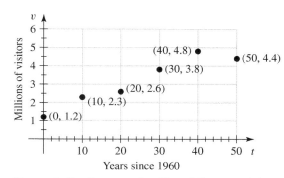

Figure 1 Scattergram for Grand Canyon data

A graph of plotted ordered pairs, such as the graph in Fig. 1, is called a **scattergram. A scattergram should have scaling on both axes and labels indicating the variable names and scale units.**

We can sketch a line that comes close to (or on) the data points of Fig. 1 (see Fig. 2).

There are many lines that come close to (or on) the data points (see Fig. 3). Each of the three lines shown in Fig. 3 does a reasonable job of describing the data.

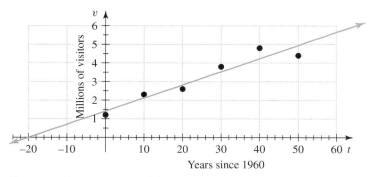

Figure 2 Linear model of Grand Canyon data

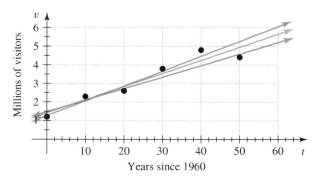

Figure 3 A few of the many lines that come close to (or on) the data points

Linear Models

In Fig. 2, we sketched a line that describes the number of visitors to the Grand Canyon. However, this description is not exact. For example, the line does not describe exactly what happened in the years 1960, 1970, 1980, 1990, 2000, or 2010, because the line does not contain any of these data points. However, the line does come close to the data points, so it suggests good approximations for those years.

If the points in a scattergram of data lie close to (or on) a line, then we say the relevant variables are **approximately linearly related.** For the Grand Canyon situation, variables t and v are approximately linearly related.

Because the line in Fig. 2 is nonvertical, it is the graph of a linear function. The process of choosing a linear function to represent the relationship between the number of visitors in a year and the number of years since 1960 is an example of *modeling*.

▶ Definition   **Model**

A **model** is a mathematical description of an authentic situation. We say the description *models* the situation.

We call the Grand Canyon linear function a *linear model*. In later chapters, we will discuss other types of models. The term "model" is being used in much the same way as it is used in "airplane model." Just as an airplane designer can use the behavior of an airplane model in a wind tunnel to predict the behavior of an actual airplane, a linear model can be used to predict what might happen in a situation in which two variables are approximately linearly related.

▶ Definition   **Linear model**

A **linear model** is a linear function, or its graph, that describes the relationship between two quantities for an authentic situation.

Every linear model is a linear function. So, depending on what we choose to emphasize, we can refer to the Grand Canyon model as a model or a function.

However, not every linear function is a linear model. Models are used only to describe situations. Functions are used both to describe situations *and* to describe certain *mathematical* relationships between two variables. For example, if the equation $y = 2x$ is not being used to describe a situation, then it is a function, not a model.

Using a Linear Model to Make Estimates and Predictions

Since all of the Grand Canyon data points lie close to our linear model, it seems reasonable that data points for the years between 1960 and 2010 that are not given in Table 3 might also lie close to the line. Similarly, it is reasonable that data points for at least a few years before 1960 or for at least a few years after 2010 might also lie near the line.

▶ **Example 2**   Using a Linear Model to Make a Prediction and an Estimate

1. Use the linear model shown in Fig. 2 to predict the number of visitors in 2018.
2. Use the linear model to estimate in what year there were 4 million visitors.

Solution

1. The year 2018 corresponds to $t = 58$, because $2018 - 1960 = 58$. To estimate the number of visitors, we locate the point on the linear model where the t-coordinate is 58. We see that the corresponding v-coordinate is about 5.5 (see Fig. 4). So, according to the model, there will be 5.5 million visitors in 2018.

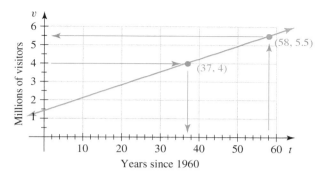

Figure 4 Using the Grand Canyon model to make a prediction and an estimate

2. To find the year in which there were 4 million visitors, we locate the point on the linear model where the v-coordinate is 4. We see that the corresponding t-coordinate is about 37. So, *according to the linear model,* there were 4 million visitors in $1960 + 37 = 1997$.

When to Use a Linear Function to Model Data

How do we determine whether an authentic situation can be described well by a linear model?

▶ **Example 3** Deciding whether to Use a Linear Function to Model Data

Consider the scattergrams of data shown in Figs. 5, 6, and 7 for situations 1, 2, and 3, respectively. For each situation, determine whether a linear function would model it well.

Solution

It appears the data points for situation 1 lie close to a line, so a linear model would describe situation 1 well. The data points for situation 2 do not lie close to any one line; a linear model would not describe situation 2 well. (In Chapters 6 and 7, we will discuss a type of nonlinear model that would describe situation 2 well.) The data points for situation 3 do not lie near a line; a linear model would not describe situation 3 well.

We create a scattergram of data to determine whether the relevant variables are approximately linearly related. If they are, we draw a line that comes close to (or on) the data points and use the line to make estimates and predictions.

WARNING

It is a common error to try to find a line that contains the greatest number of data points. Our goal is to find a line that comes close to *all* of the data points. For example, even though model 1 in Fig. 8 does not contain any of the data points shown, it fits the complete set of data points much better than does model 2, which contains three data points.

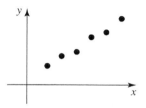

Figure 5 Scattergram for situation 1

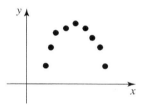

Figure 6 Scattergram for situation 2

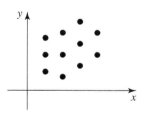

Figure 7 Scattergram for situation 3

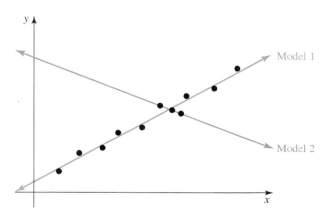

Figure 8 Comparing the fit of two models

Intercepts of a Model and Model Breakdown

In Example 4, we will find the intercepts of a linear model. By doing so, we will see that even if a model describes *known* data well, the model may not describe the situation well for all values of the independent variable.

▶ **Example 4**   Intercepts of a Model; Model Breakdown

The percentages of cell phone users who send or receive text messages multiple times per day are shown in Table 4 for various age groups.

Table 4 Percentages of Cell Phone Users Who Send or Receive Text Messages Multiple Times per Day

Age Group (years)	Age Used to Represent Age Group (years)	Percent
18–24	21.0	76
25–34	29.5	63
35–44	39.5	42
45–54	49.5	37
55–64	59.5	17

Source: *Edison Research and Arbitron*

1. Let p be the percentage of cell phone users at age a years who send or receive text messages multiple times per day. Find a linear model that describes the relationship between a and p.
2. Find the p-intercept. What does it mean in this situation?
3. Find the a-intercept. What does it mean in this situation?

Solution

1. We begin by viewing the positions of the points in the scattergram (see Fig. 9). It appears a and p are approximately linearly related, so we sketch a line that comes close to the data points.

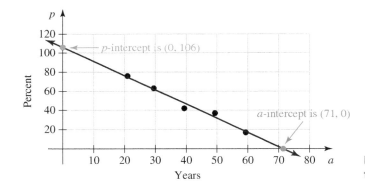

Figure 9 Intercepts of the text message model

2. The p-intercept is $(0, 106)$, or $p = 106$, when $a = 0$. According to the model, 106% of newborns who use cell phones send or receive text messages multiple times per day. Our model gives a false estimate for two reasons: Percentages cannot be larger than 100% in this situation, and newborns cannot send or receive text messages.
3. The a-intercept is $(71, 0)$, or $p = 0$, when $a = 71$. According to the model, no 71-year-old cell phone users send or receive text messages multiple times per day. This is a false estimate. A little research would show some 71-year-old cell phone users send or receive text messages multiple times per day.

To draw the text message model in Fig. 9, we used a scattergram consisting of data points representing various ages from 21.0 years to 59.5 years. In Fig. 10, we draw that portion of the model in blue, and we draw the rest of the model in red. When we use the blue portion of the model to make estimates, we are performing *interpolation*. When we use the red portions of the model, we are performing *extrapolation*.

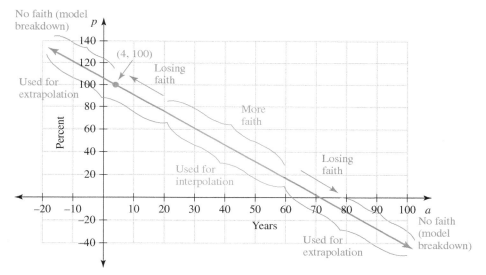

Figure 10 Interpolation versus extrapolation

▶ Definition   Interpolation, extrapolation

For a situation that can be modeled by a function whose independent variable is t,

- We perform **interpolation** when we use a part of the model whose t-coordinates are between the t-coordinates of two data points.
- We perform **extrapolation** when we use a part of the model whose t-coordinates are not between the t-coordinates of any two data points.

Although we could get large errors from interpolating with the text message model, we have more faith in our results from interpolating than from extrapolating. That's because the blue portion of the model comes close to several known data points, whereas we have no idea whether the red portion of the model comes close to *any* data points.

When we extrapolate, our faith declines more and more as we stray farther and farther from the blue portion of the text message model. In fact, we have no faith in the portion of the model from age 71 years on, because the model estimates nonpositive percentages of adults for these ages. We say *model breakdown* has occurred from age 71 years on. Similarly, model breakdown has occurred for ages less than 4 years, because the model estimates percentages greater than 100% for these ages.

▶ Definition   Model breakdown

When a model gives a prediction that does not make sense or an estimate that is not a good approximation, we say **model breakdown** has occurred.

When model breakdown occurs, it is time to modify our model or possibly rethink our modeling process. A different model might give more reasonable predictions. It could be helpful to gather more data to check our choice of model.

▶ Example 5 | Modifying a Model

Additional research yields the data shown in the first and last rows of Table 5. Use this data and the following assumptions to modify the model we found in Example 4:

- Children 3 years old and younger do not send or receive text messages multiple times per day.
- The percentage of cell phone users who send or receive text messages levels off at 5% for users over 80 years in age.
- The age of the oldest cell phone user is 116 years.

Table 5 Percentages of Cell Phone Users Who Send or Receive Text Messages Multiple Times per Day

Age Group (years)	Age Used to Represent Age Group (years)	Percent
12–17	14.5	75
18–24	21.0	76
25–34	29.5	63
35–44	39.5	42
45–54	49.5	37
55–64	59.5	17
over 64	70.0	7

Source: *Edison Research and Arbitron*

Solution

Recall that p is the percentage of cell phone users at age a years who send or receive multiple text messages per day. We sketch a scattergram of the data in Table 5, and taking into account the three assumptions, we draw a model that comes close to the data points (see Fig. 11).

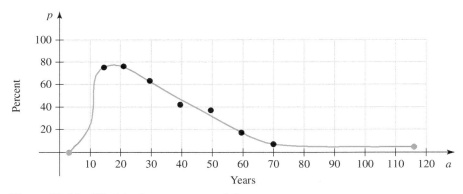

Figure 11 Modified text message model

Group Exploration

How defining the independent variable affects a model

Here you will compare two Grand Canyon models that have different definitions for the independent variable t.

1. Let v be the number (in millions) of visitors in the year that is t years *since 1960* (see Table 6). *Carefully* sketch a scattergram of the visitor data.

2. For the scattergram in Fig. 2 (page 59), the variable t is defined to be the number of years *since 1960*. Carefully sketch a line that comes close to the points in your scattergram from Problem 1 in much the same way as the line in Fig. 2 comes close to the points in Fig. 2.

Table 6 Visitors to the Grand Canyon

Year	Number of Visitors (millions)
1960	1.2
1970	2.3
1980	2.6
1990	3.8
2000	4.8
2010	4.4

Source: *National Park Service*

3. Find each result both by using your linear model from Problem 2 and by using the linear model in Fig. 2.

a. Find the *v*-intercept of the linear model.
b. Find the *t*-intercept.
c. Estimate the number of visitors in 2012.
d. Estimate when there were 3 million visitors.
e. Find the slope of the linear model.

4. For each part of Problem 3, which of your results are the same? Explain why this makes sense in terms of the two definitions of *t*.

5. For each part of Problem 3, which of your results are different? Explain why this makes sense in terms of the two definitions of *t*.

 Group Exploration

Identifying types of modeling errors

The interest rates for subsidized student loans are shown in Table 7 for various years.

Table 7 Interest Rates for Subsidized Student Loans

Years	Interest Rate (percent)
2008	6.8
2009	6.0
2010	5.7
2011	4.5
2012	3.4

Source: *New America Foundation*

Here you will explore possible causes of error for estimates and predictions based on a linear model for the interest rate data.

1. Let *r* be the interest rate (percent) for subsidized student loans at *t* years since 2005. Create a scattergram of the data.

2. Draw a line that comes close to the points in your scattergram.

3. Use your linear model to estimate the interest rate in 2012. What is the actual interest rate? Calculate the error in your estimate for 2012. (The *error* is the difference between the estimated value and the actual value.)

4. Use your linear model to predict the interest rate in 2020. Is this an accurate prediction? If not, why is the error so great?

5. Take another look at your sketch from Problem 2. Is the *t*-axis perfectly horizontal and the *r*-axis perfectly vertical? Are the scalings of both axes precise? Is your line straight? How might these considerations relate to the accuracy of an estimation or a prediction? Explain.

6. What are the coordinates of point S plotted in Fig. 12? Do you think you have found the correct first decimal place (tenths place) for these coordinates? How about the second decimal place?

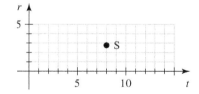

Figure 12 Problem 6

7. Problems 3–6 of this exploration suggest several possible causes of error for estimates and predictions based on a linear model. Describe the possible causes of error.

▶ Tips for Success   **Get in Touch with Classmates**

Exchange phone numbers and e-mail addresses with some classmates so that, if you must miss class, you can contact someone to find out what you missed and what homework was assigned.

Homework 2.1

For extra help ▶   MyMathLab®   Watch the videos
in MyMathLab   Download the
MyDashboard App

1. The percentages of dentistry degrees earned by women are shown in Table 8 for various years.

Table 8 Percentage of Dentistry Degrees Earned by Women

Year	Percent
1970	1
1980	13
1990	31
2000	40
2009	46

Source: *U.S. National Center for Education Statistics*

a. Let p be the percentage of dentistry degrees earned by women at t years since 1970. For example, $t = 0$ represents 1970 and $t = 10$ represents 1980. Create a scattergram of the data (see Fig. 13).

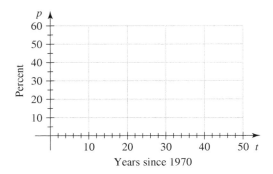

Figure 13 Exercise 1

b. Draw a line that comes close to the points in your scattergram.
c. Predict the percentage of dentistry degrees that will be earned by women in 2018. [**Note:** When responding to exercises in this text, always use sentences, not phrases.]
d. Estimate when women earned 20% of dentistry degrees.

2. The percentages of Americans who sent their tax returns to the Internal Revenue Service (IRS) electronically are shown in Table 9 for various years.

Table 9 Percentages of Tax Returns Sent Electronically

Year	Percent
2000	27
2002	36
2004	47
2006	54
2008	58
2010	70

Source: *IRS*

a. Let p be the percentage of Americans who sent their tax returns to the IRS electronically at t years since 2000. For example, $t = 0$ represents 2000 and $t = 2$ represents 2002. Create a scattergram of the data (see Fig. 14).

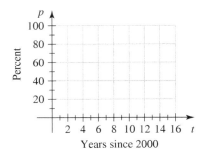

Figure 14 Exercise 2

b. Draw a line that comes close to the points in your scattergram.
c. Estimate when half of Americans sent returns electronically. [**Note:** When responding to exercises in this text, always use sentences, not phrases.]
d. By a 1998 law, the IRS was supposed to motivate 80% of taxpayers to send their returns electronically by 2007. Does your model estimate this goal was reached by then? Explain.
e. In 2005, an independent oversight board recommended giving the IRS until 2011 to reach the 80% goal. Does your model estimate this goal was reached by then? Explain.

3. Due to improved technology and public-service campaigns, the number of collisions at highway–railroad crossings per year has declined since 1992 (see Table 10).

Table 10 Numbers of Collisions at Highway–Railroad Crossings

Year	Number of Collisions (thousands)
1992	4.9
1995	4.6
2000	3.5
2005	3.1
2010	2.0
2011	2.0

Source: *Federal Railroad Administration*

Let n be the number of collisions (in thousands) for the year that is t years since 1990.

a. Create a scattergram of the data. Extend your t-axis and n-axis so you can make estimates about numbers of collisions before 1992 and predictions about future numbers of collisions. [**Note:** Include scaling on both axes and labels indicating the variable names and the scale units.]

b. Draw a line that comes close to the data points in your scattergram.

c. Use your linear model to estimate the number of collisions in 2007. Did you perform interpolation or extrapolation? Explain.

d. Use your linear model to predict in which year there will be 1.0 thousand collisions. Did you perform interpolation or extrapolation? Explain.

e. Find the n-intercept of your linear model. What does it mean in this situation?

f. Find the t-intercept. What does it mean in this situation? [**Note:** If model breakdown occurs, say so, say where, and explain why.]

4. Repeat Exercise 3, but let n be the number of collisions (in thousands) for the year that is t years *since 1985*. Which of your responses for this exercise are the same as those for Exercise 3? Explain why it makes sense that these responses are the same. Explain why it makes sense that the other responses are different.

5. The numbers of Internet users in the United States are shown in Table 11 for various years.

Table 11 Numbers of Internet Users in the United States

Year	Number of Users (millions)
2006	204
2007	212
2008	220
2009	228
2010	240

Source: *The Nielsen Company*

a. Let n be the number of Internet users (in millions) in the United States at t years since 2005. Create a scattergram of the data.

b. Sketch a line that comes close to the data points.

c. Find the n-intercept of your linear model. What does it mean in this situation? Did you perform interpolation or extrapolation? Explain.

d. Estimate by how much the number of Internet users is increasing per year.

e. Use your linear model to predict when everyone in the United States will be an Internet user. Assume the U.S. population is 315 million. Did you perform interpolation or extrapolation? Explain.

6. The temperature at which water boils (the *boiling point*) depends on elevation: The higher the elevation, the lower is the boiling point. At sea level, water boils at 212°F; at an elevation of 10,000 meters, water boils at about 151°F. Boiling points are listed in Table 12 for various elevations.

Table 12 Boiling Points of Water

Elevation (in thousands of meters)	Boiling Point (°F)
0	212
1	205
2	200
5	181
10	151
15	123

a. Let B be the boiling point (in degrees Fahrenheit) at an elevation of E thousand meters. Create a scattergram of the data.

b. Sketch a line that comes close to the data points.

c. Mount Everest, the highest mountain in the world, reaches 8850 meters at its peak. What is the boiling point of water at the peak? Did you perform interpolation or extrapolation? Explain.

d. We say water is *lukewarm* if its temperature is close to body temperature (about 98.6°F). At what elevation would boiling water feel lukewarm? Did you perform interpolation or extrapolation? Explain.

e. The cooking time required to make a hard-boiled egg depends on the water temperature. Let T be the amount of time (in minutes) it takes to cook an egg in boiling water at an elevation of E thousand meters. Sketch a *qualitative* graph that describes the relationship between E and T.

7. The percentages of Americans who believe marriages between same-sex couples should be recognized by the law as valid are shown in Table 13 for various age groups.

Table 13 Percentages of Americans Who Support Same-Sex Marriage

Age Group (years)	Age Used to Represent Age Group (years)	Percent
18–29	23.5	71
30–39	34.5	56
40–49	44.5	49
50–59	54.5	46
60–69	64.5	42
70–79	74.5	32
over 79	85.0	21

Source: *The Gallup Organization*

Let p be the percentage of Americans at age a years who believe marriages between same-sex couples should be recognized by the law as valid.

a. Create a scattergram of the data.

b. Draw a line that comes close to the data points.

c. Use your linear model to estimate at what age 65% of Americans believe same-sex couples should be recognized by the law as valid.

d. Find the p-intercept of your linear model. What does it mean in this situation?

e. Find the a-intercept of your linear model. What does it mean in this situation?

8. The percentages of Americans who currently have a personal profile page on a social networking website such as Facebook are shown in Table 14 for various age groups.

Table 14 Percentages of Americans Who Currently Have a Personal Profile Page on a Social Networking Website

Age Group (years)	Age Used to Represent Age Group (years)	Percent
12–17	14.5	78
18–24	21.0	77
25–34	29.5	65
35–44	39.5	51
45–54	49.5	35
55–64	59.5	31
over 64	70.0	13

Source: *Edison Research and Arbitron*

Let p be the percentage of Americans at age a years who have a personal profile page.
a. Create a scattergram of the data.
b. Draw a line that comes close to the data points.
c. Use your linear model to estimate at what age 70% of Americans have a profile page.
d. Find the p-intercept of your linear model. What does it mean in this situation?
e. Find the a-intercept of your linear model. What does it mean in this situation?

9. The percentages of Americans who are satisfied with the way things are in the United States are shown in Table 15 for various years.

Table 15 Percentages of Americans Who Are Satisfied

Year	Percent
1992	21
1993	28
1994	33
1995	32
1996	39
1997	49
1998	60
1999	59

Source: *The Gallup Organization*

Let p be the percentage of Americans at t years since 1990 who are satisfied with the way things are.
a. Create a scattergram of the data in Table 15.
b. Draw a line that comes close to the data points.
c. Use your line to estimate the percentage of Americans who were satisfied in 2006.
d. Data for the years 2000–2011 are shown in Table 16. Create a scattergram of the data for the years 1992–2011.
e. Compute the error in the estimation for 2006 that you made in part (c). (The *error* is the difference between the estimated percentage and the actual percentage.) Explain why the error in your estimate is so large.

Table 16 Percentages of Americans Who Are Satisfied

Year	Percent
2000	60
2002	52
2004	43
2006	31
2008	20
2011	11

Source: *The Gallup Organization*

10. The percentages of Americans living below the poverty level are shown in Table 17 for various years.

Table 17 Percentages of Americans Living Below the Poverty Level

Year	Percent
1993	15.1
1994	14.5
1995	13.8
1996	13.7
1997	13.3
1998	12.7
1999	11.9
2000	11.3

Source: *U.S. Census Bureau*

Let p be the percentage of Americans living below the poverty level at t years since 1990.
a. Create a scattergram of the data in Table 17.
b. Draw a line that comes close to the data points.
c. Use your line to estimate the percentage in 2010.
d. Data for the years 2002–2010 are shown in Table 18. Create a scattergram of the data for the years 1993–2010.

Table 18 Percentages of Americans Living Below the Poverty Level

Year	Percent
2002	12.1
2004	12.7
2006	13.3
2008	13.2
2010	15.3

Source: *U.S. Census Bureau*

e. Compute the error in the estimation for 2010 that you made in part (c). (The *error* is the difference between the estimated percentage and the actual percentage.) Explain why the absolute value of the error in your estimate is so large.

11. The annual profits of Alaska Air Group are shown in Table 19 for various years. Let p be the annual profit (in millions of dollars) at t years since 2002.
a. Without graphing, estimate the coordinates of the t-intercept for a line that comes close to the data points. What does that point mean in this situation? If you don't see how to estimate the coordinates, create a scattergram of the data first.

b. Without graphing, estimate the coordinates of the *p*-intercept for a line that comes close to the data points. What does that point mean in this situation? If you don't see how to estimate the coordinates, create a scattergram of the data first.

Table 19 **Annual Profits of Alaska Air Group**

Year	Annual Profit (millions of dollars)
2002	−68
2003	−30.8
2005	55.0
2007	91.6
2009	88.7
2010	262.6

Source: *Alaska Air Group*

12. The *windchill* (or *windchill factor*) is a measure of how cold you feel as a result of being exposed to wind. Table 20 provides some data on windchills for various temperatures when the wind speed is 10 mph.

Table 20 **Windchills for a 10-mph Wind**

Temperature (°F)	Windchill (°F)
−15	−35
−10	−28
−5	−22
5	−10
10	−4
15	3
20	9
25	15

Source: *National Weather Service Forecast Office*

Let *w* be the windchill (in degrees Fahrenheit) corresponding to a temperature of *t* degrees Fahrenheit when the wind speed is 10 mph.

a. Without graphing, estimate the coordinates of the *t*-intercept for a line that comes close to the data points. What does that point mean in this situation? If you don't see how to estimate the coordinates, create a scattergram of the data first.

b. Without graphing, estimate the coordinates of the *w*-intercept for a line that comes close to the data points. What does that point mean in this situation? If you don't see how to estimate the coordinates, create a scattergram of the data first.

Concepts

13. Describe the meaning of a linear function and a linear model. Is a linear function necessarily a model? Is a linear model necessarily a function? (See page 4 for guidelines on writing a good response.)

14. When using a line to model a situation, do we usually have more faith in a result obtained by interpolation or extrapolation? Explain. (See page 4 for guidelines on writing a good response.)

15. When modeling a situation in which the variables are approximately linearly related, different students may all do good work, yet not get the same results. Draw a scattergram and at least two reasonable linear models to show how this is possible.

16. A person collects data by doing research. If the data points lie exactly on a line, will all points on the line describe the situation exactly?

17. Which is more desirable, finding a linear model whose graph contains several, but not all, data points or finding a linear model whose graph does not contain any data points but comes close to all data points? Include some sketches of scattergrams and linear models.

18. Describe how to find a linear model for a situation and how to use the model to make estimates and predictions.

2.2 Finding Equations of Linear Models

Objectives

» Find an equation of a linear model by using data described in words.

» Find an equation of a linear model by using data displayed in a table.

In Section 2.1, we used graphs of linear functions to model data. In this section, we use *equations* of linear functions to model data.

Finding an Equation of a Linear Model by Using Data Described in Words

In Example 1, we will use data described in words to find an equation of a model.

▶ **Example 1** Finding an Equation of a Linear Model

The number of times airplanes have struck birds has increased approximately linearly from 2.6 thousand strikes in 1992 to 10.0 thousand strikes in 2011 (Source: *Federal Aviation Administration*). Let *n* be the number (in thousands) of bird strikes in the year that is *t* years since 1990. Find an equation of a linear model.

Table 21 Known Values of t and n

Years since 1990 t	Number of Bird Strikes (thousands) n
2	2.6
21	10.0

Solution

Known values of t and n are shown in Table 21.

A linear function can be put into the form $y = mx + b$, where y depends on x. Since t and n are approximately linearly related and n depends on t, we will find an equation of the form $n = mt + b$.

First, we use the data points $(2, 2.6)$ and $(21, 10.0)$ to find the slope of the model:

$$m = \frac{10.0 - 2.6}{21 - 2} = \frac{7.4}{19} \approx 0.39$$

So, we can substitute 0.39 for m in the equation $n = mt + b$:

$$n = 0.39t + b$$

Next, we can find the constant b by substituting the coordinates of the point $(2, 2.6)$ into the equation $n = 0.39t + b$ and then solving for b:

$$\begin{aligned} 2.6 &= 0.39(2) + b &&\text{Substitute 2 for t and 2.6 for n.} \\ 2.6 &= 0.78 + b &&\text{Multiply.} \\ 2.6 - 0.78 &= 0.78 + b - 0.78 &&\text{Subtract 0.78 from both sides.} \\ 1.82 &= b &&\text{Combine like terms.} \end{aligned}$$

Now we can substitute 1.82 for b in the equation $n = 0.39t + b$:

$$n = 0.39t + 1.82$$

We verify our equation by using TRACE on a graphing calculator to check that our line approximately contains the points $(2, 2.6)$ and $(21, 10.0)$. See Fig. 15.

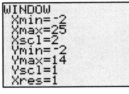 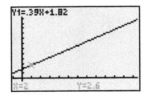 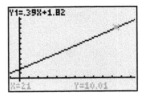

Figure 15 Checking that the model approximately contains both $(2, 2.6)$ and $(21, 10.0)$

Finding an Equation of a Linear Model by Using Data Displayed in a Table

In Example 2, we will use data shown in a table to find an equation of a linear model.

Table 22 Numbers of Apple Stores

Year	Number of Apple Stores
2003	51
2005	95
2007	169
2009	249
2011	321
2012	358

Source: *Apple, Inc.*

▶ **Example 2**   Finding an Equation of a Linear Model

The numbers of Apple stores are shown in Table 22 for various years. Let n be the number of Apple stores at t years since 2000. Find an equation of a line that comes close to the points in the scattergram of the data.

Solution

We begin by viewing the positions of the points in the scattergram (see Fig. 16). To save time and improve accuracy in plotting points, we can use a graphing calculator to view a scattergram of the data (see Fig. 17). For graphing calculator instructions, see Appendix B.8.

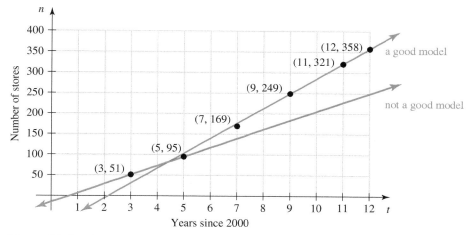

Figure 16 Apple stores scattergram

Our task is to find an equation of a line that comes close to the data points. It is not necessary to use two *data* points to find an equation, although it is often convenient and satisfactory to do so.

The red line that contains points (3, 51) and (5, 95) does *not* come close to the other data points (see Fig. 16). However, the green line that passes through points (9, 249) and (12, 358) appears to come close to the rest of the points. We will find the equation of this line.

For an equation of the form $n = mt + b$, we first use the points $(9, 249)$ and $(12, 358)$ to find m (see Fig. 18):

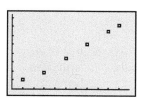

Figure 17 Graphing calculator scattergram

$$m = \frac{358 - 249}{12 - 9} = \frac{109}{3} \approx 36.33$$

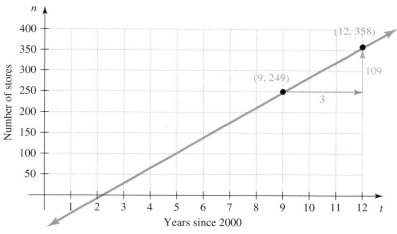

Figure 18 Two points of the Apple stores scattergram

Then we substitute 36.33 for m in the equation $n = mt + b$:

$$n = 36.33t + b$$

To find the constant b, we substitute the coordinates of the point $(9, 249)$ into the equation $n = 36.33t + b$ and then solve for b:

$249 = 36.33(9) + b$	*Substitute 9 for t and 249 for n.*
$249 = 326.97 + b$	*Multiply.*
$249 - 326.97 = 326.97 + b - 326.97$	*Subtract 326.97 from both sides.*
$-77.97 = b$	*Combine like terms.*

Now we substitute -77.97 for b in the equation $n = 36.33t + b$:

$$n = 36.33t - 77.97$$

We can check the correctness of our equation by using a graphing calculator to verify that our line approximately contains the points $(9, 249)$ and $(12, 358)$. See Fig. 19. For graphing calculator instructions, see Appendix B.10 and B.11.

WARNING

It is a common error to skip creating a scattergram when we find an equation of a model. However, we benefit in many ways by viewing a scattergram of data. First, we can determine whether the data are approximately linearly related. Second, if the data are approximately linearly related, viewing a scattergram helps us choose two good points with which to find an equation of a linear model. Third, by graphing the model with the scattergram, we can assess whether the model fits the data reasonably well.

Example 2 took four steps to find an equation of a linear model.

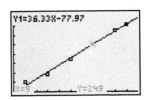

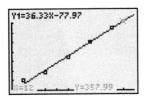

Figure 19 Checking that the model approximately contains both (9, 249) and (12, 358)

Finding an Equation of a Linear Model

To find an equation of a linear model, given some data,

1. Create a scattergram of the data.
2. Determine whether there is a line that comes close to the data points. If so, choose two points (not necessarily data points) you can use to find the equation of a linear model.
3. Find an equation of the line you identified in step 2.
4. Use a graphing calculator to verify the graph of your equation comes close to the points of the scattergram.

What should you do if you discover that a model does not fit a data set well? A good first step is to check for graphing or calculation errors. If your work appears to be correct, then try using different points to derive your equation, or increase or decrease the slope m and/or the constant term b of your equation $y = mx + b$ until the fit is good.

In Example 2, we used the linear equation $n = 36.33t - 77.97$ to describe the linear "Apple stores" model. Depending on what aspect of the model we want to emphasize, we can refer to the model as the "Apple stores model," "Apple stores function," or "equation $n = 36.33t - 77.97$."

In Example 2, we used two points to find the model $n = 36.33t - 77.97$. There is another way to find a model. Most graphing calculators have a built-in **linear regression** feature for finding an equation of a linear model. Linear regression gives the equation $n = 35.21t - 68.67$. In Fig. 20, we see both models fit the data well. For graphing calculator instructions, see Appendix B.16.

A linear equation found by linear regression is called a **linear regression equation,** and the function described by the equation is called a **linear regression function.** The graph is called a **regression line.** (You can learn more about linear regression in a statistics course.)

Now you have two ways to find the equation of a linear model. No matter which method you use, the objective is the same: Find an equation of a line that comes close to the data points.

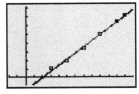

Figure 20 Comparing two Apple stores models' graphs that are so close together that there appears to be only one line

Table 23 Percentages of American Adults Who Smoke

Year	Percent Who Smoke
1970	37.4
1980	33.2
1990	25.3
2000	23.1
2010	19.4

Source: *National Center for Health Statistics*

▶ Example 3   Finding the Equation of a Linear Model

Cigarette smoking has been on the decline for the past several decades (see Table 23). Let p be the percentage of American adults who smoke at t years since 1900.

1. Use two well-chosen points to find an equation of a model that describes the relationship between t and p.
2. Find the linear regression equation and line by using a graphing calculator. Compare this model with the one you found in Problem 1.

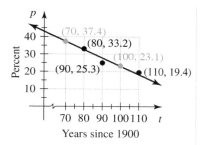

Figure 21 Smoking scattergram and linear model

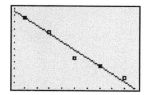

Figure 22 Verifying the smoking model

Solution

1. We see from the scattergram in Fig. 21 that a line containing the points (70, 37.4) and (100, 23.1) comes close to the rest of the data points. The zigzag lines on the t-axis near the origin indicate part of the scale is missing. This is done to show a clearer view of the data points.

   For an equation of the form $p = mt + b$, we first use the points $(70, 37.4)$ and $(100, 23.1)$ to find m:

   $$m = \frac{23.1 - 37.4}{100 - 70} = -0.48$$

   So, the equation has the form

   $$p = -0.48t + b$$

   To find b, we use the point (70, 37.4) and substitute 70 for t and 37.4 for p in the equation $p = -0.48t + b$:

$37.4 = -0.48(70) + b$	*Substitute 70 for t and 37.4 for p.*
$37.4 = -33.6 + b$	*Multiply.*
$37.4 + 33.6 = -33.6 + b + 33.6$	*Add 33.6 to both sides.*
$71 = b$	*Simplify.*

   So, the equation is $p = -0.48t + 71$.

   We can use a graphing calculator to verify the linear model contains the points (70, 37.4) and (100, 23.1) and comes close to the other data points (see Fig. 22).

2. The regression equation is $p = -0.46t + 69.17$. It is "close" to the equation $p = -0.48t + 71$. Further, both models appear to fit the data well (see Fig. 23).

 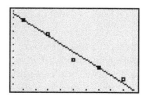

Figure 23 Comparing two smoking models' graphs that are so close together that there appears to be only one line

Group Exploration

Choosing "good points" to find a model

The revenues of IKEA are shown in Table 24 for various years. The table includes a first column that indicates a name for each data point. For example, point D refers to the point (9, 28.4).

Table 24 Annual Revenues of IKEA

Name of Point	Years since 2000	Revenue (billions of dollars)
A	6	22.3
B	7	26.2
C	8	28.2
D	9	28.4
E	10	30.8
F	11	32.8
G	12	35.4

Source: *IKEA*

1. Let r be the annual revenue (in billions of dollars) at t years since 2000. Use a graphing calculator to draw a scattergram of the data.

2. Find an equation of the line that contains the points A and B.

3. Use a graphing calculator to verify that the graph of your equation passes through both points A and B. Does the line come close to the other data points?

4. If you had used points E and F, you would have found the equation $r = 2t + 10.8$. Compare its graph with the graph you drew in Problem 3. Explain why the graphs look so different.

5. List all pairs of points that yield equations you think would be good linear models. (You do not have to find the equations.)

6. Several pairs of points from a scattergram yield equations that could serve as models of the data. Discuss how to choose two such data points to find an equation that comes reasonably close to all the data points.

7. It is not necessary to use data points to find an equation of a linear model. While viewing the IKEA scattergram, use the arrow keys on a graphing calculator to identify two nondata points you feel would yield an equation of a line that is close to the data points. For graphing calculator instructions, see Appendix B.23. Find an equation of the line that contains these two points. Then use a graphing calculator to verify that the graph of your equation comes close to the data points.

▶ Tips for Success   Verify Your Work

Use a graphing calculator to verify your work. In this section, for example, you can use a graphing calculator to check your equations. Checking your work increases your chances of catching errors and thus will likely improve your performance on homework assignments, quizzes, and tests.

Homework 2.2

For extra help ▶   MyMathLab®   Watch the videos in MyMathLab   Download the MyDashboard App

1. The number of classified documents has increased approximately linearly from 22.2 million documents in 2009 to 92.0 million documents in 2011 (Source: *The Information Security Oversight Office*). Let n be the number of documents (in millions) labeled as classified in the year that is t years since 2000. Find an equation of a linear model to describe the data.

2. The number of Americans who have a passport has increased approximately linearly from 11.1 million in 1990 to 109.8 million in 2011 (Source: *U.S. State Department*). Let n be the number (in millions) of Americans who have a passport at t years since 1900. Find an equation of a linear model to describe the data.

3. The average price (in dollars) of a television decreased approximately linearly from $912 in 2007 to $613 in 2010 (Source: *DisplaySearch*). Let p be the average price (in dollars) of a television at t years since 2000. Find an equation of a linear model to describe the data.

4. The number of little league participants has decreased approximately linearly from 2.6 million in 1997 to 2.1 million in 2011 (Source: *Little League International*). Let n be the number (in millions) of little league participants at t years since 1990. Find an equation of a linear model to describe the data.

5. The percentage of soldiers who are unavailable for combat has increased approximately linearly from 11% in 2007 to 16% in 2010 (Source: *U.S. Army*). The main causes are due to repeated deployments and health problems. Let p be the percentage of soldiers unavailable for combat at t years since 2000. Find an equation of a linear model to describe the data.

6. The number of unruly airline passengers per year has decreased approximately linearly from 176 passengers in 2007 to 131 passengers in 2011 (Source: *Federal Aviation Administration*). Let n be the number of unruly passengers in the year that is t years since 2000. Find an equation of a linear model to describe the data.

7. The average length of a 6-year-old striped bass is 27 inches, and that of a 20-year-old striped bass is 54.5 inches (Source: *daybreakfishing.com*). A striped bass's age and average length are approximately linearly related. Let L be the average length (in inches) of a striped bass at age a years. Find an equation of a linear model to describe the data.

8. For Pacific albacore tuna, the weight and mercury concentration are approximately linearly related. A 4-kilogram tuna has an average mercury concentration of 0.10 part per million. A 10-kilogram tuna has an average mercury concentration of 0.19 part per million. Let c be the average mercury concentration (in parts per million) of a Pacific albacore tuna that weighs w kilograms. Find an equation of a linear model to describe the data.

9. Find an equation of a line that comes close to the points listed in Table 25. Then use a graphing calculator to check that your line comes close to the points. [*Graphing Calculator:* See Appendix B.8 and B.10.]

Table 25 Finding a Linear Model

x	y
3	5
4	7
5	10
6	12
7	15

10. Find an equation of a line that comes close to the points listed in Table 26. Then use a graphing calculator to check that your line comes close to the points. [*Graphing Calculator:* See Appendix B.8 and B.10.]

Table 26 Finding a Linear Model

x	y
1	18
4	14
5	12
7	8
10	5

11. The percentages of births outside marriage in the United States are shown in Table 27 for various years.

Table 27 Births Outside Marriage

Year	Percent of Births outside Marriage
1970	10.7
1975	14.3
1980	18.4
1985	22.0
1990	28.0
1995	32.2
2000	33.2
2005	36.8
2010	40.8

Source: *National Center for Health Statistics*

Let p be the percentage of births outside marriage in the United States at t years since 1900.
a. Use a graphing calculator to draw a scattergram of the data.
b. Find an equation of a linear model to describe the data.
c. Draw your line and the scattergram in the same viewing window. Verify that the line passes through your two chosen points and that it comes close to all of the data points.

12. Repeat Exercise 11, but let p be the percentage of births outside marriage in the United States at t years *since 1970*. Compare the slope of your model with the slope of the model you found in Exercise 11. Compare the p-intercepts. Explain why your comparisons make sense.

13. The prices of ski rental packages from Gold Medal Sports® are shown in Table 28 for various numbers of days.

Table 28 Prices of Ski Rental Packages

Number of Days	Price of Package (dollars)
1	15.00
2	30.00
3	45.00
4	56.00
5	70.00
6	78.00

Source: *Gold Medal Sports*

Let p be the price (in dollars) of a ski rental package for n days.
a. Use a graphing calculator to draw a scattergram of the data.
b. Find an equation of a linear model to describe the data.
c. Draw your line and the scattergram in the same viewing window. Verify that the line passes through the two points you chose in finding the equation in part (b) and that it comes close to all of the data points.

14. The life expectancies at birth of Americans are shown in Table 29 for various years.
a. Let L be the life expectancy at birth (in years) of an American born t years after 1980. Use a graphing calculator to draw a scattergram of the data.

Table 29 Life Expectancies at Birth

Year of Birth	Life Expectancy (years)
1980	73.7
1985	74.7
1990	75.4
1995	75.8
2000	77.0
2005	77.9
2010	78.7

Source: *U.S. Census Bureau*

b. Find an equation of a linear model to describe the data.
c. Draw your line and the scattergram in the same viewing window. Verify that the line passes through the two points you chose in finding the equation in part (b) and that it comes close to all of the data points.

15. Table 30 shows, for various years, the percentage of Americans who are baseball fans.

Table 30 Percentages of Americans Who Are Baseball Fans

Year	Percent
1999	54
2001	51
2003	50
2005	48
2007	44
2008	43

Source: *The Gallup Organization*

Let p be the percentage of Americans who are baseball fans at t years since 1990.
a. Use a graphing calculator to draw a scattergram of the data.
b. Find an equation of a linear model to describe the data.
c. Draw your line and the scattergram in the same viewing window. Verify that the line passes through the two points you chose in finding the equation in part (b) and that it comes close to all of the data points.

16. The percentages of Americans who have been diagnosed with diabetes are shown in Table 31 for various age groups.

Table 31 Percentages of Americans Diagnosed with Diabetes, by Age Group

Age Group (years)	Age Used to Represent Age Group (years)	Percent
35–39	37	2
40–44	42	4
45–49	47	5
50–54	52	8
55–59	57	10
60–64	62	13
65–69	67	14

Source: *National Health Interview Survey*

Let p be the percentage of Americans at age a years who have been diagnosed with diabetes at some point in their lives.

a. Use a graphing calculator to draw a scattergram of the data.
b. Find an equation of a linear model to describe the data.
c. Draw your line and the scattergram in the same viewing window. Verify that the line passes through the two points you chose in finding the equation in part (b) and that it comes close to all of the data points.
d. Find the regression equation to describe the data.
e. Use a graphing calculator to graph the equations you found in parts (b) and (d) in the same viewing window. Compare the graphs.

17. Table 32 lists world record times for the women's 400-meter run. Let r be the record time (in seconds) at t years since 1900.

Table 32 Women's 400-Meter Run Record Times

Year	Runner	Country	Record Time (seconds)
1957	Marlene Mathews	Australia	57.0
1959	Maria Itkina	USSR	53.4
1962	Shin Geum Dan	North Korea	51.9
1969	Nicole Duclos	France	51.7
1972	Monika Zehrt	E. Germany	51.0
1976	Irena Szewinska	Poland	49.29
1979	Marita Koch	E. Germany	48.60
1983	Jarmila Kratochvílová	Czechoslovakia	47.99
1985	Marita Koch	E. Germany	47.60

Source: *International Association of Athletics Federations*

a. Use a graphing calculator to draw a scattergram of the data.
b. Find an equation of a linear model to describe the data.
c. Draw your line and the scattergram in the same viewing window. Verify that the line passes through the two points you chose in finding the equation in part (b) and that it comes close to all of the data points.

18. Table 33 lists world record times for the men's 400-meter run. Let r be the record time (in seconds) at t years since 1900.

Table 33 Men's 400-Meter Run Record Times

Year	Runner	Country	Record Time (seconds)
1900	Maxie Long	USA	47.8
1916	Ted Meredith	USA	47.4
1928	Emerson Spencer	USA	47.0
1932	Bill Carr	USA	46.2
1941	Graver Klemmer	USA	46.0
1950	George Rhoden	Jamaica	45.8
1960	Carl Kaufmann	Germany	44.9
1968	Lee Evans	USA	43.86
1988	Harry Reynolds	USA	43.29
1999	Michael Johnson	USA	43.18

Source: *International Association of Athletics Federations*

a. Use a graphing calculator to draw a scattergram of the data.
b. Find an equation of a linear model to describe the data.
c. Draw your line and the scattergram in the same viewing window. Verify that the line passes through the two points you chose in finding the equation in part (b) and that it comes close to all of the data points.

19. In Exercises 17 and 18, you found equations for the women's and men's 400-meter run record times. Equations that model the data well are

$$r = -0.27t + 70.45 \qquad \text{(women's model)}$$
$$r = -0.053t + 48.08 \qquad \text{(men's model)}$$

where r represents the record time (in seconds) at t years since 1900.

a. Graph both models by hand for the years from 1900 to 2050. (If you are able to use a graphing calculator to do this exercise, you may do so.)
b. Do the models predict that the women's record time will ever equal the men's record time? If so, what is that record time, and when will the record be set?
c. Do the models predict that the women's record time will ever be less than the men's record time? If so, in what years?

20. A runner's *stride rate* is the number of steps per second. The average stride rates of the top female and male runners are shown in Table 34 for various speeds.

Table 34 Top Female and Male Runners' Speeds and Average Stride Rates

Speed (feet per second)	Average Stride Rate (number of steps per second)	
	Women	Men
15.86	3.05	2.92
16.88	3.12	2.98
17.50	3.17	3.03
18.62	3.25	3.11
19.97	3.36	3.22
21.06	3.46	3.31
22.11	3.55	3.41

Source: *Biomechanical comparison of male and female runners, R. C. Nelson et al., 1977*

a. Let r be the average stride rate of a woman running at s feet per second. Find the regression equation to describe the data.
b. Let r be the average stride rate of a man running at s feet per second. Find the regression equation to describe the data.
c. Which of your two models has the r-intercept with the larger r-coordinate? What does this tell you about the graphs of the models?
d. Which model has the larger slope? What does this tell you about the graphs of the models?
e. Explain why your work in parts (c) and (d) suggests the graphs of your two models do not intersect in quadrant I (where s and r are positive). What does that mean in this situation?

21. To enroll in Intermediate Algebra, a student at the College of San Mateo (CSM) must score at least 21 points (out of 50) on a placement test. Using four semesters of data, the CSM Mathematics Department computed the percentages of students who succeeded in Intermediate Algebra (grade of A, B, or C) for various groups of scores on the placement test (see Table 35).

Table 35 Percentages of Intermediate Algebra Students Who Succeeded

Placement Score Group	Score Used to Represent Score Group	Percentage Who Succeeded in Intermediate Algebra
21–25	23	34
26–30	28	47
31–35	33	55
36–40	38	71
41–45	43	84
46–50	48	*

Source: *College of San Mateo Mathematics Department*
*There were not enough students in this group to give useful data.

a. Let p be the percentage of Intermediate Algebra students succeeding in the course who scored x points on the placement test. Use a graphing calculator to draw a scattergram of the data.

b. Find an equation of a line that you think comes close to the points in the scattergram.

c. Draw your line and the scattergram in the same viewing window. Verify that the line contains the two points you chose in finding the equation in part (b) and that it comes close to all of the data points.

22. The "crime index" refers to the number of incidents of crime. The numbers of burglaries, aggravated assaults, and all types of crime per 100,000 Americans are shown in Table 36 for various years.

Table 36 Crime Indexes

Year	Burglary	Aggravated Assault	All Types of Crime
		Crime Index (number of incidents per 100,000 people)	
1993	1099	440	5484
1995	987	418	5276
1997	919	382	4930
1999	770	334	4267
2001	742	319	4163
2003	741	295	4067
2005	727	291	3899
2007	726	287	3749
2009	716	263	3466

Source: *FBI*

a. Let A be the crime index of aggravated assaults for the year that is t years since 1990. Can the data be modeled well by a linear model? If yes, find such a model. If no, explain why not.

b. Let B be the crime index of burglaries for the year that is t years since 1990. Can the data be modeled well by a linear model? If yes, find such a model. If no, explain why not.

c. Let C be the crime index of all types of crime for the year that is t years since 1990. Can the data be modeled well by a linear model? If yes, find such a model. If no, explain why not.

d. Economist Steven D. Levitt believes crime and the economy are not related. The U.S. economy performed well from 1993 to 2000 and from 2003 to 2008, and did poorly from 2000 to 2003 and from 2008 to 2012.

   i. Explain why the aggravated-assault data support Levitt's theory.

   ii. Explain why the burglary data are less supportive (than the aggravated-assault data) of Levitt's theory.

   iii. Explain why the data for all types of crime support Levitt's theory.

Concepts

23. Three students are to find a linear model of the data in Table 37. Student A uses points $(1, 5.9)$ and $(2, 6.4)$, student B uses points $(3, 9.0)$ and $(4, 11.0)$, and student C uses points $(5, 12.1)$ and $(6, 15.5)$. Which student seems to have made the best choice of points? Explain.

Table 37 Three Students Model Data

x	y
1	5.9
2	6.4
3	9.0
4	11.0
5	12.1
6	15.5
7	16.5

24. Three students are to find a linear model of the data in Table 38. Student A uses points $(3, 13.8)$ and $(4, 10.1)$, student B uses points $(6, 7.8)$ and $(7, 4.3)$, and student C uses points $(5, 9.1)$ and $(8, 3.1)$. Which student seems to have made the best choice of points? Explain.

Table 38 Three Students Model Data

x	y
3	13.8
4	10.1
5	9.1
6	7.8
7	4.3
8	3.1
9	1.1

For Exercises 25 and 26, consider the scattergram of data and the graph of the model $y = mx + b$ in the indicated figure. Sketch the graph of a linear model that describes the data better. Then explain how you would adjust the values of m and b of the original model so it would describe the data better.

25. See Fig. 24.

Figure 24 Exercise 25

26. See Fig. 25.

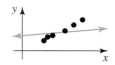

Figure 25 Exercise 26

27. Explain how to find an equation of a linear model for a given situation. Also, explain how to verify that the linear function models the situation reasonably well.

28. A student comes up with a shortcut for modeling a situation described by a table that contains several rows of data. Instead of creating a scattergram of the data, the student chooses two data points at random and uses them to find an equation of a line. Give at least two examples to illustrate what can go wrong with this shortcut.

▼2.3 Function Notation and Making Predictions

Objectives

» Use *function notation.*

» Find inputs and outputs of a function.

» Use a model to make estimates and predictions.

» Find intercepts of a model.

» Use data described in words to make estimates and predictions.

» Know the meaning of *domain* and *range* of a model.

In this section, we will discuss how to name a function. We will also find inputs and outputs of a function and use a model to make estimates and predictions. Finally, we will consider how such inputs and outputs relate to the *domain* and *range* of a model.

Function Notation

Rather than use an equation, table, graph, or words to refer to a function, it would be easier to name the function. For example, to use "f" as the name of the linear function $y = 2x + 1$, we use "$f(x)$" (read "f of x") to represent y:

$$y = f(x)$$

We refer to "$f(x)$" as *function notation.* To use function notation to write the equation of this function, we substitute $f(x)$ for y in the equation $y = 2x + 1$:

$$f(x) = 2x + 1$$

WARNING

The notation "$f(x)$" does *not* mean f times x. It is another variable name for y.

Recall from Section 1.6 that we can think of a function as a machine that sends inputs to outputs. Here we substitute 4 for x in the equation $y = 2x + 1$: $y = 2(4) + 1 = 9$. So, the input $x = 4$ leads to the output $y = 9$. Now we substitute 4 for x in the equation $f(x) = 2x + 1$:

$$f(x) = 2x + 1 \quad \text{\textit{Equation of f}}$$
$$f(4) = 2(4) + 1 \quad \text{\textit{Substitute 4 for x.}}$$
$$= 9 \quad \text{\textit{Simplify.}}$$

The equation $f(4) = 9$ means the input $x = 4$ leads to the output $y = 9$. Figure 26 shows the "machine" f sending the input 4 to the output 9.

Notice that $f(4) = 9$ is of the form

$$f(\text{input}) = \text{output}$$

Figure 26 A function "machine"

This is true for any function f.

The number $f(4)$ is the value of y when x is 4. To find $f(4)$, we say we **evaluate** the function f at $x = 4$.

▶ Example 1   Evaluating a Function

Evaluate $f(x) = -4x + 2$ at 5.

Solution

$$f(x) = -4x + 2 \quad \text{\textit{Equation of f}}$$
$$f(5) = -4(5) + 2 \quad \text{\textit{Substitute 5 for x.}}$$
$$= -18 \quad \text{\textit{Simplify.}}$$

▶

We can also use "g" to name the function $y = -4x + 2$:

$$g(x) = -4x + 2$$

The most commonly used symbols to name functions are f, g, and h.

▶ **Example 2** Evaluating Functions

For $f(x) = 2x^2 - 3x$, $g(x) = \dfrac{4x - 2}{5x - 1}$, and $h(x) = 3x - 5$, find the following (to review exponentiation and order of operations, see Sections A.5 and A.6):

1. $f(-2)$ 2. $g(3)$ 3. $h(a)$ 4. $h(a - 2)$

Solution

1.
$$f(-2) = 2(-2)^2 - 3(-2) \quad \text{\textit{Evaluate f at} }-2.$$
$$= 2(4) - 3(-2) \quad \begin{array}{l}\text{\textit{Perform exponentiation}}\\ \text{\textit{first:} }(-2)^2 = (-2)(-2) = 4\end{array}$$
$$= 8 + 6 \quad \text{\textit{Multiply.}}$$
$$= 14 \quad \text{\textit{Add.}}$$

2.
$$g(3) = \frac{4 \cdot 3 - 2}{5 \cdot 3 - 1} \quad \text{\textit{Evaluate g at 3.}}$$
$$= \frac{12 - 2}{15 - 1} \quad \text{\textit{Multiply first.}}$$
$$= \frac{10}{14} \quad \text{\textit{Subtract.}}$$
$$= \frac{5}{7} \quad \text{\textit{Simplify.}}$$

3. To find $h(a)$, we substitute a for x in the equation $h(x) = 3x - 5$:
$$h(a) = 3a - 5 \quad \text{\textit{Evaluate h at a.}}$$

4.
$$h(a - 2) = 3(a - 2) - 5 \quad \text{\textit{Evaluate h at a }- 2.}$$
$$= 3a - 6 - 5 \quad \text{\textit{Distributive law}}$$
$$= 3a - 11 \quad \text{\textit{Combine like terms.}}$$

So far, we have used equations to evaluate functions. Next, we will use a table to find an output and an input of a function.

Table 39 Input–Output Pairs of g

x	g(x)
3	12
4	9
5	8
6	9
7	12

▶ **Example 3** Using a Table to Find an Output and an Input

Some input–output pairs of a function g are shown in Table 39.

1. Find $g(7)$.
2. Find x when $g(x) = 9$.

Solution

1. From Table 39, we see the input $x = 7$ leads to the output $y = 12$. So, $g(7) = 12$.
2. To find x when $g(x) = 9$, we need to find all inputs in the table that lead to the output $y = 9$. From Table 39, we see both inputs $x = 4$ and $x = 6$ lead to the output $y = 9$. So, the values of x are 4 and 6.

In Example 4, we will use an equation to find an output and an input of a function.

▶ **Example 4** Using an Equation to Find an Output and an Input

Let $f(x) = \dfrac{3}{2}x - 1$.

1. Find $f(4)$.
2. Find x when $f(x) = -4$.

Solution

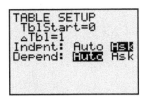

Figure 27 Putting table into "Ask" mode

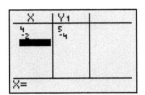

Figure 28 Verify the work

1.

$$f(4) = \frac{3}{2}(4) - 1 \quad \textit{Substitute 4 for x.}$$

$$= 6 - 1 \qquad \frac{3}{2}(4) = \frac{3}{2} \cdot \frac{4}{1} = 6$$

$$= 5 \qquad \textit{Subtract.}$$

2. We substitute -4 for $f(x)$ in $f(x) = \frac{3}{2}x - 1$ and solve for x:

$$-4 = \frac{3}{2}x - 1 \qquad \textit{Substitute } -4 \textit{ for } f(x).$$

$$2(-4) = 2 \cdot \frac{3}{2}x - 2 \cdot 1 \quad \textit{Multiply both sides by LCD, 2.}$$

$$-8 = 3x - 2 \qquad \textit{Multiply; simplify.}$$

$$-6 = 3x \qquad \textit{Add 2 to both sides.}$$

$$-2 = x \qquad \textit{Divide both sides by 3.}$$

We can verify our work in Problems 1 and 2 by putting a graphing calculator table into Ask mode (see Figs. 27 and 28). For graphing calculator instructions, see Appendix B.15.

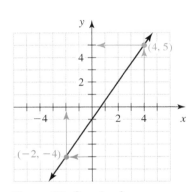

Figure 29 Graph of

$$f(x) = \frac{3}{2}x - 1$$

WARNING   Example 4 asks for both a value of y (in Problem 1) and a value of x (in Problem 2). Be sure you know which value you need to find. When you are asked for $f(x)$, what you are looking for is a value of y, not a value of x.

For $f(x) = \frac{3}{2}x - 1$, we found in Problem 1 of Example 4 that $f(4) = 5$. Since $y = 5$ when $x = 4$, we know that the ordered pair $(4, 5)$ is a solution of $f(x) = \frac{3}{2}x - 1$ and that the point $(4, 5)$ is on the graph of f (see Fig. 29). We use blue arrows to show that the input $x = 4$ leads to the output $y = 5$.

In Problem 2 of Example 4, we found that $x = -2$ when $f(x) = -4$. So, the point $(-2, -4)$ is on the graph of f. We use red arrows in Fig. 29 to show that the output $y = -4$ originates from the input $x = -2$.

▶ **Example 5**   Using a Graph to Find Values of x or $f(x)$

A graph of a function f is sketched in Fig. 30.
1. Find $f(4)$.
2. Find $f(0)$.
3. Find x when $f(x) = -2$.
4. Find x when $f(x) = 0$.

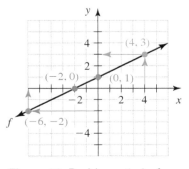

Figure 30 Problems 1–4 of Example 5

Solution
1. Recall that $y = f(x)$. The notation $f(4)$ refers to $f(x)$ when $x = 4$. So, we want the value of y when $x = 4$. The blue arrows in Fig. 30 show the input $x = 4$ leads to the output $y = 3$. Hence, $f(4) = 3$.
2. To find $f(0)$, we want the value of y when $x = 0$. The line contains the point $(0, 1)$, so $f(0) = 1$.
3. We have $y = f(x) = -2$. Thus, $y = -2$. So, we want the value of x when $y = -2$. The red arrows in Fig. 30 show the output $y = -2$ originates from the input $x = -6$. Hence, $x = -6$.
4. We have $y = f(x) = 0$. Thus, $y = 0$. The line contains the point $(-2, 0)$, so $x = -2$.

Using Function Notation with Models

Recall from Section 1.2 that when we are *not* describing an authentic situation, we treat *x* as the independent variable and *y* as the dependent variable. Here we label the independent variable, dependent variable, and function name of the equation $y = f(x)$:

dependent variable ⌐   ⌐ independent variable
$$y = f(x)$$
↑
function name

We follow this same format for a function *f* that *is* a model.

▶ Definition   Function notation

The dependent variable of a function *f* can be represented by the expression formed by writing the independent variable name within the parentheses of $f(\ )$:

$$\text{dependent variable} = f(\text{independent variable})$$

We call this representation **function notation.**

For instance, in Example 1 of Section 2.2, we found the model $n = 0.39t + 1.82$, where *n* is the number (in thousands) of times airplanes have struck birds in the year that is *t* years since 1990. Since *t* is the independent variable and *n* is the dependent variable, we can use the function name *f* to write $n = f(t)$. To use function notation to write the equation of the model, we substitute $f(t)$ for *n* in the equation $n = 0.39t + 1.82$:

$$f(t) = 0.39t + 1.82$$

In Example 6, we will use function notation in making predictions.

Table 40 Average Salaries of Faculty Members at Public Colleges and Universities

Year	Average Salary (thousands of dollars)
1980	22.1
1985	31.2
1990	41.9
1995	49.1
2000	57.7
2005	66.9
2010	78.0

Source: *American Association of University Professors*

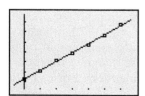

Figure 31 Check how well $s = 1.82t + 22.25$ models the data

▶ **Example 6**   Using an Equation of a Linear Model to Make Predictions

Table 40 shows the average salaries of faculty members at public colleges and universities. Let *s* be the faculty members' average salary (in thousands of dollars) at *t* years since 1980. A possible model is

$$s = 1.82t + 22.25$$

1. Verify that the function $s = 1.82t + 22.25$ models the data well.
2. Rewrite the equation $s = 1.82t + 22.25$ with the function name *f*.
3. Predict the average salary in 2018.
4. Predict when the average salary will be $95,000.

Solution

1. We draw the graph of the model and the scattergram of the data in the same viewing window (see Fig. 31). The function appears to model the data quite well.
2. Here, *t* is the independent variable and *s* is the dependent variable. Since the function name is *f*, we can write $s = f(t)$. Then we substitute $f(t)$ for *s* in the equation $s = 1.82t + 22.25$:

$$f(t) = 1.82t + 22.25$$

3. We represent the year 2018 by $t = 38$. To find the average salary, we substitute 38 for *t* in the equation $f(t) = 1.82t + 22.25$:

$$f(38) = 1.82(38) + 22.25 \quad \text{Substitute 38 for t.}$$
$$= 91.41 \quad \text{Simplify.}$$

The model predicts the average salary will be about $91.4 thousand in 2018.

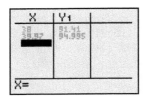

Figure 32 Verify the predictions

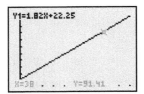

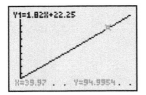

Figure 33 Verify predictions by using TRACE

4. We can represent the salary \$95,000 by $s = 95$. Since $s = f(t)$, we can write $f(t) = 95$. To find the year, we substitute 95 for $f(t)$ in the equation $f(t) = 1.82t + 22.25$ and solve for t:

$$95 = 1.82t + 22.25 \qquad \text{Substitute 95 for } f(t).$$
$$95 - 22.25 = 1.82t + 22.25 - 22.25 \qquad \text{Subtract 22.25 from both sides.}$$
$$72.75 = 1.82t \qquad \text{Combine like terms.}$$
$$\frac{72.75}{1.82} = \frac{1.82t}{1.82} \qquad \text{Divide both sides by 1.82.}$$
$$39.97 \approx t \qquad \text{Simplify.}$$

According to the model, the average salary will be \$95,000 in $1980 + 40 = 2020$. We can verify our work in both Problems 3 and 4 by using a graphing calculator table (see Fig. 32).

Or we can graphically verify our work by using TRACE (see Fig. 33).

Here we summarize how to use an equation of a model to make predictions (or estimates).

Using an Equation of a Linear Model to Make Predictions

- When making a prediction about the dependent variable of a linear model, substitute a chosen value for the independent variable in the model. Then solve for the dependent variable.
- When making a prediction about the independent variable of a linear model, substitute a chosen value for the dependent variable in the model. Then solve for the independent variable.

In Section 2.2 and this section, we discussed how to find linear models and how to use these models to make estimates and predictions. Here is a summary of this process.

Four-Step Modeling Process

To find a linear model and make estimates and predictions,

1. Create a scattergram of the data to determine whether there is a nonvertical line that comes close to the data points. If so, choose two points (not necessarily data points) that you can use to find the equation of a linear model.
2. Find an equation of your model.
3. Verify your equation by checking that the graph of your model contains the two chosen points and comes close to all of the data points.
4. Use the equation of your model to make estimates, make predictions, and draw conclusions.

In Example 6, we used f to name the function $f(t) = 1.82t + 22.25$, where $f(t)$ represents the average salary (in thousands of dollars) of faculty members at *public* colleges and universities at t years since 1980. When we use more than one function to model situations, naming the functions helps us distinguish among them. For example, we can also use a linear function to model the average salaries of faculty members at *private* colleges and universities. A good model is $s = 2.56t + 15.76$, where s is the faculty members' average salary (in thousands of dollars) at t years since 1980. We can distinguish this function from f by using g as its name:

$$g(t) = 2.56t + 15.76$$

Finding Intercepts

In Example 7, we will use a model to make a prediction and an estimate, find the intercepts of the model, and interpret the meaning of the intercepts.

▶ **Example 7**   Using Function Notation; Finding Intercepts

In Example 3 of Section 2.2, we found the equation $p = -0.48t + 71$, where p is the percentage of American adults who smoke at t years since 1900 (see Table 41).

1. Rewrite the equation $p = -0.48t + 71$ with the function name g.
2. Find $g(117)$. What does the result mean in this situation?
3. Find the value of t when $g(t) = 30$. What does it mean in this situation?
4. Find the p-intercept of the model. What does it mean in this situation?
5. Find the t-intercept of the model. What does it mean in this situation?

Table 41 American Adults
Who Smoke

Year	Percent
1970	37.4
1980	33.2
1990	25.3
2000	23.1
2010	19.4

Source: *National Center for Health Statistics*

Solution

1. To use the name g, we substitute $g(t)$ for p in the equation $p = -0.48t + 71$:

$$g(t) = -0.48t + 71$$

2. To find $g(117)$, we substitute 117 for t in the equation $g(t) = -0.48t + 71$:

$$g(t) = -0.48t + 71 \qquad \text{\textit{Equation of g}}$$
$$g(117) = -0.48(117) + 71 \qquad \text{\textit{Substitute 117 for t.}}$$
$$= 14.84 \qquad \text{\textit{Simplify.}}$$

So, $p = 14.84$ when $t = 117$. According to the model, about 14.8% of American adults will smoke in 2017.

3. We substitute 30 for $g(t)$ in the equation $g(t) = -0.48t + 71$ and solve for t:

$$g(t) = -0.48t + 71 \qquad \text{\textit{Equation of g}}$$
$$30 = -0.48t + 71 \qquad \text{\textit{Substitute 30 for g(t).}}$$
$$30 - 71 = -0.48t + 71 - 71 \qquad \text{\textit{Subtract 71 from both sides.}}$$
$$-41 = -0.48t \qquad \text{\textit{Combine like terms.}}$$
$$\frac{-41}{-0.48} = \frac{-0.48t}{-0.48} \qquad \text{\textit{Divide both sides by −0.48.}}$$
$$85.42 \approx t \qquad \text{\textit{Simplify.}}$$

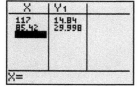

X	Y₁
117	14.84
85.42	29.998

X=

Figure 34 Verify the work

The model estimates 30% of Americans smoked in $1900 + 85.42 \approx 1985$. We can verify our work in Problems 2 and 3 by using a graphing calculator table (see Fig. 34).

4. Since the model $g(t) = -0.48t + 71$ is in slope–intercept form, the p-intercept is $(0, 71)$. So, the model estimates 71% of American adults smoked in 1900. Research would show this estimate is too high; model breakdown has occurred.
5. To find the t-intercept, we substitute 0 for $g(t)$ and solve for t:

$$0 = -0.48t + 71 \qquad \text{\textit{Substitute 0 for g(t).}}$$
$$0 + 0.48t = -0.48t + 71 + 0.48t \qquad \text{\textit{Add 0.48t to both sides.}}$$
$$0.48t = 71 \qquad \text{\textit{Combine like terms.}}$$
$$\frac{0.48t}{0.48} = \frac{71}{0.48} \qquad \text{\textit{Divide both sides by 0.48.}}$$
$$t \approx 147.92 \qquad \text{\textit{Simplify.}}$$

The t-intercept is $(147.92, 0)$. So, the model predicts no American adults will smoke in $1900 + 147.92 \approx 2048$. However, common sense suggests this event probably won't occur.

We can use TRACE to verify the p-intercept and the "zero" option to verify the t-intercept (see Fig. 35).

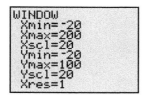

WINDOW
Xmin=-20
Xmax=200
Xscl=20
Ymin=-20
Ymax=100
Yscl=20
Xres=1

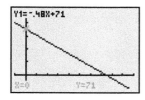

Y1=-.48X+71

X=0   Y=71

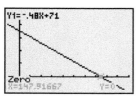

Y1=-.48X+71

Zero
X=147.91667   Y=0

Figure 35 Verify the intercepts

> ▶ **Intercepts of a Model**
>
> If a function of the form $p = mt + b$, where $m \neq 0$, is used to model a situation, then
>
> - The p-intercept is $(0, b)$.
> - To find the t-coordinate of the t-intercept, substitute 0 for p in the model's equation and solve for t.

Using Data Described in Words to Make Predictions

In most application problems in this text so far, we have been provided variable names and their definitions. In Example 8, a key step will be to create variable names and define the variables.

▶ **Example 8** Making a Prediction

The percentage of Americans with student loans who defaulted on their loans within two years of when the loans came due has increased approximately linearly from 5.0% in 2005 to 9.1% in 2010 (Source: *Department of Education*). Predict when 15% of Americans with student loans will default on their loans within two years of when the loans came due.

Solution

Let p be the percentage of Americans with student loans who defaulted on their loans within two years of when the loans came due at t years since 2000. Known values of t and p are shown in Table 42.

Since the variables t and p are approximately linearly related, we want an equation of the form $p = mt + b$. First, we use the values in Table 42 to find the slope of the model:

$$\frac{9.1 - 5.0}{10 - 5} = 0.82$$

Then we substitute 0.82 for m in the equation $p = mt + b$:

$$p = 0.82t + b$$

To find b, we use the point $(10, 9.1)$ and substitute 10 for t and 9.1 for p and then solve for b:

$$
\begin{aligned}
9.1 &= 0.82(10) + b && \text{\textit{Substitute 10 for t and 9.1 for p.}} \\
9.1 &= 8.2 + b && \text{\textit{Multiply.}} \\
9.1 - 8.2 &= 8.2 + b - 8.2 && \text{\textit{Subtract 8.2 from both sides.}} \\
0.9 &= b && \text{\textit{Combine like terms.}}
\end{aligned}
$$

Then we substitute 0.9 for b in the equation $p = 0.82t + b$:

$$p = 0.82t + 0.9$$

Finally, to predict when the percent will be 15%, we substitute 15 for p in the equation $p = 0.82t + 0.9$ and solve for t:

$$
\begin{aligned}
15 &= 0.82t + 0.9 && \text{\textit{Substitute 15 for p.}} \\
15 - 0.9 &= 0.82t + 0.9 - 0.9 && \text{\textit{Subtract 0.9 from both sides.}} \\
14.1 &= 0.82t && \text{\textit{Combine like terms.}} \\
17.20 &\approx t && \text{\textit{Divide both sides by 0.82.}}
\end{aligned}
$$

The model predicts that in $2000 + 17 = 2017$, 15% of Americans with student loans will default on their loans within two years of when the loans came due. We can verify our work by using a graphing calculator table (see Fig. 36).

Table 42 Known Values of t and p

Years since 2000 t	Percent p
5	5.0
10	9.1

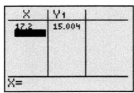

Figure 36 Verify the work

In Example 8, we defined t to be the number of years since 2000. If we had defined t to be the number of years since *1950* (or any other year), we would have obtained the same prediction of 2017, although the equation of our model would have been different. **If an exercise does not state a year from which to begin counting, choose any year.**

Domain and Range of a Model

Recall from Section 1.6 that the domain of a function is the set of all inputs and that the range of a function is the set of all outputs. For the **domain** and **range** of a model, we consider input–output pairs only when both the input and the output make sense in the situation. The domain of the model is the set of all such inputs, and the range of the model is the set of all such outputs.

▶ **Example 9**   Finding the Domain and Range of a Model

A store is open from 9 A.M. to 5 P.M., Mondays through Saturdays. Let $I = f(t)$ be an employee's weekly income (in dollars) from working t hours each week at \$10 per hour.
1. Find an equation of the model f.
2. Find the domain and range of the model f.

Solution

1. The employee's weekly income (in dollars) is equal to the pay per hour times the number of hours worked per week:

$$f(t) = 10t$$

2. To find the domain and range of the model f, we consider input–output pairs only when both the input and the output make sense in this situation. Time is the input. Since the store is open 8 hours a day, 6 days a week, the employee can work up to 48 hours each week. So, the domain is the set of numbers between 0 and 48, inclusive: $0 \le t \le 48$.

   Income is the output. Since the number of hours worked is between 0 and 48 hours, inclusive, and the pay is \$10 per hour, the range is the set of numbers between 0 and $10(48) = 480$, inclusive: $0 \le f(t) \le 480$.

   In Fig. 37, we illustrate the inputs 22, 35, and 48 being sent to the outputs 220, 350, and 480, respectively. We also label the part of the t-axis that represents the domain and the part of the I-axis that represents the range.

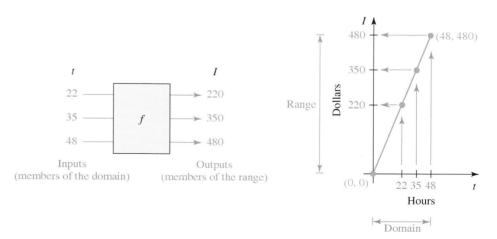

Figure 37 Domain and range of the employee income model

Group Exploration

Formula for slope

1. Let $f(x) = 2x + 1$. Find each of the following and compare all three results. [**Hint for part (b):** First, find $f(5)$ and $f(3)$. Then subtract. Finally, divide.]
   a. the slope of the graph of f
   b. $\dfrac{f(5) - f(3)}{5 - 3}$
   c. $\dfrac{f(7) - f(4)}{7 - 4}$

2. Let $g(x) = 3x + 5$. Find each of the following and compare all three results:
   a. the slope of the graph of g
   b. $\dfrac{g(3) - g(1)}{3 - 1}$
   c. $\dfrac{g(4) - g(0)}{4 - 0}$

3. Let f be a function of the form $f(x) = mx + b$. Describe $\dfrac{f(c) - f(d)}{c - d}$, where $c \neq d$. Explain.

Group Exploration

Looking ahead: Significance of the slope and the dependent variable's intercept of a model

1. A small airplane is traveling at a constant speed of 100 miles per hour. Let d be the distance (in miles) the airplane can travel in t hours.
   a. Complete Table 43.

   Table 43 Distances Traveled by an Airplane

Time (hours) t	Distance (miles) d
0	
1	
2	
3	
4	

   b. Find an equation of a linear model.
   c. Compare the slope of your model with the speed of the airplane.
   d. What is the d-intercept? What does it mean in this situation?

2. In 2010, a company was worth $10 million. Each year, its value increases by $2 million. Let V be the company's value (in millions of dollars) at t years since 2010.
   a. Complete Table 44.

   Table 44 Values of a Company

Year since 2010 t	Value (millions of dollars) V
0	
1	
2	
3	
4	

   b. Find an equation of a linear model.
   c. Compare the slope of your model with the rate at which the company's value is increasing.
   d. What is the V-intercept? What does it mean in this situation?

3. A person is in a hot-air balloon at an altitude of 1600 feet. The person begins gradually letting air out of the balloon, and the balloon descends at a rate of 200 feet per minute. Let H be the balloon's altitude (in feet) after air has been released for t minutes.
   a. Complete Table 45.

   Table 45 Altitudes of a Balloon

Time (minutes) t	Altitude (feet) H
0	
1	
2	
3	
4	

   b. Find an equation of a linear model.
   c. Compare the slope of your model with the rate at which the balloon's altitude is changing.
   d. What is the H-intercept? What does it mean in this situation?

4. In general, what is the meaning of the slope in terms of an authentic situation? What is the meaning of the dependent variable's intercept?

▶ Tips for Success   Math Journal

Do you tend to make the same mistakes repeatedly throughout a math course? If so, it might help to keep a journal in which you list errors you have made on assignments, quizzes, and tests. For each error you list, include the correct solution as well as a description of the concept needed to solve the problem correctly. Review this journal from time to time to help you avoid making these errors.

Homework 2.3

For extra help ▶ MyMathLab°   Watch the videos in MyMathLab   Download the MyDashboard App

Evaluate $f(x) = 6x - 4$ at the given value of x.

1. $f(5)$ **2.** $f(-2)$ **3.** $f\left(\dfrac{2}{3}\right)$

4. $f\left(\dfrac{5}{2}\right)$ **5.** $f(a + 2)$ **6.** $f(a - 3)$

Evaluate $g(x) = 2x^2 - 5x$ at the given value of x. (To review exponentiation and order of operations, see Sections A.5 and A.6.)

7. $g(2)$ **8.** $g(3)$ **9.** $g(-3)$ **10.** $g(-2)$

Evaluate $h(x) = \dfrac{3x - 4}{5x + 2}$ at the given value of x.

11. $h(2)$ **12.** $h(-4)$
13. $h(a - 3)$ **14.** $h(3a)$

For $f(x) = -2x + 7$, $g(x) = -3x^2 + 2x$, and $h(x) = -4$, find the following.

15. $g(-2)$ **16.** $g(-1)$ **17.** $f(5)$
18. $f(-4)$ **19.** $h(7)$ **20.** $h(-9)$

Evaluate $f(x) = -4x - 7$ at the given value of x.

21. $f(5a)$ **22.** $f(-3a)$

23. $f\left(\dfrac{a}{2}\right)$ **24.** $f\left(\dfrac{3a}{2}\right)$

25. $f(a + 4)$ **26.** $f(a - 4)$
27. $f(a - h)$ **28.** $f(a + h)$

For $f(x) = -3x + 7$, find the value of x that leads to the given value of $f(x)$.

29. $f(x) = 6$ **30.** $f(x) = 0$

31. $f(x) = \dfrac{5}{2}$ **32.** $f(x) = -\dfrac{4}{3}$

33. $f(x) = a$ **34.** $f(x) = a + 2$

For Exercises 35–38, let $f(x) = -5.95x + 183.22$. Round any results to the second decimal place.

35. Find $f(10.91)$.   **36.** Find $f(17.28)$.
37. Find x when $f(x) = 99.34$.
38. Find x when $f(x) = 72.06$.

For Exercises 39–42, refer to Table 46.

39. Find $f(2)$.   **40.** Find $f(4)$.
41. Find x when $f(x) = 2$. **42.** Find x when $f(x) = 4$.

Table 46 Values of f (Exercises 39–42)

x	f(x)
0	0
1	2
2	4
3	2
4	0

For Exercises 43–54, refer to Fig. 38.

43. Estimate $f(-6)$.   **44.** Estimate $f(0)$.

45. Estimate $f(2.5)$.   **46.** Estimate $f\left(-\dfrac{11}{2}\right)$.

47. Estimate x when $f(x) = 0$.
48. Estimate x when $f(x) = 1$.
49. Estimate x when $f(x) = 3$.
50. Estimate x when $f(x) = 3.5$.
51. Estimate x when $f(x) = \dfrac{1}{2}$. **52.** Estimate x when $f(x) = \dfrac{5}{2}$.
53. Find the domain of f.   **54.** Find the range of f.

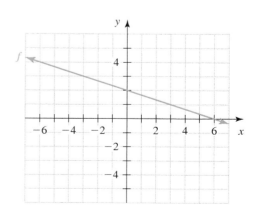

Figure 38 Exercises 43–54

For Exercises 55–58, refer to Fig. 39.

55. Find $g(-2)$.

56. Find x when $g(x) = 3$.

57. Find the domain of g.

58. Find the range of g.

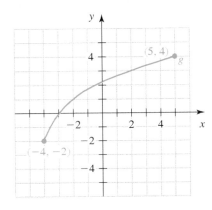

Figure 39
Exercises 55–58

For Exercises 59–62, refer to Fig. 40.

59. Find $h(1)$.

60. Find x when $h(x) = -1$.

61. Find the domain of h.

62. Find the range of h.

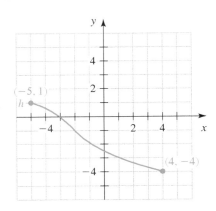

Figure 40
Exercises 59–62

Find all x-intercepts and y-intercepts. If no intercept exists, say so.

63. $f(x) = 5x - 8$

64. $f(x) = 4x + 2$

65. $f(x) = 3x$

66. $f(x) = -7x$

67. $f(x) = 5$

68. $f(x) = -2$

69. $f(x) = \dfrac{1}{2}x - 3$

70. $f(x) = -\dfrac{3}{4}x + \dfrac{1}{2}$

For Exercises 71 and 72, find the approximate x-intercept and approximate y-intercept of the graph of the equation. Round the coordinates to the second decimal place.

71. $f(x) = 2.58x - 45.21$

72. $f(x) = -4.29x + 37.58$

73. Recall that we can describe some or all of the input–output pairs of a function by means of an equation, a graph, a table, or words. Let $g(x) = -3x + 4$.
   a. Describe five input–output pairs of g by using a table.
   b. Describe the input–output pairs of g by using a graph.
   c. Describe the input–output pairs of g by using words.

74. Recall that we can describe some or all of the input–output pairs of a function by means of an equation, a graph, a table, or words. Let $f(x) = -\dfrac{3}{5}x - 1$.

a. Describe five input–output pairs of f by using a table.
b. Describe the input–output pairs of f by using a graph.
c. Describe the input–output pairs of f by using words.

75. In Exercise 11 of Homework 2.2, you found an equation close to $p = 0.76t - 42.04$ that models the percentage p of births outside marriage in the United States at t years since 1900 (see Table 47).

Table 47 Births Outside Marriage

Year	Percent of Births outside Marriage
1970	10.7
1975	14.3
1980	18.4
1985	22.0
1990	28.0
1995	32.2
2000	33.2
2005	36.8
2010	40.8

Source: *National Center for Health Statistics*

a. Rewrite the equation $p = 0.76t - 42.04$ with the function name f.
b. Find $f(118)$. What does your result mean in this situation?
c. Find the value of t so that $f(t) = 47$. What does your result mean in this situation?
d. According to the model, in what year will all births be outside marriage?
e. Estimate the percentage of births outside marriage in 1997. The actual percentage was 32.4%. What is the error in your estimate? (The error is the difference between the estimated value and the actual value.)

76. In Exercise 12 of Homework 2.2, you found an equation close to $p = 0.76t + 11.09$ that models the percentage p of births outside marriage in the United States at t years *since 1970*. Repeat Exercise 75, but use the model $p = 0.76t + 11.09$. In what instances are your answers the same? When are they different?

77. In Exercise 15 of Homework 2.2, you found an equation close to $p = -1.19t + 64.86$, where p is the percentage of Americans who are baseball fans at t years since 1990 (see Table 48).

Table 48 Percentages of Americans Who Are Baseball Fans

Year	Percent
1999	54
2001	51
2003	50
2005	48
2007	44
2008	43

Source: *The Gallup Organization*

a. Rewrite the equation $p = -1.19t + 64.86$ with the function name f.
b. Find $f(28)$. What does it mean in this situation?
c. Find t when $f(t) = 28$. What does it mean in this situation?
d. Find the p-intercept of the model. What does it mean in this situation?
e. Find the t-intercept. What does it mean in this situation?

78. First-class mail volumes are shown in Table 49 for various years.

Table 49 First-Class Mail Volumes

Year	First-Class Mail Volume (billions of pieces)
2007	95.9
2008	91.7
2009	83.8
2010	78.2
2011	73.5

Source: *U.S. Postal Service*

a. Let $v = f(t)$ be the first-class mail volume (in billions of pieces) in the year that is t years since 2000. Find an equation of f. Does the model fit the data well?

b. Find $f(18)$. What does it mean in this situation?

c. Find t when $f(t) = 18$. What does it mean in this situation?

d. Find the v-intercept. What does it mean in this situation?

e. Find the t-intercept. What does it mean in this situation?

f. Give some possible reasons why first-class mail volume has decreased so much from 2007 to 2011.

79. In Exercise 13 of Homework 2.2, you found an equation close to $p = 12.74n + 4.40$, where p is the price (in dollars) of a Gold Medal Sports ski rental package for n days (see Table 50).

Table 50 Prices of Ski Rental Packages

Number of Days	Price of Package (dollars)
1	15.00
2	30.00
3	45.00
4	56.00
5	70.00
6	78.00

Source: *Gold Medal Sports*

a. Rewrite the equation $p = 12.74n + 4.40$ with the function name f.

b. Find the p-intercept of the model. What does it mean in this situation?

c. Use f to estimate the price of renting skis for 7 days.

d. Use a graphing calculator table to find $f(1), f(2), f(3), \ldots$, and $f(6)$. Then estimate by how much p increases each time n is increased by 1. Compare these results with the slope of the graph of f. What does that mean in this situation?

e. Let $g(n) = \dfrac{f(n)}{n}$. Find $g(1)$, $g(2)$, $g(3), \ldots$, and $g(6)$. Which of these results is the least? What does that mean in this situation? [**Hint:** To find $g(2)$, first find $f(2)$. Then divide the result by 2 to get $g(2) = \dfrac{f(2)}{2}$.]

f. For ski rental packages for over 6 days, Gold Medal Sports charges a *daily* fee of $13.00 *per day*. Compare this result with your results in parts (d) and (e).

80. In Exercise 14 of Homework 2.2, you found an equation close to $L = 0.16t + 73.71$, where L is the life expectancy at birth (in years) of an American born t years after 1980 (see Table 51).

Table 51 Life Expectancies at Birth

Year of Birth	Life Expectancy (years)
1980	73.7
1985	74.7
1990	75.4
1995	75.8
2000	77.0
2005	77.9
2010	78.7

Source: *U.S. Census Bureau*

a. Use the linear model to predict the life expectancy of an American born in 2017.

b. Use the linear model to predict the birth year in which the life expectancy of an American will be 80 years.

c. Use the linear model to estimate what your (or someone else's) life expectancy was at birth. Given that you have made it to your current age, do your think your life expectancy is now less than, the same as, or more than it was at your year of birth?

d. Find the t-intercept. What does it mean in this situation?

e. Sketch by hand a *qualitative* graph to describe human life expectancy at birth during the existence of humans on Earth. [**Hint:** Your curve should be nonlinear.]

81. The number of commercial airline boardings on domestic flights increased steadily during the 1990s (see Table 52).

Table 52 Numbers of Commercial Airline Boardings on Domestic Flights

Year	Number of Boardings (millions)
1991	452
1993	487
1995	547
1997	599
1999	635
2000	666

Source: *Bureau of Transportation Statistics*

a. Let $f(t)$ be the number of commercial airline boardings on domestic flights (in millions) for the year that is t years since 1990. Use a graphing calculator to draw a scattergram of the data.

b. Find an equation of f. Does your model fit the data well?

c. Use your model f to estimate the number of boardings in 2001. The actual number was 622 million. What is the error in your estimate? (The error is the difference between the estimated value and the actual value.)

d. The number of boardings in 2001 was low due to the terrorist attacks on September 11, 2001. By making the following assumptions, estimate the amount of money airlines lost in 2001.

- All trips were round trips.
- The average number of boardings for a round trip was four (two flights out, two back).
- The average round-trip fare was $340.

82. The average gasoline taxes (in 2010 dollars) per 1000 miles driven are shown in Table 53.

Table 53 Average Gasoline Taxes per 1000 Miles Driven

Year	Average Gasoline Tax Per 1000 Miles Driven (2010 dollars)
1995	28
1998	27
2001	24
2004	23
2007	20
2010	19

Source: *Bureau of Economic Analysis; Bureau of Transportation Statistics, Bureau of Labor Statistics*

a. Let $A = f(t)$ be the average gasoline tax (in 2010 dollars) per 1000 miles driven at t years since 1990. Use a graphing calculator to draw a scattergram of the data.

b. Find an equation of f. Does your model fit the data well?

c. Find the t-intercept. What does it mean in this situation?

d. Since 1995, inflation has occurred and the average gas mileage of cars has increased. Explain how these factors have affected the gasoline tax (in 2010 dollars) per 1000 miles driven.

e. i. Teenagers drive an average of 7624 miles per year (Source: *Federal Highway Administration*). Use your model to predict the total money (in 2010 dollars) a teenager will pay in gasoline taxes during the period 2016–2018.

   ii. How much *additional* money (in 2010 dollars) would a teenager pay in gasoline taxes during the period 2016–2018 if the gasoline tax were still at the 1995 level of $28 (in 2010 dollars) per 1000 miles driven?

83. The United States and Great Britain use the Fahrenheit temperature scale, but most countries use the Celsius temperature scale. The Celsius reading 0°C is the temperature at which water freezes, and 100°C is the temperature at which water boils (at sea level). Table 54 shows equivalent Celsius and Fahrenheit temperatures.

Table 54 Equivalent Temperature Readings

Celsius Reading (°C)	Fahrenheit Reading (°F)
0	32
20	68
40	104
60	140
80	176
100	212

a. Let $F = f(C)$ be the Fahrenheit reading corresponding to a Celsius reading of C degrees. Find an equation of f.

b. The average high temperature during July in Paris is 24°C (Source: *The Weather Channel*). What is the Fahrenheit reading?

c. The average high temperature during September in Quebec is 64°F (Source: *The Weather Channel*). What is the Celsius reading?

d. The theoretical lowest possible temperature is −273.15°C. What is the Fahrenheit temperature?

84. The rate at which a cricket chirps depends on the temperature of the surrounding air. You can estimate the air temperature by counting chirps! Some data are provided in Table 55.

Table 55 Rates of Cricket Chirping

Temperature (°F)	Rate (number of chirps per minute)
50	43
60	86
70	129
80	172
90	215

Source: Eric Sloane's Weather Book, *Eric Sloane, 2005*

a. Let $g(F)$ be the number of chirps per minute a cricket makes when the temperature is F degrees Fahrenheit. Find an equation of g. Verify that the graph of your equation comes close to the points in the scattergram of the data.

b. Find $g(73)$. What does it mean in this situation?

c. Find the value of F, where $g(F) = 100$. What does your result mean in this situation?

d. What are the possible air temperatures at a field where the crickets are not chirping?

85. In Exercise 21 of Homework 2.2, you found an equation close to $p = 2.48x - 23.64$, where p is the percentage of Intermediate Algebra students at the College of San Mateo (CSM) succeeding in the course (grade of A, B, or C) who scored x points on the placement test (see Table 56).

Table 56 Percentages of Intermediate Algebra Students Who Succeeded

Placement Score Group	Score Used to Represent Score Group	Percent Who Succeeded in Intermediate Algebra
21–25	23	34
26–30	28	47
31–35	33	55
36–40	38	71
41–45	43	84
46–50	48	*

Source: *College of San Mateo Mathematics Department*
*There were not enough students in this group to give useful data.

a. Rewrite the equation $p = 2.48x - 23.64$ with the function name f.

b. Students who score below 21 points (out of 50) on the placement test cannot enroll in Intermediate Algebra. Use the model f to estimate how high the cutoff score would have to be to ensure that all students succeed in the course.

c. Use the model f to estimate for which scores no students would succeed in the course.

d. If, in one semester, 145 students scored in the 16–20-point range on the placement test, predict how many of these students would have succeeded in the course if they had been allowed to enroll in it. Would you advise CSM to lower the placement score cutoff to 16? Explain.

e. Table 57 shows the numbers of students in various placement score groups for one semester. For students who scored at least 21 points on the placement test that semester, estimate how many succeeded in the course.

Table 57 Placement Test Scores for One Semester

Placement Score Group	Number of Students
21–25	94
26–30	44
31–35	19
36–40	12
41–45	9
46–50	4

86. In Exercise 16 of Homework 2.2, you found an equation close to $p = 0.42a - 13.91$, where p is the percentage of Americans at age a years who have been diagnosed with diabetes at some point in their lives (see Table 58).

Table 58 Percentages of Americans Diagnosed with Diabetes, by Age Group

Age Group (years)	Age Used to Represent Age Group (years)	Percent
35–39	37	2
40–44	42	4
45–49	47	5
50–54	52	8
55–59	57	10
60–64	62	13
65–69	67	14

Source: *National Health Interview Survey*

a. Rewrite the equation $p = 0.42a - 13.91$ with the function name f.

b. Estimate the percentage of 40-year-old Americans who have been diagnosed with diabetes.

c. Estimate at what age 7% of Americans have been diagnosed with diabetes.

d. Find the a-intercept of the model. What does it mean in this situation?

e. The chance of any one person being diagnosed increases as the person grows older. However, 13% of all Americans over the age of 70 have been diagnosed at some point in their lives—less than the percentage for ages 65–69 years. How is this possible?

87. Public school per-student expenditures increased approximately linearly from $2.2 thousand in 1980 to $10.8 thousand in 2008 (Source: *National Education Association*). Predict the per-student expenditure in 2017.

88. The number of words in the federal tax code increased approximately linearly from 3.4 million words in 2005 to 3.8 million words in 2012 (Source: *The Tax Foundation*). Predict the number of words in the federal tax code in 2018.

89. Blood donations to American Red Cross decreased approximately linearly from 6.6 million pints in 2009 to 5.9 million pints in 2012 (Source: *American Red Cross*). Predict in which year the blood donations will be 4.5 million pints.

90. The percentage of female workers who prefer a female boss over a male boss increased approximately linearly from 10% in 1975 to 27% in 2011 (Source: *The Gallup Organization*). Predict when 30% of female workers will prefer a female boss.

91. The revenue of Kodak decreased approximately linearly from $19.0 billion in 1990 to $6.0 billion in 2011 (Source: *FactSet*).
a. The company is trying to emerge from bankruptcy protection in 2013. Predict the revenue in that year.
b. Predict when the revenue will be 0 dollars (and the company will go out of business).

92. Despite the No Child Left Behind Act of 2001, students' average math score on the SAT decreased approximately linearly from 518 points in 2006 to 514 points in 2012 (Source: *College Board*).
a. Predict the average math score on the SAT in 2017.
b. Predict when the average math score on the SAT will be 509 points.

93. The average score on the National Assessment of Educational Progress test in U.S. history was 195 points for fourth-graders who studied history about 45 minutes per week. The average score was 211 points for fourth-graders who studied history about 150 minutes per week. There is an approximate linear relationship between the number of hours fourth-graders study history per week and the average score on the test (Source: *U.S. Department of Education*). Estimate the average score for fourth-graders who study history about 200 minutes per week.

94. In Mississippi, a child is eligible for the Children's Health Insurance Program (CHIP) if the child's family meets an income limit. For a family of four, family monthly income must be no more than $3067. For a family of six, family monthly income must be no more than $4114. There is a linear relationship between family size and the income limit (Source: *CHIP*). What is the income limit of a family of seven?

95. A basement is flooded with 640 cubic feet of water. It takes 4 hours to pump out the water. Let $f(t)$ be the number of cubic feet of water that remains in the basement after t hours of pumping.
a. Find a linear equation of f. [**Hint:** You are given information about two points that can be used to find an equation.]
b. Graph f by hand. Use a graphing calculator to verify your graph.
c. What are the domain and range of the model? Explain.

96. It takes a person 5 minutes to eat all 12 ounces of ice cream in a cup. Let $f(t)$ be the number of ounces of ice cream remaining in the cup t minutes after the person began eating the ice cream.

a. Find a linear equation of f. [**Hint:** You are given information about two points that can be used to find an equation.]

b. Graph f by hand. Use a graphing calculator to verify your graph.

c. What are the domain and range of the model? Explain.

Concepts

97. A student tries to find x when $f(x) = 5$ for $f(x) = x + 2$:

$$f(5) = 5 + 2 = 7$$

Describe any errors. Then find x correctly.

98. A student tries to find $g(-5)$, where $g(x) = x^2$:

$$g(-5) = -5^2 = -25$$

Describe any errors. Then find $g(-5)$ correctly.

99. a. For $f(x) = 4x$, find $f(3)$, $f(5)$, and $f(8)$. Is the equation $f(3 + 5) = f(3) + f(5)$ a true statement?

b. For $f(x) = x^2$, find $f(2)$, $f(3)$, and $f(5)$. Is the equation $f(2 + 3) = f(2) + f(3)$ a true statement?

c. For $f(x) = \sqrt{x}$, find $f(9)$, $f(16)$, and $f(25)$. Is $f(9 + 16) = f(9) + f(16)$ a true statement?

d. Is $f(a + b) = f(a) + f(b)$ a true statement for every function f?

100. a. For $f(x) = 3x + 2$, find $f(5) - f(4)$. Compare your result with the slope of the graph of f. [**Hint:** Find $f(5)$ and $f(4)$. Then subtract.]

b. For $f(x) = 2x + 5$, find $f(7) - f(6)$. Compare your result with the slope of the graph of f.

c. For $f(x) = 4x + 1$, find $f(3) - f(2)$. Compare your result with the slope of the graph of f.

d. For $f(x) = mx + b$, find $f(a + 1) - f(a)$. Compare your result with the slope of the graph of f, and discuss what this result means. [**Hint:** Consider the slope addition property.]

101. Let t be the number of years since 2010. A student says $t = -3$ is an example of model breakdown because time can't be negative. Is the student correct? Explain.

102. A student says $f(4)$ means that $y = 4$, because $y = f(x)$. Is the student correct? Explain.

103. For a function f, assume $f(3) = 5$. Name an input and an output of f. Also, find three possible equations of f.

104. Describe the four-step modeling process in your own words.

▼2.4 Slope Is a Rate of Change

Objectives

» Calculate the *rate of change* of a quantity.

» Understand why slope is a rate of change.

» Use rate of change to help find a linear model.

» Perform a *unit analysis* of a linear model.

How quickly does a quantity change in relation to another quantity? For example, how quickly has Nevada's population increased, or how quickly has the number of hotel fires declined?

Calculating Rate of Change

The **ratio** of a to b is the fraction $\dfrac{a}{b}$. A **unit ratio** is a ratio written as $\dfrac{a}{b}$ with $b = 1$.

Suppose sea level increased *steadily* by 12 inches in the past 4 hours as it approached high tide. We can compute how much sea level changed *per hour* by finding the unit ratio of the change in sea level (12 inches) to the change in time (4 hours):

$$\frac{12 \text{ inches}}{4 \text{ hours}} = \frac{3 \text{ inches}}{1 \text{ hour}}$$

So, sea level increased by 3 inches per hour. This is an example of a *rate of change*. We say the rate of change of sea level with respect to time is 3 inches per hour. The rate of change is a *constant* because sea level increased *steadily*.

Here are some other examples of rates of change:

- The number of members of a club increases by five people per month.
- The value of a stock decreases by \$2 per week.
- The cost of a gallon of gasoline increases by 10¢ per month.

Suppose sea level increases by 5 inches in 1 hour but by 3 inches in the next hour. We can find the *average rate of change* of sea level with respect to time by finding the unit ratio of the *total* change in sea level (8 inches) to the *total* change in time (2 hours):

$$\frac{8 \text{ inches}}{2 \text{ hours}} = \frac{4 \text{ inches}}{1 \text{ hour}}$$

So, the average rate of change is 4 inches per hour.

> **Formula for Rate of Change and Average Rate of Change**
>
> Suppose a quantity y changes steadily from y_1 to y_2 as a quantity x changes steadily from x_1 to x_2. Then the **rate of change** of y with respect to x is the ratio of the change in y to the change in x:
>
> $$\frac{\text{change in } y}{\text{change in } x} = \frac{y_2 - y_1}{x_2 - x_1}$$
>
> If either quantity changes, but not steadily, then this formula is the **average rate of change** of y with respect to x.

We often refer to rate of change *with respect to time* simply as "rate of change."

▶ **Example 1**   Finding Rates of Change

1. The number of Americans who fly to Europe has decreased approximately steadily from 13.3 million fliers in 2007 to 10.8 million fliers in 2011 (Source: *U.S. Department of Commerce*). Find the average rate of change of the number of Americans who flew to Europe.
2. In Phoenix, Arizona, the average value of a two-bedroom home is $129 thousand and the average value of a four-bedroom home is $338 thousand (Source: *Trulia*). Find the average rate of change of the average value of a home with respect to the number of bedrooms.

Solution

1.
$$\frac{\substack{\text{change in the} \\ \text{number of fliers}}}{\text{change in time}} = \frac{10.8 \text{ million fliers} - 13.3 \text{ million fliers}}{\text{year } 2011 - \text{year } 2007}$$ *Change in a quantity is ending amount minus beginning amount.*

$$= \frac{-2.5 \text{ million fliers}}{4 \text{ years}}$$ *Subtract.*

$$\approx \frac{-0.63 \text{ million fliers}}{1 \text{ year}}$$ *Find unit ratio.*

The average rate of change of the annual number of Americans who flew to Europe was about -0.63 million fliers per year. So, on average, the number of Americans who flew to Europe declined yearly by about 0.63 million (630 thousand) fliers.

2. To be consistent in finding the signs of the changes, we assume that the number of bedrooms increases from two to four and that the average value increases from $129 thousand to $338 thousand:

$$\frac{\substack{\text{change in} \\ \text{average value}}}{\substack{\text{change in} \\ \text{number of bedrooms}}} = \frac{338 \text{ thousand dollars} - 129 \text{ thousand dollars}}{4 \text{ bedrooms} - 2 \text{ bedrooms}}$$ *Change in a quantity is ending amount minus beginning amount.*

$$= \frac{209 \text{ thousand dollars}}{2 \text{ bedrooms}}$$ *Subtract.*

$$= \frac{104.5 \text{ thousand dollars}}{1 \text{ bedroom}}$$ *Find unit ratio.*

The average rate of change of the average value with respect to the number of bedrooms is $104.5 thousand per bedroom. So, the average value increases by $104.5 thousand per bedroom.

Our work in Example 1 shows a connection between the sign of a rate of change and whether the changing quantity is increasing or decreasing. In Problem 2, the average rate of change was *positive,* because the average value of a home *increases* (as the number of bedrooms increases). In Problem 1, the average rate of change was *negative*, because the number of Americans who flew to Europe *decreased* (as time increased).

> ### ▶ Increasing and Decreasing Quantities
>
> Suppose a quantity p depends on a quantity t:
>
> - If p increases steadily as t increases steadily, then the rate of change of p with respect to t is positive.
> - If p decreases steadily as t increases steadily, then the rate of change of p with respect to t is negative.

Slope Is a Rate of Change

The expression

$$\frac{y_2 - y_1}{x_2 - x_1}$$

that we have been using to calculate rate of change is the same expression that we use to calculate the slope of a line. This means slope is a rate of change. We will explore this important concept in Example 2.

▶ Example 2   Comparing Slope with a Rate of Change

Suppose a student drives at a constant rate. Let d be the distance (in miles) the student can drive in t hours. Some values of t and d are shown in Table 59.

1. Create a scattergram. Then draw a linear model.
2. Find the slope of the linear model.
3. Find the rate of change of distance traveled for each given period. Compare each result with the slope of the linear model.
   a. From $t = 2$ to $t = 3$
   b. From $t = 0$ to $t = 4$

Table 59 Times and Distances

Time (hours) t	Distance (miles) d
0	0
1	60
2	120
3	180
4	240
5	300

Solution

1. We draw a scattergram and then draw a line that contains the data points (see Fig. 41).

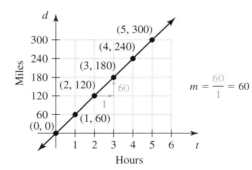

Figure 41 Car model and scattergram

2. The slope formula is $m = \dfrac{y_2 - y_1}{x_2 - x_1}$. So, with the variables t and d, we have

$$\frac{d_2 - d_1}{t_2 - t_1}$$

We arbitrarily use the points $(2, 120)$ and $(3, 180)$ to calculate the slope:

$$\frac{180 - 120}{3 - 2} = \frac{60}{1} = 60$$

So, the slope is 60. This checks with the calculation shown in Fig. 41.

3. a. Here we calculate the rate of change of distance traveled from $t = 2$ to $t = 3$:

$$\frac{\text{change in distance}}{\text{change in time}} = \frac{180 \text{ miles} - 120 \text{ miles}}{3 \text{ hours} - 2 \text{ hours}}$$ *Change in a quantity is ending amount minus beginning amount.*

$$= \frac{60 \text{ miles}}{1 \text{ hour}}$$ *Subtract.*

$$= 60 \text{ miles per hour}$$ *Divide.*

The rate of change (60 miles per hour) is equal to the slope (60).

b. Here we calculate the rate of change of distance traveled from $t = 0$ to $t = 4$:

$$\frac{\text{change in distance}}{\text{change in time}} = \frac{240 \text{ miles} - 0 \text{ miles}}{4 \text{ hours} - 0 \text{ hours}}$$ *Change in a quantity is ending amount minus beginning amount.*

$$= \frac{240 \text{ miles}}{4 \text{ hours}}$$ *Subtract.*

$$= \frac{60 \text{ miles}}{1 \text{ hour}}$$ *Find unit ratio.*

$$= 60 \text{ miles per hour}$$ *Divide.*

The rate of change (60 miles per hour) is equal to the slope (60).

In Example 2, we found that the time t and the distance traveled d are linearly related. We also found that the slope is equal to the rate of change of distance traveled with respect to time.

> **Slope Is a Rate of Change**
>
> If there is a linear relationship between quantities t and p, and if p depends on t, then the slope of the linear model is equal to the rate of change of p with respect to t.

In Problem 3 of Example 2, we calculated the same rate of change (60 miles per hour) for two different periods. In fact, the rate of change is 60 miles per hour for *any* period within the first five hours. This makes sense because the rate of change is equal to the slope of the line (60), which is a constant.

> **Constant Rate of Change**
>
> Suppose a quantity p depends on a quantity t:
>
> - If there is a linear relationship between t and p, then the rate of change of p with respect to t is constant.
> - If the rate of change of p with respect to t is constant, then there is a linear relationship between t and p.

Finding an Equation of a Linear Model

We can use rate of change to help us find an equation of a linear model.

▶ **Example 3** Finding a Model

A company's profit was $10 million in 2005 and has increased by $3 million per year. Let p be the annual profit (in millions of dollars) at t years since 2005.

1. Is there a linear relationship between t and p? Explain.
2. Find the p-intercept of the linear model.
3. Find the slope of the linear model.
4. Find an equation of the linear model.

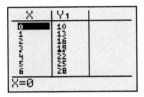

Figure 42 Verify the work

Solution

1. Since the rate of change of annual profit is a *constant* $3 million per year, the variables t and p are linearly related.
2. The profit was $10 million in 2005. Because 2005 is 0 years since 2005, we can represent this relationship by the ordered pair $(0, 10)$. So, the p-intercept of the linear model is $(0, 10)$.
3. The rate of change of annual profit is $3 million per year. So, the slope of the linear model is 3.
4. An equation of the linear model can be written in the form $p = mt + b$. Since the slope is 3 and the p-intercept is $(0, 10)$, we have $p = 3t + 10$.

    We can use a graphing calculator table to verify our equation (see Fig. 42). The ordered pair $(0, 10)$ shown in the first row of the table means the profit was $10 million in 2005, which checks. Also, as the input increases by 1, the output increases by 3. This means the annual profit increases by $3 million per year, which also checks.

Unit Analysis of a Linear Model

In Example 3, we found the linear model $p = 3t + 10$. We can perform a *unit analysis* of the model by determining the units of the expressions on both sides of the equation:

$$\underbrace{p}_{\text{millions of dollars}} = \underbrace{3}_{\substack{\text{millions of dollars} \\ \text{year}}} \cdot \underbrace{t}_{\text{years}} + \underbrace{10}_{\text{millions of dollars}}$$

We can use the fact that $\dfrac{\text{years}}{\text{year}} = 1$ to simplify the units of the expression on the right-hand side of the equation:

$$\frac{\text{millions of dollars}}{\text{year}} \cdot \text{years} + \frac{\text{millions}}{\text{of dollars}} = \frac{\text{millions}}{\text{of dollars}} + \frac{\text{millions}}{\text{of dollars}}$$

$$= \text{millions of dollars}$$

So, the units of the expressions on both sides of the equation are millions of dollars, which suggests the equation is correct.

▶ **Definition   Unit analysis**

We perform a **unit analysis** of a model's equation by determining the units of the expressions on both sides of the equation. The simplified units of the expressions on both sides of the equation should be the same.

We can perform a unit analysis of a model's equation to help verify the equation.

▶ **Example 4   Finding a Model**

A driver fills her car's 12-gallon gasoline tank and drives at a constant speed. The car consumes 0.04 gallon per mile. Let G be the number of gallons of gasoline remaining in the tank after she has driven d miles since filling up.

1. Is there a linear relationship between d and G? Explain.
2. Find the G-intercept of a linear model.
3. Find the slope of the linear model.
4. Find an equation of the linear model.
5. Perform a unit analysis of the equation.

Solution

1. Since the rate of change of gallons remaining with respect to distance traveled is a *constant* (-0.04 gallon per mile), the variables d and G are linearly related.
2. When the tank was filled, it contained 12 gallons of gasoline. We can represent this by the ordered pair $(0, 12)$, which is the G-intercept.

3. The rate of change of gasoline remaining in the tank with respect to distance traveled is −0.04 gallon per mile. So, the slope of the linear model is −0.04.
4. An equation of the linear model can be written in the form $G = md + b$. Since the slope is −0.04 and the G-intercept is $(0, 12)$, we have $G = -0.04d + 12$.
5. Here is a unit analysis of the equation $G = -0.04d + 12$:

$$\underbrace{G}_{\text{gallons}} = \underbrace{-0.04}_{\frac{\text{gallon}}{\text{mile}}} \cdot \underbrace{d}_{\text{miles}} + \underbrace{12}_{\text{gallons}}$$

We can use the fact that $\dfrac{\text{miles}}{\text{mile}} = 1$ to simplify the units of the expression on the right-hand side of the equation:

$$\frac{\text{gallon}}{\text{mile}} \cdot \text{miles} + \text{gallons} = \text{gallon} + \text{gallons}$$
$$= \text{gallons}$$

So, the units on both sides of the equation are gallons, which suggests the equation is correct.

Two Variables That Are Approximately Linearly Related

In both Examples 3 and 4, we worked with two variables that are linearly related. We will now explore the meaning of the slope of a linear model in which two variables are *approximately* linearly related.

▶ Example 5 Analyzing a Model

Sales of smartphones are shown in Table 60 for various years. Let s be smartphone annual sales (in millions of phones) at t years since 2000. A model of the situation is

$$s = 7.8t - 33.5$$

1. Use a graphing calculator to draw a scattergram and the model in the same viewing window. Check whether the line comes close to the data points.
2. What is the slope of the model? What does it mean in this situation?
3. Find the rates of change of sales from one year to the next. Compare the rates of change with the result in Problem 2.
4. Predict the sales in 2018.

Table 60 Smartphone Sales

Year	Sales (millions of phones)
2006	14.0
2007	20.7
2008	27.3
2009	36.0
2010	45.0
2011	52.0

Source: *Twice*

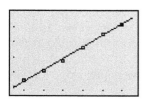

Figure 43 Smartphone scattergram and model

Solution

1. We draw the scattergram and the model in the same viewing window (see Fig. 43). For graphing calculator instructions on drawing scattergrams and models, see Appendix B.8 and B.10. The line comes close to the data points, so the model is a reasonable one.
2. The slope is 7.8, because $s = 7.8t - 33.5$ is of the form $y = mx + b$ and $m = 7.8$. According to the model, sales are increasing by 7.8 million smartphones per year.
3. The rates of change of sales are shown in Table 61. All of the rates of change are fairly close to 7.8 million smartphones per year.

Table 61 Smartphone Sales

Year	Sales (millions of phones)	Rate of Change of Sales from Previous Year (millions of phones per year)
2006	14.0	
2007	20.7	$(20.7 - 14.0) \div (2007 - 2006) = 6.7$
2008	27.3	$(27.3 - 20.7) \div (2008 - 2007) = 6.6$
2009	36.0	$(36.0 - 27.3) \div (2009 - 2008) = 8.7$
2010	45.0	$(45.0 - 36.0) \div (2010 - 2009) = 9.0$
2011	52.0	$(52.0 - 45.0) \div (2011 - 2010) = 7.0$

4. We substitute the input 18 for t in the equation $s = 7.8t - 33.5$:

$$s = 7.8(18) - 33.5 = 106.9$$

According to the model, smartphone sales will be 106.9 million phones in 2018.

In Example 5, we found that the slope of the smartphone model is 7.8, which means that, according to the model, sales increased by 7.8 million smartphones per year. In reality, sales did not increase by 7.8 million smartphones in any of the years between 2006 and 2011, inclusive. However, 7.8 million smartphones per year *is* a reasonable estimate of the *average* yearly increase.

> **Slope Is an Average Rate of Change**
>
> If two quantities t and p are approximately linearly related, and if p depends on t, then the slope of a reasonable linear model is approximately equal to the average rate of change of p with respect to t.

WARNING   It is a common error to be vague in describing the meaning of the slope of a model. For example, a description such as

The slope means it is increasing.

neither specifies the quantity that is increasing nor the rate of increase. The following statement includes the missing information:

The slope of 7.8 means sales increased by 7.8 million smartphones per year.

 Group Exploration

Slope of a linear model for approximately linearly related data

Defense spendings are shown in Table 62 for various years. Let s be the defense spending (in billions of dollars) in the year that is t years since 2000.

Table 62 Defense Spending

Year	Defense Spending (billions of dollars)
2005	495
2006	522
2007	551
2008	616
2009	661
2010	719
2011	750

Source: *Defense Department*

1. Use a graphing calculator to draw a scattergram of the data. Does it appear that the data can be modeled well by a linear function?

2. Use the data points $(6, 522)$ and $(9, 661)$ to find a linear model.

3. What is the slope of your model? According to the model, by how much will the defense spending increase each year?

4. Refer to Table 62 to find by how much the defense spending actually increased each year. List the increases in defense spending from 2005 to 2006, from 2006 to 2007, and so on. How do the actual defense spending increases compare with the slope of your model?

5. Find the average of the increases in defense spending by dividing the sum of the six increases you found in Problem 4 by the number 6. How does this average compare with the slope of your model?

Group Exploration

Looking ahead: Using a system of equations to model a situation

The revenues of the two top-selling pharmaceutical drugs, Lipitor and Nexium, are shown in Table 63 for various years. Lipitor is a cholesterol drug, and Nexium is used to treat acid reflux. Let $L(t)$ be the annual revenue of Lipitor and $N(t)$ be the annual revenue of Nexium, both in billions of dollars, at t years since 2005. The situation can be modeled by the system

$$r = L(t) = -0.33t + 8.85$$
$$r = N(t) = -0.33t + 4.81$$

1. Find the r-intercepts of the graphs of L and N. What do they mean in this situation?

2. Find the slopes of the graphs of L and N. What do they mean in this situation?

3. Your responses to Problems 1 and 2 should suggest an event that will happen in the future. Describe that event.

Table 63 Annual Revenues of Lipitor and Nexium

Year	Annual Revenue (billions of dollars)	
	Lipitor	Nexium
2006	8.6	5.1
2007	8.1	5.4
2008	7.8	5.9
2009	7.6	6.3
2010	7.2	6.3

Source: *IMS Health*

4. On a graphing calculator, use Zoom Out and then "intersect" to estimate the coordinates of the point where the graphs of L and N intersect. (For graphing calculator instructions, see Appendix B.6 and B.18.) What does it mean in terms of revenues that the graphs intersect at this point? State the year and revenue for this event.

▶ Tips for Success   **Study in a Test Environment**

Do you feel that you understand your homework assignments yet perform poorly on quizzes and tests? If so, you may not be studying enough to be ready to solve problems *in a test environment*. For example, although it is a good idea to refer to your lecture notes when you are stumped on a homework exercise, you must continue to solve similar exercises until you can solve them *without* referring to your lecture notes (unless your instructor uses open-notebook tests). The same idea applies to getting help from someone, referring to examples in the text, looking up answers in the back of the text, or any other form of support. Spend the last part of your study time completing exercises without such support. Try making up a practice quiz or test for yourself to do in a given amount of time.

Homework 2.4

For extra help ▶ **MyMathLab®**   Watch the videos in MyMathLab   Download the MyDashboard App

1. In response to rising concerns about identity theft, Fellowes, Inc.®, increased approximately steadily the number of models of paper shredders it manufactures from 2 models in 1990 to 41 models in 2012 (Source: *Fellowes*). Find the average rate of change of the number of shredder models.

2. The percentage of Americans who have trust in newspapers increased approximately linearly from 22% in 2007 to 28% in 2011 (Source: *The Gallup Organization*). Find the average rate of change of the percentage of Americans who have trust in newspapers.

3. The number of trips by Americans to Canada has declined approximately linearly from 44 million in 2000 to 11 million in 2011 (Source: *Statistics Canada*). Find the average rate of change of the number of trips.

4. Pittsburgh's population decreased approximately linearly from about 370 thousand people in 1990 to about 306 thousand people in 2010 (Source: *U.S. Census Bureau*). Find the average rate of change of population.

5. The number of executions from the death penalty decreased approximately linearly from 98 executions in 1999 to 43 executions in 2011 (Source: *Death Penalty Information Center*). Find the average rate of change of the number of executions.

6. The number of laws enacted by Congress decreased approximately linearly from 498 laws in 2004 to 383 laws in 2010 (Source: *Congressional Record*). Find the average rate of change of the number of laws enacted.

7. In-district students at Triton College pay $882 for 9 credit hours (units) of classes and $1176 for 12 credit hours of classes (Source: *Triton College*). Find the average rate of change of the total cost of classes with respect to the number of credit hours of classes.

8. In Manhattan, the average price of a two-bedroom house is $1,694,547, and that of a four-bedroom house is $6,315,496 (Source: *Trulia*). Find the average rate of change of price with respect to the number of bedrooms.

9. An Intermediate Algebra student drives a car at 70 miles per hour. Let d be the distance (in miles) the student travels in t hours.
   a. Is there a linear relationship between t and d? Explain. If the relationship is linear, find the slope and describe what it means in this situation.
   b. Find an equation of the model.

10. A train is moving at 40 miles per hour. Let d be the distance (in miles) the train travels in t hours.
   a. Create a table of values of t and d. Then make a scattergram.
   b. Is there a linear relationship between t and d? Explain. If the relationship is linear, find the slope and describe what it means in this situation.

11. The number of U.S. households that paid bills online was 66 million in 2010 and has increased by about 5.3 million per year (Source: *Forrester Research*). Let n be the number of households (in millions) that paid bills online at t years since 2010.
   a. Is there an approximate linear relationship between t and n? Explain. If the relationship is approximately linear, find the slope and describe what it means in this situation.
   b. What is the n-intercept of the model? What does it mean in this situation?
   c. Find an equation of the model.
   d. Perform a unit analysis of the equation you found in part (c).
   e. Predict the number of households that will pay bills online in 2016.

12. Retail sales of men's skin care products were $81.7 million in 2011 and have increased by about $2.6 million per year (Source: *NPD Group*). Let s be the retail sales (in millions of dollars) in the year that is t years since 2011.
   a. Is there an approximate linear relationship between t and s? Explain. If the relationship is approximately linear, find the slope and describe what it means in this situation.
   b. What is the s-intercept of the model? What does it mean in this situation?
   c. Find an equation of the model.
   d. Perform a unit analysis of the equation you found in part (c).
   e. Predict in which year retail sales of skin care products will be $100 million.

13. The unemployment rate was 7.8% in 2012 and has decreased by about 0.7 percentage point per year since then (Source: *Labor Department*). Let $g(t)$ be the unemployment rate at t years since 2012.
   a. What is the slope of the graph of g? What does it mean in this situation?

   b. Find an equation of g.
   c. Economists consider a "normal" unemployment rate to be between 5% and 6%. Sean Smith, an economics professor at the University of Central Florida, believes the unemployment rate won't decrease to 6% until after 2016. Use g to predict when the unemployment rate will be 6%. How does your result compare with Smith's prediction?
   d. Predict the unemployment rate in 2017.
   e. Find the t-intercept of the model. What does it mean in this situation?

14. The percentage of middle-income families who say it's possible to save for a secure retirement was 28% in 2011 and has decreased by 2.4 percentage points per year (Source: *Country Financial Security Index survey*). Let $f(t)$ be the percentage of middle-income families who say it's possible to save for a secure retirement at t years since 2011.
   a. What is the slope of the graph of f? What does it mean in this situation?
   b. Find an equation of f.
   c. Predict when 14% of middle-income families will say it's possible to save for a secure retirement.
   d. Find the t-intercept of the model. What does it mean in this situation?
   e. Let $g(t)$ be the number (in millions) of middle-income families at t years since 2011. A reasonable model is $g(t) = 0.035t + 15.87$ (Source: *GeoLytics*). Use the models f and g to predict the *number* of middle-income families who will say it's possible to save for a secure retirement in 2018.

15. For fall 2012, students paid $15.50 for an ID. Students could rent textbooks for $45 per course. Let $f(n)$ be the total cost (in dollars) of the ID fee and textbook rental for n courses.
   a. What is the slope of the graph of f? What does it mean in this situation?
   b. Find an equation of f.
   c. Perform a unit analysis of your equation of f.
   d. Find $f(4)$. What does it mean in this situation?
   e. Find n when $f(n) = 240.50$. What does it mean in this situation?

16. For fall 2012, students taking up to 11.99 credits (hours or units) at Lehigh Carbon Community College paid $96 per credit for tuition, $5 per semester for a student services fee, and a $12 technology fee per semester (Source: *Lehigh Carbon Community College*). Let $h(c)$ be the total one-semester cost (in dollars) of tuition and fees for a student who is taking c credits.
   a. What is the slope of the graph of h? What does it mean in this situation?
   b. Find an equation of h.
   c. Perform a unit analysis of your equation of h.
   d. Find $h(9)$. What does it mean in this situation?
   e. Find c when $h(c) = 593$. What does it mean in this situation?

17. A person drives her Honda CR-V® on a road trip. At the start of the trip, she fills up the 15.3-gallon tank with gasoline. During the trip, the car uses about 0.05 gallon of gas per mile. Let $g(x)$ be the number of gallons of gasoline remaining in the tank (which has not been refilled) after she has driven x miles.
   a. What is the slope of the graph of g? What does it mean in this situation?
   b. Find an equation of g.

c. Find the *x*-intercept of the model. What does it mean in this situation?

d. What are the domain and range of *g*?

e. If the driver will refuel the car when 1 gallon of gasoline remains in the tank, how far can she drive the car before refueling?

18. Atmospheric pressure at sea level is 1 atmosphere (atm). Under water, pressure increases by approximately 0.0303 atm for every 1-foot increase in water depth. For example, water pressure in the ocean is 1.0303 atm at a depth of 1 foot. Let $f(d)$ be the water pressure (in atm) at a water depth of *d* feet.

a. What is the slope of the graph of *f*? What does it mean in this situation?

b. Find an equation of *f*.

c. Perform a unit analysis of your equation of *f*.

d. How deep must you dive for the water pressure to be twice the pressure at sea level?

e. Crater Lake, in Oregon, is the deepest lake in the United States. Find the water pressure at 1943 feet, the lake's greatest depth.

19. Sales of energy drinks in the United States were 400 million gallons in 2012 and have increased by about 33.3 million gallons per year (Source: *Euromonitor International*).

a. Find an equation of a linear model to describe the situation. Explain what your variables represent.

b. Perform a unit analysis of the equation you found in part (a).

c. What is the slope of your model? What does it mean in this situation?

d. Predict in which year sales will reach 600 million gallons. What will be the average annual consumption per person in that year? Assume that kids under the age of 10 years don't consume energy drinks and that there will be 290 million Americans at least 10 years of age.

20. The number of U.S. brewery openings was 154 openings in 2010 and has increased by about 12.4 openings per year (Source: *Brewers Association*).

a. Find an equation of a linear model to describe the situation. Explain what your variables represent.

b. Perform a unit analysis of the equation you found in part (a).

c. What is the slope of your model? What does it mean in this situation?

d. Predict in which year there will be an average of 5 openings per state.

21. Yellow Cab of Cincinnati charges $5.75 for the first mile and $2.00 for each additional mile (Source: *Yellow Cab of Cincinnati*).

a. Find an equation of a linear model to describe the total cost of a cab fare. Explain what your variables represent.

b. If a person paid $31.75 for a cab fare, how far was the ride?

22. Some teenagers travel to Disneyland Resort in a bus. The price of a ticket for someone 10 years or older is $92, and parking costs $26 per bus (Source: *Disney*).

a. Find an equation of a linear model to describe the total cost of parking and the tickets for the teenagers. Explain what your variables represent.

b. If the total cost of parking and the tickets is $2142, how many teenagers are there?

23. The percentage of aluminum cans that were recycled in the United States was 65.1% in 2011 and has increased by about 3.6 percentage points per year (Source: *Aluminum Association*). The Aluminum Association has set a goal of a 75% recycling rate by 2015. Predict when 75% of aluminum cans will be recycled. Does your result suggest the goal will be met?

24. The percentage of Americans who have ever listened to an audio podcast was 23% in 2010 and has increased by about 3 percentage points per year (Source: *Edison Research and Arbitron*). Predict when half of Americans will have listened to an audio podcast.

25. MCI charges $46.99 per month for local calling and an additional 5 cents per minute for long-distance calling over 500 minutes (Source: *MCI*). If a person receives a monthly bill for $65.49, for how long did she talk long distance that month?

26. A Milky Way bar sells for $0.95 and a half-gallon of milk sells for $2.40 at a certain store. If a person pays a total of $14.75 for some Milky Way bars and a half-gallon of milk, how many Milky Way bars did he buy?

27. In Example 6 of Section 2.3, we made predictions with the model $s = 1.82t + 22.25$, where *s* is the average salary (in thousands of dollars) of faculty members at public colleges and universities at *t* years since 1980. What is the slope of this model? What does it mean in this situation?

28. In Exercise 78 of Homework 2.3, you found an equation close to $v = -5.83t + 137.09$ that models the first-class mail volume (in billions of pieces) in the year that is *t* years since 2000. What is the slope of this model? What does it mean in this situation?

29. In Exercise 17 of Section 2.2, you found an equation close to $r = -0.27t + 70.45$, where *r* is the record time (in seconds) for the women's 400-meter run at *t* years since 1900. What is the slope of this model? What does it mean in this situation?

30. In Example 3 of Section 2.2, we found the equation

$$p = -0.48t + 71$$

where *p* is the percentage of adult Americans who smoke at *t* years since 1900. What is the slope of this model? What does it mean in this situation?

31. In Exercise 83 of Homework 2.3, you found the equation $f(C) = 1.8C + 32$, where $f(C)$ is the Fahrenheit reading corresponding to a Celsius reading of *C* degrees. What is the slope of this model? What does it mean in this situation?

32. In Exercise 84 of Homework 2.3, you found the equation $g(F) = 4.3F - 172$, where $g(F)$ is the number of chirps per minute a cricket makes when the temperature is *F* degrees Fahrenheit. What is the slope of this model? What does it mean in this situation?

33. The percentage of the world's population that lives in rural areas has decreased for the past 50 years (see Table 64).

a. Let $f(t)$ be the percentage of the world's population that lives in rural areas at *t* years since 1950. Find an equation of *f*.

b. Find the slope of the model. What does it mean in this situation?

c. Estimate the *number* of people who will live in rural areas in 2020, when world population will be 7.6 billion.

d. Predict when 46% of the world's population will live in rural areas.

e. Find the *t*-intercept of the model. What does it mean in this situation?

Table 64 Percentages of World Population Living in Rural Areas

Year	Percent
1950	70
1960	66
1970	63
1980	61
1990	57
2000	52
2010	48

Source: *Food and Agricultural Organization of the United Nations*

34. Nevada was the fastest-growing U.S. state for the past two decades (see Table 65).

Table 65 Nevada's Population

Year	Population (millions)
1986	1.0
1990	1.2
1995	1.5
2000	2.0
2005	2.4
2010	2.7

Source: *U.S. Census Bureau*

a. Let $f(t)$ be Nevada's population (in millions) at t years since 1985. Find an equation of f.
b. What is the slope of the model? What does it mean in this situation?
c. Predict Nevada's population in 2018.
d. Find the t-intercept of the model. What does it mean in this situation?
e. Predict when Nevada's population will reach Connecticut's current population of 3.6 million.

35. Annual levels of oil production from the Outer Continental Shelf (OCS) and total annual levels of oil production in the United States (including from the OCS) are listed in Table 66 for various years.

Table 66 Oil Production

Year	Oil Production (billions of barrels) OCS	United States
1992	0.3	2.7
1995	0.4	2.4
1998	0.5	2.3
2001	0.6	2.1
2004	0.6	1.9
2007	0.5	1.8

Source: *U.S. Minerals Management Service*

a. Let $O(t)$ be the annual OCS oil production (in billions of barrels) at t years since 1990. Can the data be modeled well by using a linear model? If so, find such a model. If not, explain why not.
b. Use the data for 1998 and 2007 in Table 66 to find the average rate of change of annual OCS oil production from 1998 to 2007. Explain how your result relates to the result you found in part (a).

c. Let $U(t)$ be the total annual U.S. oil production (in billions of barrels) at t years since 1990. Can the data be modeled well by using a linear model? If so, find such a model. If not, explain why not.
d. Estimate the rate of change of the total annual U.S. oil production.
e. Predict in which year the total U.S. oil production will be 1.1 billion barrels.

36. The percentages of disposable personal incomes that Americans spent on food, both eaten at home and away from home, are shown in Table 67 for various years.

Table 67 Percentages of Disposable Personal Incomes Spent on Food

Year	Percent Eaten at Home	Eaten Away from Home
1985	7.5	4.1
1990	7.3	4.1
1995	6.5	4.1
2000	5.9	3.9
2005	5.8	4.1
2010	5.5	3.9

Source: *ERS/USDA*

a. Let $A(t)$ be the percentage of disposable personal income spent on food eaten away from home at t years since 1980. Can the data be modeled well by using a linear model? If so, find such a model. If not, explain why not.
b. Use the data for 1985 and 2005 in Table 67 to find the average rate of change of the percentage of disposable personal income spent on food eaten away from home from 1985 to 2005. Explain how your result relates to the result you found in part (a).
c. Let $H(t)$ be the percentage of disposable personal income spent on food eaten at home at t years since 1980. Can the data be modeled well by using a linear model? If so, find such a model. If not, explain why not.
d. Estimate the rate of change of the percentage of disposable personal income spent on food eaten at home.
e. Predict when 4.7% of disposable personal income will be spent on food eaten at home.

37. Table 68 shows various altitudes and the corresponding atmospheric pressures.

Table 68 Relationship Between Altitude and Pressure

Altitude (thousands of feet above sea level)	Pressure (inches of mercury)
0	29.92
1	28.86
2	27.82
3	26.82
4	25.84
5	24.89
6	23.98

Source: *Abbess Instruments*

a. Let $f(a)$ be the pressure (in inches of mercury) at altitude a (in thousands of feet above sea level). Find an equation of f.

b. What is the slope of the model? What does it mean in this situation?

c. Find the average rate of change of pressure with respect to altitude for each of the changes in altitude that follow. Compare each result with the result you found in part (b):
  i. From 1 thousand feet to 4 thousand feet
  ii. From 2 thousand feet to 5 thousand feet
  iii. From sea level to 6 thousand feet

d. Mount Elbert, in Colorado, is the second-highest mountain in the continental United States. Estimate the pressure at its peak, which is at 14,440 feet.

38. The heat index is the temperature the average person "feels" at a given humidity and air temperature. Heat indexes for various humidities when the air temperature is 75°F are shown in Table 69.

Table 69 Heat Indexes at Air Temperature of 75°F

Relative Humidity (percent)	Heat Index (degrees Fahrenheit)
0	69
20	72
40	74
60	76
80	78
100	80

Source: *National Weather Service*

a. Let $f(p)$ be the heat index (in degrees Fahrenheit) when the relative humidity is p percent (at an air temperature of 75°F). Find an equation of f.

b. What is the slope of the model? What does it mean in this situation?

c. Find the average rate of change of the heat index with respect to relative humidity (at an air temperature of 75°F) for each of the changes in relative humidity that follow. Compare each result with the result you found in part (b):
  i. From 0% humidity to 100% humidity
  ii. From 20% humidity to 80% humidity
  iii. From 40% humidity to 60% humidity

d. If the heat index is 77.6°F and the air temperature is 75°F, what is the relative humidity?

39. An airplane flies at a speed of 500 miles per hour for 3 hours. It then runs into strong headwinds and travels at a speed of 400 miles per hour for 2 more hours. Let $f(t)$ be the distance (in miles) traveled in t hours.

a. Complete a table consisting of values of t and $f(t)$. Use 0, 1, 2, 3, 4, and 5 for t. Assume it takes no time for the airplane to decelerate from 500 miles per hour to 400 miles per hour.

b. Graph the function f by hand.

c. Discuss the assumption that it takes no time for the airplane to decelerate from 500 miles per hour to 400 miles per hour. Is that possible? Explain.

d. Discuss the connections between the speeds of the airplane and the graph of f.

40. At noon, a math instructor drives at 50 miles per hour for 2 hours. During the next minute, she accelerates to 70 miles per hour, then travels at that speed for 3 more hours. (That is, she is on the road for a total of 5 hours and 1 minute.) Let d be the distance traveled (in miles) after t hours have elapsed.

a. Complete Table 70.

Table 70 Accelerating from 50 mph to 70 mph in One Minute

Time of Day	t (in hours)	d (in miles)
12:00 P.M.	0	
1:00 P.M.	1	
2:00 P.M.	2	
2:01 P.M.	2.017	
3:01 P.M.	3.017	
4:01 P.M.	4.017	
5:01 P.M.	5.017	

b. Sketch a curve that describes the relationship between t and d.

41. Let r be the annual revenue (in millions of dollars) of a company at t years since 2000. A reasonable model is shown in Fig. 44. What is the slope of the line? What does it mean in this situation?

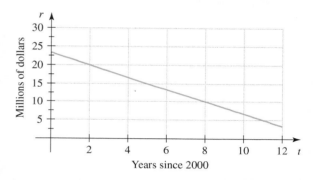

Figure 44 Revenue model

42. Let p be the population (in thousands) of a city at t years since 1980. A reasonable model is shown in Fig. 45. What is the slope of the line? What does it mean in this situation?

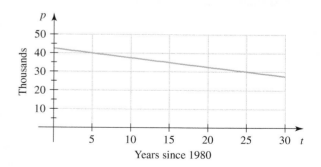

Figure 45 Population model

43. Let p be the price (in dollars) of a medium pizza with n ingredients. A reasonable model is shown in Fig. 46. What is the slope of the line? What does it mean in this situation?

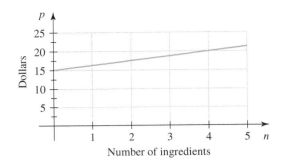

Figure 46 Pizza model

44. Let C be the total cost (in dollars) of n tickets and parking for one car at an amusement park. A reasonable model is shown in Fig. 47. What is the slope of the line? What does it mean in this situation?

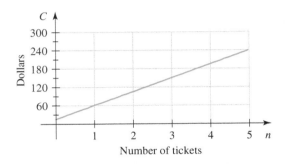

Figure 47 Amusement park model

For each scenario, sketch a qualitative graph that relates the distance d from home (in miles) to the number of minutes t that have elapsed.

45. A student drives at a constant speed. After a while, his favorite song plays on the radio, and he drives the rest of the way at a faster constant speed.

46. A commuter drives toward work at a constant speed. She notices a police car and slows down to a slower constant speed. After a while, the police car exits, and the commuter quickly resumes driving at her original constant speed.

47. A student drives toward school at a constant speed. After a while, she gets a flat tire, which takes some time to fix. She then continues to drive toward school, but at a faster constant speed to make up for lost time.

48. A student drives toward school at a constant speed. After a while, he realizes he left his graphing calculator at home. He turns around and heads home at a faster constant speed in hopes of getting to class on time. After getting his calculator, he drives toward school at an even faster constant speed.

Concepts

49. If p increases steadily as t increases steadily, then the rate of change of p with respect to t is positive. Explain why this makes sense.

50. If p decreases steadily as t increases steadily, then the rate of change of p with respect to t is negative. Explain why this makes sense.

51. Explain the statement "Slope is a rate of change." Give an example other than one of those given in the text.

52. Give an example to illustrate that if the rate of change of one quantity with respect to another quantity is constant, then there is a linear relationship between the two quantities.

Taking it to the Lab

Climate Change Lab

Most scientists are greatly concerned that the average temperature of the surface of Earth has increased by about 1°F since 1900 (see Table 71). Although this increase may not seem like much, many scientists believe an increase as small as 3.6°F could be dangerous.

Because the planet's average temperature increased by 1°F in the past century, it might seem that it would take about another two-and-a-half centuries for Earth to reach a dangerous temperature level. However, the Intergovernmental Panel on Climate Change (IPCC), composed of hundreds of scientists around the world, predicted that Earth's average temperature will rise 2.5°F to 10.4°F degrees Fahrenheit in the coming century.* Scientists from the United States and Europe have predicted that there is a 9-out-of-10 chance the global

average temperature will increase 3°F to 9°F, with a range of 4°F to 7°F most likely.[†]

Table 71 Average Surface Temperatures of Earth

Year	Average Temperature (degrees Fahrenheit)	Year	Average Temperature (degrees Fahrenheit)
1900	57.1	1960	57.2
1905	56.8	1965	57.0
1910	56.6	1970	57.3
1915	57.0	1975	57.1
1920	56.9	1980	57.6
1925	56.9	1985	57.3
1930	57.1	1990	57.8
1935	57.0	1995	57.9
1940	57.3	2000	57.8
1945	57.3	2005	58.3
1950	56.9	2010	58.3
1955	57.0	2011	58.1

Source: *NASA–GISS*

---

*IPCC, 2001: Summary for Policymakers. Adapted by author.

[†]T. M. L. Wigley and S. C. B. Raper, "Interpretation of high projections for global-mean warming," *Science* 293 (5529): 451–454, July 20, 2001. Adapted by author.

One result of the last century of global warming is that glaciers are receding and ocean levels are rising.[‡] For example, NASA scientist Bill Krabill estimates that Greenland's ice cap, the world's second largest, may be losing ice at a rate of 50 cubic kilometers per year.[§] The ice cap contained 2.85 million cubic kilometers of ice in 2000. Climatologist Jonathan Gregory of the University of Reading, in the United Kingdom, believes that by 2050 the ice cap may start an irreversible runaway melting. A total meltdown could take 1000 years.[¶]

Jonathan Overpeck, director of the Institute for the Study of Planet Earth at the University of Arizona, believes that Greenland's ice cap could melt completely in as little as 150 years and that a partial melting of Greenland's ice cap by 2100 could raise ocean levels by more than 1 meter.[∥] Coastal engineers estimate that a 1-meter rise would translate into a loss of about 100 meters of land.[**] In some areas of the world, land loss could be much greater.[††] For example, most of Florida is less than 1 meter above sea level.

Biologists note that many species throughout the world have changed their habitats in search of cooler climates.[*] One species, the golden toad, was not able to migrate and as a result has become extinct due to heat stress.[†]

Looking to the future, an international study, the most comprehensive analysis of its kind, predicts that 15 to 37 percent of all species of plants and animals—well over a million species—will become extinct by 2050.[‡] Klaus Toepfer, head of the United Nations Environment Programme (UNEP), said, "If one million species become extinct ... it is not just the plant and animal kingdoms and the beauty of the planet that will suffer. Billions of people, especially in the developing world, will suffer too as they rely on nature for such essential goods and services as food, shelter and medicines."[§]

Most scientists predict that global warming will also cause severe water shortages, create extreme weather events, and increase the number of heat-related illnesses and deaths.

Given the consensus among most scientists that global warming is occurring and that it could have catastrophic results, scientists have been searching for the cause of the warming. Most scientists believe it is largely the result of carbon dioxide emissions from the burning of fossil fuels such as oil, coal, and natural gas. Carbon dioxide emissions in the United States and in the world have increased greatly since 1950 (see Table 72).

Table 72 Carbon Dioxide Emissions from Burning of Fossil Fuels

Year	Carbon Dioxide Emissions (billions of metric tons)	
	United States	World
1950	2.4	5.8
1955	2.7	7.2
1960	2.9	9.4
1965	3.5	11.2
1970	4.3	14.7
1975	4.4	16.5
1980	4.8	19.1
1985	4.6	19.4
1990	5.0	21.6
1995	5.3	22.2
2000	5.9	23.8
2005	6.0	28.4
2010	5.6	30.6

Source: *U.S. Department of Energy*

In 1997 the United Nations negotiated a treaty called the Kyoto Protocol. The treaty's goal was to reduce annual greenhouse gas emissions to about 5% to 7% below 1990 levels by 2012. In November 2004, Russia cast the deciding vote to ratify the protocol, which took effect on February 16, 2005.

To create some flexibility in the treaty's requirements, a country that had exceeded its emissions limit could buy emissions credits from a country that was below its emissions limit. Also, a country could receive emissions credits by financing a project to help lower emissions in another country.

The treaty was legally binding for the 181 countries that ratified it.

The United States declined to ratify the Kyoto Protocol, saying that reducing emissions to the point called for by the treaty would cripple the U.S. economy. If it had ratified the treaty, the United States would have had to reduce its 2012 greenhouse gas emissions to 7% below its emissions level in 1990.

Instead of ratifying the treaty, in February 2002, the Bush administration adopted a voluntary program, called the Global Climate Change Initiative (GCCI), that includes tax incentives to motivate companies to reduce their emissions. The Bush administration set a goal of lowering the carbon intensity in 2012 to 18% below its level in 2002. *Carbon intensity* is defined as the ratio of annual carbon dioxide emissions to annual economic output.

Critics of the GCCI plan point out that if the U.S. economy is improving, then it is possible for carbon intensity to decrease *even though annual carbon dioxide emissions continue to increase.* In fact, even though annual carbon

[‡]National Snow and Ice Data Center, 2003.

[§]W. Krabill et al., "Greenland ice sheet: High-elevation balance and peripheral thinning," *Science* 289: 428–430, 2000. Adapted by author.

[¶]J. M. Gregory et al., "Climatology: Threatened loss of the Greenland ice sheet," *Nature* (April 8, 2004): 426:616. Adapted by author.

[∥]American Geophysical Union meeting, October 2002. Adapted by author.

[**]National Oceanic and Atmospheric Administration.

[††]R. J. Nicholls and F. M. J. Hoozemans, "Vulnerability to sea-level rise with reference to the Mediterranean region," *Medcoast 95*, Vol. II, October 1995. Adapted by author.

[*]T. L. Root et al., "Fingerprints of global warming on wild animals and plants," January 2, 2003, *Nature*, 421: 57–60.

[†]J. A. Pounds et al., "Biological response to climate change on a tropical mountain," 1999. *Nature (London)*, 398(6728): 611–615.

[‡]C. D. Thomas et al., "Extinction risk from climate change," January 8, 2004, *Nature*, 427: 145–148.

[§]Reported by UNEP (United Nations Environment Programme), January 8, 2004.

dioxide emissions have increased during each of the past three decades, carbon intensity has declined by 18%, 23%, and 16% in those decades! However, the projected decrease for 2002–2012 was only 13%, so modest efforts would have had to be implemented to reach the goal of 18%.[¶]

Critics such as the Earth Policy Institute and the Pew Center on Global Climate Change also say that the voluntary plan is unrealistic, because businesses will make modest efforts to reduce emissions when the economy is doing well and will make little or no effort when the economy is doing poorly. These critics argue the United States would have been more likely to respond to the Kyoto Protocol, because it was a legally binding, yet flexible, treaty.

The Obama administration spent $2.5 billion on GCCI from 2010 to 2012, helping developing countries do the following: adapt to climate change, develop clean energy infrastructures, and stop cutting down forests. The Congressional Research Service raised pros and cons of continuing such actions, including questioning whether such monies would be better spent in meeting domestic challenges, especially when the U.S. economy is struggling.[‖]

On December 11, 2011, the United Nations agreed on the Durban Platform for Enhanced Action, which includes a protocol that will apply to *all* countries, a second commitment period (beyond 2012) for the Kyoto Protocol, and the Green Climate Fund, which is meant to help developing countries in ways similar to the Obama administration's actions. The details of the plan are still being worked out. Progress on working out the details is slow, mostly because many countries fear reducing greenhouse emissions will hurt their economies.[**]

The Kyoto Protocol's goal to cut developed countries' carbon emissions to about 5% to 7% below 1990 levels was a crucial first goal, but the Intergovernmental Panel on Climate Change (IPCC) is calling for carbon dioxide emissions in 2050 to be 60% less than carbon dioxide emissions in 1990.

Many countries are condemning the United States because the Bush and Obama administrations have refused to ratify the Kyoto Protocol. Although the U.S. population in 2010 was only 5% of the world population, 18% of world carbon dioxide emissions that year was produced by the United States (see Tables 72 and 73).

Critics of the Kyoto Protocol say a fairer pact would be for all countries to commit to the same level of carbon dioxide emissions *per person*. Using the IPCC's recommendation for 2050 carbon dioxide emissions, coupled with the United Nations' prediction of 9.3 billion people in 2050,

Table 73 United States and World Populations

Year	Population (billions)	
	United States	World
1960	0.18	3.04
1970	0.21	3.71
1980	0.23	4.45
1990	0.25	5.29
2000	0.28	6.09
2010	0.31	6.85

Source: *U.S. Census Bureau*

carbon dioxide emissions should be about 0.9 metric ton per person that year.[††]

In 2010, annual carbon emissions were about 4.5 metric tons of carbon dioxide per person. Average annual carbon dioxide emissions for developing countries are 2.7 metric tons per person, which is three times the IPCC's recommendation. Even worse, average annual carbon emissions for developed countries is 10.2 metric tons per person, more than ten times the IPCC's recommendation (see Table 74).[*]

GDP, the gross domestic product, is a measure of a country's economic strength.

Table 74 GDP Ranks, Per-Person GDPs, and Per-Person Carbon Dioxide Emissions

Country	2010 GDP Rank	2010 Per-Person GDP (thousands of international dollars)	2010 Per-Person Carbon Emissions (metric tons)
Sweden	22	39.0	5.3
Switzerland	19	46.4	5.4
France	5	34.1	5.5
Italy	8	32.0	6.7
United Kingdom	6	35.7	7.9
Austria	25	40.0	8.1
Denmark	31	40.2	8.4
Japan	3	33.7	8.9
Germany	4	37.4	9.3
Belgium	21	37.6	9.9
Norway	23	57.2	10.5
Australia	15	38.2	16.0
United States	1	47.2	18.1
Netherlands	16	42.2	31.9

Source: *World Bank; Carbon Dioxide Information Analysis Center*

With annual carbon dioxide emissions of 18.1 metric tons per person in 2010, the United States would have to reduce emissions by 95% to meet the standard of 0.9 metric ton per person. This means Americans could emit only 5% of the carbon dioxide they currently emit. Imagine driving your car, heating and cooling your home, using your home appliances (including your refrigerator), using your computer, using your lights, and watching your television only 5% (one-twentieth) of the time you currently do.

[¶]"Early Release of the Annual Energy Outlook 2003" (November 2002), Energy Information Administration; and "Projected Greenhouse Gas Emissions," May 2002, *U.S. Climate Action Report 2002*, pp. 70–80, U.S. Department of State, Washington, DC.

[‖]Richard K. Lattanzio, "The Global Climate Change Initiative (GCCI): Budget Authority and Request, FY2010–FY2013," Congressional Research Service, *CRS Report for Congress*, March 15, 2012.

[**]United Nations, "Establishment of an Ad Hoc Working Group on the Durban Platform for Enhanced Action," December 11, 2011.

[††]United Nations Population Division.

[*]International Energy Agency, "CO₂ Emissions From Fuel Combustion Highlights," 2011.

Some experts, such as the engineer Alan Pears, co-director of the environmental consultancy Sustainable Solutions, believe it is possible for emissions to be significantly reduced without harming a country's economy. Norway, for instance, has a better GNP per-person ranking than the United States has, as well as significantly lower per-person carbon dioxide emissions. In fact, with the exception of the Netherlands and Australia, all of the countries listed in Table 74 have strong economies and significantly lower carbon dioxide emissions than the United States has. A scattergram of the data would show countries with a higher per-person GDP do not necessarily have higher carbon dioxide emissions.

Many states have adopted policies to reduce carbon dioxide emissions. And by using alternative sources of energy, many countries have slowed or reversed the growth of carbon dioxide emissions in recent years.[†]

In addition to national, state, and even corporate actions, individuals can help lower carbon dioxide emissions by purchasing hybrid automobiles, major appliances with the Energy Star logo, solar thermal systems to help provide hot water, and compact fluorescent light bulbs. Individuals can also carpool or use public transportation.

Analyzing the Situation

1. Let $f(t)$ be the average global temperature (in degrees Fahrenheit) at t years since 1900. Use a graphing calculator to draw a scattergram of the data in Table 71. Does it appear that Earth's average temperature increased much from 1900 to 1965? Explain.

2. **a.** Estimate the average global temperature from 1900 to 1965. [**Hint:** Divide the sum of the temperatures by the number of temperature readings.]
   b. Estimate the average global temperature from 1990 to 2000. [**Hint:** Divide the sum of the temperatures by the number of temperature readings.]
   c. Use your results in parts (a) and (b) to estimate the change in Earth's average temperature in the past century. Compare your result with the scientists' estimate of 1°F.

3. Find an equation of a model *for the years 1965 to 2011*. Verify that your model fits the data well for those years.

4. Use the model and your result from part (a) of Problem 2 to predict when the planet's average temperature will have increased by 3.6°F—a potentially dangerous climate change.

5. Use Tables 72 and 73 to verify the claims that although the U.S. population in 2010 was only 5% of world population, 18% of annual world carbon dioxide emissions were produced by the United States in that year.

6. Use the United Nations' prediction that the world population will be 9.3 billion in 2050 to verify the claim that per-person carbon dioxide emissions that year

should be about 0.9 metric ton per person for the IPCC recommendation of a 60% reduction by then.

7. Let $g(t)$ be the U.S. population (in billions) at t years since 1950. Create a scattergram of the data and then find an equation of g. Finally, verify that your model fits the data well.

8. Let $h(t)$ be U.S. carbon dioxide emissions (in billions of metric tons) in the year that is t years since 1950. Use a graphing calculator to draw a scattergram of the data, and then find an equation of h. Finally, verify that your model fits the data well.

9. **a.** Use your model g of Problem 7 to estimate U.S. population in 2011.
   b. Use your model h of Problem 8 to estimate U.S. carbon dioxide emissions in 2011.
   c. Use your results from parts (a) and (b) to estimate U.S. *per-person* carbon dioxide emissions in 2011.
   d. The actual U.S. per-person carbon dioxide emissions in 2011 were 18.0 metric tons. Is your result in part (c) an underestimate or an overestimate? Explain why this can be explained at least in part by the poor economy during the period 2008–2011.

10. Let G be the per-person GDP (in international dollars) of a country with per-person carbon emissions c (in metric tons). Use a graphing calculator to draw a scattergram of the data. Do countries with higher per-person GDPs always have higher per-person carbon emissions? Explain.

11. The numbers in the list 20, 22, 24, 26, 28 are increasing. Decide whether the ratios in the following list are increasing, decreasing, or neither:

$$\frac{20}{1}, \frac{22}{2}, \frac{24}{4}, \frac{26}{8}, \frac{28}{16}$$

12. Explain why your work in Problem 11 illustrates how it is possible for U.S. carbon intensity to decrease while U.S. annual carbon emissions increase. [**Hint:** Recall that carbon intensity is defined as the *ratio* of annual carbon emissions to annual economic output.]

13. Which seeks to lower U.S. carbon emissions more, the GCCI plan or the Kyoto Protocol? Explain. Taking into account the degree to which American companies would respond to either policy, do you think U.S. carbon emissions would be reduced more by the GCCI plan or by the Kyoto Protocol? Explain.

14. Let I be the amount of ice (in cubic kilometers) in Greenland's ice cap at t years since 2000. Assuming that Greenland's ice cap continues to melt at the current rate, find an equation that models the situation.

15. **a.** Use your model to predict the amount of ice in Greenland's ice cap in 1000 years. If a total meltdown is to occur in 1000 years, as predicted by Gregory, what must have happened to the rate of melting?
   b. If a total meltdown is to occur in 150 years, as predicted by Overpeck, what must have happened to the rate of melting?

[†]Pamela Person, "Reducing greenhouse gas emissions," Maine Center for Economic Policy, *Choices*, VII(9), Oct. 11, 2001. Adapted by author.

Used Car Lab

In this lab, you will explore the relationship between the advertised resale price of a specific make and model of a car and the car's age. Choose a car make and model (such as Honda Civic). Refer to used-car advertisements in a newspaper, car magazine, or website (such as www.edmunds.com) to find the ages and prices of about 20 cars of your chosen type. You may use more than one car of a single age, but if you use more than one source of data, be careful that you are not using the *same* car twice.

Let p be the advertised price (in dollars) of your choice of car that is a years old. (Note that a is the age of the car, not the year in which it was manufactured.)

Analyzing the Data

1. Include a table of data. State the source(s) of the data.

2. Use a graphing calculator to draw a scattergram of your data. If no line comes close to the data points, choose another make and model of car.

3. Find an equation of a linear model to describe the situation. Write your equation with the function name f.

4. Use a graphing calculator to draw a graph of your model and the scattergram in the same viewing window. Also, graph the model and scattergram by hand. How well does f model the data?

5. Use your model to estimate what the advertised price should be for your choice of car if it is 10 years old.

6. Use your model to predict when your car will be worth half as much as the cheapest price listed in your table of data.

7. Find the slope of your model. What does it mean in this situation?

8. Find the a-intercept and the p-intercept of your model. What do these intercepts mean in this situation? Do you think that f models the car situation well near the intercepts? Explain.

9. For what values of a is there model breakdown for certain? Explain.

10. Sketch a qualitative graph of the relationship between your car's price and its age for all possible ages.

Taking It One Step Further

11. Let $g(a)$ be a down payment (in dollars) of 10% of the resale price for your choice of car that is a years old. Find an equation of g.

12. Find $g(5)$. What does the result mean in this situation?

13. Compare the slope of the graph of g to the slope of the graph of f. Explain why your comparison makes sense in terms of your choice of car.

Golf Ball Lab

In this lab, you will explore the relationship between the height of a golf ball before dropping it and its height after one bounce.*

Materials

You will need at least three people and the following items:
1. a tape measure
2. a golf ball

Recording the Data

The same person should drop the golf ball each time. A second person should measure the height of the golf ball (from the bottom of the ball) before the first person drops it. The ball should be dropped from an initial height of 12 inches. A spotter should estimate the bounce height of the golf ball. Repeat this process three times. Then compute the average of the three bounce heights. Next, find average bounce heights of the golf ball for initial heights of 24 inches, 36 inches, 48 inches, 60 inches, and 72 inches. If your instructor prefers, use the data listed in Table 75.

Table 75 Drop and Bounce Heights of a Golf Ball

Drop Height (inches)	Bounce Height (inches)
12	10.0
24	20.3
36	31.0
48	44.5
60	52.0
72	64.0

Source: *J. Lehmann*

Analyzing the Data

1. Display your golf ball data in a table.

2. Let B be the bounce height (in inches) after the ball was dropped from an initial height of H inches. Use a graphing calculator to draw a scattergram of the golf ball data.

3. Find an equation of a linear model to describe the situation. Write your equation with the function name f.

4. Find the B-intercept of your model. What does it mean in this situation? If you can find a linear model with a better B-intercept, do so.

5. Use a graphing calculator to draw a graph of your model and the scattergram in the same viewing window. Also, graph the model and scattergram by hand. How well does f model the data?

---

*The Golf Ball Lab adapted from a lab written by Jim Ryan, State Center Community College District, Willow International College Center, Clovis, CA. Used by permission of James Ryan.

6. Use your model to estimate the bounce height for a drop height of 80 inches.

7. On a golf course, a golf ball is hit to a maximum height of 50 feet. What does your model estimate the bounce height to be after one bounce? Do you think this estimate is accurate? If not, will it be an underestimate or an overestimate? Explain.

8. Find the slope of your model. What does the slope mean in this situation? Explain.

9. Estimate the bounce height after three bounces for a drop height of 90 inches.

Taking It One Step Further

10. Redo the experiment with a rubber ball and then with a tennis ball. Then repeat Parts 1–5. Finally, compare the slopes of your three linear models and explain why the comparison makes sense.

Walking Student Lab

In this lab, you will explore the relationship between time and the distance between a wall and a student who is walking toward it.

Materials

You will need at least three people and the following items:
1. a timing device
2. a tape measure
3. a Texas Instruments CBR unit or a Texas Instruments CBL unit with a Vernier motion detector probe (in place of a timing device and tape measure) (optional)

Preparation

Have the student who will do the walking stand about 15 feet from a wall. If you aren't using a CBL or CBR unit, lay out the tape measure from the wall to the student's toes.

Recording of Data

Have the student walk toward the wall at a steady pace. Record the distance between the student and the wall at various times. If you are not using a CBL or CBR unit, you may need several people to assist in measuring and recording the data. Try to get at least five data points (time and distance).

If your instructor prefers, use the data listed in Table 76.

Table 76 Distances Between a Student and a Wall

Time (seconds)	Distance (feet)
0.4	10.55
1.6	8.52
3.3	5.62
4.1	4.19
5.4	1.91

Source: *J. Lehmann*

Analyzing the Data

1. Display your data in a table.
2. Let d be the distance (in feet) the student was from the wall t seconds after the student began walking. Which variable is the dependent variable?
3. Use a graphing calculator to draw a scattergram of the data.
4. Find an equation of a model to describe the situation.
5. Write your equation with the function name f.
6. Use a graphing calculator to draw a graph of your model and the scattergram in the same viewing window. Also, graph the model and scattergram by hand. How well does f model the data?
7. Is your model increasing or decreasing? Explain what this means in this situation.
8. Use your model to estimate how far the student was from the wall after 2 seconds.
9. Use your model to estimate when the student was 1 foot from the wall.
10. What is the slope of your model? What does it mean in this situation?
11. What is the d-intercept of your model? What does it mean in this situation?
12. What is the t-intercept of your model? What does it mean in this situation?
13. Use your model to estimate how far the student was from the wall after 20 seconds. Has model breakdown occurred? Explain.

Linear Model Lab: Topic of Your Choice

Your objective in this lab is to use a linear model to describe some authentic situation. Find some data on two quantities that describe a situation that has not been discussed in this text. Almanacs, newspapers, magazines, scientific journals, and the Internet are good resources. Or you can conduct an experiment. Choose something that interests you!

Analyzing the Situation

1. What two quantities did you explore? Define variables for the quantities. Include units in your definitions.
2. Which variable is the dependent variable? Which variable is the independent variable? Explain.
3. Describe how you found your data. If you conducted an experiment, provide a careful description with specific details of how you ran your experiment. If you didn't conduct an experiment, state the source of your data.
4. Include a table of your data.
5. Use a graphing calculator to draw a scattergram of your data. (If your data are not approximately linear, find some data that are.)
6. Find an equation of a linear model to describe the data.

7. What is the slope of your linear model? What does it mean in this situation?

8. Does it make sense that your variables are approximately linearly related in terms of the situation you chose to model? Explain.

9. Choose a value for your independent variable. On the basis of that chosen value, use your model to find a value for your dependent variable. Describe what your result means in the situation you are modeling.

10. Choose a value for your dependent variable. On the basis of that chosen value, use your model to find a value for your independent variable. Describe what your result means in the situation you are modeling.

11. Find the intercepts of your linear model. What do they mean in the situation you are modeling? Has model breakdown occurred at the intercepts?

12. Comment on your lab experience.
  a. For example, you might address whether the lab was enjoyable, insightful, and so on.
  b. Were you surprised by any of your findings? If so, which ones?
  c. How would you improve your process for this lab if you were to do it again?
  d. How could you improve your process if you had more time and money?

Chapter Summary

Key Points of Chapter 2

Section 2.1   Using Lines to Model Data

Scattergram	A graph of plotted ordered pairs is called a **scattergram.**
Creating a complete scattergram	A scattergram should have scaling on both axes and labels indicating the variable names and scale units.
Approximately linearly related	If the points in a scattergram of data lie close to (or on) a line, then we say the relevant variables are **approximately linearly related.**
Model	A **model** is a mathematical description of an authentic situation.
Linear model	A **linear model** is a linear function, or its graph, that describes the relationship between two quantities for an authentic situation.
Creating scattergrams and making estimates and predictions	We create a scattergram of data to determine whether the relevant variables are approximately linearly related. If they are, we draw a line that comes close to (or on) the data points and use the line to make estimates and predictions.
Interpolation and extrapolation	For a situation that can be modeled by a function whose independent variable is t, • We perform **interpolation** when we use a part of the model whose t-coordinates are between the t-coordinates of two data points. • We perform **extrapolation** when we use a part of the model whose t-coordinates are not between the t-coordinates of any two data points.
Model breakdown	When a model gives a prediction that does not make sense or an estimate that is not a good approximation, we say **model breakdown** has occurred.

Section 2.2   Finding Equations of Linear Models

Finding an equation of a linear model	To find an equation of a linear model, given some data, **1.** Create a scattergram of the data. **2.** Determine whether there is a line that comes close to the data points. If so, choose two points (not necessarily data points) that you can use to find the equation of a linear model. **3.** Find an equation of the line you identified in step 2. **4.** Use a graphing calculator to verify that the graph of your equation comes close to the points of the scattergram.

Section 2.3   Function Notation and Making Predictions

Function notation	The dependent variable of a function f can be represented by the expression formed by writing the independent variable name within the parentheses of $f(\ )$: $$\text{dependent variable} = f(\text{independent variable})$$ We call this representation **function notation.**
Four-step modeling process	To find a linear model and make estimates and predictions, **1.** Create a scattergram of the data to determine whether there is a nonvertical line that comes close to the data points. If so, choose two points (not necessarily data points) you can use to find the equation of a linear model. **2.** Find an equation of your model. **3.** Verify your equation by checking that the graph of your model contains the two chosen points and comes close to all of the data points. **4.** Use the equation of your model to make estimates, make predictions, and draw conclusions.
Making a prediction about the dependent variable	When making a prediction about the dependent variable of a linear model, substitute a chosen value for the independent variable in the model. Then solve for the dependent variable.
Making a prediction about the independent variable	When making a prediction about the independent variable of a linear model, substitute a chosen value for the dependent variable in the model. Then solve for the independent variable.
Intercepts of a model	If a function of the form $p = mt + b$, where $m \neq 0$, is used to model a situation, then • The p-intercept is $(0, b)$. • To find the t-coordinate of the t-intercept, substitute 0 for p in the model's equation and solve for t.
Domain and range of a model	For the **domain** and **range** of a model, we consider input–output pairs only when both the input and the output make sense in the situation. The domain of the model is the set of all such inputs, and the range of the model is the set of all such outputs.

Section 2.4   Slope Is a Rate of Change

Rate of change and average rate of change	Suppose a quantity y changes steadily from y_1 to y_2 as a quantity x changes steadily from x_1 to x_2. Then the **rate of change** of y with respect to x is the ratio of the change in y to the change in x: $$\frac{\text{change in } y}{\text{change in } x} = \frac{y_2 - y_1}{x_2 - x_1}$$ If either quantity changes, but not steadily, then this formula is the **average rate of change** of y with respect to x.
Increasing and decreasing quantities	Suppose a quantity p depends on a quantity t: • If p increases steadily as t increases steadily, then the rate of change of p with respect to t is positive. • If p decreases steadily as t increases steadily, then the rate of change of p with respect to t is negative.
Slope is a rate of change	If there is a linear relationship between quantities t and p, and if p depends on t, then the slope of the linear model is equal to the rate of change of p with respect to t.
Constant rate of change	Suppose a quantity p depends on a quantity t: • If there is a linear relationship between t and p, then the rate of change of p with respect to t is constant. • If the rate of change of p with respect to t is constant, then there is a linear relationship between t and p.

Section 2.4   Slope Is a Rate of Change (*Continued*)

Unit analysis	We perform a **unit analysis** of a model's equation by determining the units of the expressions on both sides of the equation. The simplified units of the expressions on both sides of the equation should be the same.
Slope is an average rate of change	If two quantities t and p are approximately linearly related, and if p depends on t, then the slope of a reasonable linear model is approximately equal to the average rate of change of p with respect to t.

Chapter 2 Review Exercises

For $f(x) = 3x^2 - 7$, $g(x) = \dfrac{2x + 5}{3x + 6}$, and $h(x) = -10x - 3$, find the following.

1. $f(3)$ **2.** $f(-3)$ **3.** $g(2)$

4. $h\left(\dfrac{3}{5}\right)$ **5.** $h(a + 3)$

For $f(x) = 2x + 3$, find the value of x that corresponds to the given value of $f(x)$.

6. $f(x) = -6$ **7.** $f(x) = \dfrac{2}{3}$ **8.** $f(x) = a + 7$

For Exercises 9–16, refer to Fig. 48.

9. Estimate $f(2)$.   **10.** Estimate $f(0)$.

11. Estimate $f(-3)$.

12. Estimate x when $f(x) = 3$.

13. Estimate x when $f(x) = 0$.

14. Estimate x when $f(x) = -1$.

15. Find the domain of f.   **16.** Find the range of f.

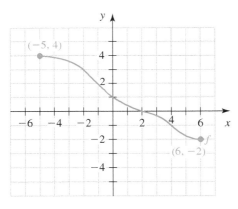

Figure 48
Exercises 9–16

For Exercises 17–20, refer to Table 77.

17. Find $f(0)$.   **18.** Find $f(2)$.

19. Find x when $f(x) = 0$.   **20.** Find x when $f(x) = 2$.

Table 77 Values of f
(Exercises 17–20)

x	$f(x)$
0	1
1	2
2	4
3	3
4	0

For Exercises 21–23, find all x-intercepts and y-intercepts of the graph of the function.

21. $f(x) = -7x + 3$ **22.** $f(x) = 4$

23. $f(x) = -\dfrac{4}{7}x + 2$

24. Find the approximate x-intercept and the approximate y-intercept of the graph of $2.56x - 9.41y = 78.25$. Round the coordinates to the second decimal place.

25. Copy the graphs of the data points and the model $y = mx + b$ in Fig. 49. Sketch the graph of a linear model that describes the data better. Then explain how you would adjust the slope and the y-intercept of the original model to describe the data better.

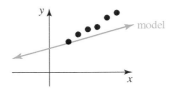

Figure 49 Exercise 25

26. A student's car has a 13-gallon gasoline tank. The car uses 1.8 gallons per hour when driven at 65 miles per hour. After filling up the gas tank, the student begins driving at 65 miles per hour and continues to drive at this speed until he runs out of gas. Let $A = f(t)$ be the amount of gasoline (in gallons) in the tank at t hours after the student filled the tank.
   a. Find an equation of f.
   b. What is the slope of the model? What does it mean in this situation?
   c. What is the A-intercept of the model? What does it mean in this situation?
   d. Perform a unit analysis of the equation you found in part (a).
   e. What is the t-intercept of the model? What does it mean in this situation?
   f. What are the domain and range of the model? Explain.

27. The median compensation (including salary and benefits) of college presidents was $870 thousand in 2010 and has increased by about $37 thousand per year since then (Source: *IRS*). Let $C(t)$ be the median annual compensation (in thousands of dollars) of college presidents at t years since 2010.
   a. Find the slope of the graph of C. What does it mean in this situation?
   b. Find an equation of C.

c. Find $C(8)$. What does it mean in this situation?

d. Find t when $C(t) = 1000$. What does it mean in this situation?

28. Sales of new light-duty vehicles decreased approximately linearly from 7.78 million vehicles in 2006 to 5.65 million vehicles in 2010 (Source: *National Automobile Dealers Association*). Find the rate of change of annual sales of new light-duty vehicles.

29. Average U.S. personal income increased approximately linearly from $14,420 in 1990 to $27,589 in 2008 (Source: *U.S. Census Bureau*). Estimate the average personal income in 2010. The actual personal income in that year was $26,059. Is your estimate an underestimate or an overestimate? Explain why this might be due to the poor economy from 2008 to 2010.

30. The Internal Revenue Service (IRS) standard mileage rate is a way of computing an automobile expense deduction on a tax return. Mileage rates for businesses are provided in Table 78 for various years. Let $M = f(t)$ be the standard mileage rate (in cents per mile) at t years since 2000.

Table 78 IRS Standard Mileage Rates for Businesses

Year	Standard Mileage Rate (cents per mile)
2000	32.5
2002	36.5
2004	37.5
2006	44.5
2008	54.5
2010	50.0
2012	55.5

Source: *IRS*

a. Find an equation of f.

b. What is the slope? What does it mean in this situation?

c. Find the M-intercept. What does it mean in this situation?

d. Predict when the standard mileage rate will be 69 cents per mile.

e. If a person will drive 12,500 miles on business trips in 2017, predict how much money she will be able to deduct for driving expenses.

f. For the first six months of 2008, the mileage rate was 50.5 cents per mile. For the rest of that year, it was 58.5 cents per mile. Explain why the estimate of 54.5 cents was used in Table 78.

31. The First Amendment says: "Congress shall make no law respecting an establishment of religion or prohibiting the free exercise thereof, or abridging the freedom of speech or of the press, or the right of the people peaceably to assemble, and to petition the government for a redress of grievances." The percentages of Americans who feel the amendment goes too far in the rights it guarantees are shown in Table 79.

Table 79 Percentages of Americans Who Feel the First Amendment Goes Too Far in the Rights It Guarantees

Year	Percent
2001	39
2003	34
2005	23
2007	25
2009	19
2011	18

Source: *State of the First Amendment 2011*

Let $f(t)$ be the percentage of Americans who think the First Amendment goes too far in the rights it guarantees at t years since 2000.

a. Find an equation of f.

b. What is the slope? What does it mean in this situation?

c. Use the model to predict when 3% of Americans will think the First Amendment goes too far in the rights it guarantees.

d. Find $f(8)$. What does it mean in this situation?

e. Find t when $f(t) = 8$. What does it mean in this situation?

f. Find the t-intercept. What does it mean in this situation?

Chapter 2 Test

For Exercises 1–10, refer to Fig. 50.

1. Estimate $f(-3)$.

2. Estimate $f(3)$.

3. Estimate $f(0)$.

4. Estimate $f(-5)$.

5. Estimate x when $f(x) = -3$.

6. Estimate x when $f(x) = -2$.

7. Estimate x when $f(x) = 0$.

8. Estimate x when $f(x) = 0.5$.

9. Find the domain of f.

10. Find the range of f.

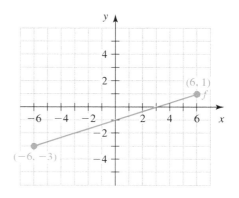

Figure 50 Exercises 1–10

Let $f(x) = -4x + 7$.

11. Find $f(-3)$.

12. Find $f(a - 5)$.

13. Find x when $f(x) = 2$.

14. Find x when $f(x) = a$.

For Exercises 15–17, find all x-intercepts and y-intercepts.

15. $f(x) = 3x - 7$

16. $g(x) = -2x$

17. $k(x) = \dfrac{1}{3}x - 8$

18. The percentages of U.S. teenagers with driver's licenses are shown in Table 80 for various ages.

Table 80　Percentages of U.S. Teens with Driver's Licenses

Age (years)	Percent
16	56.8
17	61.3
18	72.0
19	79.4
20	81.8

Source: *National Longitudinal Survey of Youth*

Let $p = f(a)$ be the percentage of teenagers at age a years who have driver's licenses.
   a. Find an equation of f.
   b. What is the slope of the model? What does it mean in this situation?
   c. Find the a-intercept. What does it mean in this situation?
   d. Estimate the percentage of 21-year-old adults who have driver's licenses.
   e. Estimate at what age all adults have driver's licenses.

19. The numbers of farmers markets are shown in Table 81 for various years. Let $f(t)$ be the number (in thousands) of farmers markets at t years since 1990.
   a. Find an equation of f.
   b. What is the slope of the model? What does it mean in this situation?
   c. Find $f(8)$. What does it mean in this situation?

d. Find t when $f(t) = 8$. What does it mean in this situation?

e. Find the t-intercept. What does it mean in this situation?

Table 81　Numbers of Farmers Markets

Year	Number of Farmers Markets (thousands)
1994	1.8
1998	2.7
2002	3.1
2006	4.4
2010	6.1

Source: *U.S. Department of Agriculture*

20. The total annual ad spending (in millions of dollars) for the NCAA basketball tournament (known as "March Madness") has increased approximately linearly from $239.1 million in 1998 to $613.8 million in 2010 (Source: *TNS Media Intelligence*). Predict the total annual ad spending for March Madness in 2017.

21. The number of states with ethanol plants was 29 states in 2012 and has increased by about 1.7 states per year since then (Source: *Renewable Fuels Association*). Let $n = f(t)$ be the number of states with ethanol plants at t years since 2012.
   a. Is there an approximate linear relationship between t and n? Explain. If the relationship is approximately linear, find the slope and describe what it means in this situation.
   b. What is the n-intercept? What does it mean in this situation?
   c. Find an equation of the model.
   d. Predict the number of states that will have ethanol plants in 2018.
   e. Predict when all states will have ethanol plants.

22. A student drives at a constant rate from home to a movie theater. The movie she wanted to see is sold out. After staying at the theater for a few minutes, she drives home, but at a slower constant rate. Sketch a qualitative graph that relates the distance d from home (in miles) to the number of hours t that have elapsed.

Systems of Linear Equations

3

Even though the women's current record time for the 400-meter run is on par with the men's record times set far back in the early 1900s, women have been improving much faster than men (see Table 1). In Example 2 of Section 3.3, we will predict when the women's record time and the men's record time will be equal.

In Chapter 2, we used a single linear model to describe an authentic situation. In this chapter, we will use two linear models to describe authentic situations. In particular, we will predict when two quantities will be equal, such as the average annual U.S. per-person consumption of milk and soft drinks. We will also predict when one quantity will be less than or greater than another quantity.

Table 1 400-Meter Run Record Times

Women		Men	
Year	Record Time (seconds)	Year	Record Time (seconds)
1957	57.0	1900	47.8
1959	53.4	1916	47.4
1962	51.9	1928	47.0
1969	51.7	1932	46.2
1972	51.0	1941	46.0
1976	49.29	1950	45.8
1979	48.60	1960	44.9
1983	47.99	1968	43.86
1985	47.60	1988	43.29
		1999	43.18

Source: *International Association of Athletics Federations*

3.1 Using Graphs and Tables to Solve Systems

Objectives

» Use graphing to make estimates and predictions about situations that can be modeled by using two linear functions.

» Know the meaning of *solution* and *solution set* of a *system of linear equations in two variables.*

» Use a graphical approach to solve systems of linear equations.

» Know the three types of linear systems of two equations.

» Use tables to solve a system of linear equations.

In this section, we will use graphs and tables to work with two or more linear equations in two variables.

Using Two Linear Models to Make a Prediction

We can use graphing to make estimates and predictions about some authentic situations that can be modeled by using two linear functions.

▶ **Example 1** Using Two Models to Make a Prediction

In the United States, life expectancies of women have been longer than life expectancies of men for many years (see Table 2). The life expectancies (in years) $W(t)$ and $M(t)$ of women and men, respectively, are modeled by the system

$$L = W(t) = 0.115t + 77.44$$
$$L = M(t) = 0.208t + 69.86$$

where t is the number of years since 1980. Use graphs of W and M to predict when life expectancies of women and men will be equal.

Table 2 U.S. Life Expectancies of Women and Men

Year of Birth	Women (years)	Men (years)
1980	77.4	70.0
1985	78.2	71.1
1990	78.8	71.8
1995	78.9	72.5
2000	79.5	74.1
2005	79.9	74.9
2009	81.3	76.2

Source: *U.S. Census Bureau*

Solution

We begin by sketching graphs of W and M on the same coordinate system (see Fig. 1).

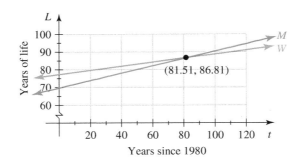

Figure 1 Life Expectancy Models of Women and Men

The intersection point is approximately (81.51, 86.81). So, the models predict that the life expectancy of both women and men will be about 86.8 years in 2062. We are not very confident about this prediction, however, because it is so far into the future.

We verify our work by using "intersect" on a graphing calculator (see Figs. 2–4). For graphing calculator instructions, see Appendix B.7 and B.18.

Figure 2 Enter the functions

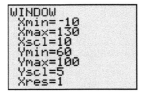

Figure 3 Set up the window

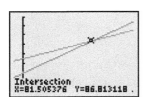

Figure 4 Find the intersection point

> #### ▶ Intersection Point of the Graphs of Two Models
>
> If the independent variable of two models represents time, then an intersection point of the graphs of the two models indicates a time when the quantities represented by the dependent variables were or will be equal.

Systems of Two Linear Equations

The two equations in Example 1 are an example of a system of linear equations in two variables. **A system of linear equations in two variables,** or a **linear system** for short, consists of two or more linear equations in two variables. Here is another example of a system of two linear equations in two variables:

$$y = 2x + 1$$
$$y = -3x + 6$$

We will work with such systems throughout this chapter.

Recall from Section 1.2 that every point on the graph of an equation represents a solution of the equation and that every point *not* on the graph represents an ordered pair that is *not* a solution. Knowing the meaning of a graph will help us greatly in this section.

▶ Example 2   Finding Ordered Pairs That Satisfy Both of Two Given Equations

Find all ordered pairs that satisfy both of the equations

$$y = 2x + 1$$
$$y = -3x + 6$$

Solution

To begin, we graph each equation on the same coordinate system (see Fig. 5).

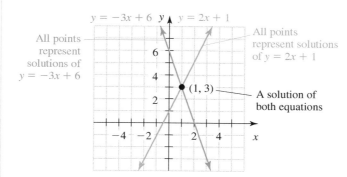

Figure 5   Intersection point is (1, 3)

For an ordered pair to be a solution of *both* equations, it must represent a point that lies on *both* lines. The intersection point $(1, 3)$ is the only point that lies on both lines. So, the ordered pair $(1, 3)$ is the only ordered pair that satisfies both equations.

We can verify that $(1, 3)$ satisfies both equations:

$$y = 2x + 1 \qquad\qquad y = -3x + 6$$
$$3 \overset{2}{=} 2(1) + 1 \qquad\qquad 3 \overset{2}{=} -3(1) + 6$$
$$3 \overset{2}{=} 3 \qquad\qquad\qquad 3 \overset{2}{=} 3$$
$$\text{true} \qquad\qquad\qquad\quad \text{true}$$

Solution Set of a System

In Example 2, we worked with the system

$$y = 2x + 1$$
$$y = -3x + 6$$

We found that the only point whose coordinates satisfy both equations is the intersection point $(1, 3)$. We call the set containing only $(1, 3)$ the *solution set of the system.*

▶ Definition   Solution of a system

We say an ordered pair (a, b) is a **solution** of a system of two equations in two variables if it satisfies both equations. The **solution set** of a system is the set of all solutions of the system. We **solve** a system by finding its solution set.

In general, **the solution set of a system of two linear equations can be found by locating any intersection point(s) of the graphs of the two equations.**

▶ Example 3   Solving a System of Two Linear Equations by Graphing

Solve the system

$$y = 2x + 4$$
$$y = -x + 1$$

Solution

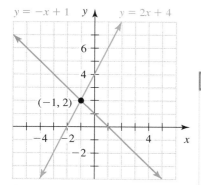

Figure 6   Intersection point is (−1, 2)

The graphs of these equations are sketched in Fig. 6. The intersection point is $(-1, 2)$. So, the solution is the ordered pair $(-1, 2)$. We can verify that $(-1, 2)$ satisfies both equations:

$$y = 2x + 4 \qquad\qquad y = -x + 1$$
$$2 \stackrel{?}{=} 2(-1) + 4 \qquad 2 \stackrel{?}{=} -(-1) + 1$$
$$2 \stackrel{?}{=} 2 \qquad\qquad 2 \stackrel{?}{=} 2$$
$$\text{true} \qquad\qquad\qquad \text{true}$$

We can also verify our work by using "intersect" on a graphing calculator (see Fig. 7).

WARNING After solving a system of two linear equations, it is a common error to check that a result satisfies only one of the two equations. It is important to check that your result satisfies *both* equations.

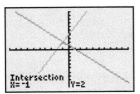

Figure 7 Verify that the intersection point is $(-1, 2)$

▶ **Example 4** Solving a System of Two Linear Equations by Graphing

Solve the system

$$\frac{1}{2}x + \frac{5}{4}y = \frac{5}{2} \qquad \textit{Equation (1)}$$
$$y = 3x - 4 \qquad \textit{Equation (2)}$$

Solution

First, we multiply both sides of equation (1) by the LCD, 4, to "clear the equation of fractions" (see Section A.11 for a review of solving an equation with fractions):

$$\frac{1}{2}x + \frac{5}{4}y = \frac{5}{2} \qquad \textit{Equation (1)}$$
$$4\left(\frac{1}{2}x + \frac{5}{4}y\right) = 4 \cdot \frac{5}{2} \qquad \textit{Multiply both sides by LCD, 4.}$$
$$4 \cdot \frac{1}{2}x + 4 \cdot \frac{5}{4}y = 4 \cdot \frac{5}{2} \qquad \textit{Distributive law}$$
$$2x + 5y = 10 \qquad \textit{Simplify.}$$
$$5y = -2x + 10 \qquad \textit{Subtract 2x from both sides.}$$
$$y = -\frac{2}{5}x + 2 \qquad \textit{Divide both sides by 5.}$$

Next, we sketch a graph of the equations $y = -\dfrac{2}{5}x + 2$ and $y = 3x - 4$ (see Fig. 8).

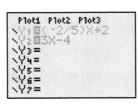

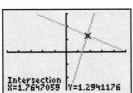

Figure 9 Using "intersect" to find the intersection point

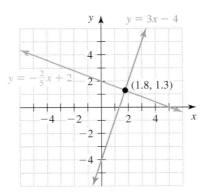

Figure 8 Approximate solution is (1.8, 1.3)

We can estimate the solution to be approximately $(1.8, 1.3)$. However, we can get a better estimate by using "intersect" on a graphing calculator (see Fig. 9).

It turns out the ordered pair $(1.7647059, 1.2941176)$ found by "intersect" is accurate to seven decimal places. For ease in calculator entry, we round the coordinates to the second decimal place and check that $(1.76, 1.29)$ satisfies both equations approximately:

$$\frac{1}{2}x + \frac{5}{4}y = \frac{5}{2} \qquad\qquad y = 3x - 4$$

$$\frac{1}{2}(1.76) + \frac{5}{4}(1.29) = \frac{5}{2} \qquad\qquad 1.29 = 3(1.76) - 4$$

$$2.4925 \approx 2.5 \qquad\qquad 1.29 \approx 1.28$$

Because $(1.76, 1.29)$ satisfies both equations approximately, we know $(1.76, 1.29)$ is a good approximation of the *exact* solution, which we will learn to find in Section 3.2.

Three Types of Linear Systems

Each of the systems in Examples 2–4 has one solution. Not all systems have exactly one solution, however.

▶ **Example 5** Solving an Inconsistent System

Solve the system

$$y = \frac{1}{2}x + 1$$

$$y = \frac{1}{2}x - 2$$

Solution

Since the two lines have equal slopes, these lines are parallel (see Fig. 10). Parallel lines do not intersect, so there is no ordered pair that satisfies both equations. The solution set is the empty set.

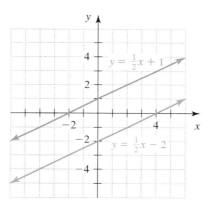

Figure 10 The solution is the empty set

A linear system whose solution set is the empty set is called an **inconsistent system.**

▶ **Example 6** Solving a Dependent System

Solve the system

$$y = 2x + 1 \qquad \textit{Equation (1)}$$

$$6x - 3y = -3 \qquad \textit{Equation (2)}$$

Solution

We write equation (2) in slope–intercept form:

$$6x - 3y = -3 \qquad\qquad \textit{Equation (2)}$$

$$2x - y = -1 \qquad\qquad \textit{Divide both sides by 3.}$$

$$-y = -2x - 1 \qquad \textit{Subtract 2x from both sides.}$$

$$y = 2x + 1 \qquad\qquad \textit{Multiply both sides by } -1.$$

So, the graphs of $6x - 3y = -3$ and $y = 2x + 1$ are the same line. The solution set of the system is the set of the infinite number of ordered pairs that correspond to points that lie on the line $y = 2x + 1$ and on the (same) line $6x - 3y = -3$.

A linear system that has an infinite number of solutions is called a **dependent system.**

In Examples 4, 5, and 6, we have seen three types of systems. We now describe these three types.

> **Types of Linear Systems**

There are three types of linear systems of two equations:

1. *One-solution system:* The lines intersect in one point. The solution set of the system contains only the ordered pair that corresponds to that point. See Fig. 11.

2. *Inconsistent system:* The lines are parallel. The solution set of the system is the empty set. See Fig. 12.

3. *Dependent system:* The lines are identical. The solution set of the system is the set of the infinite number of solutions represented by all points on the same line. See Fig. 13.

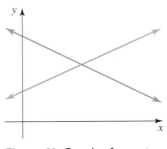

Figure 11 Graph of a system with one solution

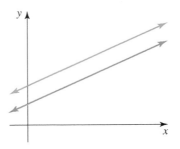

Figure 12 Graph of an inconsistent system

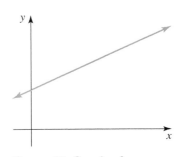

Figure 13 Graph of a dependent system

Solving a System from a Table of Solutions of Equations

We can use tables instead of graphs to solve a system.

> **Example 7**   Using a Table to Solve a System

Use a table of solutions to solve the following system of two equations:

$$y = 2x - 3$$
$$y = -3x + 7$$

Solution

Some solutions of the two equations are shown in Table 3.

Table 3 Some Solutions of $y = 2x - 3$ and $y = -3x + 7$

x	0	1	2	3	4
$y = 2x - 3$	-3	-1	1	3	5
$y = -3x + 7$	7	4	1	-2	-5

Since the ordered pair $(2, 1)$ is a solution of both equations, it is a solution of the system of equations.

The lines $y = 2x - 3$ and $y = -3x + 7$ have different slopes, so there is only one intersection point. Thus, the ordered pair $(2, 1)$ is the *only* solution of the system.

In Example 7, we used a table of solutions of two linear equations to help us find the solution of the linear system. **If an ordered pair is listed in a table as a solution of both of two linear equations, then that ordered pair is a solution of the system.**

Group Exploration

Comparing the three types of systems

1. Is the system

$$y = -2x + 3$$
$$y = -2x + 5$$

a dependent system, an inconsistent system, or a one-solution system? Explain.

2. Consider the system

$$y = 3x - 5$$
$$y = mx + b$$

where m and b are constants.

a. Find values of m and b such that the given system is inconsistent. What is the solution set of your system? Use a graphing calculator to verify your work.

b. Find values of m and b such that the given system is dependent. What is the solution set of your system?

c. Find values of m and b such that the given system is a one-solution system. Use "intersect" on a graphing calculator to find the solution.

3. Now consider this general system of two linear equations:

$$y = m_1 x + b_1$$
$$y = m_2 x + b_2$$

Discuss dependent systems, inconsistent systems, and one-solution systems in terms of $m_1, m_2, b_1,$ and b_2.

▶ **Tips for Success**   **Visualize**

To help prepare mentally and physically for competition, many exceptional athletes often visualize themselves performing well at their event throughout their training. For example, a runner training for the 100-meter dash might imagine getting set in the starting blocks, taking off right after the gunshot, being in front of the other runners, and so on, up until the moment of breaking the tape at the finish line.

In an experiment, three groups of basketball players were used to test the effectiveness of visualization. The first group warmed up by shooting baskets before a game. The second group visualized shooting baskets but did not shoot any baskets during the warm-up. The third group did not warm up or visualize before the game. The visualization group outperformed not only the group that did not warm up, but also the group that warmed up by shooting baskets!

Visualize doing all the things you feel you need to do to succeed in this course. If you do this regularly, you will have better follow-through with what you intend to do. You will also feel more confident about succeeding.

Homework 3.1

For extra help ▶ **MyMathLab®**   Watch the videos in MyMathLab   Download the MyDashboard App

Find the solution set of the system by graphing the equations by hand. If the system is inconsistent or dependent, say so. If your result is one ordered pair, check that it satisfies both equations.

1. $y = 2x + 2$
   $y = -3x + 7$

2. $y = x - 5$
   $y = -2x + 4$

3. $y = -\dfrac{1}{2}x + 3$
   $y = \dfrac{1}{3}x + 8$

4. $y = -\dfrac{1}{4}x + 3$
   $y = \dfrac{1}{2}x$

5. $y = 3(x - 1)$
   $y = -2x + 7$

6. $y = 2(x - 3)$
   $y = -3x + 4$

7. $x + 4y = 20$
   $2x - 4y = -8$

8. $2x - 3y = -6$
   $x + 3y = -3$

9. $5(y - 2) = 21 - 2(x + 3)$
   $y = 3(x - 1) + 8$

10. $3(y - 2) = 2(3x + 1) + 7$
    $y = 7 - 4(x + 2)$

11. $y = -2x + 3$
    $4y - 12 = -8x$

12. $y = 3x - 7$
    $9x - 3y = 21$

13. $4x - 6y = 24$
$6x - 9y = 18$

14. $20x - 8y = 16$
$-15x + 6y = 18$

15. $\frac{1}{2}x - \frac{1}{2}y = 1$
$\frac{1}{4}x + \frac{1}{2}y = 2$

16. $\frac{1}{3}x + \frac{1}{2}y = -3$
$\frac{1}{2}x - \frac{1}{3}y = -\frac{7}{3}$

Use "intersect" on a graphing calculator to solve the system. Round the coordinates of solutions to the second decimal place. If the system is inconsistent or dependent, say so. If your result is one ordered pair, check that it satisfies both equations approximately. **[Graphing Calculator:** *See Appendix B.18.]*

17. $y = -2.51x - 6.49$
$y = 1.74x - 1.75$

18. $y = 5.437x - 2.136$
$y = -2.752x + 3.984$

19. $2x + 5y = 7$
$3x - 4y = -13$

20. $4x - 3y = 13$
$2y + 5x = 4$

21. $\quad\quad y = 2x - 1$
$2(2x - y) = 2$

22. $\quad\quad y = 2x + 1$
$3y - 1 = 2(3x + 1)$

23. $\quad\quad y = 5x + 2$
$0.2y - x = 1$

24. $\quad\quad y = -2x + 4$
$0.5y + x = 3$

25. $\frac{1}{2}x - \frac{1}{2}y = 1$
$\frac{1}{3}x + \frac{2}{3}y = 2$

26. $\quad\quad \frac{1}{3}y + x = -2$
$-\frac{1}{4}x + \frac{1}{2}y = 2$

27. The winning times for the Olympic 500-meter speed-skating event have generally decreased since 1972 (see Table 4).

Table 4 Olympic 500-Meter Speed-Skating Times

Year	Winning Time (seconds)	
	Women	Men
1972	43.33	39.44
1976	42.76	39.17
1980	41.78	38.03
1984	41.02	38.19
1988	39.10	36.45
1992	40.33	37.14
1994	39.25	36.33
1998	38.21	35.59
2002	37.375	34.615
2006	38.285	34.880
2010	38.050	34.910

Source: *The Universal Almanac*

The winning times (in seconds) $W(t)$ and $M(t)$ for women and men, respectively, are modeled by the system

$$w = W(t) = -0.153t + 43.19$$
$$w = M(t) = -0.135t + 39.64$$

where t is the number of years since 1970.

a. Use the equations of the models to estimate the winning time for women and the winning time for men in 2010. Find the errors in your estimates.

b. Compare the slopes of the two models. What does your comparison tell you about this situation?

c. Explain why your work in parts (a) and (b) suggests that there may be a time when the women's winning time will be equal to the men's winning time.

d. Use "intersect" on a graphing calculator to predict when the women's winning time will be equal to the men's winning time. What will be that winning time?

28. Average annual U.S. per-person consumption of chicken and red meat (in pounds per person) is described for various years in Table 5.

Table 5 Average Annual U.S. Per-Person Consumption of Chicken and Red Meat

Year	Average Annual Consumption (pounds per person)	
	Chicken	Red Meat
1970	40.3	145.8
1980	48.0	136.8
1990	61.5	120.0
2000	78.0	120.7
2010	83.7	108.7
2011	84.2	104.3

Source: *U.S. Department of Agriculture*

Let $C(t)$ be the average annual per-person consumption of chicken and $R(t)$ be the average annual per-person consumption of red meat, both in pounds per person, in the year that is t years since 1970. The consumption of each can be modeled by the system

$$C(t) = 1.13t + 39.29$$
$$R(t) = -0.94t + 144.88$$

a. Use the equations of the models to estimate the consumptions of chicken and red meat in 2011. Find the errors in your estimates.

b. Compare the slopes of the two models. What does your comparison tell you about the situation?

c. Explain why your work in parts (a) and (b) suggests that there may be a time when the consumption of chicken will be equal to the consumption of red meat.

d. Use "intersect" on a graphing calculator to predict when the consumption of chicken will equal that of red meat. What will be that consumption? How confident are you?

29. The percentages of bills paid by checks and online payments are shown in Table 6 for various years.

a. Let $C(t)$ be the percentage of bills paid by checks and $W(t)$ be the percentage of bills paid by online payments, both at t years since 2000. Find equations of C and W.

Table 6 Percentages of Bills Paid by Checks and Online Payments

	Percent	
Year	Checks	Online Payments
2007	34	39
2008	31	42
2009	30	44
2010	26	45
2011	23	50

Source: *Fiserv, Inc.*

b. Use "intersect" on a graphing calculator to estimate when the percentage of bills paid by checks was equal to the percentage of bills paid by online payments. What was that percentage?

c. Predict the total percentage of bills that will be paid by checks and online payments in 2018.

30. The worldwide numbers of fixed telephone lines and cell-phone subscriptions per 100 people are shown in Table 7 for various years.

Table 7 Worldwide Numbers of Fixed Telephone Lines and Cell-Phone Subscriptions per 100 People

	Number per 100 People	
Year	Fixed Telephone Lines	Cell-Phone Subscriptions
2006	19.2	40.6
2007	19.0	50.1
2008	18.3	59.3
2009	17.7	67.9
2010	17.3	76.2

Source: *ITU World Telecommunication*

a. Let $F(t)$ be the number of fixed telephone lines per 100 people and $C(t)$ be the number of cell-phone subscriptions per 100 people, both at t years since 2000. Find equations of F and C.

b. Use "intersect" on a graphing calculator to estimate when the number of fixed telephone lines per 100 people was equal to the number of cell-phone subscriptions per 100 people.

c. Predict the total number of fixed telephone lines and cell-phone subscriptions per 100 people in 2017. Is your result greater than 100? Explain why this might be possible.

31. The percentages of households that have Internet access and broadband Internet access are shown in Table 8 for various years.

a. Let $I(t)$ be the percentage of households that have Internet access and $B(t)$ be the percentage of households that have broadband Internet access, both at t years since 2000. Find equations of I and B.

b. Use "intersect" on a graphing calculator to estimate when all households with Internet access had broadband Internet access.

c. Explain why there is model breakdown for at least one of the models I and B after the year you found in part (b).

Table 8 Percentages of Households That Have Internet Access and Broadband Internet Access

	Percent	
Year	Internet Access	Broadband Internet Access
2001	50	9
2003	55	20
2007	62	51
2009	69	64
2010	71	68

Source: *U.S. Census Bureau*

32. The percentages of women and men in the United States who are married are shown in Table 9 for various years.

Table 9 Percentages of Women and Men Who Are Married

Year	Percent of Women Who Are Married	Percent of Men Who Are Married
1990	59.7	64.3
1995	59.2	62.7
1997	57.9	61.5
2000	57.6	61.5
2004	57.1	60.3
2006	56.5	59.9
2010	55.2	58.0

Source: *U.S. Census Bureau*

a. Let $W(t)$ be the percentage of women who are married and $M(t)$ be the percentage of men who are married, both at t years since 1990. Find equations of W and M.

b. Use "intersect" on a graphing calculator to predict when the percentage of women who are married will equal the percentage of men who are married. What will be that percentage? How confident are you?

c. In 2015, there will be about 165.1 million women and 160.4 million men in the United States. Predict the total *number* of people who will be married in 2015.

33. Figure 14 shows the graphs of two linear equations. To the first decimal place, estimate the coordinates of the solution of the system.

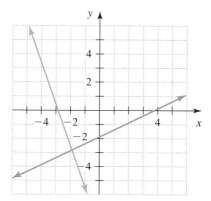

Figure 14 Exercise 33

34. Figure 15 shows the graphs of two linear equations. To the first decimal place, estimate the coordinates of the solution of the system.

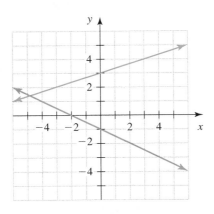

Figure 15 Exercise 34

35. Figure 16 shows the graphs of two linear equations. To the nearest integer, estimate the coordinates of the solution of the system. Explain. [**Hint:** Use the slope of each line.]

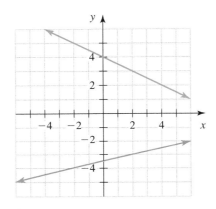

Figure 16 Exercise 35

36. Figure 17 shows the graphs of two linear equations. To the nearest integer, estimate the coordinates of the solution of the system. Explain. [**Hint:** Use the slope of each line.]

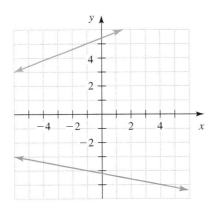

Figure 17 Exercise 36

37. Use Table 10 to solve the system

$$y = -5x + 11$$
$$y = 7x - 25$$

Table 10 Some Solutions of $y = -5x + 11$ and $y = 7x - 25$ (Exercise 37)

x	0	1	2	3	4
$y = -5x + 11$	11	6	1	-4	-9
$y = 7x - 25$	-25	-18	-11	-4	3

38. Use Table 11 to solve the system

$$y = 4x - 1$$
$$y = -3x + 6$$

Table 11 Some Solutions of $y = 4x - 1$ and $y = -3x + 6$ (Exercise 38)

x	0	1	2	3	4
$y = 4x - 1$	-1	3	7	11	15
$y = -3x + 6$	6	3	0	-3	-6

39. Some values of linear functions f and g are listed in Table 12. Estimate the solution of a system of two equations that describe f and g.

Table 12 Values of Functions f and g (Exercise 39)

x	0	1	2	3	4	5	6	7	8
$f(x)$	30	27	24	21	18	15	12	9	6
$g(x)$	2	7	12	17	22	27	32	37	42

40. Some values of linear functions f and g are listed in Table 13. Estimate the solution of a system of two equations that describe f and g.

Table 13 Values of Functions f and g (Exercise 40)

x	0	1	2	3	4	5	6	7	8
$f(x)$	99	95	91	87	83	79	75	71	67
$g(x)$	3	5	7	9	11	13	15	17	19

For Exercises 41–46, refer to Fig. 18.

41. Find $f(-4)$.   **42.** Find $g(-4)$.

43. Find x, where $f(x) = 3$.   **44.** Find x, where $g(x) = -1$.

45. Find x, where $f(x) = g(x)$.   **46.** Estimate x, where $g(x) = 0$.

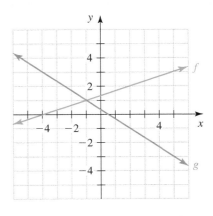

Figure 18 Exercises 41–46

Concepts

47. The graphs of $y = ax + b$ and $y = cx + d$ are sketched in Fig. 19.

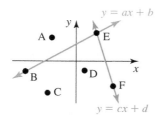

Figure 19 Exercise 47

For each part that follows, decide which one or more of the points A, B, C, D, E, or F represent ordered pairs that
a. satisfy the equation $y = ax + b$.
b. satisfy the equation $y = cx + d$.
c. satisfy both equations.
d. do not satisfy either equation.

48. Consider the system

$$y = 3x - 7$$
$$y = -2x + 3$$

Find an ordered pair that
a. satisfies $y = 3x - 7$ but does not satisfy $y = -2x + 3$.
b. satisfies $y = -2x + 3$ but does not satisfy $y = 3x - 7$.
c. satisfies both equations.
d. does not satisfy either equation.

49. Create a system of two linear equations as indicated. Verify your system graphically.

a. The solution of the system is $(2, 1)$.
b. The system is inconsistent.
c. The system is dependent.

50. Solve the system. [**Hint:** Sketch the graphs on the same coordinate system.]

$$y = 2$$
$$x = -3$$

51. Find all ordered pairs that satisfy all three equations:

$$y = x + 1$$
$$y = -2x + 7$$
$$y = 3x - 3$$

52. Find all ordered pairs that satisfy all three equations:

$$y = 2x - 5$$
$$y = 0.6x + 1$$
$$y = -1.2x + 5$$

53. Create a system of three linear equations whose solution is $(-4, 3)$. Verify your result by checking that $(-4, 3)$ satisfies all three equations. Also, verify your result graphically.

54. A system of linear equations has $(-2, 3)$ and $(4, 1)$ as solutions.
a. Find a third solution.
b. How many solutions are there?

55. A student tries to solve the system

$$y = 3x - 1$$
$$y = -2x + 9$$

After graphing the equations, she believes the solution is $(1, 2)$. She then checks whether $(1, 2)$ satisfies $y = 3x - 1$:

$$y = 3x - 1$$
$$2 \overset{?}{=} 3(1) - 1$$
$$2 \overset{?}{=} 2$$
$$\text{true}$$

The student concludes that $(1, 2)$ is the solution of the system. Describe any errors. Then solve the system correctly.

56. Describe the meaning of a solution of a system.

57. Explain why any solutions of a system of two linear equations correspond to the intersection points of the graphs of the two equations. (See page 4 for guidelines on writing a good response.)

58. Describe the three types of systems of two linear equations and how to solve these systems. Also, explain how to verify your work. (See page 4 for guidelines on writing a good response.)

▼ 3.2 Using Substitution and Elimination to Solve Systems

Objectives

» Use substitution to solve a system of two linear equations.

» Use elimination to solve a system of two linear equations.

» Solve inconsistent and dependent systems by substitution or elimination.

» Use graphs and tables to solve an equation in one variable.

In Section 3.1, we used graphs or tables of linear functions to solve linear systems. In this section, we use *equations* of linear functions to solve such systems.

Using Substitution to Solve Systems

In Example 1, we will solve a system by a technique called *substitution*.

▶ **Example 1** Solving a System by Substitution

Solve the system

$$y = x - 1 \quad \textit{Equation (1)}$$
$$3x + 2y = 13 \quad \textit{Equation (2)}$$

Solution

From equation (1), we know the value of y is equal to the value of $x - 1$. So, we substitute $x - 1$ for y in equation (2):

$$3x + 2y = 13 \quad \text{\textit{Equation (2)}}$$

$$3x + 2(x - 1) = 13 \quad \text{\textit{Substitute $x - 1$ for y.}}$$

By making this substitution, we now have an equation in terms of *one* variable. Next, we solve that equation for x:

$$3x + 2(x - 1) = 13 \quad \text{\textit{Equation in one variable}}$$

$$3x + 2x - 2 = 13 \quad \text{\textit{Distributive law}}$$

$$5x - 2 = 13 \quad \text{\textit{Combine like terms.}}$$

$$5x = 15 \quad \text{\textit{Add 2 to both sides.}}$$

$$x = 3 \quad \text{\textit{Divide both sides by 5.}}$$

This means the x-coordinate of the solution is 3. To find the y-coordinate, we substitute 3 for x in either of the original equations and solve for y:

$$y = x - 1 \quad \text{\textit{Equation (1)}}$$

$$y = 3 - 1 \quad \text{\textit{Substitute 3 for x.}}$$

$$y = 2 \quad \text{\textit{Subtract.}}$$

So, the solution is $(3, 2)$. We can check that $(3, 2)$ satisfies both of the system's equations:

$$y = x - 1 \qquad\qquad 3x + 2y = 13$$
$$2 \stackrel{?}{=} 3 - 1 \qquad\qquad 3(3) + 2(2) \stackrel{?}{=} 13$$
$$2 \stackrel{?}{=} 2 \qquad\qquad 9 + 4 \stackrel{?}{=} 13$$
$$\text{true} \qquad\qquad\qquad \text{true}$$

Instead, we can check that $(3, 2)$ is the solution by graphing the two equations and checking that $(3, 2)$ is the intersection point of the two lines (see Fig. 20). To do so on a graphing calculator, we must first solve $3x + 2y = 13$ for y:

$$y = -\frac{3}{2}x + \frac{13}{2}$$

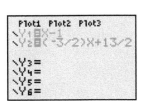

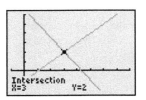

Figure 20 Verify that the intersection point is (3, 2)

> **Using Substitution to Solve a Linear System**
>
> To use **substitution** to solve a system of two linear equations,
> 1. Isolate a variable on one side of either equation.
> 2. Substitute the expression for the variable found in step 1 into the other equation.
> 3. Solve the equation in one variable found in step 2.
> 4. Substitute the solution found in step 3 into one of the original equations, and solve for the other variable.

▶ **Example 2**   Solving a System by Substitution

Solve the system

$$x - 3y = 4 \quad \text{\textit{Equation (1)}}$$

$$2x - 5y = 5 \quad \text{\textit{Equation (2)}}$$

Solution

We begin by solving for one of the variables in one of the equations. We can avoid fractions by choosing to solve equation (1) for x:

$$x - 3y = 4 \quad \text{\textit{Equation (1)}}$$

$$x = 3y + 4 \quad \text{\textit{Add 3y to both sides.}}$$

Next, we substitute $3y + 4$ for x in equation (2) and solve for y:

$$2x - 5y = 5 \qquad \text{\textit{Equation (2)}}$$
$$2(3y + 4) - 5y = 5 \qquad \text{\textit{Substitute 3y + 4 for x.}}$$
$$6y + 8 - 5y = 5 \qquad \text{\textit{Distributive law}}$$
$$y + 8 = 5 \qquad \text{\textit{Combine like terms.}}$$
$$y = -3 \qquad \text{\textit{Subtract 8 from both sides.}}$$

Finally, we substitute -3 for y in the equation $x = 3y + 4$ and solve for x:

$$x = 3(-3) + 4 \qquad \text{\textit{Substitute −3 for y.}}$$
$$x = -5 \qquad \text{\textit{Simplify.}}$$

The solution is $(-5, -3)$. We could verify our work by checking that $(-5, -3)$ satisfies *both* of the original equations.

Using Elimination to Solve Systems

In addition to solving systems by graphing or by substitution, we can solve systems by a method called *elimination*. To solve systems by this method, we will need to use the following property.

▶ **Adding Left Sides and Adding Right Sides of Two Equations**

If $a = b$ and $c = d$, then

$$a + c = b + d$$

In words, the sum of the left sides of two equations is equal to the sum of the right sides.

For example, if we add the left sides and add the right sides of the equations $2 = 2$ and $3 = 3$, we obtain the true statement $2 + 3 = 2 + 3$. We can apply this property to some pairs of equations to eliminate a variable; that is the key step in the method of elimination.

▶ **Example 3**   Solving a System by Elimination

Solve the system

$$4x - 5y = 3 \qquad \text{\textit{Equation (1)}}$$
$$3x + 5y = 11 \qquad \text{\textit{Equation (2)}}$$

Solution

We begin by adding the left sides and adding the right sides of the two equations:

$$4x - 5y = 3 \qquad \text{\textit{Equation (1)}}$$
$$\underline{3x + 5y = 11} \qquad \text{\textit{Equation (2)}}$$
$$7x + 0 = 14 \qquad \text{\textit{Add left sides and add right sides; combine like terms.}}$$

Having "eliminated" the variable y, we are left with an equation in *one* variable. Next, we solve that equation for x:

$$7x + 0 = 14$$
$$7x = 14 \qquad \text{\textit{a + 0 = a}}$$
$$x = 2 \qquad \text{\textit{Divide both sides by 7.}}$$

Then we substitute 2 for x in either of the original equations and solve for y:

$$4x - 5y = 3 \qquad \textit{Equation (1)}$$
$$4(2) - 5y = 3 \qquad \textit{Substitute 2 for x.}$$
$$8 - 5y = 3 \qquad \textit{Multiply.}$$
$$-5y = -5 \qquad \textit{Subtract 8 from both sides.}$$
$$y = 1 \qquad \textit{Divide both sides by } -5.$$

The solution is $(2, 1)$. We could check that $(2, 1)$ satisfies *both* of the original equations.

▶ **Example 4** Solving a System by Elimination

Solve the system

$$3x + 2y = 18 \qquad \textit{Equation (1)}$$
$$6x - 5y = 9 \qquad \textit{Equation (2)}$$

Solution

If we add the left sides and add the right sides of the equations as they are now, neither variable would be eliminated. Therefore, we first multiply both sides of equation (1) by -2, yielding the system

$$-6x - 4y = -36 \qquad \textit{Multiply both sides of equation (1) by } -2.$$
$$6x - 5y = 9 \qquad \textit{Equation (2)}$$

Now that the coefficients of the x terms are equal in absolute value (see Section A.3) and opposite in sign, we add the left sides and add the right sides of the equations and solve for y:

$$-6x - 4y = -36$$
$$\underline{6x - 5y = 9}$$
$$0 - 9y = -27 \qquad \textit{Add left sides and add right sides; combine like terms.}$$
$$-9y = -27 \qquad \textit{0 + a = a}$$
$$y = 3 \qquad \textit{Divide both sides by } -9.$$

We substitute 3 for y in equation (1) and solve for x:

$$3x + 2y = 18 \qquad \textit{Equation (1)}$$
$$3x + 2(3) = 18 \qquad \textit{Substitute 3 for y.}$$
$$3x + 6 = 18 \qquad \textit{Multiply.}$$
$$3x = 12 \qquad \textit{Subtract 6 from both sides.}$$
$$x = 4 \qquad \textit{Divide both sides by 3.}$$

The solution is $(4, 3)$.

▶ **Using Elimination to Solve a Linear System**

To use **elimination** to solve a system of two linear equations,

1. If needed, multiply both sides of one equation by a number (and, if necessary, multiply both sides of the other equation by another number) to get the coefficients of one variable to be equal in absolute value and opposite in sign.
2. Add the left sides and add the right sides of the equations to eliminate one of the variables.
3. Solve the equation in one variable found in step 2.
4. Substitute the solution found in step 3 into one of the original equations, and solve for the other variable.

▶ **Example 5** Solving a System by Elimination

Solve the system

$$4x - 3y = -3 \quad \text{Equation (1)}$$
$$5x + 2y = 25 \quad \text{Equation (2)}$$

Solution

To eliminate the y terms, we multiply both sides of equation (1) by 2 and multiply both sides of equation (2) by 3. That yields the system

$$8x - 6y = -6 \quad \text{Multiply both sides of equation (1) by 2.}$$
$$15x + 6y = 75 \quad \text{Multiply both sides of equation (2) by 3.}$$

The coefficients of the y terms are now equal in absolute value and opposite in sign. Next, we add the left sides and add the right sides of the equations and solve for x:

$$
\begin{aligned}
8x - 6y &= -6 \\
\underline{15x + 6y} &= \underline{75} \\
23x + 0 &= 69 \quad \text{Add left sides and add right sides; combine like terms.} \\
23x &= 69 \quad a + 0 = a \\
x &= 3 \quad \text{Divide both sides by 23.}
\end{aligned}
$$

Substituting 3 for x in equation (1) gives

$$
\begin{aligned}
4x - 3y &= -3 \quad \text{Equation (1)} \\
4(3) - 3y &= -3 \quad \text{Substitute 3 for } x. \\
12 - 3y &= -3 \quad \text{Multiply.} \\
-3y &= -15 \quad \text{Subtract 12 from both sides.} \\
y &= 5 \quad \text{Divide both sides by } -3.
\end{aligned}
$$

The solution is $(3, 5)$.

In Example 5, we eliminated y by getting the coefficients of the y terms to be equal in absolute value and opposite in sign. Note that this process is similar to finding a least common multiple.

▶ **Example 6** Using Elimination to Solve a System with Fractions

Solve the system

$$\frac{1}{3}x - \frac{1}{2}y = \frac{1}{6} \quad \text{Equation (1)}$$
$$\frac{1}{5}x + \frac{1}{4}y = \frac{13}{20} \quad \text{Equation (2)}$$

Solution

First, we clear the fractions in equation (1) by multiplying both sides by the LCD, 6, and clear the fractions in equation (2) by multiplying both sides by the LCD, 20:

$$2x - 3y = 1 \quad \text{Multiply both sides of equation (1) by 6.}$$
$$4x + 5y = 13 \quad \text{Multiply both sides of equation (2) by 20.}$$

To eliminate the variable x, we multiply both sides of $2x - 3y = 1$ by -2:

$$
\begin{aligned}
-4x + 6y &= -2 \quad \text{Multiply both sides of } 2x - 3y = 1 \text{ by } -2. \\
\underline{4x + 5y} &= \underline{13} \\
0 + 11y &= 11 \quad \text{Add left sides and add right sides; combine like terms.} \\
y &= 1 \quad \text{Divide both sides by 11.}
\end{aligned}
$$

To find the value of x, we can substitute 1 for y in any of the equations that have both x and y. We substitute 1 for y in the equation $2x - 3y = 1$ and solve for x:

$$2x - 3(1) = 1 \quad \textit{Substitute 1 for y in } 2x - 3y = 1.$$
$$2x = 4 \quad \textit{Add 3 to both sides.}$$
$$x = 2 \quad \textit{Divide both sides by 2.}$$

The solution is $(2, 1)$.

In this section and Section 3.1, we have solved many systems by graphing, substitution, and elimination. **Any linear system of two equations can be solved by graphing, substitution, or elimination. All three methods will give the same result.**

Solving Inconsistent and Dependent Systems

Each system in Examples 1–6 has one solution. What happens in using substitution or elimination when we solve an inconsistent system (empty-set solution) or a dependent system (infinitely many solutions)?

▶ **Example 7**   Using Substitution to Solve an Inconsistent System

Consider the linear system

$$y = 2x + 1 \quad \textit{Equation (1)}$$
$$y = 2x + 3 \quad \textit{Equation (2)}$$

The graphs of the equations are parallel lines (why?), so the system is inconsistent and the solution set is the empty set. What happens when we solve this system by substitution?

Solution

We substitute $2x + 1$ for y in equation (2) and solve for x:

$$y = 2x + 3 \quad \textit{Equation (2)}$$
$$2x + 1 = 2x + 3 \quad \textit{Substitute } 2x + 1 \textit{ for y.}$$
$$1 = 3 \quad \textit{Subtract 2x from both sides.}$$
$$\text{false}$$

We get the *false* statement $1 = 3$.

▶

▶ **Inconsistent System of Two Equations**

If the result of applying substitution or elimination to a linear system of two equations is a false statement, the system is inconsistent—that is, the solution set is the empty set.

▶ **Example 8**   Applying Substitution to a Dependent System

In Example 6 of Section 3.1, we found that the system

$$y = 2x + 1 \quad \textit{Equation (1)}$$
$$6x - 3y = -3 \quad \textit{Equation (2)}$$

is dependent and that the solution set is the infinite set of solutions of the equation $y = 2x + 1$. What happens when we solve this system by substitution?

Solution

We substitute $2x + 1$ for y in equation (2) and solve for x:

$$6x - 3y = -3 \quad \textit{Equation (2)}$$
$$6x - 3(2x + 1) = -3 \quad \textit{Substitute } 2x + 1 \textit{ for y.}$$
$$6x - 6x - 3 = -3 \quad \textit{Distributive law}$$
$$-3 = -3 \quad \textit{Combine like terms.}$$
$$\text{true}$$

We get the *true* statement $-3 = -3$.

▶

> **Dependent System of Two Linear Equations**
>
> If the result of applying substitution or elimination to a linear system of two equations is a true statement (one that can be put into the form $a = a$), then the system is dependent—that is, the solution is the set of ordered pairs represented by every point on the (same) line.

Using Graphing to Solve an Equation in One Variable

Some equations in *one* variable that would be difficult or impossible to solve by performing the same operations on both sides can be solved easily by graphing. To see how, consider the system of two equations in *two* variables

$$y = 2x - 4 \quad \textit{Equation (1)}$$
$$y = x - 1 \quad \textit{Equation (2)}$$

We can use substitution to solve this system. To begin, we substitute $2x - 4$ for y in equation (2):

$$2x - 4 = x - 1 \quad \textit{Substitute } 2x - 4 \textit{ for y in equation (2).}$$
$$2x - x = -1 + 4 \quad \textit{Subtract x from both sides; add 4 to both sides.}$$
$$x = 3 \quad \textit{Combine like terms.}$$

Then we substitute 3 for x in equation (1):

$$y = 2(3) - 4 = 2$$

The solution is $(3, 2)$.

Now consider solving $2x - 4 = x - 1$, which is an equation in one variable. Our earlier work shows that the solution is 3. So, the solution 3 of $2x - 4 = x - 1$ is equal to the x-coordinate of the solution $(3, 2)$ of the system

$$y = 2x - 4$$
$$y = x - 1$$

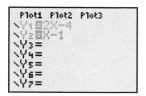

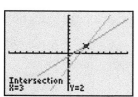

Figure 21 Solve the system

One way to find the solution 3 of the equation $2x - 4 = x - 1$ is to use "intersect" on a graphing calculator to find the x-coordinate of the intersection point $(3, 2)$ of the lines $y = 2x - 4$ and $y = x - 1$ (see Fig. 21).

> **Using Graphing to Solve an Equation in One Variable**
>
> To use graphing to solve an equation $A = B$ in one variable, x, where A and B are expressions,
>
> **1.** Use graphing to solve the system
>
> $$y = A$$
> $$y = B$$
>
> **2.** The x-coordinates of any solutions of the system are the solutions of the equation $A = B$.

▶ **Example 9** Solving an Equation in One Variable by Graphing

Solve the equation by referring to the graphs shown in Fig. 22.

1. $\dfrac{1}{4}x + 2 = -\dfrac{3}{2}x - 5$

2. $\dfrac{1}{4}x + 2 = 3$

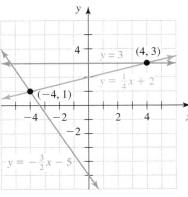

Figure 22 Graphs of $y = \frac{1}{4}x + 2$, $y = -\frac{3}{2}x - 5$, and $y = 3$

Solution

1. From Fig. 22, we see the solution of the system

$$y = \frac{1}{4}x + 2$$

$$y = -\frac{3}{2}x - 5$$

is the ordered pair $(-4, 1)$. So, the x-coordinate -4 is the solution of the equation $\frac{1}{4}x + 2 = -\frac{3}{2}x - 5$.

2. From Fig. 22, we see the solution of the system

$$y = \frac{1}{4}x + 2$$

$$y = 3$$

is the ordered pair $(4, 3)$. So, the x-coordinate 4 is the solution of the equation $\frac{1}{4}x + 2 = 3$.

Using Tables to Solve an Equation in One Variable

We can use tables rather than graphs to solve an equation in one variable.

▶ **Example 10**   Solving an Equation in One Variable by Using Tables

Use a table to solve $3x - 8 = -7x + 2$.

Solution

Recall from Section 3.1 that we can use a table to solve a system such as

$$y = 3x - 8$$

$$y = -7x + 2$$

The solution is $(1, -5)$, which has an x-coordinate of 1 (see Fig. 23). For the equation $3x - 8 = -7x + 2$, the solution is 1.

▶

Using a table to solve an equation in one variable is similar to using graphing to solve such an equation.

Figure 23 Solve the system

> ▶ **Using Tables to Solve an Equation in One Variable**
>
> To use a table to solve an equation $A = B$ in one variable, x, where A and B are expressions,
>
> 1. Use a table to solve the system
>
> $$y = A$$
> $$y = B$$
>
> 2. The x-coordinates of any solutions of the system are the solutions of the equation $A = B$.

Group Exploration

Comparing techniques of solving systems

Consider the system

$$2x + y = 4$$
$$x = 5 - 2y$$

1. Use substitution to solve the system.
2. Use elimination to solve the system.
3. Use graphing to solve the system.

4. Compare your results from Problems 1, 2, and 3.
5. Give an example of a one-solution system that is easiest to solve by substitution. Also, give an example of such a system that is easiest to solve by elimination. Finally, give an example of such a system that is easiest to solve by graphing. Explain. Solve your three systems.

Group Exploration

Using graphing to solve an equation in one variable

1. **a.** Solve

$$y = 2x + 1$$
$$y = 7 - x$$

   by substitution. Use "intersect" on a graphing calculator to verify your result.
   b. Solve $2x + 1 = 7 - x$. Check that your solution satisfies the equation.
   c. Compare your solution of the equation in part (b) with the x-coordinate of the solution of the system in part (a).

2. **a.** Solve

$$y = 3x - 5$$
$$y = x + 3$$

   by substitution. Use "intersect" to verify your result.

b. Solve $3x - 5 = x + 3$. Check that your solution satisfies the equation.
c. Compare your solution of the equation in part (b) with the x-coordinate of the solution of the system in part (a).

3. Solve $3x - 7 = 8 - 2x$ by a symbolic method. Explain how you can verify your solution by using "intersect."

4. It is difficult to find the exact solution of the equation $x^3 = 5 - x$. Use "intersect" to solve the equation, with the result rounded to the second decimal place. To enter x^3, press $\boxed{\text{X, T, }\Theta, n}$ $\boxed{\wedge}$ 3.

▶ **Tips for Success**   **Cross-Checks**

If you finish a quiz or an exam early, verify your answers with cross-checks. For example, suppose you determine by elimination that the solution of the system

$$2x + 3y = 9$$
$$4x + 5y = 17$$

is $(3, 1)$. There are several ways to verify your answer. You could check that $(3, 1)$ satisfies both equations. You could graph each equation and check that the intersection point is $(3, 1)$. Or you could solve the system by substitution.

Homework 3.2

For extra help ▶ **MyMathLab®**   Watch the videos in MyMathLab   Download the MyDashboard App

Solve the system by substitution. Verify your solution graphically or by checking that it satisfies both equations of the system.

1. $y = x - 5$
 $x + y = 9$

2. $y = 2x - 1$
 $x + y = 5$

3. $2x - 3y = -1$
 $x = 4y + 7$

4. $4x + 3y = -14$
 $y = 2x - 8$

5. $3x - 5y - 29 = 0$
 $y = 2(x - 5)$

6. $y = 3(x - 2)$
 $7x - 3y - 10 = 0$

7. $y = 99x$
 $y = 100x$

8. $y = x$
 $y = -x$

9. $y = 4x + 5$
 $y = 2x - 1$

10. $y = 11 - 3x$
 $y = 2x + 1$

11. $y = 0.2x + 0.6$
 $2y - 3x = -4$

12. $x = 2 - y$
 $0.6x + 0.3y = 0.3$

13. $4x + 3y = 2$
 $2x - y = -4$

14. $3x - y = 10$
 $2x + 5y = -16$

15. $y = \frac{1}{2}x - 5$
 $2x + 3y = -1$

16. $4x - 7y = 3$
 $x = \frac{2}{3}y + 4$

Solve the system by elimination. Verify your solution graphically or by checking that it satisfies both equations of the system.

17. $-x + 3y = -25$
 $x - 5y = 39$

18. $3x - 5y = 26$
 $-3x - 2y = 2$

19. $3x - 4y = -6$
 $5x - 4y = -2$

20. $2x + 3y = -2$
 $x + 3y = 2$

21. $2x + y = 2$
 $5x - 2y = -13$

22. $3x - 4y = 18$
 $4x - y = 11$

23. $3x - 2y = 7$
 $-6x - 5y = 4$

24. $3x + 2y = 3$
 $9x - 8y = -33$

25. $3x + 5y = 3$
 $7x - 2y = -34$

26. $-3x - 5y = -22$
 $4x - 7y = -39$

27. $8x - 9y = -43$
 $12x + 15y = 21$

28. $6x + 5y = 13$
 $9x + 4y = 2$

29. $4x - 7y = -29$
 $-5x - 2y = 4$

30. $-8x - 3y = -1$
 $6x - 5y = 37$

31. $3y = 2x - 6$
 $5x - 4y = 1$

32. $4x = 7y - 25$
 $3x + 5y = 12$

33. $0.9x + 0.4y = 1.9$
 $0.3x - 0.2y = 1.3$

34. $0.2x - 0.5y = 0.2$
 $0.8x + 1.5y = -6.2$

35. $3(2x - 1) + 4(y - 3) = 1$
 $4(x + 5) - 2(4y + 1) = 18$

36. $2(x - 3) - 3(y + 1) = -5$
 $-4(x - 2) + 5(y + 3) = 13$

37. $\frac{1}{5}x + \frac{3}{2}y = 7$
 $\frac{2}{5}x - \frac{9}{2}y = -16$

38. $-\frac{1}{2}x - \frac{1}{3}y = -1$
 $-\frac{3}{2}x + \frac{2}{3}y = -8$

39. $\frac{2}{3}x + \frac{1}{2}y = \frac{1}{6}$
 $\frac{1}{2}x + \frac{5}{4}y = \frac{11}{4}$

40. $\frac{1}{4}x + \frac{5}{2}y = 2$
 $\frac{5}{6}x - \frac{1}{3}y = -2$

Solve the system by either elimination or substitution. If the system is inconsistent or dependent, say so. For a one-solution system, verify the solution graphically or check that the solution satisfies both equations of the system.

41. $y = 2x + 5$
 $6x - 3y = -3$

42. $y = 5x - 4$
 $10x - 2y = 12$

43. $13x + 10y = -7$
 $17x - 15y = 47$

44. $3x - 5y = 10$
 $7x + 2y = 37$

45. $4x - 5y = 3$
 $-12x + 15y = -9$

46. $2x - y = -4$
 $-8x + 4y = 16$

47. $4x - 3y = 1$
 $-20x + 15y = -3$

48. $-4x + 8y = 2$
 $6x - 12y = -5$

49. $y = -2x + 4$
 $y = -4x + 10$

50. $y = 3x + 7$
 $y = -5x - 1$

51. $2(x + 3) - (y + 5) = -6$
 $5(x - 2) + 3(y - 4) = -34$

52. $-(x - 6) + 6(y + 1) = 58$
 $3(x + 1) - 4(y - 2) = -15$

53. $y = \frac{1}{2}x + 3$
 $2y - x = 6$

54. $y = -\frac{1}{3}x + 4$
 $x + 3y = 12$

55. $\frac{5}{6}x + \frac{1}{4}y = 3$
 $-\frac{1}{3}x + \frac{5}{2}y = 4$

56. $\frac{1}{2}x - \frac{3}{4}y = -4$
 $\frac{2}{3}x - \frac{1}{3}y = -4$

57. $\dfrac{x + 2y}{3} - \dfrac{x - y}{2} = \dfrac{13}{6}$
 $\dfrac{x + 3y}{2} + \dfrac{x + y}{4} = \dfrac{17}{4}$

58. $\dfrac{2x + y}{3} - \dfrac{3x - y}{6} = 1$
 $\dfrac{x + y}{3} + \dfrac{2x - y}{4} = \dfrac{31}{12}$

Use elimination or substitution to solve the system. Round the coordinates of solutions to the second decimal place. Verify your solution graphically or by checking that it satisfies both equations approximately.

59. $y = 2.58x - 8.31$
 $y = -3.25x + 7.86$

60. $y = -4.25x - 2.19$
 $y = 3.65x + 9.38$

61. $y = -0.77x + 4.84$
 $y = -2.31x - 1.49$

62. $y = -3.38x + 8.57$
 $y = -0.35x + 4.28$

For Exercises 63–68, solve the given equation or system by referring to the graphs shown in Fig. 24.

63. $\frac{1}{2}x + \frac{5}{2} = 2x + 7$

64. $\frac{1}{2}x + \frac{5}{2} = 4$

65. $\frac{1}{2}x + \frac{5}{2} = 3$

66. $2x + 7 = 3$

67. $2x + 7 = -3$

68. $y = \dfrac{1}{2}x + \dfrac{5}{2}$
$y = 2x + 7$

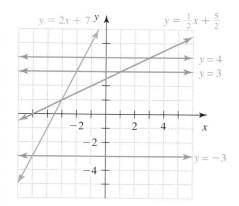

Figure 24
Exercises 63–68

For Exercises 69–74, solve the given equation or system by referring to the graphs shown in Fig. 25.

69. $\dfrac{1}{3}x + \dfrac{5}{3} = x - 1$

70. $\dfrac{1}{3}x + \dfrac{5}{3} = -3x - 5$

71. $\dfrac{1}{3}x + \dfrac{5}{3} = 2$

72. $\dfrac{1}{3}x + \dfrac{5}{3} = 0$

73. $y = \dfrac{1}{3}x + \dfrac{5}{3}$
$y = -3x - 5$

74. $y = \dfrac{1}{3}x + \dfrac{5}{3}$
$y = x - 1$

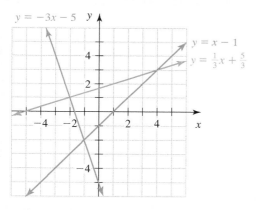

Figure 25 Exercises 69–74

Use "intersect" on a graphing calculator to solve the equation. Round the solution to the second decimal place.

75. $5x - 4 = -2x + 7$

76. $-3x - 8 = 4x + 1$

77. $-0.39x - 4.98 = 1.04x - 1.52$

78. $0.48x - 5.37 = 1.32x - 8.14$

79. $\dfrac{57}{65}x + \dfrac{91}{23} = -\dfrac{25}{73}x + \dfrac{77}{38}$

80. $\dfrac{42}{97}x + \dfrac{19}{28} = -\dfrac{14}{53}x - \dfrac{88}{37}$

For Exercises 81–86, solve the given equation or system by referring to the solutions of the functions shown in Table 14.

81. $\dfrac{1}{2}x + \dfrac{7}{2} = \dfrac{4}{5}x + 2$

82. $\dfrac{1}{2}x + \dfrac{7}{2} = \dfrac{11}{10}x + \dfrac{17}{10}$

83. $\dfrac{11}{10}x + \dfrac{17}{10} = 5$

84. $\dfrac{1}{2}x + \dfrac{7}{2} = 4$

85. $y = \dfrac{4}{5}x + 2$
$y = \dfrac{11}{10}x + \dfrac{17}{10}$

86. $y = \dfrac{1}{2}x + \dfrac{7}{2}$
$y = \dfrac{4}{5}x + 2$

Table 14 Some Solutions of Three Functions (Exercises 81–86)

x	0	1	2	3	4	5	6
$y = \dfrac{1}{2}x + \dfrac{7}{2}$	3.5	4	4.5	5	5.5	6	6.5
$y = \dfrac{4}{5}x + 2$	2	2.8	3.6	4.4	5.2	6	6.8
$y = \dfrac{11}{10}x + \dfrac{17}{10}$	1.7	2.8	3.9	5	6.1	7.2	8.3

87. Some values of linear functions f and g are listed in Table 15. Find the solution of a system of two equations that describes the functions f and g. [**Hint:** Find equations of f and g.]

Table 15 Values of Functions f and g (Exercise 87)

x	0	1	2	3	4	5	6	7	8
$f(x)$	3	7	11	15	19	23	27	31	35
$g(x)$	50	44	38	32	26	20	14	8	2

88. Some values of linear functions f and g are listed in Table 16. Find the solution of a system of two equations that describes the functions f and g. [**Hint:** Find equations of f and g.]

Table 16 Values of Functions f and g (Exercise 88)

x	0	1	2	3	4	5	6	7	8
$f(x)$	201	204	207	210	213	216	219	222	225
$g(x)$	6	11	16	21	26	31	36	41	46

Concepts

Solve the system of equations three times, once by each of the three methods: elimination, substitution, and graphing. Decide which method you prefer for the system.

89. $3x + y = 11$
$y = -2x + 9$

90. $5x - 2y = 8$
$3x + 4y = 10$

91. Consider the system

$$2x + 4y = 10$$
$$3x - 7y = 2$$

a. Solve the system by eliminating the x terms.
b. Solve the system by eliminating the y terms.
c. Compare your results in parts (a) and (b).

92. Consider the system

$$-4x + 3y = 15$$
$$5x - 4y = -19$$

a. Solve the system by eliminating the x terms.
b. Solve the system by eliminating the y terms.
c. Compare your results in parts (a) and (b).

93. A student decides to solve the system

$$y = 2x + 3$$
$$y = 2.01x + 1$$

by graphing the equations (see Fig. 26). He decides the solution is the empty set. Describe any errors. Then solve the system correctly.

 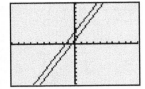

Figure 26 Graphs of two lines (Exercise 93)

94. To solve the system

$$x = 3$$
$$y = 4$$

a student adds the left sides and adds the right sides to get $x + y = 7$. She thinks the solution set is the set of points on the line $y = -x + 7$. Is the student correct? Explain.

95. Find the coordinates of points A, B, C, D, E, and F as shown in Fig. 27. The equations of lines l_1–l_4 are provided, but no attempt has been made to sketch the lines accurately, except for showing the intersection points. Verify your results graphically.

l_1: $y = 2x + 3$

l_2: $3y + x = 30$

l_3: $y + 3x = 26$

l_4: $y = 2x - 10$

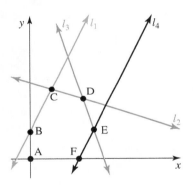

Figure 27 Exercise 95

96. Determine the constants a and b so that $(2, 3)$ is the solution of the system. Verify your result by checking that $(2, 3)$ satisfies each of your equations, and verify your result graphically.

$$7x - 4y = a$$
$$5x + 2y = b$$

97. a. Let $a, b, c, d, k,$ and p be constants such that the two equations form a one-solution system. Solve the system.

$$ax + by = c$$
$$kx + py = d$$

b. Use your result from part (a) to solve this system:

$$3x + 5y = 2$$
$$4x + 3y = 4$$

98. To solve the system

$$3x - y = 3$$
$$-2x + y = -1$$

a student adds the left sides and the right sides to get $x = 2$. He thinks that 2 is the solution. Is the student correct? Explain.

99. Describe how graphing can be used to solve an equation in one variable.

100. Explain why the solution set of a system of two linear equations either is empty, consists of exactly one solution, or consists of infinitely many solutions. Why cannot such a solution set have exactly two solutions?

101. Describe how to solve a system by elimination. Include in your discussion the result of solving a system by elimination if the system is a one-solution system, an inconsistent system, or a dependent system. Finally, describe how to solve a system by substitution.

3.3 Using Systems to Model Data

Objectives

» Use substitution and elimination to make predictions about situations described by a table of data.

» Use substitution and elimination to make predictions about situations described by rates of change.

In Section 3.1, we used a graphical approach to find the intersection point of the graphs of two linear models. In this section, we discuss how to use substitution and elimination to find such an intersection point.

Using a Table of Data to Find a System for Modeling

In Example 1, we will use two linear models from Section 3.1 and work with a table of data.

▶ Example 1 Solving a System to Make a Prediction

In Example 1 of Section 3.1, we modeled the life expectancies (in years) $W(t)$ and $M(t)$ of U.S. women and men, respectively, by the system

$$L = W(t) = 0.115t + 77.44$$
$$L = M(t) = 0.208t + 69.86$$

Table 17 U.S. Life Expectancies of Women and Men

Year of Birth	Women (years)	Men (years)
1980	77.4	70.0
1985	78.2	71.1
1990	78.8	71.8
1995	78.9	72.5
2000	79.5	74.1
2005	79.9	74.9
2009	81.3	76.2

Source: *U.S. Census Bureau*

where t is the number of years since 1980 (see Table 17). Use a symbolic method to predict when the life expectancies of women and men will be equal.

Solution

In Example 1 of Section 3.1, we found that the intersection point of the graphs of the two models represents the event when the life expectancies of women and men will be equal. We can find this intersection point by substitution (or elimination). To solve by substitution, we substitute $0.115t + 77.44$ for L in the equation $L = 0.208t + 69.86$ and solve for t:

$$0.115t + 77.44 = 0.208t + 69.86 \quad \text{Substitute } 0.115t + 77.44 \text{ for } L.$$
$$0.115t - 0.208t = 69.86 - 77.44 \quad \text{Subtract } 0.208t \text{ and } 77.44 \text{ from both sides.}$$
$$-0.093t = -7.58 \quad \text{Combine like terms.}$$
$$t \approx 81.51 \quad \text{Divide both sides by } -0.093.$$

Next, we substitute 81.51 for t in the equation $L = 0.115t + 77.44$:

$$L = 0.115(81.51) + 77.44 \approx 86.81$$

So, the approximate solution of the system is (81.51, 86.81), the same result we found in Example 1 of Section 3.1. According to the models, the life expectancy of both women and men will be about 86.8 years in 2062.

In Example 1, we used substitution to predict when the life expectancy of women will equal the life expectancy of men. Graphically, this event is described by the intersection point of the graphs of the two life-expectancy models. In general, **we can find an intersection point of the graphs of two linear models by graphing, substitution, or elimination.**

▶ Example 2 Solving a System to Make a Prediction

In Exercises 17 and 18 of Homework 2.2, you modeled world record times for the 400-meter run (see Table 18).

Table 18 400-Meter Run Record Times

	Women		Men
Year	Record Time (seconds)	Year	Record Time (seconds)
1957	57.0	1900	47.8
1959	53.4	1916	47.4
1962	51.9	1928	47.0
1969	51.7	1932	46.2
1972	51.0	1941	46.0
1976	49.29	1950	45.8
1979	48.60	1960	44.9
1983	47.99	1968	43.86
1985	47.60	1988	43.29
		1999	43.18

Source: *International Association of Athletics Federations*

The record times (in seconds) $W(t)$ and $M(t)$ for women and men, respectively, are modeled by the system

$$r = W(t) = -0.27t + 70.45$$
$$r = M(t) = -0.053t + 48.08$$

where t is the number of years since 1900. Predict when the women's record time and the men's record time will be equal.

Solution

We solve the system

$$r = -0.27t + 70.45$$
$$r = -0.053t + 48.08$$

by substitution. We do so by substituting $-0.27t + 70.45$ for r in the equation $r = -0.053t + 48.08$:

$$-0.27t + 70.45 = -0.053t + 48.08 \qquad \text{Substitute } -0.27t + 70.45 \text{ for } r.$$
$$-0.27t + 0.053t = 48.08 - 70.45 \qquad \text{Add } 0.053t \text{ to both sides; subtract } 70.45 \text{ from both sides.}$$
$$-0.217t = -22.37 \qquad \text{Combine like terms.}$$
$$t \approx 103.09 \qquad \text{Divide both sides by } -0.217.$$

Next, we substitute 103.09 for t in the equation $r = -0.27t + 70.45$ and solve for r:

$$r = -0.27(103.09) + 70.45 \approx 42.62$$

So, according to the models, the world record times for both women and men were 42.62 seconds in 2003. Model breakdown has occurred, because in 2012 the women's record time was still 47.60 seconds and the men's record time was still 43.18 seconds.

We can verify our result by using "intersect" on a graphing calculator (see Fig. 28).

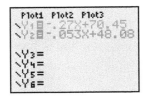

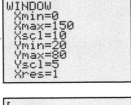

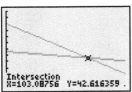

Figure 28 Verify that the intersection point is approximately (103.09, 42.62)

Using Rate of Change to Find a System for Modeling

Recall from Section 2.4 that if the rate of change of the dependent variable with respect to the independent variable is constant, then there is a linear relationship between the variables. And for the linear model that describes the relationship, the slope is equal to the constant rate of change. We use these ideas in Example 3.

▶ Example 3   Solving a System to Make a Prediction

In 2012, a 2011 Acura RL cost about $37,120 and a 2011 Chevrolet Impala LS sedan cost about $14,050. The RL depreciates by $4245 per year, and the Impala depreciates by $1200 per year (Source: *MotorTrend*). When will these 2011 cars have the same value?

Solution

Let $V = R(t)$ be the value (in dollars) of a 2011 RL and $V = C(t)$ be the value (in dollars) of a 2011 Impala, both at t years since 2012.

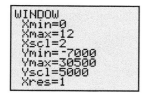

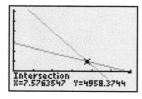

Figure 29 Verify the work

Because a 2011 RL's value decreases by a *constant* $4245 each year, the function R is linear and its slope is -4245. The V-intercept is $(0, 37,120)$, since the car is worth $37,120 at year $t = 0$. So, an equation of R is

$$V = R(t) = -4245t + 37,120$$

Similar work in finding the equation of the function C gives

$$V = C(t) = -1200t + 14,050$$

Next, we substitute $-4245t + 37,120$ for V in the equation $V = -1200t + 14,050$:

$$-4245t + 37,120 = -1200t + 14,050$$

Then we solve for t:

$$-4245t + 1200t = 14,050 - 37,120 \quad \text{Add } 1200t \text{ to both sides; subtract 37,120 from both sides.}$$
$$-3045t = -23,070 \quad \text{Combine like terms.}$$
$$t \approx 7.58 \quad \text{Divide both sides by } -3045.$$

We conclude that the cars will have the same value in approximately 8 years (in 2020). Next, we find the common value of the cars:

$$C(7.58) = -1200(7.58) + 14,050 = 4954$$

So, both cars will be worth about $4954 in 2020, according to the models. Using "intersect" on a graphing calculator gives the result that both cars will be worth about $4958 in 2020 (see Fig. 29). Our result of $4954 is $4 less than the calculator result because we evaluated C at a rounded value of t.

Group Exploration

Looking ahead: Total value

1. A cup of coffee costs $3. Find the total cost of
   a. 2 cups of coffee
   b. 4 cups of coffee
   c. 5 cups of coffee
   d. n cups of coffee

2. Let T be the total value of n objects that each have value v. Write an equation in terms of T, n, and v.

3. A pen costs $2. A notebook costs $4. Find the total cost of
   a. 3 pens and 2 notebooks
   b. 5 pens and 3 notebooks
   c. p pens and n notebooks

4. A 7000-seat theater has tickets for sale at $30 and $45. Let x be the number of $30 tickets and y be the number of $45 tickets.
   a. What is the meaning of the equation $30x + 45y = 232,500$?
   b. What is the meaning of the equation $x + y = 7000$?
   c. Solve the system

   $$30x + 45y = 232,500$$
   $$x + y = 7000$$

   What does your result mean in this situation?

▶ Tips for Success   **Study with a Classmate**

It can be helpful to meet with a friend from class and discuss what happened in class that day. Not only can you ask questions *of* each other, but also you will learn just by explaining concepts *to* each other. Explaining a concept to someone else forces you to clarify your own understanding of the concept.

Homework 3.3

For extra help ▶   MyMathLab®   Watch the videos in MyMathLab   Download the MyDashboard App

1. In Exercise 27 of Homework 3.1, the winning times (in seconds) $W(t)$ and $M(t)$ for women and men, respectively, in Olympic 500-meter speed skating are modeled by the system

$$y = W(t) = -0.153t + 43.19$$
$$y = M(t) = -0.135t + 39.64$$

where t is the number of years since 1970 (see Table 19). Use substitution or elimination to predict when the women's winning time will be equal to the men's winning time. What will be that winning time?

Table 19 Olympic 500-Meter Speed-Skating Times

	Winning Time (seconds)	
Year	Women	Men
1972	43.33	39.44
1976	42.76	39.17
1980	41.78	38.03
1984	41.02	38.19
1988	39.10	36.45
1992	40.33	37.14
1994	39.25	36.33
1998	38.21	35.59
2002	37.375	34.615
2006	38.285	34.880
2010	38.050	34.910

Source: *The Universal Almanac*

2. In Exercise 28 of Homework 3.1, the average annual U.S. per-person consumption (in pounds per person) $C(t)$ and $R(t)$ of chicken and red meat, respectively, are modeled by the system

$$y = C(t) = 1.13t + 39.29$$
$$y = R(t) = -0.94t + 144.88$$

where t is the number of years since 1970 (see Table 20).

Table 20 Average Annual U.S. Per-Person Consumption of Chicken and Red Meat

	Average Annual Consumption (pounds per person)	
Year	Chicken	Red Meat
1970	40.3	145.8
1980	48.0	136.8
1990	61.5	120.0
2000	78.0	120.7
2010	83.7	108.7
2011	84.2	104.3

Source: *U.S. Department of Agriculture*

Use substitution or elimination to predict when the annual consumption of chicken will equal that of red meat. What will be that consumption? How confident are you in this prediction?

3. In Exercise 31 of Homework 3.1, the percentages $I(t)$ and $B(t)$ of households that have Internet access and broadband Internet access, respectively, are modeled by the system

$$p = I(t) = 2.30t + 47.6$$
$$p = B(t) = 6.83t + 1.4$$

where t is the number of years since 2000 (see Table 21).

Table 21 Percentages of Households That Have Internet Access and Broadband Internet Access

	Percent	
Year	Internet Access	Broadband Internet Access
2001	50	9
2003	55	20
2007	62	51
2009	69	64
2010	71	68

Source: *U.S. Census Bureau*

a. Find the slopes of the graphs of I and B. What do they mean in this situation?
b. Since the percentage of U.S. households that have Internet access is increasing, it is not surprising that the percentage of households that have broadband Internet access is also increasing. Explain why your results in part (a) show that this is not the only reason the percentage of households with broadband Internet access is increasing.
c. Use substitution or elimination to predict when all households with Internet access will have broadband Internet access.

4. In Exercise 30 of Homework 3.1, the worldwide numbers $F(t)$ and $C(t)$ of fixed telephone lines and cell-phone subscriptions per 100 people, respectively, are modeled by the system

$$n = F(t) = -0.51t + 22.38$$
$$n = C(t) = 8.9t - 12.38$$

where t is the number of years since 2000 (see Table 22). Use substitution or elimination to estimate when the number of fixed telephone lines per 100 people was equal to the number of cell-phone subscriptions per 100 people.

Table 22 Worldwide Numbers of Fixed Telephone Lines and Cell-Phone Subscriptions per 100 People

	Number per 100 People	
Year	Fixed Telephone Lines	Cell-Phone Subscriptions
2006	19.2	40.6
2007	19.0	50.1
2008	18.3	59.3
2009	17.7	67.9
2010	17.3	76.2

Source: *ITU World Telecommunication*

5. The average annual U.S. per-person consumption of milk and soft drinks is shown in Table 23 for various years.

Table 23 Average Annual U.S. Per-Person Consumption of Milk and Soft Drinks

Year	Average Annual Consumption of Milk (gallons per person)	Year	Average Annual Consumption of Soft Drinks (gallons per person)
1970	31.3	1950	10.8
1980	27.5	1960	13.4
1985	26.7	1970	24.3
1990	25.7	1980	35.1
1995	23.9	1990	46.2
2000	22.5	2000	49.3
2005	21.0	2005	51.5

Source: *USDA/Economic Research Service*

a. Let $M(t)$ be the average annual per-person consumption of milk and $S(t)$ be the average annual per-person consumption of soft drinks, both in gallons per person, in the year that is t years since 1900. Find equations of M and S.

b. Use substitution or elimination to estimate when the annual consumption of milk was equal to the annual consumption of soft drinks. What was that consumption?

c. Use "intersect" on a graphing calculator to verify your work.

d. Because the annual per-person consumption of milk decreased from 1970 to 2005, it's not surprising that the annual per-person soft drink consumption increased during that period. But people turning from milk to soft drinks can't be the only reason annual per-person consumption of soft drinks increased. Explain by referring to the slopes of the two models.

e. In 2010, per-person consumption of milk was 20.4 gallons and per-person consumption of soft drinks was 44.7 gallons. Compare these data to those for 2005 in Table 23 and explain how the comparison relates to your response in part (d).

6. The average fuel efficiencies of domestic and imported light-duty passenger cars are shown in Table 24 for various years.

Table 24 Average Fuel Efficiencies of Domestic and Imported Cars

Year	Average Fuel Efficiency (miles per gallon)	
	Domestic	Imported
2006	30.3	29.7
2007	30.6	32.2
2008	31.2	31.8
2009	32.1	33.8
2010	33.1	35.2

Source: *U.S. Department of Transportation*

a. Let $D(t)$ be the average fuel efficiency of domestic cars and $I(t)$ be the average fuel efficiency of imported cars, both in miles per gallon, at t years since 2000. Find equations of D and I.

b. Use substitution or elimination to estimate when the fuel efficiency of domestic cars was equal to the fuel efficiency of imported cars. What was that fuel efficiency?

c. According to CAFE emissions standards, average fuel efficiency of passenger cars must be 37.8 miles per gallon in 2016. According to the models, will domestic passenger cars meet this standard? How about imported passenger cars?

d. Find the average of $D(16)$ and $I(16)$. If there will be more domestic passenger cars sold in the United States than

imported passenger cars in 2016, is your result more likely an underestimate or an overestimate of the actual average fuel efficiency of all passenger cars (both domestic and imported)? Explain.

7. Scores on tests that evaluate general knowledge and vocabulary and scores on tests that evaluate memory and information-processing speed are shown in Table 25 for various ages. (The higher the score, the better is the mental function. A score of 0 is average.)

Table 25 Age versus Mental Functioning

Age Group	Age Used to Represent Age Group	General Knowledge and Vocabulary Score	Memory and Information-Processing Speed Score
20–30	25	−0.4	1.0
30–40	35	−0.3	0.7
40–50	45	0	0.3
60–70	65	0.2	−0.2
70–80	75	0.3	−0.4

Source: *Denise Park, University of Illinois, Champaign–Urbana*

a. Let $K(a)$ be the score on general knowledge and vocabulary tests and $M(a)$ be the score on memory and information-processing speed tests, both at age a years. Find equations of K and M.

b. Use substitution or elimination to estimate at what age a person's score on general knowledge and vocabulary tests is equal to the person's score on memory and information-processing speed tests. What is that score?

c. Use "intersect" on a graphing calculator to verify your work.

8. The percentages of Americans who gamble online and at traditional casinos are shown in Table 26 for various age groups.

Table 26 Percentages of Americans Who Gamble Online and at Traditional Casinos

Age Group (years)	Age Used to Represent Age Group (years)	Percent	
		Online	Traditional Casinos
21–29	25	9	43
30–39	34.5	14	26
40–49	44.5	18	14
50–59	54.5	20	15
over 59	70	37	2

Source: *American Gaming Association*

a. Let $I(t)$ be the percentage of Americans who gamble online and let $C(t)$ be the percentage of Americans who gamble at traditional casinos, both at age a years. Find equations of I and C.

b. Use substitution or elimination to estimate at what age the percentage of Americans who gamble online is equal to the percentage of Americans who gamble at traditional casinos. What is that percentage?

c. Use "intersect" on a graphing calculator to verify your work.

9. The *Denver Post* and the *Rocky Mountain News* were competing newspapers in Denver, Colorado. Their circulations are listed in Table 27 for various years. Let $C = D(t)$ be the circulation (in thousands) of the *Denver Post* and $C = R(t)$ be the circulation (in thousands) of the

Table 27 Newspaper Circulations

Year	Denver Post Circulation (thousands)	Rocky Mountain News Circulation (thousands)
1992	255	355
1993	270	350
1994	285	345
1995	295	340

Source: *Audit Bureau of Circulations*

Rocky Mountain News, where t is the number of years since 1990. Reasonable equations of D and R are

$$C = D(t) = 13.5t + 229$$
$$C = R(t) = -5t + 365$$

a. Use substitution or elimination to estimate when the two newspapers had equal circulation.

b. The newspaper with greater circulation can usually charge more for advertisements, thus increasing its revenue. On March 1–2, 1997, both newspapers included articles claiming the other newspaper had made false reports of its circulation to the audit bureau. Use your result in part (a) to explain why it is not surprising that the competition between the two newspapers heated up in 1997.

c. Throughout the years, both newspapers increased their circulation by giving away "bonus issues" free to those who subscribed to less than a full week of newspapers. During the circulation wars from 1997 to 2000, both newspapers increased their distribution of bonus issues dramatically. In 2000, the combined circulation of the two newspapers was 826 thousand. Estimate the combined increase in the number of bonus issues from the two newspapers due to the circulation wars. [**Hint:** Begin by finding $D(10)$ and $R(10)$.]

d. Use the models D and R to estimate the combined circulation of the two newspapers in 2001.

e. In January 2001, the two newspapers joined their revenue streams under a single entity, the Denver Newspaper Agency (DNA). In 2001, the combined circulation was 638 thousand. Is your estimate in part (d) an underestimate or an overestimate? Give a possible explanation for this in terms of the circulation wars, DNA, and bonus issues.

10. World record times for the 1500-meter run are listed in Table 28.

Table 28 1500-Meter Run Record Times

Women		Men	
Year	Record Time (seconds)	Year	Record Time (seconds)
1927	318	1926	231
1936	287	1941	227
1946	277	1955	220
1957	269	1980	211
1962	259	1995	207
1993	230	1998	206

Source: *International Association of Athletics Federations*

a. Let $W(t)$ and $M(t)$ be the record times (in seconds) of women and men, respectively, at t years since 1900. Find the regression equations of W and of M.

b. Use substitution or elimination to predict when the women's record time will equal the men's record time. Verify your result by using "intersect" on a graphing calculator.

c. Now find the regression equation of the women's record times, excluding the record set in 1927. Also, find the regression equation of the men's times, excluding the record set in 1926. Use these equations to predict when the women's record time will equal the men's record time.

d. Explain why your result in part (b) is so different from that in part (c).

11. In 2012, a 2011 Ford Fusion S Sedan® cost about \$14,290 and a 2011 Cadillac DTS sedan cost about \$30,450. The Fusion depreciates by about \$1414 per year, and the DTS depreciates by about \$3740 per year (Source: *MotorTrend*).

a. Let $V = F(t)$ be the value (in dollars) of a 2011 Ford Fusion and $V = D(t)$ be the value (in dollars) of a 2011 Cadillac DTS, both at t years since 2012. Find equations of F and D.

b. Use substitution or elimination to predict when the cars will have the same value. What is that value?

c. Use "intersect" on a graphing calculator to verify your work in part (b).

12. In 2012, the price of a 2011 Honda Accord® was about \$15,905, with a depreciation of about \$1231 per year (Source: *MotorTrend*). A student had \$500 in 2012 and saves \$1700 each year. Assume the student does not earn interest on her savings.

a. Let $H(t)$ be the value (in dollars) of a 2011 Honda Accord and $S(t)$ be the student's total savings (in dollars), both at t years since 2012. Find equations of H and S.

b. Use substitution or elimination to predict when the student will be able to buy a 2011 Honda Accord for cash.

c. Use "intersect" on a graphing calculator to verify your work in part (b).

d. Now assume the student earns interest on her savings. Is your answer in part (b) an underestimate or an overestimate? Explain.

13. Nutrisystem® offers a weight-loss program that charges \$91 per week. The program includes food and phone access to weight-loss counselors (Source: *Nutrisystem*).

Weight Watchers® offers a program that charges \$12 per week for meetings plus a one-time membership fee of \$20 (Source: *Weight Watchers*). Members purchase their own food, which usually costs about \$75 per week.

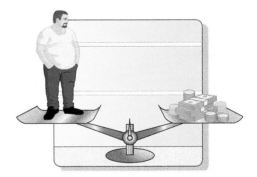

a. Let $N(t)$ be the per-person cost (in dollars) of the Nutrisystem program (including food) for t weeks. Let $W(t)$ be the per-person cost (in dollars) of the Weight Watchers program *plus food* for t weeks. Find equations of N and W.

b. Perform a unit analysis of the equations of N and W.

c. Use substitution or elimination to estimate how many weeks it will take for the total cost at Nutrisystem to equal the total cost at Weight Watchers (plus the cost of food). What is that total cost?

d. Use "intersect" on a graphing calculator to verify your work in part (c).

e. If a person joins Nutrisystem or Weight Watchers but quits 7 weeks later, which of the two weight-loss programs should he have joined? Explain.

14. Gold's Gym® offers two payment options. Option 1 requires an initial investment of $149.99 plus a monthly fee of $29.99. Option 2 requires an initial investment of $49.99 plus a monthly fee of $39.99 (Source: *Gold's Gym*). Let $f(t)$ be the total cost (in dollars) of Option 1 and $g(t)$ be the total cost (in dollars) of Option 2, both for t months.
   a. Find equations of f and g.
   b. Perform a unit analysis of the equations of f and g.
   c. Use substitution or elimination to estimate when the total cost of each payment option will be equal. What is that total cost?
   d. Use "intersect" on a graphing calculator to verify your work in part (c).
   e. If a person joins Gold's Gym but quits 10 months later, which payment option should she have chosen? Explain.

15. The percentage of U.S. electricity generated from natural gas was 24% in 2010 and has increased by about 0.9 percentage point per year (Source: *U.S. Energy Information Administration*). The percentage of U.S. electricity generated from coal was 44% in 2010 and has decreased by about 0.7 percentage point per year. Predict when the percentage of U.S. electricity generated from natural gas will be equal to that from coal. What is that percentage?

16. Total spending by advertisers on Internet ads was $21 million in 2007 and has increased by about $2 million per year (Source: *Interactive Advertising Bureau*). Total spending by advertisers on print newspaper ads was $42 million in 2007 and has decreased by about $6 million per year (Source: *Newspaper Association of America*). Predict in which year total spending on Internet ads was equal to total spending on newspaper ads. What was that total spending?

17. Average personal income in Hawaii increased approximately linearly from $24.5 thousand in 2000 to $37.6 thousand in 2010. Average personal income in Colorado increased approximately linearly from $28.9 thousand in 2000 to $38.8 thousand in 2010 (Source: *U.S. Bureau of Economic Analysis*).
   a. Let $H(t)$ be the average personal income in Hawaii and $C(t)$ be the average personal income in Colorado, both in thousands of dollars, in the year that is t years since 2000. Find equations of H and C.
   b. Use substitution or elimination to predict when average personal income in Hawaii will equal average personal income in Colorado. What is that average personal income?
   c. Use a graphing calculator table or graph to verify your work in part (b).
   d. Find the average of $H(17)$ and $C(17)$. Assuming the population of Colorado will continue to be larger than the population of Hawaii, will your result likely be an underestimate or an overestimate of the average personal income of residents of Hawaii and Colorado put together? Explain.

18. Total personal income from health care and social assistance jobs increased approximately linearly from $0.78 trillion in 2005 to $1.01 trillion in 2010. Total personal income from state and local government jobs increased approximately linearly from $0.95 trillion in 2005 to $1.14 trillion in 2010 (Source: *U.S. Bureau of Economic Analysis*).
   a. Let $H(t)$ be total personal income from health care and social assistance jobs and $G(t)$ be total personal income from state and local government jobs, both in trillions of dollars, in the year that is t years since 2000. Find equations of H and G.
   b. Use substitution or elimination to predict when total personal income from health care and social assistance jobs will equal total personal income from state and local government jobs. What is that total personal income?
   c. Use a graphing calculator table or graph to verify your work in part (b).

19. General Motors'® U.S. market share decreased approximately linearly from 22.1% in 2008 to 19.4% in 2011. Ford's® U.S. market share increased approximately linearly from 14.2% in 2008 to 16.5% in 2011 (Source: *Automakers*). Estimate when General Motors' market share will be equal to Ford's market share. What will be that market share?

20. The percentage of households with a television tuned in to ad-supported cable increased approximately linearly from 24.6% in 1994 to 51.4% in 2007. The percentage of households with a television tuned in to the major networks decreased approximately linearly from 48.5% in 1994 to 22.9% in 2007 (Source: *Nielsen*). Estimate when the percentages were equal for cable and the major networks. What was that percentage?

Concepts

21. To solve the system
$$y = f(t) = m_1 t + b_1$$
$$y = g(t) = m_2 t + b_2$$
   where m_1, b_1, m_2, and b_2 are constants, a student eliminates y and finds a noninteger value of t. He rounds the value of t *up* to an integer I.
   a. He is confused, because $f(I)$ is not equal to $g(I)$. Draw a graph to illustrate what happened.
   b. If m_1 is larger than m_2, which will be larger, $f(I)$ or $g(I)$? Draw a graph to illustrate this.

22. Describe how you can find a system of linear equations to model a situation. Also, explain how you can use the system to make an estimate or prediction about the situation.

▼3.4 Value, Interest, and Mixture Problems

Objectives

» Know a five-step problem-solving method.

» Use a system of two linear equations or a linear function to solve value, interest, and mixture problems.

In this section, we will solve problems that involve the (dollar) value of an object, the interest from an investment, or the percentage of a substance in a mixture. First, we will use a five-step problem-solving method that involves solving a linear system. Later, we will use a system of equations to find a function we can use to analyze many aspects of a given situation.

Using a Five-Step Problem-Solving Method

We begin by discussing a method we can use to solve some problems involving two quantities.

> **Five-Step Problem-Solving Method**
>
> To solve some problems in which we want to find two quantities, it is useful to perform the following five steps:
> - ***Step 1: Define each variable.*** For each quantity that we are trying to find, we usually define a variable to be that unknown quantity.
> - ***Step 2: Write a system of two equations.*** We find a system of two equations by using the variables from step 1. We can usually write both equations either by translating the information stated in the problem into mathematics or by making a substitution into a formula.
> - ***Step 3: Solve the system.*** We solve the system of equations from step 2.
> - ***Step 4: Describe each result.*** We use a complete sentence to describe the quantities found.
> - ***Step 5: Check.*** We reread the problem and check that the quantities we found agree with the given information.

Value Problems

How do we know four dimes are worth 40 cents? We find the total value of the dimes by multiplying the value of one dime (10 cents) by the number of dimes (4): $10 \cdot 4 = 40$ cents.

> **Total-Value Formula**
>
> If n objects each have value v, then their total value T is given by
> $$T = vn$$
> In words, the total value is equal to the value of one object times the number of objects.

When some objects are sold, we refer to the total money collected as the **revenue** from selling the objects.

▶ Example 1 Solving a Value Problem

A music store charges $5 for a six-string pack of electric-guitar strings and $20 for a four-string pack of electric-bass strings. If the store sells 35 packs of strings for a total revenue of $295, how many packs of each type of string were sold?

Solution

Step 1: Define each variable. Let x be the number of packs of guitar strings sold and y be the number of packs of bass strings sold.

Step 2: Write a system of two equations. The revenue from the guitar strings is equal to the price per pack times the number of packs sold: $5x$. The revenue from the bass strings is equal to the price per pack times the number of packs sold: $20y$. We add the revenue from the guitar strings and the revenue from the bass strings to find a formula of the total revenue T (in dollars):

$$T = \underset{\substack{\frac{\text{dollars}}{\text{guitar pack}}}}{5} \cdot \underset{\substack{\text{guitar packs}}}{x} + \underset{\substack{\frac{\text{dollars}}{\text{bass pack}}}}{20} \cdot \underset{\substack{\text{bass packs}}}{y}$$

To obtain our first equation, we substitute 295 for T:
$$295 = 5x + 20y$$

Since the store sells 35 packs of strings, our second equation is
$$x + y = 35$$

The system is

$$5x + 20y = 295 \quad \textit{Equation (1)}$$
$$x + y = 35 \quad \textit{Equation (2)}$$

Step 3: Solve the system. We can use elimination to solve the system. To eliminate the x terms, we multiply both sides of equation (2) by -5, yielding the system

$$5x + 20y = 295 \quad \textit{Equation (1)}$$
$$-5x - 5y = -175 \quad \textit{Multiply both sides of equation (2) by } -5.$$

Then we add the left sides and add the right sides of the equations and solve for y:

$$5x + 20y = 295$$
$$\underline{-5x - 5y = -175}$$
$$0 + 15y = 120 \quad \textit{Add left sides and right sides; combine like terms.}$$
$$y = 8 \quad \textit{Divide both sides by 15.}$$

Next, we substitute 8 for y in equation (2) and solve for x:

$$x + y = 35 \quad \textit{Equation (2)}$$
$$x + 8 = 35 \quad \textit{Substitute 8 for y.}$$
$$x = 27 \quad \textit{Subtract 8 from both sides.}$$

Step 4: Describe each result. The store sold 27 packs of guitar strings and 8 packs of bass strings.

Step 5: Check. First, we find the sum $27 + 8 = 35$, which is equal to the total number of packs of strings sold. Next, we find the total revenue from selling 27 packs of guitar strings and 8 packs of bass strings: $5 \cdot 27 + 20 \cdot 8 = 295$ dollars, which checks.

▶ **Example 2** Solving a Value Problem

The American Analog Set will play at an auditorium that has 400 balcony seats and 1600 main-level seats. If tickets for balcony seats will cost $15 less than tickets for main-level seats, what should the price be for each type of ticket so the total revenue from a sellout performance will be $70,000?

Solution

Step 1: Define each variable. Let b be the price for balcony seats and m be the price for main-level seats, both in dollars.

Step 2: Write a system of two equations. Since tickets for balcony seats will cost $15 less than tickets for main-level seats, our first equation is

$$b = m - 15$$

Since the total revenue is $70,000, our second equation is

$$b \cdot 400 + m \cdot 1600 = 70{,}000$$

The units of the expressions on both sides of the equation are dollars, which suggests that our work is correct. The system is

$$b = m - 15 \quad \textit{Equation (1)}$$
$$400b + 1600m = 70{,}000 \quad \textit{Equation (2)}$$

Step 3: Solve the system. We can use substitution to solve the system. We substitute $m - 15$ for b in equation (2) and solve for m:

$$400b + 1600m = 70{,}000 \quad \textit{Equation (2)}$$
$$400(m - 15) + 1600m = 70{,}000 \quad \textit{Substitute } m - 15 \textit{ for } b.$$
$$400m - 6000 + 1600m = 70{,}000 \quad \textit{Distributive law}$$
$$2000m - 6000 = 70{,}000 \quad \textit{Combine like terms.}$$
$$2000m = 76{,}000 \quad \textit{Add } 6000 \textit{ to both sides.}$$
$$m = 38 \quad \textit{Divide both sides by } 2000.$$

Then we substitute 38 for m in equation (1) and solve for b:

$$b = 38 - 15 = 23$$

Step 4: Describe each result. Tickets for balcony seats should be priced at $23 each, and tickets for main-level seats should be priced at $38 each.

Step 5: Check. First we find the difference in the ticket prices: $38 - 23 = 15$ dollars, which checks. Then we compute the total revenue from selling 400 of the $23 tickets and 1600 of the $38 tickets: $23 \cdot 400 + 38 \cdot 1600 = 70{,}000$ dollars, which checks.

▶

In Examples 1 and 2, we analyzed *one* aspect of a situation by working with a linear system. **If we want to analyze many aspects of a certain situation, it can help to use a system of equations to find a linear function. We can then use the function to analyze the situation in various ways.**

Example 3   Using a Function to Model a Value Situation

A 10,000-seat amphitheater will sell general-seat tickets at $45 and reserved-seat tickets at $65 for a Foo Fighters concert. Let x and y be the number of tickets that will sell for $45 and $65, respectively. Assume the show will sell out.

1. Let $T = f(x)$ be the total revenue (in dollars) from selling the $45 and $65 tickets. Find an equation of f.
2. Use a graphing calculator to sketch a graph of f for $0 \le x \le 10{,}000$. What is the slope? What does it mean in this situation?
3. Find $f(8500)$. What does it mean in this situation?
4. Find $f(11{,}000)$. What does it mean in this situation?
5. The total cost of the production is $350,000. How many of each type of ticket must be sold to make a profit of $150,000?

Solution

1. We add the revenues from the general tickets and the reserved tickets to find an equation of the total revenue T:

$$T = \underbrace{45}_{\substack{\text{dollars} \\ \text{general ticket}}} \cdot \underbrace{x}_{\substack{\text{general} \\ \text{tickets}}} + \underbrace{65}_{\substack{\text{dollars} \\ \text{reserved ticket}}} \cdot \underbrace{y}_{\substack{\text{reserved} \\ \text{tickets}}}$$

So far, we have described T in terms of x and y. Next, we describe T in terms of just x. The total number of tickets sold for a sellout performance is 10,000:

$$x + y = 10{,}000$$

Now we get y alone on one side of the equation:

$$y = 10{,}000 - x$$

Next, we substitute $10{,}000 - x$ for y in the equation $T = 45x + 65y$:

$$T = 45x + 65(10{,}000 - x) \quad \textit{Substitute } 10{,}000 - x \textit{ for } y.$$
$$= 45x + 650{,}000 - 65x \quad \textit{Distributive law}$$
$$= -20x + 650{,}000 \quad \textit{Combine like terms.}$$

So, an equation of f is

$$f(x) = -20x + 650{,}000$$

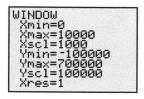

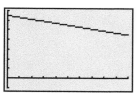

Figure 30 Graphing the revenue model

2. We draw a sketch of f in Fig. 30. The graph of f is a decreasing line with slope -20. This means that if one more ticket is sold for \$45 (and one less ticket is sold for \$65), the revenue will decrease by \$20.

3. Here, $f(8500) = -20(8500) + 650{,}000 = 480{,}000$. This means that if 8500 tickets sell for \$45 (and 1500 tickets sell for \$65), the total revenue will be \$480,000.

4. Here, $f(11{,}000) = -20(11{,}000) + 650{,}000 = 430{,}000$. This means that if $11{,}000$ tickets sell for \$45, the total revenue will be \$430,000. Since there are only 10,000 seats, model breakdown has occurred.

5. To make a profit of \$150,000, the revenue would need to be $350{,}000 + 150{,}000 = 500{,}000$ dollars. We substitute $500{,}000$ for T in the equation $T = -20x + 650{,}000$ and solve for x:

$$500{,}000 = -20x + 650{,}000 \quad \textit{Substitute 500,000 for T.}$$
$$-150{,}000 = -20x \qquad\qquad \textit{Subtract 650,000 from both sides.}$$
$$7500 = x \qquad\qquad\qquad \textit{Divide both sides by } -20.$$

So, 7500 \$45 tickets and $10{,}000 - 7500 = 2500$ \$65 tickets would need to be sold for the profit to be \$150,000.

Interest Problems

We will now model situations that involve interest from investments.

Money deposited in an account such as a savings account, certificate of deposit (CD), or mutual fund is called the **principal.** A person invests money in hopes of later getting back the principal plus additional money called the **interest,** which is a percentage of the principal (see Fig. 31). The **annual simple interest rate** is the percentage of the principal that equals the interest earned per year. So, if we invest \$100 and earn \$7 per year, then the annual simple interest rate is 7%.

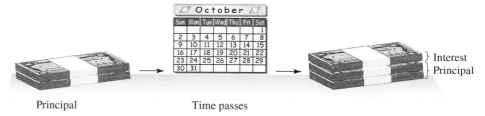

Figure 31 Invest the principal; time passes; get back the principal plus interest

▶ **Example 4**   Interest from an Investment

How much interest will a person earn by investing \$3200 in an account at 4% simple annual interest for one year?

Solution

We find 4% of 3200:

$$0.04(3200) = 128$$

The person will earn \$128 in interest.

Some people invest in a variety of accounts, including lower-risk accounts and certain higher-risk accounts. These investors might earn large amounts of interest from the higher-risk accounts but will have a safety net of principal and interest from the lower-risk accounts.

▶ **Example 5**   Solving an Interest Problem

A person plans to invest twice as much money in an Elfun Trusts account at 2.7% annual interest as in a Vanguard Morgan Growth account at 5.5% annual interest. Both interest rates are five-year averages. How much will the person have to invest in each account to earn a total of \$218 in one year?

Solution

Step 1: Define each variable. Let x be the money (in dollars) invested at 2.7% annual interest and y be the money (in dollars) invested at 5.5% annual interest.

Step 2: Write a system of two equations. The person is investing twice as much in the 2.7% account as in the 5.5% account, so our first equation is

$$x = 2y$$

Since the total interest is $218, our second equation is

interest from   interest from
2.7% account   5.5% account   total interest

$$\overbrace{0.027x} \quad + \quad \overbrace{0.055y} \quad = \quad \overbrace{218}$$

The system is

$$x = 2y \qquad \text{Equation (1)}$$
$$0.027x + 0.055y = 218 \qquad \text{Equation (2)}$$

Step 3: Solve the system. We can use substitution to solve the system. We substitute $2y$ for x in equation (2) and then solve for y:

$$0.027(2y) + 0.055y = 218 \qquad \text{Substitute 2y for x.}$$
$$0.054y + 0.055y = 218 \qquad \text{Multiply.}$$
$$0.109y = 218 \qquad \text{Combine like terms.}$$
$$y = 2000 \qquad \text{Divide both sides by 0.109.}$$

Then we substitute 2000 for y in equation (1) and solve for x:

$$x = 2y = 2(2000) = 4000$$

Step 4: Describe each result. The person should invest $4000 at 2.7% annual interest and $2000 at 5.5% annual interest.

Step 5: Check. First, we note that 4000 is twice 2000, which checks. Next, we calculate the total interest earned from investing $4000 at 2.7% and $2000 at 5.5%:

$$0.027(4000) + 0.055(2000) = 218$$

This checks, too.

▶

▶ **Example 6**   Using a Function to Model a Situation Involving Interest

A person plans to invest a total of $6000 in a Gabelli ABC mutual fund that has a three-year average annual interest of 6% and in a Presidential Bank Internet CD account at 2.25% annual interest. Let x and y be the money (in dollars) invested in the mutual fund and the CD, respectively.

1. Let $I = f(x)$ be the total interest (in dollars) earned from investing the $6000 for one year. Find an equation of f.
2. Use a graphing calculator to draw a graph of f for $0 \le x \le 6000$. What is the slope of f? What does it mean in this situation?
3. Use a graphing calculator to create a table of values of f. Explain how such a table could help the person decide how much money to invest in each account.
4. How much money should be invested in each account to earn $300 in one year?

Solution

1. The interest earned from investing x dollars in an account earning 6% annual interest is $0.06x$, and the interest earned from investing y dollars in an account earning 2.25%

annual interest is $0.0225y$ dollars. We add the two interest earnings to find the total interest earned:

$$\underbrace{I}_{\text{total interest}} = \underbrace{0.06x}_{\text{interest from 6\% account}} + \underbrace{0.0225y}_{\text{interest from 2.25\% account}}$$

Next, we describe I in terms of just x. The person plans to invest \$6000:

$$x + y = 6000$$

Then, we isolate y:

$$y = 6000 - x$$

Now we substitute $6000 - x$ for y in the equation $I = 0.06x + 0.0225y$:

$$\begin{aligned} I &= 0.06x + 0.0225(6000 - x) && \text{Substitute } 6000 - x \text{ for } y. \\ &= 0.06x + 135 - 0.0225x && \text{Distributive law} \\ &= 0.0375x + 135 && \text{Combine like terms.} \end{aligned}$$

So, our equation of f is

$$f(x) = 0.0375x + 135$$

```
WINDOW
 Xmin=0
 Xmax=6000
 Xscl=500
 Ymin=-100
 Ymax=500
 Yscl=100
 Xres=1
```

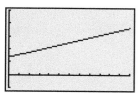

Figure 32 The revenue model

X	Y1
0	135
1000	172.5
2000	210
3000	247.5
4000	285
5000	322.5
6000	360

X=0

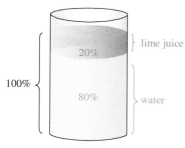

Figure 33 Table of values of f

2. We draw a graph of f in Fig. 32. The graph of f is an increasing line with slope 0.0375. This means that if one more dollar is invested at 6% (and one less dollar is invested at 2.25%), the total interest will increase by 3.75 cents.
3. We create a table in Fig. 33. The person may know she wants to invest some of the \$6000 in the safe Presidential CD account and the rest in the riskier Gabelli mutual fund, but she may not be clear as to exactly how much risk she is willing to take. By seeing some possible interest earnings, she may get a clearer idea of how much money to invest in each account.
4. We substitute 300 for I in the equation $I = 0.0375x + 135$ and solve for x:

$$\begin{aligned} 300 &= 0.0375x + 135 && \text{Substitute 300 for } I. \\ 165 &= 0.0375x && \text{Subtract 135 from both sides.} \\ 4400 &= x && \text{Divide both sides by 0.0375.} \end{aligned}$$

The person should invest \$4400 in the Gabelli mutual fund account and $6000 - 4400 = 1600$ dollars in the Presidential CD account.

Mixture Problems

Regardless of whether we are chemists or cooks, pharmacists or mechanics, we often have to mix different substances (typically liquids). Suppose that 2 ounces of lime juice is mixed with 8 ounces of water to make 10 ounces of unsweetened limeade. Note that $\frac{2}{10} = 0.20 = 20\%$ of the limeade is lime juice. We call the limeade a *20% lime-juice solution.*

Then the remaining $\frac{8}{10} = 0.80 = 80\%$ of the limeade is water. The percentage of the solution that is lime juice plus the percentage of the solution that is water is equal to 100% (all) of the solution: $20\% + 80\% = 100\%$. See Fig. 34.

So, for a 10% lime-juice solution, 10% of the solution would be lime juice and $100\% - 10\% = 90\%$ of the solution would be water. In general, **for an x% solution of two substances that are mixed, x% of the solution is one substance and $(100 - x)$% is the other substance.**

Figure 34 A 20% lime-juice solution

Example 7 Solving a Mixture Problem

A chemist needs 5 quarts of a 17% acid solution, but he has only a 15% acid solution and a 25% acid solution. How many quarts of the 15% acid solution should he mix with the 25% acid solution to make 5 quarts of a 17% acid solution?

Solution

Step 1: Define each variable. Let x be the number of quarts of 15% acid solution and y be the number of quarts of 25% acid solution.

Step 2: Write a system of two equations. Since he wants 5 quarts of the total mixture, our first equation is

$$x + y = 5$$

The total amount of pure acid doesn't change, regardless of how it is distributed in the two solutions. We find our second equation from the fact that the sum of the amounts of pure acid in both the 15% acid solution and the 25% acid solution is equal to the amount of pure acid in the desired mixture:

pure acid in   pure acid in   pure acid
15% solution   25% solution   in mixture

$$\overbrace{0.15x} \quad + \quad \overbrace{0.25y} \quad = \quad \overbrace{0.17(5)}$$

The system is

$$x + y = 5 \qquad \textit{Equation (1)}$$
$$0.15x + 0.25y = 0.85 \qquad \textit{Equation (2)}$$

Step 3: Solve the system. We can solve the system by substitution. First, we solve equation (1) for y:

$$x + y = 5 \qquad \textit{Equation (1)}$$
$$y = 5 - x \qquad \textit{Subtract x from both sides.}$$

Then we substitute $5 - x$ for y in equation (2) and solve for x:

$$0.15x + 0.25(5 - x) = 0.85 \qquad \textit{Substitute 5 − x for y.}$$
$$0.15x + 1.25 - 0.25x = 0.85 \qquad \textit{Distributive law}$$
$$-0.10x + 1.25 = 0.85 \qquad \textit{Combine like terms.}$$
$$-0.10x = -0.40 \qquad \textit{Subtract 1.25 from both sides.}$$
$$x = 4 \qquad \textit{Divide both sides by −0.10.}$$

Next, we substitute 4 for x in the equation $y = 5 - x$ and solve for y:

$$y = 5 - 4 = 1$$

Step 4: Describe each result. Four quarts of the 15% acid solution and 1 quart of the 25% acid solution are required.

Step 5: Check. First, we compute the total amount (in quarts) of pure acid in 4 quarts of 15% acid solution and 1 quart of 25% acid solution:

$$0.15(4) + 0.25(1) = 0.85$$

Next, we compute the amount (in quarts) of pure acid in 5 quarts of 17% acid solution:

$$0.17(5) = 0.85$$

Since the two results are equal, this checks. Also, $4 + 1 = 5$, which checks with the chemist wanting 5 quarts of the 17% solution.

▶

> ▶ **Example 8**   Solving a Mixture Problem

A chemist needs 8 cups of a 15% alcohol solution but has only a 20% alcohol solution. How much 20% solution and water should she mix to form the desired 8 cups of 15% solution?

Solution

Step 1: Define each variable. Let x be the number of cups of the 20% solution and y be the number of cups of water.

Step 2: Write a system of two equations. Since she wants 8 cups of the total mixture, our first equation is

$$x + y = 8$$

There is no alcohol in pure water, so we find our second equation from the fact that the amount of pure alcohol in the 20% alcohol solution is equal to the amount of pure alcohol in the desired mixture:

$$\overbrace{0.20x}^{\substack{\text{amount of pure} \\ \text{alcohol in 20\% solution}}} = \overbrace{0.15(8)}^{\substack{\text{amount of pure} \\ \text{alcohol in mixture}}}$$

The system is

$$x + y = 8 \quad \textit{Equation (1)}$$
$$0.20x = 1.2 \quad \textit{Equation (2)}$$

Step 3: Solve the system. We begin by solving equation (2) for x:

$$0.20x = 1.2 \quad \textit{Equation (2)}$$
$$x = 6 \quad \textit{Divide both sides by 0.20.}$$

Next, we substitute 6 for x in equation (1):

$$x + y = 8 \quad \textit{Equation (1)}$$
$$6 + y = 8 \quad \textit{Substitute 6 for x.}$$
$$y = 2 \quad \textit{Subtract 6 from both sides.}$$

Step 4: Describe each result. The chemist needs to mix 6 cups of the 20% alcohol solution with 2 cups of water.

Step 5: Check. First, we find $6 + 2 = 8$, which checks with the chemist wanting 8 cups of the 15% solution. Next, we compute the amount of pure alcohol in 6 cups of the 20% solution: $0.20(6) = 1.2$ cups. Finally, we compute the amount of pure alcohol in the 15% solution: $0.15(8) = 1.2$ cups. The computed amounts of pure alcohol in the 20% solution and the 15% solution are equal, so this checks.

Group Exploration

Looking ahead: Connection between a system of linear equations and a linear inequality in one variable

Recall from Example 2 of Section 3.3 that the equations

$$r = W(t) = -0.27t + 70.45 \quad \textit{Women's records}$$
$$r = M(t) = -0.053t + 48.08 \quad \textit{Men's records}$$

model 400-meter run record times (in seconds) of women and men, respectively, at t years since 1900.

1. Use a graphing calculator to draw the graphs of W and M on the same coordinate system, and find the intersection point. Then copy the graphs on a piece of paper and mark the point of intersection.

2. Now find values of t for which the models predict the women's record time will be less than the men's record time. Which years do these values of t represent? On your graph, shade the part of the t-axis that represents those years.

3. Try a *numerical* verification by using a graphing calculator. To do this, enter the functions as displayed in Fig. 35. Use the table setup displayed in Fig. 36, but replace the rectangle to the right of "TblStart=" with the t value for which the men's and women's times

will be equal. Then display the tables and use the arrow keys to verify your result from Problem 2. (See Appendix B.14 for calculator instructions.)

Figure 35 Entered functions

Figure 36 Table setup

4. Which of these two inequalities states that the women's record time is less than the men's record time?

$$W(t) < M(t) \qquad M(t) < W(t)$$

5. Substitute $-0.27t + 70.45$ for $W(t)$ and $-0.053t + 48.08$ for $M(t)$ in the inequality you chose in Problem 4. An inequality such as this is called a *linear inequality in one variable*. This inequality becomes a true statement when any of the values for t you found in Problem 2 are substituted for t in the inequality. Explain.

Homework 3.4

For extra help ▶   MyMathLab®   Watch the videos in MyMathLab   Download the MyDashboard App

1. A 5000-seat theater has tickets for sale at $27 and $40. How many tickets should be sold at each price for a sellout performance to generate a total revenue of $150,600?

2. A 9000-seat amphitheater has tickets for sale at $35 and $62. How many tickets should be sold at each price for a sellout performance to generate a total revenue of $382,500?

3. On iTunes®, the album *Plans* sells for $9.99 and the album *Codes and Keys* sells for $10.99. Both albums are by Death Cab for Cutie. If total sales of both albums in one month are 836 albums and total revenue of both albums is $9059.64, how many of each album were sold?

4. On iTunes, the album *We Were Dead Before the Ship Even Sank* sells for $9.99, and the album *No One's First, and You're Next* sells for $6.99. Both albums are by Modest Mouse. If total sales of both albums in one month are 422 albums and total revenue of both albums is $3210.78, how many of each album were sold?

5. An auditorium has 500 balcony seats and 1800 main-level seats. If tickets for balcony seats will cost $15 less than tickets for main-level seats, what should the prices be for each type of ticket so that the total revenue from a sellout performance will be $84,500?

6. An auditorium has 360 balcony seats and 1200 main-level seats. If tickets for balcony seats will cost $10 less than tickets for main-level seats, what should the prices be for each type of ticket so that the total revenue from a sellout performance will be $33,840?

7. A board of trustees of a college is considering opening a satellite college. Researchers estimate that there will be three times as many full-time students as part-time students and that full-time students will take an average of 14 units and part-time students will take an average of 3 units each semester. The charge for tuition will be $13 per unit. How many of each type of student would need to attend the new college for the total revenue to be $877,500 each semester?

8. A new college may open in the future. Full-time instructors would teach 15 units each semester. Researchers estimate that adjunct (part-time) instructors teach an average of 6 units each semester and that there is student demand for a total of 3300 units of courses. There would be enough office space for 250 instructors. To keep costs low by hiring as many adjunct instructors as possible, yet have office space for all instructors, how many full-time instructors and adjunct instructors should be hired?

9. A 20,000-seat amphitheater will sell tickets at $50 and $75 for a Green Day concert. Let x and y be the number of tickets that will sell for $50 and $75, respectively. Assume the show will sell out.
   a. Let $R = f(x)$ be the total revenue (in dollars) from selling the $50 and $75 tickets. Find an equation of f.
   b. Use a graphing calculator to draw a graph of the function f for $0 \le x \le 20{,}000$. What is the slope? What does it mean in this situation?
   c. Find $f(16{,}000)$. What does it mean in this situation?
   d. The total cost of the production is $475,000. How many of each ticket must be sold to make a profit of $600,000?

10. An 8000-seat amphitheater will sell tickets at $30 and $55 for a Garbage concert. Let x and y be the number of tickets that will sell for $30 and $55, respectively. Assume the show will sell out.
   a. Let $R = f(x)$ be the total revenue (in dollars) from selling the $30 and $55 tickets. Find an equation of f.
   b. Use a graphing calculator to draw a graph of f for $0 \le x \le 8000$. What is the slope? What does it mean in this situation?
   c. Find $f(6500)$. What does it mean in this situation?
   d. How many of each ticket must be sold for the revenue to be $250,000?

11. A 12,000-seat amphitheater will sell tickets at $45 and $70 for a Cake concert. Let x and y be the number of tickets that will sell for $45 and $70, respectively. Assume the show will sell out.
   a. Let $R = f(x)$ be the total revenue (in dollars) from selling the $45 and $70 tickets. Find an equation of f.
   b. Use a graphing calculator table to find the values $f(0)$, $f(2000)$, $f(4000)$, ..., $f(12{,}000)$. What do they mean in this situation?
   c. Describe the various possible total revenues from selling the tickets.
   d. How many of each ticket must be sold for the revenue to be $602,500?

12. A 25,000-seat amphitheater will sell tickets at $55 and $85 for a U2 concert. Let x and y be the number of tickets that will sell for $55 and $85, respectively. Assume the show will sell out.
   a. Let $R = f(x)$ be the total revenue (in dollars) from selling the $55 and $85 tickets. Find an equation of f.
   b. Use a graphing calculator table to find the values $f(0)$, $f(5000)$, $f(10{,}000)$, ..., $f(25{,}000)$. What do they mean in this situation?

c. Describe the various possible total revenues from selling the tickets.

d. How many of each ticket must be sold for the revenue to be $1,510,000?

13. For flights between Los Angeles and San Francisco, United Airlines® usually uses a 737 airplane that has 8 first-class seats and 126 coach seats. The average price of round-trip first-class tickets is $242 more than the average price of round-trip coach tickets. Assume a round-trip flight is sold out. Let x and y be the prices (in dollars) of coach and first-class tickets, respectively.

a. Let $R = f(x)$ be the total revenue (in dollars) from selling the tickets. Find an equation of f.

b. Find the slope of the graph of f. What does it mean in this situation?

c. If United Airlines wants the total revenue from the tickets for the round trip to be $14,130, what should be the average selling prices of both types of tickets?

Yes sir, the price yesterday was $350. But now it's $800, and it will go up to $1450 tomorrow. Wait that's a black-out date for that price. It will be $1725, nonrefundable, with a $500 fee for any changes.

Ahhh... will there be a movie?

14. An orchestra will perform in an auditorium with 1400 main-level seats and 300 balcony seats. Tickets for the balcony seats will cost $12 less than tickets for the main-level seats. Assume there is a sellout performance. Let x and y be the prices (in dollars) for the main-level seats and the balcony seats, respectively.

a. Let $R = f(x)$ be the total revenue (in dollars) from ticket sales. Find an equation of f.

b. Find $f(55)$. What does it mean in this situation?

c. Find the value of x when $f(x) = 101,800$. What does it mean in this situation?

For Exercises 15–22, all interest rates are five-year averages.

15. A person plans to invest $15,000. She will invest in both an American Funds New Perspective F account at 9% annual interest and an Oppenheimer Global Y account at 11% annual interest. How much should she invest in each account so the total interest in one year will be $1410?

16. A person plans to invest $9000. He will invest in both a Winslow Green Growth account at 17% annual interest and a Columbia Small Cap Growth I Z account at 10% annual

interest. How much should he invest in each account so the total interest in one year will be $1040?

17. A person plans to invest $8500. He will invest in both a GMO Growth III account at 2.3% annual interest and a Gartmore Destinations Mod Agg Svc account at 6.6% annual interest. How much should he invest in each account so the total interest in one year will be $303?

18. A person plans to invest $12,500. She will invest in both a Hartford Small Company Y account at 12.7% annual interest and a CMG Small Cap account at 10.8% annual interest. How much should she invest in each account so the total interest in one year will be $1426?

19. A person plans to invest twice as much money in a Lord Abbett Developing Growth B account at 8.2% annual interest as in a Bridgeway Micro-Cap Limited account at 21.5% annual interest. How much should the person invest in each account to earn a total of $758 in one year?

20. A person plans to invest twice as much money in an MTP Small-Cap Growth Inst I account at 8% annual interest as in a Times Square Small Cap Growth Premier account at 13% annual interest. How much should the person invest in each account to earn a total of $1885 in one year?

21. A person plans to invest three times as much in a Dreyfus Premier Worldwide Growth R account at 4.5% annual interest as in an Oppenheimer Global Opportunities Y account at 14.9% annual interest. How much should the person invest in each account to earn a total of $426 in one year?

22. A person plans to invest three times as much in a Turner Small Cap Growth account at 10.4% annual interest as in a Merrill Lynch Small Cap Growth I account at 12.2% annual interest. How much should the person invest in each account to earn a total of $217 in one year?

23. A person plans to invest a total of $10,000 in a Charter One Bank CD at 2.87% annual interest and a Dodge & Cox Balanced mutual fund that has a three-year average annual interest rate of 8.10%. Let x and y be the money (in dollars) invested in the CD and mutual fund, respectively.

a. Let $I = f(x)$ be the total interest (in dollars) earned from investing the $10,000 for one year. Find an equation of f.

b. Use a graphing calculator to draw a graph of the function f for $0 \le x \le 10,000$. What is the slope? What does it mean in this situation?

c. How much money should be invested in each account to earn a total of $400 in one year?

24. A person plans to invest a total of $5000 in a Citizens Bank CD at 2% annual interest and a Calamos Market Neutral A mutual fund that has a three-year average annual interest rate of 9.45%. Let x and y be the money (in dollars) invested in the CD and the mutual fund, respectively.

a. Let $I = f(x)$ be the total interest (in dollars) earned from investing the $5000 for one year. Find an equation of f.

b. Use a graphing calculator to draw a graph of f for $0 \le x \le 5000$. What is the slope? What does it mean in this situation?

c. How much money should be invested in each account to earn a total of $350 in one year?

25. A person plans to invest a total of $9000 in an ING Direct CD at 2.5% annual interest and a Thompson Plumb Balanced mutual fund that has a three-year average annual interest rate of 9.45%. Let x and y be the money (in dollars) invested in the CD and the mutual fund, respectively.

a. Let $I = f(x)$ be the total interest (in dollars) earned from investing the $9000 for one year. Find an equation of f.

b. Find $f(500)$. What does it mean in this situation?

c. Find the value of x when $f(x) = 500$. What does it mean in this situation?

d. Find $f(10,000)$. What does it mean in this situation?

26. A person plans to invest a total of $12,000 in a Savings Bank of Manchester CD at 1.92% annual interest and a Vanguard Wellesley Income mutual fund that has a three-year average annual interest rate of 8%. Let x and y be the money (in dollars) invested in the CD and the mutual fund, respectively.

a. Let $I = f(x)$ be the total interest (in dollars) earned from investing the $12,000 for one year. Find an equation of f.

b. Find $f(800)$. What does it mean in this situation?

c. Find the value of x when $f(x) = 800$. What does it mean in this situation?

d. Find $f(15,000)$. What does it mean in this situation?

27. A person plans to invest a total of $8000 in a LaSalle Bank CD at 1.5% annual interest and a Bridgeway Aggressive Investors 1 mutual fund that has a three-year average annual interest rate of 11.6%. Let x and y be the money (in dollars) invested in the CD and the mutual fund, respectively.

a. Let $I = f(x)$ be the total interest (in dollars) earned from investing the $8000 for one year. Find an equation of f.

b. A minimum principal of $2500 is required for the LaSalle Bank CD account. Describe the various possible total interest earnings from investing the $8000 in the accounts for one year.

c. How much of the $8000 should be invested in each account so the total interest earned in one year is $400?

28. A person plans to invest a total of $7000 in a Security Bank USA CD at 2.55% annual interest and an Artisan Mid Cap mutual fund that has a three-year average annual interest rate of 8%. Let x and y be the money (in dollars) invested in the CD and the mutual fund, respectively.

a. Let $I = f(x)$ be the total interest (in dollars) earned from investing the $7000 for one year. Find an equation of f.

b. A minimum principal of $500 is required for the Security Bank USA CD account. Describe the various possible total interest earnings from investing the $7000 in the accounts for one year.

c. How much of the $7000 should be invested in each account so the total interest earned in one year is $300?

29. A person plans to invest a total of $6000 in a Nexity Bank CD at 2.85% annual interest and an FMI Focus mutual fund that has a three-year average annual interest rate of 9%. Let x and y be the money (in dollars) invested in the CD and the mutual fund, respectively.

a. Let $I = f(x)$ be the total interest (in dollars) earned from investing the $6000 for one year. Find an equation of f.

b. Find the I-intercept of the model. What does it mean in this situation?

c. Find the x-intercept. What does it mean in this situation?

d. What is the slope? What does it mean in this situation?

30. A person plans to invest a total of $14,000 in a North Middlesex Savings Bank CD at 2.27% annual interest and a Calamos Growth A mutual fund that has a three-year average annual interest rate of 15%. Let x and y be the money (in dollars) invested in the CD and the mutual fund, respectively.

a. Let $I = f(x)$ be the total interest (in dollars) earned from investing the $14,000 for one year. Find an equation of f.

b. Find the I-intercept of the model. What does it mean in this situation?

c. Find the x-intercept. What does it mean in this situation?

d. What is the slope? What does it mean in this situation?

31. A chemist wants to mix a 10% alcohol solution and a 30% alcohol solution to make a 22% alcohol solution. How many ounces of each solution must be mixed to make 10 ounces of the 22% solution?

32. A chemist wants to mix a 10% alcohol solution and a 20% alcohol solution to make a 12% alcohol solution. How many cups of each solution must be mixed to make 5 cups of the 12% solution?

33. How many gallons each of a 5% antifreeze solution and a 20% antifreeze solution must be mixed to make 3 gallons of a 15% antifreeze solution?

34. How many liters each of a 15% antifreeze solution and a 30% antifreeze solution must be mixed to make 6 liters of a 20% antifreeze solution?

35. How many cups each of a 10% acid solution and a 25% acid solution must be mixed to make 6 cups of a 15% solution?

36. How many gallons each of a 10% acid solution and a 30% acid solution must be mixed to make 4 gallons of a 25% solution?

37. A chemist needs 5 liters of a 20% alcohol solution but has only a 25% alcohol solution. How many liters each of the 25% solution and water should she mix to make the desired 5 liters of 20% solution?

38. A chemist needs 9 ounces of a 10% alcohol solution but has only a 15% alcohol solution. How many ounces each of the 15% solution and water should he mix to make the desired 9 ounces of 10% solution?

Concepts

39. If equal amounts of a 15% alcohol solution and a 25% alcohol solution are mixed, what percentage of the mixture is alcohol? Explain.

40. If a person invests equal amounts of money in an account at 4% annual interest and an account at 6% annual interest for one year, what percentage of the total money invested will be the total interest earned? Explain.

For many worked-out examples, we wrote a system of two equations that helped us find quantities for a situation. In the exercises that follow, you will work backward. For example, given the system

$$24x + 35y = 53{,}500$$
$$x + y = 2000$$

we can relate the following to it:

A 2000-seat theater has tickets for sale at $24 and $35. How many tickets should be sold at each price for a sellout performance to generate a total revenue of $53,500?

For Exercises 41–44, describe an authentic situation for the given system. Find the unknown quantities for your situation.

41.
$$x = y - 30$$
$$9500x + 2500y = 579{,}000$$

42.
$$x + y = 9000$$
$$0.04x + 0.07y = 420$$

43.
$$x = 3y$$
$$0.05x + 0.12y = 135$$

44.
$$x + y = 10$$
$$0.15x + 0.35y = 0.27(10)$$

▼ 3.5 Using Linear Inequalities in One Variable to Make Predictions

Objectives

» Know properties of inequalities.

» Know the meaning of *satisfy, solution,* and *solution set* for a *linear inequality in one variable.*

» Solve a linear inequality in one variable, and graph the solution set.

» Solve a three-part inequality in one variable, and graph the solution set.

» Use linear inequalities to make estimates and predictions about authentic situations.

So far in this chapter, we have estimated when one quantity will be equal to another quantity. In this section, we investigate when one quantity is less than (or greater than) another quantity.

Using Models to Compare Quantities

In Example 1, we compare the one-day cost of renting a pickup truck from two companies.

▶ **Example 1**   Using Models to Compare Two Quantities

One Budget® office rents pickup trucks for $39.95 per day plus $0.19 per mile. One U-Haul® location charges $19.95 per day plus $0.49 per mile (Sources: *Budget; U-Haul*).

1. Find models that describe the one-day cost of renting a pickup truck from the companies.
2. Use graphs of your models to estimate for which mileages Budget offers the lower price.

Solution

1. Let $B(d)$ be the one-day cost (in dollars) of driving a Budget pickup truck d miles. Let $U(d)$ be the one-day cost (in dollars) of driving a U-Haul pickup truck d miles. Equations of B and U are

$$C = B(d) = 0.19d + 39.95$$
$$C = U(d) = 0.49d + 19.95$$

2. First, we sketch a graph of B and U in the same coordinate system (see Fig. 37). Note that the graph of B is below the graph of U for $d > 66.7$. Since the height of a point represents a price, we see that Budget offers the lower price for mileages over approximately 66.7 miles.

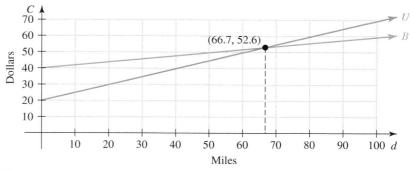

Figure 37 Budget and U-Haul models

In Example 1, we used graphing to estimate the mileages for which Budget's prices are lower than U-Haul's prices. Now we explore how to use inequalities to arrive at such an estimation. We begin by examining properties of inequalities.

Addition Property of Inequalities

In Section 1.6, we discussed the meaning of the inequality symbols $\leq$ (is less than or equal to) and $\geq$ (is greater than or equal to). In this section, we will also work with the symbols $<$ (is less than) and $>$ (is greater than). For example, the *inequality* $2 < 5$ means 2 is less than 5, which is true. The inequality $9 > 5$ means 9 is greater than 5, which is true.

What happens if we add 2 to both sides of the inequality $4 < 7$?

$$4 < 7 \qquad \textit{Original inequality}$$
$$4 + 2 \overset{?}{<} 7 + 2 \qquad \textit{Add 2 to both sides.}$$
$$6 \overset{?}{<} 9 \qquad \textit{Simplify.}$$
$$\text{true}$$

What happens if we add -2 to both sides of the inequality $4 < 7$?

$$4 < 7 \qquad \textit{Original inequality}$$
$$4 + (-2) \overset{?}{<} 7 + (-2) \qquad \textit{Add} -2 \textit{ to both sides.}$$
$$2 \overset{?}{<} 5 \qquad \textit{Simplify.}$$
$$\text{true}$$

These examples suggest the following property.

▶ **Addition Property of Inequalities**

$$\text{If } a < b, \text{ then } a + c < b + c.$$

Similar properties hold for $\leq$, $>$, and $\geq$.

Similar properties hold for subtraction as well, since subtracting a number is the same as adding the opposite of the number.

We can use a number line to illustrate that if $a < b$, then $a + c < b + c$. From Figs. 38 and 39, we see that if a lies to the left of b (that is, $a < b$), then $a + c$ lies to the left of $b + c$ (that is, $a + c < b + c$). In Fig. 38, c is negative; in Fig. 39, c is positive.

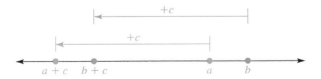

Figure 38 Adding c where c is negative

Figure 39 Adding c where c is positive

Multiplication Property of Inequalities

What if we multiply both sides of the inequality $4 < 7$ by 2?

$$4 < 7 \qquad \textit{Original inequality}$$
$$4(2) \overset{?}{<} 7(2) \qquad \textit{Multiply both sides by 2.}$$
$$8 \overset{?}{<} 14 \qquad \textit{Simplify.}$$
$$\text{true}$$

Finally, what happens if we multiply both sides of $4 < 7$ by -2?

$$4 < 7 \qquad \textit{Original inequality}$$
$$4(-2) \overset{?}{<} 7(-2) \qquad \textit{Multiply both sides by } -2.$$
$$-8 \overset{?}{<} -14 \qquad \textit{Simplify.}$$
$$\text{false}$$

The result is the false statement $-8 < -14$. We can get a *true* statement if we *reverse the inequality symbol* when we multiply both sides of $4 < 7$ by -2:

$$4 < 7 \qquad \textit{Original inequality}$$
$$4(-2) \overset{?}{>} 7(-2) \qquad \textit{Reverse inequality symbol.}$$
$$-8 \overset{?}{>} -14 \qquad \textit{Simplify.}$$
$$\text{true}$$

So, when we multiply both sides of an inequality by a *negative* number, we *reverse* the inequality symbol.

> **Multiplication Property of Inequalities**
>
> - For a *positive* number c, if $a < b$, then $ac < bc$.
> - For a *negative* number c, if $a < b$, then $ac > bc$.
>
> Similar properties hold for $\leq$, $>$, and $\geq$.
>   In words, when we multiply both sides of an inequality by a positive number, we keep the inequality symbol. When we multiply by a negative number, we reverse the inequality symbol.

Similar rules apply for division as well, since dividing by a nonzero number is the same as multiplying by its reciprocal. Therefore, **when we multiply or divide both sides of an inequality by a negative number, we reverse the inequality symbol.**
   Consider multiplying both sides of $a < b$ by -1:

$$a < b \qquad \textit{Original inequality}$$
$$-1a > -1b \qquad \textit{Multiply both sides by } -1; \textit{reverse inequality symbol.}$$
$$-a > -b \qquad -1a = -a$$

So, if $a < b$, then $-a > -b$. We can use a number line to illustrate this fact. To plot the point for $-a$, we move the point for a to the other side of the origin so that the points for $-a$ and a are the same distance from the origin (see Fig. 40).

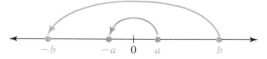

Figure 40 The points for a, b, $-a$, and $-b$

From Fig. 40, we see that if a lies to the *left* of b ($a < b$), then $-a$ lies to the *right* of $-b$ (that is, $-a > -b$).

Solving Linear Inequalities in One Variable

Here are some examples of *linear inequalities in one variable:*

$$4x - 6 < 8 \qquad 5x \leq 13 \qquad 2(x - 4) + 7 > -3 \qquad 5x \geq 2x - 6$$

▶ Definition   Linear inequality in one variable

A **linear inequality in one variable** is an inequality that can be put into one of the forms

$$mx + b < 0, \qquad mx + b \leq 0, \qquad mx + b > 0, \qquad mx + b \geq 0$$

where m and b are constants and $m \neq 0$.

We say a number **satisfies** an inequality in one variable if the inequality becomes a true statement after we have substituted the number for the variable. We call such a number a *solution* of the inequality.

▶ Example 2   Finding Solutions of an Inequality

1. Does the number 2 satisfy the inequality $3x - 5 < 7$?
2. Does the number 6 satisfy the inequality $3x - 5 < 7$?
3. Find all solutions of the inequality $3x - 5 < 7$.

Solution

1. We substitute 2 for x in the inequality $3x - 5 < 7$:

$$3(2) - 5 \overset{?}{<} 7 \qquad \textit{Substitute 2 for x.}$$
$$6 - 5 \overset{?}{<} 7 \qquad \textit{Multiply.}$$
$$1 \overset{?}{<} 7 \qquad \textit{Subtract.}$$
$$\text{true}$$

So, 2 satisfies the inequality $3x - 5 < 7$.

2. Here, we substitute 6 for x in the inequality $3x - 5 < 7$:

$$3(6) - 5 \overset{?}{<} 7 \qquad \textit{Substitute 6 for x.}$$
$$18 - 5 \overset{?}{<} 7 \qquad \textit{Multiply.}$$
$$13 \overset{?}{<} 7 \qquad \textit{Subtract.}$$
$$\text{false}$$

So, 6 does not satisfy the inequality $3x - 5 < 7$.

3. To find all solutions of the inequality, we use properties of inequalities:

$$3x - 5 < 7 \qquad \textit{Original inequality}$$
$$3x - 5 + 5 < 7 + 5 \qquad \textit{Add 5 to both sides.}$$
$$3x < 12 \qquad \textit{Combine like terms.}$$
$$\frac{3x}{3} < \frac{12}{3} \qquad \textit{Divide both sides by 3.}$$
$$x < 4 \qquad \textit{Simplify.}$$

All numbers less than 4 satisfy the inequality $3x - 5 < 7$. The solutions of the inequality are all numbers less than 4.

▶

▶ Definition   Solution of an inequality in one variable

We say a number is a **solution** of an inequality in one variable if it satisfies the inequality. The **solution set** of an inequality is the set of all solutions of the inequality. We **solve** an inequality by finding its solution set.

To solve a linear inequality in one variable, we apply properties of inequalities to get the variable alone on one side of the inequality.

▶ Example 3 Solving a Linear Inequality

Solve the inequality $-2x \geq 10$.

Solution

We divide both sides of the inequality by -2, a negative number:

$$-2x \geq 10 \qquad \textit{Original inequality}$$

$$\frac{-2x}{-2} \leq \frac{10}{-2} \qquad \textit{Divide both sides by } -2; \textit{ reverse inequality symbol.}$$

$$x \leq -5 \qquad \textit{Simplify.}$$

Since we divided by a negative number, we reversed the direction of the inequality. The solution set is the set of all numbers less than or equal to -5.

WARNING

It is a common error to forget to reverse an inequality symbol when you multiply or divide both sides of an inequality by a negative number. For instance, in Example 3, it was important that we reversed the inequality symbol $\geq$ when we divided both sides of the inequality $-2x \geq 10$ by -2.

In Example 3, we found that the solution set of $-2x \geq 10$ is the set of all real numbers less than or equal to -5. We can represent these solutions graphically on a number line by shading the part of the number line that lies to the left of -5 (see Fig. 41). We draw a filled-in circle at -5 to indicate that -5 is a solution, too.

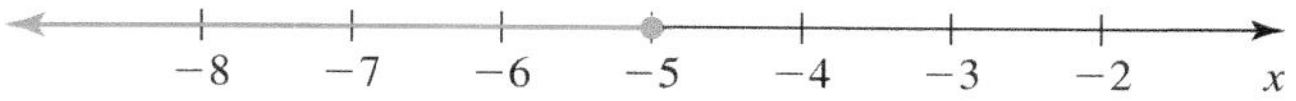

Figure 41 Graph of $x \leq -5$

If the solution set of an inequality is the set of numbers where $x < -5$, we shade the part of the number line that lies to the left of -5 but draw an *open* circle at -5 to indicate that -5 is *not* a solution (see Fig. 42).

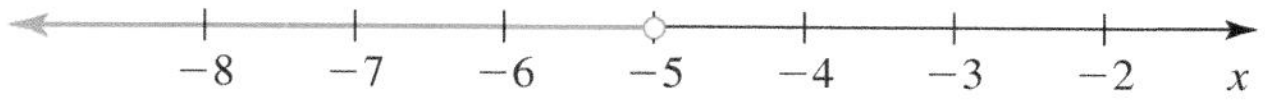

Figure 42 Graph of $x < -5$

More examples of inequalities, with matching graphs, are given in Fig. 43.

In Words	Inequality	Graph	Interval Notation
Numbers less than 2	$x < 2$	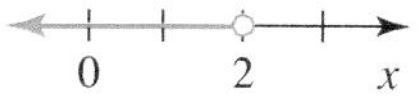	$(-\infty, 2)$
Numbers less than or equal to 2	$x \leq 2$	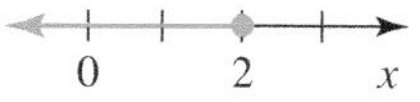	$(-\infty, 2]$
Numbers greater than 2	$x > 2$	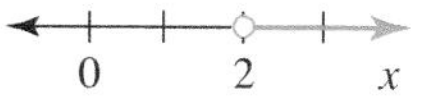	$(2, \infty)$
Numbers greater than or equal to 2	$x \geq 2$	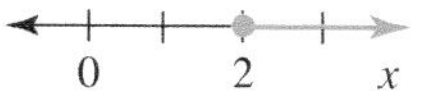	$[2, \infty)$

Figure 43 Words, inequalities, graphs, and interval notation

We can use **interval notation** to describe the solution set of an inequality. For example, we describe the numbers greater than 2 by $(2, \infty)$. We describe the numbers greater than or equal to 2 by $[2, \infty)$. We describe the set of real numbers by $(-\infty, \infty)$. More examples of interval notation are shown in Fig. 43.

Each of the four sets of numbers described in Fig. 43 is an interval. An **interval** is a set of real numbers represented by the number line or by an unbroken portion of it.

▶ Example 4   Solving a Linear Inequality

Solve $-3(4x - 5) - 1 \leq 17 - 6x$. Describe the solution set as an inequality, in a graph, and in interval notation.

Solution

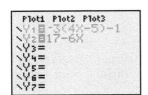

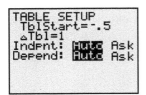

$$-3(4x - 5) - 1 \leq 17 - 6x \qquad \text{\textit{Original inequality}}$$
$$-12x + 15 - 1 \leq 17 - 6x \qquad \text{\textit{Distributive law}}$$
$$-12x + 14 \leq 17 - 6x \qquad \text{\textit{Combine like terms.}}$$
$$-12x + 14 + 6x \leq 17 - 6x + 6x \qquad \text{\textit{Add 6x to both sides.}}$$
$$-6x + 14 \leq 17 \qquad \text{\textit{Combine like terms.}}$$
$$-6x + 14 - 14 \leq 17 - 14 \qquad \text{\textit{Subtract 14 from both sides.}}$$
$$-6x \leq 3 \qquad \text{\textit{Combine like terms.}}$$
$$\frac{-6x}{-6} \geq \frac{3}{-6} \qquad \text{\textit{Divide both sides by }-6\text{; reverse inequality symbol.}}$$
$$x \geq -\frac{1}{2} \qquad \text{\textit{Simplify.}}$$

We can graph the solution set on a number line (see Fig. 44), or we can describe the solution set in interval notation as $\left[-\dfrac{1}{2}, \infty \right)$.

Figure 44 Graph of $x \geq -\dfrac{1}{2}$

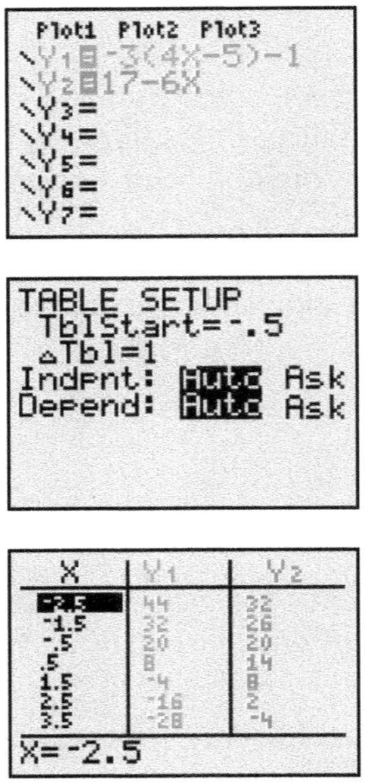

To verify our result, we check that, for inputs greater than or equal to $-\dfrac{1}{2}$, the outputs of $y = -3(4x - 5) - 1$ are less than or equal to the outputs of $y = 17 - 6x$ (see Fig. 45). We do this by setting up the table shown in the figure so that x begins at -0.5 and increases by 1. Then, we scroll up two rows so we can view both values of x that are less than -0.5 and values of x that are greater than -0.5. For graphing calculator instructions, see Appendix B.14.

Figure 45 Verify the result

▶ Example 5   Solving a Linear Inequality

Solve $\dfrac{3x + 5}{4} - \dfrac{2x - 7}{6} < \dfrac{11}{3}$. Describe the solution set as an inequality, in interval notation, and in a graph.

Solution

First, we multiply both sides of the inequality by the LCD, 12:

$$12\left(\frac{3x + 5}{4} - \frac{2x - 7}{6} \right) < 12 \cdot \frac{11}{3} \qquad \text{\textit{Multiply both sides by LCD, 12.}}$$
$$12 \cdot \frac{3x + 5}{4} - 12 \cdot \frac{2x - 7}{6} < 12 \cdot \frac{11}{3} \qquad \text{\textit{Distributive law}}$$
$$3(3x + 5) - 2(2x - 7) < 44 \qquad \text{\textit{Simplify.}}$$
$$9x + 15 - 4x + 14 < 44 \qquad \text{\textit{Distributive law}}$$
$$5x + 29 < 44 \qquad \text{\textit{Combine like terms.}}$$
$$5x + 29 - 29 < 44 - 29 \qquad \text{\textit{Subtract 29 from both sides.}}$$
$$5x < 15 \qquad \text{\textit{Combine like terms.}}$$
$$\frac{5x}{5} < \frac{15}{5} \qquad \text{\textit{Divide both sides by 5.}}$$
$$x < 3 \qquad \text{\textit{Simplify.}}$$

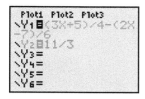

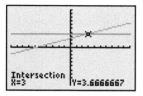

Figure 47 Verify the work

We graph the solution set, $(-\infty, 3)$, in Fig. 46.

Figure 46 Graph of $x < 3$

To verify our result, we check that, for values of x less than 3, the graph of the equation $y = \dfrac{3x + 5}{4} - \dfrac{2x - 7}{6}$ is below the horizontal line $y = \dfrac{11}{3}$. See Fig. 47.

Three-Part Inequalities

Now we will work with *three-part inequalities in one variable,* such as $3 \le x \le 7$. Recall from Section 1.6 that $3 \le x \le 7$ means the values of x are *both* greater than or equal to 3 *and* less than or equal to 7. In other words, all values of x are between 3 and 7, inclusive. To graph the solutions, we shade the part of the number line that lies between 3 and 7 (see Fig. 48). We draw filled-in circles at 3 and 7 to indicate that 3 and 7 are solutions, too.

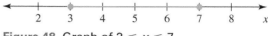

Figure 48 Graph of $3 \le x \le 7$

We describe the numbers between 3 and 7, inclusive, in interval notation by [3, 7]. More examples of three-part inequalities, with matching graphs and interval notation, are shown in Fig. 49.

In Words	Inequality	Graph	Interval Notation
Numbers between 1 and 3	$1 < x < 3$		$(1, 3)$
Numbers between 1 and 3, inclusive	$1 \le x \le 3$		$[1, 3]$
Numbers between 1 and 3, as well as 1	$1 \le x < 3$		$[1, 3)$
Numbers between 1 and 3, as well as 3	$1 < x \le 3$		$(1, 3]$

Figure 49 Words, inequalities, graphs, and interval notations

WARNING   We use notation such as $(3, 7)$ in two ways: When we work with one variable, the *interval* $(3, 7)$ is the set of numbers between 3 and 7; when we work with two variables, such as x and y, the *ordered pair* $(3, 7)$ means $x = 3$ and $y = 7$.

▶ **Example 6** Solving a Three-Part Inequality

Solve $-5 < 2x - 1 < 7$.

Solution

We can get x alone in the "middle part" of the inequality by applying the same operations to all three parts of the inequality:

$$-5 < 2x - 1 < 7 \qquad \textit{Original inequality}$$
$$-5 + 1 < 2x - 1 + 1 < 7 + 1 \qquad \textit{Add 1 to all three parts.}$$
$$-4 < 2x < 8 \qquad \textit{Combine like terms.}$$
$$\frac{-4}{2} < \frac{2x}{2} < \frac{8}{2} \qquad \textit{Divide all three parts by 2.}$$
$$-2 < x < 4 \qquad \textit{Simplify.}$$

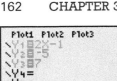

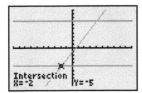

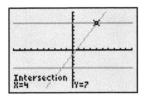

Figure 51 Verify the work

So, the solution set is the set of numbers between -2 and 4. We can graph the solution set on a number line (see Fig. 50), or we can describe the solution set in interval notation as $(-2, 4)$.

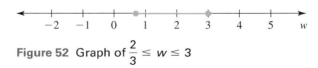

Figure 50 Graph of $-2 < x < 4$

To verify our result, we check that, for values of x between -2 and 4, the graph of $y = 2x - 1$ is between the horizontal lines $y = -5$ and $y = 7$ (see Fig. 51).

▶ **Example 7** Solving a Three-Part Inequality

Solve $\dfrac{1}{2} \le 5 - \dfrac{3}{2}w \le 4$.

Solution

$$\dfrac{1}{2} \le 5 - \dfrac{3}{2}w \le 4 \qquad \textit{Original inequality}$$

$$2 \cdot \dfrac{1}{2} \le 2 \cdot 5 - 2 \cdot \dfrac{3}{2}w \le 2 \cdot 4 \qquad \textit{Multiply all three parts by LCD, 2.}$$

$$1 \le 10 - 3w \le 8 \qquad \textit{Simplify.}$$

$$1 - 10 \le 10 - 3w - 10 \le 8 - 10 \qquad \textit{Subtract 10 from all three parts.}$$

$$-9 \le -3w \le -2 \qquad \textit{Combine like terms.}$$

$$\dfrac{-9}{-3} \ge \dfrac{-3w}{-3} \ge \dfrac{-2}{-3} \qquad \textit{Divide all three parts by } -3; \textit{ reverse inequality symbols.}$$

$$3 \ge w \ge \dfrac{2}{3} \qquad \textit{Simplify.}$$

$$\dfrac{2}{3} \le w \le 3 \qquad \textit{Write in form } a \le w \le b.$$

So, the solution set is the set of numbers between $\dfrac{2}{3}$ and 3, inclusive. We can graph the solution set on a number line (see Fig. 52), or we can describe the solution set in interval notation as $\left[\dfrac{2}{3}, 3\right]$.

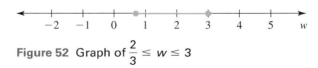

Figure 52 Graph of $\dfrac{2}{3} \le w \le 3$

Using Linear Inequalities to Make Estimates and Predictions

In Example 1, we used graphing to estimate for what mileages Budget offers a lower price than U-Haul. In Example 8, we solve an inequality to make the estimate.

▶ **Example 8** Using Models to Compare Two Quantities

In Example 1, we modeled the one-day pickup truck costs (in dollars) $B(d)$ and $U(d)$ at Budget and U-Haul, respectively, by the system

$$C = B(d) = 0.19d + 39.95$$
$$C = U(d) = 0.49d + 19.95$$

where d is the number of miles driven. Use inequalities to estimate for which mileages Budget offers the lower price.

Solution

Budget offers the lower price when

$$B(d) < U(d)$$

We substitute $0.19d + 39.95$ for $B(d)$ and $0.49d + 19.95$ for $U(d)$ to get a linear inequality in one variable:

$$0.19d + 39.95 < 0.49d + 19.95$$

Then we solve the inequality by isolating d on the left side of the inequality:

$0.19d + 39.95 < 0.49d + 19.95$	*Original inequality*
$0.19d + 39.95 - 0.49d < 0.49d + 19.95 - 0.49d$	*Subtract 0.49d from both sides.*
$-0.30d + 39.95 < 19.95$	*Combine like terms.*
$-0.30d + 39.95 - 39.95 < 19.95 - 39.95$	*Subtract 39.95 from both sides.*
$-0.30d < -20$	*Combine like terms.*
$\dfrac{-0.30d}{-0.30} > \dfrac{-20}{-0.30}$	*Divide both sides by −0.30; reverse inequality symbol.*
$d > 66.\overline{6}$	*$66.\overline{6}$ represents 66.666....*

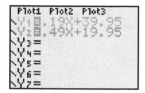

Budget offers the lower price if the truck is driven over $66.\overline{6}$ miles, about the same result we found in Example 1.

To verify our result, we check that, for inputs greater than $66.\overline{6}$, the outputs of $y = 0.19x + 39.95$ are less than the outputs of $y = 0.49x + 19.95$ (see Fig. 53). We do this by setting up the table shown in the figure so that x begins at about $66.\overline{6}$ and increases by 1. Then, we scroll up three rows so we can view values of x that are less than $66.\overline{6}$ and values that are greater than $66.\overline{6}$.

From Fig. 53, we see that Budget's costs, in column Y_1, are less than U-Haul's costs, in column Y_2, for distances above $66.\overline{6}$ miles.

Figure 53 Verify the result

 Group Exploration

Meaning of the solution set of an inequality

We solve the inequality $-3x + 7 < 1$:

$$-3x + 7 < 1$$
$$-3x + 7 - 7 < 1 - 7$$
$$-3x < -6$$
$$\frac{-3x}{-3} > \frac{-6}{-3}$$
$$x > 2$$

1. Choose a number greater than 2. Check that your number satisfies the inequality $-3x + 7 < 1$.

2. Choose two more numbers greater than 2. Check that both of these numbers satisfy the inequality $-3x + 7 < 1$.

3. Choose three numbers that are *not* greater than 2. Show that each of these numbers does *not* satisfy the inequality $-3x + 7 < 1$.

4. Explain what it means when we write $x > 2$ as the last step in solving the inequality $-3x + 7 < 1$.

▶ Tips for Success   **Form a Study Team**

You can prepare for an exam by meeting with a study team. It usually works best if you form a team with students who are at your level of ability in this course. That will allow everyone to make contributions and will make everyone feel more comfortable asking questions about troublesome concepts.

Also, spend some time studying alone. This will ensure you understand the concepts and can solve the relevant problems without help from your study team.

Homework 3.5

1. Use words, inequalities, graphs, and interval notation to complete Fig. 54.

In Words	Inequality	Graph	Interval Notation
Numbers greater than 3			
	$x < 5$	(graph, points at −4, 0 x)	
			$[-1, \infty)$

Figure 54 Exercise 1

2. Use words, inequalities, graphs, and interval notation to complete Fig. 55.

In Words	Inequality	Graph	Interval Notation
		 (graph, points at 0, 5 x)	
Numbers less than or equal to −6			
	$x \geq -3$		$(-\infty, 4)$

Figure 55 Exercise 2

Use a symbolic method to solve the inequality. Describe the solution set as an inequality, in interval notation, and in a graph. Then, use graphing calculator tables or graphs to verify your result.

3. $x + 2 \geq 5$

4. $x - 3 < 8$

5. $-4x \geq 12$

6. $-7x > 21$

7. $2w + 7 < 11$

8. $15 - 4t \leq 0$

9. $9x < 4 + 5x$

10. $-5x > -15 - 2x$

11. $2.1x - 7.4 \leq 4.36$

12. $6.6 - 5.2x > 20.64$

13. $2b - 3 > 7b + 22$

14. $6p - 2 \geq 4p - 14$

15. $3 - 2(x - 4) > 4x + 1$

16. $-5(2x + 4) + 1 \leq 3x - 3$

17. $6.2a + 61.31 < 5(3.1 - 2.7a) + 0.5$

18. $13.5 - 4.1w \leq 2(w + 6.4) - 5.9w$

19. $7(x + 1) - 8(x - 2) \leq 0$

20. $-3(2x + 1) - 2(x + 4) > 0$

21. $5r - 4(2r - 6) - 1 \geq 3(3r - 1) + r$

22. $3p - 6(4p + 3) + 4 < 5(2p - 7) - 4p$

23. $-\dfrac{2}{3}x > 4$

24. $-\dfrac{1}{4}x \leq 2$

25. $\dfrac{2}{3} - \dfrac{3}{4}t \leq \dfrac{5}{2}$

26. $\dfrac{5}{8} + \dfrac{1}{6}b > \dfrac{2}{3}$

27. $-\dfrac{1}{2}x - \dfrac{5}{6} \geq \dfrac{1}{3} + \dfrac{3}{2}x$

28. $-\dfrac{3}{4}x + \dfrac{5}{2} < \dfrac{7}{8} - \dfrac{5}{2}x$

29. $\dfrac{4c - 5}{6} \leq \dfrac{3c + 7}{4}$

30. $\dfrac{6p + 2}{8} \geq \dfrac{4p - 1}{6}$

31. $\dfrac{3x + 1}{6} - \dfrac{5x - 2}{9} > \dfrac{2}{3}$

32. $\dfrac{4x - 7}{15} + \dfrac{2x + 3}{10} < \dfrac{2}{5}$

Use a symbolic method to solve the inequality. Describe the solution set as an inequality, in interval notation, and in a graph. Then, use graphing calculator tables or graphs to verify your result.

33. $4 < x + 3 < 8$

34. $-2 < x - 4 < 3$

35. $-15 \leq 2x - 5 \leq 7$

36. $-5 \leq 3x + 1 \leq 13$

37. $-17 < 3 - 4x \leq 15$

38. $7 < 5 - 2x \leq 13$

39. $\dfrac{1}{3} \leq 4 - \dfrac{2}{3}x < 2$

40. $\dfrac{3}{4} \leq 1 - \dfrac{1}{4}x < 3$

41. In Exercise 11 of Homework 3.3, the values (in dollars) $F(t)$ and $D(t)$ for a 2011 Ford Fusion and a 2011 Cadillac DTS, respectively, are modeled by the system

$$V = F(t) = -1414t + 14{,}290$$
$$V = D(t) = -3740t + 30{,}450$$

where t is the number of years since 2012 (Source: *MotorTrend*). For what years will the value of the 2011 Fusion be less than the value of the 2011 DTS?

42. In Example 3 of Section 3.3, the values (in dollars) $R(t)$ and $C(t)$ for a 2011 Acura RL and a 2011 Chevrolet Impala LS sedan, respectively, are modeled by the system

$$V = R(t) = -4245t + 37{,}120$$
$$V = C(t) = -1200t + 14{,}050$$

where t is the number of years since 2012 (Source: *MotorTrend*). For what years will the value of the 2011 RL be less than the value of the 2011 Impala?

43. One U-Haul office rents 10-foot trucks for a one-day fee of $19.95 plus $0.69 per mile. One Penske® office charges a one-day fee of $29.95 plus $0.39 per mile (Sources: *U-Haul; Penske*).
    a. Let $U(d)$ be U-Haul's charge (in dollars) and $P(d)$ be Penske's charge (in dollars), both for driving d miles in one day. Find equations of U and P.
    b. For how many miles driven is the one-day charge at U-Haul less than the charge at Penske?

44. One Penske office rents 15-foot trucks for a one-day fee of $39.95 plus $0.29 per mile. One Budget office charges a one-day fee of $59.95 plus $0.19 per mile (Sources: *Penske; Budget*).
    a. Let $P(d)$ be Penske's charge (in dollars) for driving d miles in one day. Let $B(d)$ be Budget's charge (in dollars) for driving d miles in one day. Find equations of P and B.
    b. For how many miles driven is the one-day charge at Penske less than the charge at Budget?

45. The percentage of residents of Ohio who smoke was 20.3% in 2009 and has decreased by about 0.85 percentage point per year since then. The percentage of residents of Wisconsin who smoke was 18.8% in 2009 and has decreased by about 0.61 percentage point since then (Source: *Centers for Disease Control and Prevention*). Predict in which years the percentage of residents of Ohio who smoke will be less than the percentage of residents of Wisconsin who smoke.

46. The percentage of Americans who watched an online video in the past week was 29% in 2010 and has increased by 4.25 percentage points per year since then. The percentage of Americans who listened to online radio in the past week was 17% in 2010

and has increased by 1.25 percentage points per year since then (Source: *Edison Research and Arbitron*). Estimate in which years the percentage of Americans who listened to online radio in the past week was greater than the percentage of Americans who watched an online video in the past week.

47. The revenues from music (both singles and albums) in the format of downloads and CDs are shown in Table 29 for various years.

Table 29 Annual Revenues from Music: Downloads and CDs

| Year | Annual Revenue (billions of dollars) | |
	Downloads	CDs
2006	0.86	9.39
2007	1.23	7.47
2008	1.67	5.48
2009	1.98	4.28
2010	2.20	3.37

Source: *Recording Industry Association of America*

a. Let $D(t)$ be the annual revenue from downloaded music and $C(t)$ be the annual revenue from music CDs, both in billions of dollars, at t years since 2005. Find equations of D and C.

b. Predict in which years the revenue from downloaded music will be more than the revenue from music CDs.

c. Find the sum of the slopes of the graphs of D and C. What does it mean in this situation?

48. The annual U.S. per-person consumptions of whole milk and the annual U.S. per-person consumptions of lower fat and skim milk are shown in Table 30 for various years.

Table 30 Annual U.S. Per-Person Consumptions of Whole Milk, Lower Fat and Skim Milk

| Year | Annual Consumption (gallons per person) | |
	Whole Milk	Lower Fat and Skim Milk
1955	33.5	2.9
1965	28.8	3.7
1975	21.7	8.1
1985	14.3	12.3
1995	8.6	15.3
2005	7.0	14.1
2010	5.6	14.8

Source: *USDA/Economic Research Service*

a. Let $W(t)$ be the annual consumption of whole milk and $L(t)$ be the annual consumption of lower fat and skim milk, both in gallons per person, at t years since 1900. Find equations of W and L.

b. Estimate whether there was greater consumption of whole milk or lower fat and skim milk in 2012. By how much?

c. Estimate in which years the annual consumption of whole milk was greater than the annual consumption of lower fat and skim milk.

d. Find the sum of the slopes of the graphs of W and L. What does it mean in this situation?

49. In Example 1 of Section 3.1, birth-year life expectancies (in years) $W(t)$ and $M(t)$ for women and men, respectively, in the United States are modeled by the system

$$L = W(t) = 0.115t + 77.44$$
$$L = M(t) = 0.208t + 69.86$$

where t is the number of years since 1980 (see Table 31).

Table 31 U.S. Life Expectancies of Women and Men

Year of Birth	Women (years)	Men (years)
1980	77.4	70.0
1985	78.2	71.1
1990	78.8	71.8
1995	78.9	72.5
2000	79.5	74.1
2005	79.9	74.9
2009	81.3	76.2

Source: *U.S. Census Bureau*

a. Of those born in 2018, how much longer are women likely to live than men, on average?

b. Use a symbolic method to predict the birth years for which men will have a longer life expectancy than women. Verify your result by a graphical method.

c. A woman born in 1980 wants to choose a man to marry so that she does not outlive him.
   i. According to the linear models, should the woman marry a younger or an older man? Explain your reasoning.
   ii. What are acceptable birth years for potential husbands? [**Hint:** There is a way to do this by using an inequality. If you draw a blank, do it *by trial and error*.]

50. Zetia, Vytorin, and Lipitor are cholesterol drugs. The total market shares of Zetia and Vytorin and the market shares of Lipitor are shown in Table 32 for various years.

Table 32 Market Shares of Cholesterol Drugs

| Year | Market Share | |
	Zetia and Vytorin	Lipitor
2003	1	54
2004	5	51
2005	10	48
2006	17	44
2007	19	38

Source: *Raymond James; Wolters Kluwer*

a. Let $Z(t)$ be the total market share of Zetia and Vytorin and $L(t)$ be the market share of Lipitor, both at t years since 2000. Find equations of Z and L.

b. Find $Z(8)$ and $L(8)$. Which result is larger? What does this mean in this situation?

c. Predict when the total market share of Zetia and Vytorin will be greater than the market share for Lipitor.

d. Find the sum of the slopes of the graphs of Z and L. What does it mean in this situation?

Concepts

51. A student tries to solve the inequality $3x + 7 > 1$:

$$3x + 7 > 1$$
$$3x + 7 - 7 > 1 - 7$$
$$3x > -6$$
$$\frac{3x}{3} < \frac{-6}{3}$$
$$x < -2$$

Describe any errors. Then solve the inequality correctly.

52. A student tries to solve the inequality $-10x + 3 \leq -17$:

$$-10x + 3 \leq -17$$
$$-10x + 3 - 3 \leq -17 - 3$$
$$-10x \leq -20$$
$$\frac{-10x}{-10} \leq \frac{-20}{-10}$$
$$x \leq 2$$

Describe any errors. Then solve the inequality correctly.

53. a. List three numbers that satisfy the inequality

$$3(x - 2) + 1 \geq 7 - 4x$$

  b. List three numbers that do not satisfy the inequality

$$3(x - 2) + 1 \geq 7 - 4x$$

54. Solve the inequality $2x + 1 > 2x + 1$.

55. Find values of m and c so the solution set of the inequality $mx < c$ is the set of numbers where $x > 2$.

56. a. Is the following statement true?

$$\text{If } a < b, \text{ then } a - c < b - c.$$

  Explain.

  b. Is the following statement true?

$$\text{If } a < b \text{ and } c \neq 0, \text{ then } \frac{a}{c} < \frac{b}{c}.$$

  Explain.

57. a. Solve $x + 1 = -2x + 10$.
  b. Solve $x + 1 < -2x + 10$.
  c. Solve $x + 1 > -2x + 10$.
  d. Graph the solutions in parts (a), (b), and (c) on the same number line. Use three colors to identify the different solutions. Make observations about the solutions.
  e. Use a graphing calculator to graph $f(x) = x + 1$ and $g(x) = -2x + 10$ in the same viewing window. Explain how the observations you made in part (d) are related to these graphs.

58. a. Solve $2x - 1 = -3x + 9$.
  b. Solve $2x - 1 < -3x + 9$.
  c. Solve $2x - 1 > -3x + 9$.
  d. Graph the solutions in parts (a), (b), and (c) on the same number line. Use three colors to identify the different solutions. Make observations about the solutions.
  e. Use a graphing calculator to graph $f(x) = 2x - 1$ and $g(x) = -3x + 9$ in the same viewing window. Explain how the observations you made in part (d) are related to these graphs.

For Exercises 59–62, refer to Fig. 56. Is the statement true? Explain.

59. $f(-4) > g(-4)$ **60.** $f(2) \geq g(2)$
61. $f(-1) < g(-1)$ **62.** $f(-1) \leq g(-1)$

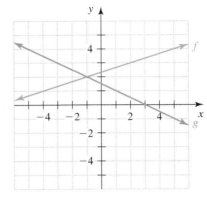

Figure 56
Exercises 59–62

63. Graphs of the linear functions f and g are sketched in Fig. 57. Approximate the solution set of the inequality $f(x) > g(x)$.

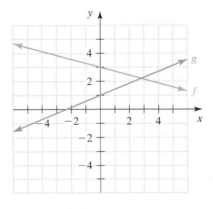

Figure 57 Exercise 63

64. Graphs of the linear functions f and g are sketched in Fig. 58. Determine which is the graph of f and which is the graph of g if the solution set of the inequality $f(x) \leq g(x)$ is the set of numbers where $x \geq 2$.

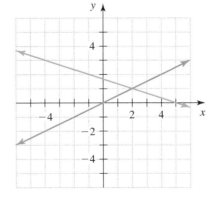

Figure 58 Exercise 64

65. Use the number line to show that if $a < b$, then $2a < 2b$.

66. Use the number line to show that if $a < b$, then $-2a > -2b$.

67. Describe how to solve a linear inequality in one variable. Include a description of when and why you need to reverse the inequality symbol. Finally, explain what you have accomplished by solving an inequality.

▼3.6 Linear Inequalities in Two Variables; Systems of Linear Inequalities

Objectives

» Graph a *linear inequality in two variables*.

» Solve a *system of linear inequalities in two variables*.

» Use a system of linear inequalities in two variables to make estimates.

Recall from Section 1.2 that a linear equation in two variables is an equation that can be put into the form $y = mx + b$ or $x = a$, where m, a, and b are constants. A **linear inequality in two variables** is an inequality that can be put into the form

$$y < mx + b \qquad \text{or} \qquad x < a$$

(or with $<$ replaced with $\leq$, $>$, or $\geq$), where m, a, and b are constants. Here are some examples:

$$y < 2x + 9 \qquad y \leq -4x - 7 \qquad 3x - 8y > 24 \qquad x \geq 5$$

First, we will work with one linear inequality in two variables. Then we will work with two or more such inequalities.

Linear Inequalities in Two Variables

We use the terms *solution*, *satisfy*, and *solution set* for an inequality in two variables in much the same way that we have used them for equations in one or two variables and inequalities in one variable.

▶ Definition   *Satisfy, solution, solution set*, and *solve* for an inequality in two variables

If an inequality in the two variables x and y becomes a true statement when a is substituted for x and b is substituted for y, we say the ordered pair (a, b) **satisfies** the inequality and call (a, b) a **solution** of the inequality. The **solution set** of an inequality is the set of all solutions of the inequality. We **solve** the inequality by finding its solution set.

We describe the solution set of an inequality by graphing all of the solutions.

▶ **Example 1**   Sketching the Graph of an Inequality

Graph $y > \dfrac{1}{2}x + 1$.

Solution

We begin by sketching a graph of $y = \dfrac{1}{2}x + 1$ (see Fig. 59).

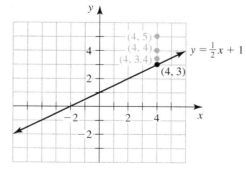

Figure 59 Some solutions of $y > \dfrac{1}{2}x + 1$ (in blue)

To investigate how to solve $y > \dfrac{1}{2}x + 1$, we choose a value of x (say, 4) and find several solutions with an x-coordinate of 4. For $y = \dfrac{1}{2}x + 1$, if $x = 4$, then $y = \dfrac{1}{2}(4) + 1 = 3$. So, the point $(4, 3)$ is on the line $y = \dfrac{1}{2}x + 1$.

For $y > \frac{1}{2}x + 1$, if $x = 4$, then

$$y > \frac{1}{2}(4) + 1$$
$$y > 3$$

So, if $x = 4$, some possible values of y are $y = 3.4$, $y = 4$, and $y = 5$. The points $(4, 3.4)$, $(4, 4)$, and $(4, 5)$ lie *above* the point $(4, 3)$, which is on the line $y = \frac{1}{2}x + 1$ (see Fig. 59).

We could choose values of x other than 4 and go through a similar argument. These investigations would suggest that the solutions of $y > \frac{1}{2}x + 1$ lie *above* the graph of $y = \frac{1}{2}x + 1$, which is true. In Fig. 60, we shade the region that contains all of the points that represent solutions of $y > \frac{1}{2}x + 1$.

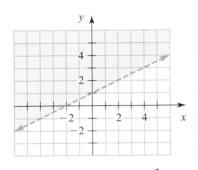

Figure 60 Graph of $y > \frac{1}{2}x + 1$

We *dash* the line $y = \frac{1}{2}x + 1$ in Fig. 60 to indicate that its points are *not* solutions of $y > \frac{1}{2}x + 1$. For example, the point $(4, 3)$ on the line $y = \frac{1}{2}x + 1$ does *not* satisfy the inequality $y > \frac{1}{2}x + 1$:

$$y > \frac{1}{2}x + 1 \quad \text{\textit{Original inequality}}$$

$$3 \overset{?}{>} \frac{1}{2}(4) + 1 \quad \text{\textit{Substitute 4 for x and 3 for y.}}$$

$$3 \overset{?}{>} 3 \quad\quad\quad \text{\textit{Simplify.}}$$

$$\text{false}$$

We can draw a graph of $y > \frac{1}{2}x + 1$ by using a graphing calculator (see Fig. 61), but we have to imagine the border $y = \frac{1}{2}x + 1$ is drawn as a dashed line. To shade above a line, press $\boxed{Y=}$ and press $\boxed{\triangleleft}$ twice. Next, press $\boxed{\text{ENTER}}$ as many times as necessary for the triangle shown in Fig. 61 to appear.

Figure 61 Graph of $y > \frac{1}{2}x + 1$ (imagine the border is a dashed line)

▶ **Example 2**   Sketching the Graph of an Inequality

Sketch a graph of $y \le \frac{3}{4}x - 1$.

Solution

The graph of $y \le \frac{3}{4}x - 1$ is the line $y = \frac{3}{4}x - 1$ and the region below that line (see Fig. 62). We use a *solid* line as the border $y = \frac{3}{4}x - 1$ to indicate that the points on the line $y = \frac{3}{4}x - 1$ are solutions of $y \le \frac{3}{4}x - 1$.

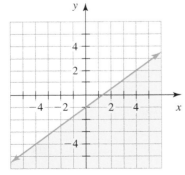

Figure 62 Graph of $y \le \frac{3}{4}x - 1$

> **Graph of an Inequality in Two Variables**

- The graph of an inequality of the form $y > mx + b$ is the region above the line $y = mx + b$. The graph of an inequality of the form $y < mx + b$ is the region below the line $y = mx + b$. For either inequality, we use a dashed line to show that $y = mx + b$ is not part of the graph.
- The graph of an inequality of the form $y \geq mx + b$ is the line $y = mx + b$ and the region above that line. The graph of an inequality of the form $y \leq mx + b$ is the line $y = mx + b$ and the region below that line.

To sketch a graph of an inequality in two variables, if the variable y is not alone on one side of the inequality, we begin by isolating it. Recall from Section 3.5 that when we multiply or divide both sides of an inequality by a negative number, we must reverse the inequality symbol.

▶ **Example 3** Sketching the Graph of an Inequality

Sketch the graph of $-2x - 3y > 6$.

Solution

First, we isolate y on one side of the inequality:

$$-2x - 3y > 6 \qquad \textit{Original inequality}$$

$$-3y > 2x + 6 \qquad \textit{Add 2x to both sides.}$$

$$\frac{-3y}{-3} < \frac{2x}{-3} + \frac{6}{-3} \qquad \textit{Divide both sides by } -3; \textit{ reverse inequality symbol.}$$

$$y < -\frac{2}{3}x - 2 \qquad \textit{Simplify.}$$

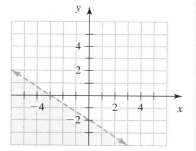

Figure 63 Graph of $-2x - 3y > 6$

The graph of $y < -\frac{2}{3}x - 2$ is the region below the line $y = -\frac{2}{3}x - 2$ (see Fig. 63).

To verify our work, we choose a point on our graph, such as $(-3, -1)$, and check that it satisfies the inequality:

$$-2x - 3y > 6 \qquad \textit{Original inequality}$$

$$-2(-3) - 3(-1) \overset{?}{>} 6 \qquad \textit{Substitute } -3 \textit{ for x and } -1 \textit{ for y.}$$

$$9 \overset{?}{>} 6 \qquad \textit{Simplify.}$$

$$\text{true}$$

To verify further, we could choose several other points on the graph and check that each point satisfies the inequality.

We could also choose several points that are not on the graph and check that each point does *not* satisfy the inequality. For example, the point $(0, 0)$ is not on the graph, and the ordered pair $(0, 0)$ does not satisfy the inequality $-2x - 3y > 6$:

$$-2x - 3y > 6 \qquad \textit{Original inequality}$$

$$-2(0) - 3(0) \overset{?}{>} 6 \qquad \textit{Substitute 0 for x and 0 for y.}$$

$$0 \overset{?}{>} 6 \qquad \textit{Simplify.}$$

$$\text{false}$$

▶

WARNING   It is a common error to think the graph of an inequality such as $-2x - 3y > 6$ is the region *above* the line $-2x - 3y = 6$, because the symbol ">" means "is greater than." However, we must first isolate y on the left side of a linear inequality before we can determine whether the graph includes the region that is above or below a line.

In fact, in Example 3, we wrote the inequality $-2x - 3y > 6$ as $y < -\dfrac{2}{3}x - 2$ and concluded the graph is the region *below* the line $y = -\dfrac{2}{3}x - 2$.

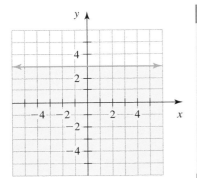

Figure 64 Graph of $y \le 3$

> ### ▶ Example 4   Sketching the Graphs of Inequalities

Sketch the graph of the inequality.

   1. $y \le 3$ **2.** $x > -4$

Solution

   1. The graph of $y \le 3$ is the horizontal line $y = 3$ and the region below that line (see Fig. 64).
   2. Ordered pairs with x-coordinates *greater than* -4 are represented by points that lie to the *right* of the vertical line $x = -4$. So, the graph of $x > -4$ is the region to the right of $x = -4$ (see Fig. 65).

Systems of Linear Inequalities in Two Variables

A **system of linear inequalities in two variables** consists of two or more linear inequalities in two variables. Here is an example:

$$y \ge -2x + 1$$
$$y < \frac{1}{2}x - 3$$

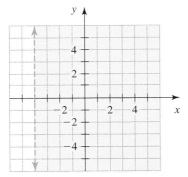

Figure 65 Graph of $x > -4$

> ### ▶ Definition   *Solution, solution set,* and *solve* for a system of inequalities in two variables

We say an ordered pair (a, b) is a **solution** of a system of inequalities in two variables if it satisfies all the inequalities in the system. The **solution set** of a system is the set of all solutions of the system. We **solve** a system by finding its solution set.

Recall from Section 3.1 that we can find the solution set of a system of two linear *equations* in two variables by locating any intersection point(s) of the graphs of the two equations. Similarly, **we can find the solution set of a system of inequalities in two variables by locating the intersection of the graphs of all of the inequalities.** This makes sense, because a solution is an ordered pair that satisfies all of the inequalities, meaning the point that represents the ordered pair lies on the graphs of all of the inequalities.

In this text, we use a graph to describe the solution set of a system of linear inequalities in two variables.

> ### ▶ Example 5   Graphing the Solution Set of a System of Inequalities

Solve the system

$$y \ge -2x + 1$$
$$y < \frac{1}{2}x - 3$$

Solution

First, we sketch the graph of $y \ge -2x + 1$ (see Fig. 66, blue region) and the graph of $y < \dfrac{1}{2}x - 3$ (see Fig. 66, red region). The graph of the solution set of the system is the intersection of the graphs of the inequalities, which is shown in Fig. 67.

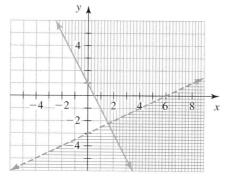

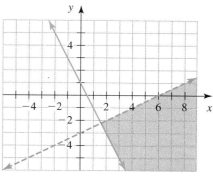

Figure 66 The solution region of
$y \geq -2x + 1$ and the solution region
of $y < \dfrac{1}{2}x - 3$

Figure 67 Graph of the solution set
of the system

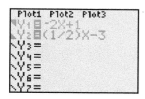

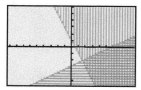

Figure 68 Verify our
work (imagine that the
border $y = \dfrac{1}{2}x - 3$ is
drawn with a dashed
line)

We can use a graphing calculator to draw a graph of the solution set of the system (see Fig. 68), where we imagine the border $y = \dfrac{1}{2}x - 3$ is drawn with a dashed line. The graph of the solution set is the region shaded by both vertical lines (in blue) and horizontal lines (in red).

▶ **Example 6**   Graphing the Solution Set of a System

Graph the solution set of the system

$$y \geq 2x - 3$$
$$y \leq -x + 5$$
$$x \geq 0$$
$$y \geq 0$$

Solution

In Fig. 69, we use arrows to indicate the graphs of each of the four inequalities. The solution set of the system is the intersection of the graphs of the four inequalities.

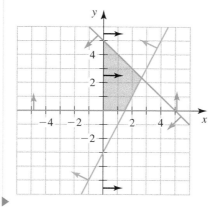

Figure 69 The graphs of $y \geq 2x - 3$, $y \leq -x + 5$,
$x \geq 0$, and $y \geq 0$

Modeling with Systems of Inequalities

We can use a system of inequalities to help us make estimates about authentic situations.

▶ **Example 7**   Using a System of Inequalities to Make Estimates

A person's life expectancy predicts how many *remaining* years the person will live. The life expectancies of U.S. females at birth and at age 20 years are shown in Table 33 for various calendar years.

Table 33 Life Expectancies of U.S. Females at Birth and at Age 20 Years

| Year | Life Expectancy (Years) | |
	At Birth	At Age 20 Years
1980	77.6	59.0
1985	78.2	59.3
1990	78.8	59.8
1995	78.9	59.9
2000	79.7	60.5
2005	79.9	60.7
2008	80.5	61.2

Source: *U.S. National Center for Health Statistics*

Let $L = B(t)$ be the life expectancy (in years) at birth and $L = T(t)$ be the life expectancy (in years) at age 20 years, both of U.S. females at t years since 1980. The linear regression models of B and T are, respectively,

$$B(t) = 0.097t + 77.66$$
$$T(t) = 0.075t + 58.95$$

1. Find a system of inequalities that describes the life expectancies of U.S. females from 0 years through 20 years old from 1985 to 2020.
2. Graph the solution set of the system of inequalities you found in Problem 1.
3. Estimate the life expectancies of U.S. females from 0 years through 20 years old in 2015.

Solution

1. The life expectancies must be less than or equal to the at-birth life expectancies ($L \leq 0.097t + 77.66$) and greater than or equal to the life expectancies at age 20 years ($L \geq 0.075t + 58.95$). We are seeking life expectancies for the calendar years from 1985 through 2020: $t \geq 5$ and $t \leq 40$. So, our system is

$$L \leq 0.097t + 77.66$$
$$L \geq 0.075t + 58.95$$
$$t \geq 5$$
$$t \leq 40$$

2. In Fig. 70, we use arrows to indicate the graphs of each of the four inequalities. The solution set of the system is the intersection of those graphs.

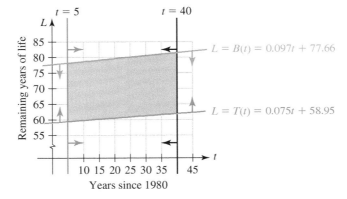

Years since 1980

Figure 70 Graph of the solution set of the system

3. The life expectancies of U.S. females from 0 years through 20 years old in the calendar year 2015 are represented by the vertical line segment above $t = 35$ on the t-axis in Fig. 71. From this line segment, we see the life expectancies are between 61.6 years and 81.1 years, inclusive.

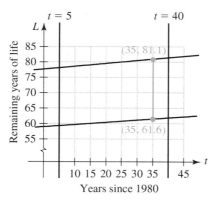

Figure 71 Life expectancies for ages 0 years through 20 years in 2015

We can also use the equations of B and T to find the life expectancies of U.S. females from 0 years through 20 years old in the calendar year 2015. To begin, we evaluate both B and T at 35:

$$B(35) = 0.097(35) + 77.66 \approx 81.1$$

$$T(35) = 0.075(35) + 58.95 \approx 61.6$$

This means the life expectancies are between 61.6 years and 81.1 years, inclusive, which checks.

Group Exploration

Meaning of solution of a system of inequalities in two variables

The graphs of $y = ax + b$ and $y = cx + d$ are sketched in Fig. 72.

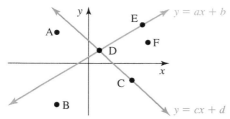

Figure 72 Graphs of $y = ax + b$ and $y = cx + d$

1. For each part, decide which one or more of the points A, B, C, D, E, and F represent ordered pairs that

a. satisfy the inequality $y < ax + b$
b. satisfy the inequality $y \geq cx + d$
c. are solutions of the system of inequalities

$$y < ax + b$$
$$y \geq cx + d$$

2. Write a system of inequalities in terms of $a, b, c, d, x,$ and y such that points B, C, and D are solutions and points A, E, and F are not solutions.

3. Write a system of inequalities in terms of $a, b, c, d, x,$ and y such that points B and C are solutions and points A, D, E, and F are not solutions.

Homework 3.6

For extra help ▶ MyMathLab®   Watch the videos in MyMathLab   Download the MyDashboard App

Graph the inequality by hand.

1. $y \geq 2x - 4$

2. $y > x + 1$

3. $y < -\dfrac{1}{2}x + 3$

4. $y \leq \dfrac{2}{3}x - 5$

5. $y \leq -2x + 6$

6. $y \geq -3x + 4$

7. $y > x$

8. $y \leq 2x$

9. $y < -\dfrac{1}{3}x$

10. $y < -\dfrac{1}{4}x$

11. $2x + 5y < 10$

12. $3x - 2y \geq 8$

13. $4x - 6y - 6 \geq 0$

14. $2y - x + 1 > 0$

15. $3(x - 2) + y \leq -2$

16. $y > -2(x - 1) + 3$

17. $y \leq 2$

18. $y < -3$

19. $x > -3$

20. $x \geq 1$

Graph by hand the solution set of the system of inequalities.

21. $y \geq \frac{1}{3}x - 2$
$y > -x + 3$

22. $y > \frac{1}{2}x + 3$
$y \leq -2x + 5$

23. $y \leq x - 4$
$y \geq -3x$

24. $y < 2x - 3$
$y < -2x$

25. $y \leq -3x + 9$
$y \geq 2x - 3$
$x \geq 0$
$y \geq 0$

26. $y \leq \frac{1}{3}x + 4$
$y \geq 2x - 5$
$x \geq 0$
$y \geq 0$

27. $y < -x + 5$
$y \leq x + 5$
$y > \frac{1}{2}x + 1$

28. $y > -x - 4$
$y \geq 2x + 6$
$y \leq \frac{1}{2}x + 6$

29. $y \leq -3$
$y \geq -5$

30. $y \leq 2$
$y > -1$

31. $2x - 4y \leq 8$
$3x + 5y \leq 10$

32. $3x - 2y < 6$
$4x + 3y > -12$

33. $x - 2y > 6$
$x + 3y \leq 3$

34. $x - 4y \geq 8$
$x + 2y < 2$

35. $1 + y \geq \frac{1}{2}(x - 4)$
$3 - y > 2(x - 1)$

36. $2 - y < 3(x + 2)$
$y - 7 \leq 2(x - 3)$

37. $5y \leq 2x + 20$
$5y \geq 2x + 5$
$x \geq 3$
$x \leq 5$

38. $4y < 3x + 20$
$4y > 3x + 8$
$x > 2$
$x < 4$

39. A person's life expectancy predicts how many *remaining* years the person will live. The life expectancies of U.S. males at birth and at age 20 years are shown in Table 34 for various calendar years.

Table 34 Life Expectancies of U.S. Males at Birth and at Age 20 Years

| Year | Life Expectancy (years) | |
	At Birth	At Age 20 Years
1980	70.1	51.9
1985	71.1	52.6
1990	71.8	53.3
1995	72.5	53.8
2000	74.3	55.3
2005	74.9	55.9
2008	75.5	56.5

Source: *U.S. National Center for Health Statistics*

Let $L = B(t)$ be the life expectancy (in years) at birth and $L = T(t)$ be the life expectancy (in years) at age 20 years, both of U.S. males at t years since 1980.
a. Find equations of B and T.
b. Find a system of inequalities that describes the life expectancies of U.S. males from 0 years through 20 years old from 1980 to 2020.
c. Graph the solution set of the system of inequalities you found in part (b).
d. Predict the life expectancies of U.S. males from 0 years through 20 years old in 2015.

40. Recall from Exercise 12 of Homework 2.1 that the windchill is a measure of how cold you feel when exposed to wind. Table 35 gives the windchills for various temperatures when the wind speed is 10 mph or 20 mph. Let $w = f(t)$ be the windchill when the wind speed is 10 mph and $w = g(t)$ be the windchill when the wind speed is 20 mph, both in degrees Fahrenheit at a temperature t in degrees Fahrenheit.

Table 35 Windchills for 10-mph and 20-mph Winds

| Temperature (degrees Fahrenheit) | Windchill (degrees Fahrenheit) | |
	10-mph Wind	20-mph Wind
−15	−35	−42
−10	−28	−35
−5	−22	−29
0	−16	−22
5	−10	−15
10	−4	−9
15	3	−2
20	9	4

Source: *National Weather Service*

a. Find equations of f and g.
b. Find a system of inequalities that describes the windchills for temperatures between −20°F and 30°F, inclusive, with wind speeds between 10 mph and 20 mph, inclusive.
c. Graph the solution set of the system of inequalities you found in part (b).
d. If the temperature is 7°F, what are the windchills for wind speeds between 10 mph and 20 mph, inclusive?

41. Recommended ski lengths are shown in Table 36 for skiers of various weights and abilities.

Table 36 Recommended Ski Lengths

| Weight (pounds) | Ski Length (centimeters) | | | |
	Beginner	Intermediate	Advanced	Expert
100.0	130	135	140	145
112.5	135	140	145	150
130.5	140	145	150	155
143.0	145	150	155	160
158.0	150	155	160	165
172.5	155	160	165	170
185.0	165	170	175	180
195.0	175	180	185	190

Source: *backcountry.com*

Let $L = B(w)$ be the recommended ski length for a beginner skier and $L = I(w)$ be the recommended ski length for an intermediate skier, both in centimeters, for a skier who weighs w pounds.
a. Find linear equations of B and I.
b. Find a system of inequalities that describes the recommended ski lengths for beginning to intermediate skiers who weigh between 130 and 150 pounds, inclusive.
c. Graph the solution set of the system of inequalities you found in part (b).
d. Estimate all recommended ski lengths for beginning to intermediate 140-pound skiers.

42. Let $L = A(w)$ be the recommended ski length for an advanced skier and $L = E(w)$ be the recommended ski length for an expert skier, both in centimeters, for a skier who weighs w pounds (see Table 36 on page 174).

    a. Find linear equations of A and E.

    b. Find a system of inequalities that describes the recommended ski lengths for advanced to expert skiers who weigh between 140 and 160 pounds, inclusive.

    c. Graph the solution set of the system of inequalities you found in part (b).

    d. Estimate all recommended ski lengths for advanced to expert 145-pound skiers.

Concepts

43. A student believes the graph of $2x - 3y < 6$ is the region below the line $2x - 3y = 6$. What would you tell the student?

44. Find three ordered pairs that are solutions of the inequality $y \leq -x - 2$, and find three ordered pairs that are not solutions.

45. Give an example of an inequality in terms of x and y for which $(3, 4)$ is a solution and $(4, 3)$ is not.

46. Give an example of an inequality in terms of x and y for which $(3, 3)$, $(-3, 3)$, and $(-3, -3)$ are solutions and $(3, -3)$ is not.

47. Graph by hand the solution set of the system

$$y \geq 2x + 1$$
$$y \leq 2x + 1$$

48. Describe the solution set of the system

$$y > 2x + 1$$
$$y < 2x + 1$$

49. a. Graph the equation or inequality by hand.

    i. $y = -2x - 3$

    ii. $y < -2x - 3$

    iii. $y \leq -2x - 3$

    iv. $y > -2x - 3$

    v. $y \geq -2x - 3$

    b. Compare the processes of graphing the equation and inequalities in part (a). How are the five processes similar? Different?

50. a. Find the solution set of the system by graphing the equations or inequalities by hand.

    i. $2x + y = 8$
        $3x - 2y = -2$

    ii. $2x + y < 8$
        $3x - 2y < -2$

    iii. $2x + y \leq 8$
        $3x - 2y \leq -2$

    iv. $2x + y \geq 8$
        $3x - 2y \geq -2$

    b. Compare the processes of solving the systems in part (a). How are the processes similar? Different?

51. Explain how to graph an inequality in two variables. When do you reverse the inequality symbol?

52. Explain how to solve a system of inequalities in two variables.

Taking it to the Lab

Climate Change Lab (continued from Chapter 2)

Recall from the Climate Change Lab in Chapter 2 that, to avoid a climate catastrophe, the IPCC has recommended that carbon dioxide emissions be lowered to 0.9 metric ton per person per year by 2050. Developed countries' carbon dioxide emissions are about 10.2 metric tons per person per year. So, these countries will have to reduce their per-person emissions significantly while trying to sustain their relatively strong economies. The United States, with carbon dioxide emissions of 18.1 metric tons per person per year, will have to reduce its emissions drastically.*

Developing countries' carbon dioxide emissions are about 2.7 metric tons per person per year. Due to their already low per-person emissions, it seems these countries will have an easier time meeting the IPCC's goal than developed countries. However, by 2050 many such countries will have become *developed* countries, and their economies will have become much stronger. As a result of this growth, their carbon dioxide emissions will greatly increase without intervention.[†]

For example, China's carbon dioxide emissions were only 1.15 metric tons per person in 1990. Due to China's booming economy, however, the country's carbon dioxide emissions in 2050 may reach 41.5 metric tons per person per year—more than 36 times the 1990 per-person level. This large increase in per-person carbon dioxide emissions will be amplified by a population increase of 480 million people in those 60 years (from 0.98 billion to 1.46 billion).[‡]

An analysis of the data in Table 37 (on p. 176) shows that developing countries' carbon dioxide emissions are growing at a greater rate than developed countries' carbon dioxide emissions. This is occurring not only because developing countries are becoming more industrialized, but also because their populations are increasing significantly.

---

*International Energy Agency, "CO$_2$ Emissions from Fuel Combustion Highlights," 2011.

[†]Carbon Dioxide Information Analysis Center (CDIAC).
[‡]United Nations Population Division.

Developed countries' economies and populations are growing at a much slower rate; in fact, most developed countries' populations will begin to decline slowly after 2020.[§]

Table 37 Carbon Dioxide Emissions

| Year | Carbon Dioxide Emissions (billion metric tons carbon) | |
	Developed Countries	Developing Countries
1980	15.0	4.1
1985	14.5	4.9
1990	15.2	6.4
1995	14.1	8.1
2000	14.6	9.2
2005	15.0	13.3
2009	14.1	16.2

Source: *Carbon Dioxide Information Analysis Center (CDIAC)*

Many challenges lie ahead for developed and developing countries, both of which will need to develop efficient systems that rely on alternative energy sources whenever possible. Citizens of developed countries will have the extra challenges of foregoing certain conveniences that up until now have been taken for granted. Developing countries will have the extra challenge of harnessing large population growths.

Analyzing the Situation

1. Let $c = f(t)$ be carbon dioxide emissions (in billions of metric tons) of developed countries in the year that is t years since 1980. Draw a scattergram by using a graphing calculator with the window shown in Fig. 73. Then find a model of the situation.

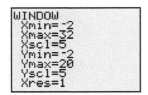

Figure 73 Window settings

2. Let $c = g(t)$ be carbon dioxide emissions (in billions of metric tons) of developing countries in the year that is t years since 1980. Use a graphing calculator to draw a scattergram, and then find a linear equation of g.

3. Compare the slopes of both models. What does the comparison tell you about the situation?

4. Explain why developing countries' carbon dioxide emissions are increasing at a greater rate than developed countries' carbon dioxide emissions.

5. Use substitution or elimination to estimate when developing countries' carbon dioxide emissions were equal to developed countries' carbon dioxide emissions. What is that carbon dioxide emission value?

6. Use your result from Problem 5 to predict the per-person carbon dioxide emissions in the year when developing countries' carbon dioxide emissions were equal to developed countries' carbon dioxide emissions. Assume world population was 6.7 billion in that year.[¶] Given that the carbon dioxide emissions in 2000 were 3.9 metric tons per person, did per-person carbon dioxide emissions increase or decrease from 2000 to the year you found in Problem 5? Explain.

7. What are the challenges that lie ahead in trying to reduce carbon dioxide emissions? What challenges are unique to developed countries? To developing countries?

Sports Lab

In Section 3.3, we predicted when the women's record time would equal the men's record time in the 400-meter run. In this lab, you will research a sporting event of your choice and use linear functions to model your data for the women's and men's versions of the event. The following websites may help you perform your research:

Track and Field Statistics
http://www.saunalahti.fi/~sut/eng/

Index to the Olympics
http://www.hickoksports.com/history/olympix.shtml

USA Swimming
www.usaswimming.org/DesktopDefault.aspx

Respond to the following instructions and questions:

1. Include tables of the women's data and the men's data you collected. State the source of your data.

2. Define any variables you used to model your data.

3. Draw sketches of scattergrams for the women's and men's data by hand in the same coordinate system. Make sure that it is clear which data points are for the women and which are for the men.

4. Find a linear function that models the women's data and a linear function that models the men's data. If you can't model your data well with linear functions, choose another sporting event.

5. Draw graphs of your functions in the same coordinate system as your scattergrams.

6. Compare the intercepts on the vertical axis for both of your linear models. What does your comparison mean in this situation?

7. Compare the slopes of your two linear models. What does your comparison mean in this situation?

8. Is there a point in time when your two models estimate (predict) that the women's performance was (will be) equal to the men's performance? If so, when did or will this happen?

---

9. Sketch a reasonable curve on paper that describes the relationship between the performance of the women and years *for all time*. Sketch a similar curve for the men. Sketch both curves in the same coordinate system.

Truck Lab

You are the owner of a large appliance store and are considering whether to continue renting delivery trucks or purchase a truck.

On average, you rent a truck twice a week and drive 100 miles on each delivery day. The rental truck costs $19.99 per day, plus $0.49 per mile. You must also pay 8% sales tax.

You can buy a delivery truck for $36,450, plus 8% sales tax. The truck will require $450 per year in maintenance, including sales tax. You estimate that repair costs will add about $600 in costs each year, including sales tax.

Because you must pay for gas and insurance regardless of whether you rent or buy, you decide that these costs will not influence your decision.

1. Let $R(t)$ be the total money (in dollars) you will pay for costs related to renting a truck for t years. Let $O(t)$ be the total money (in dollars) you will pay for costs related to owning a truck for t years. Find equations of both R and O.

2. If you choose to buy a truck, how long would you have to own the truck so that owning would be as costly as renting?

3. If you buy a truck, you can sell it later. Use the rule of thumb that a new truck loses 20% of its value as soon as you drive it off the lot. Assume that the value of the truck will decrease by $1200 each year. How long would you have to own the truck before selling it so that owning would be as costly as renting?

4. Compare your result in Part 2 with your result in Part 3. Explain why it makes sense that the results differ in this way.

5. Inflation will affect some of the costs, and if you choose to buy a truck, you may have to pay interest on a loan. Without performing calculations, discuss how these two factors would affect your answer to Part 3. Explain.

 # Chapter Summary

Key Points of Chapter 3

Section 3.1   Using Graphs and Tables to Solve Systems

Intersection point of the graphs of two models	If the independent variable of two models represents time, then an intersection point of the graphs of the two models indicates a time when the quantities represented by the dependent variables were or will be equal.
Solution of a system	We say an ordered pair (a, b) is a **solution** of a system of two equations in two variables if it satisfies both equations. The **solution set** of a system is the set of all solutions of the system. We **solve** a system by finding its solution set.
Solving a system	The solution set of a system of two linear equations can be found by locating any intersection point(s) of the graphs of the two equations.
Types of linear systems	There are three types of linear systems of two equations: **1. One-solution system:** The lines intersect in one point. The solution set of the system contains only the ordered pair that corresponds to that point. **2. Inconsistent system:** The lines are parallel. The solution set of the system is the empty set. **3. Dependent system:** The lines are identical. The solution set of the system is the set of the infinite number of solutions represented by all points on the same line.
Using a table to solve a system	If an ordered pair is listed in a table as a solution of both of two linear equations, then that ordered pair is a solution of the system consisting of the two equations.

Section 3.2   Using Substitution and Elimination to Solve Systems

Using substitution to solve a linear system	To use **substitution** to solve a system of two linear equations,

1. Isolate a variable on one side of either equation.
2. Substitute the expression for the variable found in step 1 into the other equation.
3. Solve the equation in one variable found in step 2.
4. Substitute the solution found in step 3 into one of the original equations, and solve for the other variable.

Adding left sides and adding right sides of two equations	If $a = b$ and $c = d$, then $a + c = b + d$.

Using elimination to solve a linear system	To use **elimination** to solve a system of two linear equations,

1. If needed, multiply both sides of one equation by a number (and, if necessary, multiply both sides of the other equation by another number) to get the coefficients of one variable to be equal in absolute value and opposite in sign.
2. Add the left sides and add the right sides of the equations to eliminate one of the variables.
3. Solve the equation in one variable found in step 2.
4. Substitute the solution found in step 3 into one of the original equations, and solve for the other variable.

Methods of solving a system	Any linear system of two equations can be solved by graphing, substitution, or elimination. All three methods will give the same result.

Inconsistent and dependent systems	If the result of applying substitution or elimination to a linear system of two equations is

* a false statement, the system is inconsistent—that is, the solution set is the empty set.
* a true statement (one that can be put into the form $a = a$), then the system is dependent—that is, the solution is the set of ordered pairs represented by every point on the (same) line.

Using graphing or tables to solve an equation in one variable	To use graphing or a table to solve an equation $A = B$ in one variable, x, where A and B are expressions,

1. Use graphing or a table to solve the system

$$y = A$$
$$y = B$$

2. The x-coordinates of any solutions of the system are the solutions of the equation $A = B$.

Section 3.3   Using Systems to Model Data

Intersection point of the graphs of two linear models	We can find an intersection point of the graphs of two linear models by graphing, substitution, or elimination.

Section 3.4   Value, Interest, and Mixture Problems

Five-step problem-solving method	To solve some problems in which we want to find two quantities, it is useful to perform the following five steps:

* *Step 1: Define each variable.*
* *Step 2: Write a system of two equations.*
* *Step 3: Solve the system.*
* *Step 4: Describe each result.*
* *Step 5: Check.*

Section 3.4   Value, Interest, and Mixture Problems *(Continued)*

Total-value formula	If n objects each have value v, then their total value T is given by $T = vn$.
Using a function to analyze a situation	If we want to analyze many aspects of a certain situation, it can help to use a system of equations to find a linear function. We can then use the function to analyze the situation in various ways.
Annual simple interest rate	The **annual simple interest rate** is the percentage of the **principal** that equals the **interest** earned per year.
Percentage of solution	For an $x\%$ solution of two substances that are mixed, $x\%$ of the solution is one substance and $(100 - x)\%$ is the other substance.

Section 3.5   Using Linear Inequalities in One Variable to Make Predictions

Addition property of inequalities	If $a < b$, then $a + c < b + c$. Similar properties hold for $\leq$, $>$, and $\geq$.
Multiplication property of inequalities	• For a *positive* number c, if $a < b$, then $ac < bc$. • For a *negative* number c, if $a < b$, then $ac > bc$. Similar properties hold for $\leq$, $>$, and $\geq$.
Reversing the inequality symbol	When we multiply or divide both sides of an inequality by a negative number, we reverse the inequality symbol.
Linear inequality in one variable	A **linear inequality in one variable** is an inequality that can be put into one of the forms $$mx + b < 0, \quad mx + b \leq 0, \quad mx + b > 0, \quad mx + b \geq 0$$ where m and b are constants and $m \neq 0$.
Solution of an inequality in one variable	We say a number is a **solution** of an inequality in one variable if it satisfies the inequality. The **solution set** of an inequality is the set of all solutions of the inequality. We **solve** an inequality by finding its solution set.

Section 3.6   Linear Inequalities in Two Variables; Systems of Linear Inequalities

Satisfy, solution, solution set, and *solve* for an inequality in two variables	If an inequality in two variables x and y becomes a true statement when a is substituted for x and b is substituted for y, we say the ordered pair (a, b) **satisfies** the inequality and call (a, b) a **solution** of the inequality. The **solution set** of an inequality is the set of all solutions of the inequality. We **solve** the inequality by finding its solution set.
Graph of an inequality in two variables: $y > mx + b$ or $y < mx + b$	The graph of an inequality of the form $y > mx + b$ is the region above the line $y = mx + b$. The graph of an inequality of the form $y < mx + b$ is the region below the line $y = mx + b$. For either inequality, we use a dashed line to show that $y = mx + b$ is not part of the graph.
Graph of an inequality in two variables: $y \geq mx + b$ or $y \leq mx + b$	The graph of an inequality of the form $y \geq mx + b$ is the line $y = mx + b$ and the region above that line. The graph of an inequality of the form $y \leq mx + b$ is the line $y = mx + b$ and the region below that line.
Solution, solution set, and *solve* for a system of inequalities in two variables	We say an ordered pair (a, b) is a **solution** of a system of inequalities in two variables if it satisfies all the inequalities in the system. The **solution set** of a system is the set of all solutions of the system. We **solve** a system by finding its solution set.
Intersection of graphs	We can find the solution set of a system of inequalities in two variables by locating the intersection of the graphs of all of the inequalities.

Chapter 3 Review Exercises

Find the solution set of the system by graphing the equations by hand.

1. $y = -\dfrac{3}{2}x + 1$

$y = \dfrac{1}{4}x - 6$

2. $3x - 5y = -1$

$y = -2(x - 4)$

For Exercises 3–10, solve the system by either elimination or substitution. If the system is inconsistent or dependent, say so.

3. $4x - 5y = -22$

$3x + 2y = -5$

4. $3x - 7y = 5$

$6x - 14y = -1$

5. $-4x - 5y = 3$

$10y = -8x - 6$

6. $y = 4.2x - 7.9$

$y = -2.8x + 0.5$

7. $y = 4.9x$

$-3.2y = x$

8. $3x - 5y = 21$

$y = \dfrac{1}{2}x - 4$

9. $\dfrac{3}{5}x - \dfrac{2}{3}y = 4$

$-\dfrac{6}{5}x + \dfrac{8}{3}y = -4$

10. $2(3x - 4) + 3(2y - 1) = -5$

$-3(2x + 1) + 4(y + 3) = -7$

11. Solve the system of equations three times, once by each of the three methods of elimination, substitution, and graphing:

$$2x - 5y = 15$$
$$y = -2x + 9$$

12. Create a system of two linear equations as indicated:
  a. The system is dependent.
  b. The system is inconsistent.
  c. The solution of the system is $(4, 6)$.

For Exercises 13 and 14, solve the given equation by referring to the graphs of $y = \dfrac{1}{2}x - \dfrac{5}{2}$ and $y = -\dfrac{2}{3}x - \dfrac{4}{3}$ shown in Fig. 74.

13. $\dfrac{1}{2}x - \dfrac{5}{2} = -\dfrac{2}{3}x - \dfrac{4}{3}$

14. $-\dfrac{2}{3}x - \dfrac{4}{3} = 2$

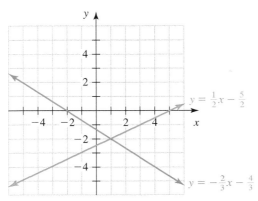

Figure 74 Exercises 13 and 14

15. Some values of functions f and g are given in Table 38. Determine two approximate solutions of the system of equations that describe the functions f and g.

Table 38 Some Values of Functions f and g (Exercise 15)

x	−4	−3	−2	−1	0	1	2	3	4
$f(x)$	2	5	8	11	14	17	20	23	26
$g(x)$	31	24	19	16	15	16	19	24	31

16. Determine the constants a and b such that $(5, 3)$ is the solution of the system.

$$2x + 3y = a$$
$$6x - 4y = b$$

Verify your result by checking that $(5, 3)$ satisfies each of your equations. Also, verify your result graphically.

17. Find the coordinates of the points A, B, C, D, E, and F as shown in Fig. 75. The equations of the sketched lines are provided, but no attempt has been made to sketch the lines accurately except for showing the intersection points.

l_1: $y = 3x + 4$

l_2: $3y + 2x = 34$

l_3: $y + 4x = 28$

l_4: $y = 3x - 14$

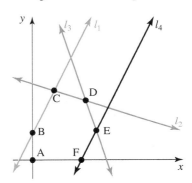

Figure 75 Exercise 17

18. Find all ordered pairs that satisfy all three equations:

$$y = -x + 2$$
$$y = -2x + 7$$
$$y = 3x - 6$$

For Exercises 19–23, use a symbolic method to solve the inequality. Describe the solution set as an inequality, in interval notation, and in a graph.

19. $3x - 8 \le 13$

20. $29.19 - 3.6a \ge 3.9(a + 2.1)$

21. $-5(2x + 3) \ge 2(3x - 4)$

22. $\dfrac{2x - 1}{4} - \dfrac{4x + 3}{6} > \dfrac{5}{3}$

23. $1 \le 2x + 5 < 11$

24. **a.** List three numbers that satisfy the inequality

$$7 - 2(3x + 5) < 4x + 1$$

  b. List three numbers that do not satisfy the inequality

$$7 - 2(3x + 5) < 4x + 1$$

25. A student tries to solve the inequality $5 - 3x \leq 11$:

$$5 - 3x \leq 11$$
$$5 - 3x - 5 \leq 11 - 5$$
$$-3x \leq 6$$
$$\frac{-3x}{-3} \leq \frac{6}{-3}$$
$$x \leq -2$$

Describe any errors. Then solve the inequality correctly.

For Exercises 26–29, refer to Fig. 76.

26. Find $f(4)$.

27. Find x where $g(x) = 0$.

28. Find x where $f(x) = g(x)$.

29. Find x where $f(x) > g(x)$.

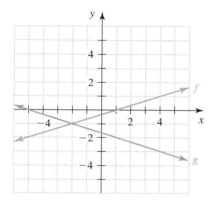

Figure 76 Exercises 26–29

30. Find values of a, b, and c such that the solution set of the inequality $ax + b > c$ is the set of numbers where $x < 5$. Use a symbolic method to verify your result.

Graph the inequality by hand.

31. $y \leq 2x - 6$

32. $4x - 2y < 8$

33. $-2(y + 3) + 4x \geq -8$

34. $y < -2$

Graph by hand the solution set of the system of inequalities.

35. $y \geq \frac{2}{5}x + 1$

$y < -\frac{1}{4}x + 2$

36. $3x - 4y \geq 12$

$6y - 2x \leq 12$

37. $x - y < 3$

$x + y < 5$

$x \geq 0$

$y \geq 0$

38. Find three ordered pairs that are solutions of the inequality $2x - 5y > 10$, and find three ordered pairs that are not.

39. The percentages of households with landlines (with or without wireless telephones) and those with only wireless phones are shown in Table 39 for various years.

Table 39 Percentages of Households with Phone Landlines and Those with Only Wireless Phones

Year	Percent	
	Landlines	Wireless-Only
2006	86.8	10.5
2007	84.4	13.6
2008	80.0	17.5
2009	75.3	22.7
2010	71.0	26.6
2011	66.2	31.6

Source: *U.S. Centers for Disease Control and Prevention*

a. Let $L(t)$ be the percentage of households with landlines and $W(t)$ be the percentage of households with only wireless phones, both at t years since 2000. Find equations of L and W.

b. Find the slopes of the two models. What do the slopes mean in this situation?

c. Predict when the percentage of households with phone landlines will be equal to the percentage of households with only wireless phones. What is that percentage?

d. Give a reason why the percentage you found in part (c) is not 50%.

e. Find values of t where $L(t) < W(t)$. What do they mean in this situation?

40. The television ratings of the baseball World Series and the average television ratings of prime-time shows on the major networks are shown in Table 40 for various years.

Table 40 Television Ratings of World Series and of Prime-Time Shows

Year	Rating of World Series	Average Rating of Prime-Time Shows on Major Networks
1973	30.7	19.2
1983	23.3	16.7
1993	17.3	12.5
2003	12.8	7.3
2007	10.6	7.9

Sources: *Fox Sports; Nielsen Media Research*

a. Let $w(t)$ be the rating of the World Series and $p(t)$ be the average rating of prime-time shows on the major networks, both at t years since 1970. Find equations of w and p.

b. Use substitution or elimination to predict when the rating of the World Series will equal the average rating of prime-time shows on the major networks. What will that rating be?

41. One Rent-A-Wreck® office rents 16-foot trucks for a one-day fee of $75 plus $0.22 per mile. One U-Haul office charges a one-day fee of $29.95 plus $0.69 per mile.

a. Let $R(d)$ be Rent-A-Wreck's charge (in dollars) and $U(d)$ be U-Haul's charge (in dollars), both for driving d miles in one day. Find equations of R and U.

b. For how many miles driven is the one-day charge at Rent-A-Wreck equal to the charge at U-Haul? What is that charge?

c. For how many miles driven is the one-day charge at Rent-A-Wreck less than the charge at U-Haul?

42. In 2012, the average price of a home in a community was $250,000, and it has increased by about $9000 each year. A family had $12,000 on January 1, 2012, and planned to save $230 each month. Predict how long it should take the family to pay a 10% down payment on an average-priced house in the community.

43. A 20,000-seat theater has tickets for sale at $55 and $70. How many tickets should be sold at each price for a sellout performance to generate a total revenue of $1,197, 500?

44. A person plans to invest $8000. She will invest in both a Hartford Global Leaders Y account at 6.8% annual interest and a Mutual Discovery Z account at 13.0% annual interest. Both interest rates are five-year averages. Let x and y be the money (in dollars) invested in the 6.8% account and the 13.0% account, respectively.
  a. Let $I = f(x)$ be the total interest (in dollars) earned from investing the $8000 for one year. Find an equation of f.
  b. Find $f(575)$. What does it mean in this situation?
  c. Find the value of x when $f(x) = 575$. What does it mean in this situation?

Chapter 3 Test

For Exercises 1–5, solve the system by either elimination or substitution. If the system is inconsistent or dependent, say so.

1. $y = 3x - 1$
     $3x - 2y = -1$

2. $2x - 5y = 3$
     $6x = 15y + 9$

3. $4x - 6y = 5$
     $6x - 9y = -2$

4. $\dfrac{2}{5}x - \dfrac{3}{4}y = 8$
     $\dfrac{3}{5}x + \dfrac{1}{4}y = 1$

5. $-4(x + 2) + 3(2y - 1) = 21$
     $5(3x - 2) - (4y + 3) = -59$

6. Create a system of two linear equations that has $(5, 2)$ as its *only* solution.

7. Solve the system of equations three times, once by each of the three methods of elimination, substitution, and graphing:
$$4x - 3y = 9$$
$$y = 2x - 5$$

8. Consider the solution set of the system
$$y = 5x - 13$$
$$y = mx + b$$
where m and b are constants. If the system's solution set is the empty set, what can you say about m? About b?

For Exercises 9–12, solve the inequality. Describe the solution set as an inequality, in interval notation, and in a graph.

9. $2 - 10x \geq 3x + 14$

10. $3(x + 4) + 1 < 5(x - 2)$

11. $2.6(t - 3.1) > 4.7t - 9.74$

12. $-\dfrac{5}{3}w + \dfrac{1}{6} \leq \dfrac{7}{4}w$

13. The graphs of f and g are sketched in Fig. 77. Solve the inequality $f(x) < g(x)$.

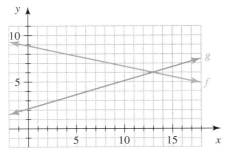
Figure 77 Exercise 13

For Exercises 14–17, refer to Fig. 78.

14. Find $f(5)$.

15. Find x where $g(x) = 3$.

16. Find x where $f(x) = g(x)$.

17. Find x where $f(x) \leq g(x)$.

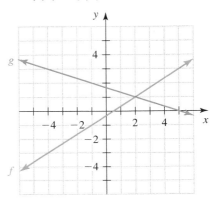
Figure 78 Exercises 14–17

18. Use "intersect" on a graphing calculator to solve the equation $\dfrac{27}{35}x - \dfrac{57}{28} = \dfrac{73}{24}x + \dfrac{41}{33}$. Round the solution to the second decimal place.

19. a. Determine three numbers that satisfy the inequality
$$3x - 11 < 7 - 6x$$
  b. Determine three numbers that do not satisfy the inequality
$$3x - 11 < 7 - 6x$$

Graph the inequality by hand.

20. $y \leq -\dfrac{2}{5}x + 3$

21. $4x - 3y < 6$

22. Graph by hand the solution set of the system of inequalities:
$$3x + 2y > 6$$
$$2x - y \geq 4$$

23. The clarity of Lake Tahoe in California is measured by the depth at which a white disk with diameter 10 inches remains visible when lowered beneath the water's surface. The clarities of Lake Tahoe in the winter and summer are shown in Table 41 for various years.
  a. Let $w(t)$ be the clarity of Lake Tahoe in the winter and $s(t)$ be the clarity of Lake Tahoe in the summer, both in feet, at t years since 1970. Find equations of w and s.

Table 41 Clarity of Lake Tahoe

Year	Clarity (feet) Winter	Clarity (feet) Summer
1970	99.4	93.5
1980	90.8	74.9
1990	84.6	75.5
2000	70.6	64.1
2010	73.0	51.9

Source: *UC Davis Tahoe Environmental Research Center*

  b. Estimate in what year the clarity in the winter was equal to the clarity in the summer. What was that clarity?

  c. Predict the average clarity throughout all of 2018.

24. The revenue of Amazon from books, CDs, and DVDs increased approximately linearly from $4.6 billion in 2007 to $7.0 billion in 2010. The revenue of Borders decreased approximately linearly from $3.7 billion in 2007 to $2.3 billion in 2010 (Source: *Amazon, Borders*).

  a. Let $A(t)$ be the annual revenue of Amazon from books, CDs, and DVDs, and let $B(t)$ be the annual revenue of Borders, both in billions of dollars, at t years since 2000. Find equations of A and B.

  b. Estimate when the annual revenue of Amazon from books, CDs, and DVDs was equal to the annual revenue of Borders. What was that revenue?

  c. For which years was the revenue of Amazon from books, CDs, and DVDs less than the revenue of Borders?

  d. What is the slope of the graph of B? What does it mean in this situation? Explain why it is not surprising that Borders went out of business in 2011.

25. How many gallons of a 10% antifreeze solution and a 20% antifreeze solution must be mixed to make 10 gallons of a 16% antifreeze solution?

26. A 10,000-seat amphitheater will sell tickets at $35 and $50 for a Blonde Redhead concert. Let x and y be the number of tickets that will sell for $35 and $50, respectively. Assume the show will sell out.

  a. Let $R = f(x)$ be the total revenue (in dollars) from selling the $35 and $55 tickets. Find an equation of f.

  b. Use a graphing calculator to draw a graph of f for $0 \le x \le 10,000$. What is the slope? What does it mean in this situation?

  c. How many of each ticket must be sold for the revenue to be $390,500?

Cumulative Review of Chapters 1–3

1. Let s be the monthly sales (in thousands of CDs) of a Weezer CD at t months after the CD is released. Sketch a qualitative graph that describes the relationship between t and s.

For Exercises 2 and 3, graph the equation.

2. $5x - 3y = 15$

3. $3(x - 4) = -2(y + 5) + 4$

4. Find the slope of the line that contains the points $(-4, 2)$ and $(3, -1)$.

5. Find an equation of the line with slope $-\dfrac{3}{5}$ that contains the point $(2, -3)$. Write your result in slope–intercept form.

6. Find an equation of the line that contains the points $(-5, -2)$ and $(-2, 3)$.

7. Find an equation of the line that contains the point $(-5, 3)$ and is perpendicular to the line $2x - 5y = 20$.

8. Find three points that lie between the lines $y = 2x + 3$ and $y = 2x + 3.1$.

For Exercises 9–11, refer to Table 42, which provides some values of four linear functions.

9. Complete Table 42.

10. Find $f(5)$.

11. Find x where $g(x) = 30$.

Table 42 Values of Four Linear Functions (Exercises 9–11)

Equation 1		Equation 2		Equation 3		Equation 4	
x	$f(x)$	x	$g(x)$	x	$h(x)$	x	$k(x)$
0	97	4		1	23	10	-28
1		5		2		11	
2		6	4	3		12	
3	58	7		4		13	
4		8		5		14	-16
5		9	43	6	-22	15	

For Exercises 12–16, let $f(x) = -\dfrac{3}{2}x + 7$.

12. Find $f(-4)$.

13. Find x where $f(x) = \dfrac{5}{3}$.

14. Find the x-intercept of the graph of f.

15. Find the y-intercept of the graph of f.

16. Sketch the graph of f.

For Exercises 17–22, refer to Fig. 79.

17. Find $g(3)$.

18. Find x where $f(x) = 1$.

19. Find the y-intercept of the graph of f.

20. Find an equation of f.

21. Find x where $f(x) = g(x)$.

22. Find x where $f(x) \le g(x)$.

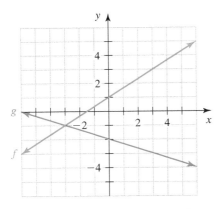

Figure 79
Exercises 17–22

For Exercises 23 and 24, solve the equation.

23. $-5x - 3(2x + 4) = 8 - 2x$

24. $\dfrac{7}{8} - \dfrac{1}{4}b = \dfrac{1}{2} + \dfrac{3}{8}b$

25. Solve for b:

$$\frac{b}{c} - d = \frac{k}{c}$$

26. Find the x-intercept and y-intercept of the graph of the equation $5x - 3y + 2 = 0$.

For Exercises 27–29, refer to the relation graphed in Fig. 80.

27. Find the domain of the relation.

28. Find the range of the relation.

29. Is the relation a function? Explain.

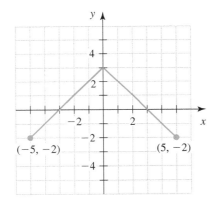

Figure 80
Exercises 27–29

Solve the system.

30. $2x + 4y = -8$
$5x - 3y = 19$

31. $3x - 7y = 14$
$y = \dfrac{3}{7}x - 2$

For Exercises 32–34, solve the given equation or system by referring to the graphs shown in Fig. 81.

32. $-\dfrac{1}{4}x - \dfrac{3}{2} = 2x + 3$

33. $-\dfrac{1}{4}x - \dfrac{3}{2} = -3$

34. $y = -\dfrac{5}{2}x + 3$
$y = -\dfrac{1}{4}x - \dfrac{3}{2}$

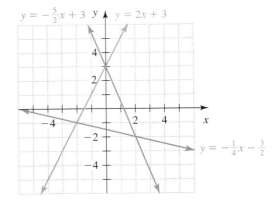

Figure 81 Exercises 32–34

35. Solve $-2(4x + 5) \ge 3(x - 7) + 1$. Describe the solution set as an inequality, in interval notation, and in a graph.

36. **a.** Solve $-3x + 6 = 0$.
   b. Solve $-3x + 6 < 0$. Graph the solution set on a number line.
   c. Graph $y = -3x + 6$.
   d. Solve the system:
   $$y = -3x + 6$$
   $$y = 4x - 1$$

37. Give an example of each of the following, and describe the solution set of each of your examples. [**Hint:** In some cases, it will be helpful to describe the solution set by using a graph.]
   a. equation in one variable
   b. equation in two variables
   c. system of two equations in two variables
   d. inequality in one variable
   e. inequality in two variables
   f. system of two inequalities in two variables

38. The numbers of foreign children adopted by American families are shown in Table 43 for various years.

Table 43 Numbers of Foreign Children Adopted by American Families

Year	Number of Adoptions (thousands)
2005	22.7
2006	20.7
2007	19.6
2008	17.5
2009	12.7
2010	11.1
2011	9.3

Source: *U.S. Department of State*

Let $n = f(t)$ be the number of foreign children (in thousands) adopted by American families in the year that is t years since 2000.

a. Find an equation of f.

b. Find $f(4)$. What does it mean in this situation?

c. Find t when $f(t) = 4$. What does the result mean in this situation?

d. Find the slope of the model. What does it mean in this situation?

e. Find the t-intercept. What does it mean in this situation?

39. The number of bicyclists younger than 16 who were hit and killed by motor vehicles was 82 children in 2009 and has declined by about 9 children each year (Source: *U.S. Department of Transportation*).

a. Let $n = f(t)$ be the number of bicyclists younger than 16 who were hit and killed by motor vehicles in the year that is t years since 2009. Find an equation of f.

b. What is the slope of the model? What does it mean in this situation?

c. Find the n-intercept. What does it mean in this situation?

d. Find the t-intercept. What does it mean in this situation?

e. For which years in the future is there model breakdown for certain? Explain.

40. The *days sales of inventory (DSI)* measures how long it takes a company to turn its inventory into sales. The DSI of Home Depot was 86.8 days in 2010 and has increased by about 2.2 days per year. The DSI of Lowes was 95.9 days in 2010 and has increased by about 3.2 days per year (Source: *Morningstar.com*).

a. Let $H(t)$ be the DSI of Home Depot and $L(t)$ be the DSI of Lowes, both in days, at t years since 2010. Find equations of H and L.

b. What are the slopes of your two models? What do they mean in this situation? Which would be better for the companies, a positive or negative slope? Explain.

c. Use substitution or elimination to estimate when the DSI of Home Depot was equal to the DSI of Lowes. What was that DSI?

d. Solve the inequality $H(t) < L(t)$. What does your result mean in this situation?

41. World record times for the 200-meter run are listed in Table 44.

Table 44 200-Meter Run Record Times

Women		Men	
Year	Record Time (seconds)	Year	Record Time (seconds)
1973	22.38	1951	20.6
1974	22.21	1963	20.3
1978	22.06	1967	20.14
1984	21.71	1979	19.72
1988	21.34	1996	19.32
		2009	19.19

Source: *International Association of Athletics Federations*

a. Let $r = W(t)$ and $r = M(t)$ be the record times (in seconds) for women and men, respectively, at t years since 1900. Find equations of W and M.

b. Find $W(118)$ and $M(118)$. What do they mean in this situation?

c. Compare the slopes of the two models. What does your comparison tell you about the situation?

d. Explain why your results from parts (b) and (c) suggest there may be a time when the women's record time will be equal to the men's record time.

e. Predict when the women's record time will equal the men's record time. What will that time be?

f. Solve $W(t) > M(t)$. What does your result mean in this situation?

g. Find the t-intercepts of the two models. What do your results mean in this situation?

h. On the same axes, sketch qualitative graphs that describe the relationship between t and r for hundreds of years into the past and future.

42. A person plans to invest twice as much in a UBS Global Equity Y account at 7.2% annual interest as in a Fidelity Worldwide account at 9.4% annual interest. Both interest rates are five-year averages. How much will the person have to invest in each account to earn a total of $595 in one year?

Exponential Functions

The most expensive slot for television advertising occurs during the Super Bowl. In 2012, a 30-second Super Bowl ad slot cost $3.5 million—about $117,000 per second! The costs of 30-second ad slots have increased greatly (see Table 1).

In Chapters 1–3, we worked with linear expressions and equations. In this chapter, we will work with a new type of expression and equation. In addition to working with linear functions, we will now use *exponential functions* to model some authentic situations. We will use these functions to make predictions. For example, in Exercise 48 of Homework 4.5, you will predict the cost of a 30-second ad slot during Super Bowl LII in 2018.

Table 1 Costs of Television Ad Slots during the Super Bowl

Super Bowl	Year	Cost for 30 Seconds (millions of dollars)
IX	1975	0.11
XIX	1985	0.5
XXIX	1995	1.0
XXXIX	2005	2.4
XLVI	2012	3.5

Source: *Ocean Media, Inc.*

4.1 Properties of Exponents

Objectives

» Know the meaning of *exponent, zero exponent,* and *negative integer exponent.*

» Know properties of exponents.

» Simplify expressions involving exponents.

» Know the meaning of *exponential function.*

» Use *scientific notation.*

In this section, we will simplify expressions involving *exponents.*

Definition of an Exponent

If n is a counting number (Section A.2), what is the meaning of b^n? The notation b^3 stands for $b \cdot b \cdot b$. So, $4^3 = 4 \cdot 4 \cdot 4 = 64$. The notation b^4 stands for $b \cdot b \cdot b \cdot b$. So, $2^4 = 2 \cdot 2 \cdot 2 \cdot 2 = 16$.

▶ **Definition** **Exponent**

For any counting number n,

$$b^n = \underbrace{b \cdot b \cdot b \cdot \ldots \cdot b}_{n \text{ factors of } b}$$

We refer to b^n as the **power,** the **nth power of b,** or **b raised to the nth power.** We call b the **base** and n the **exponent.**

The expression 3^5 is a power. It is the 5th power of 3, or 3 raised to the 5th power. For 3^5, the base is 3 and the exponent is 5. Here we label the base and the exponent of 3^5 and calculate the power:

$$3^5 = \underbrace{3 \cdot 3 \cdot 3 \cdot 3 \cdot 3}_{5 \text{ factors of } 3} = 243$$

Exponent

Base

When we calculate a power, we say we have performed an **exponentiation.**

Notice that the notation b^1 stands for one factor of b, so $b^1 = b$.

Two powers of b have specific names: We refer to b^2 as the **square of b or b squared;** we refer to b^3 as the **cube of b or b cubed.**

For an expression of the form $-b^n$, we compute b^n before finding the opposite. For example,

$$-2^4 = -(2^4) = -(2 \cdot 2 \cdot 2 \cdot 2) = -16$$

For -2^4, the base is 2, *not* -2. If we want the base to be -2, we must enclose -2 in parentheses:

$$(-2)^4 = (-2)(-2)(-2)(-2) = 16$$

We can use a graphing calculator to check both computations (see Fig. 1). To find -2^4, press $\boxed{(-)}$ **2** $\boxed{\wedge}$ **4** $\boxed{\text{ENTER}}$.

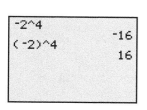

Figure 1 Compute -2^4 and $(-2)^4$

Properties of Exponents

In this section and Section 4.2, we discuss five properties of exponents.

▶ **Properties of Exponents**

If m and n are counting numbers, then

- $b^m b^n = b^{m+n}$ *Product property for exponents*
- $\dfrac{b^m}{b^n} = b^{m-n}, \quad b \neq 0$ and $m > n$ *Quotient property for exponents*
- $(bc)^n = b^n c^n$ *Raising a product to a power*
- $\left(\dfrac{b}{c}\right)^n = \dfrac{b^n}{c^n}, \quad c \neq 0$ *Raising a quotient to a power*
- $(b^m)^n = b^{mn}$ *Raising a power to a power*

In Example 1 (and the first Exploration), we will investigate why these properties make sense.

▶ **Example 1**   Meaning of Exponential Properties

1. Show that $b^2 b^3 = b^5$.
2. Show that $b^m b^n = b^{m+n}$, where m and n are counting numbers.
3. Show that $\left(\dfrac{b}{c}\right)^n = \dfrac{b^n}{c^n}$, where n is a counting number and $c \neq 0$.

Solution

1. By writing $b^2 b^3$ without exponents, we see

$$\begin{aligned} b^2 b^3 &= (bb)(bbb) && \textit{Write without exponents.} \\ &= bbbbb && \textit{Remove parentheses.} \\ &= b^5 && \textit{Write with an exponent.} \end{aligned}$$

We can verify that this result is correct for various constant bases by examining graphing calculator tables for both $y = x^2 x^3$ and $y = x^5$ (see Fig. 2). For graphing calculator instructions, see Appendix B.14.

2. We write $b^m b^n$ without exponents:

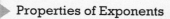

$$b^m b^n = \underbrace{(bbb\cdots b)}_{m \text{ factors}} \underbrace{(bbb\cdots b)}_{n \text{ factors}} = \underbrace{bbb\cdots b}_{m + n \text{ factors}} = b^{m+n}$$

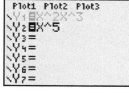

Figure 2 Comparing tables for $y = x^2 x^3$ and $y = x^5$

3. We write $\left(\dfrac{b}{c}\right)^n$, where $c \neq 0$, without exponents:

$$\left(\frac{b}{c}\right)^n = \underbrace{\left(\frac{b}{c}\right)\left(\frac{b}{c}\right)\left(\frac{b}{c}\right)\cdots\left(\frac{b}{c}\right)}_{n \text{ factors}} = \frac{\overbrace{bbb\cdots b}^{n \text{ factors}}}{\underbrace{ccc\cdots c}_{n \text{ factors}}} = \frac{b^n}{c^n}$$

Simplifying Expressions Involving Exponents

We can use properties of exponents to simplify expressions involving exponents.

> **Simplifying Expressions Involving Exponents**
>
> An expression involving exponents is simplified if
> **1.** It includes no parentheses.
> **2.** Each variable or constant appears as a base as few times as possible. For example, we write $x^2x^4 = x^6$.
> **3.** Each numerical expression (such as 7^2) has been calculated and each numerical fraction has been simplified.
> **4.** Each exponent is positive.

▶ **Example 2**   Simplifying Expressions Involving Exponents

Simplify.

1. $\left(2b^2c^3\right)^5$ **2.** $\left(3b^3c^4\right)\left(2b^6c^2\right)$ **3.** $\dfrac{3b^7c^6}{12b^2c^5}$ **4.** $\left(\dfrac{24b^7c^8}{16b^2c^5d^3}\right)^4$

Solution

1. $\left(2b^2c^3\right)^5 = 2^5\left(b^2\right)^5\left(c^3\right)^5$ *Raise factors to nth power:* $(bc)^n = b^nc^n$

$\qquad\qquad\quad = 32b^{10}c^{15}$ *Multiply exponents:* $(b^m)^n = b^{mn}$

2. $\left(3b^3c^4\right)\left(2b^6c^2\right) = (3\cdot 2)\left(b^3b^6\right)\left(c^4c^2\right)$ *Rearrange factors.*

$\qquad\qquad\qquad\quad = 6b^9c^6$ *Add exponents:* $b^mb^n = b^{m+n}$

3. $\dfrac{3b^7c^6}{12b^2c^5} = \dfrac{b^{7-2}c^{6-5}}{4}$ *Subtract exponents:* $\dfrac{b^m}{b^n} = b^{m-n}$

$\qquad\quad = \dfrac{b^5c}{4}$ *Subtract.*

4. $\left(\dfrac{24b^7c^8}{16b^2c^5d^3}\right)^4 = \left(\dfrac{3b^5c^3}{2d^3}\right)^4$ *Subtract exponents:* $\dfrac{b^m}{b^n} = b^{m-n}$

$\qquad\qquad\quad = \dfrac{\left(3b^5c^3\right)^4}{\left(2d^3\right)^4}$ *Raise numerator and denominator to nth power:* $\left(\dfrac{b}{c}\right)^n = \dfrac{b^n}{c^n}$

$\qquad\qquad\quad = \dfrac{3^4\left(b^5\right)^4\left(c^3\right)^4}{2^4\left(d^3\right)^4}$ *Raise factors to nth power:* $(bc)^n = b^nc^n$

$\qquad\qquad\quad = \dfrac{81b^{20}c^{12}}{16d^{12}}$ *Multiply exponents:* $(b^m)^n = b^{mn}$

WARNING   The expressions $3b^2$ and $(3b)^2$ are *not* equivalent expressions:

$$3b^2 = 3b \cdot b$$
$$(3b)^2 = (3b)(3b) = 9b \cdot b$$

For $3b^2$, the base is the variable b. For $(3b)^2$, the base is the product $3b$.

Here we show a typical error and the correct way to find the power $(3b)^2$:

$$(3b)^2 = 3b^2 \qquad \textit{Incorrect}$$
$$(3b)^2 = 3^2b^2 = 9b^2 \quad \textit{Correct}$$

Since the base $3b$ is a product, we need to distribute the exponent 2 to *both* factors 3 and b.

In general, when finding a power of the form $(bc)^n$, don't forget to distribute the exponent n to both factors b and c.

Zero as an Exponent

What is the meaning of b^0? If the property $\dfrac{b^m}{b^n} = b^{m-n}$ is to be true for $m = n$, then

$$1 = \frac{b^n}{b^n} = b^{n-n} = b^0, \quad b \neq 0$$

So, a reasonable definition of b^0 is 1.

▶ Definition   **Zero exponent**

For $b \neq 0$,

$$b^0 = 1$$

For example, $7^0 = 1$, $(-3)^0 = 1$, and $(ab)^0 = 1$, where $ab \neq 0$.

Negative Exponents

If n is an integer (Section A.2), what is the meaning of b^n? In particular, what is the meaning of a negative integer exponent? If the property $\dfrac{b^m}{b^n} = b^{m-n}$ is to be true for $m = 0$, then

$$\frac{1}{b^n} = \frac{b^0}{b^n} = b^{0-n} = b^{-n}, \quad b \neq 0$$

So, we should define b^{-n} to be $\dfrac{1}{b^n}$.

▶ Definition   **Negative integer exponent**

If $b \neq 0$ and n is a counting number, then

$$b^{-n} = \frac{1}{b^n}$$

In words, to find b^{-n}, take its reciprocal and switch the sign of the exponent.

For example, $3^{-2} = \dfrac{1}{3^2} = \dfrac{1}{9}$ and $b^{-5} = \dfrac{1}{b^5}$.

Next, we write $\dfrac{1}{b^{-n}}$ in another form, where $b \neq 0$ and n is a counting number:

$$\frac{1}{b^{-n}} = 1 \div b^{-n} \qquad \frac{a}{b} = a \div b$$

$$= 1 \div \frac{1}{b^n} \qquad \textit{Write power so exponent is positive: } b^{-n} = \frac{1}{b^n}$$

$$= 1 \cdot \frac{b^n}{1} \qquad \textit{Multiply by reciprocal of } \frac{1}{b^n}, \textit{which is } \frac{b^n}{1}.$$

$$= b^n \qquad \textit{Simplify.}$$

So, $\dfrac{1}{b^{-n}} = b^n$.

▶ **Negative Exponent in a Denominator**

If $b \neq 0$ and n is a counting number, then

$$\frac{1}{b^{-n}} = b^n$$

In words, to find $\frac{1}{b^{-n}}$, take its reciprocal and switch the sign of the exponent.

For example, $\frac{1}{2^{-4}} = 2^4 = 16$ and $\frac{1}{b^{-8}} = b^8$.

Simplifying More Expressions Involving Exponents

As we have seen, simplifying an expression involving exponents includes writing the expression so each exponent is positive.

▶ **Example 3**   Simplifying Expressions Involving Exponents

Simplify.

1. $9b^{-7}$ **2.** $\dfrac{5}{b^{-3}}$ **3.** $3^{-1} + 4^{-1}$

Solution

1. $9b^{-7} = 9 \cdot \dfrac{1}{b^7} = \dfrac{9}{b^7}$

2. $\dfrac{5}{b^{-3}} = 5 \cdot \dfrac{1}{b^{-3}} = 5b^3$

3. $3^{-1} + 4^{-1} = \dfrac{1}{3} + \dfrac{1}{4} = \dfrac{4}{12} + \dfrac{3}{12} = \dfrac{7}{12}$

▶

It turns out the five properties discussed at the start of this section are also true for all negative-integer exponents and the zero exponent.

▶ **Properties of Integer Exponents**

If m and n are integers, $b \neq 0$, and $c \neq 0$, then

- $b^m b^n = b^{m+n}$ *Product property for exponents*
- $\dfrac{b^m}{b^n} = b^{m-n}$ *Quotient property for exponents*
- $(bc)^n = b^n c^n$ *Raising a product to a power*
- $\left(\dfrac{b}{c}\right)^n = \dfrac{b^n}{c^n}$ *Raising a quotient to a power*
- $(b^m)^n = b^{mn}$ *Raising a power to a power*

▶ **Example 4**   Simplifying Expressions Involving Exponents

Simplify.

1. $2^{-1003}2^{1000}$

2. $\dfrac{b^{-6}}{b^{-4}}$

3. $\dfrac{35b^{-9}c^3}{25b^{-7}c^{-5}}$

Solution

1. $2^{-1003}2^{1000} = 2^{-1003+1000}$ *Add exponents: $b^m b^n = b^{m+n}$*

$\qquad\qquad\quad = 2^{-3}$ *Simplify.*

$\qquad\qquad\quad = \dfrac{1}{2^3}$ *Write powers so exponents are positive: $b^{-n} = \dfrac{1}{b^n}$*

$\qquad\qquad\quad = \dfrac{1}{8}$ *Simplify.*

2. $\dfrac{b^{-6}}{b^{-4}} = b^{-6-(-4)}$ *Subtract exponents: $\dfrac{b^m}{b^n} = b^{m-n}$*

$\qquad\quad = b^{-6+4}$ *$a - b = a + (-b)$*

$\qquad\quad = b^{-2}$ *Simplify.*

$\qquad\quad = \dfrac{1}{b^2}$ *Write powers so exponents are positive: $b^{-n} = \dfrac{1}{b^n}$*

3. $\dfrac{35b^{-9}c^3}{25b^{-7}c^{-5}} = \dfrac{7b^{-9-(-7)}c^{3-(-5)}}{5}$ *Subtract exponents: $\dfrac{b^m}{b^n} = b^{m-n}$*

$\qquad\qquad\quad = \dfrac{7b^{-2}c^8}{5}$ *Simplify.*

$\qquad\qquad\quad = \dfrac{7c^8}{5b^2}$ *Write powers so exponents are positive: $b^{-n} = \dfrac{1}{b^n}$*

▶

In the first step of Problem 2 of Example 4, we found that

$$\frac{b^{-6}}{b^{-4}} = b^{-6-(-4)}$$

WARNING   We need a subtraction symbol *and* a negative symbol in the expression on the right-hand side. It is a common error to omit writing one of these two symbols in such problems.

▶ **Example 5**   Simplifying Expressions Involving Exponents

Simplify.

1. $\dfrac{(3bc^5)^2}{(2b^{-2}c^2)^3}$

2. $\left(\dfrac{18b^{-4}c^7}{6b^{-3}c^2}\right)^{-4}$

Solution

1. $\dfrac{(3bc^5)^2}{(2b^{-2}c^2)^3} = \dfrac{3^2 b^2 (c^5)^2}{2^3 (b^{-2})^3 (c^2)^3}$ *Raise factors to a power: $(bc)^n = b^n c^n$*

$\qquad\qquad\quad = \dfrac{9b^2 c^{10}}{8b^{-6}c^6}$ *Multiply exponents: $(b^m)^n = b^{mn}$*

$\qquad\qquad\quad = \dfrac{9b^{2-(-6)}c^{10-6}}{8}$ *Subtract exponents: $\dfrac{b^m}{b^n} = b^{m-n}$*

$\qquad\qquad\quad = \dfrac{9b^8 c^4}{8}$ *Simplify.*

2. $\left(\dfrac{18b^{-4}c^7}{6b^{-3}c^2}\right)^{-4} = \left(3b^{-4-(-3)}c^{7-2}\right)^{-4}$ *Subtract exponents:* $\dfrac{b^m}{b^n} = b^{m-n}$

$= \left(3b^{-1}c^5\right)^{-4}$ *Simplify.*

$= 3^{-4}\left(b^{-1}\right)^{-4}\left(c^5\right)^{-4}$ *Raise factors to nth power:* $(bc)^n = b^n c^n$

$= 3^{-4}b^4 c^{-20}$ *Multiply exponents:* $(b^m)^n = b^{mn}$

$= \dfrac{b^4}{3^4 c^{20}}$ *Write powers so exponents are positive:* $b^{-n} = \dfrac{1}{b^n}$

$= \dfrac{b^4}{81 c^{20}}$ *Simplify.*

Definition of an Exponential Function

In this chapter and Chapter 5, we will work with *exponential functions.* Here are some examples of such functions:

$$f(x) = 2(3)^x, \qquad g(x) = -7\left(\frac{1}{2}\right)^x, \qquad h(x) = 5^x$$

Notice that, in exponential functions, the variable appears as an exponent.

▶ **Definition   Exponential function**

An **exponential function** is a function whose equation can be put into the form

$$f(x) = ab^x$$

where $a \neq 0, b > 0$, and $b \neq 1$. The constant b is called the **base.**

▶ **Example 6**   Evaluating Exponential Functions

For $f(x) = 3(2)^x$ and $g(x) = 5^x$, find the following.
1. $f(3)$ **2.** $f(-4)$ **3.** $g(a+3)$ **4.** $g(2a)$

Solution

1. $f(3) = 3(2)^3 = 3 \cdot 8 = 24$

2. $f(-4) = 3(2)^{-4} = \dfrac{3}{2^4} = \dfrac{3}{16}$

3. $g(a+3) = 5^{a+3}$ *Substitute* $a+3$ *for x in* 5^x.

$= 5^a \cdot 5^3$ *Write as product:* $b^{m+n} = b^m b^n$

$= 125(5)^a$ $5^3 = 125$; *rearrange factors:* $ab = ba$

4. $g(2a) = 5^{2a}$ *Substitute 2a for x in* 5^x.

$= (5^2)^a$ $b^{mn} = (b^m)^n$

$= 25^a$ $5^2 = 25$

WARNING   It is a common error to confuse exponential functions such as $E(x) = 2^x$ with linear functions such as $L(x) = 2x$. For the *exponential* function $E(x) = 2^x$, the variable x is an *exponent.* For the *linear* function $L(x) = 2x^1$, the variable x is a *base.*

Scientific Notation

Now we will discuss how to use exponents to describe numbers in *scientific notation.* This will enable us to describe compactly a number whose absolute value is very large or very small. For example, Earth is approximately 4,500,000,000 years old. We write 4,500,000,000 in scientific notation:

$$4.5 \times 10^9$$

The symbol "×" stands for multiplication.

As another example, light can travel 1 mile in 0.00000537 second. We write 0.00000537 in scientific notation:

$$5.37 \times 10^{-6}$$

▶ Definition   Scientific notation

A number is written in **scientific notation** if it has the form $N \times 10^k$, where k is an integer and either $-10 < N \leq -1$ or $1 \leq N < 10$.

Here are more examples of numbers in scientific notation:

$$5.2 \times 10^{17} \quad 3.638 \times 10^9 \quad -5.86 \times 10^{-12} \quad 2.13 \times 10^{-84}$$

In Example 7, we will convert some numbers from scientific notation to standard decimal notation.

▶ Example 7   Converting to Standard Decimal Notation

Simplify.

1. 5×10^3 **2.** 5×10^{-3}

Solution

1. $5 \times 10^3 = 5 \times 1000 = 5000$

We simplify $5 \times 10^3 = 5.0 \times 10^3$ by *multiplying* 5.0 by 10 three times, hence moving the decimal point three places to the *right:*

$$5.0 \times 10^3 = 5000.0 = 5000$$

three places to the right

2. $5 \times 10^{-3} = 5 \times \dfrac{1}{10^3}$ *Write powers so exponents are positive:* $b^{-n} = \dfrac{1}{b^n}$

$$= \dfrac{5}{1} \times \dfrac{1}{1000} \quad a = \dfrac{a}{1}; simplify.$$

$$= \dfrac{5}{1000} \quad Multiply.$$

$$= 0.005 \quad \dfrac{5}{1000} is\ 5\ thousandths.$$

We simplify 5.0×10^{-3} by *dividing* 5.0 by 10 three times, hence moving the decimal point three places to the *left:*

$$5.0 \times 10^{-3} = 0.005$$

three places to the left

The problems in Example 7 suggest the way to convert a number from scientific notation $N \times 10^k$ to standard decimal notation.

▶ Converting from Scientific Notation to Standard Decimal Notation

To write the scientific notation $N \times 10^k$ in standard decimal notation, we move the decimal point of the number N as follows:

• If k is *positive,* we multiply N by 10 k times; hence, we move the decimal point k places to the *right.*

• If k is *negative,* we divide N by 10 k times; hence, we move the decimal k places to the *left.*

▶ **Example 8** Converting to Standard Decimal Notation

Write the number in standard decimal notation.

1. 3.462×10^5
2. 7.38×10^{-4}

Solution

1. We *multiply* 3.462 by 10 five times; hence, we move the decimal point of 3.462 five places to the *right:*

$$3.462 \times 10^5 = 346,200.0$$

five places to the right

2. We *divide* 7.38 by 10 four times; hence, we move the decimal point of 7.38 four places to the *left:*

$$7.38 \times 10^{-4} = 0.000738$$

four places to the left

▶

In Examples 7 and 8, we converted numbers from scientific notation to standard decimal notation. In Example 9, we will investigate the way to convert numbers from standard decimal notation to scientific notation.

▶ **Example 9** Converting to Scientific Notation

Write the number in scientific notation.

1. 6,257,000,000
2. 0.00000721

Solution

1. In scientific notation, we would have

$$6.257 \times 10^k$$

We must move the decimal point of 6.257 nine places to the right to get 6,257,000,000. So, $k = 9$ and the scientific notation is

$$6.257 \times 10^9$$

2. In scientific notation, we would have

$$7.21 \times 10^k$$

We must move the decimal point of 7.21 six places to the left to get 0.00000721. So, $k = -6$ and the scientific notation is

$$7.21 \times 10^{-6}$$

▶

The problems in Example 9 suggest the way to convert a number from standard decimal notation to scientific notation.

▶ **Converting from Standard Decimal Notation to Scientific Notation**

To write a number in scientific notation, count the number of places k that the decimal point must be moved so the new number N meets the condition $-10 < N \leq -1$ or $1 \leq N < 10$:

- If the decimal point is moved to the left, then the scientific notation is written as $N \times 10^k$.

- If the decimal point is moved to the right, then the scientific notation is written as $N \times 10^{-k}$.

▶ Example 10 Converting to Scientific Notation

Write the number in scientific notation.

1. 92,900,000 (the average distance in miles between Earth and the Sun)
2. 0.0024 (the average weight, in grams, of a grain of sand)

Solution

1. For 92,900,000, the decimal point must be moved seven places to the left so the new number N is between 1 and 10. Therefore, the scientific notation is 9.29×10^7.
2. For 0.0024, the decimal point must be moved three places to the right so the new number N is between 1 and 10. Therefore, the scientific notation is 2.4×10^{-3}.

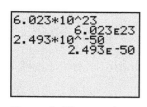

Figure 3 The numbers 6.023×10^{23} and 2.493×10^{-50}

Calculators express numbers in scientific notation so the numbers "fit" on the screen. To represent 6.023×10^{23}, most calculators use the notation 6.023 E 23, where E stands for exponent (of 10). Calculators represent 2.493×10^{-50} by 2.493 E−50 (see Fig. 3).

Group Exploration

Properties of exponents

1. In Example 1, we showed that the statement
$$b^2 b^3 = b^5$$
makes sense by first writing the expression $b^2 b^3$ without exponents. For each part that follows, show that the given statement makes sense by first writing an expression without exponents.

   a. $(bc)^4 = b^4 c^4$ **b.** $\dfrac{b^7}{b^3} = b^4, \quad b \neq 0$

   c. $(b^3)^4 = b^{12}$

2. In Example 1, we also showed that the general statements

$$b^m b^n = b^{m+n} \quad \text{and} \quad \left(\frac{b}{c}\right)^n = \frac{b^n}{c^n}, \quad c \neq 0$$

make sense for counting numbers m and n. For each part that follows, show that the general statement makes sense. Assume m and n are counting numbers.

   a. $(bc)^n = b^n c^n$

   b. $\dfrac{b^m}{b^n} = b^{m-n}, \quad$ where $m > n$ and $b \neq 0$

   c. $(b^m)^n = b^{mn}$

3. Choose values of b, c, and counting number n to show that $(b + c)^n = b^n + c^n$ is false, in general.

Group Exploration

Looking ahead: Definition of $b^{1/n}$

Throughout this exploration, assume that $(b^m)^n = b^{mn}$ for rational numbers m and n.

1. First, you will explore the meaning of $b^{1/2}$, where b is nonnegative.

   a. For now, do not use a calculator. You will explore how you should define $9^{1/2}$. You can determine a reasonable value of $9^{1/2}$ by first finding the *square* of the value:
$$\left(9^{1/2}\right)^2 = 9^{\frac{1}{2} \cdot 2} = 9^1 = 9$$
   What would be a good meaning of $9^{1/2}$? [**Hint:** Can you think of a positive number whose square equals 9?]

   b. What would be a good meaning of $16^{1/2}$? Of $25^{1/2}$?

   c. Now use a graphing calculator to find $9^{1/2}$, $16^{1/2}$, and $25^{1/2}$. For example, to find $9^{1/2}$, press **9** $\boxed{\wedge}$ $\boxed{(}$ **1** $\boxed{\div}$ **2** $\boxed{)}$ $\boxed{\text{ENTER}}$. Is the calculator interpreting $b^{1/2}$ as you would expect?

   d. What would be a good meaning of $b^{1/2}$, where b is nonnegative?

2. Now you will explore the meaning of $b^{1/3}$.

   a. For now, do not use a calculator. You will explore how you should define $8^{1/3}$. You can first find the *cube* of the value:
$$\left(8^{1/3}\right)^3 = 8^{\frac{1}{3} \cdot 3} = 8^1 = 8$$
   What would be a good meaning of $8^{1/3}$? Explain.

   b. What would be a good meaning of $27^{1/3}$? Of $64^{1/3}$?

   c. Use a graphing calculator to find $8^{1/3}$, $27^{1/3}$, and $64^{1/3}$. Is the calculator interpreting $b^{1/3}$ as you would expect?

   d. What would be a good meaning of $b^{1/3}$?

3. What would be a good meaning of $b^{1/n}$, where n is a counting number and b is nonnegative?

▶ Tips for Success   **Make Changes**

If you have not had passing scores on tests and quizzes during the first part of this course, it is time to determine what the problem is, what changes you should make, and whether you can commit to making those changes.

Sometimes students must change the way they study. For example, Rosie did poorly on exams and quizzes for the first third of the course. It was not clear why she was not passing, since she had good attendance, was actively involved in classroom work, and was doing the homework assignments. Suddenly Rosie started getting As on every quiz and test. What had happened? Rosie said, "I figured out that, to do well, it was not enough practice to do just the assigned exercises. Now I do a lot of extra exercises from each section."

Homework 4.1

For extra help ▶ **MyMathLab®**   Watch the videos in MyMathLab   Download the MyDashboard App

*Simplify without using a calculator. Then use a calculator to verify your result. [**Note:** To review order of operations, see Section A.6.]*

1. 2^{-1}

2. 3^{-2}

3. 5^0

4. $(-7)^0$

5. -4^2

6. -3^4

7. $(-4)^2$

8. $(-3)^4$

9. $(2^3)^2$

10. $(5^{-1})^{-2}$

11. $2^{-1} + 3^{-1}$

12. $\dfrac{1}{2^{-1}} + \dfrac{1}{3^{-1}}$

Simplify without using a calculator.

13. $\dfrac{7^{902}}{7^{900}}$

14. $4^{2003}4^{-2000}$

15. $13^{500}13^{-500}$

16. $(130^{-1})^{-1}$

17. $(25^3 - 411^5 + 89^2)^0$

18. $\dfrac{6^{200}}{2^{198}\,3^{199}}$

Simplify.

19. $b^7 b^{-9}$

20. $b^4 b^{-8}$

21. $(7b^{-3})(-2b^{-5})$

22. $(4b^{-9})(5b^4)$

23. $(-9b^{-7}c^5)(-8b^6c^{-5})$

24. $(-4b^{-1}c^2)(6b^3c^{-4})$

25. $(3b^2c^4)^3(2b^3c^5)^2$

26. $(4b^3c^7)^2(2b^5c^4)^3$

27. $3(b^5c)^{-2}$

28. $-6(bc^4)^{-3}$

29. $(2b^4c^{-2})^5(3b^{-3}c^{-4})^{-2}$

30. $(7b^{-4}c^{-1})^{-2}(2b^3c^{-2})^5$

31. $\dfrac{b^{-10}}{b^{15}}$

32. $\dfrac{b^{-2}}{b^2}$

33. $\dfrac{2b^{-12}}{5b^{-9}}$

34. $\dfrac{7b^{-4}}{6b^{-8}}$

35. $\dfrac{-12b^{-6}c^5}{14b^4c^5}$

36. $\dfrac{-28b^{-2}c^{-3}}{4b^{-3}c^{-1}}$

37. $\dfrac{15b^{-7}c^{-3}d^8}{-45c^2b^{-6}d^8}$

38. $\dfrac{18b^5c^3d^{-7}}{24b^{-6}c^3d^{-2}}$

39. $\dfrac{(-5b^{-3}c^4)(4b^{-5}c^{-1})}{80b^2c^{17}}$

40. $\dfrac{(3b^4c^{-1})(2b^{-7}c^{-8})}{42b^{-5}c^4}$

41. $\dfrac{(24b^3c^{-6})(49b^{-1}c^{-2})}{(28b^2c^4)(14b^{-5}c)}$

42. $\dfrac{(16b^{-2}c)(25b^4c^{-5})}{(15b^5c^{-1})(8b^{-7}c^{-2})}$

43. $\dfrac{(3b^5c^{-2})^3}{2^{-1}b^{-3}c}$

44. $\dfrac{(2b^{-7}c^4)^4}{5^{-1}b^2c^6}$

45. $\dfrac{(2b^{-4}c)^{-3}}{(2b^2c^{-5})^2}$

46. $\dfrac{(3bc^2)^{-2}}{(3b^{-3}c)^{-1}}$

47. $\left(\dfrac{6b^5c^{-2}}{7b^2c^4}\right)^2$

48. $\left(\dfrac{2bc^{-7}}{5b^{-1}c^{-2}}\right)^3$

49. $\left(\dfrac{5b^4c^{-3}}{15b^{-2}c^{-1}}\right)^{-4}$

50. $\left(\dfrac{8b^{-2}c^2}{12b^{-5}c^{-3}}\right)^{-3}$

51. $\left(\dfrac{7b^4c^{-5}}{14b^7c^{-2}}\right)^0$

52. $(42b^{-8}c^7)^{-89}(42b^{-8}c^7)^{89}$

53. $b^{-1}c^{-1}$

54. $\dfrac{1}{b^{-1}} \cdot \dfrac{1}{c^{-1}}$

55. $\dfrac{1}{b^{-1}} + \dfrac{1}{c^{-1}}$

56. $b^{-1} + c^{-1}$

Simplify. Assume n is a counting number.

57. $b^{4n}b^{3n}$

58. $b^{5n-1}b^{2n+4}$

59. $\dfrac{b^{7n-1}}{b^{2n+3}}$

60. $\dfrac{b^{3n+4}b^{n-5}}{b^{2n-3}}$

For $f(x) = 2(3)^x$ and $g(x) = 4^x$, find the following.

61. $f(3)$ **62.** $f(2)$ **63.** $f(-4)$ **64.** $f(-1)$

65. $g(a+2)$ **66.** $g(a+3)$ **67.** $g(2a)$ **68.** $g(3a)$

69. a. Complete Table 2 with output values of the function $f(x) = 2^x$. Then use a graphing calculator to verify your results.

Table 2 Input–Output Pairs of $f(x) = 2^x$ (Exercise 69)

x	$f(x)$	x	$f(x)$
-3		1	
-2		2	
-1		3	
0		4	

b. Plot the ordered pairs you found in part (a). Then guess the graph of f and sketch it by hand. Use a graphing calculator to verify your graph.

c. Use your hand-drawn graph to estimate $2^{\frac{1}{2}}$.

70. a. Complete Table 3 with output values of the function $f(x) = \left(\dfrac{1}{2}\right)^x$. Then use a graphing calculator to verify your results.

Table 3 Input–Output Pairs of $f(x) = \left(\dfrac{1}{2}\right)^x$ (Exercise 70)

x	$f(x)$	x	$f(x)$
-4		0	
-3		1	
-2		2	
-1		3	

b. Plot the ordered pairs you found in part (a). Then guess the graph of f and sketch it by hand. Use a graphing calculator to verify your graph.

c. Use your hand-drawn graph to estimate $\left(\dfrac{1}{2}\right)^{\frac{1}{2}}$.

Write the number in standard decimal form.

71. 3.965×10^2

72. 8.23172×10^3

73. 2.39×10^{-1}

74. 7.46×10^{-3}

75. 5.2×10^2

76. 7.74×10^6

77. 9.113×10^{-5}

78. 7.3558×10^{-2}

79. -6.52×10^{-4}

80. -3.006×10^{-3}

81. 9×10^5

82. 4×10^3

83. -8×10^0

84. -6.1×10^0

Write the number in scientific notation.

85. $54,260,000$

86. $173,229$

87. $23,587$

88. $6,541,883$

89. 0.00098

90. 0.08156

91. 0.0000346

92. 0.00000387

93. $-42,215$

94. $-647,000$

95. -0.00244

96. -0.000013

For Exercises 97 and 98, numbers are displayed in a graphing calculator table's version of scientific notation. Write each number shown in the Y_1 column in standard decimal form.

97. See Fig. 4.

98. See Fig. 5.

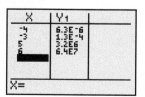

Figure 4 Exercise 97

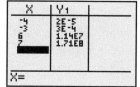

Figure 5 Exercise 98

For Exercises 99–102, the given sentence contains a number written in scientific notation. Write the number in standard decimal form.

99. The first evidence of life on Earth dates back to 3.6×10^9 years ago.

100. The Moon has an average distance from Earth of approximately 2.389×10^5 miles.

101. The hydrogen ion concentration in human blood is about 6.3×10^{-8} mole per liter.

102. The faintest sound humans can hear has an intensity of about 10^{-12} watt per square meter.

For Exercises 103–106, the given sentence contains a number (other than a date) written in standard decimal form. Write the number in scientific notation.

103. The tanker *Exxon Valdez* spilled about 10,080,000 gallons of oil in Prince William Sound, Alaska, in 1989.

104. The average distance from Earth to Alpha Centauri is about 25,000,000,000,000 miles.

105. The wavelength of violet light is about 0.00000047 meter.

106. One second is about 0.0000000317 year.

107. The numbers of bald eagle pairs in the continental United States are shown in Table 4 for various years.

Table 4 Numbers of Bald Eagle Pairs

Year	Number of Bald Eagle Pairs (thousands)
1963	0.4
1974	0.8
1986	1.9
1995	4.7
2000	6.5
2007	9.8

Source: *U.S. Fish and Wildlife Service*

Let n be the number of bald eagle pairs (in thousands) in the continental United States at t years since 1960. The situation can be described by the linear function $n = 0.21t - 1.66$ and the exponential function $n = 0.30(1.078)^t$.

a. Use a graphing calculator to draw the graphs of the two functions and, in the same viewing window, the scattergram of the data. Which function describes the situation better?

b. Use the exponential model to predict the number of bald eagle pairs in 2017.

c. Use the linear model to predict the number of bald eagle pairs in 2017. Explain why your result is so much smaller than your result from part (b). [**Hint:** Zoom out.]

108. The revenues (in billions of dollars) of Amazon are shown in Table 5 for various years.

Table 5 Annual Revenues of Amazon

Year	Annual Revenue (billions of dollars)
2002	3.9
2004	6.9
2006	10.7
2008	19.2
2010	34.2
2011	48.1

Source: *Amazon*

Let r be the annual revenue (in billions of dollars) at t years since 2000. The situation can be described by the linear function $r = 4.67t - 11.38$ and the exponential function $r = 2.2(1.32)^t$.

a. Use a graphing calculator to draw the graphs of the two functions and, in the same viewing window, the scattergram of the data. Which function describes the situation better?

b. Use the exponential model to predict the revenue in 2017.

c. Use the linear model to predict the revenue in 2017. Explain why your result is so much smaller than your result from part (b). [**Hint:** Zoom out.]

Concepts

109. Two students try to simplify $\left(5b^2\right)^{-1}$:

Student A	Student B
$\left(5b^2\right)^{-1} = -5b^{-2}$	$\left(5b^2\right)^{-1} = 5^{-1}\left(b^2\right)^{-1}$
$= \dfrac{-5}{b^2}$	$= 5^{-1}b^{-2}$
	$= \dfrac{1}{5b^2}$

Did either student simplify the expression correctly? Describe any errors.

110. Two students try to simplify an expression:

Student 1	Student 2
$\dfrac{7b^8}{b^{-3}} = 7b^{8-(-3)}$	$\dfrac{7b^8}{b^{-3}} = 7b^{8-3}$
$= 7b^{11}$	$= 7b^5$

Did either student simplify the expression correctly? Describe any errors.

111. A student tries to simplify $\dfrac{3b^{-2}c^4}{d^7}$:

$$\frac{3b^{-2}c^4}{d^7} = \frac{c^4}{3b^2d^7}$$

Describe any errors. Then simplify the expression correctly.

112. A student tries to simplify $\left(7x^4\right)^5$:

$$\left(7x^4\right)^5 = 7\left(x^4\right)^5 = 7x^{20}$$

Describe any errors. Then simplify the expression correctly.

113. It is common to confuse expressions such as 2^2, 2^{-1}, $2(-1)$, $\left(\dfrac{1}{2}\right)^2$, $\left(\dfrac{1}{2}\right)^{-1}$, -2^2, $(-2)^2$, and $\dfrac{1}{2}$. List these numbers from least to greatest. Are there any "ties"?

114. a. Simplify $\left(\dfrac{b}{c}\right)^{-2}$.

b. Simplify $\left(\dfrac{b}{c}\right)^{-n}$.

c. Use your result from part (b) to simplify $\left(\dfrac{b}{c}\right)^{-5}$ in one step.

115. Explore "0^0":

a. Simplify 5^0, 4^0, 3^0, 2^0, and 1^0. On the basis of these values, what would be a reasonable value of 0^0?

b. Simplify 0^5, 0^4, 0^3, 0^2, and 0^1. On the basis of these values, what would be a reasonable value of 0^0?

c. Why is it a good idea to leave 0^0 meaningless?

116. Simplify each expression.

a. b^{-1}
b. $\left(b^{-1}\right)^{-1}$
c. $\left(\left(b^{-1}\right)^{-1}\right)^{-1}$
d. $\left(\left(\left(b^{-1}\right)^{-1}\right)^{-1}\right)^{-1}$
e. $\underbrace{\left(\left(\left(\left(b^{-1}\right)^{-1}\right)^{-1}\right)\cdots\right)^{-1}}_{n\text{ exponents}}$

117. It is a common error to confuse the properties $b^m b^n = b^{m+n}$ and $(b^m)^n = b^{mn}$. Explain why each property makes sense, and compare the properties. Give examples to illustrate your comparison. (See page 4 for guidelines on writing a good response.)

118. Describe what it means to use exponential properties to simplify an expression. Include several examples in your description. (See page 4 for guidelines on writing a good response.)

Related Review

For $f(x) = 2x$ and $g(x) = 2^x$, find the following.

119. $f(3)$ **120.** $f(-3)$ **121.** $g(3)$ **122.** $g(-3)$

Expressions, Equations, Functions, and Graphs

Perform the indicated instruction. Then use words such as linear, exponential, function, one variable, *and* two variables *to describe the expression, equation, or system. For instance, to describe* 2x = 10, *you could say* "2x = 10 *is a linear equation in one variable."*

123. Solve:

$$y = 3x + 1$$
$$y = 2x - 4$$

124. Simplify $5(3x + 1) - 4(2x - 4)$.

125. Solve $3x + 1 = 2x - 4$.

126. Graph $f(x) = 3x + 1$ by hand.

▼ 4.2 Rational Exponents

Objectives

» Know definitions of *rational exponents*.

» Simplify expressions that have rational exponents.

In Section 4.1, we worked with integer exponents. In this section, we work with exponents that are rational numbers (Section A.2).

Definitions of Rational Exponents

How should we define $b^{1/n}$, where n is a counting number? If the exponential property $(b^m)^n = b^{mn}$ is to be true for $m = \dfrac{1}{2}$ and $n = 2$, then

$$\left(9^{\frac{1}{2}}\right)^2 = 9^{\frac{1}{2} \cdot 2} = 9^1 = 9$$

Since $(-3)^2 = 9$ and $3^2 = 9$, the statement suggests that a good meaning of $9^{1/2}$ is -3 or 3. We define $9^{1/2} = 3$. We call the nonnegative number 3 the *principal second root,* or **principal square root,** of 9, written $\sqrt{9}$.

Similarly, if the property $(b^m)^n = b^{mn}$ is to be true for $m = \dfrac{1}{3}$ and $n = 3$, then

$$\left(8^{\frac{1}{3}}\right)^3 = 8^{\frac{1}{3} \cdot 3} = 8^1 = 8$$

Since $2^3 = 8$, the statement suggests that a good meaning of $8^{1/3}$ is 2. The number 2 is called the *third root,* or **cube root,** of 8, written $\sqrt[3]{8}$.

For $(-8)^{1/3}$, a good meaning is -2, since $(-2)^3 = -8$. We do not assign a real-number value to $(-9)^{1/2}$, since no real number squared is equal to -9.

▶ **Definition** $b^{1/n}$

For the counting number n, where $n \neq 1$,

- If n is odd, then $b^{1/n}$ is the number whose nth power is b, and we call $b^{1/n}$ the **nth root of b.**
- If n is even and $b \geq 0$, then $b^{1/n}$ is the nonnegative number whose nth power is b, and we call $b^{1/n}$ the **principal nth root of b.**
- If n is even and $b < 0$, then $b^{1/n}$ is not a real number.

$b^{1/n}$ may be represented by $\sqrt[n]{b}$.

▶ **Example 1**   Simplifying Expressions Involving Rational Exponents

Simplify.

1. $25^{1/2}$ 2. $64^{1/3}$ 3. $(-64)^{1/3}$
4. $16^{1/4}$ 5. $-16^{1/4}$ 6. $(-16)^{1/4}$

Solution

1. $25^{1/2} = 5$, since $5^2 = 25$.
2. $64^{1/3} = 4$, since $4^3 = 64$.
3. $(-64)^{1/3} = -4$, since $(-4)^3 = -64$.
4. $16^{1/4} = 2$, since $2^4 = 16$.
5. $-16^{1/4} = -\left(16^{1/4}\right) = -2$.
6. $(-16)^{1/4}$ is not a real number, since the fourth power of any real number is nonnegative.

Graphing calculator checks for Problems 1, 2, and 3 are shown in Fig. 6. For example, to find $25^{1/2}$, press **25** $\boxed{\wedge}$ $\boxed{(}$ **1** $\boxed{\div}$ **2** $\boxed{)}$ $\boxed{\text{ENTER}}$. If an exponent involves an operation, you must use parentheses.

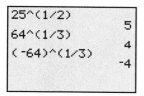

```
25^(1/2)
                5
64^(1/3)
                4
(-64)^(1/3)
                -4
```

Figure 6 Checks for Problems 1, 2, and 3

What would be a reasonable definition of $b^{m/n}$? If the properties of exponents we discussed in Section 4.1 are to hold true for rational exponents, we have

$$8^{\frac{2}{3}} = 8^{\frac{1}{3} \cdot 2} = \left(8^{\frac{1}{3}}\right)^2 = 2^2 = 4 \quad \text{or} \quad 8^{\frac{2}{3}} = 8^{2 \cdot \frac{1}{3}} = \left(8^2\right)^{\frac{1}{3}} = 64^{\frac{1}{3}} = 4$$

Likewise,

$$32^{\frac{3}{5}} = 32^{\frac{1}{5} \cdot 3} = \left(32^{\frac{1}{5}}\right)^3 = 2^3 = 8 \quad \text{or} \quad 32^{\frac{3}{5}} = 32^{3 \cdot \frac{1}{5}} = \left(32^3\right)^{\frac{1}{5}} = 32{,}768^{\frac{1}{5}} = 8$$

Also,

$$32^{-\frac{3}{5}} = \frac{1}{32^{\frac{3}{5}}} = \frac{1}{8}$$

▶ Definition   **Rational exponent**

For the counting numbers m and n, where $n \neq 1$ and b is any real number for which $b^{1/n}$ is a real number,

- $b^{m/n} = \left(b^{1/n}\right)^m = \left(b^m\right)^{1/n}$

- $b^{-m/n} = \dfrac{1}{b^{m/n}}, \quad b \neq 0$

A power of the form $b^{m/n}$ or $b^{-m/n}$ is said to have a **rational exponent.**

▶ **Example 2**   Simplifying Expressions Involving Rational Exponents

Simplify.

1. $25^{3/2}$ **2.** $(-27)^{2/3}$ **3.** $32^{-2/5}$ **4.** $(-8)^{-5/3}$

Solution

1. $25^{3/2} = (25^{1/2})^3 = 5^3 = 125$

2. $(-27)^{2/3} = \left((-27)^{1/3}\right)^2 = (-3)^2 = 9$

3. $32^{-2/5} = \dfrac{1}{32^{2/5}} = \dfrac{1}{\left(32^{1/5}\right)^2} = \dfrac{1}{2^2} = \dfrac{1}{4}$

4. $(-8)^{-5/3} = \dfrac{1}{(-8)^{5/3}} = \dfrac{1}{\left((-8)^{1/3}\right)^5} = \dfrac{1}{(-2)^5} = \dfrac{1}{-32} = -\dfrac{1}{32}$

Graphing calculator checks for Problems 1, 2, and 3 are shown in Fig. 7.

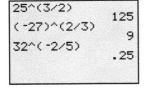

Figure 7 Checks for Problems 1, 2, and 3

▶ **Example 3**   Evaluating an Exponential Function

For $f(x) = 64^x$, $g(x) = 3(16)^x$, and $h(x) = -5(9)^x$, find the following.

1. $f\left(\dfrac{2}{3}\right)$ **2.** $g\left(\dfrac{3}{4}\right)$ **3.** $h\left(-\dfrac{1}{2}\right)$

Solution

1. $f\left(\dfrac{2}{3}\right) = 64^{2/3} = \left(64^{1/3}\right)^2 = 4^2 = 16$

2. $g\left(\dfrac{3}{4}\right) = 3(16)^{3/4} = 3\left(16^{1/4}\right)^3 = 3(2)^3 = 3 \cdot 8 = 24$

3. $h\left(-\dfrac{1}{2}\right) = -5(9)^{-1/2} = \dfrac{-5}{9^{1/2}} = -\dfrac{5}{3}$

Properties of Rational Exponents

The properties of exponents we discussed in Section 4.1 are valid for *rational* exponents.

> ### Properties of Rational Exponents
>
> If m and n are rational numbers and b and c are any real numbers for which b^m, b^n, and c^n are real numbers, then
>
> - $b^m b^n = b^{m+n}$ *Product property for exponents*
>
> - $\dfrac{b^m}{b^n} = b^{m-n}, b \neq 0$ *Quotient property for exponents*
>
> - $(bc)^n = b^n c^n$ *Raising a product to a power*
>
> - $\left(\dfrac{b}{c}\right)^n = \dfrac{b^n}{c^n}, \quad c \neq 0$ *Raising a quotient to a power*
>
> - $(b^m)^n = b^{mn}$ *Raising a power to a power*

We can use properties of exponents to help us simplify expressions involving rational exponents.

▶ **Example 4**   Simplifying Expressions Involving Rational Exponents

Simplify. Assume b is positive.

   1. $\left(4b^6\right)^{3/2}$ **2.** $\dfrac{b^{2/7}}{b^{-3/7}}$

Solution

   1. $\left(4b^6\right)^{3/2} = 4^{3/2}\left(b^6\right)^{3/2}$ *Raise factors to nth power:* $(bc)^n = b^n c^n$

        $= \left(4^{1/2}\right)^3 b^{\frac{6}{1}\cdot\frac{3}{2}}$ $b^{m/n} = (b^{1/n})^m;$ *multiply exponents:* $(b^m)^n = b^{mn}$

        $= 2^3 b^9$ $4^{\frac{1}{2}} = 2;$ *multiply.*

        $= 8b^9$ *Simplify.*

   2. $\dfrac{b^{2/7}}{b^{-3/7}} = b^{\frac{2}{7}-\left(-\frac{3}{7}\right)}$ *Subtract exponents:* $\dfrac{b^m}{b^n} = b^{m-n}$

       $= b^{\frac{2}{7}+\frac{3}{7}}$ *Simplify.*

       $= b^{5/7}$ *Add.*

▶ **Example 5**   Simplifying Expressions Involving Rational Exponents

Simplify. Assume b is positive.

   1. $b^{2/3} b^{1/2}$ **2.** $\left(\dfrac{32b^2}{b^{12}}\right)^{2/5}$

Solution

   1. $b^{2/3} b^{1/2} = b^{\frac{2}{3}+\frac{1}{2}}$ *Add exponents:* $b^m b^n = b^{m+n}$

        $= b^{\frac{4}{6}+\frac{3}{6}}$ *Find common denominator.*

        $= b^{7/6}$ *Add.*

   2. $\left(\dfrac{32b^2}{b^{12}}\right)^{2/5} = \left(32b^{2-12}\right)^{2/5}$ *Subtract exponents:* $\dfrac{b^m}{b^n} = b^{m-n}$

        $= \left(32b^{-10}\right)^{2/5}$ *Subtract.*

$$= \left(\frac{32}{b^{10}} \right)^{2/5}$$

Write powers so exponents are positive: $b^{-n} = \dfrac{1}{b^n}$

$$= \frac{32^{2/5}}{\left(b^{10} \right)^{2/5}}$$

Raise numerator and denominator to

nth power: $\left(\dfrac{b}{c} \right)^n = \dfrac{b^n}{c^n}$

$$= \frac{\left(32^{1/5} \right)^2}{b^{10 \cdot \frac{2}{5}}}$$

$b^{m/n} = \left(b^{1/n} \right)^m$ *; multiply exponents:* $\left(b^m \right)^n = b^{mn}$

$$= \frac{2^2}{b^4}$$

$32^{1/5} = 2$*; multiply.*

$$= \frac{4}{b^4}$$

Simplify.

▶ **Example 6**   Simplifying an Expression Involving Rational Exponents

Simplify $\dfrac{\left(81b^6c^{20} \right)^{1/2}}{\left(27b^{12}c^9 \right)^{2/3}}$. Assume b and c are positive.

Solution

$$\frac{\left(81b^6c^{20} \right)^{1/2}}{\left(27b^{12}c^9 \right)^{2/3}} = \frac{81^{1/2} \left(b^6 \right)^{1/2} \left(c^{20} \right)^{1/2}}{27^{2/3} \left(b^{12} \right)^{2/3} \left(c^9 \right)^{2/3}}$$

Raise factors to a power: $(bc)^n = b^n c^n$

$$= \frac{9b^{6 \cdot \frac{1}{2}} c^{20 \cdot \frac{1}{2}}}{\left(27^{1/3} \right)^2 b^{12 \cdot \frac{2}{3}} c^{9 \cdot \frac{2}{3}}}$$

$81^{1/2} = 9$; $b^{m/n} = \left(b^{1/n} \right)^m$*; multiply*

exponents: $\left(b^m \right)^n = b^{mn}$

$$= \frac{9b^3 c^{10}}{3^2 b^8 c^6}$$

$27^{1/3} = 3$*; multiply.*

$$= \frac{9b^{-5} c^4}{9}$$

Subtract exponents: $\dfrac{b^m}{b^n} = b^{m-n}$

$$= \frac{c^4}{b^5}$$

Write powers so exponents are positive: $b^{-n} = \dfrac{1}{b^n}$

▶

Group Exploration

Looking ahead: Graphical significance of a and b for $y = ab^x$

1. Use ZDecimal to graph these equations of the form $y = b^x$ in order, and describe what you observe:

$$y = 1.2^x, \quad y = 1.5^x, \quad y = 2^x, \quad \text{and} \quad y = 5^x$$

If you want a better view, set Ymin = 0. To change window settings, see Appendix B.7.

   Do the same with the equations

$$y = 0.3^x, \quad y = 0.5^x, \quad y = 0.7^x, \quad \text{and} \quad y = 0.9^x$$

2. Use ZStandard to graph these equations of the form $y = a(1.1)^x$ in order, and describe what you observe:

$$y = 2(1.1)^x, \quad y = 3(1.1)^x, \quad y = 4(1.1)^x,$$
$$\text{and} \quad y = 5(1.1)^x$$

If you want a better view, set Ymin = 0.

   Use ZStandard to do the same with the equations

$$y = -2(1.1)^x, \quad y = -3(1.1)^x, \quad y = -4(1.1)^x,$$
$$\text{and} \quad y = -5(1.1)^x$$

If you want a better view, set Ymax = 0.

3. So far, you have sketched the graphs of equations of only the forms $y = b^x$ (where $a = 1$) and $y = a(1.1)^x$ (where $b = 1.1$). Graph more equations of the form $y = ab^x$, until you are confident you know the graphical significance of the constants a and b, for any possible combination of values of a and b. If you have any new insights into the graphical significance of a and b, describe those insights.

4. Describe the graph of $y = ab^x$ in the following situations.
   a. a is positive
   b. a is negative
   c. $b > 1$
   d. $0 < b < 1$
   e. $b = 1$
   f. b is negative

5. Describe the connection between the y-intercept of the graph of $y = ab^x$ and the values of a and b.

Group Exploration

Looking ahead: Numerical significance of a and b for $f(x) = ab^x$

In this exploration, you will investigate the nature of exponential functions of the form $f(x) = ab^x$.

1. Use a graphing calculator to create a table of ordered pairs for $f(x) = 2(3)^x$, $g(x) = 64\left(\dfrac{1}{2}\right)^x$, and a third exponential function of your choice. (See Figs. 8 and 9.) Use the following values for the x-coordinates: $0, 1, 2, \ldots, 6$.

Figure 8 Enter the three functions

Figure 9 Table setup

2. a. What connection do you notice between the y-coordinates of each function and the base b of the function $y = ab^x$?
   b. Test the connection you described in part (a) by choosing yet another exponential function, and check whether it behaves as you think it should.
   c. For $f(x) = ab^x$, we have $f(0) = a$, $f(1) = ab$, $f(2) = abb$, and $f(3) = abbb$. Explain why these results suggest that your response to part (a) is correct.

3. a. What connection do you notice between the y-coordinates of each function and the coefficient a of the function $y = ab^x$?
   b. Test the connection you described in part (a) by choosing yet another exponential function, and check whether it behaves as you think it should.
   c. Use pencil and paper to find $f(0)$, where $f(x) = ab^x$. Explain why your result shows that your response to part (a) is correct.

▶ Tips for Success   **Complete Exercises without Help**

If you work an exercise by referring to a similar example in your notebook or in the text, try the exercise again without that help. If you need to refer to your source of help to solve the exercise a second time, try the exercise a third time without help. When you complete the exercise without help, reflect on which concepts you used to work the exercise, where you had difficulty, and what key idea opened the door of understanding for you. You can use a similar strategy in getting help from another student, an instructor, or a tutor.

If this sounds like a lot of work, it is! But the work is well worth it. Although it is important to complete each assignment, it is also important to learn as much as possible while progressing through it.

 # Homework 4.2

For extra help ▶ MyMathLab®   Watch the videos in MyMathLab   Download the MyDashboard App

*Simplify without using a calculator. Then use a graphing calculator to verify your result. [**Graphing Calculator:** Instructions for $x^{m/n}$: Press $\boxed{X, T, \Theta, n}\,\boxed{\wedge}\,\boxed{(}\,\boxed{m}\,\boxed{\div}\,\boxed{n}\,\boxed{)}.]*

1. $16^{1/2}$
2. $27^{1/3}$
3. $1000^{1/3}$
4. $32^{1/5}$
5. $49^{1/2}$
6. $81^{1/4}$
7. $125^{1/3}$
8. $64^{1/6}$
9. $8^{4/3}$
10. $16^{3/4}$
11. $9^{3/2}$
12. $64^{2/3}$
13. $32^{2/5}$
14. $27^{4/3}$
15. $4^{5/2}$
16. $81^{3/4}$
17. $27^{-1/3}$
18. $16^{-1/4}$
19. $-36^{-1/2}$
20. $-32^{-1/5}$
21. $4^{-5/2}$
22. $9^{-3/2}$
23. $(-27)^{-4/3}$
24. $(-32)^{-3/5}$

Simplify without using a calculator. Then use a graphing calculator to verify your result.

25. $2^{1/4}2^{3/4}$
26. $3^{7/5}3^{3/5}$
27. $\left(3^{1/2}2^{3/2}\right)^2$
28. $\left(2^{2/3}5^{1/3}\right)^3$
29. $\dfrac{7^{1/3}}{7^{-5/3}}$
30. $\dfrac{5^{4/3}}{5^{1/3}}$

For $f(x) = 81^x$, $g(x) = 4(27)^x$, and $h(x) = -2(4)^x$, find the following.

31. $f\left(\dfrac{3}{4}\right)$

32. $f\left(\dfrac{1}{4}\right)$

33. $g\left(\dfrac{1}{3}\right)$

34. $g\left(\dfrac{2}{3}\right)$

35. $g\left(-\dfrac{1}{3}\right)$

36. $g\left(-\dfrac{2}{3}\right)$

37. $h\left(\dfrac{3}{2}\right)$

38. $h\left(\dfrac{5}{2}\right)$

39. Without using a calculator, complete Table 6 with values of the function $f(x) = 16^x$. Then use a graphing calculator to verify your results.

Table 6 Values of the Function $f(x) = 16^x$

x	$f(x)$	x	$f(x)$
$-\dfrac{3}{4}$		$\dfrac{1}{4}$	
$-\dfrac{1}{2}$		$\dfrac{1}{2}$	
$-\dfrac{1}{4}$		$\dfrac{3}{4}$	
0		1	

40. Without using a calculator, complete Table 7 with values of the function $f(x) = 64^x$. Then use a graphing calculator to verify your results.

Table 7 Values of the Function $f(x) = 64^x$

x	$f(x)$	x	$f(x)$
$-\dfrac{5}{6}$		$\dfrac{1}{6}$	
$-\dfrac{2}{3}$		$\dfrac{1}{3}$	
$-\dfrac{1}{2}$		$\dfrac{1}{2}$	
$-\dfrac{1}{3}$		$\dfrac{2}{3}$	
$-\dfrac{1}{6}$		$\dfrac{5}{6}$	
0		1	

Simplify. Assume b and c are positive.

41. $b^{7/6}b^{5/6}$

42. $b^{1/5}b^{3/5}$

43. $b^{3/5}b^{-13/5}$

44. $b^{2/7}b^{-6/7}$

45. $\left(16b^8\right)^{1/4}$

46. $\left(27b^{27}\right)^{1/3}$

47. $4(25b^8c^{14})^{-1/2}$

48. $-\left(8b^{-6}c^{12}\right)^{2/3}$

49. $\left(b^{3/5}c^{-1/4}\right)\left(b^{2/5}c^{-7/4}\right)$

50. $\left(b^{-4/3}c^{1/2}\right)\left(b^{-2/3}c^{-3/2}\right)$

51. $(5bcd)^{1/5}(5bcd)^{4/5}$

52. $\left(6bc^2\right)^{5/7}\left(6bc^2\right)^{2/7}$

53. $\left[(3b^5)^3\left(3b^9c^8\right)\right]^{1/4}$

54. $\left[\left(4b^3\right)^2\left(b^2c^{12}\right)\right]^{1/4}$

55. $\dfrac{b^{-2/5}c^{11/8}}{b^{18/5}c^{-5/8}}$

56. $\dfrac{b^{3/4}c^{1/2}}{b^{-1/4}c^{-1/2}}$

57. $\left(\dfrac{9b^3c^{-2}}{25b^{-5}c^4}\right)^{-1/2}$

58. $\left(\dfrac{16b^{12}c^2}{2b^{-3}c^{-4}}\right)^{-1/3}$

59. $32^{1/5}b^{3/7}b^{2/5}$

60. $16^{1/4}b^{1/4}b^{1/3}$

61. $\dfrac{b^{5/6}}{b^{1/4}}$

62. $\dfrac{b^{-2/3}}{b^{1/7}}$

63. $\dfrac{\left(9b^5\right)^{3/2}}{\left(27b^4\right)^{2/3}}$

64. $\dfrac{\left(32b^3\right)^{3/5}}{\left(16b^3\right)^{3/2}}$

65. $\left(\dfrac{8b^{2/3}}{2b^{4/5}}\right)^{3/2}$

66. $\left(\dfrac{27b^{1/3}c^{3/4}}{8b^{-2/3}c^{1/2}}\right)^{4/3}$

67. $\dfrac{\left(8bc^3\right)^{1/3}}{\left(81b^{-5}c^3\right)^{3/4}}$

68. $\dfrac{\left(1000b^{-7}c^8\right)^{2/3}}{\left(32b^{15}c^4\right)^{3/5}}$

69. $b^{2/5}\left(b^{8/5} + b^{3/5}\right)$

70. $c^{1/3}\left(c^{8/3} - c^{5/3}\right)$

71. The amounts (in megawatts) of new solar power installed in the United States are shown in Table 8 for various years.

Table 8 Amounts of New Solar Power Installed in the United States

Year	Amount of New Solar Power Installed (megawatts)
2006	105
2007	160
2008	290
2009	435
2010	878
2011	1891
2012	3300

Source: *GTM Research*

Let A be the amount (in megawatts) of new solar power installed in the year that is t years since 2000. The situation can be described by the linear function $A = 486.96t - 3374.25$ and the exponential function $A = 2.73(1.8)^t$.

a. Use a graphing calculator to draw the graphs of the two functions and, in the same viewing window, the scattergram of the data. Which function describes the situation better?

b. Use the exponential model to predict the amount of solar power that will be installed in 2018.

c. Use the exponential model and "intersect" on a graphing calculator to predict in which year the amount of solar power installed will be 30,000 megawatts, the equivalent of more than 24 nuclear-power plants. [**Hint:** Graph the model and the horizontal line $A = 30,000$, and then use Zoom Out twice.]

72. The numbers of AP tests administered are shown in Table 9 for various years.

Table 9 Numbers of AP Tests Administered

Year	Number of AP Tests Administered (millions)
1980	0.2
1985	0.3
1990	0.5
1995	0.9
2000	1.3
2005	2.1
2010	3.3

Source: *The College Board*

Let n be the number (in millions) of AP tests administered in the year that is t years since 1980. The situation can be modeled by the linear function $n = 0.098t - 0.24$ and the exponential function $n = 0.2(1.099)^t$.

a. Use a graphing calculator to draw the graphs of the two functions and, in the same viewing window, the scattergram of the data. Which function describes the situation better?

b. Use the exponential model to predict the number of AP tests that will be administered in 2017.

c. Use the exponential model and "intersect" on a graphing calculator to predict in which year 8 million AP tests will be administered. [**Hint:** Graph the model and the horizontal line $n = 8$, and then use Zoom Out.]

Concepts

73. We can represent $\sqrt{5}$ by $5^{1/2}$. Explain.

74. To use a graphing calculator to find that $16^{1/2} = 4$, we press 16 $\boxed{\wedge}$ $\boxed{(}$ 1 $\boxed{\div}$ 2 $\boxed{)}$. If we omit the parentheses, we get the incorrect result 8. Explain.

75. A student tries to simplify $\left(36x^{36}\right)^{1/2}$:

$$\left(36x^{36}\right)^{1/2} = 36^{1/2}\left(x^{36}\right)^{1/2} = 18x^{18}$$

Describe any errors. Then simplify the expression correctly.

76. A student tries to simplify $64^{2/3}$:

$$64^{2/3} = \left(64^{1/2}\right)^3 = 8^3 = 512$$

Describe any errors. Then simplify the expression correctly.

77. Two students simplify $9^{3/2}$:

Student A
$9^{3/2} = \left(9^{1/2}\right)^3 = 3^3 = 27$

Student B
$9^{3/2} = \left(9^3\right)^{1/2} = 729^{1/2} = 27$

Explain why it makes sense the students' results are equal. Which method is easier? Explain.

78. A student tries to simplify $25^{-1/2}$:

$$25^{-1/2} = -25^{1/2} = -5$$

Describe any errors. Then simplify the expression correctly.

79. a. Identify which of the following are *not* real numbers:

$$(-9)^{1/2}, (-27)^{1/3}, (-81)^{1/4}, (-32)^{1/5}, (-1)^{1/6}, (-1)^{1/7}$$

b. Describe all of the values of b and counting number n for which $b^{1/n}$ is not a real number. Explain.

80. Use a calculator to determine which is larger, $\left(\frac{1}{2}\right)^{1/3}$ or $\left(\frac{1}{3}\right)^{1/2}$. Explain why this makes sense. [**Hint:** Use the property $\left(\frac{b}{c}\right)^n = \frac{b^n}{c^n}$.]

81. Describe how to compute a numerical expression of the form $b^{m/n}$, assuming it is a real number.

82. List the exponent definitions and properties that are discussed in this section and Section 4.1. Explain how you can recognize which definition or property will help you simplify a given expression.

Related Review

For $f(x) = 8x$ and $g(x) = 8^x$, find the following.

83. $f\left(\frac{1}{3}\right)$

84. $f\left(\frac{4}{3}\right)$

85. $g\left(\frac{1}{3}\right)$

86. $g\left(\frac{4}{3}\right)$

87. $f\left(-\frac{1}{3}\right)$

88. $f\left(-\frac{2}{3}\right)$

89. $g\left(-\frac{1}{3}\right)$

90. $g\left(-\frac{2}{3}\right)$

Expressions, Equations, Functions, and Graphs

Perform the indicated instruction. Then use words such as linear, exponential, function, one variable, *and* two variables *to describe the expression, equation, or system. For instance, to describe* $f(x) = 7(4)^x$, *you could say "$f(x) = 7(4)^x$ is an exponential function."*

91. Graph $f(x) = \frac{3}{2}x - 4$ by hand.

92. Solve:

$$y = \frac{3}{2}x - 4$$
$$y = -\frac{1}{4}x + 3$$

93. Let $f(x) = \frac{3}{2}x - 4$. Find x when $f(x) = 5$.

94. Solve $\frac{3}{2}x - 4 = -\frac{1}{4}x + 3$.

▼4.3 Graphing Exponential Functions

Objectives

» Sketch the graph of an exponential function.

» Know the graphical significance of a and b for a function of the form $f(x) = ab^x$.

» Know the *base multiplier property*, the *increasing or decreasing property*, and the *reflection property*.

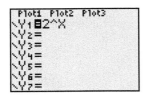

Figure 11 Enter the function

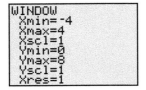

Figure 12 Set up the window

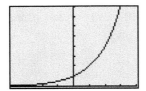

Figure 13 Graph the function

Recall from Section 4.1 that an exponential function is a function whose equation can be put into the form $f(x) = ab^x$, where $a \neq 0$, $b > 0$, and $b \neq 1$. In this section, we discuss how to use the values of a and b to help us graph an exponential function.

Graphing Exponential Functions

When graphing a certain type of function for the first time, we often begin by finding outputs for integer inputs near zero.

▶ **Example 1**   Graphing an Exponential Function with $b > 1$

Graph $f(x) = 2^x$ by hand.

Solution

First, we list input–output pairs of the function f in Table 10. Note that as the value of x increases by 1, the value of y is multiplied by 2 (the base).

Next, we plot the solutions from Table 10 in Fig. 10 and sketch an increasing curve that contains the plotted points. The graph shows that as the value of x increases by 1, the value of y is doubled.

Table 10 Input–Output Pairs of $f(x) = 2^x$

x	$f(x)$
-3	$2^{-3} = \dfrac{1}{2^3} = \dfrac{1}{8}$
-2	$2^{-2} = \dfrac{1}{2^2} = \dfrac{1}{4}$
-1	$2^{-1} = \dfrac{1}{2^1} = \dfrac{1}{2}$
0	$2^0 = 1$
1	$2^1 = 2$
2	$2^2 = 4$
3	$2^3 = 8$

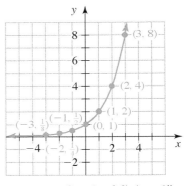

Figure 10 Graph of $f(x) = 2^x$

We can set up a window to verify our graph (see Figs. 11–13). For graphing calculator instructions, see Appendix B.7.

▶

The smooth curve sketched in Fig. 10 implies that 2^x has meaning for *any* real-number exponent x. This is indeed true. In general, for $b > 0$, b^x has meaning for any real-number exponent x. The exponents are defined so the graph of any exponential function is a smooth graph. Also, the exponential properties we have discussed for rational exponents apply to real-number exponents as well. We can use a calculator to find *real-number powers* of numbers.

Recall from Section 1.2 that every point on the graph of an equation represents a solution of the equation. Every point *not* on the graph represents an ordered pair that is *not* a solution. The graph of an exponential function is called an **exponential curve.**

▶ **Example 2**   Graphing an Exponential Function with $0 < b < 1$

Graph $g(x) = 4\left(\dfrac{1}{2}\right)^x$ by hand.

Solution

Input–output pairs of g are listed in Table 11. For example,

$$g(-1) = 4\left(\frac{1}{2}\right)^{-1} = 4\left(\frac{1}{2^{-1}}\right) = 4(2^1) = 8$$

So, $(-1, 8)$ is an input–output pair. Note that as the value of x increases by 1, the value of y is multiplied by $\frac{1}{2}$.

We plot the found points in Fig. 14 and sketch a decreasing exponential curve that contains the plotted points. The graph shows that as the value of x increases by 1, the value of y is halved.

Table 11 Input–Output
Pairs of $g(x) = 4\left(\frac{1}{2}\right)^x$

x	$g(x)$
-1	8
0	4
1	2
2	1
3	$\frac{1}{2}$

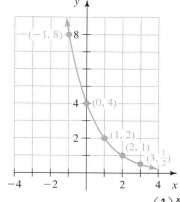

Figure 14 Graph of $y = 4\left(\frac{1}{2}\right)^x$

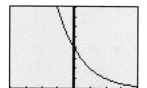

Figure 15 Graph of
$y = 4\left(\frac{1}{2}\right)^x$

We can use a graphing calculator to verify our graph (see Fig. 15).

Base Multiplier Property; Increasing or Decreasing Property

Examples 1 and 2 suggest the *base multiplier property* and the *increasing or decreasing property*.

▶ **Base Multiplier Property**

For an exponential function of the form $y = ab^x$, if the value of the independent variable increases by 1, the value of the dependent variable is multiplied by b.

We have seen two examples of this property in Examples 1 and 2. Here are two more examples of the base multiplier property:

1. For the function $f(x) = 2(3)^x$, if the value of x increases by 1, the value of y is multiplied by 3.

2. For the function $f(x) = 5\left(\frac{3}{4}\right)^x$, if the value of x increases by 1, the value of y is multiplied by $\frac{3}{4}$.

To prove the base multiplier property for the exponential function $f(x) = ab^x$, we compare outputs for the inputs k and $k + 1$, which differ by 1:

$$f(k) = ab^k \qquad f(k + 1) = ab^{k+1}$$
$$= ab^k b^1$$
$$= f(k)b$$

Since $f(k + 1) = f(k)b$, we conclude that if the value of the independent variable increases by 1, the value of the dependent variable is multiplied by b, which is what we set out to show.

For the increasing or decreasing property, we note in Example 1 that the base b is greater than 1 and the graph is increasing. In Example 2, the positive base is less than 1 and the graph is decreasing. For $f(x) = ab^x$ with $a > 0$, in general, we have the property that each multiplication by a base greater than 1 gives a larger value of y, whereas each multiplication by a positive base less than 1 gives a smaller value of y.

▶ **Increasing or Decreasing Property**

Let $f(x) = ab^x$, where $a > 0$. Then

- If $b > 1$, then the function f is increasing. We say the function **grows exponentially** (see Fig. 16).
- If $0 < b < 1$, then the function f is decreasing. We say the function **decays exponentially** (see Fig. 17).

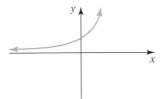

Figure 16 Typical graph of $f(x) = ab^x$, where $a > 0$ and $b > 1$

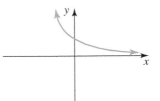

Figure 17 Typical graph of $f(x) = ab^x$, where $a > 0$ and $0 < b < 1$

Intercepts

When we sketch the graph of an exponential function, it is helpful to plot the y-intercept first. Substituting 0 for x in the general equation $y = ab^x$ gives

$$y = ab^0 = a(1) = a$$

So, the y-intercept is $(0, a)$.

▶ **y-Intercept of an Exponential Function**

For an exponential function of the form

$$y = ab^x,$$

the y-intercept is $(0, a)$.

For the function $y = 5(8)^x$, the y-intercept is $(0, 5)$. For the function $y = 4\left(\dfrac{1}{7}\right)^x$, the y-intercept is $(0, 4)$.

WARNING   For an exponential function of the form $y = b^x$ (rather than $y = ab^x$), the y-intercept is *not* $(0, b)$. By writing $y = b^x = 1b^x$, we see the y-intercept is $(0, 1)$. For example, for $y = 2^x$, the y-intercept is $(0, 1)$. See Example 1.

▶ **Example 3**   Intercepts and Graph of an Exponential Function

Let $f(x) = 6\left(\dfrac{1}{2}\right)^x$.

1. Find the *y*-intercept of the graph of *f*.
2. Find the *x*-intercept of the graph of *f*.
3. Graph *f* by hand.

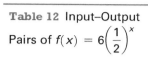

Table 12 Input–Output Pairs of $f(x) = 6\left(\frac{1}{2}\right)^x$

x	f(x)
0	6
1	3
2	$\frac{3}{2}$
3	$\frac{3}{4}$
4	$\frac{3}{8}$

Solution

1. Since $f(x) = 6\left(\frac{1}{2}\right)^x$ is of the form $f(x) = ab^x$, the *y*-intercept is $(0, a)$, or $(0, 6)$.
2. By the base multiplier property, as the value of *x* increases by 1, the value of *y* is multiplied by $\frac{1}{2}$ (see Table 12).

    When we halve a number, it becomes smaller. But no number of halvings will give a result that is zero. So, as *x* grows large, *y* will become extremely close to, but never equal, 0. Likewise, the graph of *f* gets arbitrarily close to, but never reaches, the *x*-axis (see Fig. 18). In this case, we call the *x*-axis a **horizontal asymptote.** We conclude that the function *f* has no *x*-intercepts.
3. We plot five solutions from Table 12 and sketch a decreasing exponential curve that contains the five points (see Fig. 18). If we had not already found a table of solutions, we could have plotted the *y*-intercept and plotted additional solutions by increasing the value of *x* by 1 and going half as high for the value of *y* each time.

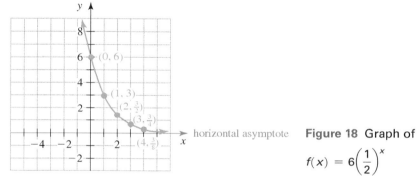

horizontal asymptote   **Figure 18** Graph of

$$f(x) = 6\left(\frac{1}{2}\right)^x$$

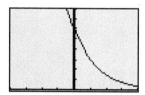

Figure 19 Graph of

$$y = 6\left(\frac{1}{2}\right)^x$$

As a check, we note that according to the increasing or decreasing property, the function *f* is decreasing, since $a > 0$ and the base, $\frac{1}{2}$, is between 0 and 1. For a more thorough check, we can use a graphing calculator to verify our graph (see Fig. 19).

In Fig. 20, the graphs of both exponential functions get closer and closer to, but never reach, the *x*-axis. For both functions, the *x*-axis is a horizontal asymptote.

Figure 20 For both exponential functions, the *x*-axis is a horizontal asymptote

Reflection Property

In Example 4, we will graph two related exponential functions that will help us understand the *reflection property*.

▶ **Example 4**   Graphs of Functions of the Form $y = ab^x$ and $y = -ab^x$

1. Sketch and compare the graphs of $f(x) = 5(3)^x$ and $g(x) = -5(3)^x$.
2. Find the domain and range of *f*.
3. Find the domain and range of *g*.

Table 13 Input–Output
Pairs of $f(x) = 5(3)^x$ and
$g(x) = -5(3)^x$

x	f(x)	g(x)
0	5	-5
1	15	-15
2	45	-45
3	135	-135
4	405	-405

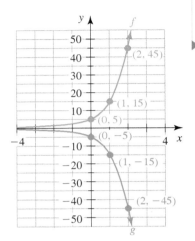

Figure 21 Graphs
of $f(x) = 5(3)^x$ and
$g(x) = -5(3)^x$

Solution

1. Input–output pairs of f and g are listed in Table 13 and plotted in Fig. 21. In Table 13, we see that for each value of x, the outputs of g are the opposites of the outputs of f. Because of this, the graph of g is the **reflection,** or mirror image, of the graph of f, with the mirror along the x-axis. We can find the graph of g by *reflecting the graph of f across the x-axis.*
2. The expression $5(3)^x$ is defined for any real number x. So, the domain of f is the set of all real numbers. From Fig. 21, we see that the range of f (the set of all outputs of f) is the set of all positive real numbers.
3. The expression $-5(3)^x$ is defined for any real number x. So, the domain of g is the set of all real numbers. From Fig. 21, we see that the range is the set of all negative real numbers.

▶ **Reflection Property**

The graphs of $f(x) = -ab^x$ and $g(x) = ab^x$ are reflections of each other across the x-axis.

We illustrate the reflection property and summarize four types of exponential curves in Figs. 22 and 23. **For all exponential functions, the x-axis is a horizontal asymptote.**

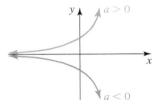

Figure 22 Typical graphs
of $f(x) = ab^x$, $b > 1$

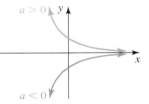

Figure 23 Typical graphs
of $f(x) = ab^x$, $0 < b < 1$

Recall that for $b > 0$, b^x has meaning for any real-number exponent x. So, **the domain of any exponential function $f(x) = ab^x$ is the set of real numbers.**

Further, Figs. 22 and 23 show that $f(x) = ab^x$ has positive outputs if $a > 0$ and negative outputs if $a < 0$. Therefore, **the range of an exponential function $f(x) = ab^x$ is the set of all positive real numbers if $a > 0$, and the range is the set of all negative real numbers if $a < 0$.**

In Example 5, we use the graph of an exponential function f to find input or output values of f.

▶ **Example 5**   Finding Values of a Function from Its Graph

The graph of an exponential function f is shown in Fig. 24.

1. Find $f(2)$.
2. Find x when $f(x) = 2$.
3. Find x when $f(x) = 0$.

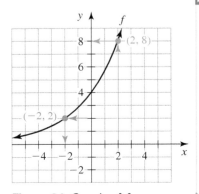

Figure 24 Graph of f

Solution

1. The blue arrows in Fig. 24 show that the input $x = 2$ leads to the output $y = 8$. We conclude that $f(2) = 8$.
2. The red arrows in Fig. 24 show that the output $y = 2$ originates from the input $x = -2$. We conclude that $x = -2$ when $f(x) = 2$.
3. Recall that the graph of an exponential function gets close to, but never reaches, the x-axis. So, there is no value of x where $f(x) = 0$.

Group Exploration

Drawing families of exponential curves

For each problem, use a graphing calculator to graph a family of curves.

1. List the equations of a family of exponential curves like the ones shown in Fig. 25.

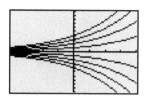

Figure 25 A family of exponential curves

2. List the equations of a family of exponential curves like the ones shown in Fig. 26. All of these curves pass through the point $(0, 2)$.

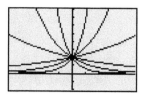

Figure 26 A family of exponential curves passing through $(0, 2)$

3. Summarize what you have learned from this exploration and this section about the coefficient a and the base b in functions of the form $f(x) = ab^x$.

Group Exploration

Looking ahead: Using trial and error to find a model

Ethanol fuel productions are shown in Table 14 for various years. Let $p = f(t)$ be the annual production (in millions of gallons) of ethanol fuel at t years since 2000.

Table 14 Annual Ethanol Fuel Productions

Year	Annual Production (millions of gallons)
2000	1.6
2001	1.8
2002	2.1
2003	2.8
2004	3.4
2005	3.9
2006	4.9
2007	6.5
2008	9.0
2009	10.6
2010	13.2
2011	13.9

Source: *Renewable Fuels Association*

1. Use a graphing calculator to draw a scattergram of the data. Would it be better to model the data with a linear or an exponential function? Explain.

2. Imagine an exponential function $f(t) = ab^t$ whose graph comes close to the data points in your scattergram. What is the p-intercept? What does this tell you about the value of a or b? Explain.

3. Guess a reasonable value of b for your function $f(t) = ab^t$. [**Hint:** The base multiplier property may help.]

4. Substitute your values of a and b from Problems 2 and 3 into the equation $f(t) = ab^t$.

5. Graph f and the scattergram in the same viewing window to see how well your model fits the data.

6. Now find better values of a and b through trial and error. When you are satisfied with your values of a and b, write the equation of f that you have found.

▶ Tips for Success   **Desire and Faith**

Accomplishing anything worthwhile, including succeeding in this course, requires substantial effort and faith that you will succeed:

> *"The secret of making something work in your lives is, first of all, the deep desire to make it work. Then the faith and belief that it can work. Then to hold that clear definite vision in your consciousness and see it working out step by step without one thought of doubt or disbelief."*

— From *Footprints on the Path*, by Eileen Caddy, © 1976, 1991.
Used by permission of Findhorn Press, Scotland, UK.

Your deep desire to succeed in this course might be to earn a degree so you can earn more money, to learn algebra for the love of learning, or to experience setting a goal and reaching it. Your faith and belief can come from knowing you, your instructor, and your college will do everything possible to ensure your success. To hold your vision of success "without one thought of doubt or disbelief" is a tall order, but the more you look for ways to succeed rather than feel discouraged, the better are your chances of success.

Homework 4.3

For extra help ▶ MyMathLab®   Watch the videos in MyMathLab   Download the MyDashboard App

Graph the given function by hand. Then use a graphing calculator to verify your graph.

1. $y = 3^x$
2. $y = 4^x$
3. $y = 10^x$
4. $y = 5^x$
5. $y = 3(2)^x$
6. $y = 2(3)^x$
7. $y = 6(3)^x$
8. $y = 3(5)^x$
9. $y = 15\left(\dfrac{1}{3}\right)^x$
10. $y = 20\left(\dfrac{1}{4}\right)^x$
11. $y = 12\left(\dfrac{1}{2}\right)^x$
12. $y = 6\left(\dfrac{2}{3}\right)^x$

Graph both functions by hand on the same coordinate system. Then use a graphing calculator to verify your graphs.

13. $f(x) = 2^x, g(x) = -2^x$

14. $f(x) = 3^x, g(x) = -3^x$

15. $f(x) = 4(3)^x, g(x) = -4(3)^x$

16. $f(x) = 2(10)^x, g(x) = -2(10)^x$

17. $f(x) = 8\left(\dfrac{1}{2}\right)^x, g(x) = -8\left(\dfrac{1}{2}\right)^x$

18. $f(x) = 6\left(\dfrac{1}{3}\right)^x, g(x) = -6\left(\dfrac{1}{3}\right)^x$

Graph the function by hand. Then use a graphing calculator to verify your graph. Find the domain and range of the function.

19. $f(x) = 5(2)^x$
20. $f(x) = 9\left(\dfrac{1}{3}\right)^x$

21. $f(x) = -8\left(\dfrac{1}{4}\right)^x$
22. $f(x) = -3(3)^x$

23. Recall that we can describe some or all of the input–output pairs of a function by means of an equation, a graph, a table, or words. Let $f(x) = 4(2)^x$.

   a. Describe five input–output pairs of f by using a table.
   b. Describe the input–output pairs of f by using a graph.
   c. Describe the input–output pairs of f by using words.

24. Recall that we can describe some or all of the input–output pairs of a function by means of an equation, a graph, a table, or words. Let $g(x) = 16\left(\dfrac{1}{2}\right)^x$.

   a. Describe five input–output pairs of g by using a table.
   b. Describe the input–output pairs of g by using a graph.
   c. Describe the input–output pairs of g by using words.

25. Input–output pairs of four exponential functions are listed in Table 15. Complete the table.

Table 15 Complete the Table (Exercise 25)

x	f(x)	g(x)	h(x)	k(x)
0	162	3	2	800
1	54	12	10	400
2	18	48		
3	6			
4				

26. Input–output pairs of four exponential functions are listed in Table 16. Complete the table.

Table 16 Complete the Table (Exercise 26)

x	f(x)	g(x)	h(x)	k(x)
0	3	64	2	100
1	6	32	6	10
2	12	16		
3	24			
4				

27. Input–output pairs of four exponential functions are listed in Table 17. Complete the table.

Table 17 Complete the Table (Exercise 27)

x	f(x)	g(x)	h(x)	k(x)
0	5			
1		80	54	
2	20			
3		20		192
4			2	768

28. Input–output pairs of four exponential functions are listed in Table 18. Complete the table.

Table 18 Complete the Table (Exercise 28)

x	f(x)	g(x)	h(x)	k(x)
0			3	400
1		3		
2	25			
3		147		
4	1		30,000	25

For Exercises 29–36, refer to Fig. 27.

29. Find $f(-3)$.

30. Find $f(-1)$.

31. Find $f(0)$.

32. Find $f(1)$.

33. Find x when $f(x) = 4$.

34. Find x when $f(x) = 2$.

35. Find x when $f(x) = 1$.

36. Find x when $f(x) = -2$.

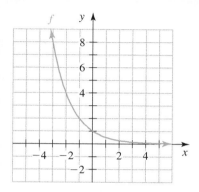

Figure 27 Graph of f—Exercises 29–36

For Exercises 37–44, refer to Table 19.

37. Find $f(3)$.

38. Find $f(6)$.

39. Find $f(5)$.

40. Find $f(0)$.

41. Find x when $f(x) = 3$.

42. Find x when $f(x) = 6$.

43. Find x when $f(x) = 24$.

44. Find x when $f(x) = 96$.

Table 19 Some Values of an Exponential Function f (Exercises 37–44)

x	$f(x)$
0	3
1	6
2	12
3	24
4	48
5	96
6	192

45. The average ticket prices to major league baseball games are shown in Table 20 for various years.

Table 20 Average Ticket Prices to Major League Baseball Games

Year	Average Ticket Price (dollars)
1950	1.54
1960	1.96
1970	2.72
1980	4.45
1991	8.84
2000	16.22
2011	26.91

Sources: *The Sporting News and the Sporting News Baseball Dope Book, 1950–85; Team Marketing Report, 1991–2004; ESPN*

a. Let $f(t)$ be the average ticket price (in dollars) to major league baseball games for the year that is t years since 1950. Use a graphing calculator to draw a scattergram of the data. Is it better to use a linear or an exponential function to model the data? Explain.

b. Draw the graph of the function $f(t) = 1.22(1.051)^t$ and the scattergram in the same viewing window. Does the graph of f come close to the data points?

c. Use f to predict the average ticket price in 2018.

d. The most expensive average ticket price in 2012 was $53.38, at Fenway Park, home of the Boston Red Sox. Use TRACE and Zoom Out on a graphing calculator to predict when the average ticket price to *all* major league baseball games will reach $53.38.

46. If you place your hand on a piano and play a note, you will feel the piano vibrate. The number of vibrations per second (hertz) of a note is called its *frequency.* If you strike the piano keys from left to right, the frequencies of the notes increase. We use some of the letters of the alphabet, sometimes in conjunction with the "sharp" symbol #, to refer to these notes (see Fig. 28). The frequencies of 13 notes in a row are listed in Table 21.

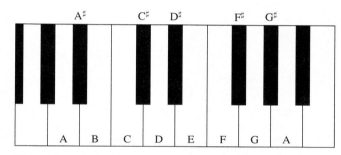

Figure 28 Notes on a piano

Table 21 Frequencies of Notes on a Piano

Note	Number of Notes above A	Frequency (in hertz)
A	0	220.0
A#	1	233.1
B	2	246.9
C	3	261.6
C#	4	277.2
D	5	293.7
D#	6	311.6
E	7	329.6
F	8	349.2
F#	9	370.0
G	10	392.0
G#	11	415.3
A	12	440.0

Source: Math and Music *by Garland and Kahn*

a. Let $f(n)$ be the frequency (in hertz) of the note that is n notes above the note A (the one with frequency 220.0 hertz). Use a graphing calculator to draw a scattergram of the data listed in Table 21. Will a linear function or an exponential function model the data better?

b. Draw the graph of the function $f(n) = 220(2)^{n/12}$ and the scattergram in the same viewing window. Does the graph come close to the data points? [***Graphing Calculator:*** For the exponential expression $220(2)^{n/12}$, press **220** $($ **2** $)$ $\wedge$ $($ $\boxed{\text{X, T, }\Theta, n}$ $\div$ **12** $)$.]

c. Estimate the frequency of the note D that is 17 notes above the note A (the one with frequency 220.0 hertz).

d. Use TRACE to find which note has a frequency of 523.25 hertz.

e. Use a graphing calculator table to find $f(0), f(12), f(24), f(36)$, and $f(48)$. What pattern do you notice? Describe this pattern in terms of the situation.

Find the x- and y-intercepts of the graph of the function.

47. $y = 7^x$

48. $y = 8(4)^x$

49. $y = 3\left(\dfrac{1}{5}\right)^x$

50. $y = -9\left(\dfrac{2}{3}\right)^x$

For Exercises 51–54, let $f(x) = 2^x + 3^x$.

51. Find $f(2)$.

52. Find $f(0)$.

53. Find $f(-2)$.

54. Find $f(-1)$.

For Exercises 55–58, let $f(x) = 3^x$.

55. Find x when $f(x) = 3$.

56. Find x when $f(x) = 9$.

57. Find x when $f(x) = 1$.

58. Find x when $f(x) = \dfrac{1}{3}$.

*For Exercises 59–70, use graphing calculator tables to compare each pair of functions f and g. What do you observe? Use exponential properties to show why this is so. [**Graphing Calculator:** For 2^{3x}, press $2 \wedge ($ 3 $\boxed{\text{X, T, }\Theta, n}$ $)$. Recall that if an exponent involves an operation, you must use parentheses.]*

59. $f(x) = 2^{3x}, g(x) = 8^x$

60. $f(x) = 2^{-x}, g(x) = \left(\dfrac{1}{2}\right)^x$

61. $f(x) = 2^{x+3}, g(x) = 8(2)^x$

62. $f(x) = 3^x 3^x, g(x) = 3^{2x}$

63. $f(x) = \dfrac{6^x}{3^x}, g(x) = 2^x$

64. $f(x) = 2^0, g(x) = 3^0$

65. $f(x) = \dfrac{3^{2x}}{3^x}, g(x) = 3^x$

66. $f(x) = 2^x 3^x, g(x) = 6^x$

67. $f(x) = x^{1/2}, g(x) = \sqrt{x}$ [***Graphing Calculator:*** For $\sqrt{x}$, press $\boxed{\text{2nd}}$ $\boxed{x^2}$ $\boxed{\text{X, T, }\Theta, n}$ $)$.]

68. $f(x) = 5^{x/3}, g(x) = (5^{1/3})^x$

69. $f(x) = 2^x, g(x) = 8^{x/3}$

70. $f(x) = 25^{x/2} \cdot 5^x, g(x) = 25^x$

Concepts

71. Graphs of four functions of the form $y = ab^x$ are shown in Fig. 29. Describe the constants a and b of each function.

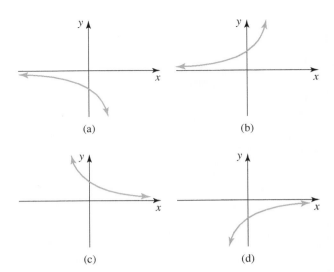

(a)   (b)

(c)   (d)

Figure 29 Exercise 71

72. The graphs of functions $f(x) = ab^x$ and $g(x) = cd^x$ are shown in Fig. 30.

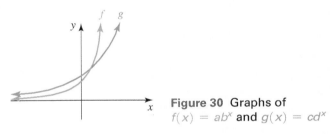

Figure 30 Graphs of $f(x) = ab^x$ and $g(x) = cd^x$

a. Which coefficient is greater, a or c? Explain.

b. Which base is greater, b or d? Explain.

73. Use a graphing calculator to graph a family of exponential curves similar to the family graphed in Fig. 31. List the equations of that family.

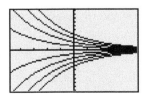

Figure 31 A family of exponential curves

74. Use a graphing calculator to graph a family of exponential curves similar to the family graphed in Fig. 32. All of these curves pass through the point $(0, -2)$. List the equations of that family.

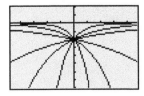

Figure 32 A family of exponential curves passing through $(0, -2)$

75. Use a graphing calculator to draw a graph similar to the one in Fig. 33. Use an equation of the form $f(x) = ab^x$, where a and b are constants you specify. What equation works?

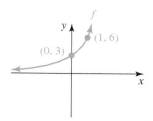

Figure 33 Exercise 75

76. Use a graphing calculator to draw a graph similar to the one in Fig. 34. Use an equation of the form $g(x) = ab^x$, where a and b are constants you specify. What equation works? Use trial and error.

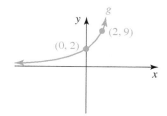

Figure 34 Exercise 76

77. Find equations of exponential functions that could correspond to the graphs shown in Fig. 35.

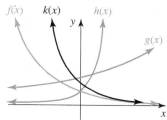

Figure 35 Exercise 77

78. a. Simplify and compare both expressions.
    i. $4(3)^2$ and 12^2 **ii.** $4^2 \cdot 3^2$ and 12^2
b. Build a graphing calculator table that shows the same input values for both functions. Explain in terms of order of operations or exponential properties why the tables are the same or different.
    i. $f(x) = 4(3)^x$ and $g(x) = 12^x$
    ii. $f(x) = 4^x \cdot 3^x$ and $g(x) = 12^x$

79. In this exercise, you will compare the function $f(x) = 100(2)^x$ with the function $g(x) = 5(3)^x$.
a. Find the y-intercept of the graph of each function.
b. What does the base multiplier property tell you about each function?
c. On the basis of your comments in parts (a) and (b), which function's outputs will eventually be much greater than the other's outputs? Explain.
d. Use a graphing calculator table to verify your comments to parts (a)–(c). To do this, enter the functions and set up a table as indicated in Figs. 36 and 37, respectively.

Figure 36 Enter the functions   **Figure 37** Set up the table

80. What are the x-intercepts and y-intercepts of the graph of a function of the form $y = ab^x$, where $b > 0$?

81. Is the statement true for $f(x) = 2^x$?
a. $f(3 + 4) = f(3) + f(4)$
b. $f(x + y) = f(x) + f(y)$

82. Is the statement true for $g(x) = 3^x$?
a. $g(2 + 5) = g(2) \cdot g(5)$
b. $g(4 + 6) = g(4) \cdot g(6)$
c. $g(2 + 4) = g(2) \cdot g(4)$
d. $g(x + y) = g(x) \cdot g(y)$

83. Let $f(x) = ab^x$, where $a > 0$. Explain why f is increasing if $b > 1$ and f is decreasing if $0 < b < 1$.

84. In an exponential function $f(x) = b^x$, the base b is a positive number not equal to 1. In this exercise, you will explore what happens if we try to define a function whose base is negative. Consider $f(x) = (-4)^x$.
a. Explain why $f\left(\dfrac{1}{2}\right)$ is undefined.
b. Explain why $f\left(\dfrac{1}{4}\right)$ is undefined.
c. List three more values of x that result in undefined outputs.

85. The graphs of the exponential functions $f(x) = -ab^x$ and $g(x) = ab^x$ are reflections of each other across the x-axis. Explain why this makes sense.

86. Explain how to sketch the graph of a function of the form $f(x) = ab^x$, where $b > 0$. Include the effect of a value of a or b on the graph.

Related Review

Graph the given function by hand. Then use a graphing calculator to verify your graph.

87. $y = 4 + 2x$
88. $y = 4(2)^x$
89. $y = -4 + 2x$
90. $y = -4(2)^x$

Find all x-intercepts and y-intercepts.

91. $y = 8 + 4x$
92. $y = 8(4)^x$

93. Some input–output pairs of the functions $f, g, h,$ and k are provided in Table 22. For each function, determine whether the given values suggest that the function is linear, exponential, or neither.

Table 22 Identifying Functions (Exercise 93)

x	$f(x)$	$g(x)$	$h(x)$	$k(x)$
0	13	4	48	5
1	9	12	24	55
2	5	36	12	555
3	1	108	6	5555
4	-3	324	3	55555

94. The graphs of the equation $y = \dfrac{1}{3}x + 2$ and an equation of the form $y = ab^x$ are shown in Fig. 38. Find the values of a and b.

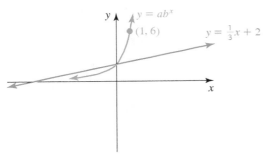

Figure 38 Exercise 94

Expressions, Equations, Functions, and Graphs

Perform the indicated instruction. Then use words such as linear, exponential, function, one variable, *and* two variables *to describe the expression, equation, or system. For instance, to describe* $3x + 5 = 7$, *you could say "$3x + 5 = 7$ is a linear equation in one variable."*

95. Graph $f(x) = 6\left(\dfrac{1}{2}\right)^x$ by hand.

96. Graph $y = -3x + 4$ by hand.

97. Find $f(-2)$, where $f(x) = 6\left(\dfrac{1}{2}\right)^x$.

98. Solve:
$$y = -3x + 4$$
$$2x - 5y = 31$$

4.4 Finding Equations of Exponential Functions

Objectives

» Use the base multiplier property to find an exponential equation.

» Solve an equation of the form $ab^n = k$ for the base b.

» Use two points to find an exponential equation.

In this section, we will discuss two ways to find an equation of an exponential function.

Using the Base Multiplier Property to Find Exponential Functions

One way to find an equation of an exponential function of the form $y = ab^x$ is to use the base multiplier property, which we discussed in Section 4.3. That is, if the value of the independent variable increases by 1, then the value of the dependent variable is multiplied by the base b.

▶ **Example 1**   Finding an Equation of an Exponential Curve

An exponential curve contains the points listed in Table 23. Find an equation of the curve.

Table 23 Solutions of an Exponential Equation

x	$f(x)$
0	3
1	6
2	12
3	24
4	48

Solution

For $f(x) = ab^x$, recall from Section 4.3 that the y-intercept is $(0, a)$. From Table 23, we see that the y-intercept is $(0, 3)$, so $a = 3$. As the value of x increases by 1, the value of y is multiplied by 2. By the base multiplier property, $b = 2$. Therefore, an equation of the curve is

$$f(x) = 3(2)^x$$

We check our result with a graphing calculator table (see Fig. 39). For graphing calculator instructions, see Appendix B.13.

 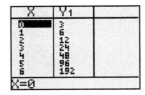

Figure 39 Verify the exponential equation $f(x) = 3(2)^x$

For Example 2, it will be helpful to review the slope addition property from Section 1.4: For a linear function of the form $y = mx + b$, if the value of the independent variable increases by 1, then the value of the dependent variable changes by the slope m.

Table 24 Input–Output Pairs for f

x	$f(x)$
0	162
1	54
2	18
3	6
4	2

Table 25 Input–Output Pairs for g

x	$g(x)$
0	50
1	46
2	42
3	38
4	34

▶ **Example 2** Linear versus Exponential Functions

1. Find a possible equation of a function whose input–output pairs are listed in Table 24.
2. Find a possible equation of a function whose input–output pairs are listed in Table 25.

Solution

1. As the value of x increases by 1 throughout Table 24, the value of y is multiplied by $\frac{1}{3}$. This suggests there is an exponential function $f(x) = a\left(\frac{1}{3}\right)^x$ whose graph contains the points in Table 24. Since the y-intercept is $(0, 162)$, we have $f(x) = 162\left(\frac{1}{3}\right)^x$.

2. As the value of x increases by 1 throughout Table 25, the value of y changes by adding -4. This suggests there is a linear function $g(x) = -4x + b$ whose graph contains the points in Table 25. Since the y-intercept is $(0, 50)$, we have $g(x) = -4x + 50$.

Solving Equations of the Form $ab^n = k$ for b

So far, we have discussed how to find an equation of an exponential curve that contains points whose x-coordinates are *consecutive* integers. Later in this section, we will discuss how to find an equation of an exponential curve that contains two given points, such as $(2, 5)$ and $(5, 63)$, whose x-coordinates are *not* consecutive integers. To use this method, we first need to discuss how to solve equations of the form $ab^n = k$ for the base b.

▶ **Example 3** One-Variable Equations Involving Exponents

Find all real-number solutions.

1. $b^2 = 25$
2. $b^3 = 8$
3. $2b^4 = 32$
4. $10b^5 = 90$
5. $b^6 = -28$

Solution

1. $b^2 = 25$ *Original equation*
   $b = -5 \text{ or } b = 5$ $(-5)^2 = 25 \text{ and } 5^2 = 25$

   So, the solutions are -5 and 5. We can use the notation ± 5 to stand for the numbers -5 and 5.

2. $b^3 = 8$ *Original equation*
   $b = 2$ $2^3 = 8$

3. $2b^4 = 32$ *Original equation*
   $b^4 = 16$ *Divide both sides by 2.*
   $b = \pm 2$ $(-2)^4 = 16 \text{ and } 2^4 = 16$

   We can check that both -2 and 2 satisfy the equation $2b^4 = 32$.

4. $10b^5 = 90$ *Original equation*
   $b^5 = 9$ *Divide both sides by 10.*
   $b = 9^{1/5}$ $9^{1/5}$ *is the number whose 5th power is 9.*
   $b \approx 1.55$ $1.55^5 \approx 9$

   We can check that 1.55 approximately satisfies the equation $10b^5 = 90$ by using a graphing calculator to verify that $10(1.55)^5 \approx 90$ (see Fig. 40).

5. The equation $b^6 = -28$ has no real-number solutions, since an even-numbered exponent gives a positive number.

```
10(1.55)^5
        89.46609688
■
```

Figure 40 Checking that 1.55 approximately satisfies $10b^5 = 90$

The problems in Example 3 suggest how to solve equations of the form $b^n = k$ for b.

> **Solving Equations of the Form $b^n = k$ for b**
>
> To solve an equation of the form $b^n = k$ for b,
>
> 1. If n is odd, the real-number solution is $k^{1/n}$.
> 2. If n is even and $k \geq 0$, the real-number solutions are $\pm k^{1/n}$.
> 3. If n is even and $k < 0$, there is no real-number solution.

> **Example 4**   One-Variable Equations Involving Exponents

Find all real-number solutions. Round any results to the second decimal place.

1. $5.42b^6 - 3.19 = 43.74$

2. $\dfrac{b^9}{b^4} = \dfrac{70}{3}$

Solution

1.

$$5.42b^6 - 3.19 = 43.74 \qquad \textit{Original equation}$$

$$5.42b^6 = 43.74 + 3.19 \qquad \textit{Add 3.19 to both sides.}$$

$$5.42b^6 = 46.93 \qquad \textit{Add.}$$

$$b^6 = \frac{46.93}{5.42} \qquad \textit{Divide both sides by 5.42.}$$

$$b = \pm\left(\frac{46.93}{5.42}\right)^{1/6} \qquad \textit{The solutions of } b^6 = k \textit{ are } \pm k^{1/6}$$
$$\textit{if } k \geq 0.$$

$$b \approx \pm 1.43 \qquad \textit{Compute.}$$

2.

$$\frac{b^9}{b^4} = \frac{70}{3} \qquad \textit{Original equation}$$

$$b^5 = \frac{70}{3} \qquad \textit{Subtract exponents: } \frac{b^m}{b^n} = b^{m-n}$$

$$b = \left(\frac{70}{3}\right)^{1/5} \qquad \textit{The solution of } b^5 = k \textit{ is } k^{1/5}.$$

$$b \approx 1.88 \qquad \textit{Compute.}$$

> **Example 5**   Solving General Equations Involving Exponents

Solve the equations for b, where n and $m - n$ are odd and $a, d + c$, and $d - c$ are nonzero.

1. $ab^n + c = d$

2. $\dfrac{b^m}{b^n} - c = d$

Solution

1.

$$ab^n + c = d \qquad \textit{Original equation}$$

$$ab^n + c - c = d - c \qquad \textit{Subtract c from both sides.}$$

$$ab^n = d - c \qquad \textit{Combine like terms.}$$

$$\frac{ab^n}{a} = \frac{d - c}{a} \qquad \textit{Divide both sides by a.}$$

$$b^n = \frac{d - c}{a} \qquad \textit{Simplify.}$$

$$b = \left(\frac{d - c}{a}\right)^{1/n} \qquad \textit{The solution of } b^n = p \textit{ is } p^{1/n} \textit{ when n is odd.}$$

2.

$$\frac{b^m}{b^n} - c = d \qquad \text{\textit{Original equation}}$$

$$\frac{b^m}{b^n} - c + c = d + c \qquad \text{\textit{Add c to both sides.}}$$

$$\frac{b^m}{b^n} = d + c \qquad \text{\textit{Combine like terms.}}$$

$$b^{m-n} = d + c \qquad \text{\textit{Subtract exponents:} } \frac{b^m}{b^n} = b^{m-n}.$$

$$b = (d + c)^{\frac{1}{m-n}} \qquad \text{\textit{The solution of } } b^k = p \text{ \textit{is} } p^{1/k} \text{ \textit{when k is odd.}}$$

Using Two Points to Find Equations of Exponential Functions

Now that we have discussed how to solve equations of the form $ab^n = k$ for b, we can discuss a second way to find an equation of an exponential function.

▶ **Example 6**   Finding an Equation of an Exponential Curve

Find an approximate equation $y = ab^x$ of the exponential curve that contains the points $(0, 3)$ and $(4, 70)$. Round the value of b to two decimal places.

Solution

Since the y-intercept is $(0, 3)$, the equation has the form $y = 3b^x$. Next, we substitute $(4, 70)$ in the equation $y = 3b^x$ and solve for b:

$$70 = 3b^4 \qquad \text{\textit{Substitute 4 for x and 70 for y.}}$$

$$3b^4 = 70 \qquad \text{\textit{If c = d, then d = c.}}$$

$$b^4 = \frac{70}{3} \qquad \text{\textit{Divide both sides by 3.}}$$

$$b = \pm\left(\frac{70}{3}\right)^{1/4} \qquad \text{\textit{The solutions of } } b^4 = k \text{ \textit{are} } \pm k^{1/4} \text{ \textit{if } } k \geq 0.$$

$$b \approx 2.20 \qquad \text{\textit{Compute; base of an exponential function is positive.}}$$

So, our equation is $y = 3(2.20)^x$; its graph contains the given point $(0, 3)$. Since we rounded the value b, the graph of the equation comes close to, but does not pass through, the given point $(4, 70)$.

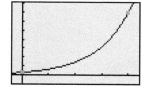

Figure 41 Verify the work

We use a graphing calculator to verify our work (see Fig. 41).

In Example 7, we will find an equation of a curve that approximates the exponential curve containing two given points. Neither point will be the y-intercept. To do this, we will use the following property.

▶ **Dividing Left Sides and Right Sides of Two Equations**

If $a = b$, $c = d$, $c \neq 0$, and $d \neq 0$, then

$$\frac{a}{c} = \frac{b}{d}$$

In words, the quotient of the left sides of two equations is equal to the quotient of the right sides.

For example, if we divide the left sides and divide the right sides of the equations $2 = 2$ and $3 = 3$, we obtain the true statement $\frac{2}{3} = \frac{2}{3}$.

▶ Example 7   Finding an Equation of an Exponential Curve

Find an approximate equation $y = ab^x$ of the exponential curve that contains $(2, 5)$ and $(5, 63)$. Round the values of a and b to two decimal places.

Solution

Since both of the ordered pairs $(2, 5)$ and $(5, 63)$ must satisfy the equation $y = ab^x$, we have the following system of equations:

$$5 = ab^2 \quad \text{Substitute 2 for x and 5 for y.}$$
$$63 = ab^5 \quad \text{Substitute 5 for x and 63 for y.}$$

It will be slightly easier to solve this system if we switch the equations to list the equation with the greater exponent of b first:

$$63 = ab^5$$
$$5 = ab^2$$

We divide the left sides and divide the right sides of the two equations to get the following result for nonzero a and b:

$$\frac{63}{5} = \frac{ab^5}{ab^2}$$

By then applying the properties $\dfrac{b^m}{b^n} = b^{m-n}$ and $\dfrac{a}{a} = 1$, where a and b are nonzero, to the right-hand side of the equation, we have an equation in terms of b (and not a):

$$\frac{63}{5} = b^3$$

We can now solve for b by finding the cube root of $\dfrac{63}{5}$:

$$b^3 = \frac{63}{5} \qquad \text{If c = d, then d = c.}$$
$$b = \left(\frac{63}{5}\right)^{1/3} \qquad \text{The solution of } b^3 = k \text{ is } k^{1/3}.$$
$$\approx 2.33 \qquad \text{Compute.}$$

So, we can substitute 2.33 for the constant b in the equation $y = ab^x$:

$$y \approx a(2.33)^x$$

To find a, we substitute the coordinates of the given point $(2, 5)$ into $y = a(2.33)^x$:

$$5 = a(2.33)^2 \quad \text{Substitute 2 for x and 5 for y.}$$
$$\frac{5}{2.33^2} = a \qquad \text{Divide both sides by 2.33}^2.$$
$$a \approx 0.92 \qquad \text{Compute.}$$

So, an equation that approximates the exponential curve that passes through $(2, 5)$ and $(5, 63)$ is $y = 0.92(2.33)^x$.

We use a graphing calculator to verify our work (see Fig. 42).

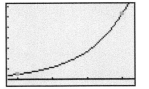

Figure 42 Check that the curve approximately contains $(2, 5)$ and $(5, 63)$

In summary, **we can find an equation of an exponential function by using the base multiplier property or by using two points. Both methods give the same result.**

Group Exploration

Comparing three ways to find exponential equations

An exponential curve contains the points listed in Table 26.

Table 26 Solutions of an Exponential Equation

x	f(x)
0	5
2	20
4	80
6	320
8	1280

1. Use the point $(0, 5)$ and one other point in Table 26 to find an equation of the curve (see Example 6).

2. Use two points in Table 26 other than $(0, 5)$ to find an equation of the curve (see Example 7).

3. Use the base multiplier property to find an equation of the curve. [**Hint:** First find $f(1)$ by recognizing a pattern.]

4. Compare your equations from Problems 1, 2, and 3.

5. An exponential curve contains the points listed in Table 27. Which method would you use to find an equation $y = ab^x$ that approximates the exponential curve? Explain. Also, find the equation. Round the value of b to two decimal places.

Table 27 Solutions of an Exponential Equation

x	f(x)
0	400
3	200
6	100
9	50
12	25

 Tips for Success **Ask Questions**

When you have a question during class time, do you ask it? Many students are reluctant to ask questions. If you tend to shy away from asking questions, keep in mind that the main idea of school is for you to learn through open communication with your instructor and other students.

If you are confused about a concept, it's likely that other students in your class are confused, too. If you ask your question, everyone else who is confused will be grateful you asked. Most instructors want students to ask questions. It helps an instructor know when students understand the material and when they are having trouble.

Homework 4.4

For extra help ▶ MyMathLab° ▦ Watch the videos in MyMathLab   Download the MyDashboard App

1. Some values of functions $f, g, h,$ and k are provided in Table 28. Find a possible equation of each function. Verify your results with a graphing calculator table.

Table 28 Values of Four Functions (Exercise 1)

x	f(x)	g(x)	h(x)	k(x)
0	4	36	5	250
1	8	12	50	50
2	16	4	500	10
3	32	$\frac{4}{3}$	5000	2
4	64	$\frac{4}{9}$	50,000	$\frac{2}{5}$

2. Some values of functions $f, g, h,$ and k are provided in Table 29. Find a possible equation of each function. Verify your results with a graphing calculator table.

Table 29 Values of Four Equations (Exercise 2)

x	f(x)	g(x)	h(x)	k(x)
0	80	4	3	3700
1	40	12	15	370
2	20	36	75	37
3	10	108	375	3.7
4	5	324	1875	0.37

3. Some values of functions $f, g, h,$ and k are provided in Table 30. Find a possible equation of each function. Verify your results with a graphing calculator table. [**Hint:** Use linear or exponential equations.]

Table 30 Values of Four Functions (Exercise 3)

x	$f(x)$	$g(x)$	$h(x)$	$k(x)$
0	100	100	2	2
1	50	50	6	6
2	25	0	10	18
3	12.5	−50	14	54
4	6.25	−100	18	162

4. Some values of functions f, g, h, and k are provided in Table 31. Find a possible equation of each function. Verify your results with a graphing calculator table. [**Hint:** Use linear or exponential equations.]

Table 31 Values of Four Functions (Exercise 4)

x	$f(x)$	$g(x)$	$h(x)$	$k(x)$
0	3	19	2	512
1	12	13	9	128
2	48	7	16	32
3	192	1	23	8
4	768	−5	30	2

Find all real-number solutions. Round your result(s) to the second decimal place. Verify that your results satisfy the equation.

5. $b^2 = 16$

6. $b^4 = 81$

7. $b^3 = 27$

8. $b^5 = 100,000$

9. $3b^5 = 96$

10. $5b^2 = 45$

11. $35b^4 = 15$

12. $44b^3 = 12$

13. $3.6b^3 = 42.5$

14. $1.7b^4 = 86.4$

15. $32.7b^6 + 8.1 = 392.8$

16. $2.1b^5 − 8.2 = 237.5$

17. $\frac{1}{4}b^3 − \frac{1}{2} = \frac{9}{4}$

18. $\frac{1}{6}b^4 + \frac{5}{3} = \frac{11}{2}$

19. $\frac{b^6}{b^2} = 81$

20. $\frac{b^{10}}{b^3} = 2187$

21. $\frac{b^8}{b^3} = \frac{79}{5}$

22. $\frac{b^9}{b^6} = \frac{2}{9}$

Solve the equation for b, where n and $m − n$ are odd and $a, d, d + c$, and $d − c$ are nonzero.

23. $b^n + c = d$

24. $b^n − c = d$

25. $ab^n − c = d$

26. $\frac{b^n}{a} + c = d$

27. $\frac{b^m}{b^n} = d$

28. $\frac{ab^m}{b^n} = d$

29. $\frac{ab^m}{b^n} + c = d$

30. $\frac{b^m}{ab^n} − c = d$

Find an approximate equation $y = ab^x$ of the exponential curve that contains the given pair of points. Round the value of b to two decimal places. Verify your result with a graphing calculator.

31. $(0, 4)$ and $(1, 8)$

32. $(0, 5)$ and $(1, 15)$

33. $(0, 3)$ and $(5, 100)$

34. $(0, 8)$ and $(4, 79)$

35. $(0, 87)$ and $(6, 14)$

36. $(0, 256)$ and $(7, 23)$

37. $(0, 5.5)$ and $(2, 73.9)$

38. $(0, 2.1)$ and $(5, 9.7)$

39. $(0, 7.4)$ and $(3, 1.3)$

40. $(0, 97.2)$ and $(4, 17.1)$

41. $(0, 39.18)$ and $(15, 3.66)$

42. $(0, 12.94)$ and $(20, 357.03)$

Find an approximate equation $y = ab^x$ of the exponential curve that contains the given pair of points. Round the values of a and b to two decimal places. Verify your result with a graphing calculator.

43. $(1, 4)$ and $(2, 12)$

44. $(2, 5)$ and $(3, 10)$

45. $(3, 4)$ and $(5, 9)$

46. $(2, 1)$ and $(5, 7)$

47. $(10, 329)$ and $(30, 26)$

48. $(11, 492)$ and $(17, 8)$

49. $(5, 8.1)$ and $(9, 2.4)$

50. $(1, 3.5)$ and $(5, 1.3)$

51. $(13, 24.71)$ and $(21, 897.35)$

52. $(4, 6.3)$ and $(10, 250.8)$

53. $(2, 73.8)$ and $(7, 13.2)$

54. $(8, 39.43)$ and $(12, 6.52)$

Concepts

55. Find an equation of the exponential curve sketched in Fig. 43. [**Hint:** Choose two points whose coordinates appear to be integers.]

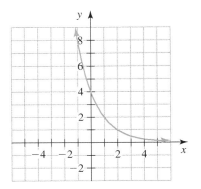

Figure 43 Graph of f—Exercise 55

56. Find an equation of the exponential curve sketched in Fig. 44.

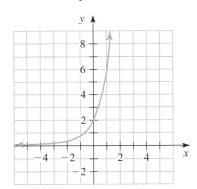

Figure 44 Graph of f—Exercise 56

57. Find an equation of the exponential curve sketched in Fig. 45.

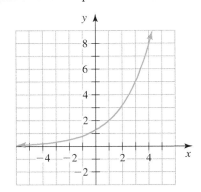

Figure 45 Graph of f—Exercise 57

58. Find an equation of the exponential curve sketched in Fig. 46.

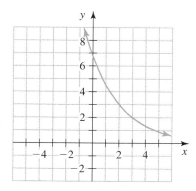

Figure 46 Graph of *f*—Exercise 58

59. Solve the system. [**Hint:** Think graphically.]

$$y = 6(4)^x$$
$$y = 6\left(\frac{1}{3}\right)^x$$

60. Solve the system. [**Hint:** Think graphically.]

$$y = 7(3)^x$$
$$y = 4(3)^x$$

61. a. Is there an exponential curve that contains the given point? If so, find an equation of the curve. If not, explain.
    i. $(0, 2)$ **ii.** $(2, 0)$
  b. Is there an exponential curve that contains the points $(2, -1)$ and $(3, 1)$? If so, find an equation of the curve. If not, explain.

62. a. Is there an exponential curve that passes through the given points? If so, find an equation of the curve. If not, explain.
    i. $(0, 5)$ and $(1, 5)$ **ii.** $(0, 3)$ and $(7, 3)$
  b. Is there an exponential curve that passes through two given points that have the same *y*-coordinate? Explain.

63. Describe the base multiplier property and explain why it makes sense. Include an example.

64. Describe how to find the equation of an exponential curve that contains two given points. Include both the case in which one of the points is the *y*-intercept and the case in which neither of the points is the *y*-intercept.

Related Review

Find all real-number solutions or simplify, whichever is appropriate. Round your solution(s) to the second decimal place.

65. $\dfrac{b^7}{b^2}$ **66.** $\dfrac{b^8}{b^4}$

67. $\dfrac{b^7}{b^2} = 76$ **68.** $\dfrac{b^8}{b^4} = \dfrac{65}{3}$

69. $\dfrac{8b^3}{6b^{-1}}$ **70.** $\dfrac{10b^{-7}}{15b^{-2}}$

71. $\dfrac{8b^3}{6b^{-1}} = \dfrac{3}{7}$ **72.** $\dfrac{10b^{-7}}{15b^{-2}} = \dfrac{4}{7}$

Let L be a linear function and E be an exponential function. Assume the graphs of both L and E contain the pair of given points. Find

equations of L and E. Use a graphing calculator to draw the graphs of L and E in the same viewing window.

73. $(0, 2)$ and $(1, 6)$ **74.** $(2, 8)$ and $(5, 2)$

The graph of a function contains the given pair of points. Could the function be linear, exponential, either linear or exponential, or neither? Explain.

75. $(5, 3)$ and $(7, 6)$ **76.** $(2, 6)$ and $(4, 6)$

77. In this exercise, you will compare the linear function $L(x) = 2x + 100$ with the exponential function $E(x) = 3(2)^x$.
  a. Find the *y*-intercept of the graph of both functions.
  b. For functions *L* and *E*, describe what happens to the value of *y* as the value of *x* increases by 1.
  c. On the basis of your responses to parts (a) and (b), which function's outputs will eventually dominate the other's outputs? Explain.
  d. Use a graphing calculator table to verify your responses to parts (a)–(c). To do this, enter the functions and set up a table as indicated in Figs. 47 and 48, respectively.

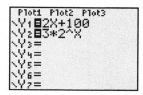

Figure 47 Enter the functions

Figure 48 Set up a table

78. Is it possible for a linear function and an exponential function to have the indicated number of intersection points? If so, give equations of the two functions. If not, explain. [**Hint:** First sketch some graphs.]
  a. 3 intersection points
  b. 2 intersection points
  c. 1 intersection point
  d. 0 intersection points

Expressions, Equations, Functions, and Graphs

Perform the indicated instruction. Then use words such as linear, exponential, function, one variable, *and* two variables *to describe the expression, equation, or system.*

79. Graph $f(x) = 3(2)^x$ by hand.

80. Find all real-number solutions of $2b^6 = 259$. Round any result(s) to the second decimal place.

81. Find $f(-3)$, where $f(x) = 3(2)^x$.

82. Simplify $\dfrac{8b^{-3}c^6}{12b^2c^3}$.

▼ 4.5 Using Exponential Functions to Model Data

Objectives

» Find an equation of an *exponential model* by using the base multiplier property.

» Model a *half-life* situation.

» Find an equation of an exponential model by using data described in words.

» Find an equation of an exponential model by using data displayed in a table.

» For a model $f(t) = ab^t$, know the meaning of the coefficient a and the base b in terms of the situation being modeled.

» Make estimates and predictions by using an exponential model.

Table 32 Values of a Bacteria Model

t (hours)	$B = f(t)$ (millions)
0	3
1	6
2	12
3	24
4	48

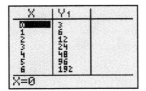

Figure 50 Table for bacteria model

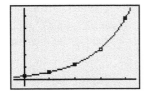

Figure 51 Graph of bacteria model

In Section 4.4, we found equations of exponential functions. In this section, we use that skill to model authentic situations.

Using the Base Multiplier Property to Find a Model

We can use the base multiplier property to find an exponential model.

▶ **Definition**   Exponential model, exponentially related, approximately exponentially related

An **exponential model** is an exponential function, or its graph, that describes the relationship between two quantities for an authentic situation. If all of the data points for a situation lie on an exponential curve, then we say the independent and dependent variables are **exponentially related.** If no exponential curve contains all of the data points, but an exponential curve comes close to all of the data points (and perhaps contains some of them), then we say the variables are **approximately exponentially related.**

▶ **Example 1**   Modeling with an Exponential Function

Suppose that a peach has 3 million bacteria on it at noon on Monday and that one bacterium divides into two bacteria every hour, on average (see Fig. 49).

$t = 0$

$t = 1$

$t = 2$ **Figure 49** A result of bacteria dividing every hour

Let $B = f(t)$ be the number of bacteria (in millions) on the peach at t hours after noon on Monday.

1. Find an equation of f.
2. Predict the number of bacteria on the peach at noon on Tuesday.

Solution

1. We complete a table of values of f based on the assumption that one bacterium divides into two bacteria every hour (see Table 32).

   As the value of t increases by 1, the value of B changes by greater and greater amounts, so it would *not* be appropriate to model the data by using a linear function. Note, though, that as the value of t increases by 1, the value of B is multiplied by 2, so we *can* model the situation by using an *exponential* model of the form $f(t) = a(2)^t$. The B-intercept is $(0, 3)$, so $f(t) = 3(2)^t$.

   We use a graphing calculator table and graph to verify our work (see Figs. 50 and 51).

2. We use $t = 24$ to represent noon on Tuesday. We substitute 24 for t in our equation of f:

$$f(24) = 3(2)^{24} = 50,331,648$$

According to the model, there would be 50,331,648 million bacteria. To omit writing "million," we must add six zeros to 50,331,648—that is, 50,331,648,000,000. There would be about 50 trillion bacteria at noon on Tuesday.

For an exponential function $y = ab^t$, the y-intercept is $(0, a)$. So, **if $y = ab^t$ is an exponential model where y is a quantity at time t, then the coefficient a is the value of that quantity present at time $t = 0$.** For example, the bacteria model $f(t) = 3(2)^t$ has coefficient 3, which represents the 3 million bacteria that were present at time $t = 0$ (noon on Monday).

We can use an exponential function to model the value of an investment that earns r percent interest compounded annually. The term **r percent interest compounded annually** means the interest earned each year equals r percent of the principal *and any interest earned in previous years* (all of which becomes part of the investment).

▶ **Example 2**   Modeling with an Exponential Function

A person invests $5000 in an account that earns 6% interest compounded annually.

1. Let $V = f(t)$ be the value (in dollars) of the account at t years after the money is invested. Find an equation of f.
2. What will be the value after 10 years?

Solution

Table 33 Values of a Compounded-Interest (6%) Account

t	$V = f(t)$
0	5000.00
1	$5000.00(1.06) = 5300.00$
2	$5300.00(1.06) = 5618.00$
3	$5618.00(1.06) = 5955.08$
4	$5955.08(1.06) \approx 6312.38$

1. Each year, the investment value is equal to the previous year's value (100% of it) plus 6% of the previous year's value. So, the value is equal to 106% of the previous year's value. For example, after one year, the value will be 106% of $5000, or $1.06(5000) = 5300$ dollars. After two years, the value will be $1.06(5300) = 5618$ dollars. See Table 33.

   As the value of t increases by 1, the value of V is multiplied by 1.06. So, f is the exponential function $f(t) = a(1.06)^t$. Since the value of the account at the start is $5000, we have $a = 5000$. So, $f(t) = 5000(1.06)^t$.

2. To find the value in 10 years, we substitute 10 for t:

$$f(10) = 5000(1.06)^{10} \approx 8954.24$$

The value will be $8954.24 in 10 years.

In Example 2, we used the function $f(t) = 5000(1.06)^t$ to model the value of the 6% compounded-interest account. Note that subtracting 1 from the base 1.06 gives the interest rate in decimal form:

$$b - 1 = 1.06 - 1 = 0.06 = \text{interest rate (in decimal form)}$$

Half-Life Applications

If a quantity decays exponentially, we can describe how quickly it decays by its *half-life*.

▶ Definition   Half-life

If a quantity decays exponentially, the **half-life** is the amount of time it takes for that quantity to be reduced to half (see Fig. 52).

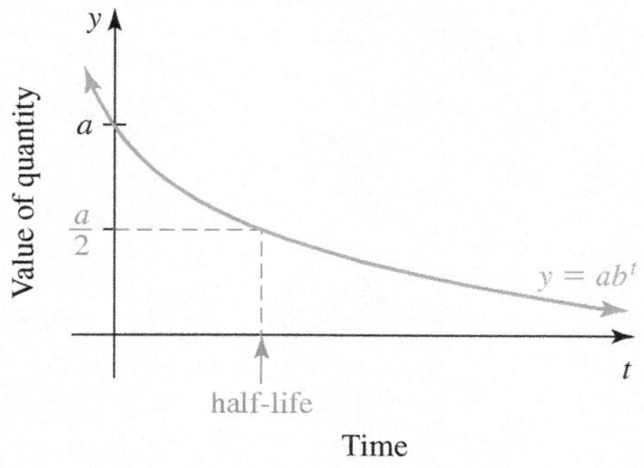

Figure 52 Half-life of a quantity

For example, the half-life of the radioactive element hydrogen-3 is 12.3 years, which means every 12.3 years the number of hydrogen-3 atoms is reduced to half. The half-lives of some radioactive elements are much different from that of hydrogen-3. For instance, polonium-214 has a half-life of 0.164 millisecond, and uranium-238 has a half-life of 4.5 billion years!

▶ **Example 3**   Modeling with an Exponential Function

The world's worst nuclear accident occurred in Chernobyl, Ukraine, on April 26, 1986. Immediately afterward, 28 people died from acute radiation sickness. So far, about 25,000 people have died from the accident, mostly due to the release of the radioactive element cesium-137 (Source: *Medicine Worldwide*).

Cesium-137 has a half-life of 30 years. Let $P = f(t)$ be the percent of the cesium-137 that remains at t years since 1986.

1. Find an equation of f.
2. Describe the meaning of the base of f.
3. What percent of the cesium-137 will remain in 2014?

Solution

1. We discuss two methods of finding an equation of f.

   Method 1   At time $t = 0$, 100% of the cesium-137 is present. At time $t = 30$, there will be $\frac{1}{2}(100) = 50$ percent. At time $t = 60$, there will be $\frac{1}{2} \cdot \frac{1}{2}(100) = 25$ percent. We organize these results, and one more calculation, in Table 34.

   From Table 34, we see that the situation can be modeled well with an exponential function. Each exponent in the second column of the table is equal to the value of t in the first column, divided by 30. Thus, the equation of f is

   $$f(t) = 100\left(\frac{1}{2}\right)^{t/30}$$

   We can use a graphing calculator table and graph to verify our equation (see Figs. 53 and 54). We can write this equation in the form $f(t) = ab^t$:

   $$f(t) = 100\left(\frac{1}{2}\right)^{t/30} = 100\left(\left(\frac{1}{2}\right)^{\frac{1}{30}}\right)^t$$

   Since $\left(\frac{1}{2}\right)^{1/30} \approx 0.977$, we can write

   $$f(t) = 100(0.977)^t$$

   Method 2   Instead of recognizing a pattern from a table, we can find an equation of f by using the points $(0, 100)$ and $(30, 50)$. Since the P-intercept is $(0, 100)$, we have

   $$P = f(t) = 100b^t$$

   To find b, we substitute the coordinates of $(30, 50)$ into the equation $f(t) = 100b^t$:

$50 = 100b^{30}$	*Substitute 30 for t and 50 for f(t).*
$100b^{30} = 50$	*If c = d, then d = c.*
$b^{30} = \dfrac{50}{100}$	*Divide both sides by 100.*
$b^{30} = \dfrac{1}{2}$	*Simplify.*
$b = \pm\left(\dfrac{1}{2}\right)^{1/30}$	*The solution of $b^{30} = k$ is $\pm k^{1/30}$.*
$b \approx 0.977$	*Compute; base of an exponential function is positive.*

   So, an equation of f is $f(t) = 100(0.977)^t$, the same equation we found earlier.

2. The base of f is 0.977. Each year, 97.7% of the previous year's cesium-137 is present. In other words, the cesium-137 decays by 2.3% each year.

3. Since $2014 - 1986 = 28$, we substitute 28 for t in the equation $f(t) = 100(0.977)^t$:

   $$f(28) = 100(0.977)^{28} \approx 52.13$$

   In 2014, about 52.1% of the cesium-137 will remain.

Table 34 Percentages of Cesium-137 That Remain

Year t	Percent P
0	$100 = 100\left(\frac{1}{2}\right)^0$
30	$100 \cdot \frac{1}{2} = 100 \cdot \left(\frac{1}{2}\right)^1$
60	$100 \cdot \frac{1}{2} \cdot \frac{1}{2} = 100\left(\frac{1}{2}\right)^2$
90	$100 \cdot \frac{1}{2} \cdot \frac{1}{2} \cdot \frac{1}{2} = 100\left(\frac{1}{2}\right)^3$
t	$100\left(\frac{1}{2}\right)^{t/30}$

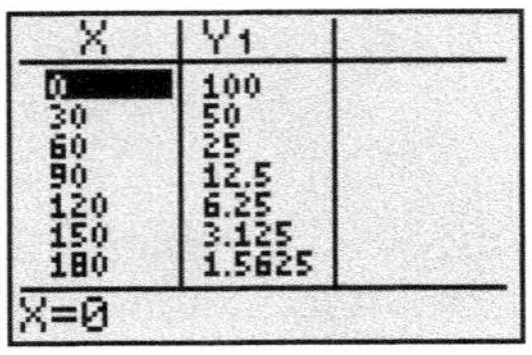

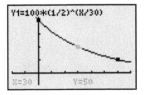

X	Y1
0	100
30	50
60	25
90	12.5
120	6.25
150	3.125
180	1.5625

X=0

Figure 53 Table for f

Y1=100*(1/2)^(X/30)

X=30   Y=50

Figure 54 Graph of f and the points $(0, 100)$, $(30, 50)$, and $(60, 25)$

> ### Meaning of the Base of an Exponential Model

If $f(t) = ab^t$, where $a > 0$, models a quantity at time t, then the percent rate of change is constant. In particular,

- If $b > 1$, then the quantity grows exponentially at a rate of $b - 1$ percent (in decimal form) per unit of time.
- If $0 < b < 1$, then the quantity decays exponentially at a rate of $1 - b$ percent (in decimal form) per unit of time.

In Example 2, we found the compounded-interest model $f(t) = 5000(1.06)^t$. Since $1.06 - 1 = 0.06$, the base 1.06 indicates that the value grows exponentially by 6% per year.

In Example 3, we found the cesium-137 model $f(t) = 100(0.977)^t$. Since $1 - 0.977 = 0.023$, the base 0.977 indicates that the cesium-137 decays exponentially by 2.3% per year.

Finding a Model by Using Data Described in Words

Instead of using the base multiplier property, we can sometimes find an equation of a model by using two data points described in words.

> **Example 4** Modeling with an Exponential Function

The number of severe near collisions on airplane runways has decayed approximately exponentially from 67 in 2000 to 16 in 2010 (Source: *Federal Aviation Administration*). Predict the number of severe near collisions in 2018.

Table 35 Known Values of t and n

Years since 2000	Number of Severe Near Collisions
0	67
10	16

Solution

Let n be the number of severe near collisions on airplane runways in the year that is t years since 2000. Known values of t and n are shown in Table 35.

Because the variables t and n are approximately exponentially related, we want an equation of the form $n = ab^t$. From Table 35, we see that the n-intercept is $(0, 67)$. So, the equation is of the form

$$n = 67b^t$$

To find b, we substitute the coordinates of $(10, 16)$ into the equation $n = 67b^t$ and then solve for b:

$$16 = 67b^{10} \qquad \text{Substitute 10 for } t \text{ and 16 for } n.$$
$$67b^{10} = 16 \qquad \text{If } c = d, \text{ then } d = c.$$
$$b^{10} = \frac{16}{67} \qquad \text{Divide both sides by 67.}$$
$$b = \left(\frac{16}{67}\right)^{1/10} \qquad \text{The solution of } b^{10} = k \text{ is } k^{1/10}.$$
$$b \approx 0.867$$

Then we substitute 0.867 for b in the equation $n = 67b^t$:

$$n = 67(0.867)^t$$

Finally, to predict the number of severe near collisions in 2018, we substitute $2018 - 2000 = 18$ for t in the equation $n = 67(0.867)^t$ and solve for n:

$$n = 67(0.867)^{18} \approx 5.13$$

The model predicts that there will be about 5 severe near collisions in 2018. We use a graphing calculator table (see Fig. 55) to check that each of the three ordered pairs $(0, 67)$, $(10, 16)$, and $(18, 5.13)$ approximately satisfies the equation $n = 67(0.867)^t$.

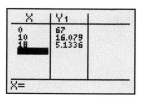

Figure 55 Verify the work

Finding an Exponential Model by Using Data Displayed in a Table

In Example 5, we will find an equation of an exponential model by using data shown in a table.

▶ **Example 5**   Modeling with an Exponential Function

The numbers of viewers of the Major League Baseball (MLB) All-Star Game are shown in Table 36 for various years. Let $f(t)$ be the number of viewers (in millions) of the All-Star Game at t years since 1980.

1. Find an equation of f.
2. What is the coefficient a of the model $f(t) = ab^t$? What does it mean in this situation?
3. What is the base b of the model $f(t) = ab^t$? What does it mean in this situation?
4. Predict the number of viewers of the All-Star Game in 2018.

Table 36 Numbers of Viewers of MLB All-Star Game

Year	Number of Viewers (millions)
1982	34
1985	28
1990	24
1995	20
2000	15
2005	12
2010	12
2011	11

Source: *Nielsen Media Research, Inc.*

Solution

1. We use a graphing calculator to view a scattergram of the data (see Fig. 56). Because the points "bend upward," the scattergram suggests we can model the data better with an exponential function than with a linear function. If we imagine an exponential curve that contains the points $(15, 20)$ and $(31, 11)$, it appears the curve might come close to the other data points. To find an equation of this curve, we substitute the coordinates of the points $(15, 20)$ and $(31, 11)$ into the equation $f(t) = ab^t$:

$$11 = ab^{31}$$
$$20 = ab^{15}$$

Next, we divide the two left sides and divide the two right sides and solve for b:

$$\frac{11}{20} = \frac{ab^{31}}{ab^{15}} \qquad \textit{Divide left sides and divide right sides.}$$

$$\frac{11}{20} = b^{16} \qquad \textit{Simplify; subtract exponents: } \frac{b^m}{b^n} = b^{m-n}$$

$$b = \pm\left(\frac{11}{20}\right)^{1/16} \qquad \textit{The solutions of } b^{16} = k \textit{ are } \pm k^{1/16}.$$

$$\approx 0.963 \qquad \textit{Compute; base of an exponential function is positive.}$$

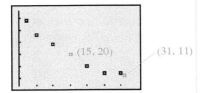

Figure 56 All-Star Game scattergram

So, an equation is $f(t) = a(0.963)^t$. To find a, we substitute the coordinates of $(15, 20)$ into the equation:

$$20 = a(0.963)^{15} \qquad \textit{Substitute 15 for t and 20 for f(t).}$$

$$a = \frac{20}{0.963^{15}} \qquad \textit{Divide both sides by 0.963}^{15}.$$

$$\approx 35.21 \qquad \textit{Compute.}$$

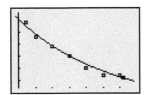

Figure 57 Check how well the model fits the data

The equation is $f(t) = 35.21(0.963)^t$. The graph in Fig. 57 shows that our exponential model fits the data well.

2. The coefficient of $f(t) = 35.21(0.963)^t$ is 35.21. So, the n-intercept is $(0, 35.21)$. This means there were about 35 million viewers of the All-Star Game in 1980. A little research would show that the actual number of viewers was 36 million, so the model's estimate is pretty accurate.
3. The base of $f(t) = 35.21(0.963)^t$ is $b = 0.963$. Because $1 - b = 1 - 0.963 = 0.037$, we conclude the number of viewers is decaying exponentially by 3.7% per year.
4. To predict the number of viewers in 2018, we evaluate f at $2018 - 1980 = 38$:

$$f(38) = 35.21(0.963)^{38} \approx 8.40$$

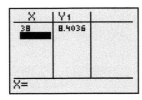

Figure 58 Verify the work

There will be about 8 million viewers in 2018. We use a graphing calculator table to verify our work (see Fig. 58).

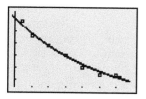

Figure 59 Compare the fit of models *f* and *r*

We used two points to find the exponential model $f(t) = 35.21(0.963)^t$ in Example 5. We can also find an exponential model by using a graphing calculator's *exponential regression*. Exponential regression gives the model $r(t) = 34.86(0.962)^t$. In Fig. 59, we see that both of the models fit the data well. For graphing calculator instructions, see Appendix B.16.

We call the equation $r(t) = 34.86(0.962)^t$ the **exponential regression equation** for the given data. We refer to its graph as an **exponential regression curve.**

The bases of both models are approximately equal. The base 0.963 of *f* estimates that the number of viewers of the MLB All-Star Game is decaying exponentially by 3.7% each year. The base 0.962 of *r* estimates that the number of viewers is decaying exponentially by 3.8% each year.

At this point in the course, we have a choice between modeling some data with a linear function or modeling the same data with an exponential function. For some authentic situations, we will know which type of model to use on the basis of our knowledge of the situation. For other situations, we can decide by viewing a scattergram of the data. Here we review the four-step modeling process.

▶ **Four-Step Modeling Process**

To find a model and then make estimates and predictions,

1. Create a scattergram of the data. Decide whether a line or an exponential curve comes close to the points.
2. Find an equation of your function.
3. Verify your equation by checking that the graph comes close to all of the data points.
4. Use your equation of the model to draw conclusions, make estimates, and/or make predictions.

If you discover that a model does not fit a data set well, a good first step is to check for any graphing or calculation errors. If your work appears to be correct, then try using different points to find your equation. Another option is to increase or decrease one or both of the constants in your equation until the fit is good.

Group Exploration

Comparing a linear model with an exponential model

In 1950, world population was 2.5 billion. In 1987, it was 5.0 billion (Source: *U.S. Census Bureau*).

1. First, assume world population is growing exponentially. Let $E(t)$ be the world's population (in billions) at *t* years since 1950. Find an equation of *E*.

2. Now assume world population is growing linearly. Let $L(t)$ be the world's population (in billions) at *t* years since 1950. Find an equation of *L*.

3. Use your equations of *E* and *L* to make two predictions of the world's population for each of the years that follow.
   a. 2020   **b.** 2050   **c.** 2150

4. Use the window settings shown in Fig. 60 to compare the graphs of *E* and *L*.

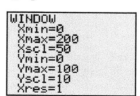

Figure 60 Compare the graphs of the exponential and linear models

5. Will there be much difference in the world's population if it grows exponentially or linearly in the short run? in the long run? Explain.

▶ Tips for Success   **Show What You Know**

Even if you don't know how to do one step of a problem, show your instructor you understand the other parts of the problem. Check with your instructor first, but you may earn partial credit if you pick a number (which would probably be incorrect) to be the result for the one step and then show what you would do with that number in the remaining steps of the solution.

For example, suppose you want to find an equation of the line that passes through the points $(4, 7)$ and $(5, 9)$, but you have forgotten how to find the slope of the line. You could write,

I've drawn a blank on finding the slope. However, if the slope is 3, then

$$y = 3x + b$$
$$7 = 3(4) + b$$
$$7 = 12 + b$$
$$-5 = b$$

Therefore, $y = 3x - 5$.

You could point out that you know your result is incorrect, because the graph of $y = 3x - 5$ does not pass through the point $(5, 9)$. Also, seeing your result (with a graph) may jog your memory about finding the slope and allow you to go back and do the problem correctly.

Homework 4.5

For extra help ▶ **MyMathLab®**   Watch the videos in MyMathLab   Download the MyDashboard App

1. Suppose a rumor is spreading that eating pickles will raise your IQ. Assume 40 Americans have heard the rumor as of today and each day the number of Americans (past and present) who have heard it triples. Let $f(t)$ be the number of Americans (past and present) who have heard the rumor at t days since today.
   a. Find an equation of f.
   b. How many Americans (past and present) will have heard the rumor 10 days from now?
   c. How many Americans (past and present) will have heard the rumor 15 days from now? Has model breakdown occurred? [**Hint:** Assume the U.S. population is 306 million.]

2. Suppose a flu epidemic has broken out at your school. Assume that on February 10, 20 people have the flu and that each day the number of people (past and present) who have gotten the flu triples. Let $f(t)$ be the number of people (past and present) who have gotten the flu by the day that is t days since February 10.
   a. Find an equation of f.
   b. Find $f(4)$. What does it mean in this situation?
   c. Find $f(10)$. What does it mean in this situation?

3. The name of the search engine Google™ is a play on the word "googol," which refers to the number 1 followed by one hundred zeros.
   a. In 2012, Google's index contained 30 trillion web pages. According to founders Larry Page and Sergey Brin, the size of the index doubles every year. Let $f(t)$ be the number of web pages (in trillions) in Google's index at t years since 2012. Find an equation of f.
   b. Predict the number of web pages Google's index will contain in 2018.

   c. If the web pages in Google's index in 2018 were printed and stacked in one pile, what would be the height (in miles) of that pile? [**Hint:** Take a stack of 500 pages of computer paper to be 2 inches tall.]

4. The total number of hours people spent listening to Pandora Radio was 1 billion hours in 2009 and has approximately doubled each year (Source: *Pandora Media, Inc.*).
   a. Let $H = f(t)$ be the total number (in billions) of listener hours in the year that is t years since 2009. Find an equation of f.
   b. What is the H-intercept of the model? What does it mean in this situation?
   c. Predict the total number of listener hours in 2017. Assuming the world population will be 7.3 billion in that year, predict the average annual number of listener hours per person.

5. The market share of eBooks (the percentage of revenue from all books) was 8.3% in 2010 and has grown by about 108% per year since then (Source: *German Book Office New York*). That is, each year the market share is about 2.08 times the previous year's market share.
   a. Let $M = f(t)$ be the market share of eBooks at t years since 2010. Find an equation of f.
   b. What is the M-intercept? What does it mean in this situation?
   c. What is the base b of $f(t) = ab^t$? What does it mean in this situation?
   d. Predict the market share in 2013. Assuming the revenue of all books will be $5 billion in that year, predict the revenue from eBooks.

6. The number of U.S. natural catastrophes (events that cost at least $1 million) was 250 catastrophes in 2010 and has grown by about 5% per year (Source: *Munich Reinsurance Company*). That is, each year there are about 1.05 times the number of natural catastrophes as in the previous year.
  a. Let $n = f(t)$ be the number of U.S. natural catastrophes in the year that is t years since 2010.
  b. What is the n-intercept? What does it mean in this situation?
  c. What is the base b of $f(t) = ab^t$? What does it mean in this situation?
  d. Predict the number of U.S. natural catastrophes in 2018. Use your result to predict the average number of U.S. natural catastrophes per day in 2018.

7. a. About 2.5 million TiVo® subscribers got TiVo through DIRECTV® in 2007, and that number has grown by about 50% per year (Source: *TiVo*). That is, each year there are about 1.5 times as many subscribers as in the preceding year. Let $D(t)$ be the number (in millions) of such subscribers at t years since 2007. Find an equation of D.
  b. About 1.71 million people were stand-alone TiVo subscribers in 2007, and that number has grown by about 120% per year (Source: *TiVo*). That is, each year there are about 2.2 times as many subscribers as in the preceding year. Let $S(t)$ be the number (in millions) of such subscribers at t years since 2007. Find an equation of S.
  c. Use "intersect" on a graphing calculator to find the intersection point of the graphs of D and S. What does it mean in this situation? [**Hint:** Use the window settings shown in Fig. 61.]

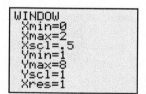

Figure 61 Exercise 7c

8. The average number of cable channels per household was 135 channels in 2010 and has grown by about 8% per year (Source: *Nielsen Media*). That is, each year, there have been about 1.08 times the number of channels as in the previous year.
  a. Let $f(t)$ be the average number of cable channels at t years since 2010. Find an equation of f.
  b. Predict the average number of cable channels per household in 2017.
  c. Currently, people must subscribe to bundles of channels rather than individual channels. On a weekly basis, subscribers watch only 12% of the channels to which they subscribe, on average. The Federal Communications Commission has urged Congress to eliminate bundling. Predict the average number of channels per household in 2017 if that happens.

9. Someone invests $3000 in an account at 8% interest compounded annually. Let $f(t)$ be the value (in dollars) of the account at t years after she has invested the $3000.
  a. Find an equation of f.
  b. What is the base b of your model $f(t) = ab^t$? What does it mean in this situation?
  c. What is the coefficient a of your model $f(t) = ab^t$? What does it mean in this situation?
  d. What will be the account's value in 15 years?

10. A person invests $7000 at 10% interest compounded annually. Let $f(t)$ be the value (in dollars) of the account at t years after he has deposited the $7000.
  a. Find an equation of f.
  b. What is the base b of your model $f(t) = ab^t$? What does it mean in this situation?
  c. What is the coefficient a of $f(t) = ab^t$? What does it mean in this situation?
  d. What will be the account's value in 10 years? Explain why the value has more than doubled, even though the investment earned 10% for 10 years.

11. A person invests $4000 in stocks today, and their value doubles every 6 years. Let $f(t)$ be the value (in dollars) of the investment at t years from now.
  a. Find an equation of f.
  b. Find the value of the investment 20 years from now.

12. Someone invests $2800 in stocks today, and their value doubles every 11 years. Let $g(t)$ be the value (in dollars) of the investment at t years from now.
  a. Find an equation of g.
  b. Find the value of the investment 25 years from now.

13. A person invests $5000 at 6% interest compounded annually for 3 years and then invests the balance (the $5000 plus the interest earned) in an account at 8% interest for 5 years. Find the value of the investment after the 8 years.

14. A person invests $3500 at 3% interest compounded annually for 4 years and then invests the balance (the $3500 plus the interest earned) in an account at 7% interest for 9 years. Find the value of the investment after the 13 years have elapsed.

15. Suppose a college bookstore sells 984 copies of a new (not used) textbook in 2011. Each year from 2011 to 2014, the new-textbook sales are half of the previous year's sales (due to used-textbook sales). Let $s = g(t)$ be the sales of copies of the new textbook in the year that is t years since 2011.
  a. Find an equation of g.
  b. What is the s-intercept of the model? What does it mean in this situation?
  c. Find $g(3)$. What does it mean in this situation?
  d. What is the half-life of new-textbook sales?

16. A storage tank contains niobium-97m, a radioactive element. The percentage of the element that remains is halved each hour. Let $p = f(t)$ be the percentage of niobium-97m that remains at t hours since the element was placed in the tank.
  a. Find an equation of f.
  b. What is the p-intercept of the model? What does it mean in this situation?
  c. Find $f(9)$. What does it mean in this situation?
  d. What is the half-life of niobium-97m?

17. A storage tank contains radium-226, a radioactive element with a half-life of 1600 years. Let $f(t)$ be the percentage of radium-226 that remains at t years since the element was placed in the tank.
  a. Find an equation of f.
  b. What percentage of the radium-226 will remain after 100 years?
  c. What percentage of the radium-226 will remain after 3200 years? Explain how you can find this result without using the equation of f.

18. A storage tank contains californium-251, a radioactive element with a half-life of about 900 years. Let $g(t)$ be the percentage of californium-251 that remains at t years since the element was placed in the tank.
   a. Find an equation of g.
   b. What percentage of the californium-251 will remain after 600 years?
   c. What percentage of the californium-251 will remain after 3600 years? Explain how you can find this result without using the equation of g.

19. A thyroid cancer patient ingests a single dose of radioactive iodine-131 to kill the cancer cells. Iodine-131 has an *effective half-life* of 7.56 days—some is lost to radioactive decay, and some is removed through urination. Let $f(t)$ be the percentage of the iodine-131 that remains in the patient's body at t days since he ingested the iodine-131.
   a. Find an equation of f.
   b. For 3 days after ingesting the iodine-131, the patient must stay at least 1 meter away from other people, because the radiation he emits could be harmful. What percentage of the iodine-131 will remain in his body after 3 days?
   c. The patient can safely spend a lot of time near a child when at most 5% of the iodine-131 remains. Use "intersect" on a graphing calculator to estimate when that time will be. [**Hint:** Use ZStandard followed by Zoom Out.]

20. A physician injects a patient with thallium-201 to determine how well blood flows to the patient's heart muscle. Thallium-201 has an *effective half-life* of 2.3 days—some is lost to exponential decay, and some is removed through the digestive and urinary tracts. Let $f(t)$ be the percentage of the thallium-201 that remains in the patient's body at t days since she was injected.
   a. Find an equation of f.
   b. What percentage of thallium-201 will remain after 5 days?
   c. Use "intersect" on a graphing calculator to estimate when only 10% of the thallium-201 will remain. [**Hint:** Use ZStandard followed by Zoom Out.]

21. The half-life of caffeine in a person's bloodstream is about 6 hours. If a person's bloodstream contains 80 milligrams of caffeine, how much of that caffeine will remain after 14 hours?

22. The half-life of aspirin in a person's bloodstream is about 15 minutes. If a person's bloodstream contains 200 milligrams of aspirin, how much of that aspirin will remain after 40 minutes?

23. The number of wireless Internet users in the United States grew approximately exponentially from 12 million users in 2003 to 105 million users in 2010 (Source: *Computer Industry Almanac*). Estimate the number of wireless Internet users in 2012.

24. The enrollment in private, for-profit colleges grew approximately exponentially from 0.6 million students in 2000 to 2.3 million students in 2011 (Source: *National Center for Education Statistics*). Predict the enrollment in 2017.

25. For those who have private health insurance, per-person annual spending on healthcare grows approximately exponentially with age. The average annual spending of 21-year-old adults is $198 and the average annual spending of 60-year-old adults is $715 (Source: *Thomson Reuters*). Estimate the average annual spending on healthcare by 30-year-old adults who have private health insurance.

26. Hard-copy sales of *Encyclopedia Britannica* decayed approximately exponentially from 108 thousand encyclopedias in 1994 to 8 thousand encyclopedias in 2011 (Source: *Kellog School of Management*). Estimate the hard-copy sales in 2012. Explain why it is not surprising that *Encyclopedia* went out of print in 2012.

27. World population is provided in Table 37 for various years.

Table 37 World Population

Year	Population (billions)
1930	2.070
1940	2.295
1950	2.500
1960	3.050
1970	3.700
1980	4.454
1990	5.279
2000	6.080
2012	7.044

Source: *U.S. Census Bureau*

Let $p = f(t)$ be the world's population (in billions) at t years since 1900.
   a. Use a graphing calculator to draw a scattergram to describe the data. Is it better to use a linear or an exponential function to model the data? Explain.
   b. Find an equation of f.
   c. Find $f(110)$. What does it mean in this situation? Have you performed interpolation or extrapolation? Explain.
   d. Find $f(118)$. What does it mean in this situation? Have you performed interpolation or extrapolation? Explain.

28. The numbers of men's colleges, not including seminaries, are shown in Table 38 for various years.

Table 38 Numbers of Men's Colleges

Year	Number of Men's Colleges
1967	145
1975	80
1985	27
1995	11
2012	4

Source: *National Association of Independent Colleges and Universities*

Let $n = f(t)$ be the number of men's colleges at t years since 1960.
   a. Use a graphing calculator to draw a scattergram to describe the data. Is it better to use a linear or an exponential function to model the data? Explain.
   b. Find an equation of f.
   c. Find $f(45)$. What does it mean in this situation? Have you performed interpolation or extrapolation? Explain.
   d. Find $f(58)$. What does it mean in this situation? Have you performed interpolation or extrapolation? Explain.

29. The number of Starbucks stores worldwide has increased substantially since 1991 (see Table 39).

Table 39 Numbers of Starbucks Stores Worldwide

Year	Number of Stores
1991	116
1993	272
1995	676
1997	1412
1999	2135
2001	4709
2003	7225

Source: *Starbucks Corporation*

Let $n = f(t)$ be the number of Starbucks stores worldwide at t years since 1990.
a. Find an equation of f.
b. What is the percentage rate of growth of Starbucks stores?
c. Use f to estimate the number of stores in 2008. At the end of 2008, there were 15,256 stores (after 500 store closures during 2008). Is the percentage rate of growth of stores for the period 1991–2003 the same as for the period 2003–2008? Explain.
d. Use "intersect" on a graphing calculator to estimate when there were 3,000 stores. [**Hint:** Graph $n = 3,000$.]

30. Percentages of adults surveyed who plan to attend a Halloween party this year are shown in Table 40 for various age groups.

Table 40 Percentages of Adults Who Plan to Attend a Halloween Party

Age Group (years)	Age Used to Represent Age Group (years)	Percent
18–24	21.0	44
25–34	29.5	34
35–44	39.5	25
45–54	49.5	14
55–64	59.5	10
65 or over	70.0	6

Source: *International Mass Retail Association*

Let $p = f(t)$ be the percentage of adults at age t years who plan to attend a Halloween party this year.
a. Find an equation of f.
b. Find $f(26)$. What does it mean in this situation?
c. Use f to estimate the *number* of 42-year-old adults who plan to attend a Halloween party. Assume there are about 4.6 million 42-year-old adults.
d. What is the base b of the model $r(t) = ab^t$? What does it mean in this situation?
e. Use "intersect" on a graphing calculator to estimate at what age 12% of adults plan to attend a Halloween party. [**Hint:** Graph $p = 12$.]

31. The University of Michigan offers a $500,000 life insurance policy. Monthly rates for nonsmoking faculty are shown in Table 41 for various ages.

Table 41 University of Michigan Life Insurance Monthly Rates for Nonsmoking Faculty

Age Group (years)	Age Used to Represent Age Group (years)	Monthly Rate (dollars)
30–34	32	15.00
35–39	37	18.50
40–44	42	26.00
45–49	47	46.00
50–54	52	75.50
55–59	57	118.00
60–64	62	195.50
65–69	67	326.60

Source: *University of Michigan*

Let $g(t)$ be the monthly rate (in dollars) for a nonsmoking faculty member at t years of age.
a. Find an equation of g.
b. What is the coefficient a of your model $g(t) = ab^t$? What does it mean in this situation?
c. What is the base b of your model $g(t) = ab^t$? What does it mean in this situation?
d. Find $g(35)$. What does it mean in this situation?
e. For many life insurance policies, monthly rates for women are different from monthly rates for men. Assume these rates depend on life expectancy only. Given that the life expectancy of women is higher than that of men, would women or men pay higher monthly rates? Explain.

32. A person's heart attack risk can be estimated by using *Framingham point scores*, which are based on such factors as age, cholesterol level, blood pressure, and smoking habits. Men's risks of having a heart attack in the next 10 years are shown in Table 42 for various scores.

Table 42 Risks of Having a Heart Attack

Framingham Point Scores	Risk (percent)
0	1
5	2
10	6
15	20
17	30

Sources: *The Journal of the American Medical Association; Framingham Heart Study*

Let $f(s)$ be a man's risk of having a heart attack in the next 10 years if his score is s points.

a. Find an equation of f.

b. A 47-year-old man with high cholesterol has high blood pressure but does not smoke. His score is 11 points. What is the risk he will have a heart attack in the next 10 years?

c. Another 47-year-old man has the same cholesterol level and blood pressure as the man described in part (b). However, this man's score is 5 points higher, because he smokes. What is the risk that he will have a heart attack in the next 10 years?

d. What is the coefficient a of your model $f(s) = ab^s$? What does it mean in this situation?

e. What is the base b of your model $f(s) = ab^s$? What does it mean in this situation?

33. From 1790 to 1860, U.S. population grew rapidly (see Table 43).

Table 43 U.S. Population

Year	Population (millions)	Population Ratio (current to previous)
1790	3.9	—
1800	5.3	1.36
1810	7.2	
1820	9.6	
1830	12.9	
1840	17.1	
1850	23.2	
1860	31.4	

Source: *U.S. Census Bureau*

a. Complete the third column of Table 43. The first entry is 1.36, since $\dfrac{1800 \text{ population}}{1790 \text{ population}} = \dfrac{5.3}{3.9} \approx 1.36$.

b. What do you observe about the ratios in the third column?

c. On the basis of your observation in part (b), is it better to use an exponential or a linear function to model the data? Explain.

d. Let $f(t)$ be the U.S. population (in millions) at t years since 1790. Find an equation of an exponential function that models the data from 1790 to 1860.

e. Complete the third column of Table 44.

Table 44 U.S. Population

Year	Population (millions)	Population Ratio (current to previous)
1860	31.4	—
1870	39.8	
1880	50.2	
1890	62.9	
1900	76.0	

Source: *U.S. Census Bureau*

f. Is it likely f gives reasonable population estimates after 1860? Explain.

g. Use f to estimate the population in 2012. The actual population was 313.9 million. What is the error in your estimate?

34. The amounts of the federal debt are listed in Table 45 for various years.

Table 45 Federal Debt Amounts

Year	Federal Debt (billions of dollars)
1960	291
1970	381
1980	909
1990	3206
2000	5629
2010	13,529

Source: *U.S. Office of Management and Budget*

a. Let $D = f(t)$ be the federal debt (in billions of dollars) at t years since 1960. Find an equation of f.

b. Predict the federal debt in 2018.

c. If the federal debt were paid off in 2018 by each U.S. citizen contributing an equal amount of money, how much would each person have to pay? Assume the population will be about 335 million in 2018.

d. Predict the federal debt in 2050.

e. If the federal debt were paid off in 2050 by each U.S. citizen contributing an equal amount of money, how much would each person have to pay? Assume the population will be about 439 million in 2050. Explain why some people want to reduce or eliminate the debt now rather than later.

35. The average numbers of lightning deaths per million people per year are shown in Table 46 for various decades, and the percentages of Americans who live in rural areas are shown in the table for various years.

Table 46 Average Numbers of Lightning Deaths per Million People per Year; Percentages of Americans Who Live in Rural Areas

Decade	Year Used to Represent Decade	Lightning Fatality Rate	Year	Percentage of Americans Who Live in Rural Areas
1940–1949	1945	2.4	1950	36.0
1950–1959	1955	1.1	1960	30.1
1960–1969	1965	0.7	1970	26.3
1970–1979	1975	0.5	1980	26.3
1980–1989	1985	0.4	1990	24.8
1990–1999	1995	0.2	2000	22.0
2000–2010	2005	0.1	2010	21.0

Source: *Lopez and Holle 1998; Storm Data; U.S. Census Bureau*

a. Let $f(t)$ be the lightning fatality rate (average number of lightning deaths per million people per year) at t years since 1900. Use your graphing calculator to find the regression equation of f.

b. Predict the lightning fatality rate in 2017. Round your result to the second decimal place.

c. Use your result in part (b) to predict the *number* of lightning deaths in 2017. Assume the U.S. population will be 332 million in that year.

d. The ratio of injuries to deaths, both from lightning, appears to be 10 to 1 (Source: *Cherington et al. 1999*). Use your result in part (c) to predict the number of injuries from lightning in 2017.

e. Let $g(t)$ be the percentage of Americans who live in rural areas at t years since 1900. Use your graphing calculator to find the exponential regression equation of g.

f. It has been hypothesized that the lightning fatality rate has decreased due to the migration of Americans from rural areas to urban ones (Source: *Annual Rates of Lightning Fatalities by Country, Holle 2008*). Explain why this is probably not the only reason by comparing the meaning of the bases of the functions *f* and *g*.

36. Table 47 compares the economic strength of a country with the percentage of the population that was involved in producing agriculture. *Gross national product* (*GNP*) is a measure of the amount of goods and services a country produces.

Table 47 Percentage of Population in Agriculture versus GNP

Country	Percent of Population in Agriculture	GNP per Person (dollars)
United States	1	43,743
Great Britain	1	37,632
France	2	35,854
Canada	2	32,546
Australia	3	32,170
Italy	3	29,999
Japan	5	38,984
New Zealand	9	25,942
Slovenia	9	17,352
Korea (North and South)	12	10,975
Latvia	16	6757
Chile	17	5865
Panama	23	4626
Brazil	25	3455
Columbia	32	2292
Bolivia	36	1009
Bangladesh	50	467
Vietnam	60	623

Source: *United Nations*

a. Let $f(p)$ be the GNP per person (in dollars) for a country in which p percent of the population was involved in agriculture. Use a graphing calculator to find the regression equation of f.

b. Use a graphing calculator to sketch a scattergram of the data and your model on the same coordinate system. Does the model fit the data well?

c. What is the base b of your function $f(p) = ab^p$? What does it mean in this situation? Explain why this makes sense in terms of productivity.

d. Which country's data point is farthest from the regression curve? What does the position of the point in relation to the other data points and the regression curve suggest about this situation? [**Hint:** Zoom in.]

Concepts

37. A storage tank contains a radioactive element. Let $p = f(t)$ be the percentage of the element that remains at t years since the element was placed in the tank. A graph of f is shown in Fig. 62.
a. What is the half-life of the element?
b. What percentage of the element will remain in the tank after 40 years?

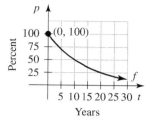

Figure 62 The graph of the model *f*

38. A storage tank contains a radioactive element. Let $p = g(t)$ be the percentage of the element that remains at t years since the element was placed in the tank. Some values of g are shown in Table 48.

Table 48 Percentages of a Radioactive Element

Year t	Percent $g(t)$
0	100.0
1	79.4
2	63.0
3	50.0
4	39.7
5	31.5
6	25.0

a. What is the half-life of the element?
b. What percentage of the element will remain in the tank after 12 years?

Consider the scattergram of data and the graph of the model $f(t) = ab^t$ in the figure. Sketch the graph of an exponential model that describes the data better; then explain how you would adjust the values of a and b of the original model to describe the data better.

39. See Fig. 63.

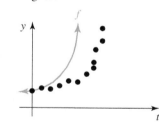

Figure 63 Exercise 39

40. See Fig. 64.

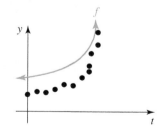

Figure 64 Exercise 40

41. Explain how you can tell whether to model a situation with a linear model, exponential model, or neither.

42. Assume $f(t) = ab^t$, where $a > 0$, models a quantity at time t.
a. Explain why the quantity grows exponentially at a rate of $b - 1$ percent (in decimal form) if $b > 1$.
b. Explain why the quantity decays exponentially at a rate of $1 - b$ percent (in decimal form) if $0 < b < 1$.

43. Describe how to use the base multiplier property to find an exponential model for a given situation.

44. Explain how to find an exponential model for a situation described by a table of data. Also, explain how to use the model to make an estimate or prediction for the situation.

Related Review

45. In this exercise, you will explore two types of interest-bearing accounts.
   a. Suppose $800 is deposited into a savings account that earns 3% interest compounded annually. Let $C(t)$ be the value (in dollars) of the account at t years after the $800 has been deposited. Find an equation of C.
   b. Now suppose $800 is deposited into a savings account that earns 3% simple interest. Recall from Section 3.4 that the term *simple interest* means the interest earned each year is 3% of the $800 only. Let $S(t)$ be the value (in dollars) of the account at t years after the $800 has been deposited. Find an equation of S. [**Hint:** Each year, the balance increases by $800(0.03) = 24$ dollars.]
   c. Find $C(1)$, $C(2)$, $S(1)$, and $S(2)$. Explain in terms of the situation why it makes sense that $C(1)$ is equal to $S(1)$ but that $C(2)$) is not equal to $S(2)$.
   d. Compare $C(20)$ with $S(20)$. What does your comparison mean in this situation?

46. On Monday, 20 people receive a prank e-mail warning them zombies are on the loose. On Tuesday, 40 more people receive the e-mail.
   a. Assume the number of people receiving the e-mail is growing exponentially. Let $E(t)$ be the number of people who receive the e-mail on the day that is t days since Monday. Find an equation of E.
   b. Now assume the number of people receiving the e-mail is growing linearly. Let $L(t)$ be the number of people who receive the e-mail on the day that is t days since Monday. Find an equation of L.
   c. Compare $E(7)$ with $L(7)$. What does your comparison mean in this situation?
   d. Compare $E(28)$ with $L(28)$. What does your comparison mean in this situation?
   e. Use a graphing calculator to draw the graphs of E and L on the same coordinate system. Compare the graphs.
   f. Is there much difference in the numbers of people who will receive the e-mail if it grows exponentially or linearly? Explain.

47. Retail sales in China are shown in Table 49 for various years.

Table 49 Annual Retail Sales in China

Year	Annual Retail Sales (trillions of dollars)
2006	0.51
2007	0.65
2008	0.84
2009	0.97
2010	1.14

Source: *Access Asia*

   a. Let $f(t)$ be annual retail sales (in trillions of dollars) in China at t years since 2000. Use a graphing calculator to draw a scattergram of the data. Is it better to use a linear or exponential function to model the data? Explain.

   b. Find an equation of f.
   c. Predict the retail sales in China in 2017.
   d. In 2011, U.S. retail sales were $4.65 trillion (Source: *U.S. Department of Commerce*). Predict in which year retail sales in China will reach that level.

48. The costs of 30-second ad slots during the Super Bowl have increased greatly (see Table 50).

Table 50 Costs of Television Ad Slots during the Super Bowl

Super Bowl	Year	Cost for 30 Seconds (millions of dollars)
IX	1975	0.11
XIX	1985	0.5
XXIX	1995	1.0
XXXIX	2005	2.4
XLVI	2012	3.5

Source: *Ocean Media, Inc.*

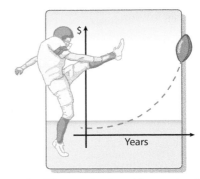

   a. First, assume the 30-second ad cost is growing linearly. Let $L(t)$ be the 30-second ad cost (in millions of dollars) at t years since 1950. Find an equation of L.
   b. Now assume the 30-second ad cost is growing exponentially. Let $E(t)$ be the 30-second ad cost (in millions of dollars) at t years since 1950. Find an equation of E.
   c. Describe how close each model comes to the points in the scattergram.
   d. Use L and E to estimate the cost of a 30-second ad slot during Super Bowl I in 1967. The actual cost was $40,000. Which function estimates that cost better?
   e. Find the slope of the graph of L and the base b of $E(t) = ab^t$, and describe what they mean in this situation.
   f. In Super Bowl XLIV in 2010, a 30-second ad slot cost $2.65 million, the first decline in cost since 2003. Use E to help estimate the total loss in revenue from ad slots during Super Bowl XLIV, likely due to a poor economy. [**Hint:** First find $E(60)$.]
   g. Use E to predict the cost of a 30-second ad slot during Super Bowl LII in 2018.

Expressions, Equations, Functions, and Graphs

Give an example of the following. Then solve, simplify, or graph, as appropriate.

49. exponential equation in one variable

50. linear function

51. exponential function

52. system of two linear equations in two variables

53. expression involving exponents

Taking it to the Lab

Stringed Instrument Lab

Many stringed instruments (such as guitars, banjos, and basses) have thin metal strips called *frets* across the neck and underneath the strings. Frets are precisely placed so that the instruments produce the 12 chromatic notes of our Western musical scale. In this lab, you will discover where the frets of a stringed instrument must be placed to produce the 12 chromatic notes. You can apply what you learn to determine where violinists and cellists must put their fingers to produce these 12 notes.

Materials
You will need the following materials:
1. a stringed instrument with frets
2. a meterstick or tape measure

Recording of Data
Measure the length (in centimeters) of one of the strings of the instrument from the *nut* to the *bridge* (see Fig. 65). This is the length of an *open string*. Then measure the length (in centimeters) of the same string from the 12th fret to the bridge.

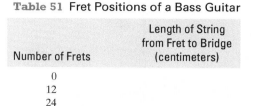

Table 51 Fret Positions of a Bass Guitar

Number of Frets	Length of String from Fret to Bridge (centimeters)
0	
12	
24	
36	
48	
n	

4. Let $f(n)$ be the distance (in centimeters) from the nth fret to the bridge. On the basis of the entries in Table 51, is f linear, quadratic, exponential, or none of these? Explain.

5. Find an equation of f.

6. Use your equation of f to find the distance between the fifth fret and the bridge.

7. Use a graphing calculator table to find the appropriate distances for all the frets of the instrument. Compare these values with the actual distances.

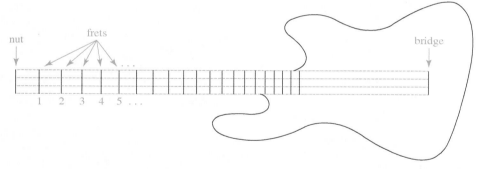

Figure 65 A bass guitar

Analyzing the Data
1. Compare the sound produced by plucking the open string with that produced by plucking the string when it is pressed just before the 12th fret (toward the nut). The higher pitched note is called the *octave* of the lower note. How do distances between the nut and the bridge and between the 12th fret and the bridge compare?

2. You probably found that when you halve the length of an open string, you can produce the octave of the open string. Since the Western chromatic musical scale has 12 notes from each note to its octave, this means that the 12th fret should be placed in the middle of the nut and the bridge. Where should the 24th fret be placed to achieve the next octave?

3. Complete Table 51.

8. On a 1974 Fender® Jazz bass, one of the strings has an open-string length of 86.5 cm. Explain how the Fender music technician knew where to put the frets.

9. In this lab, you observed that an octave is achieved by halving a string. Explain why it follows that the frets of an instrument are closer together when they are closer to the bridge.

Cooling Water Lab

In this lab, you will relate the temperature of some heated water to the amount of time that the water has been cooling.

In case the necessary measuring devices are not available for this experiment, some sample data are listed in Table 52.

Table 52 Temperatures of Water

Time (minutes)	Water Temperature (°C)	Difference Between Water Temperature and Room Temperature (°C)
0	83.49	
5	71.22	
10	63.09	
15	57.23	
20	52.65	
25	48.83	
30	45.63	

Source: *J. Lehmann*
*Room temperature = 21.7°C

Materials

To do this lab, you will need the following materials:

1. hot water

2. a coffee cup

3. a temperature probe that measures temperatures in degrees Celsius. Or measure temperatures in degrees Fahrenheit and use the formula $C = \dfrac{F - 32}{1.8}$ to convert from degrees Fahrenheit to degrees Celsius. *If you are using a thermometer as the temperature probe, make sure that it can handle hot water; otherwise it might break or even explode.*

4. a timing device

Preparation

Heat some water and pour it into a coffee cup. Set the cup on a counter or table to cool. Choose an environment where the temperature of the air will not change much during the 30-minute experiment.

Recording of Data

Record the temperature of the air at the start of the experiment and then again at the end. If the room temperatures at the beginning and end of the experiment are significantly different, redo the experiment in an environment where the room temperature will not change much. Also, record the water temperature every five minutes for 30 minutes.

Analyzing the Data

1. Find the average of the room temperature in degrees Celsius at the start and end of the experiment. This average will be referred to as *the* room temperature. If you are using the sample data in Table 52, the room temperature when it was collected was 21.7°C.

2. Display the water temperature data in the first two columns of a table like Table 52.

3. For each water temperature reading, compute the difference between the water temperature and the room temperature. Enter these differences in the third column of your table.

4. Let $D = f(t)$ be the difference between the water and room temperatures (in degrees Celsius) at t minutes after the water is allowed to cool. Create a scattergram by hand, comparing D with t for your cooling-water data.

5. Use a graphing calculator to draw a scattergram of the data.

6. Find an equation of f.

7. Use a graphing calculator to draw a graph of your model and the scattergram in the same viewing window. Also, graph the model and scattergram by hand. How well does f model the data?

8. If your model is linear, what is the meaning of the slope? If your model is exponential, what is the meaning of the base?

9. Use your model to estimate the water temperature at 22 minutes.

10. Use your model to estimate the water temperature at 1 hour.

11. What will be the temperature of the water when it stops cooling? Does f predict when this temperature will be reached? According to f, how much time will it take for this to happen? Is this a reasonable prediction? Explain.

Exponential Lab: Topic of Your Choice

Your objective in this lab is to find some authentic data that appear to be exponential and then model them with an exponential function. Your function should model a situation that has not been discussed in this text. Your first task will be to find the data. Almanacs, newspapers, magazines, scientific journals, and the Internet are good resources. Or you can conduct an experiment to obtain your data.

Analyzing the Data

1. What two variables did you explore? [**Hint:** Describe the units of the variables.]

2. Which variable is the dependent variable? Which variable is the independent variable? Explain.

3. Does it make sense to you why an exponential function would model your situation best? Explain.

4. State the source of your data. If you conducted an experiment, provide a careful description with specific details of how you ran your experiment.

5. Include a table of your data.

6. Use a graphing calculator to draw a scattergram of your data.

7. Find an equation of an exponential model to describe the data.

8. Use a graphing calculator to graph your exponential model and the scattergram in the same viewing window. Graph your model and the scattergram by hand. How well does your model fit the data?

9. What is the base b of your exponential model? What does it mean in this situation?

10. What is the coefficient a of your exponential model? What does it mean in this situation?

11. Find any intercepts of your exponential model. What do they mean in this situation?

12. Choose an input of your model. Find the output that comes from the input. What does your result mean in this situation?

13. Comment on your lab experience.

   a. For example, you might address whether this lab was enjoyable, insightful, and so on.

   b. Were you surprised by any of your findings? If so, which ones?

   c. How would you improve your lab procedure if you did this lab again?

   d. How would you improve your procedure if you had more time and money?

Chapter Summary

Key Points of Chapter 4

Section 4.1 Properties of Exponents

Exponent

For any counting number n,

$$b^n = \underbrace{b \cdot b \cdot b \cdot \ldots \cdot b}_{n \text{ factors of } b}$$

We refer to b^n as the **power**, the **nth power of b**, or **b raised to the nth power.** We call b the **base** and n the **exponent.**

Simplifying expressions involving exponents

An expression involving exponents is simplified if

1. It includes no parentheses.

2. Each variable or constant appears as a base as few times as possible.

3. Each numerical expression has been calculated, and each numerical fraction has been simplified.

4. Each exponent is positive.

Finding $-b^n$

For an expression of the form $-b^n$, we compute b^n before finding the opposite.

Definitions of b^0 and b^{-n}

For $b \neq 0$,

- $b^0 = 1$

- $b^{-n} = \dfrac{1}{b^n}$, where n is a counting number.

Negative exponent in a denominator

If $b \neq 0$ and n is a counting number, then $\dfrac{1}{b^{-n}} = b^n$.

Properties of integer exponents

If m and n are integers, $b \neq 0$, and $c \neq 0$, then

- $b^m b^n = b^{m+n}$ **Product property for exponents**

- $\dfrac{b^m}{b^n} = b^{m-n}$ **Quotient property for exponents**

- $(bc)^n = b^n c^n$ **Raising a product to a power**

- $\left(\dfrac{b}{c}\right)^n = \dfrac{b^n}{c^n}$ **Raising a quotient to a power**

- $(b^m)^n = b^{mn}$ **Raising a power to a power**

Exponential function

An **exponential function** is a function whose equation can be put into the form $f(x) = ab^x$, where $a \neq 0$, $b > 0$, and $b \neq 1$. The constant b is called the **base.**

Scientific notation

A number is written in **scientific notation** if it has the form $N \times 10^k$, where k is an integer and either $-10 < N \leq -1$ or $1 \leq N < 10$.

Section 4.1   Properties of Exponents (*Continued*)

Converting from scientific notation to standard decimal notation	To write the scientific notation $N \times 10^k$ in standard decimal notation, we move the decimal point of the number N as follows: • If k is *positive*, we multiply N by 10 k times; hence, we move the decimal point k places to the *right*. • If k is *negative*, we divide N by 10 k times; hence, we move the decimal point k places to the *left*.
Converting from standard decimal notation to scientific notation	To write a number in scientific notation, count the number of places k that the decimal point must be moved so the new number N meets the condition $-10 < N \le 1$ or $1 \le N < 10$: • If the decimal point is moved to the left, then the scientific notation is written as $N \times 10^k$. • If the decimal point is moved to the right, then the scientific notation is written as $N \times 10^{-k}$.

Section 4.2   Rational Exponents

Definition of $b^{1/n}$	For the counting number n, where $n \ne 1$, • If n is odd, then $b^{1/n}$ is the number whose nth power is b, and we call $b^{1/n}$ the **nth root of b.** • If n is even and $b \ge 0$, then $b^{1/n}$ is the nonnegative number whose nth power is b, and we call $b^{1/n}$ the **principal nth root of b.** • If n is even and $b < 0$, then $b^{1/n}$ is not a real number. $b^{1/n}$ may be represented by $\sqrt[n]{b}$.
Rational exponent	For the counting numbers m and n, where $n \ne 1$ and b is any real number for which $b^{1/n}$ is a real number, • $b^{m/n} = (b^{1/n})^m = (b^m)^{1/n}$ • $b^{-m/n} = \dfrac{1}{b^{m/n}}, b \ne 0$
Properties of rational exponents	If m and n are rational numbers and b and c are any real numbers for which b^m, b^n, and c^n are real numbers, then • $b^m b^n = b^{m+n}$ **Product property for exponents** • $\dfrac{b^m}{b^n} = b^{m-n}, b \ne 0$ **Quotient property for exponents** • $(bc)^n = b^n c^n$ **Raising a product to a power** • $\left(\dfrac{b}{c}\right)^n = \dfrac{b^n}{c^n}, c \ne 0$ **Raising a quotient to a power** • $(b^m)^n = b^{mn}$ **Raising a power to a power**

Section 4.3   Graphing Exponential Functions

Base multiplier property	For an exponential function of the form $y = ab^x$, if the value of the independent variable increases by 1, the value of the dependent variable is multiplied by b.
Increasing or decreasing property	Let $f(x) = ab^x$, where $a > 0$. Then • If $b > 1$, then the function f is increasing. We say the function **grows exponentially.** • If $0 < b < 1$, then the function f is decreasing. We say the function **decays exponentially.**
y-intercept of an exponential function	For an exponential function of the form $y = ab^x$, the y-intercept is $(0, a)$.
Reflection property	The graphs of $f(x) = -ab^x$ and $g(x) = ab^x$ are **reflections** of each other across the x-axis.
Horizontal asymptote	For all exponential functions, the x-axis is a horizontal asymptote.
Domain	The domain of any exponential function $f(x) = ab^x$ is the set of real numbers.
Range	The range of an exponential function $f(x) = ab^x$ is the set of all positive real numbers if $a > 0$, and the range is the set of all negative real numbers if $a < 0$.

Section 4.4   Finding Equations of Exponential Functions

Solving $b^n = k$ for b

To solve an equation of the form $b^n = k$ for b,
- If n is odd, the solution is $k^{1/n}$.
- If n is even and $k \geq 0$, the solutions are $\pm k^{1/n}$.
- If n is even and $k < 0$, there is no real-number solution.

Dividing left sides and right sides of two equations

If $a = b$, $c = d$, $c \neq 0$, and $d \neq 0$, then $\dfrac{a}{c} = \dfrac{b}{d}$.

Finding an equation

We can find an equation of an exponential function by using the base multiplier property or by using two points. Both methods give the same result.

Section 4.5   Using Exponential Functions to Model Data

Exponential model, exponentially related, approximately exponentially related

An **exponential model** is an exponential function, or its graph, that describes the relationship between two quantities for an authentic situation. If all of the data points for a situation lie on an exponential curve, then we say the independent and dependent variables are **exponentially related.** If no exponential curve contains all of the data points, but an exponential curve comes close to all of the data points (and perhaps contains some of them), then we say the variables are **approximately exponentially related.**

Quantity present at time $t = 0$

If $y = ab^t$ is an exponential model where y is a quantity at time t, then the coefficient a is the value of that quantity present at time $t = 0$.

r percent interest compounded annually

The term **r percent interest compounded annually** means the interest earned each year equals r percent of the principal and any interest earned in previous years (all of which becomes part of the investment).

Half-life

If a quantity decays exponentially, the **half-life** is the amount of time it takes for that quantity to be reduced to half.

Meaning of the base b

If $f(t) = ab^t$, where $a > 0$, models a quantity at time t, then the percent rate of change is constant. In particular,
- If $b > 1$, then the quantity grows exponentially at a rate of $b - 1$ percent (in decimal form) per unit of time.
- If $0 < b < 1$, then the quantity decays exponentially at a rate of $1 - b$ percent (in decimal form) per unit of time.

Four-step modeling process

To find a model and then make estimates and predictions,
1. Create a scattergram of the data. Decide whether a line or an exponential curve comes close to the points.
2. Find an equation of your function.
3. Verify your equation by checking that the graph comes close to all of the data points.
4. Use your equation of the model to draw conclusions, make estimates, and/or make predictions.

Chapter 4 Review Exercises

Simplify. Assume b and c are positive.

1. $\dfrac{2^{-400}}{2^{-405}}$

2. $\dfrac{4b^{-3}c^{12}}{16b^{-4}c^3}$

3. $(2b^{-5}c^{-2})^3(3b^4c^{-6})^{-2}$

4. $\dfrac{(20b^{-2}c^{-9})(27b^5c^3)}{(18b^3c^{-1})(30b^{-1}c^{-4})}$

5. $32^{4/5}$ **6.** $16^{-3/4}$ **7.** $\dfrac{b^{-1/3}}{b^{4/3}}$ **8.** $\dfrac{(16b^8c^{-4})^{1/4}}{(25b^{-6}c^4)^{3/2}}$

9. $\left(\dfrac{32b^2c^5}{2b^{-6}c^1}\right)^{1/4}$

10. $\left(8^{2/3}b^{-1/3}c^{3/4}\right)\left(64^{-1/3}b^{1/2}c^{-5/2}\right)$

Simplify. Assume n is a counting number.

11. $b^{2n-1}b^{4n+3}$ **12.** $\dfrac{b^{n/2}}{b^{n/3}}$

13. Use properties of exponents to show why $3^{2x} = 9^x$.

For $f(x) = 3(5)^x$ and $g(x) = 6^x$, find the following.

14. $f(-2)$ **15.** $g(a + 2)$

For $f(x) = 49^x$ and $g(x) = 2(81)^x$, find the following.

16. $f\left(\dfrac{1}{2}\right)$ **17.** $g\left(-\dfrac{3}{4}\right)$

Write the number in standard decimal form.

18. 4.4487×10^7 **19.** 3.85×10^{-5}

Write the number in scientific notation.

20. 54,000,000   **21.** -0.00897

22. Graph $f(x) = 2(3)^x$ by hand.

Graph the function by hand. Find its domain and range.

23. $h(x) = -3(2)^x$ **24.** $g(x) = 12\left(\dfrac{1}{2}\right)^x$

Find all real-number solutions of the equation. Round any result(s) to the second decimal place.

25. $3.9b^7 = 283.5$ **26.** $5b^4 - 13 = 67$

27. $\dfrac{1}{3}b^2 - \dfrac{1}{5} = \dfrac{2}{3}$

28. Some values of the functions f, g, h, and k are provided in Table 53. For each function, determine whether the given values suggest that the function is linear, exponential, or neither. If the function could be linear or exponential, find a possible equation for it.

Table 53 Values of Four Functions (Exercises 28–30)

x	$f(x)$	$g(x)$	$h(x)$	$k(x)$
1	30	5	2	96
2	26	15	3	48
3	22	45	6	24
4	18	135	11	12
5	14	405	18	6

For Exercises 29 and 30, refer to Table 53.

29. Find $f(4)$.   **30.** Find x when $k(x) = 6$.

For Exercises 31 and 32, find an approximate equation $y = ab^x$ of the exponential curve that contains the given pair of points. Round the values of a and b to two decimal places.

31. $(0, 2)$ and $(5, 3)$ **32.** $(3, 30)$ and $(9, 7)$

33. Consider the scattergram of data and the graph of the model $f(x) = ab^t$ in Fig. 66. Sketch the graph of an exponential model that describes the data better; then explain how you would adjust the values of a and b of the original model to describe the data better.

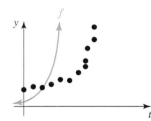

Figure 66 Exercise 33

34. Suppose $2000 is deposited into an account that earns 7% interest compounded annually. Let $f(t)$ be the value (in dollars) of the account at t years after the $2000 is deposited.
   a. Find an equation of f.
   b. Find the value of the account after 5 years.

35. A corporation's annual revenue has doubled every year. The revenue in 2010 was $17 thousand.
   a. Let $g(t)$ be the annual revenue (in thousands of dollars) at t years since 2010. Find an equation of g.
   b. Predict the revenue in 2018.

36. A storage tank contains carbon-14, a radioactive element with a half-life of 5730 years. Let $f(t)$ be the percentage of carbon-14 that remains at t years since the element was placed in the tank.

a. Find an equation of f.
b. Predict the percentage of carbon-14 remaining after 100 years.

37. The number of homes that are unoccupied has grown approximately exponentially from 8.5 million homes in 1980 to 14.3 million homes in 2010 (Source: *U.S. Census Bureau*). Predict the number of homes that will be unoccupied in 2017.

38. The prices of one ounce of gold are shown in Table 54 on January 1 of various years.

Table 54 Prices of Gold

Year	Price (dollars per ounce)
2000	282
2002	278
2004	416
2006	530
2008	846
2010	1121
2012	1599

Source: *Kitco Metals, Inc.*

a. Let $f(t)$ be the price (in dollars per ounce) of gold on January 1 at t years since 2000. Use a graphing calculator to draw a scattergram of the data. Is it better to use a linear or an exponential function to model the data? Explain.
b. Find an equation of f.
c. What is the coefficient a of your model $f(t) = ab^t$? What does it mean in this situation?
d. What is the base b of your model $f(t) = ab^t$? What does it mean in this situation?
e. Find $f(18)$. What does it mean in this situation?

39. Zimride is a website where people at least 18 years old can offer and get paid for shared car rides. The numbers of users of the site are shown in Table 55 for various years.

Table 55 Numbers of Users of Zimride

Year	Number of Users (thousands)
2007	6
2008	10
2009	35
2010	105
2011	200
2012	400

Source: *Zimride*

a. Let $n = f(t)$ be the number (in thousands) of users of Zimride at t years since 2000. Find an equation of f.
b. Find the percentage rate of growth of the number of users of Zimride.
c. Predict the number of users of Zimride in 2017.
d. Use "intersect" on a graphing calculator to predict when all people at least 18 years old will be users of Zimride. Assume there will be 260 million people at least 18 years old in that year. [**Hint:** Enter the model and the horizontal line $n = 260,000$, use ZoomFit, and then Zoom Out. See Appendix B.6 for graphing calculator instructions.]

Chapter 4 Test

Simplify.

1. $32^{2/5}$

2. $-8^{-4/3}$

Simplify. Assume b and c are positive.

3. $\left(2b^3c^8\right)^3$

4. $\left(\dfrac{4b^{-3}c}{25b^5c^{-9}}\right)^0$

5. $\dfrac{b^{1/2}}{b^{1/3}}$

6. $\dfrac{25b^{-9}c^{-8}}{35b^{-10}c^{-3}}$

7. $\left(\dfrac{6b(b^3c^{-2})}{3b^2c^5}\right)^2$

8. $\dfrac{\left(25b^8c^{-6}\right)^{3/2}}{\left(7b^{-2}\right)\left(2c^3\right)^{-1}}$

9. Use properties of exponents to show that $8^{x/3}2^{x+3} = 8(4)^x$.

For $f(x) = 4^x$, find the following.

10. $f(-2)$

11. $f\left(-\dfrac{3}{2}\right)$

For Exercises 12 and 13, graph the function by hand. Find its domain and range.

12. $f(x) = -5(2)^x$

13. $f(x) = 18\left(\dfrac{1}{3}\right)^x$

14. For each graph in Fig. 67, find an equation of an exponential function that could fit the graph.

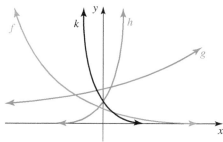

Figure 67 Exercise 14

15. Some values of a function f are provided in Table 56. Find an equation of f in terms of t.

Table 56 Values of a
Function f (Exercise 15)

t	$f(t)$
0	160
1	80
2	40
3	20
4	10
5	5

16. Find all real-number solutions of $3b^6 + 5 = 84$. Round any result(s) to the second decimal place.

Find an approximate equation $y = ab^x$ of an exponential curve that contains the given pair of points. Round the values of a and b to two decimal places.

17. $(0, 70)$ and $(6, 20)$

18. $(4, 9)$ and $(7, 50)$

For Exercises 19–21, refer to Fig. 68.

19. Find $f(0)$.

20. Find x when $f(x) = 3$.

21. Find an equation of f.

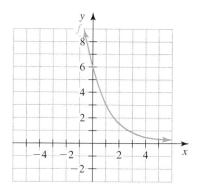

Figure 68 Exercises 19–21

22. On March 1, there are 400 leaves on a tree. For a while, the total number of leaves triples each week. Let $f(t)$ be the total number of leaves on the tree at t weeks since March 1.
  a. Find an equation of f.
  b. Find $f(6)$. What does it mean in this situation?
  c. Find $f(52)$. What does it mean in this situation?

23. The numbers of fraud complaints by consumers are shown in Table 57 for various years.

Table 57 Numbers of Fraud
Complaints by Consumers

Year	Number of Complaints (millions)
2005	0.6
2006	0.7
2007	0.7
2008	0.9
2009	1.0
2010	1.2
2011	1.5

Source: *Federal Trade Commission*

  a. Let $f(t)$ be the number (in millions) of fraud complaints by consumers in the year that is t years since 2000. Find an equation of f.
  b. What is the base b of your model $f(t) = ab^t$? What does it mean in this situation?
  c. What is the coefficient a of your model $f(t) = ab^t$? What does it mean in this situation?
  d. Predict the number of complaints in 2018.
  e. Predict what *percentage* of the U.S. population will file fraud complaints in 2020. Assume the U.S. population will be 341 million in that year and that no one will file more than one complaint.

5 Logarithmic Functions

Have you heard of "green" buildings? They are buildings designed to meet certain environmental standards. The numbers of buildings with Leadership in Energy and Environmental Design (LEED) certification for being green are shown in Table 1 for various years. In Exercise 18 of Homework 5.5, you will predict when there will be an average of 2000 LEED-certified green buildings per state.

In Chapter 4, we worked with exponential functions. In this chapter, we will work with *logarithmic functions,* which are closely related to exponential functions. We will also discuss how to simplify *logarithmic expressions* and solve *logarithmic equations in one variable.* In Section 4.5, we made predictions for the dependent variable of an exponential model—but not for the independent variable. In Section 5.5, we will be able to make predictions for the independent variable, such as when the minimum salary for major league baseball players will be $1 million.

Table 1 Numbers of LEED-Certified Green Buildings

Year	Number of Buildings with LEED Certification
2002	28
2004	183
2006	660
2008	2113
2010	7267

Source: *United States Green Building Council*

▼ 5.1 Composite Functions

Objectives

» Know the meaning of *composite function.*

» Use tables to evaluate a composite function.

» Use equations to evaluate a composite function.

» Find an equation of a composite function.

» Use graphs to evaluate a composite function.

» Use a composite function to model an authentic situation.

In this section, we will discuss how to combine two functions to make a new function called the *composite function.*

Definition of a Composite Function

Years ago, vending machines did not accept dollar bills. Suppose a student puts a dollar bill into a change machine and gets four quarters. Then the student puts the quarters into an old-fashioned vending machine and gets a bag of chips (see Fig. 1). So the output (quarters) of the change maker is used as the input of the old-fashioned vending machine.

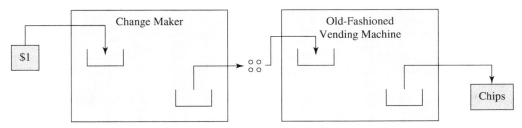

Figure 1 Action of change maker followed by action of old-fashioned vending machine

Now suppose the student puts the dollar bill directly into a modern vending machine and gets the bag of chips (see Fig. 2).

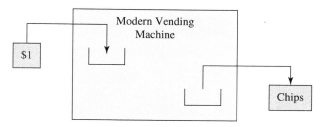

Figure 2 Action of modern vending machine

Note that the modern vending machine combines the actions of making change and then selling chips.

Similarly, we can create a function that combines the "actions" of two functions, where the output of the first function is used as the input of the second function. For example, we will next combine the tasks of finding the total cost of some tickets and then computing the sales tax. Let $C = g(n)$ be the total cost of n tickets and let $f(C)$ be the sales tax for C dollars worth of tickets (see Tables 2 and 3).

Table 2 Input–Output Pairs of g

Number of Tickets n	Total Cost (dollars) $g(n)$
2	40
3	60
4	80
5	100

Table 3 Input–Output Pairs of f

Total Cost of Tickets (dollars) C	Sales Tax (dollars) $f(C)$
40	3.20
60	4.80
80	6.40
100	8.00

Table 4 Input–Output Pairs of the Composition of f and g

Number of Tickets n	Sales Tax (dollars) $(f \circ g)(n)$
2	3.20
3	4.80
4	6.40
5	8.00

To find the sales tax on 2 tickets, we first refer to the first row of Table 2 and see that the total cost of 2 tickets is $40. Then we refer to the first row of Table 3 and see that the sales tax on $40 worth of tickets is $3.20. In conclusion, the sales tax on 2 tickets is $3.20.

We can repeat the process for 3, 4, and 5 tickets and summarize the information in Table 4, leaving out the middle step of showing the cost of the tickets. The pairs of numbers in Table 4 are input–output values of a function called the *composition of f and g*, written $f \circ g$.

In Fig. 3, we show the input–output action of g followed by the input–output action of f. Since the output of g, $g(n)$, is used as the input of f, the final output is $f(g(n))$.

Figure 3 Action of g followed by action of f

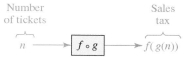

Figure 4 Action of $f \circ g$

In Fig. 4, we show the input–output action of $f \circ g$. Note that $f \circ g$ combines the actions of g and f, much like the modern vending machine combines the actions of the change maker and the old-fashioned vending machine.

▶ Definition   Composite function

If f and g are functions, x is in the domain of g, and $g(x)$ is in the domain of f, then we can form the **composite function** $f \circ g$:

$$(f \circ g)(x) = f(g(x))$$

We say $f \circ g$ is the **composition of f and g.**

Using Tables to Evaluate a Composite Function

In Example 1, we will use tables to evaluate the composition of two functions.

▶ **Example 1**   Using Tables to Evaluate a Composite Function

All of the input–output pairs of functions g and f are shown in Tables 5 and 6, respectively.

Table 5 Input–Output Pairs for g

x	$g(x)$
0	8
1	5
2	9
3	6
4	7

Table 6 Input–Output Pairs for f

x	$f(x)$
5	30
6	27
7	24
8	21
9	18

1. Find $(f \circ g)(0)$.
2. Use a table to describe five input–output pairs of $f \circ g$.

Table 7 Input–Output Pairs for $f \circ g$

x	$h(x)$
0	$f(g(0)) = f(8) = 21$
1	$f(g(1)) = f(5) = 30$
2	$f(g(2)) = f(9) = 18$
3	$f(g(3)) = f(6) = 27$
4	$f(g(4)) = f(7) = 24$

Solution

1. $(f \circ g)(0) = f(g(0))$ *Definition of $f \circ g$*

   $= f(8)$ *From the first row of Table 5, we see that $g(0) = 8$.*

   $= 21$ *From the fourth row of Table 6, we see that $f(8) = 21$.*

2. We repeat the process used in Problem 1 for the inputs 1, 2, 3, and 4 and show the work in Table 7, including the work from Problem 1.

Evaluating a Composite Function

Instead of using tables, we can use equations of functions to evaluate their composition.

▶ **Example 2**   Evaluating a Composite Function

Let $f(x) = 2x - 5$ and $g(x) = 3x + 6$.
1. Find $(f \circ g)(4)$.   2. Find $(g \circ f)(4)$.

Solution

1.

   $(f \circ g)(4) = f(g(4))$ *Definition of composite function*

   $= f(18)$ *$g(4) = 3(4) + 6 = 18$*

   $= 2(18) - 5$ *Substitute 18 for x in $f(x) = 2x - 5$.*

   $= 31$ *Compute.*

2.

   $(g \circ f)(4) = g(f(4))$ *Definition of composite function*

   $= g(3)$ *$f(4) = 2(4) - 5 = 3$*

   $= 3(3) + 6$ *Substitute 3 for x in $g(x) = 3x + 6$.*

   $= 15$ *Compute.*

Note that the results of Problems 1 and 2 of Example 2 are not equal. **In general, the outputs $(f \circ g)(a)$ and $(g \circ f)(a)$ may or may not be equal.**

Finding an Equation of a Composite Function

To prepare for Example 3, consider the function $f(x) = 5x$. To find $f(4)$, we substitute 4 for x in $f(x) = 5x$:

$$f(4) = 5(4)$$

Similarly, to find $f(x - 3)$, we substitute $x - 3$ for x in $f(x) = 5x$:

$$f(x - 3) = 5(x - 3)$$

▶ **Example 3** Finding Equations of Composite Functions

Let $f(x) = 5x$ and $g(x) = x - 3$.

1. Find an equation of $f \circ g$.   **2.** Find an equation of $g \circ f$.

Solution

1. Since $g(x) = x - 3$, we can substitute $x - 3$ for $g(x)$ in the second step:

$$
\begin{aligned}
(f \circ g)(x) &= f(g(x)) &&\text{\textit{Definition of composite function}} \\
&= f(x - 3) &&\text{\textit{Substitute x − 3 for g(x).}} \\
&= 5(x - 3) &&\text{\textit{Substitute x − 3 for x in f(x) = 5x.}} \\
&= 5x - 15 &&\text{\textit{Distributive law}}
\end{aligned}
$$

2. Since $f(x) = 5x$, we can substitute $5x$ for $f(x)$ in the second step:

$$
\begin{aligned}
(g \circ f)(x) &= g(f(x)) &&\text{\textit{Definition of composite function}} \\
&= g(5x) &&\text{\textit{Substitute 5x for f(x).}} \\
&= 5x - 3 &&\text{\textit{Substitute 5x for x in g(x) = x − 3.}}
\end{aligned}
$$

Similar to what we noticed in Example 2, the results of Problems 1 and 2 in Example 3 are different. **In general, $f \circ g$ and $g \circ f$ may or may not be the same function.**

WARNING $f(g(x))$ is *not* the product of $f(x)$ and $g(x)$. The product of $f(x)$ and $g(x)$ is written $f(x)g(x)$. Here we compare $f(x)g(x)$ and $f(g(x))$, using the functions $f(x) = 5x$ and $g(x) = x - 3$ from Example 3:

$$
\begin{aligned}
f(x)g(x) &= 5x(x - 3) & f(g(x)) &= f(x - 3) \\
&= 5x^2 - 15x & &= 5(x - 3) \\
& & &= 5x - 15
\end{aligned}
$$

Note that the results are quite different.

▶ **Example 4** Finding Equations of Composition Functions

Let $f(x) = 2^x$ and $g(x) = x + 4$.

1. Find an equation of $f \circ g$.   **2.** Find an equation of $g \circ f$.

Solution

1. Since $g(x) = x + 4$, we can substitute $x + 4$ for $g(x)$ in the second step:

$$
\begin{aligned}
(f \circ g)(x) &= f(g(x)) &&\text{\textit{Definition of composite function}} \\
&= f(x + 4) &&\text{\textit{Substitute x + 4 for g(x).}} \\
&= 2^{x+4} &&\text{\textit{Substitute x + 4 for x in f(x) = 2^{x}.}}
\end{aligned}
$$

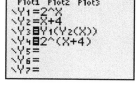

We verify our work by creating a graphing calculator table for $y = f(g(x))$ and $y = 2^{x+4}$. See Fig. 5. (The command $Y_1(Y_2(X))$ is the calculator's notation for composing functions. To enter an equation by using Y_n references, see Appendix B.25.)

2. Since $f(x) = 2^x$, we can substitute 2^x for $f(x)$ in the second step:

$$
\begin{aligned}
(g \circ f)(x) &= g(f(x)) &&\text{\textit{Definition of composite function}} \\
&= g(2^x) &&\text{\textit{Substitute 2^{x} for f(x).}} \\
&= 2^x + 4 &&\text{\textit{Substitute 2^{x} for x in g(x) = x + 4.}}
\end{aligned}
$$

Figure 5 Verify the work

▶ **Example 5** Evaluating and Finding an Equation of a Composite Function

Let $f(x) = -3x + 8$ and $g(x) = 4x - 5$.

1. Find $(f \circ g)(2)$.
2. Find an equation of $f \circ g$.
3. Use the equation of $f \circ g$ to find $(f \circ g)(2)$.

Solution

1.

$$(f \circ g)(2) = f(g(2)) \qquad \text{\textit{Definition of composite function}}$$
$$= f(3) \qquad g(2) = 4(2) - 5 = 3.$$
$$= -3(3) + 8 \qquad \text{\textit{Substitute 3 for x in f(x) = -3x + 8.}}$$
$$= -1 \qquad \text{\textit{Compute.}}$$

2. Since $g(x) = 4x - 5$, we can substitute $4x - 5$ for $g(x)$ in the second step:

$$(f \circ g)(x) = f(g(x)) \qquad \text{\textit{Definition of composite function}}$$
$$= f(4x - 5) \qquad \text{\textit{Substitute 4x - 5 for g(x).}}$$
$$= -3(4x - 5) + 8 \qquad \text{\textit{Substitute 4x - 5 for x in f(x) = -3x + 8.}}$$
$$= -12x + 15 + 8 \qquad \text{\textit{Distributive law}}$$
$$= -12x + 23 \qquad \text{\textit{Combine like terms.}}$$

3.

$$(f \circ g)(2) = -12(2) + 23 \qquad \text{\textit{Substitute 2 for x in (f $\circ$ g)(x) = -12x + 23.}}$$
$$= -1 \qquad \text{\textit{Compute.}}$$

So, $(f \circ g)(2)$ is equal to -1, which is the same result we found in Problem 1.

▶ **Example 6**   Expressing a Function as a Composition of Two Functions

If $h(x) = (7x + 3)^5$, find equations of the functions f and g such that $h(x) = (f \circ g)(x)$.

Solution

To form $f(g(x))$, we substitute $g(x)$ for x in $f(x)$. Similarly, to form $(7x + 3)^5$, we can substitute $7x + 3$ for x in x^5. This suggests that $g(x) = 7x + 3$ and $f(x) = x^5$. We check by performing the composition:

$$(f \circ g)(x) = f(g(x)) = f(7x + 3) = (7x + 3)^5$$

There are other possible answers. For example, $g(x) = 7x$ and $f(x) = (x + 3)^5$ also work:

$$(f \circ g)(x) = f(g(x)) = f(7x) = (7x + 3)^5$$

Using Graphs to Evaluate a Composite Function

Instead of using tables or equations to evaluate a composition, we can use graphs of functions.

▶ **Example 7**   Using Graphs to Evaluate a Composite Function

Refer to the graphs in Fig. 6 to find $(f \circ g)(5)$.

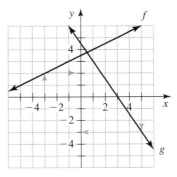

Figure 6 Graphs of f and g

Solution

The blue arrows in Fig. 6 show that $g(5) = -3$. So, we can substitute -3 for $g(5)$ in the second step:

$$
\begin{aligned}
(f \circ g)(5) &= f(g(5)) && \text{\small\textit{Definition of composite function}} \\
&= f(-3) && \text{\small\textit{Substitute }}-3\text{\small\textit{ for }}g(5). \\
&= 2 && \text{\small\textit{The red arrows in Fig. 6 show that }}f(-3) = 2.
\end{aligned}
$$

Using a Composite Function to Model an Authentic Situation

Near the start of this section, we used tables to evaluate the composition of two models. In Example 8, we will use an equation to evaluate the composition of two models.

▶ Example 8 Using a Composite Function to Model a Situation

Let $f(Q)$ be the number of cups in Q quarts, and let $g(x)$ be the number of ounces in x cups.

1. Find an equation of f.
2. Find an equation of g.
3. Find an equation of $g \circ f$.
4. Find $(g \circ f)(5)$. What does it mean in this situation?

Solution

1. Since there are 4 cups in one quart, $f(Q) = 4Q$.
2. Since there are 8 ounces in one cup, $g(x) = 8x$.
3. $(g \circ f)(Q) = g(f(Q)) = g(4Q) = 8(4Q) = 32Q$
4. $(g \circ f)(5) = 32(5) = 160$

The function f converts units of quarts to units of cups, and the function g converts units of cups to units of ounces, so $g \circ f$ converts units of quarts to units of ounces (see Fig. 7).

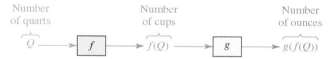

Figure 7 Action of f followed by action of g

So, $(g \circ f)(5) = 160$ means there are 160 ounces in 5 quarts.

▶ Example 9 Using a Composition Function to Model a Situation

In Exercise 6 of Homework 2.1, you used a line to describe the relationship between elevation and boiling point (see Table 8). A reasonable model is $f(E) = -5.9E + 211.3$, where $F = f(E)$ is the boiling point (in Fahrenheit degrees) at an elevation of E thousand meters. Table 9 shows equivalent Fahrenheit and Celsius temperatures. A reasonable model is $c(F) = 0.56F - 17.78$, where $c(F)$ is the Celsius reading corresponding to a Fahrenheit reading of F degrees.

Table 8 Boiling Points of Water

Elevation (thousands of meters)	Boiling Point (°F)
0	212
1	205
2	200
5	181
10	151
15	123

Table 9 Equivalent Temperature Readings

Fahrenheit Reading (°F)	Celsius Reading (°C)
32	0
68	20
104	40
140	60
176	80
212	100

1. Let $h(E)$ be the boiling point (in Celsius degrees) at elevation E thousand meters. Find an equation of h.
2. Find $h(7)$. What does it mean in this situation?

Solution

1. Note that $f(E)$ is the boiling point (in Fahrenheit degrees) at E thousand meters. Since c converts Fahrenheit readings to equivalent Celsius readings, $c(f(E))$ is the boiling point (in *Celsius* degrees) at E thousand meters. So, $h(E) = c(f(E))$. Here we find the equation of h:

$$
\begin{aligned}
h(E) &= c(f(E)) & & \text{\textit{h is the composition of c and f.}} \\
&= c(-5.9E + 211.3) & & \text{\textit{Substitute} } -5.9E + 211.3 \text{ \textit{for} } f(x). \\
&= 0.56(-5.9E + 211.3) - 17.78 & & \text{\textit{Substitute} } -5.9E + 211.3 \text{ \textit{for F in}} \\
& & & c(F) = 0.56F - 17.78. \\
&= -3.304E + 118.328 - 17.78 & & \text{\textit{Distributive law}} \\
&= -3.304E + 100.548 & & \text{\textit{Combine like terms.}}
\end{aligned}
$$

2. $h(7) = -3.304(7) + 100.548 = 77.42$

The model estimates that at an elevation of 7 thousand meters, the boiling point is about 77 degrees Celsius. We use a graphing calculator to verify our work in Problems 1 and 2 (see Fig. 8).

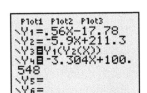

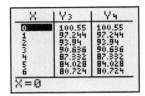

Figure 8 Verify the work

Group Exploration

Composition of two linear functions

1. For each pair of functions given in parts (a), (b), and (c), find an equation of $f \circ g$. Is $f \circ g$ a linear function? If it is, compare the slope of the graph of $f \circ g$ to the product of the slopes of the graphs of f and g.
   a. $f(x) = 2x + 6$ and $g(x) = 4x + 3$
   b. $f(x) = 3x - 2$ and $g(x) = 5x + 4$
   c. $f(x) = m_1 x + b_1$ and $g(x) = m_2 x + b_2$

2. What can you say about the composition of two linear functions? What can you say about the slope of the graph of the composition? [**Hint:** See part (c).]

3. The graphs of two functions are sketched in Fig. 9. Sketch the graph of $f \circ g$. [**Hint:** Find $(f \circ g)(0)$. Then refer to Problem 2.]

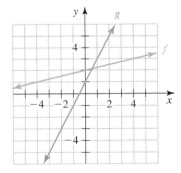

Figure 9 Graphs of two linear functions

Group Exploration

Looking ahead: Inverse function

A company's profit in 2010 was \$5 million. Each year, the profit increases by \$2 million. Let $p = f(t)$ be the profit (in millions of dollars) for the year that is t years after 2010.

1. Find an equation of f. Write the equation in function notation. Also, write the equation with the variables p and t.

2. Use an equation of f to predict when the company will have a profit of \$21 million.

3. In Problem 1, you found an equation with p and t. Solve this equation for t.

4. Substitute 21 for p in the equation you found in Problem 3, and solve for t.

5. Compare your results for Problems 2 and 4.

6. Enter the equation you found in Problem 3 into a graphing calculator to help you complete Table 10.

Table 10 From Profit to Year

Profit (millions of dollars) p	Years since 2010 t
21	
22	
23	
24	
25	

7. In Problems 2 and 4, you used two different methods to find when the company will have a profit of $21 million. If the company wants to know when it might attain 15 different profit levels, which method would be better to use? Explain.

Homework 5.1

For extra help ▶ **MyMathLab®**   ▤ Watch the videos in MyMathLab   Download the MyDashboard App

All of the values of functions g and f are shown in Table 11. For Exercises 1–8, refer to this table.

1. Find $(f \circ g)(0)$.

2. Find $(f \circ g)(3)$.

3. Find $(g \circ f)(0)$.

4. Find $(g \circ f)(3)$.

5. Find $(g \circ g)(1)$.

6. Find $(f \circ f)(4)$.

7. Use a table to describe five input–output pairs of $f \circ g$.

8. Use a table to describe five input–output pairs of $g \circ f$.

Table 11 Input–Output Pairs for g and f (Exercises 1–8)

x	$g(x)$	x	$f(x)$
0	4	0	1
1	0	1	3
2	3	2	0
3	2	3	4
4	1	4	2

All of the values of functions g and f are shown in Table 12. For Exercises 9–16, refer to this table.

9. Find $(f \circ g)(8)$.

10. Find $(f \circ g)(7)$.

11. Find $(g \circ f)(8)$.

12. Find $(g \circ f)(7)$.

13. Find $(f \circ f)(6)$.

14. Find $(g \circ g)(6)$.

15. Use a table to describe five input–output pairs of $g \circ f$.

16. Use a table to describe five input–output pairs of $f \circ g$.

Table 12 Input–Output Pairs for g and f (Exercises 9–16)

x	$g(x)$	x	$f(x)$
5	7	5	8
6	5	6	5
7	6	7	9
8	9	8	6
9	8	9	7

For each pair of functions, find **(a)** $(f \circ g)(2)$; **(b)** $(g \circ f)(2)$.

17. $f(x) = 4x + 1$ and $g(x) = 3x - 6$

18. $f(x) = -x + 6$ and $g(x) = 5 - 4x$

19. $f(x) = 6x - 8$ and $g(x) = \dfrac{8}{x}$

20. $f(x) = 5x - 4$ and $g(x) = \dfrac{6}{x}$

21. $f(x) = 2(3)^x$ and $g(x) = 4x - 5$

22. $f(x) = 3(2)^x$ and $g(x) = 3x - 2$

23. $f(x) = \dfrac{x + 1}{5x - 7}$ and $g(x) = 16 - 3x^2$

24. $f(x) = \dfrac{3x + 6}{x + 2}$ and $g(x) = 2x^2 - 5$

For each pair of functions, find **(a)** an equation of $f \circ g$; **(b)** an equation of $g \circ f$; **(c)** $(f \circ g)(3)$; **(d)** $(g \circ f)(3)$.

25. $f(x) = x + 4$ and $g(x) = 2x$

26. $f(x) = x - 8$ and $g(x) = 4x$

27. $f(x) = 3x - 7$ and $g(x) = 2x - 4$

28. $f(x) = -4x + 5$ and $g(x) = 3x + 1$

29. $f(x) = 2^x$ and $g(x) = x + 2$

30. $f(x) = 3^x$ and $g(x) = 5 - x$

31. $f(x) = x^4$ and $g(x) = x - 1$

32. $f(x) = x^5$ and $g(x) = x - 2$.

For Exercises 33–40, refer to Fig. 10. Find the following.

33. $(f \circ g)(-2)$

34. $(f \circ g)(-6)$

35. $(g \circ f)(5)$

36. $(g \circ f)(-3)$

37. $(f \circ f)(-5)$

38. $(g \circ g)(4)$

39. The y-intercept of the graph of $f \circ g$

40. The y-intercept of the graph of $g \circ g$

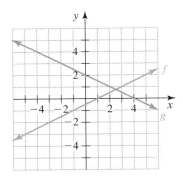

Figure 10 Exercises 33–40

For Exercises 41–46, refer to Fig. 11. Find the following.

41. $(f \circ g)(2)$ **42.** $(f \circ g)(6)$ **43.** $(g \circ f)(2)$

44. $(g \circ f)(1)$ **45.** $(f \circ f)(0)$ **46.** $(g \circ g)(0)$

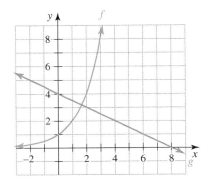

Figure 11 Exercises 41–46

Find equations of f and g such that $h(x) = f(g(x))$.

47. $h(x) = 5^{x-9}$ **48.** $h(x) = 8^{x+3}$

49. $h(x) = 2^x + 6$ **50.** $h(x) = 7^x - 5$

51. $h(x) = (5x - 2)^2$ **52.** $h(x) = (4x + 8)^3$

53. $h(x) = \dfrac{1}{3x - 7}$ **54.** $h(x) = \dfrac{1}{4x + 5}$

55. Let $f(t)$ be the U.S. population (in millions) at t years since 2000. Let $g(p)$ be the weight (in billions of pounds) of french fries consumed annually by p million Americans. What does $(g \circ f)(19) = 9.8$ mean in this situation?

56. Let $f(I)$ be the amount (in thousands of dollars) of federal income tax an American has to pay if their personal income is I thousand dollars. Let $g(t)$ be the median personal income (in thousands of dollars) of an American at t years since 2005. What does $(f \circ g)(12) = 14$ mean in this situation?

57. Let $f(p)$ be the number (in thousands) of Americans who will purchase The Kills album *No Wow* at price p dollars. Let $g(n)$ be the revenue (in millions of dollars) from selling n thousand albums. What does $(g \circ f)(8.99) = 2.3$ mean in this situation?

58. Let $g(t)$ be the number (in thousands) of couches sold by a company in the year that is t years since 2010. Let $f(n)$ be the revenue (in millions of dollars) from selling n thousand couches. What does $(f \circ g)(8) = 5$ mean in this situation?

59. Let $f(y)$ be the number of feet in y yards, and let $g(x)$ be the number of inches in x feet.
   a. Find equations of f and g.

b. Find an equation of $g \circ f$.
   c. Find $(g \circ f)(5)$. What does it mean in this situation?

60. Let $f(Q)$ be the value (in cents) of Q quarters, and let $g(D)$ be the number of quarters worth D dollars.
   a. Find equations of f and g.
   b. Find an equation of $f \circ g$.
   c. Find $(f \circ g)(3)$. What does it mean in this situation?

61. Let $f(M)$ be the number of seconds in M minutes, and let $g(H)$ be the number of minutes in H hours.
   a. Find equations of f and g.
   b. Find an equation of $f \circ g$.
   c. Find $(f \circ g)(3)$. What does it mean in this situation?

62. There are 2.54 centimeters in 1 inch. Let $f(I)$ be the number of centimeters in I inches, and let $g(x)$ be the number of inches in x feet.
   a. Find equations of f and g.
   b. Find an equation of $f \circ g$.
   c. Find $(f \circ g)(4)$. What does it mean in this situation?

63. The gas mileage of a car is 25 miles per gallon. Assume gasoline costs \$4.25 per gallon. Let $f(d)$ be the amount (in gallons) of gasoline used in driving d miles. Let $g(x)$ be the cost (in dollars) of x gallons of gasoline.
   a. Find equations of f and g.
   b. Find an equation of $g \circ f$.
   c. Find $(g \circ f)(300)$. What does it mean in this situation?

64. A U.S. dollar is worth 0.63 British pound. A British pound is worth 132 Japanese yen. Let $f(d)$ be the number of British pounds worth d U.S. dollars. Let $g(p)$ be the number of Japanese yen worth p British pounds.
   a. Find equations of f and g.
   b. Find an equation of $g \circ f$.
   c. Find $(g \circ f)(10)$. What does it mean in this situation?

65. In Exercise 11 of Homework 2.2, you found an equation close to $f(t) = 0.76t - 42.04$, where $f(t)$ is the percentage of births outside marriage at t years since 1900 (see Table 13).

Table 13 Births Outside Marriage

Year	Percent of Births outside Marriage
1970	10.7
1975	14.3
1980	18.4
1985	22.0
1990	28.0
1995	32.2
2000	33.2
2005	36.8
2010	40.8

Source: *National Center for Health Statistics*

a. The percentage $g(p)$ of births from *married* couples is given by $g(p) = 100 - p$, where p is the percentage of births outside of marriage. Explain why this makes sense.
   b. Let $h(t)$ be the percentage of births from *married* couples at t years since 1900. Determine which of the following is true: $h(t) = (f \circ g)(t)$ or $h(t) = (g \circ f)(t)$. Explain.
   c. Find an equation of h.
   d. Find $h(117)$. What does it mean in this situation?
   e. Find t when $h(t) = 52$. What does it mean in this situation?

66. In Exercise 16 of Homework 2.2, you found an equation close to $f(a) = 0.42a - 13.91$, where $f(a)$ is the percentage of Americans at age a years who have been diagnosed with diabetes at some point in their lives (see Table 14).

Table 14 Percentages of Americans Diagnosed with Diabetes, by Age Group

Age Group (years)	Age Used to Represent Age Group (years)	Percent
35–39	37	2
40–44	42	4
45–49	47	5
50–54	52	8
55–59	57	10
60–64	62	13
65–69	67	14

Source: *National Health Interview Survey*

a. The percentage $g(p)$ of Americans who have *never* been diagnosed with diabetes is given by $g(p) = 100 - p$, where p is the percentage of Americans who have been diagnosed with diabetes. Explain why this makes sense.

b. Let $h(a)$ be the percentage of Americans at age a years who have *never* been diagnosed with diabetes. Determine which of the following is true: $h(a) = (f \circ g)(a)$ or $h(a) = (g \circ f)(a)$. Explain.

c. Find an equation of h.

d. Find $h(50)$. What does it mean in this situation?

e. What is the slope of the graph of h? What does it mean in this situation? Explain why it makes sense that the slope is the opposite of the slope of the graph of f.

67. In Exercise 47 of Homework 3.5, you found an equation close to $D(t) = 0.34t + 0.56$, where $D(t)$ is the annual revenue (in billions of dollars) from downloaded music at t years since 2005 (see Table 15).

Table 15 Annual Revenues from Downloaded Music

Year	Annual Revenue (billions of dollars)
2006	0.86
2007	1.23
2008	1.67
2009	1.98
2010	2.20

Source: *Recording Industry Association of America*

a. The value (in *millions* of dollars) $M(b)$ of b billion dollars is given by $M(b) = 1000b$. Explain why this makes sense.

b. Let $h(t)$ be the annual revenue (in *millions* of dollars) from downloaded music at t years since 2005. Determine which of the following is true: $h(t) = (D \circ M)(t)$ or $h(t) = (M \circ D)(t)$. Explain.

c. Find an equation of h.

d. Find $h(-1)$. What does it mean in this situation?

e. What is the t-intercept of the graph of h? What does it mean in this situation? Compare the t-intercept of the graph of h with the t-intercept of the graph of D. Explain why your comparison makes sense.

68. In Exercise 27 of Chapter 2 Review Exercises, you found the equation $C(t) = 37t + 870$, where $C(t)$ is the median compensation (in thousands of dollars) of college presidents in the year that is t years since 2010.

a. The value (in *millions* of dollars) $M(d)$ of d thousand dollars is given by $M(d) = \dfrac{d}{1000}$. Explain why this makes sense.

b. Let $h(t)$ be the median compensation (in *millions* of dollars) of college presidents in the year that is t years since 2010. Determine which of the following is true: $h(t) = (C \circ M)(t)$ or $h(t) = (M \circ C)(t)$. Explain.

c. Find an equation of h.

d. Find $h(7)$. What does it mean in this situation?

e. What is the t-intercept of the graph of h? Compare it with the t-intercept of the graph of C. Explain why your comparison makes sense.

69. In Exercise 83 of Homework 2.3, you found the equation $f(C) = 1.8C + 32$, where $f(C)$ is the Fahrenheit reading that corresponds to the Celsius reading of C degrees (see Table 16).

Table 16 Equivalent Temperature Readings

Celsius Reading (°C)	Fahrenheit Reading (°F)
0	32
20	68
40	104
60	140
80	176
100	212

In Exercise 84 of Homework 2.3, you found the equation $g(F) = 4.3F - 172$, where $g(F)$ is the number of chirps per minute a cricket makes when the temperature is F degrees Fahrenheit (see Table 17).

Table 17 Rates of Cricket Chirping

Temperature (°F)	Rate (number of chirps per minute)
50	43
60	86
70	129
80	172
90	215

a. Let $h(C)$ be the number of chirps per minute a cricket makes when the temperature is C degrees Celsius. Determine which of the following is true: $h(C) = (f \circ g)(C)$ or $h(C) = (g \circ f)(C)$. Explain.

b. Find an equation of h.

c. Estimate the rate crickets chirp when the temperature is 23°C.

d. Estimate the temperature in Celsius degrees at which crickets chirp 200 times per minute.

70. In Exercise 82 of Homework 2.3, you found an equation close to $f(t) = -0.64t + 31.48$, where $f(t)$ is the average gasoline tax (in 2010 dollars) per 1000 miles driven at t years since 1990 (see Table 18).

a. If the average gasoline tax were $15 per 1000 miles driven, how much would a person who drives 12 thousand miles per year pay in gasoline taxes *per year*?

b. Let $g(R)$ be the average gasoline tax (in 2010 dollars) paid per person *per year*, where R is the average gasoline tax (in 2010 dollars) per 1000 miles driven. The average number of miles Americans drive per year is 13.5 thousand miles (Source: *Federal Highway Administration*). Find an equation of g. [**Hint:** Part (a) might suggest what to do.]

c. Let $h(t)$ be the average gasoline tax (in 2010 dollars) paid per person *per year* at t years since 1990. Determine which of the following is true: $h(t) = (f \circ g)(t)$ or $h(t) = (g \circ f)(t)$. Explain.

d. Find an equation of h.

e. Find $h(27)$. What does it mean in this situation?

f. Find t when $h(t) = 175$. What does it mean in this situation?

Table 18 Average Gasoline Taxes per 1000 Miles Driven

Year	Average Gasoline Tax per 1000 Miles Driven (2010 dollars)
1995	28
1998	27
2001	24
2004	23
2007	20
2010	19

Source: *Bureau of Economic Analysis, Bureau of Transportation Statistics, Bureau of Labor Statistics*

Concepts

71. Let $f(x) = x + 8$ and $g(x) = x + 5$. A student tries to find an equation of $f \circ g$:

$$(f \circ g)(x) = (x + 8)(x + 5)$$
$$= x^2 + 13x + 40$$

Describe any errors. Then find an equation of $f \circ g$ correctly.

72. Let $f(x) = 2^x$ and $g(x) = x + 3$. A student tries to find an equation of $f \circ g$:

$$(f \circ g)(x) = f(x + 3)$$
$$= 2^x + 3$$

Describe any errors. Then find an equation of $f \circ g$ correctly.

73. Let $f(x) = 4x - 2$ and $g(x) = -7x + 3$. A student tries to find an equation of $f \circ g$:

$$(f \circ g)(x) = -7(4x - 2) + 3$$
$$= -28x + 14 + 3$$
$$= -28x + 17$$

Describe any errors. Then find an equation of $f \circ g$ correctly.

74. Let $f(x) = 2x - 9$ and $g(x) = -7x + 3$. A student tries to find an equation of $f \circ g$:

$$(f \circ g)(x) = 2(-7x + 3)$$
$$= -14x + 6$$

Describe any errors. Then find an equation of $f \circ g$ correctly.

75. Let $f(x) = 5x - 6$ and $g(x) = 4x - 10$.

a. Find $(f \circ g)(3)$.

b. Find $(g \circ f)(3)$.

c. Are your results from parts (a) and (b) equal?

76. Let $f(x) = 3x + 6$ and $g(x) = 5x + 2$.

a. Find an equation of $f \circ g$.

b. Find an equation of $g \circ f$.

c. Are the functions $f \circ g$ and $g \circ f$ the same? Explain.

77. Let $f(x) = 4x - 7$ and $g(x) = 3x - 2$.

a. Find $g(2)$. Then use the result to find $(f \circ g)(2)$.

b. Find an equation of $f \circ g$.

c. Use your result from part (b) to find $(f \circ g)(2)$. Compare the result with your result from part (a).

78. a. For each part, use the given definitions of f and g to find an equation of $f \circ g$.

   i. $f(x) = x - 3$ and $g(x) = x + 3$

   ii. $f(x) = \dfrac{x}{4}$ and $g(x) = 4x$

   iii. $f(x) = 5x$ and $g(x) = \dfrac{x}{5}$

b. What do you notice about your results of parts (a.i), (a.ii), and (a.iii)? Why does this make sense?

c. Let $g(x) = x - 2$. Find an equation of a function f such that $(f \circ g)(x) = x$.

79. Let $f(x) = 2x$. Find an equation for the function.

a. $f \circ f$

b. $f \circ (f \circ f)$

c. $f \circ (f \circ (f \circ f))$

d. $\underbrace{f \circ (f \circ (f \circ \ldots \circ f) \ldots)}_{n \text{ functions}}$

80. Let $f(x) = x + 2$. Find an equation for the function.

a. $f \circ f$

b. $f \circ (f \circ f)$

c. $f \circ (f \circ (f \circ f))$

d. $\underbrace{f \circ (f \circ (f \circ \ldots \circ f) \ldots)}_{n \text{ functions}}$

81. Give an example of functions f and g such that $f \circ g$ and $g \circ f$ are different functions. Your example should be different than those in the textbook.

82. What is the meaning of a composite function? Give an example.

Related Review

83. Suppose that the function f has domain set A and range set B and that the function g has domain set B and range set C.

a. Explain why $g \circ f$ is a function. [**Hint:** Recall that a function is a relation in which each input leads to exactly one output.]

b. What are the domain and range of $g \circ f$?

84. Table 19 lists all of the input–output pairs of functions f and g. Find the domain and range of $f \circ g$. [**Hint:** Recall that for $(f \circ g)(x)$ to be defined, x must be in the domain of g and $g(x)$ must be in the domain of f.]

Table 19 Input–Output Pairs for g and f (Exercise 84)

x	$g(x)$	x	$f(x)$
0	10	3	9
1	9	4	10
2	8	5	11
3	7	6	12
4	6	7	13

Expressions, Equations, Functions, and Graphs

Perform the indicated instruction. Then use words such as linear, exponential, function, one variable, *and* two variables *to describe the expression, equation, or system.*

85. Graph $f(x) = 2(3)^x$ by hand.

86. Find an approximate equation $y = ab^x$ of an exponential curve that contains the points $(4, 15)$ and $(9, 12)$. Round a and b to the second decimal place.

87. Graph $f(x) = 2 + 3x$ by hand.

88. Find an equation of a line that contains the points $(4, 15)$ and $(9, 12)$.

▼5.2 Inverse Functions

Objectives

» Know the meaning of *inverse of a function, invertible function,* and *one-to-one function.*

» Know the *reflection property of inverse functions.*

» Graph the inverse of a function.

» Find an equation of the inverse of a model.

» Find an equation of the inverse of a function that is not a model.

In this section, we will study a type of function that has a special relationship to a given function. It is called the *inverse* of a function. We will begin the section with an example that will allow us to develop a definition of the inverse of a function. Then we will describe inverses of functions by using first tables, then graphs, and finally equations.

Definition of an Inverse of a Function

Although the United States and several other countries use the Fahrenheit scale (in °F) to measure temperature, most countries use the Celsius scale (in °C). A comparison of the two scales is shown in Table 20.

If an American visiting Europe hears the local temperature will reach 20°C, it would be helpful to be able to convert 20°C to 68°F. There is a function g that converts Celsius inputs to Fahrenheit outputs (see Fig. 12). We let C be the Celsius temperature and F be the Fahrenheit temperature.

Table 20 Celsius and Fahrenheit Equivalent Readings

Celsius (°C)	Fahrenheit (°F)
0	32
20	68
40	104
60	140
80	176
100	212

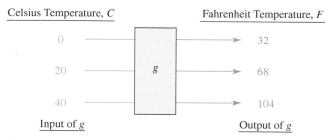

Figure 12 The function g converts Celsius temperatures to Fahrenheit temperatures

If a European visiting the United States hears the local temperature will reach 68°F, it would be helpful to be able to convert 68°F to 20°C. If we reverse the arrows of Fig. 12, we have an input–output diagram of a new relation (see Fig. 13). For each Fahrenheit temperature, there is exactly one Celsius temperature, so the new relation is also a function. We call this function the *inverse* of g and show it as "g^{-1}" (read "g-inverse").

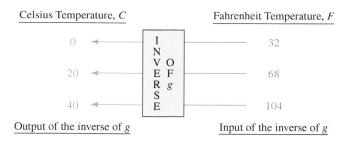

Figure 13 The inverse of g converts Fahrenheit temperatures back to Celsius temperatures

There are two key observations we can make about g^{-1}:

1. g^{-1} sends outputs of g to inputs of g. For example, g sends the input 0 to the output 32 and g^{-1} sends 32 to 0 (see Figs. 12 and 13). Using symbols, we write

$$g(0) = 32 \quad \text{and} \quad g^{-1}(32) = 0$$

We say these two statements are **equivalent,** which means one statement implies the other and vice versa.

2. g^{-1} undoes g. For example, g sends 0 to 32 and g^{-1} undoes this action by sending 32 *back* to 0 (see Fig. 14).

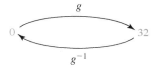

Figure 14 g^{-1} undoes g

The **inverse of a function** f is a relation that sends b to a if $f(a) = b$. The inverse of a function is not necessarily a function. If the inverse of a function f is also a function, we say f is **invertible** and use "f^{-1}" as a name for the inverse of f. We say f^{-1} is the **inverse function of** f.

> **Property of an Inverse Function**
>
> For an invertible function f, the following statements are equivalent:
> $$f(a) = b \qquad \text{and} \qquad f^{-1}(b) = a$$
> In words: If f sends a to b, then f^{-1} sends b to a. If f^{-1} sends b to a, then f sends a to b.

▶ **Example 1**   Evaluating an Inverse Function

Let f be an invertible function where $f(2) = 5$. Find $f^{-1}(5)$.

Solution

Since f sends 2 to 5, it follows that f^{-1} sends 5 back to 2. So, $f^{-1}(5) = 2$.
▶

Table 21 Input–Output Values of f

x	$f(x)$
0	1
1	3
2	9
3	27
4	81

▶ **Example 2**   Evaluating f and f^{-1}

Some values of an invertible function f are shown in Table 21. Find the following.
1. $f(3)$
2. $f^{-1}(9)$

Solution
1. $f(3) = 27$, because f sends 3 to 27.
2. Since f sends 2 to 9, we conclude that f^{-1} sends 9 back to 2. Therefore, $f^{-1}(9) = 2$.
▶

WARNING

The -1 in "$f^{-1}(x)$" is *not* an exponent. It is part of the function notation "f^{-1}"— which stands for the inverse of the function f. Here, we simplify 3^{-1} and use the values of f shown in Table 21 to find $f^{-1}(3)$:

$$3^{-1} = \frac{1}{3} \Big\} \quad \text{"-1" is an exponent: Use } b^{-n} = \frac{1}{b^n}$$

$$f^{-1}(3) = 1 \Big\} \quad \begin{array}{l}\text{"f^{-1}" stands for the inverse of f;}\\ \text{f sends 1 to 3, so f^{-1} sends 3 back to 1.}\end{array}$$

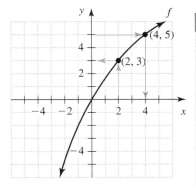

Figure 15 Graph of an invertible function f

▶ **Example 3**   Evaluating f and f^{-1}

The graph of an invertible function f is shown in Fig. 15.
1. Find $f(2)$.
2. Find $f^{-1}(5)$.

Solution
1. The blue arrows in Fig. 15 show that f sends 2 to 3. So, $f(2) = 3$.
2. The function f sends 4 to 5. So, f^{-1} sends 5 back to 4 (see the red arrows). Therefore, $f^{-1}(5) = 4$.

All linear functions with nonzero slope and all exponential functions are invertible. (We will see why at the end of this section.) Therefore, we can use the notation f^{-1} whenever we describe the inverse of either of these two types of functions.
▶

Table 22 Input–Output Values of *f*

x	f(x)
0	16
1	8
2	4
3	2
4	1

Table 23 Input–Output Values of *f*$^{-1}$

x	f^{-1}(x)
1	4
2	3
4	2
8	1
16	0

Figure 16 *g* sends values of *C* to values of *F*

Figure 17 *g*$^{-1}$ sends values of *F* to values of *C*

▶ **Example 4**   Finding Input–Output Values of an Inverse Function

Let $f(x) = 16\left(\dfrac{1}{2}\right)^x$.

1. Find five input–output values of f^{-1}.

2. Find $f^{-1}(8)$.

Solution

1. We begin by finding input–output values of f (see Table 22). Since f^{-1} sends outputs of f to inputs of f, we conclude that f^{-1} sends 16 to 0, 8 to 1, 4 to 2, 2 to 3, and 1 to 4. We list these results, from the smallest to the largest input, in Table 23.

2. From Table 23, we see that f^{-1} sends the input 8 to the output 1, so $f^{-1}(8) = 1$.

Let's return to the function g that converts Celsius temperatures to Fahrenheit temperatures. Consider the input–output diagrams of g and g^{-1} in Figs. 16 and 17. We've noted that to find the inverse of g, we reverse the arrow for g. But also notice that if we reverse the arrow for g^{-1}, we get the arrow for g. This suggests that the inverse of g^{-1} is g, which is true. So, g and g^{-1} are inverses of each other.

▶ **f and f^{-1} Are Inverses of Each Other**

If f is an invertible function, then

- f^{-1} is invertible and
- f and f^{-1} are inverses of each other.

Graphing Inverse Functions

Next, we discuss how to graph the inverse of an invertible function.

▶ **Example 5**   Comparing the Graphs of a Function and Its Inverse

Sketch the graphs of $f(x) = 2^x$, f^{-1}, and $y = x$ on the same set of axes.

Solution

We list some input–output values of f and f^{-1} in Tables 24 and 25.

Table 24 Input–Output Pairs for *f*

x	f(x)
−3	$\frac{1}{8}$
−2	$\frac{1}{4}$
−1	$\frac{1}{2}$
0	1
1	2
2	4

Table 25 Input–Output Pairs for *f*$^{-1}$

x	f^{-1}(x)
$\frac{1}{8}$	−3
$\frac{1}{4}$	−2
$\frac{1}{2}$	−1
1	0
2	1
4	2

From Tables 24 and 25, we see that if a point (a, b) is on the graph of f, then the point (b, a) is on the graph of f^{-1}. This observation will lead us to a key step in graphing inverses in future problems.

Next, we plot the input–output pairs of f with blue dots, plot the input–output pairs of f^{-1} with red dots, and sketch the line $y = x$ (see Fig. 18).

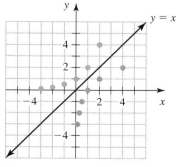

Figure 18 Some points of the graph of *f* (in blue), some points of the graph of *f*$^{-1}$ (in red), and the line *y* = *x*

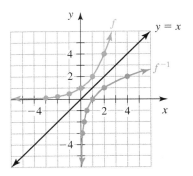

Figure 19 The graphs of f, f^{-1}, and $y = x$

If we were to draw the blue dots in wet ink and fold the paper along the line $y = x$, the ink would make dots where the red dots are. We say the red dots are the *reflection* of the blue dots across the line $y = x$.

In Fig. 19, we sketch a graph of $f(x) = 2^x$ with a blue exponential curve. By reflecting all the blue points on the graph of f across the line $y = x$, we obtain the red graph of f^{-1}. The graph of f^{-1} is the reflection of the graph of $f(x) = 2^x$ across the line $y = x$.

> **Reflection Property of Inverse Functions**
>
> For an invertible function f, the graph of f^{-1} is the reflection of the graph of f across the line $y = x$.

In Example 5, we saw that if a point (a, b) is on the graph of f, then the point (b, a) is on the graph of the inverse of f.

> **Graphing an Inverse Function**
>
> For an invertible function f, we sketch the graph of f^{-1} by the following steps:
>
> 1. Sketch the graph of f.
> 2. Choose several points that lie on the graph of f.
> 3. For each point (a, b) chosen in step 2, plot the point (b, a).
> 4. Sketch the curve that contains the points plotted in step 3.

> **Example 6**   Graphing an Inverse Function

Let $f(x) = \dfrac{1}{3}x - 1$. Sketch the graph of f, f^{-1}, and $y = x$ on the same set of axes.

Solution

We apply the four steps to graph the inverse function:

Step 1: Sketch the graph of f: See Fig. 20.

Step 2: Choose several points that lie on the graph of f: $(-6, -3), (-3, -2), (0, -1),$ $(3, 0),$ and $(6, 1)$.

Step 3: For each point (a, b) chosen in step 2, plot the point (b, a): We plot $(-3, -6),$ $(-2, -3), (-1, 0), (0, 3),$ and $(1, 6)$ in Fig. 21.

Step 4: Sketch the curve that contains the points plotted in step 3: The points from step 3 lie on a line. See Fig. 21.

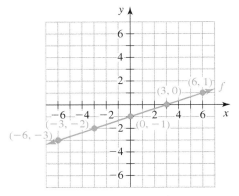

Figure 20 Graph of $f(x) = \dfrac{1}{3}x - 1$

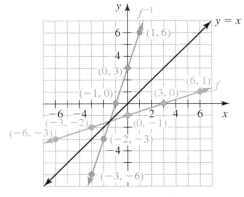

Figure 21 Graphs of $f(x) = \dfrac{1}{3}x - 1, y = x,$ and f^{-1}

Finding an Equation of the Inverse of a Model

So far, we have described inverse functions by using tables and graphs. We now describe them by using equations. To begin, we will use a three-step process to find an equation of the inverse of a model.

Table 26 Numbers of Worldwide E-Mails Sent Daily

Year	Number of E-Mails Sent Daily (billions)
2000	15
2002	35
2004	65
2006	88
2007	97

Source: *IDC*

Figure 22 *f* sends values of *t* to values of *n*

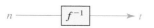

Figure 23 f^{-1} sends values of *n* to values of *t*

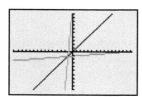

Figure 24 Check that the graph of f^{-1} is the reflection of *f* across the line $y = x$

▶ **Example 7** Finding an Equation of the Inverse of a Model

The numbers (in billions) of worldwide e-mail messages sent daily are shown in Table 26 for various years. Let $n = f(t)$ be the number (in billions) of e-mails sent daily at t years since 2000. A reasonable model is

$$f(t) = 12.1t + 14$$

1. Find an equation of f^{-1}.
2. Find $f(15)$. What does it mean in this situation?
3. Find $f^{-1}(210)$. What does it mean in this situation?
4. What is the slope of f? What does it mean in this situation?
5. What is the slope of f^{-1}? What does it mean in this situation?

Solution

1. Since f sends values of t to values of n, f^{-1} sends values of n to t (see Figs. 22 and 23). To find an equation of f^{-1}, we want to write t in terms of n. Here are three steps to follow to find an equation of f^{-1}:

   Step 1: We replace $f(t)$ with n: $n = 12.1t + 14$.

   Step 2: We solve the equation for t:

   $$n = 12.1t + 14 \quad \text{\textit{Equation from step 1}}$$
   $$n - 14 = 12.1t \quad \text{\textit{Subtract 14 from both sides.}}$$
   $$\frac{n}{12.1} - \frac{14}{12.1} = t \quad \text{\textit{Divide both sides by 12.1.}}$$

   An approximate equation is $t = 0.083n - 1.16$.

   Step 3: Since f^{-1} sends values of n to values of t, we have $f^{-1}(n) = t$. So, we can substitute $f^{-1}(n)$ for t in the equation $t = 0.083n - 1.16$:

   $$f^{-1}(n) = 0.083n - 1.16$$

   To verify our work, we use ZStandard followed by ZSquare to check that the graph of f^{-1} is the reflection of the graph of f across the line $y = x$ (see Fig. 24).

2. $f(15) = 12.1(15) + 14 = 195.5$. Since f sends values of t to values of n, it follows that $n = 195.5$ when $t = 15$. According to the model f, 195.5 billion e-mails will be sent daily in 2015.

3. $f^{-1}(210) = 0.083(210) - 1.16 = 16.27$. Since f^{-1} sends values of n to values of t, it follows that $t = 16.27$ when $n = 210$. According to the model f^{-1}, 210 billion e-mails will be sent daily in 2016.

4. The slope of the graph of $f(t) = 12.1t + 14$ is 12.1. This means the rate of change of n with respect to t is 12.1. According to the model f, the number of e-mails sent daily increases by 12.1 billion e-mails each year.

5. The slope of the graph of $f^{-1}(n) = 0.083n - 1.16$ is 0.083. This means the rate of change of t with respect to n is 0.083. According to the model f^{-1}, 0.083 year passes each time the number of e-mails sent daily increases by 1 billion e-mails.

In Example 7, we performed three steps to find an equation of the inverse of a model.

> **Three-Step Process for Finding the Inverse of a Model**
>
> To find the inverse of an invertible *model f*, where $p = f(t)$,
>
> 1. Replace $f(t)$ with p.
> 2. Solve for t.
> 3. Replace t with $f^{-1}(p)$.

Finding an Equation of the Inverse of a Function That Is Not a Model

We can take three similar steps, followed by one more step, to find an equation of the inverse of a function that is *not* a model.

▶ **Example 8**   Finding the Inverse of a Function That Is Not a Model

Find the inverse of $f(x) = 2x - 3$.

Solution

Step 1: Substitute y for $f(x)$: $y = 2x - 3$.

Step 2: Solve for x:

$$y = 2x - 3 \qquad \textit{Equation from step 1}$$
$$y + 3 = 2x \qquad \textit{Add 3 to both sides.}$$
$$2x = y + 3 \qquad \textit{If } a = b, \textit{ then } b = a.$$
$$\frac{2x}{2} = \frac{y}{2} + \frac{3}{2} \qquad \textit{Divide both sides by 2.}$$
$$x = \frac{1}{2}y + \frac{3}{2} \qquad \textit{Simplify.}$$

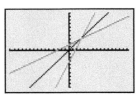

Step 3: Replace x with $f^{-1}(y)$: $f^{-1}(y) = \frac{1}{2}y + \frac{3}{2}$.

Step 4: When a function is not a model, we usually want the input variable to be x. So, we rewrite the equation $f^{-1}(y) = \frac{1}{2}y + \frac{3}{2}$ in terms of x:

$$f^{-1}(x) = \frac{1}{2}x + \frac{3}{2}$$

Figure 25 Check that the graph of f^{-1} is the reflection of f across the line $y = x$

To verify our work, we use ZStandard followed by ZSquare to check that the graph of f^{-1} is the reflection of the graph of f across the line $y = x$ (see Fig. 25).

▶

When finding the inverse of a function f, we must keep in mind whether f is a model. If the function is not a model, we perform all four steps as shown in Example 8. However, if the function is a model, we perform only the first three steps, so the variables retain their original meaning.

> ▶ **Four-Step Process for Finding the Inverse of a Function That Is Not a Model**
>
> Let f be an invertible function that is *not* a model. To find the inverse of f, where $y = f(x)$,
>
> 1. Replace $f(x)$ with y.
> 2. Solve for x.
> 3. Replace x with $f^{-1}(y)$.
> 4. Write the equation of f^{-1} in terms of x.

So far, we have used tables and graphs to describe the inverse of an exponential function, such as $f(x) = 2^x$. Can we find an equation of the inverse of $f(x) = 2^x$? To find such an equation, we would have to solve the equation $y = 2^x$ for x. We cannot do this by using familiar operations such as adding or subtracting. Nonetheless, the inverse of an exponential function is a powerful tool that we will continue to explore throughout the rest of this chapter.

Composing an Invertible Function with Its Inverse

Let's return one last time to the function g that converts Celsius temperatures to Fahrenheit temperatures. In Fig. 26, we show the input–output action of g followed by the input–output action of g^{-1}.

Figure 26 Action of g followed by action of g^{-1}

Note that the final output, C, is the same as the original input. This means $(g^{-1} \circ g)(C) = C$, which is a symbolic way of saying g^{-1} undoes g.

In Fig. 27, we show the input–output action of g^{-1} followed by the input–output action of g.

Figure 27 Action of g^{-1} followed by action of g

Note that the final output, F, is the same as the original input. This means $(g \circ g^{-1})(F) = F$, which is a symbolic way of saying g undoes g^{-1}.

> ## Composing an Invertible Function with Its Inverse
>
> If f is an invertible function, then
>
> - $(f^{-1} \circ f)(x) = x$, where x is in the domain of f, and
> - $(f \circ f^{-1})(x) = x$, where x is in the domain of f^{-1}.

▶ **Example 9** Composing an Invertible Function with Its Inverse

In Example 8, we found that the inverse of $f(x) = 2x - 3$ is the function $f^{-1}(x) = \dfrac{1}{2}x + \dfrac{3}{2}$. Show that the following are true.

1. $(f^{-1} \circ f)(x) = x$
2. $(f \circ f^{-1})(x) = x$

Solution

1.
$$
\begin{aligned}
(f^{-1} \circ f)(x) &= f^{-1}(f(x)) && \text{\textit{Definition of composite function}} \\
&= f^{-1}(2x - 3) && \text{\textit{Substitute } 2x - 3 \text{ for } f(x).} \\
&= \frac{1}{2}(2x - 3) + \frac{3}{2} && \text{\textit{Substitute } 2x - 3 \text{ for } x \text{ in } f^{-1}(x) = \frac{1}{2}x + \frac{3}{2}.} \\
&= \frac{1}{2} \cdot 2x - \frac{1}{2} \cdot 3 + \frac{3}{2} && \text{\textit{Distributive law}} \\
&= x - \frac{3}{2} + \frac{3}{2} && \text{\textit{Multiply; simplify.}} \\
&= x && \text{\textit{Combine like terms.}}
\end{aligned}
$$

2. $(f \circ f^{-1})(x) = f(f^{-1}(x))$ *Definition of composite function*

$$= f\left(\frac{1}{2}x + \frac{3}{2}\right) \quad \textit{Substitute } \frac{1}{2}x + \frac{3}{2} \textit{ for } f^{-1}(x).$$

$$= 2\left(\frac{1}{2}x + \frac{3}{2}\right) - 3 \quad \textit{Substitute } \frac{1}{2}x + \frac{3}{2} \textit{ for } x \textit{ in } f(x) = 2x - 3.$$

$$= 2 \cdot \frac{1}{2}x + 2 \cdot \frac{3}{2} - 3 \quad \textit{Distributive law}$$

$$= x + 3 - 3 \quad \textit{Multiply; simplify.}$$

$$= x \quad \textit{Combine like terms.}$$

After finding the inverse of an invertible function f, we can verify our work by one of two ways. We can check that the graph of f^{-1} is the reflection of the graph of f across the line $y = x$, or we can check that $(f^{-1} \circ f)(x) = x$ and that $(f \circ f^{-1})(x) = x$.

One-to-One Functions

Figure 28 f sends both -2 and 2 to 4

Figure 29 The inverse of f sends 4 to both -2 and 2

We said earlier in this section that the inverse of a function is not necessarily a function. Consider $f(x) = x^2$. Note that $f(-2) = 4$ and $f(2) = 4$. So, f sends both of the inputs -2 and 2 to the output 4 (see Fig. 28). Therefore, the inverse of f sends the input 4 to the *two* outputs -2 and 2 (see Fig. 29). Thus, the inverse of f is not a function. Note that the inverse of f is not a function because an output of f originates from more than one input of f.

If each output of a function originates from exactly one input, we say the function is **one-to-one. A one-to-one function is invertible.** All exponential functions are one-to-one and, hence, invertible. To see why, recall that all exponential functions are either increasing functions or decreasing functions. If f is an increasing exponential function, then $a < b$ implies that $f(a) < f(b)$. See Fig. 30. If f is a decreasing exponential function, then $a < b$ implies that $f(a) > f(b)$. See Fig. 31. Both implications show that if two inputs a and b are different, then their outputs $f(a)$ and $f(b)$ are different, too. It follows that each output originates from exactly one input.

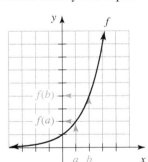

Figure 30 Graph of an increasing exponential function

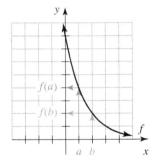

Figure 31 Graph of a decreasing exponential function

Using similar approaches, we could show that all linear functions with nonzero slope are one-to-one and, hence, invertible. Or we could show that such a function is invertible by finding the equation of the inverse of the function; you are asked to do this in Exercise 99.

Group Exploration

Looking ahead: A logarithm is an exponent

1. a. Solve $2^x = 16$. **b.** Solve $2^x = 32$.
   c. Approximate the solution of $2^x = 24$ by using trial and error. Your result should be correct up to four decimal places. [**Hint:** Parts (a) and (b) should suggest a reasonable first guess. Then you can use calculator tables to speed up the trial-and-error process.]

2. Approximate the solution of $3^x = 15$ by using trial and error. We call the solution $\log_3(15)$, where *log* is shorthand for *logarithm*.

3. Approximate the solution of $10^x = 500$. We call the solution $\log_{10}(500)$.

▶ Tips for Success   **Review Material**

At various times throughout this course, you can improve your understanding of algebra by reviewing material you have learned so far. Re-solve problems, redo explorations, and consider again key points from previous chapters.

Homework 5.2

For extra help ▶   MyMathLab°   Watch the videos in MyMathLab   Download the MyDashboard App

1. Let f be an invertible function where $f(4) = 7$. Find $f^{-1}(7)$.
2. Let g be an invertible function where $g^{-1}(3) = 2$. Find $g(2)$.

Some values of an invertible function f are given in Table 27. For Exercises 3–10, refer to this table.

3. Find $f(4)$.   4. Find $f(2)$.
5. Find $f^{-1}(4)$.   6. Find $f^{-1}(2)$.
7. Use a table to describe five input–output values of f^{-1}.
8. Find x when $f(x) = 2$.
9. Find $f^{-1}(f(6))$.
10. Find $f(f^{-1}(6))$.

Table 27 Values of f
(Exercises 3–10)

x	$f(x)$
2	10
3	8
4	6
5	4
6	2

Some values of an invertible function g are given in Table 28. For Exercises 11–18, refer to this table.

11. Find $g(2)$.   12. Find $g(6)$.
13. Find $g^{-1}(2)$.   14. Find $g^{-1}(6)$.
15. Use a table to describe six input–output values of g^{-1}.
16. Find x when $g(x) = 6$.
17. Find $g^{-1}(g(4))$.
18. Find $g(g^{-1}(486))$.

Table 28 Values of g
(Exercises 11–18)

x	$g(x)$
1	2
2	6
3	18
4	54
5	162
6	486

19. Complete Table 29 by using the table of values of f to complete the table of values of f^{-1}.

Table 29 Finding Values of f^{-1}
(Exercise 19)

x	$f(x)$	x	$f^{-1}(x)$
1	34	4	
2	28	10	
3	22	16	
4	16	22	
5	10	28	
6	4	34	

20. Complete Table 30 by using the table of values of f to complete the table of values of f^{-1}.

Table 30 Finding Values of f^{-1}
(Exercise 20)

x	$f(x)$	x	$f^{-1}(x)$
2	5	2	
3	2	3	
4	3	4	
5	6	5	
6	4	6	

Let $f(x) = 3(2)^x$.

21. Use a table to describe five input–output values of f^{-1}.
22. Find $f(2)$.   23. Find $f(3)$.
24. Find $f^{-1}(24)$.   25. Find $f^{-1}(3)$.
26. Find x when $f(x) = 6$.

Graph the given function, its inverse, and $y = x$ by hand on the same set of axes. Label each graph as f, f^{-1}, or $y = x$.

27. $f(x) = 3(2)^x$ 28. $f(x) = 2(3)^x$
29. $f(x) = 3^x$ 30. $f(x) = 4^x$
31. $f(x) = 2x$ 32. $f(x) = 3x$
33. $f(x) = 3x - 2$ 34. $f(x) = 2x - 5$
35. $f(x) = \frac{1}{2}x + 1$ 36. $f(x) = \frac{2}{3}x - 1$
37. $f(x) = 4\left(\frac{1}{2}\right)^x$ 38. $f(x) = 6\left(\frac{1}{3}\right)^x$
39. $f(x) = \left(\frac{1}{3}\right)^x$ 40. $f(x) = \left(\frac{1}{2}\right)^x$

For Exercises 41–46, refer to Fig. 32, which shows the graph of an invertible function g.

41. Find $g(2)$.

42. Find $g(-1)$.

43. Find $g^{-1}(2)$.

44. Find $g^{-1}(-3)$.

45. Find $g^{-1}(0)$.

46. Graph g^{-1} by hand.

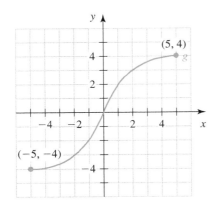

Figure 32 Exercises 41–46

For Exercises 47–52, refer to Fig. 33, which shows the graph of an invertible function f.

47. Find $f(2)$.

48. Find $f(-1)$.

49. Find $f^{-1}(4)$.

50. Find $f^{-1}(0)$.

51. Graph f^{-1} by hand.

52. Find $f^{-1}(1)$.

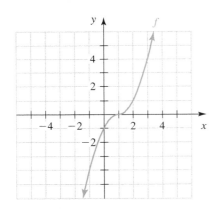

Figure 33 Exercises 47–52

53. In Exercise 11 of Homework 2.2, you found an equation close to $p = f(t) = 0.76t - 42.04$ that models the percentage p of births outside marriage at t years since 1900 (see Table 31).

Table 31 Births outside Marriage

Year	Percent
1970	10.7
1975	14.3
1980	18.4
1985	22.0
1990	28.0
1995	32.2
2000	33.2
2005	36.8
2010	40.8

Source: *National Center for Health Statistics*

a. Find an equation of f^{-1}.

b. Find $f(100)$. What does it mean in this situation?

c. Find $f^{-1}(100)$. What does it mean in this situation?

d. What is the slope of f^{-1}? What does it mean in this situation?

54. In Exercise 34 of Homework 2.4, you found an equation close to $p = f(t) = 0.074t + 0.86$ that models Nevada's population p (in millions) at t years since 1985 (see Table 32).

Table 32 Nevada's Population

Year	Population (millions)
1986	1.0
1990	1.2
1995	1.5
2000	2.0
2005	2.4
2010	2.7

Source: *U.S. Census Bureau*

a. Find an equation of f^{-1}.

b. Find $f(3)$. What does it mean in this situation?

c. Find $f^{-1}(3)$. What does it mean in this situation?

d. What is the slope of f^{-1}? What does it mean in this situation?

55. The percentages of households with two or more working computers are shown in Table 33 for various years.

Table 33 Percentages of Households with Two or More Working Computers

Year	Percent
2004	26
2005	30
2006	32
2007	37
2008	37
2009	42
2010	45

Source: *Edison Research and Arbitron*

Let $p = f(t)$ be the percentage of households with two or more working computers at t years since 2000.

a. Use a graphing calculator to draw a scattergram of the data. Can the data be modeled better by using a linear or an exponential function? Explain.

b. Find an equation of f.

c. Find an equation of f^{-1}.

d. Use f to predict when 69% of households will have two or more working computers.

e. Now use f^{-1} to predict when 69% of households will have two or more working computers.

f. Compare your results in parts (d) and (e).

56. The numbers of cremations in the United States are shown in Table 34 for various years. Let $p = f(t)$ be the percentage of bodies that are cremated in the year that is t years since 1990.

a. Use a graphing calculator to draw a scattergram of the data. Can the data be modeled better by using a linear or an exponential function? Explain.

Table 34 Percentages of Bodies That Are Cremated

Year	Percent
1995	19.2
1998	24.1
2000	26.2
2003	29.5
2005	32.3
2007	34.3
2010	40.6

Source: *Cremation Association of North America*

b. Find an equation of *f.*
c. Find an equation of f^{-1}.
d. Use *f* to predict in which year half of people who die will be cremated.
e. Now use f^{-1} to predict in which year half of people who die will be cremated.
f. Compare your results from parts (d) and (e).

57. Credit scores measure financial responsibility. Credit scores of Americans are shown in Table 35 for various age groups.

Table 35 Credit Scores of Americans

Age Group (years)	Age Used to Represent Age Group (years)	Average Credit Score (points)
18–29	23.5	637
30–39	34.5	654
40–49	44.5	675
50–59	54.5	697
60–69	64.5	722
70 or more	75	747

Source: *Experian*

Let $c = f(a)$ be the average credit score (in points) of adults at *a* years of age.

a. Use a graphing calculator to draw a scattergram of the data. Can the data be modeled better by using a linear or an exponential function? Explain.
b. Find a linear equation of *f.*
c. Find an equation of f^{-1}.
d. The average credit score of all adults is 677 points. Use f^{-1} to estimate the (single) age of adults whose average credit score is 677 points.
e. The highest possible score is 830 points. Use f^{-1} to estimate the age of adults whose average credit score is 830 points. (The oldest American ever was Sarah Knauss, who died at age 119 years.)
f. What is the slope of the graph of f^{-1}? What does it mean in this situation?

58. The percentages of Americans who went to the movies at least once in the past year are shown in Table 36 for various age groups.

Table 36 Percentages of Americans Who Go to the Movies

Age Group (years)	Age Used to Represent Age Group (years)	Percent
18–24	21.0	88
25–34	29.5	79
35–44	39.5	73
45–54	49.5	65
55–64	59.5	46
65–74	69.5	38
over 74	80	28

Source: *U.S. National Endowment for the Arts*

Let $p = f(a)$ be the percentage of Americans at age *a* years who go to the movies.

a. Use a graphing calculator to draw a scattergram of the data. Can the data be modeled better by using a linear or an exponential function? Explain.
b. Find an equation of *f.*
c. Find an equation of f^{-1}.
d. Use f^{-1} to estimate at what age half of Americans go to the movies.
e. What is the slope of the graph of f^{-1}? What does it mean in this situation?

Find the inverse of the given function. Use a graphing calculator to verify your work by graphing f, f^{-1}, and y = x on the same set of axes.

59. $f(x) = x + 8$ **60.** $f(x) = x - 6$

61. $f(x) = -4x$ **62.** $f(x) = 5x$

63. $f(x) = \dfrac{x}{7}$ **64.** $f(x) = -\dfrac{x}{2}$

65. $f(x) = -6x - 2$ **66.** $f(x) = 3x - 8$

67. $f(x) = 0.4x - 7.9$ **68.** $f(x) = -6.25x + 12.5$

69. $f(x) = \dfrac{7}{3}x + 1$ **70.** $f(x) = \dfrac{8}{5}x + 4$

71. $f(x) = -\dfrac{5}{6}x - 3$ **72.** $f(x) = -\dfrac{2}{5}x - 8$

73. $f(x) = \dfrac{6x - 2}{5}$ **74.** $f(x) = \dfrac{2x - 7}{4}$

75. $f(x) = 7 - 8(x + 1)$ **76.** $f(x) = 2(x - 1) + 5$

77. $f(x) = x$ **78.** $f(x) = -x$

79. $f(x) = x^3$ **80.** $f(x) = x^5$

*For Exercises 81–86, show that (**a**) $(f^{-1} \circ f)(x) = x$; (**b**) $(f \circ f^{-1})(x) = x$.*

81. $f(x) = x + 7$ and $f^{-1}(x) = x - 7$

82. $f(x) = 4x$ and $f^{-1}(x) = \dfrac{1}{4}x$

83. $f(x) = 2x - 5$ and $f^{-1}(x) = \dfrac{1}{2}x + \dfrac{5}{2}$

84. $f(x) = 4x + 1$ and $f^{-1}(x) = \dfrac{1}{4}x - \dfrac{1}{4}$

85. $f(x) = \dfrac{3}{4}x - 2$ and $f^{-1}(x) = \dfrac{4}{3}x + \dfrac{8}{3}$

86. $f(x) = \dfrac{7}{6}x + 3$ and $f^{-1}(x) = \dfrac{6}{7}x - \dfrac{18}{7}$

87. Let $f(x) = 5x - 9$.
   a. Find an equation of f^{-1}.
   b. Find $f(4)$.
   c. Find $f^{-1}(4)$.

88. Let $g(x) = \dfrac{3}{5}x - 1$.
   a. Find an equation of g^{-1}.
   b. Find $g(20)$.
   c. Find $g^{-1}(20)$.

89. Recall that we can describe some or all of the input–output pairs of a function by means of an equation, a graph, a table, or words. Let $f(x) = 3x - 5$.
   a. Describe the input–output pairs of f^{-1} by using an equation.
   b. Describe five input–output pairs of f^{-1} by using a table.
   c. Describe the input–output pairs of f^{-1} by using a graph.
   d. Describe the input–output pairs of f^{-1} by using words.

90. Recall that we can describe some or all of the input–output pairs of a function by means of an equation, a graph, a table, or words. Let $g(x) = \dfrac{4}{5}x + 2$.
   a. Describe the input–output pairs of g^{-1} by using an equation.
   b. Describe five input–output pairs of g^{-1} by using a table.
   c. Describe the input–output pairs of g^{-1} by using a graph.
   d. Describe the input–output pairs of g^{-1} by using words.

Concepts

91. A student says that $g(x) = \dfrac{x}{2}$ is the inverse of the function $f(x) = 2^x$. Is the student correct? Explain.

92. A student tries to show $f^{-1}(f(x)) = x$ for $f(x) = x + 3$:

$$f^{-1}(f(x)) = \frac{1}{f}(f(x)) = x$$

Describe any errors. Then do the work correctly.

93. Explain why it makes sense that the function $g(x) = x - 5$ is the inverse of the function $f(x) = x + 5$.

94. Explain why it makes sense that the function $g(x) = \dfrac{x}{3}$ is the inverse of the function $f(x) = 3x$.

95. Explain why it makes sense that if a function g is the inverse of an invertible function f, then f is the inverse function of g.

96. If a function f is invertible, then $(f^{-1} \circ f)(x) = x$ and $(f \circ f^{-1})(x) = x$. Explain why this makes sense.

97. Is the function $f(x) = 3$ one-to-one? Is it invertible? Explain.

98. Is the function $f(x) = x^4$ one-to-one? Is it invertible? Explain.

99. In this exercise, you will show that all linear functions with nonzero slope are invertible.
   a. Let $f(x) = mx + b$, where $m \neq 0$. Find an equation of the inverse of f.
   b. Explain why your work in part (a) shows that the inverse of f is a function.

100. Explain how to find the inverse of an invertible linear function. Also, explain the meaning of an inverse function. (See page 4 for guidelines on writing a good response.)

Related Review

101. Let $f(x) = 2x - 3$ and $g(x) = \dfrac{1}{2}x + 3$.
   a. Find any points of intersection of the graphs of f and g.
   b. Find an equation of f^{-1}.
   c. Find an equation of g^{-1}.
   d. Find any points of intersection of the graphs of f^{-1} and g^{-1}.
   e. What do you observe about your results from parts (a) and (d)? Explain why this makes sense in terms of a property of an inverse function.

102. Let $f(x) = 3x + 5$.
   a. Solve the equation $3x + 5 = 11$.
   b. Find an equation of f^{-1}.
   c. Find $f^{-1}(11)$.
   d. What do you observe about your results from parts (a) and (c)? Explain why this makes sense in terms of a property of an inverse function.
   e. Use f^{-1} to solve each of the following equations.
      i. $3x + 5 = 17$
      ii. $3x + 5 = 2$
      iii. $3x + 5 = -6$

Expressions, Equations, Functions, and Graphs

Perform the indicated instruction. Then use words such as linear, exponential, function, one variable, *and* two variables *to describe the expression, equation, or system.*

103. Solve: $3x - 5y = 10$
       $7x + 4y = 39$

104. Simplify $\left(\dfrac{25b^7 c^{-3}}{49b^3 c^{-9}} \right)^{1/2}$.

105. Graph $3x - 5y = 10$ by hand.

106. Find all real-number solutions of $6b^5 = 349$. Round any results to the second decimal place.

▼ 5.3 Logarithmic Functions

Objectives

» Know the meaning of *logarithm* and *logarithmic function*.

» Find logarithms and evaluate logarithmic functions.

» Know properties of logarithmic functions.

» Graph logarithmic functions.

» Use logarithms to model authentic situations.

Table 37 Input–Output Pairs of $f(x) = 2^x$

x	$f(x)$
0	2^0
1	2^1
2	2^2
3	2^3
4	2^4

Table 38 Input–Output Pairs of f^{-1}

x	$f^{-1}(x)$
2^0	0
2^1	1
2^2	2
2^3	3
2^4	4

In Section 5.2, we discussed the inverse of a function. In this section, we will focus on the inverse of an exponential function, which can be used to measure the energy released by earthquakes and the noise level of sounds.

Definition of a Logarithm

Consider the function $f(x) = 2^x$. Input–output values of f and f^{-1} are shown in Tables 37 and 38.

From Table 38, we see that $f^{-1}(2^3) = 3$. The output 3 is the *exponent* of the input 2^3. In fact, all of the outputs in Table 38 are *exponents* of the corresponding inputs. We know $f^{-1}(2^6) = 6$, since 6 is the exponent of 2^6. Likewise, $f^{-1}(2^7) = 7$.

For $f(x) = 2^x$, the function f^{-1} is so useful we give it a specific name and call it $\log_2$ (read "logarithm, base 2"). So, we write $\log_2(2^3) = 3$, $\log_2(2^6) = 6$, and so on.

To find $\log_2(32)$, we first write 32 as a power of 2:

$$\log_2(32) = \log_2(2^5) = 5$$

So, $\log_2(32) = 5$ because $2^5 = 32$. Likewise, $\log_2(16) = 4$ because $2^4 = 16$. In general,

$$\log_2(a) = k \quad \text{if} \quad 2^k = a$$

We define $\log_3$ in a similar way:

$$\log_3(a) = k \quad \text{if} \quad 3^k = a$$

For example, $\log_3(9) = 2$, since $3^2 = 9$. The logarithm 2 is the *exponent* on the base 3 that gives 9.

▶ **Definition Logarithm**

For $b > 0$, $b \neq 1$, and $a > 0$,

the **logarithm $\log_b(a)$** is the number k such that $b^k = a$.

In words, $\log_b(a)$ is the exponent on the base b that gives a. We call b the **base** of the logarithm.

In short, a logarithm is an exponent.

▶ **Example 1 Finding Logarithms**

Find the logarithm.

1. $\log_7(49)$ 2. $\log_8(64)$ 3. $\log_3(81)$
4. $\log_5(125)$ 5. $\log_4(64)$ 6. $\log_{10}(100,000)$

Solution

1. $\log_7(49) = 2$, since $7^2 = 49$.
2. $\log_8(64) = 2$, since $8^2 = 64$.
3. $\log_3(81) = 4$, since $3^4 = 81$.
4. $\log_5(125) = 3$, since $5^3 = 125$.
5. $\log_4(64) = 3$, since $4^3 = 64$.
6. $\log_{10}(100,000) = 5$, since $10^5 = 100,000$.

▶ **Definition Common logarithm**

A **common logarithm** is a logarithm with base 10. We write $\log(a)$ to represent $\log_{10}(a)$.

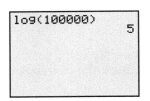

Figure 34 Use a graphing calculator to find that $\log(100,000) = 5$

For example, $\log(100,000)$ represents $\log_{10}(100,000)$. We can use the "log" key on a calculator to find base-10 logarithms. In Fig. 34, we find that $\log(100,000) = 5$.

It is important to keep in mind that a logarithm is an exponent. In Example 2, we use properties of exponents to find more logarithms.

▶ **Example 2** Finding Logarithms

Find the logarithm.

1. $\log_7(7)$ 2. $\log_4(1)$ 3. $\log_3\left(\dfrac{1}{9}\right)$

4. $\log_6\left(\sqrt{6}\right)$ 5. $\log_b\left(b^5\right)$ 6. $\log(0.001)$

Solution

1. $\log_7(7) = 1$, since $7^1 = 7$.
2. $\log_4(1) = 0$, since $4^0 = 1$.
3. $\log_3\left(\dfrac{1}{9}\right) = -2$, since $3^{-2} = \dfrac{1}{3^2} = \dfrac{1}{9}$.
4. $\log_6\left(\sqrt{6}\right) = \dfrac{1}{2}$, since $6^{\frac{1}{2}} = \sqrt{6}$.
5. $\log_b\left(b^5\right) = 5$, since $b^5 = b^5$.
6. Remember that "$\log(a)$" is shorthand for $\log_{10}(a)$, so $\log(0.001) = -3$, because
$$10^{-3} = \dfrac{1}{10^3} = \dfrac{1}{1000} = 0.001.$$

▶

Properties of Logarithms

What are the general properties of logarithms? In the discussion that follows, we assume that $b > 0$ and $b \neq 1$.

In Example 2, we found that $\log_7(7) = 1$. In general, $\log_b(b) = 1$, since $b^1 = b$. We also found that $\log_4(1) = 0$. In general, $\log_b(1) = 0$, since $b^0 = 1$.

▶ **Properties of Logarithms**

For $b > 0$ and $b \neq 1$,

- $\log_b(b) = 1$
- $\log_b(1) = 0$

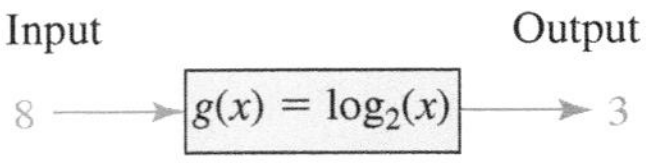

Input   Output

$8 \longrightarrow \boxed{g(x) = \log_2(x)} \longrightarrow 3$

Figure 35 Illustration of $g(8) = \log_2(8) = 3$

Recall that $\log_2$ is the name of a function. When we write $\log_2(8) = 3$, we mean the function $\log_2$ sends the input 8 to the output 3 (see Fig. 35). What follows is the general definition of a logarithmic function.

▶ **Definition** Logarithmic function

A **logarithmic function, base b,** is a function that can be put into the form
$$f(x) = \log_b(x)$$
where $b > 0$ and $b \neq 1$.

The nonpositive numbers are not in the domain of $\log_2$. Consider $\log_2(0)$. No exponent on the base 2 gives 0. Now consider $\log_2(-8)$. No exponent on the base 2 gives a negative number. In general, **the domain of a logarithmic function $\log_b$ is the set of all positive real numbers**.

The function $\log_2$ is the inverse of $f(x) = 2^x$. From our work in Section 5.2, we can conclude that $f(x) = 2^x$ is also the inverse of $\log_2$.

> ### Logarithmic and Exponential Functions Are Inverses of Each Other

- For an exponential function $f(x) = b^x$, $f^{-1}(x) = \log_b(x)$.
- For a logarithmic function $g(x) = \log_b(x)$, $g^{-1}(x) = b^x$.

In words, $g(x) = \log_b(x)$ and $f(x) = b^x$ are inverse functions of each other.

> **Example 3** Finding an Inverse Function

Find the inverse of the function.

1. $f(x) = 4^x$ **2.** $h(x) = \log_9(x)$

Solution

1. $f^{-1}(x) = \log_4(x)$
2. $h^{-1}(x) = 9^x$

> **Example 4** Evaluating f and f^{-1}

Let $f(x) = 3^x$.

1. Find $f(4)$.   **2.** Find $f^{-1}(9)$.

Solution

1. $f(4) = 3^4 = 81$
2. $f^{-1}(9) = \log_3(9) = 2$

Recall from Section 5.2 that if a function f is invertible, then $f^{-1}(f(x)) = x$, where x is in the domain of f. For the exponential function $f(x) = b^x$ and its inverse $f^{-1}(x) = \log_b(x)$, this implies that

$$\log_b(b^x) = x$$

Also recall the property $f(f^{-1}(x)) = x$, where x is in the domain of f^{-1}. This implies that

$$b^{\log_b(x)} = x, \text{ where } x > 0$$

> ### Composing Logarithmic and Exponential Functions with the Same Base

For $b > 0$ and $b \neq 1$,

- $\log_b(b^x) = x$
- $b^{\log_b(x)} = x$, where $x > 0$

> **Example 5** Composing Logarithmic and Exponential Functions with the Same Base

Simplify.

1. $\log_5(5^9)$ **2.** $6^{\log_6(3)}$

Solution

1. $\log_5(5^9) = 9$, because $\log_b(b^x) = x$.
2. $6^{\log_6(3)} = 3$, because $b^{\log_b(x)} = x$.

Graphing a Logarithmic Function

Because a logarithmic function is the inverse of an exponential function, we can use the four-step graphing method of Section 5.2 to help us graph a logarithmic function.

▶ Example 6   Graphing a Logarithmic Function

Sketch the graph of $y = \log_3(x)$.

Solution

The inverse of $f(x) = 3^x$ is $f^{-1}(x) = \log_3(x)$. So, we can apply the four-step method to graph the inverse of f:

Step 1: Sketch the graph of f: See Fig. 36.

Step 2: Choose several points on the graph of f: $\left(-1, \dfrac{1}{3}\right)$, $(0, 1)$, $(1, 3)$, and $(2, 9)$.

Step 3: For each point (a, b) chosen in step 2, plot point (b, a): We plot $\left(\dfrac{1}{3}, -1\right)$, $(1, 0)$, $(3, 1)$, and $(9, 2)$ in Fig. 37.

Step 4: Sketch the curve that contains the points plotted in step 3: See Fig. 37. The red curve is the graph of $y = \log_3(x)$.

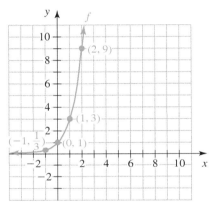

Figure 36 Graph of $f(x) = 3^x$

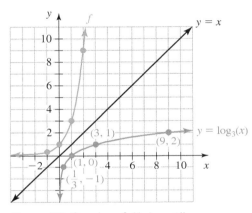

Figure 37 Graphs of $f(x) = 3^x$, $y = \log_3(x)$, and $y = x$

To graph a logarithmic function $y = \log_b(x)$, we use the four-step graphing method from Section 5.2 to sketch the inverse of $f(x) = b^x$.

Using Logarithms to Model Authentic Situations

Scientists often use logarithms to rescale measurements of objects or phenomena when the measurements tend to be very small $\left(\text{e.g., } 3.2 \times 10^{-8}\right)$ or very large $\left(\text{e.g., } 7.9 \times 10^{13}\right)$. For example, scientists use logarithms for measurements of amplitudes of earthquakes, noise levels of sounds, and pH values of solutions.

The energy released by an earthquake is sometimes measured on the *Richter scale*. The *Richter number*, R, of an earthquake is given by

$$R = \log\left(\frac{A}{A_0}\right)$$

where A is the amplitude (maximum value) of a seismic wave and A_0, called the *reference amplitude*, is the amplitude of the smallest seismic wave that a seismograph can detect.

Oh, NO!!

A mean trick to play on a seismographer

Hee hee!

▶ **Example 7** Richter Numbers

In 1906, an earthquake in San Francisco had an amplitude 2×10^8 times the reference amplitude A_0. In 1989, an earthquake in San Francisco had an amplitude 8×10^6 times A_0.

1. Find the Richter number of both earthquakes.
2. Find the ratio of the amplitudes of the 1906 and 1989 earthquakes.

Solution

1. The Richter number of the 1906 earthquake is

$$R = \log\left(\frac{2 \times 10^8 A_0}{A_0}\right) \quad \textit{Substitute } 2 \times 10^8 A_0 \textit{ for A.}$$
$$= \log\left(2 \times 10^8\right) \quad \textit{Simplify.}$$
$$\approx 8.3 \quad \textit{Compute.}$$

The Richter number of the 1989 earthquake is

$$R = \log\left(\frac{8 \times 10^6 A_0}{A_0}\right) \quad \textit{Substitute } 8 \times 10^6 A_0 \textit{ for A.}$$
$$= \log\left(8 \times 10^6\right) \quad \textit{Simplify.}$$
$$\approx 6.9 \quad \textit{Compute.}$$

2. The ratio of the amplitudes of the 1906 earthquake and the 1989 earthquake is

$$\frac{2 \times 10^8 A_0}{8 \times 10^6 A_0} = 25$$

So, the 1906 earthquake had an amplitude 25 times greater than that of the 1989 earthquake.

▶

Group Exploration

Looking ahead: Power property for logarithms

1. Use a calculator to compare $\log\left(3^2\right)$ with $2\log(3)$.
2. Use a calculator to compare $\log\left(7^4\right)$ with $4\log(7)$.
3. Use a graphing calculator table to compare values of $f(x) = \log\left(x^3\right)$ and $g(x) = 3\log(x)$. Also, compare the graphs of f and g in the same viewing window.

4. Use a graphing calculator table to compare values of $f(x) = \log\left(x^5\right)$ and $g(x) = 5\log(x)$. Also, compare the graphs of f and g in the same viewing window.
5. What do Problems 1–4 suggest about $\log\left(x^p\right)$? Test your observation.

Homework 5.3

For extra help ▶ **MyMathLab®** Watch the videos in MyMathLab Download the MyDashboard App

Find the logarithm.

1. $\log_9(81)$
2. $\log_6(36)$
3. $\log_3(27)$
4. $\log_5(625)$
5. $\log_4(256)$
6. $\log_3(243)$
7. $\log_6(216)$
8. $\log_2(64)$
9. $\log(100)$
10. $\log(1000)$
11. $\log_4\left(\frac{1}{4}\right)$
12. $\log_3\left(\frac{1}{3}\right)$
13. $\log_2\left(\frac{1}{8}\right)$
14. $\log_3\left(\frac{1}{81}\right)$
15. $\log\left(\frac{1}{10,000}\right)$
16. $\log\left(\frac{1}{100}\right)$
17. $\log_5(1)$
18. $\log_8(1)$

19. $\log_9(9)$ **20.** $\log_4(4)$

21. $\log_9(3)$ **22.** $\log_{36}(6)$

23. $\log_8(2)$ **24.** $\log_{32}(2)$

25. $\log_7(\sqrt{7})$ **26.** $\log_2(\sqrt{2})$

27. $\log_5(\sqrt[4]{5})$ **28.** $\log_7(\sqrt[3]{7})$

29. $\log_2(\log_2(16))$ **30.** $\log_2(\log_3(81))$

31. $\log(\log(10))$ **32.** $\log_3(\log_3(27))$

33. $\log_b(b)$ **34.** $\log_b(1)$

35. $\log_b(b^4)$ **36.** $\log_b(b^6)$

37. $\log_b\left(\dfrac{1}{b^5}\right)$ **38.** $\log_b\left(\dfrac{1}{b^3}\right)$

39. $\log_b(\sqrt{b})$ **40.** $\log_b(\sqrt[5]{b})$

41. $\log_b(\log_b(b))$ **42.** $\log_2\left(\log_b(\sqrt{b})\right)$

Find the inverse of the given function.

43. $f(x) = 3^x$ **44.** $g(x) = 8^x$

45. $h(x) = 10^x$ **46.** $g(x) = \left(\dfrac{1}{3}\right)^x$

47. $f(x) = \log_5(x)$ **48.** $g(x) = \log_4(x)$

49. $h(x) = \log(x)$ **50.** $f(x) = \log_{\frac{1}{2}}(x)$

Let $f(x) = 2^x$.

51. Find $f(2)$.   **52.** Find $f(4)$.

53. Find $f^{-1}(2)$.   **54.** Find $f^{-1}(4)$.

Let $g(x) = \log_3(x)$.

55. Find $g(3)$.   **56.** Find $g(81)$.

57. Find $g^{-1}(3)$.   **58.** Find $g^{-1}(2)$.

For Exercises 59–62, refer to the values of the function $f(x) = 3^x$ *listed in Table 39.*

59. Find $f(1)$.   **60.** Find $f(3)$.

61. Find $f^{-1}(1)$. Also, write your result as a logarithm.

62. Find $f^{-1}(3)$. Also, write your result as a logarithm.

Table 39 Values of $f(x) = 3^x$
(Exercises 59–62)

x	f(x)
0	1
1	3
2	9
3	27
4	81

Simplify.

63. $\log_2(2^6)$ **64.** $\log_4(4^3)$

65. $5^{\log_5(8)}$ **66.** $3^{\log_3(9)}$

67. $\log(10^7)$ **68.** $\log(10^2)$

69. $10^{\log(3)}$ **70.** $10^{\log(4)}$

Graph the function by hand.

71. $y = \log_2(x)$ **72.** $y = \log_4(x)$ **73.** $y = \log(x)$

74. $y = \log_6(x)$ **75.** $y = \log_{\frac{1}{2}}(x)$ **76.** $y = \log_{\frac{1}{3}}(x)$

77. Recall that we can describe some or all of the input–output pairs of a function by means of an equation, a graph, a table, or words. Let $f(x) = \log_5(x)$.
   a. Describe five input–output pairs of f by using a table.
   b. Describe the input–output pairs of f by using a graph.
   c. Describe the input–output pairs of f by using words.

78. Recall that we can describe some or all of the input–output pairs of a function by means of an equation, a graph, a table, or words. Let $g(x) = \log_{\frac{1}{4}}(x)$.
   a. Describe five input–output pairs of g by using a table.
   b. Describe the input–output pairs of g by using a graph.
   c. Describe the input–output pairs of g by using words.

79. a. Solve the equation $5^x = 25$.
   b. Find $\log_5(25)$.
   c. Explain why the results of parts (a) and (b) are the same.

80. a. Find $\log(100)$.
   b. Complete Table 40.

Table 40 Values of $\log(x)$
(Exercise 80)

x	log (x)
0.001	
0.01	
0.1	
1	
10	
100	
1000	

   c. Examine the entries in Table 40, and describe all patterns that you observe.

81. In 2004, an earthquake in the Indian Ocean had an amplitude 1.6×10^9 times the reference amplitude A_0. In 1985, an earthquake in Mexico City had an amplitude 6.3×10^7 times A_0.
   a. Find the Richter number of the Indian Ocean earthquake.
   b. Find the Richter number of the Mexico City earthquake.
   c. Find the ratio of the amplitudes of the Indian Ocean and Mexico City earthquakes.

82. In 1920, an earthquake in Gansu, China, had an amplitude 4.0×10^8 times the reference amplitude A_0. In 1980, an earthquake in Naples, Italy, had an amplitude 1.6×10^7 times A_0.
   a. Find the Richter number of the Gansu earthquake.
   b. Find the Richter number of the Naples earthquake.
   c. Find the ratio of the amplitudes of the Gansu and Naples earthquakes.

83. The loudness of sound can be measured on a *decibel scale*. The sound level L (in decibels) of a sound is given by

$$L = 10 \log\left(\frac{I}{I_0}\right)$$

where I is the intensity of the sound $\left(\text{in watts per square meter, W/m}^2\right)$ and $I_0 = 10^{-12}$ W/m^2. The constant I_0 is the approximate intensity of the softest sound a human can hear. Find the decibel values of the sounds listed in Table 41.

Table 41 Examples of Sound Intensities

Sound	Intensity of Sound (W/m²)
Faintest sound heard by humans	10^{-12}
Whisper	10^{-10}
Inside a running car	10^{-8}
Conversation	10^{-6}
Noisy street corner	10^{-4}
Soft-rock concert	10^{-2}
Threshold of pain	1

84. The acidity or alkalinity of a solution is measured on a *pH scale*. The pH of a solution is given by

$$\text{pH} = -\log\left(H^+\right)$$

where H^+ is the hydrogen ion concentration (in moles per liter) of the solution. Distilled water has a pH of 7. Acidic solutions have a pH less than 7, and basic (alkaline) solutions have a pH greater than 7. Most solutions have a pH between 1 and 14. Find the pH of each solution listed in Table 42, and determine whether the solution is acidic or basic. Round your results to the first decimal place.

Table 42 Hydrogen Ion Concentrations of Some Solutions

Solution	Hydrogen Ion Concentration (moles per liter)
Vinegar	1.6×10^{-3}
Human blood	6.3×10^{-8}
Shampoo	7.4×10^{-10}
Orange juice	6.3×10^{-4}
Hydrochloric acid	2.5×10^{-2}

Concepts

For Exercises 85–88, match the function with its graph in Fig. 38.

85. $f(x) = b^x, 0 < b < 1$ **86.** $g(x) = b^x, b > 1$

87. $h(x) = \log_b(x), 0 < b < 1$ **88.** $k(x) = \log_b(x), b > 1$

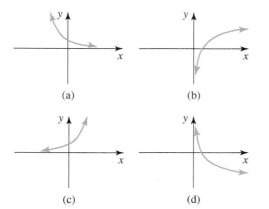

(a)   (b)

(c)   (d)

Figure 38 Exercises 85–88

89. Without computing the values of $\log_2(7)$ and $\log_3(7)$, determine which is larger. Explain.

90. a. Is $\log_3(0)$ defined? Explain.
 b. Is $\log_3(-27)$ defined? Explain.
 c. What is the domain of $f(x) = \log_3(x)$? Explain.

91. Give an example of an exponential function f of the form $f(x) = b^x$. List five input–output pairs of f. Then list five input–output pairs of f^{-1}. What is another name for f^{-1}?

92. Explain how to find a logarithm. Also, explain why a logarithmic function is the inverse of a function.

Related Review

93. In this exercise, you will compare the logarithmic function $f(x) = \log_2(x)$, the linear function $g(x) = 2x$, and the exponential function $h(x) = 2^x$.
 a. Complete Table 43.

Table 43 Complete the Table (Exercise 93)

x	$f(x)$	$g(x)$	$h(x)$
1			
2			
4			
8			
16			

 b. As the inputs in Table 43 increase, for which function are the outputs growing at the fastest rate? the next-fastest rate?

94. a. Sketch the graphs of the functions $f(x) = 3(2)^x$ and $g(x) = -3(2)^x$ on the same coordinate system. Are the graphs reflections of each other across the x-axis?
 b. Sketch the graphs of the functions $f(x) = \frac{1}{3}x$ and $g(x) = -\frac{1}{3}x$ on the same coordinate system. Are the graphs reflections of each other across the x-axis?
 c. Considering your observations in parts (a) and (b), graph the functions $f(x) = \log_2(x)$ and $g(x) = -\log_2(x)$ by hand on the same coordinate system.

Show that **(a)** $\left(f^{-1} \circ f\right)(x) = x;$ **(b)** $\left(f \circ f^{-1}\right)(x) = x.$

95. $f(x) = 3^x + 5$ and $f^{-1}(x) = \log_3(x - 5)$

96. $f(x) = 4^x - 7$ and $f^{-1}(x) = \log_4(x + 7)$

97. $f(x) = 5(2)^x - 6$ and $f^{-1}(x) = \log_2\left(\dfrac{x + 6}{5}\right)$

98. $f(x) = 8^{x-1} + 2$ and $f^{-1}(x) = \log_8(x - 2) + 1$

Expressions, Equations, Functions, and Graphs

Perform the indicated instruction. Then use words such as linear, exponential, logarithmic, function, one variable, *and* two variables *to describe the expression, equation, or system.*

99. Find an approximate equation $y = ab^x$ of an exponential curve that contains the points $(3, 5)$ and $(7, 89)$. Round a and b to the second decimal place.

100. Graph $f(x) = -\dfrac{4}{3}x - 1$ by hand.

101. Simplify $4b^{2/3}c^{-5/4}\left(2b^{-1/5}c^{3/4}\right)$.

102. Find $f^{-1}(2)$, where $f(x) = -\dfrac{4}{3}x - 1$.

▼5.4 Properties of Logarithms

Objectives

» Convert equations in *logarithmic form* to *exponential form* and vice versa.

» Know the *power property for logarithms.*

» Use properties of logarithms to solve exponential and logarithmic equations.

» Solve equations in one variable by graphing.

In this section, we will discuss some properties of logarithms and how to use these properties to solve exponential and logarithmic equations in one variable.

Exponential/Logarithmic Forms Property

In Section 5.3, we discussed how to find logarithms. For example,

$$\log_2(8) = 3 \quad \text{since} \quad 2^3 = 8$$

We say that the equation $\log_2(8) = 3$ is in *logarithmic form* and that the equation $2^3 = 8$ is in *exponential form*. The forms $\log_2(8) = 3$ and $2^3 = 8$ are equivalent.

Here are more examples of equations in equivalent logarithmic and exponential forms:

Logarithmic form	*Exponential form*
$\log_2(16) = 4$	$2^4 = 16$
$\log_3(9) = 2$	$3^2 = 9$
$\log_5(125) = 3$	$5^3 = 125$
$\log(100,000) = 5$	$10^5 = 100,000$

▶ **Exponential/Logarithmic Forms Property**

For $a > 0$, $b > 0$, and $b \neq 1$, the equations

$$\log_b(a) = c \quad \text{and} \quad b^c = a$$

are equivalent.

The equation $\log_b(a) = c$ is in **logarithmic form** and the equation $b^c = a$ is in **exponential form.** Either form can replace the other when you solve a problem.

▶ **Example 1**   Solving Equations in Logarithmic Form

Solve for x.

1. $\log_4(x) = 3$ **2.** $\log(3x - 2) = 2$

Solution

1. We write $\log_4(x) = 3$ in exponential form and solve for x:

$$4^3 = x \quad \textit{Write in exponential form.}$$
$$64 = x \quad \textit{Simplify.}$$

2. We write $\log(3x - 2) = 2$ in exponential form and solve for x:

$$10^2 = 3x - 2 \quad \textit{Write in exponential form.}$$
$$100 = 3x - 2 \quad \textit{Simplify.}$$
$$102 = 3x \quad \textit{Add 2 to both sides.}$$
$$34 = x \quad \textit{Divide both sides by 3.}$$

▶

A logarithmic equation in one variable is an equation in one variable that contains one or more logarithms. Here are some examples of logarithmic equations in one variable:

$$\log_3(x) = 4 \qquad \log_b(87) = 6 \qquad 3\log_2(t) - 7 = 8 \qquad \log_5(x^4) + \log_5(3x) = 3$$

▶ **Example 2**   Solving Logarithmic Equations in One Variable

Solve for x.

1. $6\log_9(t) + 1 = 4$ **2.** $\log_3(x^4) = 2$

Solution

1. We get $\log_9(t)$ alone on the left side of the equation and solve for t:

$$6\log_9(t) + 1 = 4 \qquad \textit{Original equation}$$
$$6\log_9(t) = 3 \qquad \textit{Subtract 1 from both sides.}$$
$$\log_9(t) = \frac{1}{2} \qquad \textit{Divide both sides by 6.}$$
$$9^{1/2} = t \qquad \textit{Write in exponential form.}$$
$$3 = t \qquad \textit{Simplify.}$$

2. We write $\log_3(x^4) = 2$ in exponential form and solve for x:

$$3^2 = x^4 \qquad \textit{Write in exponential form.}$$
$$x^4 = 9 \qquad \textit{If } c = d, \textit{ then } d = c; \textit{ simplify.}$$
$$x = \pm 9^{1/4} \qquad \textit{The solution of } x^4 = k \textit{ is } \pm k^{1/4} \textit{ if } k \geq 0.$$
$$x \approx \pm 1.7321 \qquad \textit{Compute.}$$

In most cases throughout this chapter, we will round approximate solutions to the fourth decimal place.

In Example 3, we will solve some more logarithmic equations—this time for the *base* of a logarithm. A key step will still be to write an equation in logarithmic form in exponential form instead.

▶ **Example 3**   Solving for the Base of a Logarithm

Solve for b.

1. $\log_b(81) = 4$ **2.** $\log_b(67) = 5$

Solution

1. We write $\log_b(81) = 4$ in exponential form and solve for b:

$$b^4 = 81 \qquad \textit{Write in exponential form.}$$
$$b = \pm 81^{1/4} \qquad \textit{The solution of } b^4 = k \textit{ is } \pm k^{1/4}.$$
$$b = 3 \qquad \textit{Simplify; the base of a logarithm is positive.}$$

2. We write $\log_b(67) = 5$ in exponential form and solve for b:

$$b^5 = 67 \qquad \textit{Write in exponential form.}$$
$$b = 67^{1/5} \qquad \textit{The solution of } b^5 = k \textit{ is } k^{1/5}.$$
$$b \approx 2.3185 \qquad \textit{Compute.}$$

In summary, **for an equation of the form $\log_b(x) = k$, we can solve for b or x by writing the equation in exponential form.**

Power Property for Logarithms

An exponential equation in one variable is an equation in one variable in which an exponent contains a variable. Here are some examples of exponential equations in one variable:

$$3^x = 50 \qquad 5(2)^x = 71 \qquad 4(7)^x + 5 = 785 \qquad 4^{3x-2} = 391$$

An important property called the **power property for logarithms** will help us solve exponential equations.

> **Power Property for Logarithms**
>
> For $x > 0, b > 0$, and $b \neq 1$,
> $$\log_b\left(x^p\right) = p \log_b(x)$$
> In words, a logarithm of a power of x is the exponent times the logarithm of x.

For example, $\log_3\left(x^5\right) = 5 \log_3(x)$. Also, $\log_2\left(x^7\right) = 7 \log_2(x)$.

A proof of the power property for logarithms follows: Let $k = \log_b(x)$. The exponential form of this equation is $b^k = x$. Taking the exponent p on both sides and simplifying gives

$$\left(b^k\right)^p = x^p \quad \textit{Raise both sides to the power p.}$$
$$b^{kp} = x^p \quad \textit{Multiply exponents: } (b^m)^n = b^{mn}$$

A logarithmic form of this equation is

$$\log_b\left(x^p\right) = kp$$
$$= pk \qquad \textit{Commutative law}$$
$$= p \log_b(x) \quad \textit{Substitute } \log_b(x) \textit{ for k.}$$

Therefore

$$\log_b\left(x^p\right) = p \log_b(x)$$

This statement is what we set out to prove.

Next, we describe the **logarithm property of equality,** which also is helpful in solving exponential equations.

> **Logarithm Property of Equality**
>
> For positive real numbers a, b, and c, where $b \neq 1$, the equations
> $$a = c \quad \text{and} \quad \log_b(a) = \log_b(c)$$
> are equivalent.

If we have the equation $a = c$ and then write $\log(a) = \log(c)$, we say we "take the log of both sides" of the equation $a = c$.

To solve an equation in exponential form, such as $3^x = 17$, we first take the log of both sides and then apply the power property for logarithms.

▶ **Example 4**　Solving an Exponential Equation

Solve the equation $2^x = 12$.

Solution

$$2^x = 12 \qquad \textit{Original equation}$$
$$\log(2^x) = \log(12) \qquad \textit{Take the log of both sides.}$$
$$x\log(2) = \log(12) \qquad \textit{Power property: } \log_b(x^p) = p \log_b(x)$$
$$x = \frac{\log(12)}{\log(2)} \qquad \textit{Divide both sides by } \log(2).$$
$$x \approx 3.5850 \qquad \textit{Compute.}$$

We check that 3.5850 approximately satisfies the equation $2^x = 12$:

$$2^{3.5850} \approx 12.0003 \approx 12$$

WARNING   When we compute a quotient of logarithms on a graphing calculator, it pays to watch the use of parentheses. Here we show a correct and an incorrect way to compute $\dfrac{\log(12)}{\log(2)}$:

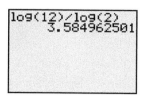

Calculator Entry	Calculator's Interpretation	
$\log(12)\;\boxed{\div}\;\log(2)\boxed{\text{ENTER}}$:	$\dfrac{\log(12)}{\log(2)}$	*Correct*
$\log(12\;\boxed{\div}\;\log(2\boxed{\text{ENTER}}$:	$\log\left(\dfrac{12}{\log(2)}\right)$	*Incorrect*

Figure 39 Compute $\dfrac{\log(12)}{\log(2)}$

The correct computation is shown in Fig. 39.

▶ **Example 5** Solving an Exponential Equation

Solve $3(4)^x = 71$.

Solution

$$3(4)^x = 71 \qquad \textit{Original equation}$$

$$4^x = \frac{71}{3} \qquad \textit{Divide both sides by 3.}$$

$$\log(4^x) = \log\left(\frac{71}{3}\right) \qquad \textit{Take the log of both sides.}$$

$$x\log(4) = \log\left(\frac{71}{3}\right) \qquad \textit{Power property: } \log_b(x^p) = p\log_b(x)$$

$$x = \frac{\log\left(\dfrac{71}{3}\right)}{\log(4)} \qquad \textit{Divide both sides by } \log(4).$$

$$x \approx 2.2824 \qquad \textit{Compute.}$$

We check that 2.2824 approximately satisfies the equation $3(4)^x = 71$:

$$3(4)^{2.2824} \approx 71.0008 \approx 71$$

▶

WARNING   Since $3(4)^x \neq (3\cdot 4)^x$, we *cannot* begin to solve $3(4)^x = 71$ in Example 5 by saying

$$3(4)^x = 71$$
$$\log[3(4)^x] = \log(71)$$
$$x\log(3\cdot 4) = \log(71) \qquad \textit{Cannot do this, since } 3(4)^x \neq (3\cdot 4)^x.$$

That is why we began by dividing both sides of $3(4)^x = 71$ by 3.

In general,

$$\log_b(ax^p) \neq p\log_b(ax)$$

To solve some equations of the form $ab^x = c$ for x, we divide both sides of the equation by a, and then take the log of both sides. Next, we use the power property for logarithms.

▶ **Example 6** Solving an Exponential Equation

Solve $5^{3w-1} = 17$.

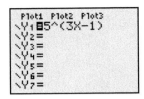

Figure 40 Verify the work

Solution

$$5^{3w-1} = 17 \qquad \text{\textit{Original equation}}$$

$$\log(5^{3w-1}) = \log(17) \qquad \text{\textit{Take the log of both sides.}}$$

$$(3w-1)\log(5) = \log(17) \qquad \text{\textit{Power property:}}\ \log_b(x^p) = p\log_b(x)$$

$$3w - 1 = \frac{\log(17)}{\log(5)} \qquad \text{\textit{Divide both sides by}}\ \log(5).$$

$$3w = \frac{\log(17)}{\log(5)} + 1 \qquad \text{\textit{Add 1 to both sides.}}$$

$$w = \frac{\dfrac{\log(17)}{\log(5)} + 1}{3} \qquad \text{\textit{Divide both sides by 3.}}$$

$$w \approx 0.9201 \qquad \text{\textit{Compute.}}$$

We use a graphing calculator table to check that, for the function $y = 5^{3x-1}$, the input 0.9201 leads approximately to the output 17 (see Fig. 40).

▶

▶ Example 7 Solving an Exponential Equation

Solve $7(2)^x - 4 = 20 + 3(2)^x$.

Solution

$$7(2)^x - 4 = 20 + 3(2)^x \qquad \text{\textit{Original equation}}$$

$$7(2)^x - 3(2)^x = 24 \qquad \text{\textit{Subtract}}\ 3(2)^x\ \text{\textit{from both sides; add 4 to both sides.}}$$

$$4(2)^x = 24 \qquad 7(2)^x - 3(2)^x = (7-3)(2)^x = 4(2)^x$$

$$2^x = 6 \qquad \text{\textit{Divide both sides by 4.}}$$

$$\log(2^x) = \log(6) \qquad \text{\textit{Take the log of both sides.}}$$

$$x\log(2) = \log(6) \qquad \text{\textit{Power property:}}\ \log_b(x^p) = p\log_b(x)$$

$$x = \frac{\log(6)}{\log(2)} \qquad \text{\textit{Divide both sides by}}\ \log(2).$$

$$x \approx 2.5850 \qquad \text{\textit{Compute.}}$$

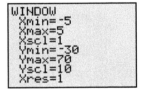

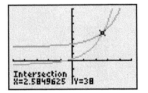

Figure 41 Verify the work

An approximate solution is 2.5850. Recall from Section 3.2 that we can use "intersect" on a graphing calculator to solve an equation in one variable. In Fig. 41, we graph the equations $y = 7(2)^x - 4$ and $y = 20 + 3(2)^x$ and find an approximate intersection point $(2.5850, 38)$, which has x-coordinate 2.5850. So, an approximate solution of the original equation is 2.5850, which checks.

▶

▶ Example 8 Solving a General Exponential Equation

Solve the equation $ab^x + c = d$ for x, where $b > 0$, $b \neq 1$, and the constants have values for which the equation has exactly one real-number solution.

Solution

$$ab^x + c = d \qquad \text{\textit{Original equation}}$$

$$ab^x + c - c = d - c \qquad \text{\textit{Subtract c from both sides.}}$$

$$ab^x = d - c \qquad \text{\textit{Combine like terms.}}$$

$$\frac{ab^x}{a} = \frac{d-c}{a} \qquad \text{\textit{Divide both sides by a.}}$$

$$b^x = \frac{d-c}{a} \qquad \text{\textit{Simplify.}}$$

$$\log(b^x) = \log\left(\frac{d-c}{a}\right) \quad \text{\textit{Take the log of both sides.}}$$

$$x\log(b) = \log\left(\frac{d-c}{a}\right) \quad \text{\textit{Power property:}} \log_b(x^p) = p\log_b(x)$$

$$x = \frac{\log\left(\dfrac{d-c}{a}\right)}{\log(b)} \quad \text{\textit{Divide both sides by}} \log(b).$$

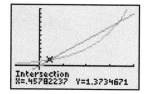

Intersection
X=.45782237 Y=1.3734671

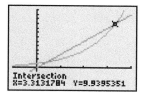

Intersection
X=3.3131784 Y=9.9395351

Figure 42 Solve the system

Solving Equations in One Variable by Using Graphs

Recall from Section 3.2 that some equations that are impossible to solve by performing operations on both sides can be solved by graphing. We will work with one such equation in Example 9.

▶ **Example 9** Using Graphing to Solve an Equation in One Variable

Use graphing to solve $2^x = 3x$.

Solution

We use "intersect" on a graphing calculator to find the solutions of the system

$$y = 2^x$$
$$y = 3x$$

See Fig. 42.

The approximate solutions of the system are (0.4578, 1.3735) and (3.3132, 9.9395). The x-coordinates of these ordered pairs, 0.4578 and 3.3132, are the approximate solutions of the equation $2^x = 3x$.

Group Exploration

Comparing the power property with other statements

Consider the following equations, where $x > 0$, $a > 0$, $b > 0$, and $b \neq 1$:

$$\log_b(x^p) = p\log_b(x)$$
$$\log_b[a(x^p)] = p\log_b(ax)$$
$$\log_b[(ax)^p] = p\log_b(ax)$$

1. Which, if any, of these equations are true in general? Explain why in terms of the power property for logarithms.

2. Show that the other equation or equations are false by using the substitutions $b = 10$, $a = 10$, $x = 10$, and $p = 2$.

3. Three students tried to solve $5(4)^x = 30$. Which students, if any, solved the equation correctly? Describe any errors and where they occurred.

Student 1's work

$$5(4)^x = 30$$
$$4^x = 6$$
$$\log(4^x) = \log(6)$$
$$x\log(4) = \log(6)$$
$$x = \frac{\log(6)}{\log(4)}$$
$$x \approx 1.2925$$

Student 2's work

$$5(4)^x = 30$$
$$\log[5(4)^x] = \log(30)$$
$$x\log[5(4)] = \log(30)$$
$$x\log(20) = \log(30)$$
$$x = \frac{\log(30)}{\log(20)}$$
$$x \approx 1.1353$$

Student 3's work

$$5(4)^x = 30$$
$$20^x = 30$$
$$\log(20^x) = \log(30)$$
$$x\log(20) = \log(30)$$
$$x = \frac{\log(30)}{\log(20)}$$
$$x \approx 1.1353$$

▶ Tips for Success   **Take a Break**

Have you ever had trouble solving a problem but returned to the problem hours later and found it easy to solve? By taking a break, you can return to the problem with a different perspective and renewed energy. You've also given your subconscious mind a chance to reflect on the problem while you take your break. You can strategically take advantage of this phenomenon by allocating time at two different points in your day to complete your homework assignment.

Homework 5.4

For extra help ▶ MyMathLab®   Watch the videos in MyMathLab   Download the MyDashboard App

Write the equation in exponential form. Assume all constants are positive and not equal to 1.

1. $\log_3(243) = 5$ 　　　　**2.** $\log_2(32) = 5$
3. $\log(100) = 2$ 　　　　　**4.** $\log(10{,}000) = 4$
5. $\log_b(a) = c$ 　　　　　**6.** $\log_r(s) = t$
7. $\log(m) = n$ 　　　　　**8.** $\log(y) = z$

Write the equation in logarithmic form. Assume all constants are positive and not equal to 1.

9. $5^3 = 125$ 　　　　　　**10.** $2^5 = 32$
11. $10^3 = 1000$ 　　　　　**12.** $10^5 = 100{,}000$
13. $y^w = x$ 　　　　　　　**14.** $r^s = t$
15. $10^p = q$ 　　　　　　**16.** $10^x = y$

Solve.

17. $\log_4(x) = 2$ 　　　　　**18.** $\log_2(x) = 3$
19. $\log(x) = -2$ 　　　　　**20.** $\log(x) = -3$
21. $\log_4(x) = 0$ 　　　　　**22.** $\log_9(x) = 0$
23. $\log_{27}(t) = \dfrac{4}{3}$ 　　　　**24.** $\log_{16}(p) = \dfrac{3}{4}$
25. $2\log_8(2x - 5) = 4$ 　　**26.** $3\log_5(4x + 1) = 9$
27. $4\log_{81}(x) - 3 = -2$ 　**28.** $3\log_8(x) + 5 = 6$
29. $\log_2(\log_3(y)) = 3$ 　　**30.** $\log_3(\log_2(p)) = -1$

Solve. Round any solutions to the fourth decimal place.

31. $\log_6(x^3) = 2$ 　　　　　**32.** $\log_4(x^5) = 3$

Solve for b. Round any approximate solutions to the fourth decimal place.

33. $\log_b(49) = 2$ 　　　　　**34.** $\log_b(16) = 2$
35. $\log_b(8) = 3$ 　　　　　**36.** $\log_b(125) = 3$
37. $\log_b(16) = 5$ 　　　　　**38.** $\log_b(95) = 9$

Solve. Round any approximate solutions to the fourth decimal place. Verify your result by checking that it satisfies or approximately satisfies the original equation.

39. $4^x = 9$ 　　　　　　　**40.** $10^x = 50$
41. $5(4)^x = 80$ 　　　　　**42.** $3(2)^x = 17$

43. $3.83(2.18)^t = 170.91$
44. $1.73(4.09)^w = 526.44$
45. $8 + 5(2)^x = 79$ 　　　　**46.** $20 = -3 + 4(2)^x$
47. $2^{4x+5} = 17$ 　　　　　　**48.** $8 = 3^{7x-1}$
49. $6(3)^x - 7 = 85 + 4(3)^x$
50. $5^x + 7 = 50 - 3(5)^x$
51. $4^{3p} \cdot 4^{2p-1} = 100$ 　　**52.** $3^{2r} \cdot 3^{r-4} = 97$
53. $3^x = -8$ 　　　　　　　**54.** $1^x = 13$

Solve. Round any approximate solutions to the fourth decimal place.

55. $\log_4(x) = 3$ 　　　　　**56.** $\log_3(x) = 4$
57. $3(4)^t + 15 = 406$ 　　　**58.** $2(6)^w - 17 = 3$
59. $\log_b(73) = 5$ 　　　　　**60.** $\log_b(19) = 4$
61. $3\log_{27}(y - 1) = 2$ 　　**62.** $2\log_4(3r + 2) = 5$
63. $3(2)^{4x-2} = 83$ 　　　　**64.** $5(4)^{2x+1} = 974$

For Exercises 65–70, estimate any solutions of the equation or system by referring to the graphs shown in Fig. 43.

65. $2^x = 4\left(\dfrac{1}{2}\right)^x$ 　　　　**66.** $2^x = 4 - x$

67. $4\left(\dfrac{1}{2}\right)^x = 4 - x$ 　　**68.** $2^x = 5$

69. $4\left(\dfrac{1}{2}\right)^x = 1$ 　　　　**70.** $y = 2^x$
$y = 4\left(\dfrac{1}{2}\right)^x$

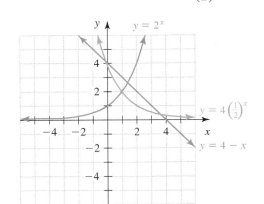

Figure 43 Exercises 65–70

Use "intersect" on a graphing calculator to solve the equation. Round any solutions to the fourth decimal place.

71. $3^x = 5 - x$

72. $2^x = 5 - 2x$

73. $7\left(\frac{1}{2}\right)^x = 2x$

74. $8\left(\frac{1}{3}\right)^x = x$

75. $\log(x + 1) = 3 - \frac{2}{5}x$

76. $6 - x = 3\log(x + 5)$

For Exercises 77–82, solve the given equation or system by referring to the values of $y = 3^{x-1}$, $y = 12\left(\frac{1}{2}\right)^x$, and $y = x - \frac{3}{2}$ shown in Table 44.

77. $3^{x-1} = 12\left(\frac{1}{2}\right)^x$

78. $12\left(\frac{1}{2}\right)^x = x - \frac{3}{2}$

79. $3^{x-1} = 81$

80. $12\left(\frac{1}{2}\right)^x = 6$

81. $y = 12\left(\frac{1}{2}\right)^x$
$y = x - \frac{3}{2}$

82. $y = 3^{x-1}$
$y = 12\left(\frac{1}{2}\right)^x$

Table 44 Some Values of Three Functions

x	1	2	3	4	5	6
$y = 3^{x-1}$	1	3	9	27	81	243
$y = 12\left(\frac{1}{2}\right)^x$	6	3	1.5	0.75	0.375	0.1875
$y = x - \frac{3}{2}$	−0.5	0.5	1.5	2.5	3.5	4.5

In Exercises 83–90, solve for x. Assume $b > 0$, $b \neq 1$, and the constants have values for which the equation has exactly one real-number solution.

83. $ab^x = c$

84. $\frac{b^x}{a} = c$

85. $b^x + c = d$

86. $b^x - c = d$

87. $ab^x - c = d$

88. $\frac{b^x}{a} + c = d$

89. $ab^{x+p} - c = d$

90. $ab^{kx} + c = d$

Concepts

91. A student tries to solve $3(8^x) = 7$:

$$3(8)^x = 7$$
$$\log[3(8)^x] = \log(7)$$
$$x\log[3(8)] = \log(7)$$
$$x\log(24) = \log(7)$$
$$x = \frac{\log(7)}{\log(24)}$$
$$x \approx 0.6123$$

Describe any errors. Then solve the equation correctly.

92. A student tries to solve $2(3)^x = 10$:

$$2(3)^x = 10$$
$$6^x = 10$$
$$\log(6^x) = \log(10)$$
$$x\log(6) = 1$$
$$x = \frac{1}{\log(6)}$$
$$x \approx 1.2851$$

Describe any errors. Then solve the equation correctly.

Let $f(x) = 4^x$. Round any approximate results to the fourth decimal place.

93. Find $f(4)$.

94. Find $f^{-1}(16)$.

95. Find x when $f(x) = 3$.

96. Find x when $f^{-1}(x) = 3$.

For Exercises 97–100, let $g(x) = \log_2(x)$. Round any approximate results to the fourth decimal place.

97. Find $g(8)$.

98. Find $g^{-1}(4)$.

99. Find a when $g(a) = 5$.

100. Find a when $g^{-1}(a) = 5$.

101. Determine whether the statement is true. Explain.

a. $\frac{\log_2(4)}{\log_2(16)} = \frac{4}{16}$

b. $\frac{\log_3(1)}{\log_3(27)} = \frac{1}{27}$

c. $\frac{\log(1000)}{\log(10{,}000)} = \frac{1000}{10{,}000}$

d. $\frac{\log_b(c)}{\log_b(d)} = \frac{c}{d}$, where b, c, and d are positive, $b \neq 1$, and $d \neq 1$.

102. Determine whether the statement is true. Explain. [**Hint:** For parts (a), (b), and (c), use the "log" key on a calculator.]

a. $\log(4 \cdot 3^2) = 2\log(4 \cdot 3)$

b. $\log(5 \cdot 2^3) = 3\log(5 \cdot 2)$

c. $\log(6 \cdot 10^4) = 4\log(6 \cdot 10)$

d. $\log(ax^p) = p\log(ax)$, where a and x are positive.

103. a. Use ZDecimal to graph $f(x) = \log(x^3) - 3\log(x) + 1$. Describe the graph in words.

b. Explain why the graph of f is in neither quadrant II nor quadrant III.

c. Use properties of logarithms to write the right-hand side of the equation of f as a constant. Use your result to explain why the graph that you found in part (a) makes sense.

104. The incorrect work that follows shows that the logarithm of any positive number is 0. Describe any errors. Assume $b > 0$, $b \neq 1$, and $k > 0$:

$$\log_b(k) = \log_b(k \cdot 1) = \log_b(k \cdot 5^0) = 0 \cdot \log_b(5k) = 0$$

105. Describe the power property for logarithms. Give an example. Does the power property imply that $x^p = px$? Explain.

106. Describe how to use the power property for logarithms to solve an exponential equation.

Related Review

Solve. Find the exact solution if the equation is linear. For other types of equations, round the solution(s) to the fourth decimal place.

107. $5(3p - 7) - 9p = -4p + 23$

108. $99 - 2(3)^x = 12$

109. $5b^6 - 88 = 56$

110. $\log_b(75) = 4$

111. $\dfrac{3}{8}r = \dfrac{5}{6}r - \dfrac{2}{3}$

112. $\log_2(3x + 7) = 4$

Expressions, Equations, Functions, and Graphs

Perform the indicated instruction. Then use words such as linear, exponential, logarithmic, function, one variable, *and* two variables *to describe the expression, equation, or system.*

113. Solve $\log_2(x) = -5$.

114. Find an equation of a line that contains the points $(-2, -4)$ and $(3, 5)$.

115. Graph $y = \log_2(x)$ by hand.

116. Find the inverse of the function $f(x) = 3x - 7$.

▼ 5.5 Using the Power Property with Exponential Models to Make Predictions

Objectives

» Use the power property for logarithms with exponential models to make predictions.

» Use the half-life of carbon-14 to date archeological artifacts and fossils.

In Section 4.5, we used exponential functions to model data. In this section, we will use exponential functions with the power property for logarithms to make predictions about the independent variable of the function.

▶ Example 1   Using the Power Property to Make a Prediction

A person invests \$7000 in a bank account with a yearly interest rate of 6% compounded annually. When will the balance be \$10,000?

Solution

Let $B = f(t)$ be the balance (in thousands of dollars) after t years or any fraction thereof. From our work with compounded-interest accounts in Section 4.5, we know we can model the situation well by using an exponential model of the form $f(t) = ab^t$ with y-intercept $(0, a)$. The B-intercept is $(0, 7)$, for \$7000 when $t = 0$, so $a = 7$ and $f(t) = 7b^t$. By the end of each year, the account has increased by 6% of the previous year's balance, so $b = 1.06$. Thus,

$$f(t) = 7(1.06)^t$$

To find when the balance is \$10,000 ($B = 10$), we substitute 10 for $f(t)$ and solve for t:

$$10 = 7(1.06)^t \qquad \textit{Substitute 10 for } f(x).$$

$$\frac{10}{7} = 1.06^t \qquad \textit{Divide both sides by 7.}$$

$$\log\left(\frac{10}{7}\right) = \log\left(1.06^t\right) \qquad \textit{Take the log of both sides.}$$

$$\log\left(\frac{10}{7}\right) = t \log(1.06) \qquad \textit{Power property: } \log_b(x^p) = p\log_b(x)$$

$$t = \frac{\log\left(\dfrac{10}{7}\right)}{\log(1.06)} \qquad \textit{If } c = d, \textit{ then } d = c; \textit{divide both sides by } \log(1.06).$$

$$t \approx 6.1212 \qquad \textit{Compute.}$$

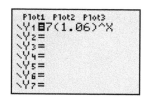

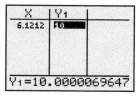

Figure 44 Verify the work

So, it will take about 6 years and 45 days for the balance to reach $10,000. We use a graphing calculator table to check that, for the function $y = 7(1.06)^x$, the input 6.1212 leads approximately to the output 10 (see Fig. 44).

▶

> To make a prediction about the independent variable t of an exponential model of the form $f(t) = ab^t$, we substitute a value for $f(t)$ and divide both sides of the equation by the coefficient a. Next, we take the log of both sides of the equation and use the power property to help solve for t.

▶ **Example 2** Using the Power Property to Make a Prediction

The infant mortality rate is the number of deaths of infants under one year old per 1000 births.* In 1915, the rate was almost 100 deaths per 1000 infants, or 1 death per 10 infants. The infant mortality rate has decreased substantially since then (see Table 45).

1. Let $I = f(t)$ be the infant mortality rate (number of deaths per 1000 infants) at t years since 1900. Find an equation of f.
2. What is the percent rate of decay for infant mortality rates?
3. Find $f^{-1}(4.7)$. What does the result mean in this situation?

Table 45 Infant Mortality Rates

Year	Rate (number of deaths per 1000 infants)
1915	99.9
1920	85.8
1930	64.6
1940	47.0
1950	29.2
1960	26.0
1970	20.0
1980	12.6
1990	9.2
2000	6.9
2010	6.2
2012	6.0

Source: *National Center for Health Statistics*

Solution

1. The scattergram in Fig. 45 shows that the points "bend" and that an exponential function will model the data better than a linear function.

   We use the points $(40, 47)$ and $(110, 6.2)$ to find an equation of the form $I = ab^t$. We substitute the coordinates of the two chosen points into $f(t) = ab^t$:

   $$6.2 = ab^{110}$$
   $$47 = ab^{40}$$

   We divide the left sides and divide the right sides of the equations and solve for b:

   $$\frac{6.2}{47} = \frac{ab^{110}}{ab^{40}}, \quad \text{where } a \neq 0 \text{ and } b \neq 0 \qquad \textit{Divide left sides and divide right sides.}$$

   $$\frac{6.2}{47} = b^{70} \qquad \textit{Simplify; subtract exponents: } \frac{b^m}{b^n} = b^{m-n}$$

   $$b = \left(\frac{6.2}{47}\right)^{1/70} \qquad \textit{The solution of } b^{70} = k \text{ is } k^{1/70}.$$

   $$b \approx 0.971 \qquad \textit{Compute.}$$

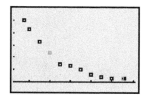

Figure 45 Scattergram of the data

So, $f(t) = a(0.971)^t$. We substitute the coordinates of $(110, 6.2)$ into the equation $f(t) = a(0.971)^t$ and solve for a:

$$6.2 = a(0.971)^{110} \qquad \textit{Substitute 110 for t and 6.2 for f(t).}$$

$$a = \frac{6.2}{0.971^{110}} \qquad \textit{Divide both sides by 0.917}^{110}.$$

$$a \approx 157.86 \qquad \textit{Compute.}$$

Thus, $f(t) = 157.86(0.971)^t$. In Fig. 46, the model appears to fit the data very well.

2. The base b is 0.971. Since $1 - 0.971 = 0.029$, we conclude that the model estimates the infant mortality rate has decayed by 2.9% per year.
3. Since f sends values of t to values of I, f^{-1} sends values of I to values of t (see Figs. 47 and 48).

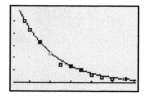

Figure 46 Verifying the model

---

*The rate does not include fetal deaths.

Figure 47 *f* sends values of *t* to values of *I*

Figure 48 f^{-1} sends values of *I* to values of *t*

Therefore, $f^{-1}(4.7)$ represents the year (since 1900) when the infant mortality rate will be 4.7 deaths per 1000 infants. To find the year, we substitute 4.7 for $f(t)$ in the equation $f(t) = 157.86(0.971)^t$ and solve for *t*:

$$4.7 = 157.86(0.971)^t \qquad \text{\textit{Substitute 4.7 for f(t).}}$$

$$\frac{4.7}{157.86} = 0.971^t \qquad \text{\textit{Divide both sides by 157.86.}}$$

$$\log\left(\frac{4.7}{157.86}\right) = \log(0.971^t) \qquad \text{\textit{Take the log of both sides.}}$$

$$\log\left(\frac{4.7}{157.86}\right) = t\log(0.971) \qquad \text{\textit{Power property:} } \log_b(x^p) = p\log_b(x)$$

$$t = \frac{\log\left(\dfrac{4.7}{157.86}\right)}{\log(0.971)} \qquad \text{\textit{Divide both sides by log (0.971).}}$$

$$t \approx 119.41 \qquad \text{\textit{Compute.}}$$

The model predicts the infant mortality rate will be 4.7 deaths per 1000 infants in 2019.

Before we perform more modeling, it will be helpful to know a fact related to the base multiplier property (Section 4.3). For an exponential function $y = f(t) = ab^t$, we know by the base multiplier property that, as the value of *t* increases by 1, the value of *y* is multiplied by the base *b*. Also, if the value of *y* is multiplied by *M* in going from $t = 0$ to $t = k$, then the value of *y* will continue to be multiplied by *M* each time *t* is increased by *k*. To see this, recall that $f(0) = a$ and note that

$$f(k) = ab^k = aM, \quad \text{so} \quad b^k = M$$

We can use the fact that $b^k = M$ to show that if $t = 0$ is increased by *k* a total of *n* times, then *y* is multiplied by *M* a total of *n* times:

$$f(nk) = ab^{nk} = a(b^k)^n = a(M)^n$$

We use this idea in Example 3.

Table 46 Federal Debt Amounts

Year	Federal Debt (billions of dollars)
1960	291
1970	381
1980	909
1990	3206
2000	5629
2010	13,529

Source: *U.S. Office of Management and Budget*

▶ **Example 3**   Using the Power Property to Estimate Doubling Time

In Exercise 34 of Homework 4.5, you may have found the equation $f(t) = 291(1.08)^t$, where $f(t)$ is the federal debt (in billions of dollars) at *t* years since 1960 (see Table 46). Estimate how often the federal debt doubles.

Solution

In 1960, the federal debt was \$291 billion. We find the year when the debt was $2(291) = 582$ billion dollars (twice as large) by substituting 582 for $f(t)$ in the equation $f(t) = 291(1.08)^t$ and solving for *t*:

$$582 = 291(1.08)^t \qquad \text{\textit{Substitute 582 for f(t).}}$$

$$2 = 1.08^t \qquad \text{\textit{Divide both sides by 291.}}$$

$$\log(2) = \log(1.08^t) \qquad \text{\textit{Take the log of both sides.}}$$

$$\log(2) = t\log(1.08) \qquad \text{\textit{Power property:} } \log_b(x^p) = p\log_b(x)$$

$$t = \frac{\log(2)}{\log(1.08)} \qquad \text{\textit{Divide both sides by log (1.08).}}$$

$$t \approx 9.01 \qquad \text{\textit{Compute.}}$$

According to the exponential function f, it took about 9 years to double the 1960 debt. By the discussion preceding this example, we can conclude that f predicts the debt will double *every* 9 years.

▶

Recall from Section 4.5 that the half-life of an element is the amount of time it takes for the number of atoms to be reduced to half. All organisms are, in part, composed of the elements carbon-12 and carbon-14. Carbon-14 is radioactive. After an animal or plant dies, its carbon-14 decays exponentially with a half-life of 5730 years. However, the amount of carbon-12 remains constant. Scientists know the ratio of carbon-14 to carbon-12 in *living* organisms. Hence, scientists can determine how long ago an organism lived by measuring the decreased ratio of carbon-14 to carbon-12 in a bone, a piece of wood, or another artifact that was once living and was owned or used by the organism.

▶ **Example 4** Using the Power Property to Make an Estimate

A violent volcanic eruption and subsequent collapse of the former Mount Mazama created Crater Lake, the deepest lake in the United States. Scientists found a charcoal sample from a tree that burned in the eruption. If only 39.40% of the carbon-14 remains in the sample, when did Crater Lake form?

Solution

Let $P = f(t)$ be the percentage of carbon-14 that remains at t years after the sample formed. Since the percentage is halved every 5730 years, we will find an exponential equation of the form

$$f(t) = ab^t$$

At time $t = 0$, 100% (all) of the carbon-14 remained, so the P-intercept is $(0, 100)$. Therefore, $a = 100$ and $f(t) = 100b^t$. At time $t = 5730$, $\frac{1}{2}(100) = 50\%$ of the carbon-14 remained. So, we substitute the coordinates of the point $(5730, 50)$ into the equation $f(t) = 100b^t$ and solve for b:

$$50 = 100b^{5730} \quad \text{Substitute 5730 for } t \text{ and 50 for } f(t).$$
$$0.5 = b^{5730} \quad \text{Divide both sides by 100.}$$
$$b = \pm 0.5^{1/5730} \quad \text{The solutions of } b^{5730} = k \text{ are } \pm k^{1/5730}.$$
$$b \approx 0.999879 \quad \text{Compute; the base of an exponential function is positive.}$$

The equation is $f(t) = 100(0.999879)^t$. We use more digits than usual for the base, as even a small change in it would greatly affect estimates well into the past (or future).
To estimate the age of the sample, we substitute 39.40 for $f(t)$ and solve for t:

$$39.40 = 100(0.999879)^t \quad \text{Substitute 39.40 for } f(t).$$
$$0.3940 = 0.999879^t \quad \text{Divide both sides by 100.}$$
$$\log(0.3940) = \log(0.999879^t) \quad \text{Take the log of both sides.}$$
$$\log(0.3940) = t\log(0.999879) \quad \text{Power property: } \log_b(x^p) = p\log_b(x)$$
$$t = \frac{\log(0.3940)}{\log(0.999879)} \quad \text{Divide both sides by log (0.999879).}$$
$$t \approx 7697 \quad \text{Compute.}$$

So, the age of Crater Lake (and the sample) is approximately 7697 years.

▶

Group Exploration ————————————————————

Finding an equation of the inverse of an exponential model

In Example 1, we found the model $B = f(t) = 7(1.06)^t$, where B is the balance (in thousands of dollars) of an account after t years. The starting balance is \$7000, and the interest rate is 6% compounded annually. In this exploration, you will find the equation of the inverse function f^{-1}.

1. Substitute B for $f(t)$ in the equation $f(t) = 7(1.06)^t$.

2. Solve your equation for t.

3. Replace t with $f^{-1}(B)$ in your equation. You now have an equation of f^{-1}.

4. Use your equation of f^{-1} to find $f^{-1}(12)$. What does it mean in this situation?

5. Use a graphing calculator to help you complete Table 47.

6. How could the information in your completed table help an investor?

Table 47 Values of f^{-1}

B	$f^{-1}(B)$
7	
8	
9	
10	
11	
12	
13	
14	

Group Exploration ————————————————————

Looking ahead: Product and quotient properties for logarithms

1. **a.** Use a calculator to compare $\log(2 \cdot 3)$ with $\log(2) + \log(3)$.
   b. Use a calculator to compare $\log(7 \cdot 2)$ with $\log(7) + \log(2)$.
   c. Use a calculator to compare $\log(4 \cdot 6)$ with $\log(4) + \log(6)$.
   d. What do parts (a)–(c) of this exploration suggest about $\log(xy)$? Check whether your observation is true for other values of x and y. (Your observation is referred to as the *product property for logarithms*.)

2. Determine how $\log\left(\dfrac{x}{y}\right)$ can be expressed in terms of two logarithms. [**Hint:** Choose specific values for x and y. Then compute $\log\left(\dfrac{x}{y}\right)$, $\log(x)$, and $\log(y)$, and compare the values.] Check whether your observation is true for other values of x and y. (Your observation is referred to as the *quotient property* for logarithms.)

Homework 5.5

For extra help ▶ MyMathLab®   Watch the videos in MyMathLab   Download the MyDashboard App

1. A person invests \$2000 in an account at 5% interest compounded annually. Let $V = f(t)$ be the value (in dollars) of the account after t years or any fraction thereof.
   a. Find an equation of f.
   b. What is the V-intercept? What does it mean in this situation?
   c. What will be the value of the investment in five years?
   d. When will the value of the investment be \$3000?

2. A person invests \$12,500 in an account at 8% interest compounded annually. Let $V = f(t)$ be the value (in dollars) of the account after t years or any fraction thereof.
   a. Find an equation of f.
   b. What is the V-intercept? What does it mean in this situation?

   c. What will be the value of the investment in four years?
   d. When will the value of the investment be \$20,000?

3. A person invests \$9300 in an account at 6% interest compounded annually. When will the value of the investment be \$13,700?

4. A person invests \$4500 in an account at 3% interest compounded annually. When will the value of the investment be \$5900?

5. A person invests \$6000 in an account at 10% interest compounded annually. When will the value of the investment be doubled? Explain why it will take less than 10 years, even though the rate is 10%.

6. A person invests $4000 in an account at 5% interest compounded annually. When will the value of the investment be doubled? Explain why it will take less than 20 years, even though the rate is 5%.

7. The U.S. annual production of ethanol, used as fuel for automobiles, was 13.9 billion gallons in 2011 and has grown by about 19% per year since then (Source: *Department of Energy*). Predict when annual ethanol production will reach 40 billion gallons.

8. The number of Iraqi students enrolled at U.S. colleges and universities was 616 students in 2011 and has grown by about 27% per year since then (Source: *Institute of International Education*). Predict when 3000 Iraqi students will enroll in U.S. colleges and universities.

9. Suppose a rumor is spreading in the United States that tomato juice causes hair loss. Assume 30 people have heard the rumor as of today and each day the number of people (both past and present) who will have heard the rumor triples. Let $f(t)$ be the number of people (both past and present) who will have heard the rumor at t days since today.
   a. Find an equation of f.
   b. What is the number of Americans (both past and present) who will have heard the rumor 8 days from now?
   c. Predict when all Americans (both past and present) will have heard the rumor. Assume the U.S. population is 315 million.

10. There are 4 million bacteria on a peach at noon on Tuesday. Assume a bacterium divides into two bacteria every hour, on average. Let $f(t)$ be the number of bacteria (in millions) on the peach at t hours after Tuesday noon.
   a. Find an equation of f.
   b. Find $f(24)$. What does it mean in this situation?
   c. Find $f^{-1}(8000)$. What does it mean in this situation?

11. According to the U.S. Occupational Safety and Health Administration standard, an average person can listen to 8 hours of sound per day at a sound level of 90 decibels without experiencing hearing loss. Recall from Exercise 83 of Homework 5.3 that a decibel is a unit for measurement of sound intensity. For each increase of 5 decibels, the exposure time must be cut in half. For example, an average person can listen to 4 hours of sound per day at a sound level of 95 decibels without experiencing hearing loss. (One overexposure may result in temporary, but probably not permanent, hearing loss.)

   Some examples of sound being made at various decibel levels are listed in Table 48.

Table 48 Examples of Decibel Levels

Sound Level (decibels)	Example
0	Faintest sound heard by humans
20	Whisper
40	Inside a running car
60	Conversation
80	Noisy street corner
100	Soft-rock concert
120	Threshold of pain

Source: *From* Math and Music *by Trudi Hammel Garland and Charity Vaughan Kahn, p. 140. Copyright © 1993 Pearson Education, Inc. or its affiliates. Used by permission. All Rights Reserved.*

   a. Let $T = f(d)$ be the number of hours of safe exposure time in one day to a sound at a level d decibels *above 90 decibels*. Find an equation of f.
   b. Many rock bands play at about 114 decibels. Use your equation of f to predict how long they can play at concerts so their fans do not experience hearing loss. On the basis of your result, do you think these types of fans experience hearing loss? Assume most people are not wearing earplugs.
   c. Many rock concerts last about 3 hours. At what sound level should the bands play so fans who attend a lot of concerts will not experience hearing loss?

12. In a weightless environment, astronauts lose about 1.5% of the calcium in their bodies per month (Source: *NASA*). Suppose some astronauts flew to Mars. Assuming the astronauts did not lose or gain calcium while on Mars, they would lose 17% of the calcium in their bodies due to the round trip. Estimate the number of months the round trip would take (not counting the time spent on Mars).

13. First prize for the World Series of Poker's main event has grown approximately exponentially from $0.21 million in 1975 to $8.53 million in 2012 (Source: *Harrah's Entertainment*). Predict when the first prize will be $19 million.

14. Electronic cigarette sales have grown approximately exponentially from 0.05 million units in 2008 to 2.5 million units in 2011 (Source: *Tobacco Vapor Electronic Cigarette Association*). Each unit has three parts: battery, charger, and nicotine-containing cartridge. Predict in which year sales will reach 1.676 *billion* units.

15. The timber harvests in the Tongass National Forest in Alaska have decayed approximately exponentially from 471 million board feet in 1990 to 36 million board feet in 2010 (Source: *U.S. Forest Service*). Predict when the timber harvest will be 13 million board feet.

16. The revenue from personal breathalyzers to test for alcohol impairment has grown approximately exponentially from $27.9 million in 2005 to $215.2 million in 2011 (Source: *WinterGreen Research*). Predict in which year the revenue will be $641.9 million. WinterGreen Research predicts this will happen in 2016. Does this market-analysis firm believe the percentage rate of change of revenue per year will be greater than, less than, or equal to that during the period 2005–2011? Explain.

17. The numbers of Twitter employees are shown in Table 49 for various years.

Table 49 Numbers of Twitter Employees

Year	Number of Employees
2008	8
2009	29
2010	130
2011	350
2012	900

Source: *AllThingsD.com*

Let $f(t)$ be the number of Twitter employees at t years since 2005.
  a. Use a graphing calculator to draw a scattergram of the data. Is it better to model the data by using a linear or an exponential function? Explain.
  b. Find an equation of f.
  c. What is the base b of your model $f(t) = ab^t$? What does it mean in this situation?
  d. Predict the number of Twitter employees in 2014.
  e. Predict when the number of Twitter employees will equal 394 thousand, which is the population of Cleveland, Ohio.

18. The numbers of LEED-certified green buildings in the United States are shown in Table 50 for various years.

Table 50 Numbers of LEED-Certified Green Buildings

Year	Number of Buildings with LEED Certification
2002	28
2004	183
2006	660
2008	2113
2010	7267

Source: *United States Green Building Council*

Let $f(t)$ be the number of LEED-certified green buildings in the United States at t years since 2000.
  a. Use a graphing calculator to draw a scattergram of the data. Is it better to model the data by using a linear or an exponential function? Explain.
  b. Find an equation of f.
  c. What is the base b of your model $f(t) = ab^t$? What does it mean in this situation?
  d. Predict the number of LEED-certified green buildings in 2015.
  e. Predict when there will be an average of 2000 LEED-certified green buildings *per state*.

19. The numbers of polio cases in the world are shown in Table 51 for various years. Let $f(t)$ be the number of polio cases (in thousands) in the year that is t years since 1980.
  a. Use a graphing calculator to draw a scattergram of the data. Is it better to model the data by using a linear or an exponential function? Explain.
  b. Find an equation of f.
  c. Predict the number of polio cases in 2018.
  d. Predict in which year there will be 1 case of polio.
  e. Find the approximate half-life of the number of polio cases. [**Hint:** Use f to estimate the number of cases in 1980. Then use f to estimate when there was half that number of cases.]

Table 51 Numbers of Polio Cases Worldwide

Year	Number of Polio Cases (thousands)
1988	350
1992	138
1996	33
2000	4
2004	1.3
2008	1.7
2011	0.7

Source: *World Health Organization*

20. The numbers of Russian children adopted by American parents are shown in Table 52 for various years.

Table 52 Numbers of Russian Children Adopted by American Parents

Year	Number of Children
2004	5862
2005	4631
2006	3702
2007	2303
2008	1857
2009	1586
2010	1079
2011	962

Source: *U.S. Department of State*

Let $f(t)$ be the number of Russian children adopted by American parents in the year that is t years since 2000.
  a. Use a graphing calculator to draw a scattergram of the data. Is it better to model the data by using a linear or an exponential function? Explain.
  b. Find an equation of f.
  c. Predict the number of Russian children that will be adopted by American parents in 2018. How many adoptions will that be per state, on average?
  d. Predict in which year only one Russian child will be adopted by American parents.
  e. Find the approximate half-life of the number of Russian children adopted by American parents. [**Hint:** Use f to estimate the number of adoptions in 2000. Then use f to estimate in which year the number of adoptions was half that amount.]

21. In Exercise 27 of Homework 4.5, you may have found an equation close to $f(t) = 1.21(1.0161)^t$, where $p = f(t)$ models world population (in billions) at t years since 1900 (see Table 53).

Table 53 World Population

Year	World Population (billions)
1930	2.070
1940	2.295
1950	2.500
1960	3.050
1970	3.700
1980	4.454
1990	5.279
2000	6.080
2012	7.044

Source: *U.S. Census Bureau*

a. The United Nations predicts world population will reach 9.3 billion in 2050. Use *f* to predict when world population will reach 9.3 billion.

b. Use a graphing calculator to draw a scattergram to describe the part of the data in Table 53 *from 1970 to 2012*. Is it better to use a linear or an exponential function to model the data? Explain. Find an equation for such a function. Use the function notation "*g*" for this function.

c. Use *g* to predict when world population will reach 9.3 billion. Is that year before or after the predicted year you found in part (a)? Why does this make sense?

d. The United Nations describes a possible post-2050 scenario in which world population will reach 9.3 billion in 2050 and increase to 10.1 billion in 2100. Draw by hand a scattergram of all of the data shown in Table 53, and plot points for the scenario's predictions for 2050 and 2100. Graph the functions *f* and *g* by hand. Then sketch a model that describes the scenario better than the functions *f* and *g* do.

22. The minimum and average salaries for major league baseball players are shown in Table 54 for various years.

Table 54 Salaries for Major League Baseball Players

Year	Minimum Salary (thousands of dollars)	Average Salary (thousands of dollars)
1970	12	29
1975	16	45
1980	30	144
1985	60	372
1990	100	579
1995	109	1071
2000	200	1998
2005	316	2633
2010	400	3015
2012	480	3440

Source: *baseball-reference.com*

Let $M(t)$ be the minimum salary and $A(t)$ be the average salary, both in thousands of dollars, at *t* years since 1970.
a. Find regression equations of *M* and *A*.
b. Predict the minimum salary and the average salary in 2018.
c. What is the percentage rate of growth of minimum salaries? of average salaries?
d. In Exercise 45 of Homework 4.3, you may have worked with the model $f(t) = 1.22(1.051)^t$, where $f(t)$ is the average ticket price (in dollars) to major league baseball games at *t* years since 1950. What is the percentage rate of growth of average ticket prices? Can the growth in minimum salaries or average salaries be accounted for by the growth in average ticket prices alone? Explain.
e. Predict when the minimum salary will be $1 million.

23. The percentages of seniors with severe memory impairment (based on memory tests) are shown in Table 55 for various age groups. Let $p = f(t)$ be the percentage of seniors at age *t* years with severe memory impairment.
a. Find an equation of *f*.
b. What is the base *b* of your model $f(t) = ab^t$? What does it mean in this situation?
c. Estimate what percentage of 70-year-old seniors have severe memory impairment.

Table 55 Percentages of Seniors with Severe Memory Impairment

Age Group (years)	Age Used to Represent Age Group (years)	Percent
65–69	67	1.1
70–74	72	2.5
75–79	77	4.5
80–84	82	6.4
over 84	88	12.9

Source: *Federal Interagency Forum on Aging-Related Statistics*

d. Estimate at what age 10% of seniors have severe memory impairment.
e. In Exercise 7 of Homework 3.3, you may have found that there is a linear relationship between an adult's age and an adult's score on a test measuring memory and information-processing speed. Would that *linear* relationship necessarily conflict with an *exponential* relationship between a senior's age and the percentage of seniors with severe memory impairment? Explain.

24. Saks Fifth Avenue® offered a promotional sale in which customers could receive a gift card. The values of the gift cards are shown in Table 56 for various expenditures.

Table 56 Saks Fifth Avenue Gift Card Values

Expenditure Group (dollars)	Expenditure Used to Represent Expenditure Group (dollars)	Gift Card Value (dollars)
250–499	375	25
500–999	750	50
1000–1999	1500	100
2000–2999	2500	200
3000 or more	3500	450

Source: *Saks Fifth Avenue*

Let $v = f(s)$ be the value (in dollars) of a gift card that a customer who spends *s* dollars will receive.
a. Find an equation of *f*.
b. What is the coefficient *a* of your model $f(s) = ab^s$? What does it mean in this situation?
c. What is the base *b* of your model $f(s) = ab^s$? What does it mean in this situation?
d. Customer A spends $2000, customer B spends $2500, and customer C spends $2999. According to your model *f*, what are the values of the gift cards that these customers will receive? Compare these values with the actual values of the gift cards they will receive.
e. Use your model to estimate for what expenditure a customer would receive a $700 gift card.
f. If a new promotion is to include a gift card for $700, as well as gift cards for the values shown in Table 56, determine reasonable expenditure groups for $450 and $700 gift cards.

25. In a study of 10 of the most selective U.S. colleges and universities, researchers found that a student applicant has a better chance of being accepted to a college through early decision (students apply early and colleges decide early) than by regular decision. Table 57 shows a comparison of SAT scores (out of 1600) and acceptance rates by both systems.

Table 57 Percentages of Applicants Accepted by Early Decision and Regular Decision

| SAT Score Group | Score Used to Represent SAT Score Group | Percent | |
		Early Decision	Regular Decision
1100–1190	1145	21	10
1200–1290	1245	35	17
1300–1390	1345	52	31
1400–1490	1445	70	48
1500–1600	1550	93	72

Source: *Professor Christopher Avery, Kennedy School of Government, Harvard University*

For students who score s points, let $E(s)$ and $R(s)$ be the percentages of early-decision and regular-decision applicants, respectively, who are accepted.
a. Find regression equations of E and R.
b. What percentage of early-decision applicants who score 1425 points get accepted? What about regular-decision applicants who score 1425 points?
c. For what score do half of early-decision applicants get accepted? What about regular-decision applicants?
d. The study concluded that students who apply for early decision have the equivalent of 100 points added to their SAT score, compared with students applying for regular decision. What do your results from part (c) suggest the equivalent number of added points to be?
e. Use "intersect" on a graphing calculator to find the intersection point of the graphs of E and R. What does it mean in this situation? [Challenge: Use substitution and the property $\dfrac{b^t}{c^t} = \left(\dfrac{b}{c}\right)^t$, where b and c are positive, to find the intersection point.]

You're planning pretty far ahead, but by applying to our ultra-early decision system, your newborn need score only 1 point on the SAT to be accepted!

26. New York Life offers a $250,000 life insurance policy. Quarterly rates for women and men are shown in Table 58 for various ages.

Table 58 New York Life Quarterly Rates for a $250,000 Policy

| Age (years) | Quarterly Rate (dollars) | |
	Women	Men
35	25.00	28.75
40	33.75	35.75
45	51.25	57.50
50	70.00	87.50
55	104.50	145.00
60	145.75	230.75
64	220.00	355.00

Source: *New York Life*

Let $W(t)$ and $M(t)$ be the quarterly rates (in dollars) for women and men, respectively, both at t years of age.
a. Find regression equations of W and M.
b. For a $250,000 policy, how much would a 52-year-old woman pay per quarter? How much would a 52-year-old man pay per quarter?
c. At what age would a woman pay $120 per quarter for a $250,000 policy? At what age would a man pay that much for a $250,000 policy?
d. Due to Montana insurance regulations, both sexes must pay the same quarterly rates. So, New York Life uses the male rates for all residents of Montana. Estimate how much more a 62-year-old woman would pay per quarter for a $250,000 policy if she lived in Montana rather than in some other state.
e. Use "intersect" on a graphing calculator to find the intersection point of the graphs of W and M. What does it mean in this situation? [Challenge: Use substitution and the property $\dfrac{b^t}{c^t} = \left(\dfrac{b}{c}\right)^t$, where b and c are positive, to find the intersection point.]

27. Physicians use gallium citrate-67 to detect certain types of cancer, including lymphoma. Gallium citrate-67 has an effective half-life of 3.25 days—some is lost to radioactive decay, and some is removed through the digestive and urinary tracts. A patient who is breast-feeding is injected with the radioactive element.
a. Let $f(t)$ be the percentage of the gallium citrate-67 that remains in the patient's body at t days since she was injected. Find an equation of f.
b. A scan of the gallium citrate-67 is performed 2 days after the injection. What percentage of the element remains?
c. The patient can resume breast-feeding when only 0.39% of the gallium citrate-67 remains. When can she resume breast-feeding?

28. Physicians use technetium-99m to locate stress fractures in bones. Technetium-99m has an effective half-life of 5.3 hours—some is lost to radioactive decay, and some is removed through urination. A patient with a possible stress fracture in his foot is injected with the radioactive element.
a. Let $f(t)$ be the percentage of the technetium-99m that remains in the patient's body at t hours since he was injected. Find an equation of f.

b. What percentage of the technetium-99m will remain after 1 day?

c. When will only 1% of the technetium-99m remain?

29. Scientists used a sample of spruce wood from the Two Creeks Forest Bed in Wisconsin to date an advance of the continental ice sheet into the United States during the last Ice Age. If 24.46% of the carbon-14 remains in the sample, when did the ice sheet advance? (Assume this advance killed the tree.) The half-life of carbon-14 is 5730 years.

30. A mummy was on display at a museum in Niagara Falls until it was sold in 1999. A few years later, researchers identified the mummy as the ancient Egyptian pharaoh Rameses I. The mummy was eventually returned to Egypt. If 69.57% of the carbon-14 in the mummy remains, estimate how long ago Rameses I lived. The half-life of carbon-14 is 5730 years.

31. An archeologist discovers a tool made of wood.

a. If 50% of the wood's carbon-14 remains, how old is the wood? Explain how you can find this result without using an equation. The half-life of carbon-14 is 5730 years.

b. If 25% of the wood's carbon-14 remains, how old is the wood? Explain how you can find this result without using an equation.

c. If 10% of the wood's carbon-14 remains, how old is the wood? First, guess an approximate age without solving an equation. Explain how you decided on your estimate. Then, use an equation to find the age.

32. A person drinks a cup of coffee. Assume the caffeine enters his bloodstream immediately and there was no caffeine in his bloodstream before he drank the coffee. The half-life of caffeine in a person's bloodstream is about 6 hours. A cup of coffee contains about 240 milligrams of caffeine.

a. Let $f(t)$ be the number of milligrams of caffeine in the person's bloodstream at t hours after he drank the coffee. Find an equation of f.

b. The person drinks the coffee at 8 A.M. and goes to bed at 11 P.M. Use f to predict the amount of caffeine in his bloodstream when he goes to bed.

c. The person drinks another cup of coffee 24 hours after the first cup. How much caffeine will be in his bloodstream from these 2 cups of coffee just after he drank the second cup? Explain how you can find this result without using an equation.

d. Now assume the person drinks the cup of coffee at 8 A.M. and then drinks a cup of coffee every morning at 8 A.M. from then on. Sketch a qualitative graph that describes the relationship between caffeine in his bloodstream and time. Describe any assumptions that you make.

33. A storage tank contains a liquid radioactive element with a half-life of 100 years. It will be relatively safe for the contents to leak from the tank when 0.01% of the radioactive element remains. How long must the tank remain intact for this storage procedure to be safe?

34. A storage tank contains a liquid radioactive element with a half-life of 500 years. It will be relatively safe for the contents to leak from the tank when 0.02% of the radioactive element remains. How long must the tank remain intact for this storage procedure to be safe?

Concepts

35. Suppose the same amount of principal is deposited in an account at 3% interest compounded annually as in an account at 6% interest compounded annually. After how many years will there be twice as much money in the 6% account as in the 3% account? [**Hint:** For each account, find an expression that describes the value of the account, where t is the number of years the principal P (in dollars) has been invested. Set the ratio of the expression for the 6% account and the expression for the 3% account equal to 2 and solve for t.]

36. Describe how you can use the power property for logarithms to make estimates and predictions.

Related Review

37. A teacher ran an experiment to compare the weight of a bar of soap with the number of days he had used it in the shower (see Table 59).

Table 59 Weight of a Bar of Soap versus Number of Days of Use

Number of Days	Weight (grams)
0	124
4	103
7	84
11	58
17	27
20	12
22	6

Source: *Rex Boggs, Glenmore State High School, Rockhampton, Queensland, Australia*

Let $w = f(t)$ be the weight (in grams) of the bar of soap after t days of use.

a. Find a linear equation and an exponential equation of f. Which model describes the situation better?

b. Estimate when the bar of soap weighed 45 grams.

c. If your model is linear, find the slope. If your model is exponential, find the base b of $f(t) = ab^t$. What does your result mean in this situation?

d. On day 23, the bar of soap broke into two pieces and went down the drain. Use the model to estimate when there would have been no soap left. Has model breakdown occurred? Explain.

38. Due to inflation, an item that cost $10,000 in 1980 cost $26,720 in 2012. Costs comparable to $10,000 in 1980 are shown in Table 60 for various years. Let $c = f(t)$ be the cost (in dollars) in the year that is t years since 1980 that is comparable to $10,000 in 1980.

a. Use a graphing calculator to draw a scattergram of the data. Is it better to model the data by using a linear or an exponential function? Explain.

b. Find an equation of f.

c. If your model is linear, find the slope. If your model is exponential, find the base b of $f(t) = ab^t$. What does your result mean in this situation?

d. What is the c-intercept? What does it mean in this situation?

Table 60 Costs Comparable to $10,000 in 1980

Year	Comparable Cost (dollars)
1980	10,000
1985	12,893
1990	15,559
1995	18,059
2000	20,367
2005	23,030
2010	25,279
2012	26,720

Source: *Bureau of Labor Statistics*

e. Use *f* to predict when the cost of $29,000 would be comparable to the cost of $10,000 in 1980.

Expressions, Equations, Functions, and Graphs

Perform the indicated instruction. Then use words such as linear, exponential, logarithmic, function, one variable, *and* two variables *to describe the expression, equation, or system.*

39. Simplify $\dfrac{-25b^{3/8}}{40b^{2/5}}$.

40. Find the inverse of $f(x) = \dfrac{2}{5}x - 3$.

41. Solve $4(6)^x - 31 = 180$. Round any solutions to the fourth decimal place.

42. Graph $f(x) = \dfrac{2}{5}x - 3$ by hand.

▼ 5.6 More Properties of Logarithms

Objectives

» Know the *product, quotient,* and *change-of-base properties* for logarithms.

» Use properties of logarithms to simplify expressions and solve equations.

» Use a calculator to evaluate a logarithm with a base other than 10.

In Section 5.4, we studied some properties of logarithms. In this section, we will discuss three more.

Product Property for Logarithms

We can use the **product property for logarithms** to add two logarithms that have the same base.

> ▶ **Product Property for Logarithms**
>
> For $x > 0$, $y > 0$, $b > 0$, and $b \neq 1$,
>
> $$\log_b(x) + \log_b(y) = \log_b(xy)$$
>
> In words, the sum of logarithms is the logarithm of the product of their inputs.

For example, for $x > 0$, $\log_3(5) + \log_3(x) = \log_3(5x)$. A proof of the product property for logarithms follows.

Let $m = \log_b(x)$ and $n = \log_b(y)$. Writing both equations in exponential form, we have

$$x = b^m$$
$$y = b^n$$

Multiplying the left sides and multiplying the right sides yields

$$xy = (b^m)(b^n) \quad \text{Multiply left sides and multiply right sides.}$$
$$= b^{m+n} \quad \text{Add exponents: } b^m b^n = b^{m+n}$$

Writing $xy = b^{m+n}$ in logarithmic form gives

$$m + n = \log_b(xy)$$

Substituting $\log_b(x)$ for *m* and $\log_b(y)$ for *n* yields

$$\log_b(x) + \log_b(y) = \log_b(xy)$$

This statement is what we set out to prove.

▶ **Example 1**   Using the Product Property for Logarithms

Simplify. Write the sum of logarithms as a single logarithm.

1. $\log_b(2x) + \log_b(x)$ 　　　　 **2.** $3 \log_b(x^2) + 2 \log_b(6x)$

Solution

1. $\log_b(2x) + \log_b(x) = \log_b(2x \cdot x)$ 　 *Product property:* $\log_b(x) + \log_b(y) = \log_b(xy)$

　　　　　　　　　　　　 $= \log_b(2x^2)$ 　　 *Add exponents:* $b^m b^n = b^{m+n}$

2. $3 \log_b(x^2) + 2 \log_b(6x) = \log_b(x^2)^3 + \log_b(6x)^2$ 　 *Power property:*
　　　　　　　　　　　　　　　　　　　　　　　　　　　　　　$p \log_b(x) = \log_b(x^p)$

　　　　　　　　　　　　 $= \log_b[(x^2)^3 \cdot (6x)^2]$ 　 *Product property:*
　　　　　　　　　　　　　　　　　　　　　　　　　　　$\log_b(x) + \log_b(y) = \log_b(xy)$

　　　　　　　　　　　　 $= \log_b[x^6 \cdot 36x^2]$ 　　 *Multiply exponents; raise*
　　　　　　　　　　　　　　　　　　　　　　　　　 factors to 2nd power.

　　　　　　　　　　　　 $= \log_b(36x^8)$ 　　　 *Add exponents:* $b^m b^n = b^{m+n}$

WARNING　　For us to apply the product property for logarithms, the coefficient of each logarithm must be 1. So, in Problem 2 of Example 1, we first applied the power property to get coefficients of 1:

$$3 \log_b(x^2) + 2 \log_b(6x) = \log_b(x^2)^3 + \log_b(6x)^2$$

Then we applied the product property.

Quotient Property

We use the product property to simplify the sum of two logarithms with the same base. We use the **quotient property for logarithms** to simplify the *difference* of two logarithms with the same base.

▶ **Quotient Property for Logarithms**

For $x > 0$, $y > 0$, $b > 0$, and $b \neq 1$,

$$\log_b(x) - \log_b(y) = \log_b\left(\frac{x}{y}\right)$$

In words, the difference of two logarithms is the logarithm of the quotient of their inputs.

For example, for $x > 0$, $\log_4(x) - \log_4(7) = \log_4\left(\frac{x}{7}\right)$. You are asked to prove the quotient property in Exercise 50.

▶ **Example 2**   Product and Quotient Properties

Simplify. Write the result as a single logarithm with a coefficient of 1.

1. $\log_b(6w^7) - \log_b(w^2)$ 　　　　 **2.** $2 \log_b(3p) + 3 \log_b(p^2) - 4 \log_b(2p)$

Solution

1. $\log_b(6w^7) - \log_b(w^2) = \log_b\left(\frac{6w^7}{w^2}\right)$ 　 *Quotient property:*
　　　　　　　　　　　　　　　　　　　　　 $\log_b(x) - \log_b(y) = \log_b\left(\frac{x}{y}\right)$

　　　　　　　　　　　　 $= \log_b(6w^5)$ 　 *Subtract exponents:* $\frac{b^m}{b^n} = b^{m-n}$

2. $2\log_b(3p) + 3\log_b(p^2) - 4\log_b(2p)$

$= \log_b(3p)^2 + \log_b(p^2)^3 - \log_b(2p)^4$ *Power property:* $p\log_b(x) = \log_b(x^p)$

$= \log_b[(3p)^2(p^2)^3] - \log_b(2p)^4$ *Product property:*
$\qquad\qquad\qquad\qquad\qquad\qquad\qquad\qquad \log_b(x) + \log_b(y) = \log_b(xy)$

$= \log_b\dfrac{(3p)^2(p^2)^3}{(2p)^4}$ *Quotient property:*
$\qquad\qquad\qquad\qquad\qquad \log_b(x) - \log_b(y) = \log_b\left(\dfrac{x}{y}\right)$

$= \log_b\dfrac{9p^2 \cdot p^6}{16p^4}$ *Raise factors to a power; multiply*
$\qquad\qquad\qquad\qquad\quad$ *exponents.*

$= \log_b\dfrac{9p^8}{16p^4}$ *Add exponents:* $b^m b^n = b^{m+n}$

$= \log_b\dfrac{9p^4}{16}$ *Subtract exponents:* $\dfrac{b^m}{b^n} = b^{m-n}$

Solving Logarithmic Equations

We can use the power, product, and quotient properties to solve logarithmic equations.

▶ **Example 3**   Solving a Logarithmic Equation

Solve $2\log_5(3x) + 4\log_5(2x) = 3$.

Solution

$\quad 2\log_5(3x) + 4\log_5(2x) = 3$ *Original equation*

$\quad\quad \log_5(3x)^2 + \log_5(2x)^4 = 3$ *Power property:* $p\log_b(x) = \log_b(x^p)$

$\quad\quad\quad \log_5[(3x)^2(2x)^4] = 3$ *Product property:* $\log_b(x) + \log_b(y) = \log_b(xy)$

$\quad\quad\quad\quad \log_5[9x^2(16x^4)] = 3$ *Raise factors to a power:* $(bc)^n = b^n c^n$

$\quad\quad\quad\quad\quad \log_5(144x^6) = 3$ *Add exponents:* $b^m b^n = b^{m+n}$

$\quad\quad\quad\quad\quad\quad\quad 5^3 = 144x^6$ *Write in exponential form.*

$\quad\quad\quad\quad\quad\quad\quad x^6 = \dfrac{125}{144}$ *Divide both sides by* 144.

Although there is a negative sixth root of $\dfrac{125}{144}$, the original equation contains $4\log_5(2x)$, and the domain of a logarithmic function is the set of *positive* numbers. So, $2x$ must be positive; hence, x must be positive:

$$x = \left(\frac{125}{144}\right)^{1/6}$$
$$x \approx 0.9767$$

▶ **Example 4**   Solving a Logarithmic Equation

Solve $5\log_7(t^3) - 2\log_7(3t) = 2$

Solution

$\quad 5\log_7(t^3) - 2\log_7(3t) = 2$ *Original equation*

$\quad\quad \log_7(t^3)^5 - \log_7(3t)^2 = 2$ *Power property:* $p\log_b(x) = \log_b(x^p)$

$\quad\quad\quad\quad \log_7\dfrac{(t^3)^5}{(3t)^2} = 2$ *Quotient property:* $\log_b(x) - \log_b(y) = \log_b\left(\dfrac{x}{y}\right)$

$$\log_7 \frac{t^{15}}{9t^2} = 2 \qquad \textit{Multiply exponents; raise factors to 2nd power.}$$

$$\log_7 \frac{t^{13}}{9} = 2 \qquad \textit{Subtract exponents: } \frac{b^m}{b^n} = b^{m-n}$$

$$7^2 = \frac{t^{13}}{9} \qquad \textit{Write in exponential form.}$$

$$t^{13} = 441 \qquad \textit{Multiply both sides by 9.}$$

$$t = 441^{1/13} \qquad \textit{The solution of } b^{13} = k \textit{ is } k^{1/13}.$$

$$t \approx 1.5974 \qquad \textit{Compute.}$$

We solved the equations in Examples 3 and 4 by first applying the power property so the coefficient of each logarithm was 1. Next, we combined the logarithms on one side of the equation by using the product property or the quotient property. Then we solved the equation by using techniques discussed in Section 5.4.

Change-of-Base Property

The "log" key on a calculator finds logarithms, base 10. We use the **change-of-base property** to find logarithms for bases other than 10.

> ▶ **Change-of-Base Property**
>
> For $a > 0$, $b > 0$, $a \neq 1$, $b \neq 1$, and $x > 0$,
>
> $$\log_b(x) = \frac{\log_a(x)}{\log_a(b)}$$

For example, $\log_3(5) = \dfrac{\log_2(5)}{\log_2(3)}$. Also, $\log_3(5) = \dfrac{\log_4(5)}{\log_4(3)}$ and $\log_3(5) = \dfrac{\log(5)}{\log(3)}$. We are free to write a logarithm in terms of any new base, including base 10.

To prove the change-of-base property, we let $k = \log_b(x)$. In exponential form, we have

$$b^k = x$$

Next, we take $\log_a$ of both sides and solve for k:

$$\log_a(b^k) = \log_a(x) \qquad \textit{Take the } \log_a \textit{ of both sides.}$$

$$k \log_a(b) = \log_a(x) \qquad \textit{Power property: } \log_a(b^k) = k \log_a(b)$$

$$k = \frac{\log_a(x)}{\log_a(b)} \qquad \textit{Divide both sides by } \log_a(b).$$

But $k = \log_b(x)$, so, by substitution, we have

$$\log_b(x) = \frac{\log_a(x)}{\log_a(b)}$$

which is what we set out to prove.

To find a logarithm to a base other than 10, we use the change-of-base property to convert to $\log_{10}$; then we can use the log key on a calculator.

Figure 49 Compute $\dfrac{\log(12)}{\log(2)}$

▶ **Example 5**   Converting to $\log_{10}$

Find $\log_2(12)$.

Solution

We can use the change-of-base property to write $\log_2(12)$ in terms of base 10:

$$\log_2(12) = \frac{\log(12)}{\log(2)}$$

Using the log key on a calculator, we compute $\dfrac{\log(12)}{\log(2)} \approx 3.5850$ (see Fig. 49). So, $\log_2(12) \approx 3.5850$.

▶ **Example 6**   Using the Change-of-Base Property

Write $\dfrac{\log_7(x)}{\log_7(4)}$ as a single logarithm.

Solution

By the change-of-base property, we have $\dfrac{\log_7(x)}{\log_7(4)} = \log_4(x)$.

In Section 5.3, we sketched the graph of a logarithmic function. From now on, we can use a graphing calculator to verify such a graph by converting the logarithmic function to $\log_{10}$.

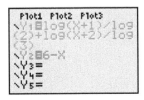

Figure 50 Graph of $y = \dfrac{\log(x)}{\log(3)}$

▶ **Example 7**   Using a Graphing Calculator to Graph a Logarithmic Function

Use a graphing calculator to draw the graph of $y = \log_3(x)$.

Solution

By the change-of-base property, we have $y = \log_3(x) = \dfrac{\log(x)}{\log(3)}$. Using the log key on a graphing calculator, we enter the function and draw the graph (see Fig. 50). This graph verifies the graph that we sketched by hand in Example 6 of Section 5.3.

Recall from Sections 3.2 and 5.4 that some equations in one variable that are impossible to solve by performing operations on both sides can be solved by graphing. We will work with one such equation in Example 8.

▶ **Example 8**   Using Graphing to Solve an Equation in One Variable

Use graphing to solve $\log_2(x + 1) + \log_3(x + 2) = 6 - x$.

Solution

We use the change-of-base property on the left side of the equation to write

$$\frac{\log(x + 1)}{\log(2)} + \frac{\log(x + 2)}{\log(3)} = 6 - x$$

Then we use "intersect" on a graphing calculator to solve the system

$$y = \frac{\log(x + 1)}{\log(2)} + \frac{\log(x + 2)}{\log(3)}$$
$$y = 6 - x$$

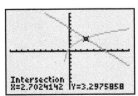

Figure 51 Solve the system

See Fig. 51.

The approximate solution of the system is $(2.7024, 3.2976)$. The x-coordinate, 2.7024, is the approximate solution of the equation $\log_2(x + 1) + \log_3(x + 2) = 6 - x$.

Comparing Properties of Logarithms

How do the properties of logarithms compare? Throughout this discussion, we assume that x, y, a, and b are positive and that a and b are not equal to 1.

The quotient property for logarithms tells us that a difference of logarithms is equal to a logarithm of a quotient:

$$\log_b(x) - \log_b(y) = \log_b\left(\frac{x}{y}\right)$$

The change-of-base property tells us that a logarithm is equal to a quotient of logarithms (with a "new" base):

$$\log_b(x) = \frac{\log_a(x)}{\log_a(b)}$$

WARNING   It is a common error to confuse the quotient property and the change-of-base property for logarithms. In general,

$$\log_b(x) - \log_b(y) \neq \frac{\log_b(x)}{\log_b(y)}$$

and

$$\log_b\left(\frac{x}{y}\right) \neq \frac{\log_b(x)}{\log_b(y)}$$

Group Exploration

Function of a sum

1. Substitute 2 for x and 3 for y and use a calculator to help you decide whether the resulting statement is true or false.
   a. $\log(x + y) = \log(x) + \log(y)$
   b. $2^{x+y} = 2^x + 2^y$
   c. $(x + y)^2 = x^2 + y^2$
   d. $\sqrt{x + y} = \sqrt{x} + \sqrt{y}$

2. All of the statements in Problem 1 are of the form $f(x + y) = f(x) + f(y)$. Is the statement

$f(x + y) = f(x) + f(y)$ true for every function f? Explain.

3. According to the distributive law, $a(x + y) = ax + ay$. Explain why this statement is true for all values of a but the statement $f(x + y) = f(x) + f(y)$ is not true for all functions f.

4. Give an example of a function f such that the statement $f(x + y) = f(x) + f(y)$ is true.

Homework 5.6

For extra help ▶ MyMathLab®   Watch the videos in MyMathLab   Download the MyDashboard App

Simplify. Write your result as a single logarithm with a coefficient of 1.

1. $\log_b(x) + \log_b(3x)$
2. $\log_b(5x) + \log_b(x)$
3. $\log_b(8x) - \log_b(2)$
4. $\log_b(24x) - \log_b(6)$
5. $4\log_b(t) + \log_b(5t)$
6. $\log_b(7w) + 3\log_b(w)$
7. $\log_b(3x^2) - 5\log_b(x)$
8. $\log_b(6x^4) - 7\log_b(x)$
9. $2\log_b(3x) + 3\log_b(x^3)$
10. $4\log_b(x^2) + 5\log_b(x)$
11. $3\log_b(2m) + 5\log_b(m^2) - \log_b(3m)$
12. $2\log_b(3k) + 4\log_b(k^3) - \log_b(5k)$

Solve. Round any solutions to the fourth decimal place.

13. $\log_5(6x) + \log_5(x) = 2$
14. $\log_3(x) + \log_3(6x) = 3$
15. $\log_2(9x) - \log_2(3) = 5$
16. $\log_4(12x) - \log_4(6) = 3$
17. $\log_7(w^2) + 2\log_7(3w) = 2$
18. $4\log_3(2r) + \log_3(r^3) = 4$
19. $\log(x^{13}) - 2\log(x^4) = 1$

20. $\log(x^9) - 3\log(x^2) = 3$

21. $3\log(x^2) + 4\log(2x) = 2$

22. $2\log(2x) + 3\log(x^4) = 4$

23. $3\log_5(p^4) - 5\log_5(2p) = 3$

24. $4\log_2(k^2) - 3\log_2(2k) = 4$

Evaluate. Round your result to the fourth decimal place.

25. $\log_3(7)$ **26.** $\log_2(11)$

27. $\log_9(3.58)$ **28.** $\log_{12}(2.88)$

29. $\log_8\left(\dfrac{1}{70}\right)$ **30.** $\log_{\frac{1}{2}}(7)$

Solve by using "intersect" on a graphing calculator. Round any solutions to the fourth decimal place.

31. $\log(x + 5) + \log(x + 2) = 3 - x$

32. $\log(x + 1) + \log(x + 4) = 8 - 2x$

33. $\log_5(x + 3) + \log_2(x + 4) = -2x + 9$

34. $\log_3(x + 2) + \log_4(x + 1) = -x + 7$

35. $\log_2(x + 4) + \log_3(x + 5) = 2^x + 1$

36. $\log_3(x + 6) + \log_2(x + 8) = 3^x + 2$

For Exercises 37–40, write the expression as a single logarithm.

37. $\dfrac{\log_2(x)}{\log_2(7)}$ **38.** $\dfrac{\log_4(x)}{\log_4(5)}$

39. $\dfrac{\log_b(r)}{\log_b(s)}$ **40.** $\dfrac{\log_b(p)}{\log_b(q)}$

For Exercises 41–44, let $g(x) = \log_{12}(x)$. Find each output. Round your result to the fourth decimal place.

41. $g(17)$ **42.** $g(50)$ **43.** $g(8)$ **44.** $g(5)$

Concepts

45. Three students try to solve the equation $3(2^x) = 7$:

Student 1's work

$3(2)^x = 7$

$2^x = \dfrac{7}{3}$

$\log(2^x) = \log\left(\dfrac{7}{3}\right)$

$x\log(2) = \log\left(\dfrac{7}{3}\right)$

$x = \dfrac{\log\left(\dfrac{7}{3}\right)}{\log(2)}$

Student 2's work

$3(2)^x = 7$

$2^x = \dfrac{7}{3}$

$x = \log_2\left(\dfrac{7}{3}\right)$

Student 3's work

$3(2)^x = 7$

$\log[3(2)^x] = \log(7)$

$\log(3) + \log(2^x) = \log(7)$

$\log(2^x) = \log(7) - \log(3)$

$x\log(2) = \log(7) - \log(3)$

$x = \dfrac{\log(7) - \log(3)}{\log(2)}$

Which student(s) solved the equation correctly? Explain.

46. A student tries to write the expression $3\log_2(x) + \log_2(x^2)$ as a single logarithm:

$$3\log_2(x) + \log_2(x^2) = 3\log_2(x \cdot x^2)$$
$$= 3\log_2(x^3)$$

Describe any errors. Then write the expression correctly as a single logarithm.

47. Which of the following expressions are equal?

$$\log_b(b^2) \qquad \log_b(b^6) - \log_b(b^4) \qquad \log_b(b^6) \qquad 2$$
$$\log_b\left(\dfrac{b^6}{b^4}\right) \qquad \dfrac{\log_b(b^6)}{\log_b(b^4)}$$

48. a. Use ZDecimal to graph $f(x) = \log(100x) - \log(x)$. Describe the graph in words.

   b. Explain why the graph of f is in neither quadrant II nor quadrant III.

   c. Use properties of logarithms to write the right-hand side of the equation of f as a constant. Use your result to explain why the graph that you found in part (a) makes sense.

49. Clearly, $\log_b(x) - \log_b(x) = 0$. Use a property of logarithms to write $\log_b(x) - \log_b(x)$ in another form to show that $\log_b(1) = 0$. Assume that $b > 0$, $x > 0$, and $b \neq 1$.

50. Prove the quotient property for logarithms. [**Hint:** Try to find a creative way to use the product property, followed by the power property, with the expression $\log_b\left(\dfrac{x}{y}\right)$.]

51. a. Simplify $\log_2(x^3) + \log_2(x^5)$.

   b. Solve $\log_2(x^3) + \log_2(x^5) = 7$. Round any solutions to the fourth decimal place.

   c. Compare the process of simplifying an expression with solving an equation.

   d. Explain how simplifying an expression can help when you are solving an equation.

52. List the properties for logarithms discussed in this section and in Section 5.4. Explain how each property can be used. Give examples to illustrate your points.

Related Review

Simplify by writing your result as a single logarithm with a coefficient of 1, or solve, as appropriate. Round any solutions to the fourth decimal place.

53. $\log_2(x^4) + \log_2(x^3)$

54. $\log_2(t^9) - \log_2(t^5) = 5$

55. $\log_2(x^4) + \log_2(x^3) = 4$

56. $\log_2(t^9) - \log_2(t^5)$

57. $2\log_9(x^3) - 3\log_9(2x) = 2$

58. $3\log_5(3x) + 2\log_5(x^2)$

59. $2\log_9(x^3) - 3\log_9(2x)$

60. $3\log_5(3x) + 2\log_5(x^2) = 3$

Simplify. If an expression contains two logarithms, write your result as a single logarithm with a coefficient of 1.

61. $\left(16b^{16}c^{-7}\right)^{1/4}\left(27b^{27}c^5\right)^{1/3}$

62. $\dfrac{\left(25b^9c^{-6}\right)^{1/2}}{\left(81b^3c^{-8}\right)^{1/4}}$

63. $3\log_b\left(2x^5\right) + 2\log_b\left(3x^4\right)$

64. $4\log_b\left(3x^2\right) - 5\log_b\left(2x^7\right)$

Solve the system.

65. $y = 3x - 7$
    $y = -2x + 3$

66. $y = \dfrac{1}{2}x - 4$

    $y = -\dfrac{2}{3}x + 3$

67. $y = \log_2\left(4x^2\right) - 3$
    $y = \log_2(x) + 2$

68. $y = 2 + \log_3\left(3x^2\right)$
    $y = 8 - \log_3(9x)$

Expressions, Equations, Functions, and Graphs

Perform the indicated instruction. Then use words such as linear, exponential, logarithmic, function, one variable, *and* two variables *to describe the expression, equation, or system.*

69. Solve:

$$2x - 3y = 6$$
$$y = \dfrac{2}{3}x - 2$$

70. Solve $\log_3(2m - 1) = 5$.

71. Graph $2x - 3y = 6$ by hand.

72. Find $f(5)$, where $f(x) = \log_3(2x - 1)$.

▼ 5.7 Natural Logarithms

Objectives

» Know the meaning of a *natural logarithm.*

» Evaluate natural logarithms.

» Use properties of natural logarithms to simplify expressions and solve equations.

» Use exponential models with base e to make estimates and predictions.

In Chapter 4 and in this chapter, we have worked with exponential and logarithmic functions with various values of the base. In statistics and calculus, it is helpful to use a special constant called e as the base for these two types of functions. In this section, we will describe this constant and use it as the base for logarithmic and exponential functions.

Definition of Natural Logarithm

In this section, we discuss a logarithm with a special base called e, where e is an irrational number:

$$e \approx 2.718281828459045\ldots$$

To the nearest ten-thousandth, $e = 2.7183$.

Many equations for useful models contain e. For example, the equation for one type of "bell curve" is

$$f(x) = \dfrac{e^{-0.5x^2}}{\sqrt{2\pi}}$$

The graph of f has the shape of a bell (see Fig. 52). Bell curves can be used to model heights of women (or men), IQs, widths of trunks of redwood trees, and many other quantities.

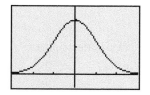

Figure 52 Graph of

$f(x) = \dfrac{e^{-0.5x^2}}{\sqrt{2\pi}}$

▶ Definition   Natural logarithm

A **natural logarithm** is a logarithm with base e. We write $\ln(a)$ to represent $\log_e(a)$.

Throughout the discussion that follows, assume that $a > 0, b > 0$, and $b \neq 1$.

Recall from Section 5.3 that $\log_b(a)$ is the exponent on the base b that gives a. So, **for $a > 0$, $\ln(a)$ is the exponent on the base e that gives a.**

Recall from Section 5.4 that $\log_b(a) = c$ and $b^c = a$ are equivalent forms. In terms of base e, this means $\ln(a) = c$ and $e^c = a$ are equivalent forms.

▶ **Exponential/Natural Logarithmic Forms Property**

For $a > 0$, the equations

$$\ln(a) = c \quad \text{and} \quad e^c = a$$

are equivalent.

The equation $\ln(a) = c$ is in logarithmic form, and the equation $e^c = a$ is in exponential form. Either form can replace the other when you solve a problem.

The key on most graphing calculators that is labeled "ln" or "LN" will give you the natural logarithm of a number.

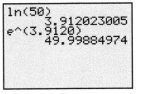

Figure 53 Computing ln(50)

▶ **Example 1** Finding a Natural Logarithm

Use a calculator to find $\ln(50)$.

Solution

By pressing $\boxed{\text{LN}}$ 50 $\boxed{)}$ $\boxed{\text{ENTER}}$, we get $\ln(50) \approx 3.9120$ (see Fig. 53). This means that $e^{3.9120} \approx 50$. We check that $e^{3.9120} \approx 50$ by pressing $\boxed{\text{2nd}}$ $\boxed{\text{LN}}$ 3.9120 $\boxed{)}$ $\boxed{\text{ENTER}}$.

▶

We can find the natural logarithm of powers of e without using a calculator.

▶ **Example 2** Finding a Natural Logarithm

Find $\ln(e^5)$.

Solution

$$\ln\left(e^5\right) = \log_e\left(e^5\right) \quad \textit{Definition of natural logarithm}$$
$$= 5 \quad \textit{Simplify.}$$

▶

From Example 2, we see that for the function ln, the input e^5 leads to the output 5. So, the *positive* real number e^5 is in the domain of ln. Recall from Section 5.3 that for *any* logarithmic function, the domain is the set of all positive real numbers.

Solving Logarithmic and Exponential Equations

In Example 3, we solve two logarithmic equations.

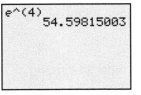

Figure 54 Computing e^4

▶ **Example 3** Solving Logarithmic Equations

Solve the equation.

1. $\ln(x) = 4$ **2.** $3\ln(4x) - 2 = 5$

Solution

1. We write $\ln(x) = 4$ in the exponential form $e^4 = x$. The approximate solution is 54.5982 (see Fig. 54).

2.
$$3\ln(4x) - 2 = 5 \quad \textit{Original equation}$$
$$3\ln(4x) = 7 \quad \textit{Add 2 to both sides.}$$
$$\ln(4x) = \frac{7}{3} \quad \textit{Divide both sides by 3.}$$
$$e^{7/3} = 4x \quad \textit{Write in exponential form.}$$
$$\frac{e^{7/3}}{4} = x \quad \textit{Divide both sides by 4.}$$
$$x \approx 2.5781 \quad \textit{Compute.}$$

We check that 2.5781 approximately satisfies the equation $3\ln(4x) - 2 = 5$:

$$3\ln[4(2.5781)] - 2 \approx 5.00004 \approx 5$$

▶

▶ **Example 4**   Solving an Exponential Equation

Solve $5e^{x-1} = 100$.

Solution

$$5e^{x-1} = 100 \qquad \text{\textit{Original equation}}$$
$$e^{x-1} = 20 \qquad \text{\textit{Divide both sides by 5.}}$$
$$\ln(20) = x - 1 \qquad \text{\textit{Write in logarithmic form.}}$$
$$\ln(20) + 1 = x \qquad \text{\textit{Add 1 to both sides.}}$$
$$x \approx 3.9957 \qquad \text{\textit{Compute.}}$$

We check that 3.9957 approximately satisfies the equation $5e^{x-1} = 100$:

$$5e^{3.9957-1} \approx 99.9968 \approx 100$$

▶

How do the properties for $\log_b(x)$ correspond to the properties for $\ln(x)$? Assume that $x > 0, y > 0, b > 0$, and $b \neq 1$ unless stated otherwise. The following properties apply:

Properties of Logarithms

$\log_b(1) = 0$

$\log_b(b) = 1$

$\log_b(b^x) = x,$
   for real number x
$b^{\log_b(x)} = x$

$\log_b(x^p) = p \log_b(x)$

$\log_b(x) + \log_b(y) = \log_b(xy)$

$\log_b(x) - \log_b(y) = \log_b\left(\dfrac{x}{y}\right)$

Properties of Natural Logarithms

$\ln(1) = 0$ — *The natural logarithm of 1 is 0.*

$\ln(e) = 1$ — *The natural logarithm of e is 1.*

$\ln(e^x) = x,$
   for real number x — *Composing $y = \ln(x)$ with $y = e^x$*
$e^{\ln(x)} = x$ — *Composing $y = e^x$ with $y = \ln(x)$*

$\ln(x^p) = p \ln(x)$ — *Power property*

$\ln(x) + \ln(y) = \ln(xy)$ — *Product property*

$\ln(x) - \ln(y) = \ln\left(\dfrac{x}{y}\right)$ — *Quotient property*

We can use the power property for natural logarithms to solve exponential equations.

▶ **Example 5**   Solving an Equation

Solve $2(5)^t + 3 = 63$.

Solution

$$2(5)^t + 3 = 63 \qquad \text{\textit{Original equation}}$$
$$2(5)^t = 60 \qquad \text{\textit{Subtract 3 from both sides.}}$$
$$5^t = 30 \qquad \text{\textit{Divide both sides by 2.}}$$
$$\ln(5^t) = \ln(30) \qquad \text{\textit{Take the natural logarithm of both sides.}}$$
$$t \ln(5) = \ln(30) \qquad \text{\textit{Power property: } \ln(x^p) = p\ln(x)}$$
$$t = \frac{\ln(30)}{\ln(5)} \qquad \text{\textit{Divide both sides by ln(5).}}$$
$$t \approx 2.1133 \qquad \text{\textit{Compute.}}$$

We check that 2.1133 approximately satisfies the equation $2(5)^t + 3 = 63$:

$$2(5)^{2.1133} + 3 \approx 63.0017 \approx 63$$

▶

In Example 5, we used ln to solve an exponential equation. In Section 5.4, we used log to solve exponential equations. It does not matter whether we use ln or log to solve an exponential equation such as $2(5)^t + 3 = 63$. Both methods require about the same amount of work and give the same result.

In Example 6, we use the power and quotient properties for logarithms to simplify a logarithmic expression.

▶ **Example 6**   Power and Quotient Properties

Write $5 \ln(x^3) - 3 \ln(2x)$ as a single logarithm with a coefficient of 1. Simplify the result.

Solution

$$5 \ln(x^3) - 3 \ln(2x) = \ln(x^3)^5 - \ln(2x)^3 \quad \text{\textit{Power property: } } p\ln(x) = \ln(x^p)$$

$$= \ln \frac{(x^3)^5}{(2x)^3} \quad \text{\textit{Quotient property: } } \ln(x) - \ln(y) = \ln\left(\frac{x}{y}\right)$$

$$= \ln \frac{x^{15}}{8x^3} \quad \text{\textit{Multiply exponents; raise factors to 3rd power.}}$$

$$= \ln \frac{x^{12}}{8} \quad \text{\textit{Subtract exponents: } } \frac{b^m}{b^n} = b^{m-n}$$

We verify our work by comparing tables for the functions $y = 5 \ln(x^3) - 3 \ln(2x)$ and $y = \ln \frac{x^{12}}{8}$ (see Fig. 55).

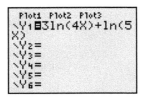

Figure 55 Verify the work

▶

▶ **Example 7**   Solving an Equation

Solve $3 \ln(4x) + \ln(5x) = 7$.

Solution

$$3 \ln(4x) + \ln(5x) = 7 \quad \text{\textit{Original equation}}$$

$$\ln(4x)^3 + \ln(5x) = 7 \quad \text{\textit{Power property: } } p\ln(x) = \ln(x^p)$$

$$\ln\left[(4x)^3(5x)\right] = 7 \quad \text{\textit{Product property: } } \ln(x) + \ln(y) = \ln(xy)$$

$$\ln\left[64x^3(5x)\right] = 7 \quad \text{\textit{Raise factors to nth power: } } (bc)^n = b^n c^n$$

$$\ln(320x^4) = 7 \quad \text{\textit{Add exponents: } } b^m b^n = b^{m+n}$$

$$e^7 = 320x^4 \quad \text{\textit{Write in exponential form.}}$$

$$x^4 = \frac{e^7}{320} \quad \text{\textit{Divide both sides by 320.}}$$

Although there is a negative fourth root of $\frac{e^7}{320}$, the original equation contains $3 \ln(4x)$, and the domain of a (natural) logarithm function is the set of *positive* numbers. So, $4x$ must be positive. Hence, x must be positive:

$$x = \left(\frac{e^7}{320}\right)^{1/4}$$

$$x \approx 1.3606$$

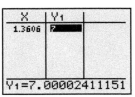

We use a graphing calculator table to check that, for the function $y = 3 \ln(4x) + \ln(5x)$, the input 1.3606 leads approximately to the output 7 (see Fig. 56).

Figure 56 Verify the work   ▶

Table 61 Numbers of BlackBerry Subscribers

Year	Number of Subscribers (millions)
2000	0.03
2002	0.32
2004	1.07
2006	5.0
2008	16
2010	50

Source: *Research in Motion*

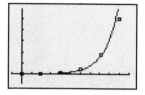

Figure 57 Verify the fit

Exponential Models with Base *e*

So far, we have worked with exponential models of the form $f(t) = ab^t$. In calculus, it is often helpful to write such models in the form $f(t) = ae^{kt}$, where a and k are constants.

▶ **Example 8**   Using a Model with Base *e* to Make a Prediction

The BlackBerry® is a wireless handheld device. The numbers of BlackBerry subscribers are shown in Table 61 for various years. Let $f(t)$ be the number of BlackBerry subscribers (in millions) at t years since 2000. A possible equation of f is

$$f(t) = 0.05e^{0.72t}$$

1. Verify that f models the situation well.
2. Predict when there will be 500 million subscribers.

Solution

1. We draw the graph of f and the scattergram of the data in the same viewing window (see Fig. 57). It appears that f is a reasonable model.
2. To predict when there will be 500 million subscribers, we substitute 500 for $f(t)$ and solve for t:

$$500 = 0.05e^{0.72t} \qquad \text{\textit{Substitute 500 for f(x).}}$$

$$\frac{500}{0.05} = e^{0.72t} \qquad \text{\textit{Divide both sides by 0.05.}}$$

$$\ln\left(\frac{500}{0.05}\right) = \ln\left(e^{0.72t}\right) \qquad \text{\textit{Take the natural logarithm of both sides.}}$$

$$\ln\left(\frac{500}{0.05}\right) = 0.72t \qquad \text{\textit{ln}}\left(e^a\right) = a$$

$$t = \frac{\ln\left(\dfrac{500}{0.05}\right)}{0.72} \qquad \text{\textit{Divide both sides by 0.72.}}$$

$$t \approx 12.79 \qquad \text{\textit{Compute.}}$$

The model predicts there will be 500 million subscribers in 2013.

 Group Exploration

Newton's law of cooling

A hot potato is taken out of an oven and allowed to cool to room temperature. Let p be the temperature (in degrees Fahrenheit) of the potato at t minutes after it is removed from the oven.

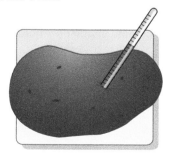

1. Sketch a qualitative graph that describes the relationship between t and p.
2. Newton's law of cooling states that

$$p - r = ae^{-kt}$$

where r is room temperature (in degrees Fahrenheit) and a and k are constants. The room temperature is 70°F. Substitute $r = 70$ into the equation.
3. The temperature of the potato was 350°F when it was removed from the oven. Find the value of the constant a, and substitute it into your equation.
4. The temperature of the potato was 200°F 5 minutes later. Find the value of k, and substitute it into your equation.
5. Isolate p on one side of your equation. Then use a graphing calculator to draw the graph of your equation. Compare your graph with your sketch in Problem 1.
6. What will be the temperature of the potato after a long time? Explain.
7. Estimate at what temperature a potato can be comfortably eaten. How long will it take for the potato to reach that temperature?

▶ Tips for Success   **Calm Down during a Test**

If you get flustered during a test, close your eyes, take a couple of deep breaths, and think about something pleasant or nothing at all for a moment. This short break might give you some perspective and help you relax.

Homework 5.7

For extra help ▶ MyMathLab®   ▦ Watch the videos in MyMathLab   ◉ Download the MyDashboard App

Use a calculator to find the natural logarithm. Round your result to the fourth decimal place.

1. $\ln(54.8)$ **2.** $\ln(37.28)$ **3.** $\ln\left(\dfrac{1}{2}\right)$ **4.** $\ln\left(\dfrac{5}{8}\right)$

Simplify. Verify your result by using a graphing calculator.

5. $\ln\left(e^4\right)$ **6.** $\ln\left(e^6\right)$ **7.** $\ln(e)$ **8.** $\ln(1)$

9. $\ln\left(\dfrac{1}{e}\right)$ **10.** $\ln\left(\dfrac{1}{e^2}\right)$ **11.** $\dfrac{1}{2}\ln\left(e^6\right)$ **12.** $\ln\left(\sqrt{e}\right)$

13. $e^{\ln 7}$ **14.** $e^{\ln 4}$

Solve the equation. Round any solutions to the fourth decimal place. Use graphing calculator tables or graphs to verify your result.

15. $\ln(x) = 2$ **16.** $\ln(x) = 5$

17. $\ln(p + 5) = 3$ **18.** $\ln(t - 4) = 5$

19. $7e^x = 44$ **20.** $3e^x = 85$

21. $5\ln(3x) + 2 = 7$ **22.** $2\ln(5x) - 3 = 1$

23. $4e^{3m-1} = 68$ **24.** $7e^{2p+10} = 100$

25. $e^{3x-5} \cdot e^{2x} = 135$ **26.** $e^{2x-3} \cdot e^x = 83$

27. $3.1^x = 49.8$ **28.** $2.4^x = 63.5$

29. $3(6)^x - 1 = 97$ **30.** $5(2)^x + 3 = 264$

31. $5e^x - 20 = 2e^x + 67$ **32.** $7e^x - 12 = 3e^x + 44$

Simplify. Write the expression as a single logarithm with a coefficient of 1. Use graphing calculator tables or graphs to verify your result.

33. $\ln(4x) + \ln\left(3x^4\right)$ **34.** $\ln\left(8x^2\right) + \ln(4x)$

35. $\ln\left(25x^4\right) - \ln\left(5x^3\right)$ **36.** $\ln\left(6x^3\right) - \ln\left(2x^4\right)$

37. $2\ln\left(w^4\right) + 3\ln(2w)$ **38.** $4\ln(3r) + 5\ln\left(r^3\right)$

39. $3\ln(3x) - 2\ln\left(x^2\right)$ **40.** $2\ln\left(x^3\right) - 3\ln(2x)$

41. $3\ln(2k) + 4\ln\left(k^2\right) - \ln\left(k^7\right)$

42. $5\ln\left(p^2\right) + 2\ln(3p) - \ln\left(p^9\right)$

Solve the equation. Round any solutions to the fourth decimal place. Check your result.

43. $\ln(3x) + \ln(x) = 4$

44. $\ln(2x) + \ln(5x) = 6$

45. $\ln\left(4w^5\right) - 2\ln\left(w^2\right) = 5$

46. $\ln\left(7r^{15}\right) - 3\ln\left(r^4\right) = 1$

47. $2\ln(3x) + 2\ln\left(x^3\right) = 8$

48. $4\ln(2x) + 3\ln\left(x^5\right) = 9$

49. $5\ln(2m) - 3\ln\left(m^4\right) = 7$

50. $3\ln(4y) - 4\ln\left(y^3\right) = 5$

Solve by using "intersect" on a graphing calculator. Round any solutions to the fourth decimal place.

51. $e^x = 5 - x$

52. $2e^x = 9 - 2x$

53. $3\ln(x + 2) = -2x + 6$

54. $2\ln(x + 1) = -x + 7$

55. $3\ln(x + 3) = 0.7x + 2$

56. $4\ln(x + 5) = x + 5$

For Exercises 57–60, let $f(x) = 4\ln(x)$.

57. Find $f\left(e^5\right)$.

58. Find $f\left(\dfrac{1}{e^3}\right)$.

59. Find x when $f(x) = -8$.

60. Find x when $f(x) = 2$.

61. Assume the equation $ae^{bx} = c$ has a solution for x, where $a \neq 0$ and $b \neq 0$. Solve for x.

62. Assume the equation $ae^{bx+d} + k = c$ has a solution for x, where $a \neq 0$ and $b \neq 0$. Solve for x.

63. Pointing a laser at aircraft, which can temporarily blind pilots, is a serious offense with a maximum punishment of 20 years in prison and a \$250,000 fine. The numbers of laser incidents involving aircraft are shown in Table 62 for various years.

Table 62 Numbers of Laser Incidents Involving Aircraft

Year	Number
2005	283
2006	446
2007	675
2008	988
2009	1527
2010	2836

Source: *Federal Aviation Administration*

Let $n = f(t)$ be the number of laser incidents involving aircraft in the year that is t years since 2000. An equation of f is

$$f(t) = 29.89e^{0.45t}$$

a. Use a graphing calculator to draw the graph of the model and, in the same viewing window, the scattergram of the data. Does the model fit the data well?

b. Find the *n*-intercept. What does it mean in this situation?

c. Predict when there will be 60,000 laser incidents involving aircraft.

d. Cockpits have been illuminated in 67% of laser incidents involving aircraft. Predict the number of times cockpits will be illuminated in 2018.

64. Americans for Prosperity is a conservative interest group that promotes less regulation and lower government spending. The annual budgets of the group are shown in Table 63 for various years.

Table 63 Annual Budget of Americans for Prosperity

Year	Annual Budget (millions of dollars)
2007	7
2008	12
2009	28
2010	40
2011	50
2012	129

Source: *Americans for Prosperity*

Let $B = f(t)$ be the annual budget (in millions of dollars) of Americans for Prosperity at t years since 2000. An equation of f is

$$f(t) = 0.16e^{0.55t}$$

a. Use a graphing calculator to draw the graph of the model and, in the same viewing window, the scattergram of the data. Does the model fit the data well?

b. Find the *B*-intercept. What does it mean in this situation?

c. Predict the annual budget in 2017.

d. Predict when the annual budget will reach $1.8 *billion*.

65. A person buys a cup of coffee and drinks it in the store. The coffee's temperature y (in degrees Fahrenheit) is given by

$$y = 70 + 137e^{-0.06t}$$

where t is the number of minutes since he bought the coffee.

a. What was the temperature of the coffee when the person bought it?

b. If the person begins drinking the coffee when it reaches 180°F, how much time must he wait after buying it?

c. Use a graphing calculator table or graph to estimate the room temperature of the *store*.

66. A person makes a cup of tea. The tea's temperature y (in degrees Fahrenheit) is given by

$$y = 68 + 132e^{-0.05t}$$

where t is the number of minutes since the person made the tea.

a. What was the temperature of the tea when the person made it?

b. If the person waits 5 minutes to begin drinking the tea, what is the temperature of the tea then?

c. The tea is *lukewarm* at a temperature of about 98.6°F. If the person lets the tea sit until it is lukewarm, how much time has gone by since she made it?

67. A cable hangs between two poles that are 20 feet apart (see Fig. 58). The height of the cable (in feet) is given by

$$h(x) = 10\left(e^{0.03x} + e^{-0.03x}\right), \quad -10 \le x \le 10$$

where x is the horizontal position (in feet) as indicated in Fig. 58.

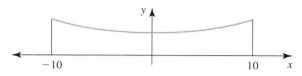

Figure 58 Exercise 67

a. Find the height of the cable at either pole.

b. Find $h(6)$. What does it mean in this situation?

c. How high is the cable where it is closest to the ground?

68. A cable hangs between two poles that are 30 feet apart (see Fig. 59). The height of the cable (in feet) is given by

$$h(x) = 20\left(e^{0.05x} + e^{-0.05x}\right), \quad -15 \le x \le 15$$

where x is the horizontal position (in feet) as indicated in Fig. 59.

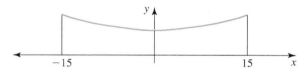

Figure 59 Exercise 68

a. Find $h(-8)$. What does it mean in this situation?

b. How high is the cable where it is closest to the ground?

c. Explain why there is model breakdown for $x < -15$ and for $x > 15$.

Concepts

69. Two students try to solve the equation $2^x = 7$:

Student 1's work	Student 2's work
$2^x = 7$	$2^x = 7$
$\ln(2^x) = \ln(7)$	$\log(2^x) = \log(7)$
$x \ln(2) = \ln(7)$	$x \log(2) = \log(7)$
$x = \dfrac{\ln(7)}{\ln(2)}$	$x = \dfrac{\log(7)}{\log(2)}$

Which student(s) solved the equation correctly? Explain.

70. A student tries to simplify $\log\left(e^8\right)$:

$$\log\left(e^8\right) = 8$$

Is the work correct? Explain.

71. Which expressions are equal? Assume that $x > 0$ and $x \neq 1$.

$$3\ln(x) \quad \ln\left(x^7\right) - \ln\left(x^4\right) \quad 2\ln(x)\ln(x) \quad \frac{\ln\left(x^7\right)}{\ln\left(x^4\right)}$$

$$\ln\left(x^3\right) \qquad \ln(3x)$$

72. a. Solve $e^x = 30$ by writing the equation in logarithmic form.

b. Solve $e^x = 30$ by taking the natural logarithm of both sides of the equation.

c. Compare your results in parts (a) and (b).

73. Explain in your own words why $\ln(e) = 1$.

74. Explain in your own words why $\ln(1) = 0$.

75. a.   i. To solve $3^x = 58$, begin by taking the natural logarithm of both sides.

     ii. To solve $3^x = 58$, begin by taking the common log (base 10) of both sides.

     iii. Compare your results in parts (i) and (ii).

  b. Create an equation of the form $b^x = c$, where b and c are positive and $b \neq 1$.

     i. To solve your equation, begin by taking the natural logarithm of both sides.

     ii. To solve your equation, begin by taking the common log (base 10) of both sides.

     iii. Compare your results in parts (i) and (ii).

  c. Summarize the main point of this exercise.

76. Explain how to use the power property for natural logarithms to solve an exponential equation in one variable.

Related Review

Simplify by writing your result as a single logarithm with a coefficient of 1, or solve, as appropriate. Round any solutions to the fourth decimal place.

77. $\ln(x^8) - \ln(x^3)$

78. $2\ln(4x) + 3\ln(x^2)$

79. $\ln(x^8) - \ln(x^3) = 4$

80. $2\ln(4x) + 3\ln(x^2) = 7$

Solve. Find the exact solution if the equation is linear. For any other type of equation, round the solution(s) to the fourth decimal place.

81. $3e^x - 5 = 7$

82. $4\log_2(x^2) - 2\log_2(3x) = 5$

83. $7 - 3(2t - 4) = 5t + 6$

84. $\log(w - 17) = 2$

85. $\dfrac{b^7}{b^3} = 16$

86. $3\ln(2x) + 4\ln(x^2) = 7$

Expressions, Equations, Functions, and Graphs

Give an example of the following. Then solve, simplify, or graph, as appropriate.

87. expression involving exponents

88. system of two linear equations in two variables

89. logarithmic equation in one variable

90. sum of two natural logarithmic expressions

91. linear function

92. exponential function

Taking it to the Lab

China and India Populations Lab

In this lab, you will compare the populations of China and India.*

Collecting the Data

For both countries, you will find populations for every five years since 1950, plus make a projection for the current year.

1. Go to www.census.gov/population/international/data/idb/ informationGateway.php. Under "Select Country(ies)," hold the CTRL key and select China and India. Under "Select Year(s)," hold the CTRL key and select the years that are multiples of 5 between 1950 and the present (1950, 1955, 1960, etc.). The current year should already be highlighted. (Mac users: If the control key doesn't work, try using the command key.) Then click "Submit."

2. Record the data or print the screen.

Analyzing the Data

1. Include tables of data for China's population and India's population.

2. Define the variables for your models. [**Hint:** Describe the units of the variables.]

3. Which variables are the independent variables? Which variables are the dependent variables? If you round the data, describe how.

4. Use a graphing calculator to draw scattergrams of the data. Copy the scattergrams on paper. For both countries, discuss whether a linear or an exponential function is the better choice of model. Explain.

5. For both countries, find an equation of a model.

6. For both countries, use a graphing calculator to graph your model and your scattergram in the same viewing window. Also, graph your model and scattergram by hand. How well does your model fit the data?

7. Which country has the larger current population? Use your models to estimate the difference in the current populations.

8. Use "intersect" on a graphing calculator to predict when the populations will be equal.

9. Go to www.census.gov to find an estimate of the current world population. Use a model to predict when China's population will reach that size. Use a model to predict when India's population will reach that size. In terms of the types of functions used to model the populations, explain why the two results are so different.

*"Taking it to the Lab: China and India Populations Lab" adapted from a lab written by Cheryl Gregory, College of San Marco, CA. Used by permission of Cheryl Gregory.

10. Use your models to predict when the sum of the populations of China and India will reach the current world population. Explain how you found your result.

Folding Paper Lab

In this lab, you will investigate the thickness of a sheet of paper by folding it many times.

Materials

To do this lab, you will need the following materials:

1. an $8\frac{1}{2}$-inch-by-11-inch piece of paper

2. a ruler

Preparation

Fold the piece of paper in half six times very carefully, each time without unfolding.

Recording of Data

Use the ruler to measure the thickness of the folded paper.

Analyzing the Data

1. What is the thickness of the folded paper (after six folds)? Include units.

2. Use your answer to Part 1 to estimate the thickness of the paper when it is unfolded. Include units.

3. Let $f(n)$ be the thickness of the paper if it has been folded n times. Find an equation of f. What are the units of $f(n)$?

4. Can you fold the paper a seventh time? If not, use f to predict the thickness if it could be folded seven times. If

you can, keep folding the paper until you cannot fold it any more and predict the thickness if it could be folded one more time.

5. How thick would the folded paper be if you could fold it 15 times? Would the folded paper be taller or shorter than you?

6. After how many folds would the folded paper be at least as tall as a football field is long (that is, 120 yards long if you include the end zones)?

7. After how many folds would the thickness of the folded paper match the distance to the Moon? (The average distance to the Moon is approximately 238,857 miles. There are 5280 feet in 1 mile.)

8. The situation in this lab is limited by your inability to fold the paper many times. Instead of folding a piece of paper, you could cut a piece of paper in half, then stack the two halves. Next, you could cut the stack of papers and restack the two piles of papers. Cutting the stack in two each time and then restacking achieves the same thickness as folding the paper in two. By cutting and stacking, can the result described in Part 7 be achieved? Explain.

Exponential/Logarithmic Lab: Topic of Your Choice

Repeat the Exponential Lab: Topic of Your Choice, but choose a different situation. Also, choose an output of your model. Find the input that originates from that output. What does the result mean in this situation?

Chapter Summary

Key Points of Chapter 5

Section 5.1   Composite Functions

Composite function	If f and g are functions, x is in the domain of g, and $g(x)$ is in the domain of f, then we can form the **composite function** $f \circ g$: $(f \circ g)(x) = f(g(x))$. We say $f \circ g$ is the **composition of f and g**.

Section 5.2   Inverse Functions

Inverse of a function f	The **inverse of a function f** is a relation that sends b to a if $f(a) = b$.
Invertible function	If the inverse of a function f is also a function, we say f is **invertible** and use "f^{-1}" as a name for the inverse of f.
Property of an inverse function	For an invertible function f, the following statements are equivalent: $f(a) = b$ and $f^{-1}(b) = a$.

Section 5.2   Inverse Functions (*Continued*)

f and f^{-1} are inverses of each other	If f is an invertible function, then • f^{-1} is invertible, • f and f^{-1} are inverses of each other, • $\left(f^{-1} \circ f\right)(x) = x$, where x is in the domain of f, and • $\left(f \circ f^{-1}\right)(x) = x$, where x is in the domain of f^{-1}.
Reflection property of inverse functions	For an invertible function f, the graph of f^{-1} is the reflection of the graph of f across the line $y = x$.
Graphing an inverse function	For an invertible function f, we sketch the graph of f^{-1} by the following steps: **1.** Sketch the graph of f. **2.** Choose several points that lie on the graph of f. **3.** For each point (a, b) chosen from step 2, plot the point (b, a). **4.** Sketch the curve that contains the points plotted in step 3.
Three-step process for finding the inverse of a model	To find the inverse of an invertible *model* f, where $p = f(t)$, **1.** Replace $f(t)$ with p. **2.** Solve for t. **3.** Replace t with $f^{-1}(p)$.
Four-step process for finding the inverse of a function that is not a model	Let f be an invertible function that is *not* a model. To find the inverse of f, where $y = f(x)$, **1.** Replace $f(x)$ with y. **2.** Solve for x. **3.** Replace x with $f^{-1}(y)$. **4.** Write the equation of f^{-1} in terms of x.
One-to-one function	If each output of a function originates from exactly one input, we say that the function is **one-to-one**.

Section 5.3   Logarithmic Functions

Definition of a logarithm	For $b > 0$, $b \neq 1$, and $a > 0$, the **logarithm $\log_b(a)$** is the number k such that $b^k = a$. In words, $\log_b(a)$ is the exponent on the base b that gives a. We call b the **base** of the logarithm.
Common logarithm	A **common logarithm** is a logarithm with base 10. We write $\log(a)$ to represent $\log_{10}(a)$.
Properties of logarithms	For $b > 0$ and $b \neq 1$, • $\log_b(b) = 1$ • $\log_b(1) = 0$ • $\log_b(b^x) = x$ • $b^{\log_b(x)} = x$, where $x > 0$
Logarithmic function	A **logarithmic function, base b,** is a function that can be put into the form $f(x) = \log_b(x)$, where $b > 0$ and $b \neq 1$.
Domain of a logarithmic function	The domain of a logarithmic function $\log_b$ is the set of all positive real numbers.
Logarithmic and exponential functions are inverses of each other	For an exponential function $f(x) = b^x$, $f^{-1}(x) = \log_b(x)$. For a logarithmic function $g(x) = \log_b(x)$, $g^{-1}(x) = b^x$.
Graphing $y = \log_b(x)$	To graph a logarithmic function $y = \log_b(x)$, use the four-step graphing method from Section 5.2 to sketch the inverse of $f(x) = b^x$.

Section 5.3   Logarithmic Functions (*Continued*)

Richter number	The *Richter number, R,* of an earthquake is given by $$R = \log\left(\frac{A}{A_0}\right)$$ where A is the amplitude (maximum value) of a seismic wave and A_0, called the *reference amplitude,* is the amplitude of the smallest seismic wave that a seismograph can detect.

Section 5.4   Properties of Logarithms

Exponential/logarithmic forms property	For $a > 0, b > 0$, and $b \neq 1, \log_b(a) = c$ and $b^c = a$ are equivalent.
Logarithmic equation in one variable	A **logarithmic equation in one variable** is an equation in one variable that contains one or more logarithms.
Solving $\log_b(x) = k$	For an equation of the form $\log_b(x) = k$, we can solve for b or x by writing the equation in exponential form.
Exponential equation in one variable	An **exponential equation in one variable** is an equation in one variable in which an exponent contains a variable.
Power property for logarithms	For $x > 0, b > 0$, and $b \neq 1, \log_b(x^p) = p\log_b(x)$.
Logarithm property of equality	For positive real numbers a, b, and c, where $b \neq 1$, the equations $a = c$ and $\log_b(a) = \log_b(c)$ are equivalent.
Solving $ab^x = c$ for x	To solve some equations of the form $ab^x = c$ for x, we divide both sides of the equation by a and then take the log of both sides. Next, we use the power property for logarithms.

Section 5.5   Using the Power Property with Exponential Models to Make Predictions

Making a prediction	To make a prediction about the independent variable t of an exponential model of the form $f(t) = ab^t$, we substitute a value for $f(t)$ and divide both sides of the equation by the coefficient a. Next, we take the log of both sides of the equation and use the power property to help solve for t.

Section 5.6   More Properties of Logarithms

Properties of logarithms	For $x > 0, y > 0, a > 0, b > 0, a \neq 1$, and $b \neq 1$, • $\log_b(x) + \log_b(y) = \log_b(xy)$ Product property for logarithms • $\log_b(x) - \log_b(y) = \log_b\left(\frac{x}{y}\right)$ Quotient property for logarithms • $\log_b(x) = \dfrac{\log_a(x)}{\log_a(b)}$ Change-of-base property
Finding $\log_b(a)$ where $b \neq 10$	To find a logarithm to a base other than 10, we use the change-of-base property for logarithms to convert to $\log_{10}$; then we can use the log key on a calculator.

Section 5.7   Natural Logarithms

Approximation of e	To the nearest ten-thousandth, $e = 2.7183$.
Definition of a natural logarithm	A **natural logarithm** is a logarithm with base e. We write $\ln(a)$ to represent $\log_e(a)$.
Meaning of $\ln(a)$	For $a > 0, \ln(a)$ is the exponent on the base e that gives a.
Exponential/natural logarithmic forms property	For $a > 0$, the equations $\ln(a) = c$ and $e^c = a$ are equivalent.

Section 5.7 Natural Logarithms (*Continued*)

Properties of natural logarithms

$\ln(1) = 0$

$\ln(e) = 1$

$\ln(e^x) = x$

For $x > 0$ and $y > 0$,

- $e^{\ln(x)} = x$
- $\ln(x^p) = p\ln(x)$ Power property for natural logarithms
- $\ln(x) + \ln(y) = \ln(xy)$ Product property for natural logarithms
- $\ln(x) - \ln(y) = \ln\left(\dfrac{x}{y}\right)$ Quotient property for natural logarithms

Chapter 5 Review Exercises

All of the values of functions g and f are shown in Table 64. For Exercises 1–7, refer to this table.

1. Find $f(2)$.
2. Find $f^{-1}(2)$.
3. Find $(f \circ g)(1)$.
4. Find $(g \circ f)(1)$.
5. Find $(g^{-1} \circ g)(3)$.
6. Find $(f \circ g^{-1})(0)$.
7. Use a table to describe five input–output pairs of $f \circ g$.

Table 64 Input–Output Pairs for f and g (Exercises 1–7)

x	f(x)	x	g(x)
0	2	0	3
1	4	1	2
2	3	2	1
3	0	3	4
4	1	4	0

For each pair of functions in Exercises 8–10, find (a) an equation of $f \circ g$; (b) an equation of $g \circ f$; (c) $(f \circ g)(3)$; (d) $(g \circ f)(3)$.

8. $f(x) = 5x - 2$ and $g(x) = -4x + 7$
9. $f(x) = 4(2)^x$ and $g(x) = 2x - 4$
10. $f(x) = \log_3(x)$ and $g(x) = x + 6$
11. Let $h(x) = e^{x-5}$. Find equations of f and g so that $h(x) = f(g(x))$.
12. A book sells for $8. The sales tax in Michigan is 6%. Let $f(n)$ be the total cost (in dollars) of n of the books. Let $g(d)$ be the sales tax (in dollars) on a purchase in Michigan worth d dollars.
    a. Find equations of f and g.
    b. Find an equation of $g(f(n))$.
    c. Find $g(f(7))$. What does it mean in this situation?

Graph f, f^{-1}, and $y = x$ by hand on the same set of axes.

13. $f(x) = 2x - 3$
14. $f(x) = 3^x$

15. The numbers of FBI background checks for firearm purchases are shown in Table 65 for various years.

Table 65 Numbers of FBI Background Checks for Firearm Purchases

Year	Number of Background Checks (millions)
2005	9
2006	10
2007	11
2008	13
2009	14
2010	15
2011	16

Source: *FBI*

Let $n = f(t)$ be the number (in millions) of FBI background checks for firearm purchases in the year that is t years since 2000.

a. Use a graphing calculator to draw a scattergram of the data. Can the data be modeled better by using a linear or an exponential function? Explain.
b. Find an equation of f.
c. Find $f(18)$. What does it mean in this situation?
d. Find $f^{-1}(18)$. What does it mean in this situation?
e. Although states charge various amounts for background checks, assume the average charge is $15 per check. Let $C(n)$ be the total cost (in millions of dollars) of n million background checks. Find an equation of C.
f. Let $h(t)$ be the total cost (in millions of dollars) of FBI background checks for all firearm purchases in the year that is t years since 2000. Determine which of the following is true: $h(t) = (f \circ C)(t)$ or $h(t) = (C \circ f)(t)$. Explain.
g. Find an equation of h.
h. Find $h(17)$. What does it mean in this situation?

For Exercises 16 and 17, (a) find the inverse of the given function; (b) show that $(f^{-1} \circ f)(x) = x$; (c) show that $(f \circ f^{-1})(x) = x$.

16. $f(x) = 3x$

17. $f(x) = \dfrac{5}{6}x - 2$

Evaluate the logarithmic function at the given value. Round approximate results to the fourth decimal place.

18. $\log_5(25)$

19. $\log(100{,}000)$

20. $\log_3\left(\dfrac{1}{9}\right)$

21. $\ln\left(\dfrac{1}{e^3}\right)$

22. $\log_4(\sqrt[3]{4})$

23. $\log_3(7)$

24. $\ln(5)$

25. $\log_b(b^7)$

For Exercises 26 and 27, find the inverse of the function.

26. $h(x) = 3^x$

27. $h(x) = \log(x)$

28. Sketch the graph of $y = \log_4(x)$ by hand.

29. Write the equation $d^x = k$ in logarithmic form.

30. Write the equation $\log_y(w) = r$ in exponential form.

Solve. Round any approximate solutions to the fourth decimal place.

31. $6(2)^x = 30$

32. $\log_3(x) = -4$

33. $4.3(9.8)^x - 3.3 = 8.2$

34. $\log_b(83) = 6$

35. $5\log_{32}(m) - 3 = -1$

36. $5(4)^{3r-7} = 40$

37. $2^{4t} \cdot 2^{3t-5} = 94$

For Exercises 38–40, find any solutions of the equation or system by referring to the graphs shown in Fig. 60.

38. $\log_2(x) = -\dfrac{3}{4}x + 5$

39. $2^x - 3 = -2$

40. $y = \log_2(x)$

 $y = -\dfrac{3}{4}x + 5$

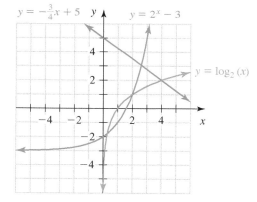

Figure 60 Exercises 38–40

For Exercises 41–44, let $f(x) = 3^x$.

41. Find $f(4)$.

42. Find $f^{-1}(25)$.

43. Find x when $f(x) = 6$.

44. Find x when $f^{-1}(x) = 6$.

45. Suppose \$8000 is deposited into an account that earns 5% interest compounded annually. Let $f(t)$ be the value (in dollars) of the account after t years or any fraction thereof.
   a. Find a formula of f.
   b. Find the value of the account after 9 years.
   c. After how many years will the value of the account double?

46. On April 1, a tree has 30 leaves. Each week, the number of leaves quadruples (increases by four times). Let $f(t)$ be the number of leaves on the tree at t weeks since April 1.
   a. Find an equation of f.
   b. Predict the number of leaves at 5 weeks after April 1.
   c. Predict when there will be 100,000 leaves.

47. National health spendings from all sources, public and private, are shown in Table 66 for various years.

Table 66 National Health Spendings

Year	National Health Spending (trillions of dollars)
1970	0.1
1975	0.2
1980	0.3
1985	0.4
1990	0.7
1995	1.0
2000	1.3
2005	2.0
2010	2.6

Source: *Centers for Medicare and Medicaid Services*

Let $s = f(t)$ be the national health spending (in trillions of dollars) in the year that is t years since 1970.
   a. Find an equation of f.
   b. What is the s-intercept of the model? What does it mean in this situation?
   c. What is the percentage rate of growth of national health spending?
   d. Predict the national health spending in 2019.
   e. Predict in what year the national health spending will be \$5 trillion.

48. A student ran an experiment to investigate the relationship between the length of a rubber band and the weight applied to one end of it. He hooked one end of a rubber band to a horizontal pole supported between two chairs. He attached a bag to the other end of the rubber band. Then, he recorded the lengths of the rubber band with various numbers of tape cassettes in the bag (see Table 67).

Table 67 Lengths of a Rubber Band Stretched by Tape Cassettes

Number of Cassettes	Length of Rubber Band (inches)
0	10.00
1	12.00
2	15.38
3	19.50
4	28.31
5	33.50
6	45.45
7	64.15

Source: *Michael S.*

   a. Let $f(n)$ be the length (in inches) of the rubber band stretched by n cassettes. Find an equation of f.
   b. What is the base b of your function $f(n) = ab^n$? What does it mean in this situation?

c. What is the coefficient a of your function $f(n) = ab^n$? What does it mean in this situation?

d. Estimate the length of the rubber band if it were stretched by eight cassettes. Describe two scenarios in which model breakdown might occur for your estimate.

e. Estimate the number of cassettes needed to stretch the rubber band to 139 inches. If model breakdown occurs for your estimate from part (d), does that imply model breakdown occurs for the estimate you made in this part? Explain.

49. A storage tank contains cobalt-60, which has a half-life of 5.3 years. Predict when 15% of the cobalt-60 will remain.

For Exercises 50–53, simplify. Write your result as a single logarithm with a coefficient of 1.

50. $\log_b(p) + \log_b(6p) - \log_b(2p)$

51. $3\log_b(2x) + 2\log_b(3x)$

52. $4\log_b(x^2) - 2\log_b(x^5)$

53. $\dfrac{\log_b(w)}{\log_b(y)}$

54. Which of the following expressions are equal?

$$\log_b(b^5) - \log_b(b^2) \qquad 3 \qquad \log_b(b^5)$$

$$\log_b(b^3) \qquad \frac{\log_b(b^5)}{\log_b(b^2)} \qquad \log_b\!\left(\frac{b^5}{b^2}\right)$$

Solve. Round any solutions to the fourth decimal place.

55. $2\log_9(3w) + 3\log_9(w^2) = 5$

56. $5\log_6(2x) - 3\log_6(4x) = 2$

Simplify. Write your result as a single logarithm with a coefficient of 1.

57. $3\ln(4x) + 2\ln(2x)$

58. $\ln(2m^7) - 4\ln(m^3) + 3\ln(m^2)$

Solve. Round any solutions to the fourth decimal place.

59. $4e^x = 75$

60. $-3\ln(p) + 7 = 1$

61. $3\ln(t^5) - 5\ln(2t) = 7$

Chapter 5 Test

*For each pair of functions in Exercises 1 and 2, find (**a**) an equation of $f \circ g$; (**b**) an equation of $g \circ f$; (**c**) $(f \circ g)(2)$; (**d**) $(g \circ f)(2)$.*

1. $f(x) = 3x + 4$ and $g(x) = 2x - 5$

2. $f(x) = 3^x$ and $g(x) = x - 4$

For Exercises 3–6, refer to Fig. 61, which shows the graphs of invertible functions f and g.

3. Find $(f \circ g)(1)$.

4. Find $(g \circ f)(1)$.

5. Find $g^{-1}(3)$.

6. Graph f^{-1} by hand.

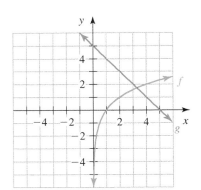

Figure 61 Exercises 3–6

7. Graph $f(x) = 3x - 6$, f^{-1}, and $y = x$ by hand on the same set of axes.

8. The prices of an adult one-day ticket to Walt Disney World® are shown in Table 68 for various years. Let $p = f(t)$ be the price (in dollars) of an adult one-day ticket at t years since 2000.

Table 68 Prices of an Adult One-Day Ticket to Walt Disney World

Year	Ticket Price (dollars)
2000	46
2002	50
2004	58
2006	67
2008	75
2010	82
2012	89

Source: *The Walt Disney Company*

a. Find an equation of f.

b. Use f to estimate the price of an adult one-day ticket in 2011.

c. Find an equation of f^{-1}.

d. Use f^{-1} to predict when the price of an adult one-day ticket will be \$110.

e. Sales tax of 6.5% is charged for tickets at Walt Disney World. Let $S(d)$ be the sales tax (in dollars) on a ticket worth d dollars. Find an equation of S.

f. Let $h(t)$ be the sales tax (in dollars) on an adult one-day ticket at t years since 2000. Determine which of the following is true: $h(t) = (f \circ S)(t)$ or $h(t) = (S \circ f)(t)$. Explain.

g. Find an equation of h.

h. Find $h(17)$. What does it mean in this situation?

9. Find the inverse of the function $g(x) = \dfrac{2x - 9}{5}$.

Evaluate. Round approximate results to the fourth decimal place.

10. $\log_2(16)$

11. $\log_4\!\left(\dfrac{1}{64}\right)$

12. $\log_7(10)$

13. $\log(0.1)$

14. $\log_b(\sqrt{b})$

15. $\ln\left(\dfrac{1}{e^2}\right)$

For Exercises 16 and 17, find the inverse of the function.

16. $h(x) = 4^x$

17. $f(x) = \log_5(x)$

18. Write $s^k = w$ in logarithmic form.

19. Write $\log_c(a) = d$ in exponential form.

For Exercises 20–22, solve. Round any solutions to the fourth decimal place.

20. $\log_b(50) = 4$

21. $6(2)^x - 9 = 23$

22. $\log_4(7p + 5) = -\dfrac{3}{2}$

23. Use "intersect" on a graphing calculator to solve the equation $4^x - 8 = -\dfrac{1}{2}x + 3$. Round any solutions to the second decimal place.

24. The tuition rates at Princeton University are shown in Table 69 for the academic years ending in the indicated year. Let $r = f(t)$ be the tuition rate (in dollars per year) at t years since 1950.

   a. Find an equation of f.
   b. What is the r-intercept of the model? What does it mean in this situation?
   c. What is the percentage rate of growth of the tuition rate?
   d. Predict the tuition rate in 2017.
   e. Predict when the tuition rate at Princeton will be $80,000 per year.

Table 69 Tuition Rates at Princeton

Year	Tuition Rates (dollars per year)
1950	600
1960	1450
1970	2350
1980	5585
1990	14,390
2000	25,430
2010	36,640
2012	38,650

Source: *Princeton University*

25. Scientists wanted to date a sample of cloth wrappings of a mummified bull from a pyramid in Dashur, Egypt. If 78.04% of the carbon-14 remains in the sample, estimate the age of the mummy. The half-life of carbon-14 is 5730 years.

Simplify. Write your result as a single logarithm with a coefficient of 1.

26. $\log_b(x^3) + \log_b(5x)$

27. $3\log_b(4p^2) - 2\log_b(8p^5) + \log_b(2p^4)$

For Exercises 28 and 29, solve. Round any solutions to the fourth decimal place.

28. $\log_3(x) + \log_3(2x) = 5$

29. $2\log_4(x^4) - 3\log_4(3x) = 3$

30. Simplify $2\ln(5w) + 3\ln(w^6)$. Write your result as a single logarithm with a coefficient of 1.

Solve. Round any solutions to the fourth decimal place.

31. $2e^{3x-1} = 54$

32. $7\ln(t - 2) - 1 = 4$

Cumulative Review of Chapters 1–5

Solve. Round approximate results to the fourth decimal place.

1. $2(4)^{5x-1} = 17$

2. $\log_3(x - 5) = 4$

3. $3b^7 - 18 = 7$

4. $8 + 2e^x = 15$

5. $4\log_5(3x^2) + 3\log_5(6x^4) = 3$

6. $7 - 3(4w - 2) = 2(3w + 5) - 4(2w + 1)$

For Exercises 7 and 8, estimate any solutions of the equation by referring to the graphs of $f(x) = 3^x$, $g(x) = 9\left(\dfrac{1}{3}\right)^x$, and $h(x) = x - 1$ shown in Fig. 62.

7. $3^x = 9\left(\dfrac{1}{3}\right)^x$

8. $9\left(\dfrac{1}{3}\right)^x = x - 1$

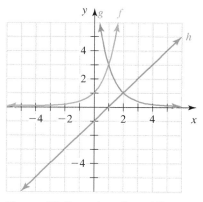

Figure 62 Exercises 7 and 8

For Exercises 9 and 10, solve the system.

9.
$$x = 2y - 5$$
$$4x - 5y = -14$$

10.
$$3(2 - 4x) = -10 - 2y$$
$$2x - 3y = -8$$

11. Solve the inequality $8x - 3 \geq -3(4x - 5)$. Describe the solution set as an inequality, in interval notation, and in a graph.

Simplify.

12. $\left(4b^{-3}c^2\right)^3 \left(5b^{-7}c^{-1}\right)^2$ **13.** $\dfrac{8b^{1/3}c^{-1/2}}{6b^{-1/2}c^{3/4}}$

Simplify. Write your result as a single logarithm with a coefficient of 1.

14. $4\log_b\left(x^7\right) - 2\log_b(7x)$

15. $3\ln\left(p^6\right) + 4\ln\left(p^2\right)$

For Exercises 16–21, refer to Table 70.

16. Find an equation of f.

17. Find an equation of g.

18. Find the slope of the graph of h.

19. Find $k(5)$.

20. Find $(g \circ k)(8)$.

21. Find $f^{-1}(5)$.

Table 70 Values of Four Functions (Exercises 16–21)

x	$f(x)$	x	$g(x)$	x	$h(x)$	x	$k(x)$
0	5	0	25	4	83	3	160
1	15	1	28	5	76	4	80
2	45	2	31	6	69	5	40
3	135	3	34	7	62	6	20
4	405	4	37	8	55	7	10
5	1215	5	40	9	48	8	5

For Exercises 22–25, graph the function by hand.

22. $y = 8\left(\dfrac{1}{2}\right)^x$

23. $y = -\dfrac{2}{5}x + 3$

24. $2(2x - y) + 2y = 3(4 + y)$

25. $y = \log_2(x)$

26. Find an equation of a line that contains the points $(-4, 7)$ and $(5, -3)$.

27. Find an equation of an exponential curve that contains the points $(3, 85)$ and $(7, 13)$.

28. Let $f(x) = x - 3$ and $g(x) = 2^x$.
   a. Find $(f \circ g)(5)$.
   b. Find an equation of $g \circ f$.

Let $f(x) = 2(3)^x$. Round approximate results to the fourth decimal place.

29. Find $f(-4)$.

30. Graph f by hand.

31. Graph f^{-1} by hand.

32. Find $f^{-1}(35)$.

Find the logarithm.

33. $\log_3\left(\dfrac{1}{81}\right)$ **34.** $\log_b\left(\sqrt[7]{b}\right)$

35. Find $\log_8(73)$. Round your result to the fourth decimal place.

For Exercises 36–40, refer to Fig. 63.

36. Find $g(-1)$.

37. Find $(f \circ g)(3)$.

38. Find an equation of f.

39. Graph f^{-1} by hand.

40. Find $f^{-1}(2)$.

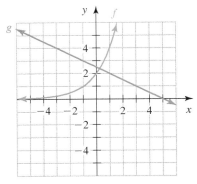

Figure 63 Exercises 36–40

For Exercises 41 and 42, find the inverse of the function.

41. $f(x) = \dfrac{2}{7}x - 3$

42. $g(x) = 8^x$

43. Sketch a graph of a relation that is not a function. Next, create a table of five ordered pairs of the relation. Explain why your relation is not a function.

44. Compare the function $f(x) = 3x + 2$ with the function $g(x) = 2(3)^x$.
   a. Find the y-intercept of the graphs of both functions.
   b. For both f and g, describe what happens to the value of y as the value of x increases by 1.
   c. For a large input value of x, which function will have a greater output value of y? Explain.
   d. Graph f and g by hand on the same coordinate system.

45. Let f be the linear function and g be the exponential function whose graphs contain the points $(4, 3)$ and $(7, 8)$.
   a. Find an equation of f.
   b. Find an equation of g.
   c. Use a graphing calculator to draw the graphs of f and g in the same viewing window.

46. Let $f(x) = 3x$ and $g(x) = 3^x$.
   a. Find $f(2)$ and $g(2)$.
   b. Find an equation of f^{-1} and an equation of g^{-1}.
   c. Find $f^{-1}(81)$ and $g^{-1}(81)$.

47. One U-Haul office rents pickup trucks for a one-day fee of $19.95 plus $0.69 per mile. One Budget office charges a one-day fee of $29.95 plus $0.45 per mile (Sources: *U-Haul; Budget*).
   a. Let $U(x)$ be U-Haul's charge and $B(x)$ be Budget's charge, both in dollars, for driving x miles in one day. Find equations of U and B.
   b. Find the slopes of the graphs of U and B. What do they mean in this situation?
   c. For how many miles driven is the one-day charge at U-Haul equal to the one-day charge at Budget?
   d. Solve the inequality $U(x) < B(x)$. What does your result mean in this situation?

48. A 15,000-seat amphitheater has tickets for sale at $43 and $60. How many tickets should be sold at each price for a sellout performance to generate a total revenue of $721,500?

49. The annual revenue of Whole Foods Market was $9.0 billion in 2010 and has grown by about 14% per year since then (Source: *Whole Foods Market*).
  a. Let $r = f(t)$ be the annual revenue (in billions of dollars) of Whole Foods Market at t years since 2010. Find an equation of f.
  b. What is the r-intercept of the model? What does it mean in this situation?
  c. What is the base b of your function $f(t) = ab^t$? What does it mean in this situation?
  d. Predict when the annual revenue will be $25 billion.

50. The numbers of tuberculosis cases in the United States are shown in Table 71 for various years.

Table 71 Tuberculosis Cases in the United States

Year	Number of Cases (thousands)
1955	69.9
1960	55.5
1970	37.1
1980	27.7
1990	25.7
2000	16.3
2010	11.2

Source: *Centers for Disease Control and Prevention*

Let $n = f(t)$ be the number (in thousands) of tuberculosis cases in the year that is t years since 1950.
  a. Find an equation of f.
  b. What is the n-intercept? What does it mean in this situation?
  c. What is the percent rate of decay of the number of cases? What does it mean in this situation?
  d. Find $f(9)$. What does it mean in this situation?
  e. Find $f^{-1}(9)$. What does it mean in this situation?

  f. Find the approximate half-life of the number of cases. [**Hint**: Use f to estimate the number of cases in 1950. Then use f to estimate when the number of cases was half that amount.]

51. The numbers of women who placed in the top 100 of the New York City Marathon are shown in Table 72 for various years.

Table 72 Numbers of Women Who Placed in the Top 100 of the NYC Marathon

Year	Number
1981	0
1986	3
1991	5
1996	8
2001	14
2006	13
2011	15

Source: *nycmarathon.org*

Let $n = f(t)$ be the number of women who placed in the top 100 of the New York City Marathon at t years since 1980.
  a. Find an equation of f.
  b. If your model is linear, find the slope. If your model is exponential, find the base b of $f(t) = ab^t$. What does your result mean in this situation?
  c. What is the t-intercept? What does it mean in this situation?
  d. The marathon was canceled in 2012 due to Hurricane Sandy. Estimate the number of women who would have placed in the top 100 if the marathon had not been canceled.
  e. Find an equation of f^{-1}.
  f. Find $f^{-1}(20)$. What does it mean in this situation?
  g. The number of men who placed in the top 100 is given by $g(n) = 100 - n$, where n is the number of women who placed in the top 100. Let $h(t) = (g \circ f)(t)$. Find an equation of h.
  h. Find $h(37)$. What does it mean in this situation?

6

Polynomial Functions

Do you have a cell phone? If so, how much do you usually pay each month to use it? The average monthly cell phone bill has actually decreased since 2004 (see Table 1). In Exercise 95 of Homework 6.2, you will predict the total amount of money paid by all cell phone subscribers in a certain year.

So far, we have studied linear, exponential, and logarithmic functions. In this chapter, we will work with *polynomial expressions* and *polynomial functions*. We will perform operations with polynomial expressions and solve *polynomial equations* in one variable. We will also use polynomial functions to model authentic situations, such as the number of participants in the Ironman World Championship. We will use these functions to make predictions, such as the enrollment at colleges and universities in 2017.

Table 1 Average Monthly Cell Phone Bills and Numbers of Subscribers

Year	Average Bill (dollars per month)	Number of Subscribers (millions)
1998	39.43	69.2
2000	45.27	109.5
2002	48.40	140.8
2004	50.64	182.1
2006	50.56	233.0
2008	50.07	270.3
2010	47.21	302.9

Source: *Cellular Telecommunications & Internet Association*

6.1 Adding and Subtracting Polynomial Expressions and Functions

Objectives

» Know the meaning of *term, monomial, polynomial, degree, coefficient, like terms, polynomial function, quadratic function, parabola, vertex,* and *cubic function.*

» Add and subtract polynomials.

» Evaluate polynomial functions.

» Recognize typical graphs of quadratic functions and cubic functions.

» Find *sum functions* and *difference functions.*

» Use sum functions and difference functions to describe authentic situations.

In this section, we will discuss how to add and subtract expressions called *polynomials.* We will discuss how to combine two *polynomial functions* to form a "new" function and how to use some of these new functions to model authentic situations.

Polynomials

A **term** is a constant, a variable, or a product of a constant and one or more variables raised to powers. Here are some examples of terms: $3x^6$, x, -3, $x^{1/2}$, and $-2x^3y^{-5}$.

A **monomial** is a constant, a variable, or a product of a constant and one or more variables raised to *counting-number* powers. Here are some examples of monomials:

$$3x^6 \quad x \quad -3 \quad -5x^7y^4$$

A **polynomial,** or **polynomial expression,** is a monomial or a sum of monomials. Here are some examples of polynomials:

$$5x^3 - 2x^2 + 7x - 4 \quad 4x^5y^2 - x^2 \quad 4x + 1 \quad 5 \quad x \quad -2x^3$$

The polynomial $4x^3 - 8x^2 + 6x - 9$ is a *polynomial in one variable.* It has four terms: $4x^3$, $-8x^2$, $6x$, and -9. We usually write polynomials in one variable so the exponents of the terms decrease from left to right, which is called **descending order.** If a polynomial contains more than one variable, we usually write the polynomial so the exponents of one of the variables decrease from left to right.

The **degree of a term** in one variable is the exponent on the variable. For example, the degree of the term $7x^4$ is 4. The degree of a term in two or more variables is the sum of the exponents on the variables. For example, the term $2x^3y^5$ has degree $3 + 5 = 8$. The **degree of a polynomial** is the largest degree of any nonzero term of the polynomial. For example, the polynomial $4x^5 - 9x^3 + 1$ has degree 5. A constant polynomial, such as 7, has degree 0.

Polynomials with degrees 1, 2, or 3 have special names:

Degree	Name	Examples
1	linear (first-degree) polynomial	$4x + 9, -6x$
2	quadratic (second-degree) polynomial	$7x^2 - 3x + 8, x^2 + 5$
3	cubic (third-degree) polynomial	$-5x^3 - 4x^2 + 8x + 2, 8x^3 + 7x$

▶ **Example 1**   Describing Polynomials

Use words such as *linear, quadratic, cubic, polynomial, degree, one variable,* and *two variables* to describe the expression.

1. $-3x^2 + 8x - 4$ **2.** $5x^3 - 2x^2 + 9x + 1$ **3.** $6a^5b^2 - 9a^3b^3 - 2ab^4$

Solution

1. The term $-3x^2$ has degree 2, which is larger than the degrees of the other terms. So, $-3x^2 + 8x - 4$ is a quadratic (second-degree) polynomial in one variable.
2. The term $5x^3$ has degree 3, which is larger than the degrees of the other terms. So, $5x^3 - 2x^2 + 9x + 1$ is a cubic (third-degree) polynomial in one variable.
3. The term $6a^5b^2$ has degree 7 (the sum of the exponents of the variables), which is larger than the degrees of the other terms. So, $6a^5b^2 - 9a^3b^3 - 2ab^4$ is a seventh-degree polynomial in two variables.

▶

Combining Like Terms

The **coefficient** of a term is the constant factor of the term. For the term $-7x^3$, the coefficient is -7. For the term x^2, the coefficient is 1, because $x^2 = 1x^2$. For the term 5, the coefficient is 5. The coefficients of a polynomial are the coefficients of the terms. For example, the coefficients of the polynomial $3x^3 + 6x^2 - 4x - 9$ are 3, 6, -4, and -9. The **leading coefficient** of a polynomial is the coefficient of the term with the largest degree. For $3x^3 + 6x^2 - 4x - 9$, the leading coefficient is 3.

Like terms either are constant terms or are variable terms that contain the same variable(s) raised to exactly the same power(s). For example, the terms $2x^3y^5$ and $7x^3y^5$ are like terms, because both terms have an x with the exponent 3 and a y with the exponent 5. The terms $6x^5$ and $8x^2$ are **unlike terms** (not like terms), because the exponents of x are different.

We can combine like terms by using the distributive law. For example,

$$2x^3 + 4x^3 = (2 + 4)x^3 = 6x^3$$

Note that we can find $2x^3 + 4x^3$ in one step by adding the coefficients:

$$2x^3 + 4x^3 = 6x^3$$
$$2 \ + \ 4 \ = 6$$

Similarly, we can find $7x^2 - 3x^2$ by adding the coefficients:

$$7x^2 - 3x^2 = 4x^2$$
$$7 + (-3) = 4$$

However, we can't add the coefficients in $2x^4 + 5x^3$, because $2x^4$ and $5x^3$ are not like terms. There is no helpful way to use the distributive law for unlike terms.

> ### Combining Like Terms
>
> To combine like terms, add the coefficients of the terms.

▶ Example 2   Combining Like Terms

Combine like terms when possible.

1. $5x^3 - 4x^2 + 2x^3 - x^2$
2. $3p^3t^2 + p^2t - 8p^3t^2 + 7p^2t$

Solution

1. We rearrange the terms so the terms with x^3 are adjacent and the terms with x^2 are adjacent:

$$5x^3 - 4x^2 + 2x^3 - x^2 = 5x^3 + 2x^3 - 4x^2 - x^2 \quad \text{Rearrange terms.}$$
$$= 7x^3 - 5x^2 \quad \text{Combine like terms.}$$

2.
$$3p^3t^2 + p^2t - 8p^3t^2 + 7p^2t \quad \text{Rearrange terms.}$$
$$= 3p^3t^2 - 8p^3t^2 + p^2t + 7p^2t$$
$$= -5p^3t^2 + 8p^2t \quad \text{Combine like terms.}$$

Addition of Polynomials

Now that we know how to combine like terms, we can add polynomials.

> ### Adding Polynomials
>
> To add polynomials, combine like terms.

▶ Example 3   Adding Polynomials

Find the sum $\left(5a^2 - 7ab + 3b^2\right) + \left(2a^2 - 4ab - 9b^2\right)$.

Solution

$$\left(5a^2 - 7ab + 3b^2\right) + \left(2a^2 - 4ab - 9b^2\right)$$
$$= 5a^2 + 2a^2 - 7ab - 4ab + 3b^2 - 9b^2 \quad \text{Rearrange terms.}$$
$$= 7a^2 - 11ab - 6b^2 \quad \text{Combine like terms.}$$

Subtraction of Polynomials

We can use the fact that $a - b = a - 1b$ to help us subtract two polynomials.

▶ Example 4   Subtracting Polynomials

Find the difference $\left(7x^2 - 2x + 5\right) - \left(6x^2 - 4x + 1\right)$.

Solution

To begin, we write $\left(7x^2 - 2x + 5\right) - \left(6x^2 - 4x + 1\right)$ as $\left(7x^2 - 2x + 5\right) - 1\left(6x^2 - 4x + 1\right)$ and distribute the -1:

$$\left(7x^2 - 2x + 5\right) - \left(6x^2 - 4x + 1\right)$$
$$= \left(7x^2 - 2x + 5\right) - 1\left(6x^2 - 4x + 1\right) \quad a - b = a - 1b$$
$$= 7x^2 - 2x + 5 - 6x^2 + 4x - 1 \quad \text{Distributive law}$$
$$= 7x^2 - 6x^2 - 2x + 4x + 5 - 1 \quad \text{Rearrange terms.}$$
$$= x^2 + 2x + 4 \quad \text{Combine like terms.}$$

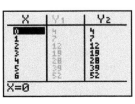

Figure 1 Verify the work

We use a graphing calculator table to verify the work (see Fig. 1).

> **Subtracting Polynomials**
>
> To subtract polynomials, first distribute -1; then combine like terms.

Now that we are familiar with polynomial expressions, we turn our attention to *polynomial functions*.

Quadratic Functions

The following are examples of *polynomial functions:*

$$f(x) = 3x^5 - 9x^4 + 8x^2 + 1 \qquad g(x) = 4x^2 - 3x + 5 \qquad h(x) = \frac{2}{3}x$$

A **polynomial function** is a function whose equation can be put into the form $f(x) = P$, where P is a polynomial in terms of the variable x. If P is a quadratic (second-degree) polynomial, we call the function a *quadratic function*.

> **Definition** Quadratic function
>
> A **quadratic function** is a function whose equation can be put into the form
>
> $$f(x) = ax^2 + bx + c$$
>
> where $a \neq 0$. This form is called the **standard form.**

For example, the function $f(x) = 8x^2 - 2x + 7$ is quadratic, because it is in the form $f(x) = ax^2 + bx + c$, with $a = 8$, $b = -2$, and $c = 7$.

▶ **Example 5** Evaluating a Quadratic Function

For $f(x) = -2x^2 + 5x - 1$, find the following.

1. $f(4)$ **2.** $f(-3)$ **3.** $f(0)$

Solution

1. $f(4) = -2(4)^2 + 5(4) - 1 = -2(16) + 5(4) - 1 = -13$
2. $f(-3) = -2(-3)^2 + 5(-3) - 1 = -2(9) + 5(-3) - 1 = -34$
3. $f(0) = -2(0)^2 + 5(0) - 1 = -2(0) + 5(0) - 1 = -1$

We use a graphing calculator table to verify our work (see Fig. 2).

The function $f(x) = x^2$ is quadratic, because it is in the form $f(x) = ax^2 + bx + c$, with $a = 1$, $b = 0$, and $c = 0$.

▶ **Example 6** Graphing a Quadratic Function

Sketch the graph of $f(x) = x^2$.

Solution

First, we list some input–output pairs of $f(x) = x^2$ in Table 2. Then, we plot the corresponding points and sketch a curve that contains the points (see Fig. 3).

We use ZStandard followed by ZSquare on a graphing calculator to verify our graph (see Fig. 4).

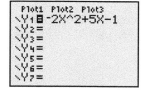
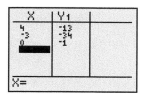

Figure 2 Verify the work

Table 2 Input–Output Pairs of $f(x) = x^2$

x	$f(x)$
-3	$(-3)^2 = 9$
-2	$(-2)^2 = 4$
-1	$(-1)^2 = 1$
0	$0^2 = 0$
1	$1^2 = 1$
2	$2^2 = 4$
3	$3^2 = 9$

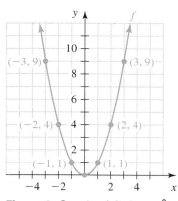

Figure 3 Graph of $f(x) = x^2$

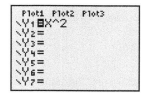
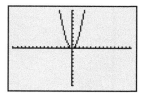

Figure 4 Verify the work

The graph of a quadratic function is called a **parabola.** The curve sketched in Fig. 3 is a parabola. Two more examples of parabolas are sketched in Figs. 5 and 6.

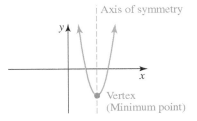

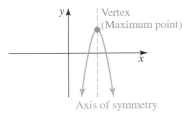

Figure 5 A parabola that opens upward

Figure 6 A parabola that opens downward

There is a difference between parabolas and lines that is worth noting. The lowest point of a parabola that *opens upward* (see Fig. 5) is called the **minimum point.** The highest point of a parabola that *opens downward* (see Fig. 6) is called the **maximum point.** The minimum point or maximum point of a parabola is called the **vertex** of the parabola. In contrast, lines do not have a lowest or highest point.

The vertical line that passes through a parabola's vertex is called the **axis of symmetry** (see Figs. 5 and 6). The part of the parabola that lies to the left of the axis of symmetry is the mirror reflection of the part that lies to the right.

▶ **Example 7**   Using a Graph to Find Values of a Function

A graph of a quadratic function f is sketched in Fig. 7.

1. Find $f(4)$.
2. Find x when $f(x) = -3$.
3. Find x when $f(x) = 5$.
4. Find x when $f(x) = 6$.

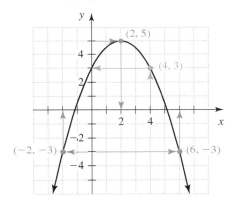

Figure 7 Graph of a quadratic function

Solution

1. The blue arrows in Fig. 7 show that the input $x = 4$ leads to the output $y = 3$. So, $f(4) = 3$.
2. The red arrows in Fig. 7 show that the output $y = -3$ originates from the two inputs $x = -2$ and $x = 6$. That is, $f(-2) = -3$ and $f(6) = -3$. So, the values of x are -2 and 6 when $f(x) = -3$.
3. The green arrows in Fig. 7 show that the output $y = 5$ originates from the single input $x = 2$. That is, $f(2) = 5$. So, the value of x is 2 when $f(x) = 5$. (There is a single input because the vertex $(2, 5)$ is the only point on the parabola that has a y-coordinate equal to 5.)
4. No point of the downward-opening parabola is above the vertex, which has a y-coordinate of 5. So, there is no point on the parabola with $f(x) = 6$.

By considering the shape of any parabola that opens upward or downward, we see that each (output) value of y in the range originates from either one or two (input) values of x in the domain.

Cubic Function

If a polynomial function can be put into the form $f(x) = P$, where P is a cubic (third-degree) polynomial, we call the function a *cubic function*.

▶ Definition **Cubic function**

A **cubic function** is a function whose equation can be put into the form

$$f(x) = ax^3 + bx^2 + cx + d$$

where $a \neq 0$.

Table 3 Input–Output Pairs of $f(x) = x^3$

x	$f(x)$
-3	$(-3)^3 = -27$
-2	$(-2)^3 = -8$
-1	$(-1)^3 = -1$
0	$0^3 = 0$
1	$1^3 = 1$
2	$2^3 = 8$
3	$3^3 = 27$

Here are some examples of cubic functions:

$$f(x) = -5x^3 + 9x^2 - 7x + 2 \qquad g(x) = 8x^3 - 5x + 1 \qquad h(x) = x^3 - 4x^2$$

▶ **Example 8** Graphing a Cubic Function

Sketch the graph of $f(x) = x^3$.

Solution

First, we list some input–output pairs of $f(x) = x^3$ in Table 3. Then, we plot the corresponding points and sketch a curve that contains the points (see Fig. 8).

Four graphs of typical cubic functions are shown in Fig. 9.

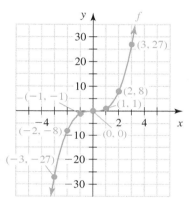

Figure 8 Graph of $f(x) = x^3$

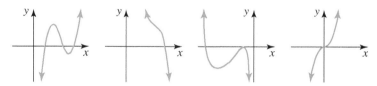

Figure 9 Graphs of typical cubic functions

Sum Function and Difference Function

We can add two functions or subtract two functions to form another function.

▶ Definition **Sum function, difference function**

If f and g are functions and x is in the domain of both functions, then we can form the following functions:

- **Sum function $f + g$**, where $(f + g)(x) = f(x) + g(x)$
- **Difference function $f - g$**, where $(f - g)(x) = f(x) - g(x)$

For $f(x) = 5x$ and $g(x) = 3x$, we have $(f + g)(x) = f(x) + g(x) = 5x + 3x = 8x$. So, $(f + g)(x) = 8x$. And $(f - g)(x) = f(x) - g(x) = 5x - 3x = 2x$. So, $(f - g)(x) = 2x$.

▶ **Example 9** Finding a Sum Function and a Difference Function

Let $f(x) = 5x^2 - x + 3$ and $g(x) = -2x^2 + 9x - 7$.

1. Find an equation of the sum function $f + g$.
2. Find $(f + g)(2)$.
3. Find an equation of the difference function $f - g$.
4. Find $(f - g)(2)$.

Solution

1. $(f + g)(x) = f(x) + g(x)$ *Definition of sum function*

$= \left(5x^2 - x + 3\right) + \left(-2x^2 + 9x - 7\right)$ *Substitute $5x^2 - x + 3$ for $f(x)$ and $-2x^2 + 9x - 7$ for $g(x)$.*

$= 5x^2 - 2x^2 - x + 9x + 3 - 7$ *Rearrange terms.*

$= 3x^2 + 8x - 4$ *Combine like terms.*

2. $(f + g)(2) = 3(2)^2 + 8(2) - 4 = 24$

3. $(f - g)(x) = f(x) - g(x)$ *Definition of difference function*

$= \left(5x^2 - x + 3\right) - \left(-2x^2 + 9x - 7\right)$ *Substitute $5x^2 - x + 3$ for $f(x)$ and $-2x^2 + 9x - 7$ for $g(x)$.*

$= \left(5x^2 - x + 3\right) - 1\left(-2x^2 + 9x - 7\right)$ $a - b = a - 1b$

$= 5x^2 - x + 3 + 2x^2 - 9x + 7$ *Distributive law*

$= 5x^2 + 2x^2 - x - 9x + 3 + 7$ *Rearrange terms.*

$= 7x^2 - 10x + 10$ *Combine like terms.*

4. $(f - g)(2) = 7(2)^2 - 10(2) + 10 = 18$

Modeling with Sum Functions and Difference Functions

Suppose A and B represent quantities. Then $A + B$ represents the sum of the two quantities.

The difference $A - B$ tells us how much more there is of one quantity than the other quantity. For example, suppose $A = 8$ and $B = 5$. Then $A - B = 8 - 5 = 3$ tells us A is 3 more than B. Now suppose $A = 5$ and $B = 8$. Then $A - B = 5 - 8 = -3$ tells us A is 3 less than B.

▶ **The Meaning of the Sign of a Difference**

If a difference $A - B$ is positive, then A is more than B. If a difference $A - B$ is negative, then A is less than B.

In Example 10, we use a sum function and a difference function to describe an authentic situation.

Table 4 College Enrollments

Year	Enrollment (millions)	
	Women	Men
1995	7.9	6.3
2000	8.6	6.7
2005	10.0	7.5
2008	10.9	8.2
2010	12.1	9.1

Source: *National Center for Education Statistics*

▶ **Example 10** Using a Sum Function and a Difference Function to Model a Situation

Women's and men's enrollments at U.S. colleges and universities are shown in Table 4 for various years. The enrollments (in millions) $W(t)$ and $M(t)$ for women and men, respectively, are modeled by the system

$$W(t) = 0.014t^2 - 0.08t + 7.96$$
$$M(t) = 0.012t^2 - 0.12t + 6.65$$

where t is the number of years since 1990.

1. Find an equation of the sum function $W + M$.
2. Perform a unit analysis of the expression $W(t) + M(t)$.
3. Find $(W + M)(27)$. What does it mean in this situation?
4. Find an equation of the difference function $W - M$.
5. Find $(W - M)(27)$. What does it mean in this situation?

Solution

1. $(W + M)(t) = W(t) + M(t)$ — *Definition of sum function*

$= (0.014t^2 - 0.08t + 7.96)$ — *Substitute $0.014t^2 - 0.08t + 7.96$ for $W(t)$*
$+ (0.012t^2 - 0.12t + 6.65)$ — *and $0.012t^2 - 0.12t + 6.65$ for $M(t)$.*

$= 0.026t^2 - 0.20t + 14.61$ — *Combine like terms.*

2. For the expression $W(t) + M(t)$, we have

$$\underbrace{W(t)}_{\text{millions of female students}} + \underbrace{M(t)}_{\text{millions of male students}}$$

The units of the expression are millions of students.

3. $(W + M)(27) = 0.026(27)^2 - 0.20(27) + 14.61 \approx 28.16$

This means the total enrollment for women and men in $1990 + 27 = 2017$ will be about 28.2 million students, according to the model.

4. $(W - M)(t) = W(t) - M(t)$ — *Definition of difference function*

$= (0.014t^2 - 0.08t + 7.96)$ — *Substitute $0.014t^2 - 0.08t + 7.96$*
$- 1(0.012t^2 - 0.12t + 6.65)$ — *for $W(t)$ and $0.012t^2 - 0.12t + 6.65$*
for $M(t)$; $a - b = a - 1b$

$= 0.014t^2 - 0.08t + 7.96$ — *Distributive law*
$- 0.012t^2 + 0.12t - 6.65$

$= 0.002t^2 + 0.04t + 1.31$ — *Combine like terms.*

5. $(W - M)(27) = 0.002(27)^2 + 0.04(27) + 1.31 \approx 3.85$

This means in 2017 women's enrollment will exceed men's enrollment by about 3.9 million students, according to the model.

Group Exploration

Using a difference function to solve a system

1. Let $f(x) = -3x + 7$ and $g(x) = 2x - 3$.
   a. Graph by hand the functions f and g on the same coordinate system.
   b. Find an equation of the difference function $f - g$.
   c. Find $(f - g)(1)$. Refer to your graphs in part (a) to explain why your result is positive.
   d. Find $(f - g)(3)$. Refer to your graphs in part (a) to explain why your result is negative.
   e. Find $(f - g)(2)$. Refer to your graphs in part (a) to explain why your result is 0.
   f. Refer to your graphs in part (a) to solve the system

   $$y = -3x + 7$$
   $$y = 2x - 3$$

   Explain why your work in part (e) shows that the x-coordinate of the solution of the system is 2.

2. Let $f(x) = -x + 5$ and $g(x) = 2x - 4$.
   a. Find an equation of the difference function $f - g$.
   b. Find x when $(f - g)(x) = 0$.
   c. Without using graphing, substitution, or elimination, state the x-coordinate of the solution of the system that follows. Then use any method to find the y-coordinate of the solution.

   $$y = -x + 5$$
   $$y = 2x - 4$$

▶ Tips for Success   **Complete the Rest of the Assignment**

If you have spent a good amount of time trying to solve an exercise but can't, consider going on to the next exercise in the assignment. The next exercise may involve a different concept or a more familiar situation. After completing the rest of the assignment, you may be able to complete the exercise you skipped. One explanation is that you may have learned or remembered some concept in a later exercise that relates to the exercise with which you were struggling.

Homework 6.1

For extra help ▶ MyMathLab® ▦ Watch the videos in MyMathLab ⬤ Download the MyDashboard App

Use words such as linear, quadratic, cubic, polynomial, degree, one variable, *and* two variables *to describe the expression.*

1. $5x^2 - 6x + 2$

2. $4x^3 + 2x^2 + 9$

3. $-2x^3 - 4x^2 + 5x - 1$

4. $-7x^2 - 5$

5. $6p^4q^3 + 3p^2q^4 - 2q^5$

6. $3m^6n^2 - 9m^3n^2 + 8mn^3$

Combine like terms when possible. Use a graphing calculator table to verify your work when possible.

7. $6x^2 - 3x - 2x^2 + 4x$

8. $4x^2 - 7x + 3x^2 - 9x$

9. $-5x^3 - 4x + 2x^2 - 7x^3 + 5 - x$

10. $-7x^2 + 6x - 4x^3 - 1 + 2x^3 - x^2$

11. $4a^4b^2 - 7ab^3 - 9a^4b^2 + 2ab^3$

12. $2m^3n + 4mn^2 - 8m^3n - 7mn^2$

13. $2x^4 - 4x^3y + 2x^2y^2 + x^3y - 2x^2y^2 + xy^3$

14. $3r^4 - r^3t - 4r^2t^2 + 6rt^2 + 4r^2t^2 - 4rt^3$

Perform the addition. Use a graphing calculator table to verify your work when possible.

15. $(3x^2 - 5x - 2) + (6x^2 + 2x - 7)$

16. $(5x^2 + 3x - 6) + (-7x^2 - 5x + 1)$

17. $(-2x^3 + 4x - 3) + (5x^3 - 6x^2 + 2)$

18. $(-5x^3 - 8x^2 + 4) + (-4x^3 + x - 9)$

19. $(8a^2 - 7ab + 2b^2) + (3a^2 + 4ab - 7b^2)$

20. $(6t^2 + 2tw - w^2) + (-4t^2 - 9tw - 3w^2)$

21. $(2m^4p + m^3p^2 - 7m^2p^3) + (m^3p^2 + 7m^2p^3 - 8mp^3)$

22. $(x^3y - 5x^2y^2 + 2xy^3) + (5x^2y^2 - 4xy^3 + 7y^4)$

Perform the subtraction. Use a graphing calculator table to verify your work when possible.

23. $(2x^2 + 4x - 7) - (9x^2 - 5x + 4)$

24. $(6x^2 + 3x - 1) - (4x^2 - 8x + 3)$

25. $(6x^3 - 3x^2 + 4) - (-7x^3 + x - 1)$

26. $(5x^3 - x + 6) - (-9x^3 + 4x^2 - 6)$

27. $(8m^2 + 3mp - 5p^2) - (-2m^2 - 7mp - 4p^2)$

28. $(b^2 - 6bc + 4c^2) - (5b^2 + 3bc - 2c^2)$

29. $(a^3b - 5a^2b^2 + ab^3) - (5a^2b^2 - 7ab^3 + b^3)$

30. $(6x^4y + x^3y^2 - 3x^2y^3) - (4x^3y^2 - 3x^2y^3 - 5xy^4)$

For the functions $f(x) = -2x^2 - 5x + 3$, $g(x) = 3x^2 - 8x - 1$, *and* $h(x) = 2x^3 - 4x$, *find the following.*

31. $f(3)$

32. $f(-4)$

33. $g(-4)$

34. $g(2)$

35. $f(0)$

36. $g(0)$

37. $h(3)$

38. $h(2)$

39. $h(-2)$

40. $h(-1)$

For Exercises 41–48, refer to Fig. 10.

41. Estimate $f(-1)$.

42. Estimate $f(0)$.

43. Estimate $f(1)$.

44. Estimate $f(2)$.

45. Estimate a when $f(a) = 3$.

46. Estimate a when $f(a) = 0$.

47. Estimate a when $f(a) = -1$.

48. Estimate a when $f(a) = -2$.

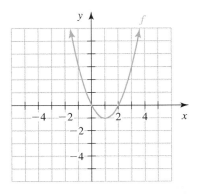

Figure 10
Exercises 41–48

For Exercises 49–56, refer to Table 5, which lists values of a quadratic function f.

49. Find $f(0)$.

50. Find $f(3)$.

51. Find $f(4)$.

52. Find $f(6)$.

53. Find x when $f(x) = 19$.

54. Find x when $f(x) = 3$.

55. Find x when $f(x) = 1$.

56. Find x when $f(x) = 0$.

Table 5 Some Values of a Quadratic Function f (Exercises 49–57)

x	$f(x)$
0	19
1	9
2	3
3	1
4	3
5	9
6	19

57. Consider the quadratic function f described in Table 5.
   a. Find x when $f(x) = 9$.
   b. Explain why f does not have an inverse function.

58. The values of a quadratic function f are listed in Table 6. Estimate the x-intercept(s) and the y-intercept(s).

Table 6 Values of a Function f (Exercise 58)

x	$f(x)$
-3	5.35
-2	0.17
-1	-3.61
0	-5.99
1	-6.97
2	-6.55
3	-4.73
4	-1.51
5	3.11
6	9.13

Graph the function by hand. To begin, substitute the values -2, -1, 0, 1, *and* 2 *for* x. *Make other substitutions as necessary. Use a graphing calculator to verify your work.*

59. $f(x) = 2x^2$ **60.** $f(x) = 3x^2$

61. $f(x) = -2x^2$ **62.** $f(x) = -3x^2$

63. $f(x) = 3x^3$ **64.** $f(x) = 2x^3$

65. $f(x) = -3x^3$ **66.** $f(x) = -2x^3$

For $f(x) = 4x^2 - 2x + 8$, $g(x) = 7x^2 + 5x - 1$, *and* $h(x) = -3x^2 - 4x - 9$, *find an equation of the given function; then evaluate the function at the indicated value.*

67. $f + g$, $(f + g)(3)$ **68.** $f + h$, $(f + h)(3)$

69. $f - h$, $(f - h)(4)$ **70.** $g - h$, $(g - h)(4)$

For $f(x) = 2x^3 - 4x + 1$, $g(x) = -3x^2 + 5x - 3$, *and* $h(x) = x^3 - 3x^2 + 2x$, *find an equation of the given function; then evaluate the function at the indicated value.*

71. $f + g$, $(f + g)(2)$ **72.** $f + h$, $(f + h)(2)$

73. $f - h$, $(f - h)(-1)$ **74.** $g - h$, $(g - h)(-1)$

75. In Exercise 5 of Homework 3.3, the annual U.S. consumption (in gallons per person) $M(t)$ and $S(t)$ of milk and soft drinks, respectively, is modeled by the system

$$M(t) = -0.28t + 36.67$$
$$S(t) = 0.82t + 8.96$$

where t is the number of years since 1950 (see Table 7).

Table 7 Annual U.S. Consumption of Milk and Soft Drinks

Year	Average Annual Consumption of Milk (gallons per person)	Year	Average Annual Consumption of Soft Drinks (gallons per person)
1970	31.3	1950	10.8
1980	27.5	1960	13.4
1985	26.7	1970	24.3
1990	25.7	1980	35.1
1995	23.9	1990	46.2
2000	22.5	2000	49.3
2005	21.0	2005	51.5

Source: *USDA/Economic Research Service*

a. Find an equation of the sum function $M + S$.
b. Perform a unit analysis of the expression $M(t) + S(t)$.
c. Find $(M + S)(53)$. What does it mean in this situation?
d. Find an equation of the difference function $M - S$.
e. Find $(M - S)(53)$. What does it mean in this situation?

76. In Exercise 28 of Homework 3.1, annual U.S. consumption (in pounds per person) $C(t)$ and $R(t)$ of chicken and red meat, respectively, is modeled by the system

$$C(t) = 1.13t + 39.29$$
$$R(t) = -0.94t + 144.88$$

where t is the number of years since 1970 (see Table 8).

Table 8 Annual U.S. Consumption of Chicken and Red Meat

Year	Annual Consumption (pounds per person)	
	Chicken	Red Meat
1970	40.3	145.8
1980	48.0	136.8
1990	61.5	120.0
2000	78.0	120.7
2010	83.7	108.7
2011	84.2	104.3

Source: *U.S. Department of Agriculture*

a. Find an equation of the sum function $C + R$.
b. Perform a unit analysis of the expression $C(t) + R(t)$.
c. Find $(C + R)(48)$. What does it mean in this situation?
d. Find an equation of the difference function $C - R$.
e. Find $(C - R)(48)$. What does it mean in this situation?

77. If you are driving and spot an object in the road, the distance it will take you to stop is equal to the sum of the following:
  • The **reaction distance** is the distance you will continue to travel before you hit the brakes.
  • The **braking distance** is the distance you will travel as you are braking.
The reaction and braking distances are shown in Table 9 for various driving speeds.
a. Let $R(s)$ be the reaction distance (in feet) when driving at s miles per hour. Find an equation of R.
b. The braking distance (in feet) $B(s)$ can be modeled by the function $B(s) = 0.063s^2$, where s is the driving speed (in mph) just before braking. Find an equation of the sum function $R + B$.

Table 9 Reaction and Braking Distances

Driving Speed (miles per hour)	Reaction Distance (feet)	Braking Distance (feet)
20	44	25
30	66	57
40	88	101
50	110	158
60	132	227
70	154	310
80	176	404

Source: *National Highway Traffic Safety Administration*

c. Perform a unit analysis of the expression $R(s) + B(s)$.
d. Find $(R + B)(26)$. What does it mean in this situation?
e. Low-beam headlights can illuminate objects up to 160 feet away. Suppose a person is driving 38 mph at night and then slams on the brakes when she sees a tree lying across the road. Will she hit the tree? Explain.

78. The United States' market share $U(t)$ of world manufacturing output can be modeled by the function $U(t) = -0.47t + 24.68$, where t is the number of years since 2000 (see Table 10). China's market share $C(t)$ can be modeled by the function $C(t) = 0.13t^2 - 0.54t + 11.24$, where t is the number of years since 2000.

Table 10 United States' and China's Market Shares of Manufacturing Output

Year	Market Share (percent) United States	Market Share (percent) China
2004	22.8	11.1
2005	22.5	11.9
2006	21.7	12.8
2007	21.4	13.9
2008	20.8	15.0
2009	20.6	17.2
2010	20.0	18.9

Source: *United Nations*

a. Find an equation of the sum function $U + C$.
b. Perform a unit analysis of the expression $U(t) + C(t)$.
c. Find $(U + C)(17)$. What does it mean in this situation?
d. Find an equation of the difference function $U - C$.
e. Find $(U - C)(17)$. What does it mean in this situation?

Concepts

79. A student tries to find the difference of the polynomials $6x^2 + 8x + 5$ and $2x^2 + 4x + 3$:

$$\left(6x^2 + 8x + 5\right) - \left(2x^2 + 4x + 3\right)$$
$$= 6x^2 + 8x + 5 - 2x^2 + 4x + 3$$
$$= 4x^2 + 12x + 8$$

Describe any errors. Then find the difference correctly.

80. Let f and g be functions, both with independent variable x. A student says that $(f + g)(x) = f(x) + g(x)$ as a result of the distributive law. Explain why the student is incorrect. Then create two functions f and g so you can show the meaning of $(f + g)(x) = f(x) + g(x)$.

81. Let $f(x) = 3x + 7$ and $g(x) = 5x + 2$.
a. Find equations of the difference function $f - g$ and the difference function $g - f$.
b. Find $(f - g)(2)$ and $(g - f)(2)$. Compare the results.
c. Find $(f - g)(4)$ and $(g - f)(4)$. Compare the results.
d. Find $(f - g)(7)$ and $(g - f)(7)$. Compare the results.
e. Summarize your findings from parts (b)–(d). Explain why this makes sense.

82. a. Is it possible for the sum of two quadratic polynomials to be the given type of polynomial? If yes, give an example. If no, explain.
i. cubic
ii. quadratic
iii. linear
iv. constant
b. Summarize the possible results for the sum of two quadratic polynomials.

83. If $A - B = -10$, explain why this means A is 10 less than B.

84. Use the distributive law to explain why $3x^4 + 2x^4 = 5x^4$.

85. Describe how to add two polynomials. Describe how to subtract two polynomials. (See page 4 for guidelines on writing a good response.)

86. Explain how it is sometimes useful to use a sum function or difference function to model an authentic situation. (See page 4 for guidelines on writing a good response.)

Related Review

For Exercises 87–92, match the given type of function to the appropriate graph in Fig. 11.

87. $f(x) = mx + b, m < 0$ and $b > 0$
88. $f(x) = mx + b, m > 0$ and $b < 0$

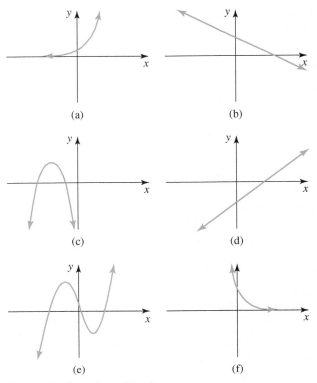

Figure 11 Exercises 87–92

89. $f(x) = ax^2 + bx + c$

90. $f(x) = ax^3 + bx^2 + cx + d$

91. $f(x) = ab^x, a > 0$ and $b > 1$

92. $f(x) = ab^x, a > 0$ and $0 < b < 1$

For $f(x) = 2x - 3$ and $g(x) = 4x + 5$, find an equation of the given function; then evaluate the function at the indicated value.

93. $f \circ g, (f \circ g)(3)$

94. $g \circ f, (g \circ f)(3)$

95. $f - g, (f - g)(2)$

96. $g - f, (g - f)(2)$

Expressions, Equations, Functions, and Graphs

Perform the indicated instruction. Then use words such as lin-ear, quadratic, cubic, exponential, logarithmic, polynomial, degree, function, one variable, and two variables to describe the expression, equation, or system.

97. Simplify $\left(\dfrac{25b^5 c^{-7}}{4b^{-3}c} \right)^{1/2}$.

98. Solve $7(3)^x - 51 = 83$. Round any solutions to the fourth decimal place.

99. Graph $f(x) = -2(2)^x$ by hand.

100. Solve $7(3x) - 51 = 83$. Round any solutions to the fourth decimal place.

▼ 6.2 Multiplying Polynomial Expressions and Functions

Objectives

» Know the meaning of *binomial* and *trinomial*.

» Multiply polynomials.

» Simplify the square of a binomial.

» Find the product of two *binomial conjugates.*

» Evaluate quadratic functions, and write them in standard form.

» Find *product functions.*

» Use product functions to describe authentic situations.

In Section 6.1, we added and subtracted polynomials and worked with sum functions and difference functions. In this section, we will multiply polynomials and work with *product functions.*

Monomials, Binomials, and Trinomials

We refer to a polynomial as a **monomial,** a **binomial,** or a **trinomial,** depending on whether it has one, two, or three nonzero terms, respectively:

Name	Examples	Meaning
monomial	$4x^7, \quad x^3, \quad -9x^2y^3, \quad -3$	one nonzero term
binomial	$4x^2 - 9, \quad 5x^3 + x^2, \quad -2y + 5$	two nonzero terms
trinomial	$5x^3 - 3x + 6, \quad 3x^2 + 7x + 2$	three nonzero terms

Multiplication of Monomials

We can use the product property for exponents (Section 4.1) to help us multiply monomials.

> **Example 1** Finding the Product of Two Monomials

Find the product $4x^3y^2(-2xy^6)$.

Solution

We rearrange factors so the coefficients are adjacent, the powers of x are adjacent, and the powers of y are adjacent:

$$4x^3y^2(-2xy^6) = 4(-2)\left(x^3x^1\right)\left(y^2y^6\right) \quad \text{\small{Rearrange factors; } } x = x^1$$
$$= -8x^4y^8 \quad \text{\small{Multiply; add exponents: } } b^m b^n = b^{m+n}$$

WARNING   An expression such as $4x^3y^2(-2xy^6)$ is *not* the same as an expression such as $4x^3y^2 - 2xy^6$: The first expression is a product, whereas the second is a difference. We can tell that $4x^3y^2(-2xy^6)$ is a product because there is no operation symbol between the expressions $4x^3y^2$ and $(-2xy^6)$.

Multiplication of a Monomial and a Polynomial

We can use the distributive law to help us find the product of a monomial and a polynomial.

> **Example 2** Finding the Product of a Monomial and a Polynomial

Find the product.

1. $-4x(6x + 3)$

2. $7p^2t(3p^2t - 2pt^2 + 5t^3)$

Solution

1.
$$-4x(6x + 3) = -4x \cdot 6x - 4x \cdot 3 \quad \textit{Distributive law}$$
$$= -24x^2 - 12x \quad \textit{x} \cdot \textit{x} = \textit{x}^2$$

2. $7p^2t(3p^2t - 2pt^2 + 5t^3)$
$$= 7p^2t \cdot 3p^2t - 7p^2t \cdot 2pt^2 + 7p^2t \cdot 5t^3 \quad \textit{Distributive law}$$
$$= 21p^4t^2 - 14p^3t^3 + 35p^2t^4 \quad \textit{Add exponents: } b^m b^n = b^{m+n}$$

Multiplication of Two Polynomials

We can also use the distributive law to help us find the product of two binomials. For instance, we can find the product $(a + b)(c + d)$ by using the distributive law three times:

$$(a + b)(c + d) = a(c + d) + b(c + d) \quad \textit{Distribute } (c + d).$$
$$= ac + ad + bc + bd \quad \textit{Distribute a and distribute b.}$$

By examining the expression $ac + ad + bc + bd$, we can find the product $(a + b)(c + d)$ more directly by adding the four products formed by multiplying each term in the first sum by each term in the second sum:

$$(a + b)(c + d) = ac + ad + bc + bd$$

After using this technique, we combine like terms if possible.

> ### Multiplying Two Polynomials
>
> To multiply two polynomials, multiply each term in the first polynomial by each term in the second polynomial. Then combine like terms if possible.

▶ Example 3   Finding the Product of Two Binomials

Find the product.

1. $(x + 4)(x + 8)$ **2.** $(5p - 6w)(3p + 2w)$

Solution

1.
$$(x + 4)(x + 8) = x \cdot x + x \cdot 8 + 4 \cdot x + 4 \cdot 8 \quad \textit{Multiply pairs of terms.}$$
$$= x^2 + 8x + 4x + 32 \quad \textit{x} \cdot \textit{x} = \textit{x}^2$$
$$= x^2 + 12x + 32 \quad \textit{Combine like terms.}$$

2. $(5p - 6w)(3p + 2w)$
$$= 5p \cdot 3p + 5p \cdot 2w - 6w \cdot 3p - 6w \cdot 2w \quad \textit{Multiply pairs of terms.}$$
$$= 15p^2 + 10pw - 18pw - 12w^2 \quad \textit{x} \cdot \textit{x} = \textit{x}^2$$
$$= 15p^2 - 8pw - 12w^2 \quad \textit{Combine like terms.}$$

▶ Example 4   Finding Products

Find the product.

1. $(2a^2 - 5b^2)(4a^2 - 3b^2)$ **2.** $4x(x^2 + 2)(x - 3)$

Solution

1. $(2a^2 - 5b^2)(4a^2 - 3b^2)$
$$= 2a^2 \cdot 4a^2 - 2a^2 \cdot 3b^2 - 5b^2 \cdot 4a^2 + 5b^2 \cdot 3b^2 \quad \textit{Multiply pairs of terms.}$$
$$= 8a^4 - 6a^2b^2 - 20a^2b^2 + 15b^4 \quad \textit{Add exponents: } b^m b^n = b^{m+n}$$
$$= 8a^4 - 26a^2b^2 + 15b^4 \quad \textit{Combine like terms.}$$

Figure 12 Verify the work

2. We begin by multiplying $4x$ by both terms in the binomial $x^2 + 2$:

$$4x\left(x^2 + 2\right)(x - 3) = \left(4x \cdot x^2 + 4x \cdot 2\right)(x - 3) \qquad \text{Distributive law}$$
$$= \left(4x^3 + 8x\right)(x - 3) \qquad \text{Add exponents: } b^m b^n = b^{m+n}$$
$$= 4x^3 \cdot x - 4x^3 \cdot 3 + 8x \cdot x - 8x \cdot 3 \qquad \text{Multiply pairs of terms.}$$
$$= 4x^4 - 12x^3 + 8x^2 - 24x \qquad \text{Add exponents: } b^m b^n = b^{m+n}$$

We use a graphing calculator table to verify our work (see Fig. 12).

We can find the product of two polynomials of any degree in a similar fashion. The key is to multiply each term in the first polynomial by each term in the second polynomial. Then combine like terms.

▶ **Example 5** Finding the Products of Two Polynomials

Find the product.

1. $(2x + y)\left(5x^2 - 3xy + 4y^2\right)$ **2.** $\left(x^2 - 3x + 2\right)\left(x^2 + x - 5\right)$

Solution

1. To begin, we multiply each term in the first polynomial by each term in the second polynomial:

$$(2x + y)\left(5x^2 - 3xy + 4y^2\right)$$

$$= 2x \cdot 5x^2 - 2x \cdot 3xy + 2x \cdot 4y^2 + y \cdot 5x^2 - y \cdot 3xy + y \cdot 4y^2 \quad \begin{array}{l}\text{Multiply pairs}\\\text{of terms.}\end{array}$$
$$= 10x^3 - 6x^2y + 8xy^2 + 5x^2y - 3xy^2 + 4y^3 \quad \begin{array}{l}\text{Add exponents:}\\b^m b^n = b^{m+n}\end{array}$$
$$= 10x^3 - 6x^2y + 5x^2y + 8xy^2 - 3xy^2 + 4y^3 \quad \text{Rearrange terms.}$$
$$= 10x^3 - x^2y + 5xy^2 + 4y^3 \quad \text{Combine like terms.}$$

2. $\left(x^2 - 3x + 2\right)\left(x^2 + x - 5\right)$

$$= x^2 \cdot x^2 + x^2 \cdot x - x^2 \cdot 5 - 3x \cdot x^2 - 3x \cdot x + 3x \cdot 5 + 2 \cdot x^2 + 2 \cdot x - 2 \cdot 5$$
$$= x^4 + x^3 - 5x^2 - 3x^3 - 3x^2 + 15x + 2x^2 + 2x - 10$$
$$= x^4 + x^3 - 3x^3 - 5x^2 - 3x^2 + 2x^2 + 15x + 2x - 10$$
$$= x^4 - 2x^3 - 6x^2 + 17x - 10$$

We use a graphing calculator table to verify our work (see Fig. 13).

Figure 13 Verify the work

Square of a Binomial

How do we square a sum? The square of the binomial $x + 3$ is $(x + 3)^2$:

$$(x + 3)^2 = (x + 3)(x + 3) \qquad y^2 = yy$$
$$= x^2 + 3x + 3x + 9 \qquad \text{Multiply pairs of terms.}$$
$$= x^2 + 6x + 9 \qquad \text{Combine like terms.}$$

We have simplified $(x + 3)^2$ by writing it as $x^2 + 6x + 9$. We **simplify the square of a binomial** by writing it as an expression that does not have parentheses.

Now, we generalize and simplify $(A + B)^2$:

$$(A + B)^2 = (A + B)(A + B) \qquad y^2 = yy$$
$$= A^2 + AB + BA + B^2 \qquad \text{Multiply pairs of terms.}$$
$$= A^2 + 2AB + B^2 \qquad \text{Combine like terms.}$$

So, $(A + B)^2 = A^2 + 2AB + B^2$. We can use similar steps to find the property $(A - B)^2 = A^2 - 2AB + B^2$.

> ▶ **Squaring a Binomial**
>
> $$(A + B)^2 = A^2 + 2AB + B^2 \quad \textit{Square of a sum}$$
> $$(A - B)^2 = A^2 - 2AB + B^2 \quad \textit{Square of a difference}$$
>
> In words, the square of a binomial equals the first term squared, plus (or minus) twice the product of the two terms, plus the second term squared.

We can instead simplify $(x + 3)^2$ by substituting x for A and 3 for B in the formula for the square of a sum:

$$(A + B)^2 = A^2 + 2 \ A \ B + B^2$$
$$(x + 3)^2 = x^2 + 2 \cdot x \cdot 3 + 3^2 \quad \textit{Substitute x for A and 3 for B.}$$
$$= x^2 + 6x + 9 \quad \textit{Simplify.}$$

The result is the same as our result from writing $(x + 3)^2$ as $(x + 3)(x + 3)$ and then multiplying. So, there are two ways to simplify $(x + 3)^2$. Similarly, there are two ways to simplify the square of any binomial. If you experiment with both methods in the homework, you will be able to make an informed choice of method for future problems.

▶ **Example 6**   Simplifying Squares of Binomials

Simplify.

1. $(x + 7)^2$ **2.** $(5t - 4w)^2$ **3.** $\left(3r^2 + 2y^2\right)^2$

Solution

1. We substitute x for A and 7 for B:

$$(A + B)^2 = A^2 + 2 \ A \ B + B^2$$
$$(x + 7)^2 = x^2 + 2 \cdot x \cdot 7 + 7^2 \quad \textit{Substitute.}$$
$$= x^2 + 14x + 49 \quad \textit{Simplify.}$$

Another way to simplify $(x + 7)^2$ is to write it as $(x + 7)(x + 7)$ and then multiply each term in the first binomial by each term in the second binomial:

$$(x + 7)^2 = (x + 7)(x + 7) \quad b^2 = bb$$
$$= x^2 + 7x + 7x + 49 \quad \textit{Multiply pairs of terms.}$$
$$= x^2 + 14x + 49 \quad \textit{Combine like terms.}$$

2. We substitute $5t$ for A and $4w$ for B:

$$(A - B)^2 = A^2 - 2 \ A \ B + B^2$$
$$(5t - 4w)^2 = (5t)^2 - 2 \cdot 5t \cdot 4w + (4w)^2 \quad \textit{Substitute.}$$
$$= 25t^2 - 40tw + 16w^2 \quad \textit{Simplify.}$$

Another way to simplify $(5t - 4w)^2$ is to write it as $(5t - 4w)(5t - 4w)$ and then multiply each term in the first binomial by each term in the second binomial:

$$(5t - 4w)^2 = (5t - 4w)(5t - 4w) \quad b^2 = bb$$
$$= 25t^2 - 20tw - 20tw + 16w^2 \quad \textit{Multiply pairs of terms.}$$
$$= 25t^2 - 40tw + 16w^2 \quad \textit{Combine like terms.}$$

3. $\left(3r^2 + 2y^2\right)^2 = \left(3r^2\right)^2 + 2\left(3r^2\right)\left(2y^2\right) + \left(2y^2\right)^2 \quad \textit{(A + B)}^2 = \textit{A}^2 + \textit{2AB} + \textit{B}^2;$
                                                                                substitute $3r^2$ for A and $2y^2$ for B.

$$= 9r^4 + 12r^2y^2 + 4y^4 \quad \textit{Simplify.}$$

In Example 6, we found that both $x^2 + 14x + 49$ and $25t^2 - 40tw + 16w^2$ are *squares* of binomials. Both of these *trinomials* are called perfect-square trinomials. A **perfect-square trinomial** is a trinomial equivalent to the square of a binomial.

Here we compare squaring a product with squaring a sum:

$$(AB)^2 = A^2B^2 \qquad \textit{Square of a product}$$
$$(A + B)^2 = A^2 + 2AB + B^2 \qquad \textit{Square of a sum}$$

WARNING

It is a common error to omit the middle term in squaring a binomial—for instance,

$$(x + 5)^2 = x^2 + 25 \qquad \textit{Incorrect}$$
$$(x + 5)^2 = x^2 + 10x + 25 \qquad \textit{Correct}$$

When simplifying $(A + B)^2$, don't omit the middle term $2AB$ of $A^2 + 2AB + B^2$. Likewise, when simplifying $(A - B)^2$, don't omit the middle term $-2AB$ of $A^2 - 2AB + B^2$.

Finding the Product of Binomial Conjugates

Binomials such as $2x + 5$ and $2x - 5$ are said to be binomial conjugates. We say the sum of two terms and the difference of the same two terms are **binomial conjugates** of each other.

How do we find the product of the binomial conjugates $A + B$ and $A - B$? We multiply as we would for any other two binomials:

$$(A + B)(A - B) = A^2 - AB + AB - B^2 \qquad \textit{Multiply pairs of terms.}$$
$$= A^2 - B^2 \qquad \textit{Combine like terms.}$$

We see that the product of $A + B$ and $A - B$ is a *difference of two squares*, $A^2 - B^2$.

> **Product of Binomial Conjugates**
>
> $$(A + B)(A - B) = A^2 - B^2$$
>
> In words, the product of two binomial conjugates is the difference of the square of the first term and the square of the second term.

By the commutative law of multiplication, we have

$$(A - B)(A + B) = A^2 - B^2$$

> **Example 7** Multiplying Binomial Conjugates

Find the product.

1. $(x + 6)(x - 6)$
2. $(3p - 8q)(3p + 8q)$
3. $\left(4m^2 - 7rt\right)\left(4m^2 + 7rt\right)$
4. $(x + 3)(x - 3)\left(x^2 + 9\right)$

Solution

1. We substitute x for A and 6 for B:

$$(A + B)(A - B) = A^2 - B^2$$
$$\downarrow \quad \downarrow \quad \downarrow \quad \downarrow \qquad \downarrow \quad \downarrow$$
$$(x + 6)\ (x - 6) = x^2 - 6^2 \qquad \textit{Substitute.}$$
$$= x^2 - 36 \qquad \textit{Simplify.}$$

2. We substitute $3p$ for A and $8q$ for B:

$$(A - B)\ (A + B) = A^2 - B^2$$
$$\downarrow \quad \downarrow \quad \downarrow \quad \downarrow \qquad \downarrow \quad \downarrow$$
$$(3p - 8q)(3p + 8q) = (3p)^2 - (8q)^2 \qquad \textit{Substitute.}$$
$$= 9p^2 - 64q^2 \qquad \textit{Simplify.}$$

3. $\left(4m^2 - 7rt\right)\left(4m^2 + 7rt\right) = \left(4m^2\right)^2 - \left(7rt\right)^2 \qquad (A - B)(A + B) = A^2 - B^2$
$$= 16m^4 - 49r^2t^2 \qquad \textit{Simplify.}$$

4. $(x + 3)(x - 3)(x^2 + 9) = (x^2 - 9)(x^2 + 9)$ *(A + B)(A - B) = A² - B²*

$\qquad\qquad\qquad\qquad\qquad = (x^2)^2 - 9^2$ *(A - B)(A + B) = A² - B²*

$\qquad\qquad\qquad\qquad\qquad = x^4 - 81$ *Simplify.*

Function Notation

So far in this section, we have been working with polynomial expressions. Now we will apply the skills we have learned to polynomial functions.

▶ **Example 8**   Evaluating a Quadratic Function

For $f(x) = x^2 - 5x$, find the following.

1. $f(a - 3)$
2. $f(a + 2) - f(a)$

Solution

1. $f(a - 3) = (a - 3)^2 - 5(a - 3)$ *Substitute a − 3 for x.*

$\qquad\qquad = a^2 - 6a + 9 - 5a + 15$ *(A − B)² = A² − 2AB + B²; distributive law*

$\qquad\qquad = a^2 - 11a + 24$ *Combine like terms.*

2. $f(a + 2) - f(a)$

$\qquad = \left[(a + 2)^2 - 5(a + 2)\right] - \left(a^2 - 5a\right)$ *Substitute a + 2 for x; substitute a for x.*

$\qquad = a^2 + 4a + 4 - 5a - 10 - a^2 + 5a$ *(A + B)² = A² + 2AB + B²; distributive law; subtract.*

$\qquad = 4a - 6$ *Combine like terms.*

Recall from Section 6.1 that a quadratic function in the form $f(x) = ax^2 + bx + c$ is in standard form.

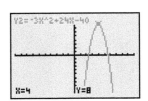

▶ **Example 9**   Writing a Quadratic Function in Standard Form

Write $f(x) = -3(x - 4)^2 + 8$ in standard form.

Solution

We begin by simplifying $(x - 4)^2$, because we work with exponents before we multiply or add:

$$f(x) = -3(x - 4)^2 + 8 \qquad \text{\textit{Original equation}}$$
$$= -3\left(x^2 - 8x + 16\right) + 8 \qquad \textit{(A - B)² = A² - 2AB + B²}$$
$$= -3x^2 + 24x - 48 + 8 \qquad \textit{Distributive law}$$
$$= -3x^2 + 24x - 40 \qquad \textit{Combine like terms.}$$

We use graphing calculator graphs to verify our work (see Fig. 14).

Figure 14 Verify the work

Product Function

In Section 6.1, we worked with sum functions and difference functions. Now we will work with *product functions*. For example, if $f(x) = 2x$ and $g(x) = x + 3$, then it follows that $f(x) \cdot g(x) = 2x(x + 3) = 2x^2 + 6x$. The function $f(x) \cdot g(x) = 2x^2 + 6x$ is called the product function of f and g.

▶ **Definition   Product function**

If f and g are functions and x is in the domain of both functions, then we can form the **product function** $f \cdot g$:

$$(f \cdot g)(x) = f(x) \cdot g(x)$$

▶ **Example 10** Finding the Product Function

Let $f(x) = 3x + 7$ and $g(x) = 5x - 2$.

1. Find an equation of the product function $f \cdot g$.
2. Find $(f \cdot g)(2)$.
3. Find an equation of the composite function $f \circ g$.
4. Find $(f \circ g)(2)$.

Solution

1. $(f \cdot g)(x) = f(x) \cdot g(x)$ *Definition of product function*

             $= (3x + 7)(5x - 2)$ *Substitute $3x + 7$ for $f(x)$ and $5x - 2$ for $g(x)$.*

             $= 15x^2 - 6x + 35x - 14$ *Multiply pairs of terms.*

             $= 15x^2 + 29x - 14$ *Combine like terms.*

2. $(f \cdot g)(2) = 15(2)^2 + 29(2) - 14 = 104$

3. $(f \circ g)(x) = f(g(x))$ *Definition of composition*

             $= f(5x - 2)$ *Substitute $5x - 2$ for $g(x)$.*

             $= 3(5x - 2) + 7$ *Substitute $5x - 2$ for x in $f(x) = 3x + 7$.*

             $= 15x - 6 + 7$ *Distributive law*

             $= 15x + 1$ *Combine like terms.*

4. $(f \circ g)(2) = 15(2) + 1 = 31$

▶

WARNING   It is a common error to confuse the product function $f \cdot g$ with the composite function $f \circ g$. Our work in Example 10 shows that these two functions are not the same in general. Sometimes we can find a meaningful model by finding the product of two models.

▶ **Example 11** Using a Product Function to Model a Situation

The annual cost of state corrections (prisons and related costs) per person in the United States can be modeled by the function

$$C(t) = 3.3t + 89$$

where $C(t)$ is the annual cost (in dollars per person) at t years since 1990 (see Table 11). The U.S. population can be modeled by the function

$$P(t) = 2.8t + 254$$

where $P(t)$ is the population (in millions) at t years since 1990.

Table 11 Costs of State Corrections; U.S. Population

Year	Cost (dollars per person)	U.S. Population (millions)
1998	113	275.9
2000	125	282.2
2002	135	287.8
2004	134	293.0
2006	135	298.6
2008	154	304.4

Source: *U.S. Census Bureau*

1. Check that the models fit the data well.
2. Find an equation of the product function $C \cdot P$.
3. Perform a unit analysis of the expression $C(t) \cdot P(t)$.
4. Find $(C \cdot P)(28)$. What does it mean in this situation?
5. Use a graphing calculator graph to determine whether the function $C \cdot P$ is increasing, decreasing, or neither for values of t between 0 and 30. What does your result mean in this situation?

Solution

1. We check the fit of the cost model in Fig. 15 and the fit of the population model in Fig. 16. The models appear to fit the data fairly well.

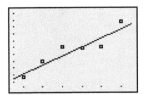

Figure 15 Cost scattergram and model

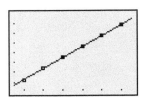

Figure 16 Population scattergram and model

2. $(C \cdot P)(t) = C(t) \cdot P(t)$ *Definition of product function*

$= (3.3t + 89)(2.8t + 254)$ *Substitute $3.3t + 89$ for $C(t)$ and $2.8t + 254$ for $P(t)$.*

$= 9.24t^2 + 838.2t + 249.2t + 22{,}606$ *Multiply pairs of terms.*

$= 9.24t^2 + 1087.4t + 22{,}606$ *Combine like terms.*

3. For the expression $C(t) \cdot P(t)$, we have

$$\underbrace{C(t)}_{\dfrac{\text{dollars}}{\text{person}}} \cdot \underbrace{P(t)}_{\text{millions of people}}$$

The units of the expression are millions of dollars.

4. $(C \cdot P)(28) = 9.24(28)^2 + 1087.4(28) + 22{,}606 \approx 60{,}297$. This means the total cost of state corrections will be about $60,297 million ($60.297 billion) in 2018, according to the model.

5. To graph the model, we enter the function, then press ⌗WINDOW⌗, and set Xmin to be 0 and Xmax to be 30. Then we use ZoomFit to draw the graph (see Fig. 17). For values of t between 0 and 30, the model is increasing. This means the total cost of state corrections has been increasing since 1990 and will continue to increase until 2020.

Plot1 Plot2 Plot3
\Y₁⊟9.24X^2+1087
.4X+22606
\Y₂=
\Y₃=
\Y₄=
\Y₅=
\Y₆=

WINDOW
 Xmin=0
 Xmax=30
 Xscl=5
 Ymin=22606
 Ymax=63544
 Yscl=5000
 Xres=1

Figure 17 Graph of the function $C \cdot P$

Group Exploration

Looking ahead: Factoring trinomials

In Problem 1 of Example 3, we found that the product $(x + 4)(x + 8)$ is equivalent to $x^2 + 12x + 32$. Working backward, we write $x^2 + 12x + 32 = (x + 4)(x + 8)$, and we call the process *factoring*. We say $(x + 4)(x + 8)$ is a factored polynomial. In general, a *factored polynomial* is a product of two or more polynomials.

1. Complete Table 12.

Table 12 Multiplying Some Quadratic Polynomials

Factored Polynomial	Last Terms	Product of Factored Polynomial	Coefficient of x	Constant Term
$(x + 3)(x + 4)$	3 and 4	$x^2 + 7x + 12$	7	12
$(x + 5)(x - 3)$	5 and -3	$x^2 + 2x - 15$	2	-15
$(x - 2)(x + 6)$				
$(x - 4)(x - 3)$				

2. For each row of Table 12, what connection do you notice between the last terms of the factored polynomial and the coefficient of x of the product of the factored polynomial? Explain why this happens.

3. For each row of Table 12, what connection do you notice between the last terms of the factored polynomial and the constant term of the product of the factored polynomial? Explain why this happens.

4. **a.** Do the observations you have made in this exploration apply to the polynomial $(2x + 3)(x + 4)$? If so, show that they do. If not, explain why not in terms of how you find the product $(2x + 3)(x + 4)$.

   b. Do the observations you have made in this exploration apply to the polynomial $(x + 5)(3x + 4)$? If so, show that they do. If not, explain why not in terms of how you find the product $(x + 5)(3x + 4)$.

   c. Discuss, in general, when your observations apply and when they do not.

▶ Tips for Success   Review Your Notes as Soon as Possible

Do you get confused by notes you wrote during class, even though the class activities made sense to you? If this happens a lot, review your notes as soon after class as possible. Even reviewing your notes for just a few minutes between classes will help. This will increase your likelihood of remembering what you learned in class and will give you the opportunity to add more comments to your notes while the class experience is fresh in your mind. Teaming with a classmate to review notes can also be helpful.

Homework 6.2

For extra help ▶ MyMathLab®   Watch the videos in MyMathLab   Download the MyDashboard App

Find the product. Use a graphing calculator table to verify your work when possible.

1. $3x^2(6x^4)$
2. $5x^3(7x^6)$
3. $2a^3b^5(-4a^2b^3)$
4. $7w^4y^3(-3w^3y^6)$
5. $-6x(5x - 2)$
6. $-9x(4x - 4)$
7. $5ab^2(4a^2 - 7ab + 3b^2)$
8. $-7w^2y(6w^2 + 2wy - 8y^2)$
9. $(x + 3)(x + 6)$
10. $(x + 9)(x + 2)$
11. $(3m - 2)(5m + 4)$
12. $(4p - 7)(2p + 3)$
13. $(8x - 3)(4x - 1)$
14. $(5x - 6)(3x - 2)$
15. $(1.7x - 2.4)(2.3x + 1.2)$
16. $(3.5x - 1.3)(2.2x - 4.7)$
17. $(2a + 5b)(3a - 7b)$
18. $(8p + t)(7p - 4t)$
19. $(4x - 9y)(5x - 2y)$
20. $(3m - 4p)(3m - 6p)$
21. $(2a^2 - 5b^2)(7a^2 + 3b^2)$
22. $(4a^2 - 9b^2)(3a^2 - 2b^2)$
23. $3x^2(2x - 5)(4x + 1)$
24. $2x^2(3x + 2)(2x - 5)$
25. $5x(x^2 + 3)(x - 4)$
26. $2x(x^2 - 7)(x + 3)$
27. $(3x + 2)(4x^2 + 5x - 3)$
28. $(5x + 3)(2x^2 - 7x - 4)$
29. $(a + b)(a^2 - ab + b^2)$
30. $(a - b)(a^2 + ab + b^2)$
31. $(4x - 3y)(2x^2 - xy + 5y^2)$
32. $(3x - 5y)(4x^2 + 2xy - y^2)$
33. $(x^2 + 2x - 3)(x^2 - x + 2)$
34. $(x^2 - 4x + 1)(x^2 - 3x + 2)$
35. $(2x^2 + xy - 3y^2)(x^2 - 2xy + y^2)$
36. $(x^2 + 2xy - y^2)(3x^2 - xy - 2y^2)$

Simplify. Use a graphing calculator table to verify your work when possible.

37. $(x + 5)^2$
38. $(x + 9)^2$
39. $(x - 8)^2$
40. $(x - 1)^2$
41. $(3x + 5)^2$
42. $(7x + 2)^2$
43. $(2.6x - 3.2)^2$
44. $(6.7x + 1.9)^2$
45. $(4a + 3b)^2$
46. $(3p + 7t)^2$
47. $(2x^2 - 6y^2)^2$
48. $(5m^2 - 4p^2)^2$
49. $-2x(2x + 5)^2$
50. $-5x(3x + 2)^2$

Find the product. Use a graphing calculator table to verify your work when possible.

51. $(x - 4)(x + 4)$
52. $(x - 7)(x + 7)$
53. $(3x + 6)(3x - 6)$
54. $(5x + 9)(5x - 9)$
55. $(2r - 8t)(2r + 8t)$
56. $(7m - 4n)(7m + 4n)$
57. $(3rt - 9w)(3rt + 9w)$
58. $(7ab - 5c)(7ab + 5c)$
59. $(8a^2 + 3b^2)(8a^2 - 3b^2)$
60. $(5p^2 + 7q^2)(5p^2 - 7q^2)$
61. $(x - 2)(x + 2)(x^2 + 4)$
62. $(x - 1)(x + 1)(x^2 + 1)$
63. $(3a + 2b)(3a - 2b)(9a^2 + 4b^2)$
64. $(2m - 5n)(2m + 5n)(4m^2 + 25n^2)$

For $f(x) = x^2 - 3x$, find the following.

65. $f(5b)$
66. $f(6b)$
67. $f(c + 4)$
68. $f(c + 1)$
69. $f(b - 3)$
70. $f(b - 2)$
71. $f(a + 2) - f(a)$
72. $f(a + 3) - f(a)$
73. $f(a + h) - f(a)$
74. $f(a) - f(a - h)$

For Exercises 75–80, write the quadratic function in standard form. Use a graphing calculator table or graph to verify your work.

75. $f(x) = (x + 6)^2$
76. $f(x) = (x - 5)^2$

77. $f(x) = 2(x + 3)^2 + 1$

78. $f(x) = 4(x - 2)^2 - 7$

79. $f(x) = -3(x - 5)^2 - 1$

80. $f(x) = -2(x + 4)^2 + 3$

For $f(x) = 2x - 3$, $g(x) = 3x + 2$, $h(x) = 2x^2 - 4x + 3$, and $k(x) = 3x^2 + x - 5$, find an equation of the given product function; then evaluate the product function at the indicated value.

81. $f \cdot g$, $(f \cdot g)(3)$

82. $g \cdot h$, $(g \cdot h)(3)$

83. $f \cdot h$, $(f \cdot h)(2)$

84. $h \cdot k$, $(h \cdot k)(2)$

85. $f \cdot f$, $(f \cdot f)(4)$

86. $g \cdot g$, $(g \cdot g)(4)$

For $f(x) = 4x + 1$, $g(x) = 5x + 3$, $h(x) = 3x^2 - x - 2$, and $k(x) = 2x^2 - 4x + 3$, find an equation of the given product function; then evaluate the product function at the indicated value.

87. $f \cdot g$, $(f \cdot g)(-1)$

88. $g \cdot f$, $(g \cdot f)(-1)$

89. $f \cdot h$, $(f \cdot h)(-2)$

90. $g \cdot k$, $(g \cdot k)(-2)$

91. $h \cdot h$, $(h \cdot h)(1)$

92. $k \cdot k$, $(k \cdot k)(1)$

93. The average value per acre of U.S. farmland (in dollars per acre) $V(t)$ is modeled by the function $V(t) = 62t + 508$, where t is the number of years since 1990 (see Table 13). The amount of U.S. farmland (in millions of acres) $A(t)$ is modeled by the function $A(t) = -3.3t + 978$, where t is the number of years since 1990.

Table 13 Values and Acres of U.S. Farmland

Year	Average Value (dollars per acre)	Amount of Farmland (millions of acres)
1993	740	968
1995	840	961
1997	930	956
1999	1030	948
2001	1150	941
2003	1270	939
2005	1407	928
2007	1634	921
2008	1646	920

Sources: *National Agriculture Statistics Service; Agricultural Statistics Board*

a. Check that the models fit the data well.

b. Find an equation of the product function $V \cdot A$.

c. Perform a unit analysis of the expression $V(t) \cdot A(t)$.

d. Find $(V \cdot A)(27)$. What does it mean in this situation?

e. Use a graphing calculator graph to determine whether the function $V \cdot A$ is increasing, decreasing, or neither for values of t between 0 and 27. What does your result mean in this situation? Explain how that is possible, given that the amount of farmland has been decreasing.

94. World Internet population (in billions) is modeled by $W(t) = 0.084t + 0.32$, where t is the number of years since 2000 (see Table 14). The number of web pages viewed per person per day is modeled by $N(t) = t + 31$, where t is the number of years since 2000.

Table 14 World Populations and Numbers of Web Pages Viewed per Person per Day

Year	World Internet Population (in billions)	Pages Viewed per Person per Day
2006	0.817	37
2007	0.903	38
2008	0.988	39
2009	1.072	40
2010	1.152	41

Source: *J.P. Morgan*

a. Check that the models fit the data well.

b. Find an equation of the product function $W \cdot N$.

c. Perform a unit analysis of the expression $(W \cdot N)(t)$.

d. Find $(W \cdot N)(17)$. What does it mean in this situation?

e. Predict the total number of pages that will be viewed by everyone in the world *throughout* 2018.

f. Use a graphing calculator graph to determine whether the function $W \cdot N$ is increasing, decreasing, or neither for values of t between 0 and 20. What does your result mean in this situation?

95. The average monthly cell phone bill (in dollars per month) $B(t)$ is modeled by the function $B(t) = -0.197t^2 + 6.15t + 3$, where t is the number of years since 1990 (see Table 15). The number of cell phone subscribers (in millions) $N(t)$ is modeled by the function $N(t) = 20t - 92$, where t is the number of years since 1990.

Table 15 Average Monthly Cell Phone Bills and Numbers of Subscribers

Year	Average Bill (dollars per month)	Number of Subscribers (millions)
1998	39.43	69.2
2000	45.27	109.5
2002	48.40	140.8
2004	50.64	182.1
2006	50.56	233.0
2008	50.07	270.3
2010	47.21	302.9

Source: *Cellular Telecommunications & Internet Association*

a. Check that the models fit the data well.

b. Find an equation of the product function $B \cdot N$.

c. Perform a unit analysis of the expression $B(t) \cdot N(t)$.

d. Find $(B \cdot N)(24)$. What does it mean in this situation?

e. Use a graphing calculator graph to determine whether the function $B \cdot N$ is increasing, decreasing, or neither for values of t between 14 and 20. What does your result mean in this situation? Explain how this is possible, given that the average bill decreased from 2004 to 2010.

96. In Example 6 of Section 2.3, we modeled the average salaries of professors at public colleges and universities. A reasonable model is $S(t) = 1.8t + 22$, where $S(t)$ is the average salary (in thousands of dollars) at t years since 1980 (see Table 16). The number of such professors (in thousands) $N(t)$ is modeled by the function $N(t) = 0.6t^2 + 9t + 670$, where t is the number of years since 1980.

Table 16 Average Salaries and Numbers of Professors

Year	Average Salary (thousands of dollars per professor)	Year	Number of Professors (thousands)
1980	22.1	1980	686
1985	31.2	1985	715
1990	41.9	1991	826
1995	49.1	1995	932
2000	57.7	2001	1174
2005	66.9	2005	1290
2010	78.0	2009	1439

Sources: *American Association of University Professors; U.S. National Center for Education Statistics*

a. Check that the models fit the data well.
b. Find an equation of the product function $S \cdot N$.
c. Perform a unit analysis of the expression $S(t) \cdot N(t)$.
d. Find $(S \cdot N)(38)$. What does it mean in this situation?
e. Use a graphing calculator graph to determine whether the function $S \cdot N$ is increasing, decreasing, or neither for values of t between 0 and 40. What does your result mean in this situation?

Concepts

97. A student tries to simplify $(x + 8)^2$:
$$(x + 8)^2 = x^2 + 64$$
Describe any errors. Then simplify the expression correctly.

98. A student tries to simplify $(2x - 9y)^2$:
$$(2x - 9y)^2 = 4x^2 - 81y^2$$
Describe any errors. Then simplify the expression correctly.

99. a. Use a graphing calculator table to show that $(x + 2)^2$ and $x^2 + 2^2$ are not equivalent.
 b. Simplify $(x + 2)^2$.
 c. Use a graphing calculator table to show that $(x + 2)^2$ and your result in part (b) are equivalent.

100. a. Use a graphing calculator table to show that $(x - 4)^2$ and $x^2 - 4^2$ are not equivalent.
 b. Simplify $(x - 4)^2$.
 c. Use a graphing calculator table to show that $(x - 4)^2$ and your result in part (b) are equivalent.

101. A student tries to find the product $7x(-2x)$:
$$7x(-2x) = 5x$$
Describe any errors. Then find the product correctly.

102. A student tries to simplify $(3x + 5)^2$:
$$(3x + 5)^2 = 9x^2 + 15x + 25$$
Describe any errors. Then simplify the expression correctly.

103. Which expressions are equivalent?
$(2x - 5)(3x + 4)$ $6x^2 + 7x - 20$ $3x(2x - 2) - x - 20$
$(3x - 4)(2x + 5)$ $6x^2 - 7x - 20$ $(3x + 4)(2x - 5)$

104. Which expressions are equivalent?
$(8x + 1)(x - 4)$ $(4x - 2)(2x + 2)$ $8x^2 - 31x - 4$
$8x^2 + 31x - 4$ $(x - 4)(8x + 1)$ $4(2x^2 - 1) - 31x$

105. Show that the property $(A - B)^2 = A^2 - 2AB + B^2$ is correct.

106. Describe the various types of products of polynomials and squares of binomials we have discussed in this section. Describe how to find such products and simplify such squares.

Related Review

For $f(x) = x^2$, $g(x) = 4x - 5$, $h(x) = 2x^2 - 3x + 1$, and $k(x) = x + 3$, find an equation of the given function; then evaluate the function at the indicated value.

107. $g - h, (g - h)(-2)$
108. $g + h, (g + h)(-2)$
109. $h \cdot k, (h \cdot k)(-1)$
110. $g \cdot h, (g \cdot h)(-1)$
111. $f \circ g, (f \circ g)(3)$
112. $g \circ f, (g \circ f)(3)$
113. $h \circ k, (h \circ k)(2)$
114. $k \circ h, (k \circ h)(2)$

Find the product or simplify to help you decide whether the function is linear or quadratic. Use a graphing calculator graph to verify your work.

115. $f(x) = (2x - 5)(3x - 1)$
116. $f(x) = (4x - 7)(4x + 7)$
117. $f(x) = x^2 - (x + 1)^2$
118. $f(x) = (x + 6)^2 - (x - 6)^2$

Simplify. Write your result as a single logarithm with a coefficient of 1.

119. $\log_b(x + 5) + \log_b(x - 3)$
120. $\log_b(x - 4) + \log_b(x - 7)$
121. $2\log_b(w - 3) + \log_b(w + 3)$
122. $\log_b(p - 2) + 2\log_b(p + 2)$

Expressions, Equations, Functions, and Graphs

Perform the indicated instruction. Then use words such as linear, quadratic, cubic, exponential, logarithmic, polynomial, degree, function, one variable, *and* two variables *to describe the expression, equation, or system.*

123. Find the product $4x(3x + 5)(2x - 3)$.

124. Graph $f(x) = 9\left(\dfrac{1}{3}\right)^x$ by hand.

125. Write $f(x) = -3(x - 4)^2 + 5$ in standard form.

126. Simplify $\left(\dfrac{3b^4 c^{-5}}{9b^{-2}c^{-3}}\right)^{-2}$.

▼ 6.3 Dividing Polynomials: Long Division and Synthetic Division

Objectives

» Divide a polynomial by a monomial.

» Use long division to divide a polynomial by a binomial.

» Perform synthetic division.

In Sections 6.1 and 6.2, we discussed how to add, subtract, and multiply polynomials. In this section, we will divide polynomials.

Dividing by a Monomial

First, we will discuss how to divide a polynomial by a monomial. Recall the following rule about adding fractions with a common denominator:

$$\frac{A}{B} + \frac{C}{B} = \frac{A + C}{B}, \text{ where } B \neq 0$$

To divide by a monomial, we will go backward.

> **▶ Dividing by a Monomial**
>
> If A, B, and C are monomials and B is nonzero, then
>
> $$\frac{A + C}{B} = \frac{A}{B} + \frac{C}{B}$$
>
> In words: To divide a polynomial by a monomial, divide each term of the polynomial by the monomial.

WARNING   It is a common error to divide only some of the terms of the polynomial by the monomial. Remember to divide *every* term of the polynomial by the monomial.

```
Plot1 Plot2 Plot3
\Y1◻(12X^4-5X^2+
6X)/(3X)
\Y2◻4X^3-(5/3)X+
2
\Y3=
\Y4=
\Y5=
```

X	Y₁	Y₂
1	4.3333	4.3333
2	30.667	30.667
3	105	105
4	251.33	251.33
5	493.67	493.67
6	856	856
7	1362.3	1362.3
X=1		

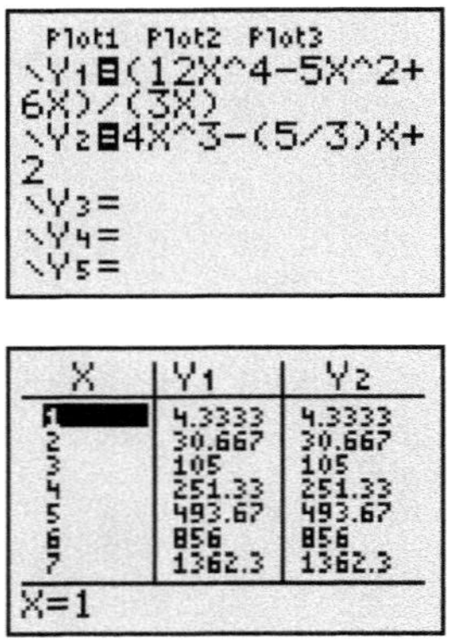

Figure 18 Verify the work

▶ **Example 1**   Dividing by a Monomial

Find the quotient $\dfrac{12x^4 - 5x^2 + 6x}{3x}$.

Solution

$$\frac{12x^4 - 5x^2 + 6x}{3x} = \frac{12x^4}{3x} - \frac{5x^2}{3x} + \frac{6x}{3x} \quad \textit{Divide each term by 3x: } \frac{A - C + D}{B} = \frac{A}{B} - \frac{C}{B} + \frac{D}{B}$$

$$= 4x^3 - \frac{5}{3}x + 2 \quad \textit{Simplify; subtract exponents: } \frac{x^m}{x^n} = x^{m-n}$$

We use a graphing calculator table to verify our work (see Fig. 18).

Recall that for each division calculation, there is a related multiplication calculation. For example, since $\dfrac{8}{2} = 4$, it follows that $2 \cdot 4 = 8$. We can use this concept to perform another check of our work in Example 1. To check that

$$\frac{12x^4 - 5x^2 + 6x}{3x} = 4x^3 - \frac{5}{3}x + 2$$

we multiply $3x$ and $4x^3 - \dfrac{5}{3}x + 2$:

$$3x\left(4x^3 - \frac{5}{3}x + 2\right) = 3x\left(4x^3\right) - 3x\left(\frac{5}{3}x\right) + 3x(2)$$

$$= 12x^4 - 5x^2 + 6x$$

which checks.

> **Example 2** Dividing by a Monomial

Find the quotient $\dfrac{6x^4y + 8x^3y^3 - 4x^2y^4}{-2x^2y}$.

Solution

$$\dfrac{6x^4y + 8x^3y^3 - 4x^2y^4}{-2x^2y} = \dfrac{6x^4y}{-2x^2y} + \dfrac{8x^3y^3}{-2x^2y} - \dfrac{4x^2y^4}{-2x^2y}$$

Divide each term by $-2x^2y$: $\dfrac{A + C - D}{B} = \dfrac{A}{B} + \dfrac{C}{B} - \dfrac{D}{B}$

$$= -3x^2 - 4xy^2 + 2y^3$$

Simplify; subtract exponents: $\dfrac{x^m}{x^n} = x^{m-n}$

We verify our work by finding the product $-2x^2y\left(-3x^2 - 4xy^2 + 2y^3\right)$:

$$-2x^2y\left(-3x^2 - 4xy^2 + 2y^3\right) = 6x^4y + 8x^3y^3 - 4x^2y^4$$

Using Long Division to Divide by a Binomial

We can use long division to divide a polynomial by a binomial. The steps are similar to performing long division with numbers. Here we review how to use long division to divide 3547 by 14:

```
                        2 5 3     ← Quotient
      Divisor  →   1 4 ) 3 5 4 7   ← Dividend
                      − 2 8 ↓      2·14 = 28
                        7 4        Subtract and bring down next digit of dividend.
                      − 7 0 ↓      5·14 = 70
                          4 7      Subtract and bring down next digit of dividend.
                        − 4 2      3·14 = 42
      Remainder  →         5      Subtract.
```

We conclude

$$\dfrac{3547}{14} = 253 + \dfrac{5}{14}$$

Recall that we can verify our work by checking that

Divisor	Quotient	Remainder	Dividend
↓	↓	↓	↓
14 ·	253 +	5 =	3547

which is true.

> **Example 3** Dividing by a Binomial

Divide: $\dfrac{2x^2 + 11x + 15}{x + 3}$.

Solution

The steps are similar to performing long division with numbers. To begin, we divide $2x^2$ (the first term of $2x^2 + 11x + 15$) by x (the first term of $x + 3$): $\dfrac{2x^2}{x} = 2x$.

$$
\begin{array}{r}
2x \\
x + 3 \overline{)\, 2x^2 + 11x + 15} \\
2x^2 + 6x
\end{array}
$$

$\dfrac{2x^2}{x} = 2x$

$2x(x + 3) = 2x^2 + 6x$

To subtract $2x^2 + 6x$, we change the signs of $2x^2$ and $6x$ and add:

$$
\begin{array}{r}
2x \\
x + 3 \overline{)\, 2x^2 + 11x + 15\,} \\
2x^2 + 6x \\
\hline
5x
\end{array}
$$

Change signs.   Add.

Next, we bring down the 15:

$$
\begin{array}{r}
2x \\
x + 3 \overline{)\, 2x^2 + 11x + 15\,} \\
-2x^2 - 6x \downarrow \\
\hline
5x + 15
\end{array}
$$

Bring down the 15.

Then we repeat the process.

$$
\begin{array}{r}
2x + 5 \\
x + 3 \overline{)\, 2x^2 + 11x + 15\,} \\
-2x^2 - 6x \\
\hline
5x + 15 \\
5x + 15 \\
\hline
0
\end{array}
\qquad \frac{5x}{x} = 5
$$

Change signs. $5(x + 3) = 5x + 15$ Add.

We conclude

$$\frac{2x^2 + 11x + 15}{x + 3} = 2x + 5$$

We verify our work by checking that

Divisor	Quotient	Remainder	Dividend
↓	↓	↓	↓

$$(x + 3) \cdot (2x + 5) + 0 = 2x^2 + 11x + 15$$

which is true.

▶ **Example 4** Dividing by a Binomial

Divide: $\dfrac{6x^2 + 11x - 7}{2x + 5}$.

Solution

To begin, we divide $6x^2$ (the first term of $6x^2 + 11x - 7$) by $2x$ (the first term of $2x + 5$): $\dfrac{6x^2}{2x} = 3x$.

$$
\begin{array}{r}
3x \\
2x + 5 \overline{)\, 6x^2 + 11x - 7\,} \\
6x^2 + 15x \downarrow \\
\hline
-4x - 7
\end{array}
\qquad \frac{6x^2}{2x} = 3x
$$

Change signs. $3x(2x + 5) = 6x^2 + 15x$

Add. Then bring down the -7.

Then we repeat the process.

$$
\begin{array}{r}
3x - 2 \\
2x + 5 \overline{)\, 6x^2 + 11x - 7\,} \\
-6x^2 - 15x \\
\hline
-4x - 7 \\
4x + 10 \\
\hline
3
\end{array}
\qquad \frac{-4x}{2x} = -2
$$

Change signs. $-2(2x + 5) = -4x - 10$ Add.

We conclude

$$\frac{6x^2 + 11x - 7}{2x + 5} = 3x - 2 + \frac{3}{2x + 5}$$

To verify our work, we simplify $(2x + 5)(3x - 2) + 3$:

Divisor   Quotient   Remainder

↓   ↓   ↓

$$(2x + 5) \cdot (3x - 2) + 3 = 6x^2 - 4x + 15x - 10 + 3$$
$$= 6x^2 + 11x - 7 \leftarrow \text{Dividend}$$

Since the result is the dividend, this checks.

▶ **Example 5**   Dividing a Polynomial with Missing Terms

Divide: $\dfrac{27x^3 - 8}{3x - 2}$.

Solution

Since the dividend, $27x^3 - 8$, doesn't have x^2 or x terms, we use $0x^2$ and $0x$ as placeholders:

$$27x^3 + 0x^2 + 0x - 8$$

This way, like terms will line up when we perform long division:

$$
\begin{array}{r}
9x^2 + 6x + 4 \\
3x - 2 \overline{)\,27x^3 + 0x^2 + 0x - 8} \\
\end{array}
$$

Change signs. $27x^3 - 18x^2$ *Use $0x^2$ and $0x$ as placeholders.*
      $9x^2(3x - 2) = 27x^3 - 18x^2$

      $18x^2 + 0x$ *Add; then bring down $0x$.*

Change signs. $18x^2 - 12x$ *$6x(3x - 2) = 18x^2 - 12x$*

      $12x - 8$ *Add; then bring down -8.*

Change signs. $12x - 8$ *$4(3x - 2) = 12x - 8$*

        0 *Add.*

We conclude

$$\frac{27x^3 - 8}{3x - 2} = 9x^2 + 6x + 4$$

We use a graphing calculator table to verify our work (see Fig. 19).

Figure 19 Verify the work

▶ **Example 6**   Dividing a Polynomial with Missing Terms

Divide: $\dfrac{1 + 5x^3 - 4x + 2x^2}{x^2 - 3}$.

Solution

First, we write the dividend in decreasing order: $5x^3 + 2x^2 - 4x + 1$. Also, since the divisor, $x^2 - 3$, doesn't have an x term, we use $0x$ as a placeholder:

$$x^2 + 0x - 3$$

Just like in Example 5, this will allow like terms to line up:

$$
\begin{array}{r}
5x + 2 \\
x^2 + 0x - 3 \overline{)\,5x^3 + 2x^2 - 4x + 1} \\
\end{array}
$$

Change signs. $5x^3 + 0x^2 - 15x$ *$5x(x^2 + 0x - 3) = 5x^3 + 0x^2 - 15x$*

      $2x^2 + 11x + 1$ *Add; then bring down the 1.*

Change signs. $2x^2 + 0x - 6$ *$2(x^2 + 0x - 3) = 2x^2 + 0x - 6$*

      $11x + 7$ *Add.*

We conclude

$$\frac{5x^3 + 2x^2 - 4x + 1}{x^2 - 3} = 5x + 2 + \frac{11x + 7}{x^2 - 3}$$

To verify our work, we simplify $(x^2 - 3)(5x + 2) + (11x + 7)$:

Divisor   Quotient   Remainder
↓   ↓   ↓

$(x^2 - 3)$ · $(5x + 2)$ + $(11x + 7)$ $= 5x^3 + 2x^2 - 15x - 6 + 11x + 7$
$= 5x^3 + 2x^2 - 4x + 1 \leftarrow$ Dividend

Since the result is the dividend, this checks.

Synthetic Division

When we divide a polynomial by a binomial of the form $x - a$, we can use a method called *synthetic division*, which uses the ideas of long division but is more efficient. To take our first step toward synthetic division, consider dividing $3x^3 - 7x^2 + 10x - 12$ by $x - 2$. Here we perform long division twice, the first time showing the variables and the second time not showing them:

$$\begin{array}{r} 3x^2 - x + 8 \\ x-2\overline{)3x^3 - 7x^2 + 10x - 12} \\ \underline{3x^3 + 6x^2} \\ -x^2 + 10x \\ \underline{-x^2 + 2x} \\ 8x - 12 \\ \underline{8x + 16} \\ 4 \end{array}$$

$$\begin{array}{r} 3 - 1\ \ 8 \\ 1-2\overline{)3 - 7\ \ \ 10 - 12} \\ \underline{3 + 6} \\ -1\ \ \ 10 \\ \underline{-1\ \ \ 2} \\ 8 - 12 \\ \underline{8 + 16} \\ 4 \end{array}$$

We conclude

$$\frac{3x^3 - 7x^2 + 10x - 12}{x - 2} = 3x^2 - x + 8 + \frac{4}{x - 2}$$

In Example 7, we will perform the division yet one more time, now using synthetic division.

▶ **Example 7**   Performing Synthetic Division

Use synthetic division to divide: $\dfrac{3x^3 - 7x^2 + 10x - 12}{x - 2}$.

Solution

When performing synthetic division, there is no need to write the coefficient of x of the divisor $x - 2$. The method already takes the divisions by x into account. Also, instead of dividing by the constant term -2, we divide by its opposite: 2. That way, we can add without having to change signs first.

$\underline{2|}\ \ 3\ \ \ -7\ \ \ 10\ \ \ -12$ *Write 2 of x − 2 and the coefficients of $3x^3 − 7x^2 + 10x − 12$.*
     ↓
     3   *Bring down the 3.*

$\underline{2|}\ \ 3\ \ \ -7\ \ \ 10\ \ \ -12$
            6   *Multiply 3 by 2 to get 6.*
     3

$$\begin{array}{r|rrrr}
2 & 3 & -7 & 10 & -12 \\
  &   & 6 &   &   \\
\hline
  & 3 & -1 &   &
\end{array}$$

Add −7 and 6 to get −1.

$$\begin{array}{r|rrrr}
2 & 3 & -7 & 10 & -12 \\
  &   & 6 & -2 &   \\
\hline
  & 3 & -1 & 8 &
\end{array}$$

Multiply −1 by 2 to get −2.
Add 10 and −2 to get 8.

$$\begin{array}{r|rrrr}
2 & 3 & -7 & 10 & -12 \\
  &   & 6 & -2 & 16 \\
\hline
  & 3 & -1 & 8 & 4
\end{array}$$

Multiply 8 by 2 to get 16.
Add −12 and 16 to get 4.

$$3x^2 \quad -1x \quad +8 \quad \text{Remainder}$$

So, the result is $3x^2 - x + 8$ with remainder 4. We conclude

$$\frac{3x^3 - 7x^2 + 10x - 12}{x - 2} = 3x^2 - x + 8 + \frac{4}{x - 2}$$

This checks with our work just before this example.

Recall that **to perform synthetic division, the divisor must be of the form $x - a$.** The first step is to write the dividend in descending order. Then we write a inside the $\rfloor$ and write the coefficients of the dividend outside it.

▶ **Example 8**   Performing Synthetic Division

Use synthetic division to divide: $\dfrac{x^2 - 1 - 39x + 3x^3}{x + 4}$.

Solution

First, we write the dividend in descending order: $3x^3 + x^2 - 39x - 1$. Next we use synthetic division. Note that $x + 4 = x - (-4)$. So, we write -4 inside the $\rfloor$:

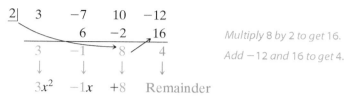

$$\begin{array}{r|rrrr}
-4 & 3 & 1 & -39 & -1 \\
   &   & -12 & 44 & -20 \\
\hline
   & 3 & -11 & 5 & -21
\end{array}$$

$$3x^2 \quad -11x \quad +5 \quad \text{Remainder}$$

The quotient is $3x^2 - 11x + 5$ with remainder -21. We conclude

$$\frac{x^2 - 1 - 39x + 3x^3}{x + 4} = 3x^2 - 11x + 5 - \frac{21}{x + 4}$$

▶ **Example 9**   Performing Synthetic Division when There Are Missing Terms

Use synthetic division to divide: $\dfrac{-2p^3 + 22p - 12}{p - 3}$.

Solution

Because the dividend $-2p^3 + 22p - 12$ does not have a p^2 term, we use 0 as a placeholder:

$$
\begin{array}{r|rrrr}
3 & -2 & 0 & 22 & -12 \\
  &   & -6 & -18 & 12 \\
\hline
  & -2 & -6 & 4 & 0
\end{array}
$$

We conclude

$$\frac{-2p^3 + 22p - 12}{p - 3} = -2p^2 - 6p + 4$$

Homework 6.3

For extra help ▶ MyMathLab®   ▦ Watch the videos in MyMathLab   Download the MyDashboard App

Divide. Use a graphing calculator table to verify your work.

1. $\dfrac{3x^5 + 7x^3}{x}$

2. $\dfrac{2x^6 + 9x^2}{x^2}$

3. $\dfrac{6x^3 + 12x^2}{3x}$

4. $\dfrac{8x^3 + 20x}{4x}$

5. $\dfrac{20p^9 - 5p^6 + 15p^3}{5p^3}$

6. $\dfrac{10c^5 + 8c^3 - 4c^2}{2c^2}$

7. $\dfrac{16x^5 - 3x^4 - 24x^3}{-8x^2}$

8. $\dfrac{18x^5 + 5x^4 - 6x^3}{-6x^3}$

Divide. Verify your work by multiplying.

9. $\dfrac{4x^5 - 8x^4 + 7x^2}{2x^4}$

10. $\dfrac{20x^6 - 35x^4 - 10x^2}{5x^3}$

11. $\dfrac{-8k^4 - 6k^3 + 12k}{-4k^2}$

12. $\dfrac{-2b^5 + 9b^4 - 15b}{-3b^3}$

13. $\dfrac{x^4y + x^3y^2 - xy^4}{xy}$

14. $\dfrac{x^5y - x^4y^2 - x^2y^4}{xy}$

15. $\dfrac{10m^4r^2 + 3m^2r^3 + 4mr^4}{2mr^2}$

16. $\dfrac{6w^5p + 12w^4p^2 + 2w^3p^3}{6w^2p}$

17. $\dfrac{12x^6y^4 + 18x^5y^2 - 8x^4y}{-4x^3y^2}$

18. $\dfrac{18x^5y - 9x^2y^3 + 7xy^4}{-3xy^2}$

Perform long division. To verify your work, check that the product of the divisor and the quotient plus the remainder is the dividend.

19. $\dfrac{3x^2 + 14x + 8}{x + 4}$

20. $\dfrac{2x^2 + 11x + 15}{x + 3}$

21. $\dfrac{4x^2 - 22x + 10}{x - 5}$

22. $\dfrac{5x^2 - 7x - 6}{x - 2}$

23. $\dfrac{6p^2 + 19p + 12}{3p + 2}$

24. $\dfrac{8w^2 + 26w + 7}{2w + 6}$

25. $\dfrac{4x^2 + 2x - 23}{2x + 5}$

26. $\dfrac{15x^2 + 14x - 6}{3x + 4}$

27. $\dfrac{10x^2 - 7x + 3}{5x - 1}$

28. $\dfrac{12x^2 - 23x + 2}{4x - 1}$

29. $\dfrac{2m - 9 + 20m^2}{4m - 2}$

30. $\dfrac{10b^2 - 35 + 27b}{5b - 4}$

Perform long division. Use a graphing calculator table to verify your work.

31. $\dfrac{4x^3 + 12x^2 + 15x + 13}{2x + 3}$

32. $\dfrac{15x^3 - 4x^2 - 24x - 11}{5x + 2}$

33. $\dfrac{17p + 12p^3 - 14 - 22p^2}{3p - 4}$

34. $\dfrac{7 - 13w^2 + 6w^3 - 9w}{2w - 5}$

35. $\dfrac{x^2 + 7}{x + 3}$

36. $\dfrac{x^2 + 5}{x + 2}$

37. $\dfrac{8x^3 - 125}{2x - 5}$

38. $\dfrac{27x^3 - 64}{3x - 4}$

39. $\dfrac{3x^3 - 10x^2 + 7}{3x - 1}$

40. $\dfrac{6x^3 - 11x^2 + 5}{2x - 1}$

41. $\dfrac{3x^3 - 4x^2 + 9x - 16}{x^2 + 3}$

42. $\dfrac{2x^3 - 5x^2 + 4x - 7}{x^2 + 2}$

43. $\dfrac{6y^3 + 9y^2 - 4y - 7}{3y^2 - 2}$

44. $\dfrac{10b^3 - 6b^2 - 20b + 17}{2b^2 - 4}$

Perform synthetic division. Use a graphing calculator table to verify your work.

45. $\dfrac{3x^3 - 10x^2 + 10x - 4}{x - 2}$

46. $\dfrac{2x^3 - 11x^2 + 18x - 9}{x - 3}$

47. $\dfrac{-x^3 - 4x^2 + 5x + 23}{x + 4}$

48. $\dfrac{4x^3 + 18x^2 - 7x + 15}{x + 5}$

49. $\dfrac{3k^2 - 7k + 1}{k - 1}$

50. $\dfrac{2w^2 - 5w - 10}{w + 1}$

51. $\dfrac{-11x^2 - 17 + 8x + 2x^3}{x - 5}$

52. $\dfrac{7 + 3x^3 - 9x - 2x^2}{x - 2}$

53. $\dfrac{3x^3 + 11x^2 + 14}{x + 4}$

54. $\dfrac{2x^3 - 7x^2 + 5}{x + 3}$

Concepts

55. A student tries to find a quotient:

$$\frac{6x^2 + 7x}{2x^2} = \frac{6x^2}{2x^2} + 7x$$
$$= 3 + 7x$$
$$= 7x + 3$$

Describe any errors. Then find the quotient correctly.

56. A student tries to find a quotient:

$$\frac{3x^5 - 6x^2}{7x^4} = \frac{3x^5}{7x^4} - \frac{6x^2}{7x^4}$$
$$= \frac{3x}{7} - \frac{6x^2}{7}$$

Describe any errors. Then find the quotient correctly.

57. A student tries to find the quotient $\dfrac{2x^2 + 10x + 12}{x + 3}$:

$$\begin{array}{r} -2x - 4 \\ x + 3 \overline{)\, 2x^2 + 10x + 12} \\ \underline{-2x^2 - 6x} \\ 4x + 12 \\ \underline{-4x - 12} \\ 0 \end{array}$$

$$\frac{2x^2 + 10x + 12}{x + 3} = -2x - 4$$

Describe any errors. Then find the quotient correctly.

58. A student tries to find the quotient $\dfrac{3x^3 - 7x^2 + 3x - 2}{x + 2}$:

$$\begin{array}{r|rrrr} 2 & 3 & -7 & 3 & -2 \\ & & 6 & -2 & 2 \\ \hline & 3 & -1 & 1 & 0 \end{array}$$

$$\frac{3x^3 - 7x^2 + 3x - 2}{x + 2} = 3x^2 - x + 1$$

Describe any errors. Then find the quotient correctly.

59. A student tries to find the quotient $\dfrac{4x^3 - 10x^2 - 9x + 15}{x - 3}$:

$$\begin{array}{r|rrrr} 3 & 4 & -10 & -9 & 15 \\ & & 12 & 6 & -9 \\ \hline & 4 & 2 & -3 & 6 \end{array}$$

$$\frac{4x^3 - 10x^2 - 9x + 15}{x - 3} = 4x^3 + 2x^2 - 3x + 6$$

Describe any errors. Then find the quotient correctly.

60. a. Find the product $(x + 2)(x + 5)$.

    b. Use long division to find the quotient $\dfrac{x^2 + 7x + 10}{x + 5}$.

    c. Explain how your work in parts (a) and (b) is related.

61. Give an example of a polynomial and a monomial such that the quotient of the polynomial and the monomial is $2x^2 - 3x + 7$.

62. Give an example of a polynomial and a binomial such that the quotient of the polynomial and the binomial is $5x - 2$.

63. When a certain polynomial is divided by the binomial $x - 3$, the result is $2x - 5 + \dfrac{4}{x - 3}$. What is the polynomial?

64. If the division of two polynomials has remainder 0, what does the product of the divisor and quotient equal? Explain.

65. When we divide a polynomial by a monomial, we divide each term of the polynomial by the monomial. Explain why this make sense.

66. Give several reasons why long division of polynomials is similar to long division of numbers.

67. Describe how to divide a polynomial by a monomial.

68. Describe how to divide a polynomial by a binomial.

69. Describe when synthetic division can be used and how to perform it.

70. Describe how to verify your work after you divide a polynomial by a binomial.

Related Review

Perform the indicated operation. Use a graphing calculator table to verify your work.

71. $\left(6x^2 - x - 2\right)(3x - 2)$

72. $\left(8x^2 - 10x - 3\right)(4x + 1)$

73. $\left(6x^2 - x - 2\right) - (3x - 2)$

74. $\left(8x^2 - 10x - 3\right) - (4x + 1)$

75. $\dfrac{6x^2 - x - 2}{3x - 2}$

76. $\dfrac{8x^2 - 10x - 3}{4x + 1}$

77. $(3x - 2)^2$

78. $(4x + 1)^2$

Expressions, Equations, Functions, and Graphs

Perform the indicated instruction. Then use words such as linear, quadratic, cubic, exponential, logarithmic, polynomial, degree, *function,* one variable, *and* two variables *to describe the expression, equation, or system.*

79. Solve:

$$3x - 2y = 9$$
$$4x - y = 7$$

80. Graph $3x - 2y = 4$.

81. Solve $4\log_2(3x) + \log_2\left(5x^3\right) = 8$.

82. Solve $5 - (2x - 3) \leq x + 4$.

▼ 6.4 Factoring Trinomials of the Form $x^2 + bx + c$; Factoring Out the GCF

Objectives

» Know that multiplying and *factoring* are reverse processes.

» Factor a trinomial of the form $x^2 + bx + c$.

» Know the meaning of a *prime* polynomial.

» Factor out the *greatest common factor (GCF)* of a polynomial.

» *Completely factor* polynomials.

» Know when to factor out the opposite of the GCF of a polynomial.

We know how to multiply 2 and 5, as follows: $2 \cdot 5 = 10$. Can we work backward? Here, we *factor* the number 10: $10 = 2 \cdot 5$. Note that factoring 10 is the reverse of multiplying 2 and 5. Next, we will make similar observations about polynomials.

Multiplying Polynomials versus Factoring Polynomials

In Section 6.2, we found products of polynomials; for example,

$$(x + 2)(x + 3) = x^2 + 3x + 2x + 6 \quad \text{\textit{Multiply pairs of terms.}}$$
$$= x^2 + 5x + 6 \quad \text{\textit{Combine like terms.}}$$

In this section, we will learn how to work backward. That is, we will learn how to write $x^2 + 5x + 6$ as a product. This process is called *factoring*.

We **factor** a polynomial by writing it as a product. We say $(x + 2)(x + 3)$ is a **factored polynomial** and both $(x + 2)$ and $(x + 3)$ are factors of the polynomial.

> ### ▶ Comparing Multiplying with Factoring
>
> Multiplying and factoring are reverse processes. For example,
>
> $$\text{Multiplying}$$
> $$\overrightarrow{}$$
> $$(x + 2)(x + 3) = x^2 + 5x + 6$$
> $$\overleftarrow{}$$
> $$\text{Factoring}$$

Factoring a Trinomial of the Form $x^2 + bx + c$

To see how to factor $x^2 + 5x + 6$, let's take another look at how we find the product $(x + 2)(x + 3)$:

$$\overset{\text{last terms}}{(x + 2)(x + 3)} = x^2 + 3x + 2x + 2 \cdot 3$$
$$= x^2 + 5x + 6$$

$$\underset{\substack{\text{sum of} \\ \text{last terms} \\ 2 + 3 = 5}}{\uparrow} \quad \underset{\substack{\text{product of} \\ \text{last terms} \\ 2 \cdot 3 = 6}}{\uparrow}$$

For $x^2 + 5x + 6$, notice that the coefficient of x is 5, which is the sum of 2 and 3, the *last terms* of $(x + 2)(x + 3)$. Also, the constant term of $x^2 + 5x + 6$ is 6, which is the product of 2 and 3. Now we find the product $(x + p)(x + q)$:

$$(x + p)(x + q) = x^2 + qx + px + pq \quad \text{\textit{Multiply pairs of terms.}}$$
$$= x^2 + px + qx + pq \quad \text{\textit{Rearrange terms.}}$$
$$= x^2 + (p + q)x + pq \quad \text{\textit{Distributive law}}$$

In the result, we see that the coefficient of x is the sum of the last terms p and q and that the constant term is the product of the last terms p and q. This observation can help us factor some quadratic trinomials.

Trinomials with Positive Constant Terms

For the trinomial $x^2 + 5x + 6$, the constant term, 6, is positive. In Examples 1 and 2, we will factor two more trinomials whose constant term is positive.

▶ **Example 1**   Factoring a Trinomial of the Form $x^2 + bx + c$

Factor $x^2 + 11x + 24$.

Solution

To factor $x^2 + 11x + 24$, we need two integers whose product is 24 and whose sum is 11. We try only positive integers, since both their product and their sum must be positive. Here are the possibilities:

$$\begin{array}{cc} \textbf{Product} = 24 & \textbf{Sum} = \textbf{11?} \\ 1(24) = 24 & 1 + 24 = 25 \\ 2(12) = 24 & 2 + 12 = 14 \\ 3(8) = 24 & 3 + 8 = 11 \leftarrow \text{Success!} \\ 4(6) = 24 & 4 + 6 = 10 \end{array}$$

Since $3(8) = 24$ and $3 + 8 = 11$, we conclude that the last terms of the factors are 3 and 8:

$$x^2 + 11x + 24 = (x + 3)(x + 8)$$

We check the result by finding the product $(x + 3)(x + 8)$:

$$(x + 3)(x + 8) = x^2 + 8x + 3x + 24 = x^2 + 11x + 24$$

By the commutative law, $(x + 3)(x + 8) = (x + 8)(x + 3)$, so we can write the factors $x + 3$ and $x + 8$ in either order.

▶

We now summarize how to factor a trinomial of the form $x^2 + bx + c$.

▶ **Factoring $x^2 + bx + c$**

To factor $x^2 + bx + c$, look for two integers p and q whose product is c and whose sum is b. That is, $pq = c$ and $p + q = b$. If such integers exist, the factored polynomial is

$$(x + p)(x + q)$$

▶ **Example 2**   Factoring a Trinomial of the Form $x^2 + bx + c$

Factor $x^2 - 8x + 16$.

Solution

To factor $x^2 - 8x + 16$, we need two integers whose product is 16 and whose sum is -8. Since the product 16 is positive, the two integers must have the same sign. Therefore, both integers must be negative, because the sum -8 is negative. Here are the possibilities:

$$\begin{array}{cc} \textbf{Product} = 16 & \textbf{Sum} = -8? \\ -1(-16) = 16 & -1 + (-16) = -17 \\ -2(-8) = 16 & -2 + (-8) = -10 \\ -4(-4) = 16 & -4 + (-4) = -8 \leftarrow \text{Success!} \end{array}$$

Since $-4(-4) = 16$ and $-4 + (-4) = -8$, we conclude that the last terms of the factors are -4 and -4:

$$x^2 - 8x + 16 = (x - 4)(x - 4) = (x - 4)^2$$

Our result, $(x - 4)^2$, is the square of a binomial. So, the original expression, $x^2 - 8x + 16$, is a perfect-square trinomial (Section 6.2).

We use a graphing calculator table to verify our work (see Fig. 20).

Figure 20 Verify the work

When the constant term of a trinomial is positive, we need to consider only certain possibilities for the factors of that constant term. In Example 1, we worked with only *positive* factors of the positive constant term, because the coefficient of the middle term was *positive*. In Example 2, we worked with only *negative* factors of the positive constant term, because the coefficient of the middle term was *negative*.

▶ **Factoring $x^2 + bx + c$ with c Positive**

To factor a trinomial of the form $x^2 + bx + c$ with a positive constant term c,

- If b is positive, look for two *positive* integers whose product is c and whose sum is b. For example,

$$x^2 + 10x + 16 = (x + 2)(x + 8)$$

Positive b Positive c Both last terms are positive.

- If b is negative, look for two *negative* integers whose product is c and whose sum is b. For example,

$$x^2 - 9x + 18 = (x - 3)(x - 6)$$

Negative b Positive c Both last terms are negative.

Trinomials with Negative Constant Terms

How do we factor a quadratic trinomial for which the constant term is negative?

▶ **Example 3**   Factoring a Trinomial of the Form $x^2 + bx + c$

Factor $w^2 - 3w - 18$.

Solution

To factor $w^2 - 3w - 18$, we need two integers whose product is -18 and whose sum is -3. Since the product -18 is negative, the two integers must have different signs. Here are the possibilities:

Product $= -18$	**Sum $= -3$?**
$1(-18) = -18$	$1 + (-18) = -17$
$2(-9) = -18$	$2 + (-9) = -7$
$3(-6) = -18$	$3 + (-6) = -3 \leftarrow$ Success!
$6(-3) = -18$	$6 + (-3) = 3$
$9(-2) = -18$	$9 + (-2) = 7$
$18(-1) = -18$	$18 + (-1) = 17$

Since $3(-6) = -18$ and $3 + (-6) = -3$, we conclude that the last terms of the factors are 3 and -6:

$$w^2 - 3w - 18 = (w + 3)(w - 6)$$

We check the result by finding the product $(w + 3)(w - 6)$:

$$(w + 3)(w - 6) = w^2 - 6w + 3w - 18 = w^2 - 3w - 18$$

When the constant term of a trinomial is negative, the integers whose product equals that negative constant term have different signs. For instance, in Example 3, we worked with only integers with different signs whose product is -18.

> **Factoring $x^2 + bx + c$ with c Negative**
>
> To factor a trinomial of the form $x^2 + bx + c$ with a negative constant term c, look for two integers with *different* signs whose product is c and whose sum is b. For example,
>
> $$x^2 + 2x - 15 = (x - 3)(x + 5)$$
>
> Negative c The last terms have different signs.

We can use a similar method to factor trinomials that have two variables.

> **Example 4** Factoring a Trinomial with Two Variables

Factor $a^2 + 6ab + 8b^2$.

Solution

To help us find the last terms, we write the trinomial in the form $a^2 + (6b)a + 8b^2$. We need two monomials whose product is $8b^2$ and whose sum is $6b$. So, the last terms are $2b$ and $4b$:

$$a^2 + 6ab + 8b^2 = (a + 2b)(a + 4b)$$

We check by finding the product $(a + 2b)(a + 4b)$:

$$(a + 2b)(a + 4b) = a^2 + 4ab + 2ab + 8b^2 = a^2 + 6ab + 8b^2$$

Prime Polynomials

Just as a prime number has no positive factors other than itself and 1, a polynomial that cannot be factored is called **prime.**

Consider the polynomial $x^2 + 5x + 10$. To factor this polynomial, we need two integers whose product is 10 and whose sum is 5. We try only positive integers, since both their product and sum must be positive. Here are the possibilities:

Product $= 10$	**Sum** $= 5$?
$1(10) = 10$	$1 + 10 = 11$
$2(5) = 10$	$2 + 5 = 7$

Neither of the possible sums equals 5, so we conclude that the trinomial $x^2 + 5x + 10$ is prime.

> **Example 5** Identifying a Prime Polynomial

Factor $-14 + 6x + x^2$.

Solution

First, we write $-14 + 6x + x^2$ in descending order to avoid confusion about the coefficients:

$$x^2 + 6x - 14$$

To factor $x^2 + 6x - 14$, we need two integers whose product is -14 and whose sum is 6. Since the product -14 is negative, the two integers must have different signs. Here are the possibilities:

Product $= -14$	Sum $= 6$?
$1(-14) = -14$	$1 + (-14) = -13$
$2(-7) = -14$	$2 + (-7) = -5$
$7(-2) = -14$	$7 + (-2) = 5$
$14(-1) = -14$	$14 + (-1) = 13$

Because none of the sums equal 6, we conclude that the trinomial $x^2 + 6x - 14$ is prime. So, the original trinomial $-14 + 6x + x^2$ is prime.

Factoring Out the GCF

Consider the polynomial $3x + 12$. Note that 3 is a common factor of both $3x$ (where $3x = 3 \cdot x$) and 12 (where $12 = 3 \cdot 4$):

$$3x + 12 = 3 \cdot x + 3 \cdot 4$$

We use the distributive law to *factor out* the common factor 3:

$$3x + 12 = 3 \cdot x + 3 \cdot 4 = 3(x + 4)$$

So, we factor $3x + 12$ as $3(x + 4)$. We check the result by finding the product $3(x + 4)$:

$$3(x + 4) = 3x + 12$$

▶ **Example 6**   Factoring Out a Common Factor

Factor.

1. $10x^2 - 15x$ **2.** $8x^3 + 20x^2$

Solution

1. The expression $5x$ is a common factor of $10x^2 = 5x \cdot 2x$ and $15x = 5x \cdot 3$. So, we use the distributive law to factor out $5x$:

$$10x^2 - 15x = 5x \cdot 2x - 5x \cdot 3 \quad \text{\small 5x is a common factor.}$$
$$= 5x(2x - 3) \quad \text{\small Factor out 5x.}$$

2. The expression $4x^2$ is a common factor of $8x^3 = 4x^2 \cdot 2x$ and $20x^2 = 4x^2 \cdot 5$. So, we use the distributive law to factor out $4x^2$:

$$8x^3 + 20x^2 = 4x^2 \cdot 2x + 4x^2 \cdot 5 \quad \text{\small 4x}^2 \text{\small is a common factor.}$$
$$= 4x^2(2x + 5) \quad \text{\small Factor out 4x}^2.$$

In Problem 2 of Example 6, notice that $2x$ is also a common factor of $8x^3 = 2x \cdot 4x^2$ and $20x^2 = 2x \cdot 10x$. So, we could have factored $8x^3 + 20x^2$ by factoring out $2x$ rather than $4x^2$:

$$8x^3 + 20x^2 = 2x(4x^2 + 10x)$$

However, this result is not *completely factored;* we can still factor $4x^2 + 10x$ by factoring out $2x$:

$$8x^3 + 20x^2 = 2x(4x^2 + 10x) = 2x \cdot 2x(2x + 5) = 4x^2(2x + 5)$$

Although we have found the same final result, it was more efficient to factor out $4x^2$, which has a larger coefficient and a higher degree than $2x$. We call $4x^2$ the *greatest common factor* of $8x^3$ and $20x^2$.

▶ Definition   Greatest common factor

The **greatest common factor (GCF)** of two or more terms is the monomial with the largest coefficient and the highest degree that is a factor of all the terms.

For both polynomials in Example 6, the common factor we factored out of the polynomial was the GCF. In Example 7, we factor another polynomial by factoring out the GCF.

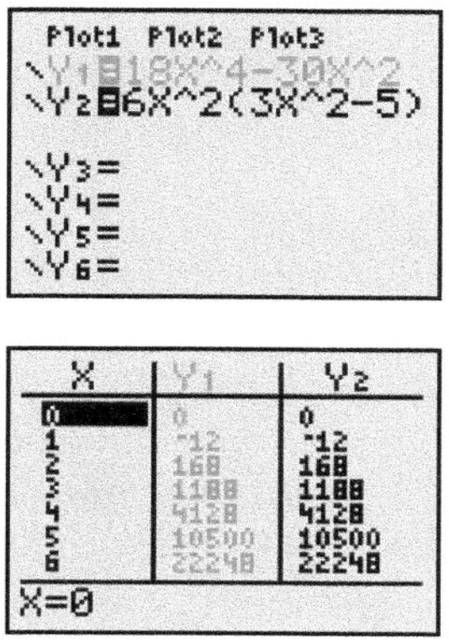

▶ **Example 7**   Factoring Out the GCF

Factor $18x^4 - 30x^2$.

Solution

We begin by factoring $18x^4$ and $30x^2$:

$$18x^4 = 2 \cdot 3 \cdot 3 \cdot x \cdot x \cdot x \cdot x$$
$$30x^2 = 2 \cdot 3 \cdot 5 \cdot x \cdot x$$

There are four common factors: 2, 3, x, and x. So, the GCF is $6x^2$:

$$18x^4 - 30x^2 = 6x^2 \cdot 3x^2 - 6x^2 \cdot 5 \qquad \text{$6x^2$ is the GCF.}$$
$$= 6x^2(3x^2 - 5) \qquad \text{Factor out $6x^2$.}$$

We use a graphing calculator table to verify our work (see Fig. 21).

Figure 21 Verify the work

After you factor a polynomial, verify your work by finding the product of your result or by using a graphing calculator table.

So far, we have factored out the GCF for some binomials with one variable. We can also factor out the GCF for polynomials with more than two terms and more than one variable.

▶ **Example 8**   Factoring Out the GCF

Factor $14p^4t + 21p^2t^2 - 70pt$.

Solution

We begin by factoring $14p^4t$, $21p^2t^2$, and $70pt$:

$$14p^4t = 2 \cdot 7 \cdot p \cdot p \cdot p \cdot p \cdot t$$
$$21p^2t^2 = 3 \cdot 7 \cdot p \cdot p \cdot t \cdot t$$
$$70pt = 2 \cdot 5 \cdot 7 \cdot p \cdot t$$

There are three common factors: 7, p, and t. So, the GCF is $7pt$:

$$14p^4t + 21p^2t^2 - 70pt = 7pt \cdot 2p^3 + 7pt \cdot 3pt - 7pt \cdot 10 \qquad \text{$7pt$ is the GCF.}$$
$$= 7pt(2p^3 + 3pt - 10) \qquad \text{Factor out $7pt$.}$$

Completely Factoring Polynomials

After we factor the GCF out of a polynomial, we must check whether the result can be factored further by using factoring techniques discussed earlier in this section. If a result cannot be factored further, it is said to be **completely factored.**

▶ **Example 9**   Completely Factoring a Polynomial

Factor $3x^3 + 21x^2 + 36x$.

Solution

The GCF of $3x^3$, $21x^2$, and $36x$ is $3x$:

$$3x^3 + 21x^2 + 36x = 3x(x^2 + 7x + 12)$$

To factor $x^2 + 7x + 12$, we need two integers whose product is 12 and whose sum is 7. Since the product and sum must be positive, we try only positive integers:

	Product $= 12$	**Sum** $= 7$?
(We have temporarily	$1(12) = 12$	$1 + 12 = 13$
put aside the	$2(6) = 12$	$2 + 6 = 8$
GCF, $3x$.)	$3(4) = 12$	$3 + 4 = 7 \leftarrow$ Success!

Because $3(4) = 12$ and $3 + 4 = 7$, we conclude that the last terms of the factors are 3 and 4:

$$x^2 + 7x + 12 = (x + 3)(x + 4)$$

So,

$$3x^3 + 21x^2 + 36x = 3x(x^2 + 7x + 12) = 3x(x + 3)(x + 4)$$

▶

To factor $3x^3 + 21x^2 + 36x$ in Example 9, we first factored out the GCF, $3x$, and then factored the resulting trinomial, $x^2 + 7x + 12$. In general, **when the leading coefficient of a polynomial is positive and the GCF is not 1, first factor out the GCF.** (We will soon discuss what to do when the leading coefficient of a polynomial is negative.)

WARNING   When we factor a trinomial by looking for integers whose product and sum are the appropriate values, we can easily forget about the GCF by the time we have found the other factors. If there is more factoring to be done after you have factored out the GCF, write a note several lines down that reminds you to include the GCF in your result.

▶ **Example 10**   Completely Factoring a Polynomial

Factor $5x^3y^2 - 10x^2y^3 - 40xy^4$.

Solution

The GCF of $5x^3y^2$, $10x^2y^3$, and $40xy^4$ is $5xy^2$:

$$5x^3y^2 - 10x^2y^3 - 40xy^4 = 5xy^2(x^2 - 2xy - 8y^2)$$
$$= 5xy^2[x^2 - (2y)x - 8y^2]$$

To factor $x^2 - (2y)x - 8y^2$, we need two monomials whose product is $-8y^2$ and whose sum is $-2y$. So, the last terms are $-4y$ and $2y$:

$$x^2 - 2xy - 8y^2 = (x - 4y)(x + 2y)$$

Hence,

$$5x^3y^2 - 10x^2y^3 - 40xy^4 = 5xy^2(x^2 - 2xy - 8y^2) = 5xy^2(x - 4y)(x + 2y)$$

▶

WARNING   It is a common error to forget to *completely* factor a polynomial. In Example 10, we factored the GCF, $5xy^2$, out of $5x^3y^2 - 10x^2y^3 - 40xy^4$:

$$5x^3y^2 - 10x^2y^3 - 40xy^4 = 5xy^2(x^2 - 2xy - 8y^2) \quad \textit{Not completely factored}$$

We were not done factoring, because we could still factor $x^2 - 2xy - 8y^2$:

$$5xy^2(x^2 - 2xy - 8y^2) = 5xy^2(x - 4y)(x + 2y) \quad \textit{Completely factored}$$

When factoring a polynomial, always *completely* factor it.

Factoring Out the Opposite of the GCF of a Polynomial

How do we factor a polynomial in which the leading coefficient is negative? Consider the polynomial $-2r^4 + 18r^3 - 40r^2$, which has a negative leading coefficient: -2.

> ### Factoring when the Leading Coefficient Is Negative
>
> When the leading coefficient of a polynomial is negative, first factor out the opposite of the GCF.

▶ **Example 11** Factoring Out the Opposite of the GCF

Factor $-2r^4 + 18r^3 - 40r^2$.

Solution

For $-2r^4 + 18r^3 - 40r^2$, the GCF is $2r^2$. The leading coefficient of $-2r^4 + 18r^3 - 40r^2$ is -2, which is negative. So, we first factor out the opposite of the GCF:

$$-2r^4 + 18r^3 - 40r^2 = -2r^2(r^2 - 9r + 20)$$ *Factor out $-2r^2$, opposite of GCF.*

$$= -2r^2(r - 5)(r - 4)$$ *Find two integers whose product is 20 and whose sum is -9.*

We use a graphing calculator table to verify our work (see Fig. 22).

▶

Figure 22 Verify the work

In summary, there are two aspects to factoring that are important to remember:

1. If the leading coefficient of a polynomial is positive and the GCF is not 1, first factor out the GCF. If the leading coefficient is negative, first factor out the opposite of the GCF.

2. Always *completely* factor a polynomial.

Group Exploration

Factors of an expression and x-intercepts of the graph of a function

In this exploration, you will explore a connection between factors of a polynomial of the form $x^2 + bx + c$ and x-intercepts of the graph of the polynomial function $f(x) = x^2 + bx + c$.

1. Factor $x^2 + x - 2$.

2. Use ZDecimal to draw a graph of the function $f(x) = x^2 + x - 2$. What are the x-intercepts?

3. What connection do you notice between your result in Problem 1 and the x-intercepts of the graph of f? Explain why this connection makes sense.

4. The graph of a function $g(x) = x^2 + bx + c$ is sketched in the indicated figures. Use the graph to help you factor $x^2 + bx + c$. Then find the values of b and c.

a. Fig. 23

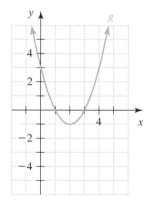

Figure 23 Graph of $g(x) = x^2 + bx + c$

b. Fig. 24

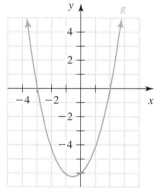

Figure 24 Graph of $g(x) = x^2 + bx + c$

Homework 6.4

For extra help ▶ **MyMathLab®**   Watch the videos in MyMathLab   Download the MyDashboard App

Factor when possible. Use a graphing calculator table to verify your work when possible.

1. $x^2 + 11x + 28$
2. $x^2 + 17x + 30$
3. $x^2 - 8x + 12$
4. $x^2 - 8x + 15$
5. $r^2 - 4r - 32$
6. $k^2 - 2k - 24$
7. $x^2 + 5x - 14$
8. $x^2 + 3x - 40$
9. $x^2 - 7x - 12$
10. $x^2 - 11x - 18$
11. $x^2 + 10x + 25$
12. $x^2 + 14x + 49$
13. $t^2 - 18t + 81$
14. $w^2 - 16w + 64$
15. $4x - 5 + x^2$
16. $12 + x^2 - 13x$
17. $a^2 + 12ab + 20b^2$
18. $p^2 + 17pt + 16t^2$
19. $w^2 - 5wy + 4y^2$
20. $x^2 - 10xy + 21y^2$
21. $p^2 + 3pq - 28q^2$
22. $r^2 + 4rt - 12t^2$
23. $b^2 + 4bc - 16c^2$
24. $w^2 + 2wy - 32y^2$
25. $p^2 - 6pq - 16q^2$
26. $m^2 - mr - 42r^2$

Factor when possible. Use a graphing calculator table to verify your work when possible.

27. $3x + 21$
28. $5x + 20$
29. $16x^2 - 12x$
30. $21x^2 - 35x$
31. $9y^5 + 18y^3$
32. $16w^4 + 24w^2$
33. $3ab - 12a^2b$
34. $25p^2q - 45pq^3$
35. $18a^4b^2 + 12a^2b^3$
36. $32x^3y + 40x^2y^4$
37. $-14x^5y + 63x^2y^2$
38. $-22x^3y^3 + 33xy^2$
39. $2x^2 + 12x + 18$
40. $7x^2 + 21x + 14$
41. $3x^2 - 3x - 18$
42. $4x^2 - 4x - 80$
43. $15k - 50 + 5k^2$
44. $-36 + 6t^2 + 6t$
45. $-4x^2 + 24x - 36$
46. $-2x^2 + 24x - 72$
47. $-x^2 + 11x - 10$
48. $-x^2 - 2x + 35$
49. $3w^2 - 27w - 60$
50. $2p^2 - 20p - 32$
51. $4x^3 - 24x^2 + 32x$
52. $2x^3 - 10x^2 + 12x$
53. $a^4 - 21a^3 + 20a^2$
54. $t^4 - 5t^3 - 36t^2$
55. $5x^2y + 45xy^2 + 40y^3$
56. $2x^3 + 18x^2y + 28xy^2$
57. $4x^4y - 12x^3y^2 - 40x^2y^3$
58. $3a^3b - 3a^2b^2 - 36ab^3$
59. $-2x^3y^2 + 16x^2y^3 - 32xy^4$
60. $-5x^4y + 20x^3y^2 - 20x^2y^3$

Concepts

61. A student tries to factor $2x^2 + 16x + 30$:

$$2x^2 + 16x + 30 = 2(x^2 + 8x + 15)$$

Describe any errors. Then factor the polynomial correctly.

62. A student tries to factor $x^2 + 10x + 24$:

$$x^2 + 10x + 24 = (x + 4)(x + 6)$$
$$= x^2 + 6x + 4x + 24$$
$$= x^2 + 10x + 24$$

Describe any errors. Then factor the polynomial correctly.

63. A student tries to factor $12x^3 + 18x^2$:

$$12x^3 + 18x^2 = 2x^2(6x + 9)$$

Describe any errors. Then factor the polynomial correctly.

64. Two students try to factor the polynomial $x^2 + 14x + 48$:

Student A	**Student B**
$x^2 + 14x + 48$	$x^2 + 14x + 48$
$= (x + 6)(x + 8)$	$= (x + 8)(x + 6)$

Are both students, one student, or neither student correct? Explain.

65. Which polynomials are equivalent?

$$(x - 3)(x + 6) \qquad x^2 - 3x - 18 \qquad x^2 - 9x - 18$$
$$x^2 + 3x - 18 \qquad (x + 6)(x - 3)$$

66. Which polynomials are equivalent?

$$x^2 + 4x - 45 \qquad (x + 5)(x - 9) \qquad x^2 - 4x - 45$$
$$x^2 - 45 \qquad (x - 9)(x + 5)$$

67. a. Factor $x^2 - 5x + 4$.
   b. Use ZDecimal on a graphing calculator to graph the function $f(x) = x^2 - 5x + 4$. What are the x-intercepts?
   c. What connection do you notice between your result in part (a) and the x-intercepts of the graph of f? Explain why this connection makes sense.

68. a. Factor $x^2 - 6x + 8$.
   b. Use ZDecimal on a graphing calculator to graph the function $f(x) = x^2 - 6x + 8$. What are the x-intercepts?
   c. What connection do you notice between your result in part (a) and the x-intercepts of the graph of f? Explain why this connection makes sense.

69. Give three examples of a quadratic polynomial in which $x + 4$ is a factor.

70. Give three examples of a cubic polynomial in which $x - 6$ is a factor.

71. Find all possible values of k such that $x^2 + kx + 28$ can be factored.

72. Find all possible values of k such that $x^2 + kx - 32$ can be factored.

73. Compare the process of factoring a polynomial with that of multiplying polynomials.

74. Describe the various factoring techniques addressed in this section. Give an example to illustrate each technique. Finally, explain how to recognize polynomials to which each technique applies.

Related Review

If the polynomial is not factored, then factor it. If it is factored, then find the product.

75. $(x + 5)(x - 3)$
76. $3(3x - 2)(2x - 5)$
77. $k^2 - 7k - 30$
78. $6p^2 - 22p + 20$
79. $(7x - 5)(7x + 5)$
80. $(2x^2 - x + 3)(3x^2 + 4x - 2)$
81. $81r^2 - 49$
82. $9y^2 - 42y + 49$

Expressions, Equations, Functions, and Graphs

Perform the indicated instruction. Then use words such as linear, quadratic, cubic, exponential, logarithmic, polynomial, degree, function, one variable, *and* two variables *to describe the expression, equation, or system.*

83. Factor $x^2 + 3x - 28$.

84. Find an approximate equation $y = ab^x$ of an exponential curve that contains the points $(3, 98)$ and $(8, 9)$. Round a and b to the second decimal place.

85. Find the product $(3w - 4)(2w^2 + 3w - 5)$.

86. Solve $3(2)^{2x-1} = 238$. Round any solutions to the fourth decimal place.

▼6.5 Factoring Polynomials

Objectives

» *Factor* a polynomial with four terms *by grouping.*

» *Factor a trinomial by trial and error.*

» Know how to rule out possibilities when factoring by trial and error.

» *Factor a trinomial by grouping.*

In this section, we will first factor some polynomials that have four terms by using a technique called *factoring by grouping*. Then we will factor trinomials of the form $ax^2 + bx + c$ where $a \neq 1$. (In Section 6.4, we did so where $a = 1$.) We will discuss two methods: trial and error, and writing such a trinomial as a polynomial with four terms so we can try to factor by grouping. These two methods give equivalent results.

Factoring a Polynomial with Four Terms by Grouping

In Section 6.4, we factored out a monomial GCF. For example, here we factor out the monomial w from the polynomial $x(w) + 3(w)$:

$$x(w) + 3(w) = (x + 3)(w)$$

We can also factor out a binomial GCF. For example, here we factor out the binomial $y + 5$ from the polynomial $x(y + 5) + 3(y + 5)$:

$$x(y + 5) + 3(y + 5) = (x + 3)(y + 5)$$

We can factor some polynomials that contain four terms by first factoring the first two terms and the last two terms. For example,

$$\underbrace{xy + 5x}_{\text{factor}} + \underbrace{3y + 15}_{\text{factor}} = x(y + 5) + 3(y + 5) \quad \textit{Factor both pairs of terms.}$$
$$= (x + 3)(y + 5) \quad \textit{Factor out GCF, } y + 5.$$

We call this method *factoring by grouping*.

▶ Example 1   Factoring by Grouping

Factor $3x^3 - 18x^2 - 2x + 12$.

Solution

We begin by factoring the first two terms and the last two:

$$3x^3 - 18x^2 - 2x + 12 = 3x^2(x - 6) - 2(x - 6) \quad \textit{Factor both pairs of terms.}$$
$$= (3x^2 - 2)(x - 6) \quad \textit{Factor out GCF, } x - 6.$$

We verify the result by finding the product $(3x^2 - 2)(x - 6)$:

$$(3x^2 - 2)(x - 6) = 3x^3 - 18x^2 - 2x + 12$$

WARNING   It is a common error to think a polynomial such as $3x^2(x - 6) - 2(x - 6)$ in Example 1 is factored. Even though both terms $3x^2(x - 6)$ and $2(x - 6)$ are factored, the entire expression $3x^2(x - 6) - 2(x - 6)$ is a difference, not a product. The polynomial $(3x^2 - 2)(x - 6)$ in Example 1 *is* factored, because it is a product.

When trying to factor a polynomial with four terms, consider trying to factor it by grouping.

> ▶ **Factoring by Grouping**
>
> For a polynomial with four terms, we **factor by grouping** (if it can be done) by
>
> **1.** Factoring the first two terms and the last two terms.
> **2.** Factoring out the binomial GCF.

Figure 25 Verify the work

▶ **Example 2** Factoring by Grouping

Factor $10x^3 - 6x^2 + 5x - 3$.

Solution

$$10x^3 - 6x^2 + 5x - 3 = 2x^2(5x - 3) + 1(5x - 3) \quad \textit{Factor both pairs of terms.}$$
$$= (2x^2 + 1)(5x - 3) \quad \textit{Factor out GCF, } 5x - 3.$$

We use a graphing calculator to verify our work (see Fig. 25).

▶

▶ **Example 3** Factoring by Grouping

Factor $ax + bx - ay^2 - by^2$.

Solution

$$ax + bx - ay^2 - by^2 = x(a + b) - y^2(a + b) \quad \textit{Factor both pairs of terms.}$$
$$= (x - y^2)(a + b) \quad \textit{Factor out GCF, } a + b.$$

We verify the result by finding the product $(x - y^2)(a + b)$:

$$(x - y^2)(a + b) = ax + bx - ay^2 - by^2$$

▶

Method 1: Factoring Trinomials by Trial and Error

One way to factor trinomials of the form $ax^2 + bx + c$ is to make educated guesses at the factorization and then find the product of these guesses to see if any of them work. This method is called **factoring by trial and error.**

▶ **Example 4** Factoring by Trial and Error

Factor $3x^2 + 14x + 8$.

Solution

If we can factor $3x^2 + 14x + 8$, the result will be of the form

$$(3x + ?)(x + ?)$$

The product of the last terms must be 8, so the last terms must be 1 and 8 or 2 and 4, where we can write each pair in either order. We can rule out negative last terms in the factors, because the middle term of $3x^2 + 14x + 8$ has the positive coefficient 14. We decide between the two pairs of possible last terms by multiplying:

$$(3x + 1)(x + 8) = 3x^2 + 24x + x + 8 = 3x^2 + 25x + 8$$
$$(3x + 8)(x + 1) = 3x^2 + 3x + 8x + 8 = 3x^2 + 11x + 8$$
$$(3x + 2)(x + 4) = 3x^2 + 12x + 2x + 8 = 3x^2 + 14x + 8 \leftarrow \text{Success!}$$
$$(3x + 4)(x + 2) = 3x^2 + 6x + 4x + 8 = 3x^2 + 10x + 8$$

So, $3x^2 + 14x + 8 = (3x + 2)(x + 4)$. We use a graphing calculator table to verify our work (see Fig. 26).

▶

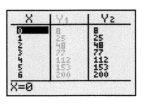

Figure 26 Verify the work

In trying to factor a polynomial, once we find the factored polynomial, there is no need to multiply the other possibilities. In Example 4, we multiplied all possible factorizations of $3x^2 + 14x + 8$ only to show how to organize the work in case the last possibility is the correct one.

To use the method shown in Example 4, it is helpful to be able to multiply two binomials in one step. Consider the product of $5x + 2$ and $3x + 2$:

$$(5x + 2)(3x + 2) = 15x^2 + 10x + 6x + 4$$
$$= 15x^2 + 16x + 4$$

To find the product in one step, we must combine the like terms $10x$ and $6x$ mentally. Note that these like terms come from the product of the two *outer terms* and the product of the two *inner terms* of $(5x + 2)(3x + 2)$:

Add these
terms mentally.

outer terms

$$(5x + 2)(3x + 2) = 15x^2 + 10x + 6x + 4$$
$$= 15x^2 + 16x + 4$$

inner terms

▶ **Example 5**   Factoring by Trial and Error

Factor $2x^2 - 5x - 25$.

Solution

If we can factor $2x^2 - 5x - 25$, the result will be of the form

$$(2x + ?)(x + ?)$$

The product of the last terms must be -25, so the last terms must be 1 and -25, 5 and -5, or -1 and 25, where we can write each pair in either order. We decide among the three pairs of possible last terms by multiplying:

$$(2x + 1)(x - 25) = 2x^2 - 49x - 25$$
$$(2x - 25)(x + 1) = 2x^2 - 23x - 25$$
$$(2x + 5)(x - 5) = 2x^2 - 5x - 25 \quad \leftarrow \text{Success!}$$
$$(2x - 5)(x + 5) = 2x^2 + 5x - 25$$
$$(2x - 1)(x + 25) = 2x^2 + 49x - 25$$
$$(2x + 25)(x - 1) = 2x^2 + 23x - 25$$

Therefore, $2x^2 - 5x - 25 = (2x + 5)(x - 5)$.

▶ **Factoring $ax^2 + bx + c$ by Trial and Error**

To **factor a trinomial** of the form $ax^2 + bx + c$ **by trial and error,** identify possible products by using the fact that if the trinomial can be factored as a product of two binomials, then the product of the coefficients of the first terms of the binomials is equal to a and the product of the last terms of the binomials is equal to c. For example,

Coefficients of first terms:
$5 \cdot 3 = 15 = a$

$$15x^2 + 26x + 8 = (5x + 2)(3x + 4)$$

$a = 15$ $b = 26$ $c = 8$

Last terms:
$2 \cdot 4 = 8 = c$

To find the correct factored expression, multiply the possible products and identify those for which the coefficient of x is b.

Ruling Out Possibilities While Factoring by Trial and Error

Example 6 shows how to rule out possible factorizations to help speed up the process of factoring.

▶ **Example 6**   Ruling Out Possibilities

Factor $10x^2 - 19x + 6$.

Solution

If we can factor $10x^2 - 19x + 6$, the result will be in one of these two forms:

$$(10x + ?)(x + ?) \quad (5x + ?)(2x + ?)$$

The product of the last terms must be 6, so the last terms must be -1 and -6, or -2 and -3, where we can write each pair in either order. We can rule out positive last terms, because the middle term of $10x^2 - 19x + 6$ has a negative coefficient, -19.

Since the terms of $10x^2 - 19x + 6$ do not have a common factor of 2, we can also rule out products that have a factor of 2. For example, we can rule out $(10x - 6)(x - 1)$, because it has a factor of 2:

$$(10x - 6)(x - 1) = 2(5x - 3)(x - 1)$$

We decide among the remaining possible last terms by multiplying:

$$(10x - 1)(x - 6) = 10x^2 - 61x + 6$$
Contains factor of 2, rule out: $(10x - 2)(x - 3)$
$$(10x - 3)(x - 2) = 10x^2 - 23x + 6$$
Contains factor of 2, rule out: $(5x - 1)(2x - 6)$
$$(5x - 6)(2x - 1) = 10x^2 - 17x + 6$$
$$(5x - 2)(2x - 3) = 10x^2 - 19x + 6 \leftarrow \text{Success!}$$
Contains factor of 2, rule out: $(5x - 3)(2x - 2)$

So, $10x^2 - 19x + 6 = (5x - 2)(2x - 3)$.

▶

Factoring Out the GCF, Then Factoring by Trial and Error

When factoring a polynomial, recall from Section 6.4 that if the GCF is not 1, then we first factor out the GCF and continue factoring if possible. Always completely factor a polynomial.

▶ **Example 7**   Completely Factoring a Polynomial

Factor $6x^3y^2 + 26x^2y^3 + 24xy^4$.

Solution

To factor $6x^3y^2 + 26x^2y^3 + 24xy^4$, we first factor out the GCF, $2xy^2$:

$$2xy^2\left(3x^2 + 13xy + 12y^2\right)$$

If we can factor further, the result will be in the form

$$2xy^2(3x + ?)(x + ?)$$

The product of the last terms must be $12y^2$, so the last terms must be y and $12y$, $2y$ and $6y$, or $3y$ and $4y$, where we can write each pair in either order. Since we have factored out the GCF, we rule out any possibility in which one of the binomials has a monomial factor. We decide among the remaining possibilities by multiplying:

(We have temporarily put aside the GCF, $2xy^2$.)

$$(3x + y)(x + 12y) = 3x^2 + 37xy + 12y^2$$
Contains factor of 3, rule out: $(3x + 12y)(x + y)$
$$(3x + 2y)(x + 6y) = 3x^2 + 20xy + 12y^2$$
Contains factor of 3, rule out: $(3x + 6y)(x + 2y)$
Contains factor of 3, rule out: $(3x + 3y)(x + 4y)$
$$(3x + 4y)(x + 3y) = 3x^2 + 13xy + 12y^2 \leftarrow \text{Success!}$$

So, $6x^3y^2 + 26x^2y^3 + 24xy^4 = 2xy^2\left(3x^2 + 13xy + 12y^2\right) = 2xy^2(3x + 4y)(x + 3y)$.

▶

Method 2: Factoring Trinomials by Grouping

Instead of using trial and error to factor a trinomial, we can factor by grouping.

To factor a trinomial of the form $x^2 + bx + c$, recall from Section 6.4 that we look for two integers whose product is c and whose sum is b. To factor a trinomial of the form $ax^2 + bx + c$, we must look for two integers whose product is ac and whose sum is b.

> **▶ Factoring $ax^2 + bx + c$ by Grouping**
>
> To **factor a trinomial** of the form $ax^2 + bx + c$ **by grouping** (if it can be done),
> 1. Find pairs of numbers whose product is ac.
> 2. Determine which of the pairs of numbers from step 1 has the sum b. Call this pair of numbers m and n.
> 3. Write the bx term as $mx + nx$:
> $$ax^2 + bx + c = ax^2 + mx + nx + c$$
> 4. Factor $ax^2 + mx + nx + c$ by grouping.
>
> Another name for this technique is the **ac method.**

▶ Example 8   Factoring a Trinomial by Grouping

Factor $3x^2 + 14x + 8$ by grouping.

Solution

Here, $a = 3$, $b = 14$, and $c = 8$.

Step 1: Find the product ac: $ac = 3(8) = 24$.

Step 2: We want to find two numbers m and n that have the product $ac = 24$ and the sum $b = 14$:

Product = 24	**Sum = 14?**
$1(24) = 24$	$1 + 24 = 25$
$2(12) = 24$	$2 + 12 = 14 \leftarrow$ Success!
$3(8) = 24$	$3 + 8 = 11$
$4(6) = 24$	$4 + 6 = 10$

Since $2(12) = 24$ and $2 + 12 = 14$, we conclude that the two numbers m and n are 2 and 12.

Step 3: We write the bx term, $14x$, as the sum $mx + nx$:
$$3x^2 + 14x + 8 = 3x^2 + 2x + 12x + 8$$

Step 4: We factor $3x^2 + 2x + 12x + 8$ by grouping:
$$3x^2 + 2x + 12x + 8 = x(3x + 2) + 4(3x + 2) \quad \text{Factor both pairs of terms.}$$
$$= (x + 4)(3x + 2) \quad \text{Factor out GCF, } (3x + 2).$$

In step 3 of Example 8, we could switch the mx and nx terms to get $3x^2 + 12x + 2x + 8$ and still be able to factor by grouping in step 4. (Try it.)

In Example 4, we used trial and error to factor $3x^2 + 14x + 8$ as $(3x + 2)(x + 4)$. In Example 8, we factored it as $(x + 4)(3x + 2)$ by using grouping. The two results are equivalent. In general, the results from factoring a trinomial by trial and error and factoring a trinomial by grouping are equivalent.

▶ Example 9   Factoring a Trinomial by Grouping

Factor $6x^2 - 7x + 2$ by grouping.

Solution

Here, $a = 6$, $b = -7$, and $c = 2$.

Step 1: Find the product ac: $ac = 6(2) = 12$.

Step 2: We want to find two numbers m and n that have the product $ac = 12$ and the sum $b = -7$:

Product = 12	**Sum = -7?**
$-1(-12) = 12$	$-1 + (-12) = -13$
$-2(-6) = 12$	$-2 + (-6) = -8$
$-3(-4) = 12$	$-3 + (-4) = -7 \leftarrow$ Success!

Since $-3(-4) = 12$ and $-3 + (-4) = -7$, we conclude that the two numbers m and n are -3 and -4.

Step 3: We write $6x^2 - 7x + 2 = 6x^2 - 3x - 4x + 2$.

Step 4: We factor $6x^2 - 3x - 4x + 2$ by grouping:

$$6x^2 - 3x - 4x + 2 = 3x(2x - 1) - 2(2x - 1) \quad \text{Factor both pairs of terms.}$$
$$= (3x - 2)(2x - 1) \quad \text{Factor out GCF, } (2x - 1).$$

▶ **Example 10**   Factoring Out the GCF, Then Factoring by Grouping

Factor $20x^4 - 40x^3 - 25x^2$.

Solution

First, we factor out the GCF, $5x^2$:

$$20x^4 - 40x^3 - 25x^2 = 5x^2\left(4x^2 - 8x - 5\right)$$

Next, we use grouping to try to factor $4x^2 - 8x - 5$, where $a = 4$, $b = -8$, and $c = -5$.

Step 1: Find the product ac: $ac = 4(-5) = -20$.

Step 2: We want to find two numbers m and n that have the product $ac = -20$ and the sum $b = -8$:

	Product = -20	**Sum = -8?**
(We have temporarily	$1(-20) = -20$	$1 + (-20) = -19$
put aside the	$2(-10) = -20$	$2 + (-10) = -8 \leftarrow$ Success!
GCF, $5x^2$.)	$4(-5) = -20$	$4 + (-5) = -1$
	$5(-4) = -20$	$5 + (-4) = 1$
	$10(-2) = -20$	$10 + (-2) = 8$
	$20(-1) = -20$	$20 + (-1) = 19$

Since $2(-10) = -20$ and $2 + (-10) = -8$, we conclude that the two numbers m and n are 2 and -10.

Step 3: We write $4x^2 - 8x - 5 = 4x^2 + 2x - 10x - 5$.

Step 4: We factor $4x^2 + 2x - 10x - 5$ by grouping:

$$4x^2 + 2x - 10x - 5 = 2x(2x + 1) - 5(2x + 1) \quad \text{Factor both pairs of terms.}$$
$$= (2x - 5)(2x + 1) \quad \text{Factor out GCF, } (2x + 1).$$

So, $20x^4 - 40x^3 - 25x^2 = 5x^2\left(4x^2 - 8x - 5\right) = 5x^2(2x - 5)(2x + 1)$. We use a graphing calculator table to verify our work (see Fig. 27).

Figure 27 Verify the work

Group Exploration

Factoring polynomials

1. A student tries to factor $2x^2 - 17x - 30$:

$$2x^2 - 17x - 30 = (2x - 5)(x - 6)$$

Multiply $(2x - 5)(x - 6)$ to show the work is incorrect. Then factor $2x^2 - 17x - 30$ correctly.

2. A student tries to factor $2x^2 + 10x + 12$:

$$2x^2 + 10x + 12 = (2x + 4)(x + 3)$$

Explain why the work is not correct. Then factor the polynomial correctly.

3. A student tries to factor $x^3 - 3x^2 + 2x - 6$:

$$x^3 - 3x^2 + 2x - 6 = x^2(x - 3) + 2(x - 3)$$

Explain why the student has not succeeded in factoring the given expression. Then factor it correctly.

4. A student tries to factor $2x^2 - x - 6$. Since the product of -3 and 2 is -6 and the sum of -3 and 2 is -1, the student does the following work:

$$2x^2 - x - 6 = (2x - 3)(x + 2)$$

Find the product $(2x - 3)(x + 2)$ to show the work is incorrect. Explain what is wrong with the student's reasoning. Then factor the polynomial correctly.

Group Exploration

Looking ahead: Factoring the difference of two squares

1. Find the product $2(x + 4)$. Then factor $2x + 8$. Compare finding the product $2(x + 4)$ with factoring $2x + 8$.

2. Find the product.
   a. $(x - 3)(x + 3)$ **b.** $(x - 4)(x + 4)$
   c. $(x - 5)(x + 5)$ **d.** $(2x - 7)(2x + 7)$

3. Factor the polynomial.
   a. $x^2 - 9$ **b.** $x^2 - 36$
   c. $16x^2 - 25$ **d.** $9x^2 - 4$

4. Describe in general how to factor the difference of two squares.

▶ **Tips for Success**   **Choose a Good Time and Place to Study**

To improve your effectiveness at studying, take stock of when and where you are best able to study. Tracy, a student who lives in a sometimes distracting household, completes her assignments at the campus library just after she attends her classes. Gerome, a morning person, gets up early so he can study before classes. Being consistent in the time and location for studying can help, too. Research has shown that after a person repeats a daily activity for about 21 days, the activity becomes habit. Even if it takes willpower to shuffle your schedule so you can study at your prime time and location, things will start to feel comfortable and familiar within three weeks.

Homework 6.5

For extra help ▶   MyMathLab®   Watch the videos in MyMathLab   Download the MyDashboard App

Factor when possible. Use a graphing calculator table to verify your work when possible.

1. $x^3 + 3x^2 + 4x + 12$
2. $x^3 + 2x^2 + 5x + 10$
3. $5x^3 - 20x^2 + 3x - 12$
4. $2x^3 - 4x^2 + 5x - 10$
5. $6m^3 - 15m^2 + 2m - 5$
6. $15k^3 - 10k^2 + 3k - 2$
7. $10x^3 + 25x^2 - 2x - 5$
8. $6x^3 + 9x^2 - 2x - 3$
9. $ax - 3ay - 2bx + 6by$
10. $ax - 5ay - 3bx + 15by$
11. $5a^2x + 2a^2y - 5bx - 2by$
12. $3ax + 7ay - 3b^2x - 7b^2y$

For Exercises 13–50, factor when possible. Use a graphing calculator table to verify your work when possible.

13. $3x^2 + 11x + 10$
14. $5x^2 + 13x + 6$
15. $2x^2 - x - 15$
16. $3x^2 - 19x - 14$

17. $5p^2 - 21p + 4$
18. $7t^2 - 24t + 9$
19. $4x^2 + 16x + 15$
20. $6x^2 + 19x + 8$
21. $9x^2 - 4x - 8$
22. $8x^2 - 5x - 6$
23. $1 + 9w^2 - 6w$
24. $-10m + 1 + 25m^2$
25. $15x^2 + x - 6$
26. $8x^2 + 9x - 14$
27. $6x^2 - 17x + 12$
28. $4x^2 - 21x + 20$
29. $16y^2 - 29y - 6$
30. $12w^2 - 19w - 10$
31. $10a^2 + 21ab + 9b^2$
32. $8m^2 + 26mn + 15n^2$
33. $20x^2 + 17xy - 3y^2$
34. $16p^2 + 31pt - 2t^2$
35. $6w^2 - 3wy - 4y^2$
36. $9m^2 - 5mp - 6p^2$
37. $4r^2 - 20ry + 25y^2$
38. $9b^2 - 24bc + 16c^2$
39. $6x^2 + 26x - 20$
40. $6x^2 + 9x - 60$
41. $-12x^2 + 3x + 9$
42. $-10x^2 - 8x + 24$
43. $12x - 32x^2 + 16x^3$
44. $-65x^2 + 25x + 30x^3$

45. $30x^4 + 4x^3 - 2x^2$

46. $56x^4 - 44x^3 + 8x^2$

47. $36t^3 + 48t^2w + 16tw^2$

48. $8x^2y - 40xy^2 + 50y^3$

49. $20a^3b^2 + 30a^2b^3 - 140ab^4$

50. $15a^3b - 36a^2b^2 + 12ab^3$

Factor when possible. Use a graphing calculator table to verify your work when possible.

51. $x^2 - 6x - 40$

52. $x^2 + 3x - 18$

53. $3w^3 - 6w^2 + 5w - 10$

54. $5t^3 + 15t^2 - 4t - 12$

55. $3x^4 - 21x^3y - 54x^2y^2$

56. $6a^2b^3 - 36ab^4 + 48b^5$

57. $m^2 - 11mp - 30p^2$

58. $r^2 - 11rt - 24t^2$

59. $6x^2 - 19x + 10$

60. $8x^2 + 37x - 15$

61. $x^2 + xy - 30y^2$

62. $x^2 - 3xy - 28y^2$

63. $-6r^3 + 24r^2 - 24r$

64. $-5k^3 + 40k^2 - 80k$

65. $-10 + 12x^2 + 2x$

66. $3x - 6 + 30x^2$

67. $a^2x - 3a^2y - 2bx + 6by$

68. $2ax - 4ay - 3bx + 6by$

69. $x^2 - 10x - 16$

70. $x^2 - 13x - 12$

71. $10p^3t^2 + 22p^2t^3 - 24pt^4$

72. $24w^4y - 44w^3y^2 - 40w^2y^3$

Concepts

73. A student tries to factor $x^3 + 5x^2 - 3x - 15$:

$$x^3 + 5x^2 - 3x - 15 = x^2(x + 5) - 3(x + 5)$$

Describe any errors. Then factor the expression correctly.

74. A student tries to factor $4x^2 + 8x + 3$:

$$4x^2 + 8x + 3 = 4x(x + 2) + 3$$

Describe any errors. Then factor the expression correctly.

75. A student tries to factor the polynomial $3x^2 - 9x - 30$:

$$3x^2 - 9x - 30 = (3x - 15)(x + 2)$$

Describe any errors. Then factor the polynomial correctly.

76. A student tries to factor the polynomial $4x^2 + 32x + 60$:

$$4x^2 + 32x + 60 = (2x + 6)(2x + 10)$$
$$= 2(x + 3)(2)(x + 5)$$
$$= 4(x + 3)(x + 5)$$

Is the work correct? If no, explain. If yes, is there an easier method?

77. Which of the following expressions are equivalent?

$$2(x - 2)(x - 6) \quad 2(x^2 - 8x + 12) \quad 2x^2 - 16x + 24$$
$$(x - 2)(2x - 12) \quad (x - 2)(2x - 6) \quad (2x - 2)(x - 6)$$
$$2(x - 4)^2 - 8 \quad (2x - 4)(x - 6)$$

78. Factor $x^2 + 6x + 8$ using grouping. Then factor $x^2 + 6x + 8$ by the method discussed in Section 6.4. Which method is easier? Explain.

79. Explain why it is a good idea to factor out the GCF of $8x^2 + 40x + 48$ before using any other factoring technique. Then factor the polynomial.

80. Describe the various factoring techniques addressed in this section and in Section 6.4. Give an example to illustrate each technique. Explain how to recognize polynomials to which each technique applies.

Related Review

If the polynomial is not factored, then factor it. If the polynomial is factored, then find the product.

81. $12x^3 - 27x$

82. $2x^3 - 20x^2 + 42x$

83. $-2(3p + 5)(4p - 3)$

84. $5y(2y - 3)(2y + 3)$

85. $2x^3 - 5x^2 - 18x + 45$

86. $24x^2 - 48x - 3x^3$

87. $(3k + 4)(2k^2 - k + 3)$

88. $(w^2 - 5)(w - 7)$

Expressions, Equations, Functions, and Graphs

Perform the indicated instruction. Then use words such as linear, quadratic, cubic, exponential, logarithmic, polynomial, degree, function, one variable, *and* two variables *to describe the expression, equation, or system.*

89. Simplify $-2x(3x - 5)^2$.

90. Solve $3(2t - 5) - 2(2t + 3) = 12$.

91. Factor $8x^3 - 40x^2 + 50x$.

92. Find the product $(5x - 2)(3x^2 - 4x + 2)$.

▼ 6.6 Factoring Special Binomials; A Factoring Strategy

Objectives

» Factor differences of squares.

» Factor sums of cubes and differences of cubes.

» Know a factoring strategy.

In this section, we will first discuss how to factor three special types of binomials: differences of squares, sums of cubes, and differences of cubes. Then we will discuss a factoring strategy to help us sift through the many factoring techniques we have discussed in this chapter and select the best techniques to completely factor a given polynomial.

The Difference of Two Squares

In Section 6.2, we found the product of two binomial conjugates by using the property $(A + B)(A - B) = A^2 - B^2$. The expression $A^2 - B^2$ is the difference of two squares. To factor a difference of two squares, we can use that property in reverse.

▶ Difference of Two Squares

$$A^2 - B^2 = (A + B)(A - B)$$

In words, the difference of the squares of two terms is the product of the sum of the terms and the difference of the terms.

▶ Example 1   Factoring Differences of Two Squares

Factor.
   1. $x^2 - 49$
   2. $36w^2 - 25y^2$

Solution
   1. Since $x^2 - 49 = (x)^2 - (7)^2$, we substitute x for A and 7 for B:

$$A^2 - B^2 = (A + B)(A - B)$$
$$x^2 - 49 = x^2 - 7^2 = (x + 7)(x - 7)$$

   2. Since $36w^2 - 25y^2 = (6w)^2 - (5y)^2$, we substitute $6w$ for A and $5y$ for B:

$$A^2 - B^2 = (A + B)(A - B)$$
$$36w^2 - 25y^2 = (6w)^2 - (5y)^2 = (6w + 5y)(6w - 5y)$$

WARNING   The binomial $x^2 + 25$ is prime. It is a common error to think this polynomial can be factored as $(x + 5)^2$, but if you simplify $(x + 5)^2$, you'll see that the result is $x^2 + 10x + 25$, not $x^2 + 25$. In general, **except for factoring out the GCF, a sum of squares cannot be factored.**

▶ Example 2   Factoring Differences of Two Squares

Factor.
   1. $4x^3 - 36x$
   2. $16p^4 - 1$

Solution
   1. To factor $4x^3 - 36x$, we first factor out the GCF, $4x$:

$$4x^3 - 36x = 4x(x^2 - 9) \qquad \text{Factor out GCF, } 4x.$$
$$= 4x(x + 3)(x - 3) \quad A^2 - B^2 = (A + B)(A - B)$$

   2. The binomial $16p^4 - 1$ is a difference of squares, since $(4p^2)^2 = 16p^4$ and $1^2 = 1$:

$$16p^4 - 1 = (4p^2)^2 - 1^2 \qquad \text{Write as difference of squares.}$$
$$= (4p^2 + 1)(4p^2 - 1) \qquad A^2 - B^2 = (A + B)(A - B)$$
$$= (4p^2 + 1)(2p + 1)(2p - 1) \quad \begin{array}{l} 4p^2 + 1 \text{ is prime:} \\ A^2 - B^2 = (A + B)(A - B) \end{array}$$

We use a graphing calculator table to verify our work (see Fig. 28).

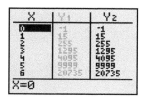

Figure 28 Verify the work

The Sum or Difference of Two Cubes

So far, we have discussed how to factor a difference of squares. We can also factor a sum of cubes and factor a difference of cubes.

To see how to factor the sum of two cubes, we begin by multiplying the expressions $A + B$ and $A^2 - AB + B^2$:

$$(A + B)(A^2 - AB + B^2) = A \cdot A^2 - A \cdot AB + A \cdot B^2 + B \cdot A^2 - B \cdot AB + B \cdot B^2$$
$$= A^3 - A^2B + AB^2 + A^2B - AB^2 + B^3$$
$$= A^3 + B^3$$

So, $(A + B)(A^2 - AB + B^2) = A^3 + B^3$. The right-hand side of the equation, $A^3 + B^3$, is a sum of two cubes. By similar work, we can also find a property for the difference of two cubes.

> **Sum or Difference of Two Cubes**
>
> $$A^3 + B^3 = (A + B)(A^2 - AB + B^2) \quad \text{\textit{Sum of two cubes}}$$
> $$A^3 - B^3 = (A - B)(A^2 + AB + B^2) \quad \text{\textit{Difference of two cubes}}$$

We can use these two properties to factor any polynomial that is a sum or difference of two cubes. To use the properties, it will help to memorize the following cubes:

$$2^3 = 8 \qquad 3^3 = 27 \qquad 4^3 = 64 \qquad 5^3 = 125 \qquad 10^3 = 1000$$

▶ **Example 3**   Factoring a Sum and a Difference of Two Cubes

Factor.

1. $x^3 + 8$

2. $x^3 - 125$

Solution

1.

$$A^3 + B^3 = (A + B)(A^2 - A\ B + B^2)$$

$$x^3 + 8 = x^3 + 2^3 = (x + 2)(x^2 - x \cdot 2 + 2^2) \quad \text{\textit{Factor.}}$$
$$= (x + 2)(x^2 - 2x + 4) \quad \text{\textit{Simplify.}}$$

The trinomial $x^2 - 2x + 4$ is prime, so we have completely factored $x^3 + 8$.

2.

$$A^3 - B^3 = (A - B)(A^2 + A\ B + B^2)$$

$$x^3 - 125 = x^3 - 5^3 = (x - 5)(x^2 + x \cdot 5 + 5^2) \quad \text{\textit{Factor.}}$$
$$= (x - 5)(x^2 + 5x + 25) \quad \text{\textit{Simplify.}}$$

The trinomial $x^2 + 5x + 25$ is prime, so we have completely factored $x^3 - 125$. We use a graphing calculator table to verify our work (see Fig. 29).

Figure 29 Verify the work

▶ **Example 4**   Factoring a Sum and a Difference of Two Cubes

Factor.

1. $64t^3 + 27w^3$

2. $3x^5 - 24x^2y^3$

Solution

1. $64t^3 + 27w^3 = (4t)^3 + (3w)^3$ *Write as a sum of cubes.*

$$= (4t + 3w)((4t)^2 - 4t \cdot 3w + (3w)^2) \quad \begin{array}{l} A^3 + B^3 = \\ (A + B)(A^2 - AB + B^2) \end{array}$$

$$= (4t + 3w)(16t^2 - 12tw + 9w^2) \quad \text{\textit{Simplify.}}$$

The trinomial $16t^2 - 12tw + 9w^2$ is prime, so we have completely factored $64t^3 + 27w^3$.

2. For $3x^5 - 24x^2y^3$, first we factor out the GCF, $3x^2$:

$$3x^5 - 24x^2y^3 = 3x^2(x^3 - 8y^3) \qquad \text{\textit{Factor out GCF, } } 3x^2.$$
$$= 3x^2(x^3 - (2y)^3) \qquad \text{\textit{Write as a difference of cubes.}}$$
$$= 3x^2(x - 2y)(x^2 + x \cdot 2y + (2y)^2) \qquad \text{\textit{$A^3 - B^3 =$}}$$
$$\qquad\qquad\qquad\qquad\qquad\qquad\qquad \text{\textit{$(A - B)(A^2 + AB + B^2)$}}$$
$$= 3x^2(x - 2y)(x^2 + 2xy + 4y^2) \qquad \text{\textit{Simplify.}}$$

The trinomial $x^2 + 2xy + 4y^2$ is prime, so we have completely factored $3x^5 - 24x^2y^3$.

Consider the properties for the sum of cubes and the difference of cubes:

$$A^3 + B^3 = (A + B)(A^2 - AB + B^2) \qquad A^3 - B^3 = (A - B)(A^2 + AB + B^2)$$

Provided we have first factored out the GCF (or its opposite), and A and B are first-degree monomials, we can assume the trinomials $A^2 - AB + B^2$ and $A^2 + AB + B^2$ are prime.

▶ **Example 5**   Factoring the Difference of Two Sixth Powers

Factor $n^6 - p^6$.

Solution

Since $n^6 = (n^3)^2$ and $p^6 = (p^3)^2$, we can begin to factor the binomial by using the property for a difference of two squares:

$$n^6 - p^6$$
$$= (n^3)^2 - (p^3)^2 \qquad \text{\textit{Write as a difference of two squares.}}$$
$$= (n^3 + p^3)(n^3 - p^3) \qquad \text{\textit{$A^2 - B^2 = (A + B)(A - B)$}}$$
$$= (n + p)(n^2 - np + p^2)(n - p)(n^2 + np + p^2) \qquad \text{\textit{$A^3 + B^3 = (A + B)(A^2 - AB + B^2)$;}}$$
$$\qquad\qquad\qquad\qquad\qquad\qquad\qquad\qquad\qquad \text{\textit{$A^3 - B^3 = (A - B)(A^2 + AB + B^2)$}}$$

Although we could have started to factor $n^6 - p^6$ by writing it as a difference of two cubes, $(n^2)^3 - (p^2)^3$, this would have led to very challenging factoring after we had used the property for a difference of two cubes.

A Factoring Strategy

We will now discuss a five-step factoring strategy that will help us determine the best factoring techniques to use to factor a given polynomial completely.

▶ **Five-Step Factoring Strategy**

These five steps can be used to factor many polynomials (steps 2–4 can be applied to the entire polynomial or to a factor of the polynomial):

1. If the leading coefficient is positive and the GCF is not 1, factor out the GCF. If the leading coefficient is negative, factor out the opposite of the GCF.

2. For a binomial, try using one of the properties for the difference of two squares, the sum of two cubes, or the difference of two cubes.

3. For a trinomial of the form $ax^2 + bx + c$,
 a. If $a = 1$, try to find two integers whose product is c and whose sum is b.
 b. If $a \neq 1$, try to factor by using trial and error or by grouping.

4. For an expression with four terms, try factoring by grouping.

5. Continue applying steps 2–4 until the polynomial is completely factored.

▶ **Example 6** Factoring a Polynomial

Factor $x^4 - 2x^3 + 1000x - 2000$.

Solution

Since $x^4 - 2x^3 + 1000x - 2000$ has four terms, we try to factor it by grouping:

$$x^4 - 2x^3 + 1000x - 2000$$
$$= x^3(x - 2) + 1000(x - 2) \;\Big\}$$
$$= (x^3 + 1000)(x - 2) \qquad\qquad \Big\} \quad \textit{Factor by grouping.}$$
$$= (x + 10)(x^2 - 10x + 100)(x - 2) \quad \textit{A}^3 + \textit{B}^3 = (\textit{A} + \textit{B})(\textit{A}^2 - \textit{AB} + \textit{B}^2)$$

▶ **Example 7** Factoring a Polynomial

Factor $10x^2 - 15x + 40x^3$.

Solution

First, we write $10x^2 - 15x + 40x^3$ in descending order:

$$10x^2 - 15x + 40x^3 = 40x^3 + 10x^2 - 15x \qquad \textit{Rearrange terms.}$$
$$= 5x(8x^2 + 2x - 3) \qquad \textit{Factor out GCF, 5x.}$$
$$= 5x(4x + 3)(2x - 1) \qquad \textit{Factor by trial and error.}$$

We use a graphing calculator table to verify our work (see Fig. 30).

Figure 30 Verify the work

▶ **Example 8** Factoring a Polynomial

Factor $50t^2w^2 - 8w^4$.

Solution

For $50t^2w^2 - 8w^4$, the GCF is $2w^2$. First, we factor out $2w^2$:

$$50t^2w^2 - 8w^4 = 2w^2(25t^2 - 4w^2)$$

Since the factor $25t^2 - 4w^2$ has two terms, we check to see whether it is the difference of two squares, which it is. So, we have

$$50t^2w^2 - 8w^4 = 2w^2(25t^2 - 4w^2) = 2w^2(5t + 2w)(5t - 2w)$$

▶ **Example 9** Factoring a Polynomial

Factor $3a^3b - 21a^2b^2 + 18ab^3$.

Solution

For $3a^3b - 21a^2b^2 + 18ab^3$, the GCF is $3ab$. First, we factor out $3ab$:

$$3a^3b - 21a^2b^2 + 18ab^3 = 3ab(a^2 - 7ab + 6b^2)$$

Since the factor $a^2 - 7ab + 6b^2$ is a trinomial with leading coefficient 1, we try to find two monomials whose product is $6b^2$ and whose sum is $-7b$. The monomials are $-b$ and $-6b$, so we have

$$3a^3b - 21a^2b^2 + 18ab^3 = 3ab(a^2 - 7ab + 6b^2) = 3ab(a - b)(a - 6b)$$

◆▼ Group Exploration

Looking ahead: Zero factor property

1. What can you say about A or B if $AB = 0$?
2. What can you say about A or B if $A(B - 1) = 0$?
3. What can you say about x if $x(x - 1) = 0$?

4. Solve $x^2 - x = 0$. [**Hint:** Does this have something to do with Problem 3?]
5. Solve $2x^2 - 6x = 0$.   6. Solve $x^2 - 8x + 15 = 0$.

Homework 6.6

Factor when possible. Use a graphing calculator table to verify your work when possible.

1. $x^2 - 25$
2. $x^2 - 9$
3. $a^2 - 36$
4. $t^2 - 81$
5. $4x^2 - 49$
6. $25x^2 - 16$
7. $9x^2 + 100$
8. $49x^2 + 4$
9. $16p^2 - 25t^2$
10. $81k^2 - 49r^2$
11. $75x^2 - 12$
12. $45x^2 - 20$
13. $18a^3b - 32ab^3$
14. $50m^3t - 72mt^3$
15. $16x^4 - 81$
16. $81x^4 - 1$
17. $t^4 - w^4$
18. $a^4 - 81b^4$

Factor when possible. Use a graphing calculator table to verify your work when possible.

19. $x^3 + 27$
20. $x^3 + 64$
21. $x^3 - 8$
22. $x^3 - 27$
23. $m^3 + 1$
24. $r^3 - 1$
25. $8x^3 + 27$
26. $27x^3 + 64$
27. $125x^3 - 8$
28. $1000x^3 - 27$
29. $27p^3 + 8t^3$
30. $8w^3 + 125y^3$
31. $27x^3 - 64y^3$
32. $64c^3 - 125d^3$
33. $5x^3 + 40$
34. $10x^3 + 640$
35. $2x^4 - 54xy^3$
36. $4x^5 - 32x^2y^3$
37. $k^6 - 1$
38. $t^6 - 64$
39. $64x^6 - y^6$
40. $x^6 - y^6$

For Exercises 41–82, factor when possible. Use a graphing calculator table to verify your work when possible.

41. $a^2 - 3ab - 28b^2$
42. $p^2 - 9pt + 20t^2$
43. $2x^4 - 16xy^3$
44. $4x^3y - 4y^4$
45. $-7x - 18 + x^2$
46. $2x + x^2 - 80$
47. $4x^3y - 8x^2y^2 - 96xy^3$
48. $2x^4y + 24x^3y^2 + 70x^2y^3$
49. $-k^2 + 12k - 36$
50. $-t^2 + 18t - 81$
51. $4x^2 + 9x + 6$
52. $8x^2 - 13x + 10$
53. $x^3 - 2x^2 - 9x + 18$
54. $4x^3 - x^2 - 16x + 4$
55. $6x^4 - 33x^3 + 45x^2$
56. $15x^4 + 55x^3 - 20x^2$
57. $32m^2 - 98t^2$
58. $75r^2 - 27y^2$
59. $8x^2 + 10x - 3$
60. $6x^2 + 11x - 10$
61. $12x^2y - 26xy^2 - 10y^3$
62. $36x^4 - 21x^3y + 3x^2y^2$
63. $x^2 - 11x - 24$
64. $x^2 - 13x - 36$
65. $125x^3 + 27$
66. $64x^3 + 125$
67. $p^2 + 18p + 81$
68. $r^2 + 20r + 100$
69. $20x^3 - 8x^2 - 5x + 2$
70. $9x^3 + 27x^2 - x - 3$
71. $49x^2 + 14x + 1$
72. $64x^2 - 16x + 1$
73. $25x^2 + 81y^2$
74. $36m^2 + 49n^2$
75. $2w^3y + 250y^4$
76. $5a^3b^2 + 5000b^5$

77. $-3x^3 + 3x^2 + 90x$
78. $-2x^3 + 20x^2 - 32x$
79. $27x^3 - 75x$
80. $98x^3 - 18x$
81. $81p^4 - 16q^4$
82. $16m^4 - n^4$

Concepts

83. A student tries to factor $x^3 - 8$:
$$x^3 - 8 = (x - 2)(x^2 + 4x + 4)$$
Describe any errors. Then factor the expression correctly.

84. A student tries to factor $x^3 + 27$:
$$x^3 + 27 = (x + 3)(x^2 + 3x + 9)$$
Describe any errors. Then factor the expression correctly.

85. A student tries to factor $4x^2 + 100$:
$$4x^2 + 100 = 4(x^2 + 25) = 4(x + 5)(x + 5) = 4(x + 5)^2$$
Describe any errors. Then factor the expression correctly.

86. A student tries to factor $x^3 + a^3$:
$$x^3 + a^3 = (x + a)(x^2 - 2ax + a^2)$$
Describe any errors. Then factor the expression correctly.

87. a. Factor $x^2 - 4$.
b. Use ZStandard on a graphing calculator to graph the function $f(x) = x^2 - 4$. (For a closer look, try ZDecimal.) What are the x-intercepts?
c. What connection do you notice between your result in part (a) and the x-intercepts of the graph of f? Explain why this connection makes sense.

88. a. Factor $x^3 - x^2 - 4x + 4$.
b. Use ZStandard on a graphing calculator to graph the function $f(x) = x^3 - x^2 - 4x + 4$. (For a closer look, try ZDecimal.) What are the x-intercepts?
c. What connection do you notice between your result in part (a) and the x-intercepts of the graph of f? Explain why this connection makes sense.

89. Show that $A^3 - B^3 = (A - B)(A^2 + AB + B^2)$ by finding the product $(A - B)(A^2 + AB + B^2)$.

90. Show that $A^2 + AB + B^2$ is prime when $A = x$ and $B = y$.

91. Describe how to factor a difference of two squares, a sum of two cubes, and a difference of two cubes.

92. Describe, in your own words, a strategy for factoring polynomials.

Related Review

If the expression is not factored, then factor it. If the expression is factored, then find the product.

93. $(3x - 7)(3x + 7)$
94. $(8x + 1)(8x - 1)$
95. $36p^2 - 49$
96. $81c^2 - 25$
97. $(t - 5)(t^2 + 5t + 25)$
98. $(w + 3)(w^2 - 3w + 9)$
99. $27p^3 + 1$
100. $8m^3 - 125$

Expressions, Equations, Functions, and Graphs

Perform the indicated instruction. Then use words such as linear, quadratic, cubic, exponential, logarithmic, polynomial, degree, function, one variable, and two variables to describe the expression, equation, or system.

101. Graph $2(3x - 2y) = 3x + 4$ by hand.

102. Solve $\log_3(4w + 2) = 4$.

103. Solve:

$$3x - 5y = 21$$
$$2x + 7y = -17$$

104. Simplify $\left(8b^{-6}c^3\right)^{2/3}\left(4b^4c^{-6}\right)^{1/2}$.

▼ 6.7 Using Factoring to Solve Polynomial Equations

Objectives

» Know the *zero factor property.*

» Use factoring to solve *quadratic equations in one variable.*

» Find the *x*-intercept(s) of the graph of a polynomial function.

» Know a connection between the *x*-intercepts of the graph of a function and the solutions of a related equation in one variable.

» Use factoring to solve *cubic equations in one variable.*

» Use graphing to solve a polynomial equation in one variable.

» Use a *quadratic model* to make estimates and predictions about an authentic situation.

» Solve area-of-rectangle problems.

In this section, we will discuss how to use factoring to help us solve equations. We will use this skill to help us make estimates and predictions about some authentic situations.

Zero Factor Property

In Section 6.1, we graphed quadratic equations in *two* variables. In this section, we will solve quadratic equations in *one* variable, such as

$$x^2 - 3x - 28 = 0 \qquad 25x^2 - 49 = 0 \qquad 12x = 9x^2 + 4$$

A **quadratic equation in one variable** is an equation that can be put into the form

$$ax^2 + bx + c = 0$$

where a, b, and c are constants and $a \neq 0$. The connection between solving a quadratic equation and factoring an expression lies in the *zero factor property*.

▶ **Zero Factor Property**

Let A and B be real numbers.

$$\text{If } AB = 0, \text{ then } A = 0 \text{ or } B = 0.$$

In words, if the product of two numbers is zero, then at least one of the numbers must be zero.

Solving Quadratic Equations in One Variable

We can use the zero factor property to help us solve some quadratic equations in one variable.

▶ **Example 1**   Solving a Quadratic Equation

Solve $(x - 5)(x + 2) = 0$.

Solution

$$\begin{aligned}
(x - 5)(x + 2) &= 0 && \text{\textit{Original equation}} \\
x - 5 = 0 \quad &\text{or} \quad x + 2 = 0 && \text{\textit{Zero factor property}} \\
x = 5 \quad &\text{or} \qquad\quad x = -2 && \text{\textit{Add 5 to both sides./Subtract 2 from both sides.}}
\end{aligned}$$

We check that both 5 and -2 satisfy the original equation:

Check $x = 5$	**Check $x = -2$**
$(x - 5)(x + 2) = 0$	$(x - 5)(x + 2) = 0$
$(5 - 5)(5 + 2) \overset{?}{=} 0$	$(-2 - 5)(-2 + 2) \overset{?}{=} 0$
$0(7) \overset{?}{=} 0$	$-7(0) \overset{?}{=} 0$
$0 \overset{?}{=} 0$	$0 \overset{?}{=} 0$
true	true

So, the solutions are 5 and -2.

▶

▶ **Example 2** Solving a Quadratic Equation

Solve $w^2 - 2w - 8 = 0$.

Solution

$$w^2 - 2w - 8 = 0 \qquad \text{\textit{Original equation}}$$
$$(w + 2)(w - 4) = 0 \qquad \text{\textit{Factor left side.}}$$
$$w + 2 = 0 \quad \text{or} \quad w - 4 = 0 \quad \text{\textit{Zero factor property}}$$
$$w = -2 \quad \text{or} \quad w = 4 \quad \text{\textit{Subtract 2 from both sides./}}$$
$$\text{\textit{Add 4 to both sides.}}$$

We check that both -2 and 4 satisfy the original equation:

Check $w = -2$	**Check $w = 4$**
$w^2 - 2w - 8 = 0$	$w^2 - 2w - 8 = 0$
$(-2)^2 - 2(-2) - 8 \overset{?}{=} 0$	$4^2 - 2(4) - 8 \overset{?}{=} 0$
$4 + 4 - 8 \overset{?}{=} 0$	$16 - 8 - 8 \overset{?}{=} 0$
$0 \overset{?}{=} 0$	$0 \overset{?}{=} 0$
true	true

So, the solutions are -2 and 4.

The key step in solving a quadratic equation of the form $ax^2 + bx + c = 0$ is to factor the left side of the equation so we can apply the zero factor property.

Connection between x-Intercepts and Solutions

There is an important connection between x-intercepts of the graph of a function and the solutions of a related equation in one variable. We begin to investigate this connection in Example 3.

▶ **Example 3** Finding x-Intercepts of the Graph of a Quadratic Function

Find the x-intercepts of the graph of $f(x) = x^2 - 7x + 10$.

Solution

To find the x-intercepts, we substitute 0 for $f(x)$ and solve for x:

$$0 = x^2 - 7x + 10 \qquad \text{\textit{Substitute 0 for f(x).}}$$
$$0 = (x - 5)(x - 2) \qquad \text{\textit{Factor right-hand side.}}$$
$$x - 5 = 0 \quad \text{or} \quad x - 2 = 0 \quad \text{\textit{Zero factor property}}$$
$$x = 5 \quad \text{or} \quad x = 2$$

So, the x-intercepts are $(2, 0)$ and $(5, 0)$. We use "zero" on a graphing calculator to verify our work (see Fig. 31).

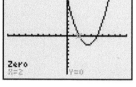

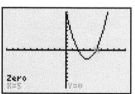

Figure 31 Verify the work

In general, we find the x-intercepts of the graph of $f(x) = ax^2 + bx + c$ by solving the equation $ax^2 + bx + c = 0$.

▶ **Connection Between x-Intercepts and Solutions**

Let f be a function. If k is a real-number solution of the equation $f(x) = 0$, then $(k, 0)$ is an x-intercept of the graph of the function f. Also, if $(k, 0)$ is an x-intercept of the graph of f, then k is a solution of $f(x) = 0$.

This property suggests that we can verify our solutions of a quadratic equation $ax^2 + bx + c = 0$ by using a graphing calculator to find the x-intercepts of the graph of $f(x) = ax^2 + bx + c$.

Solving More Quadratic Equations

In Example 4, we solve quadratic equations and use a graphing calculator to verify our work.

> **Example 4** Solving Quadratic Equations

Solve.

1. $4x^2 + 26x + 30 = 0$ **2.** $x^2 - 10x + 25 = 0$

Solution

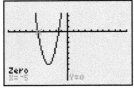

Zero
X=-1.5   Y=0

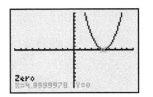

Zero
X=-5   Y=0

Figure 32 Verify the work

1.
$$4x^2 + 26x + 30 = 0 \quad \textit{Original equation}$$
$$2\left(2x^2 + 13x + 15\right) = 0 \quad \textit{Factor out GCF, 2.}$$
$$2(2x + 3)(x + 5) = 0 \quad \textit{Completely factor left side.}$$

Now we can apply a variation of the zero factor property: If $2AB = 0$, then $A = 0$ or $B = 0$. Here, we take $2x + 3$ to be A and $x + 5$ to be B:

$$2x + 3 = 0 \qquad \text{or} \qquad x + 5 = 0 \qquad \textit{Zero factor property}$$
$$2x = -3 \qquad \text{or} \qquad x = -5$$
$$x = -\frac{3}{2} \qquad \text{or} \qquad x = -5$$

We use "zero" on a graphing calculator to check that the x-intercepts of the graph of $f(x) = 4x^2 + 26x + 30$ are $\left(-\dfrac{3}{2}, 0\right)$ and $(-5, 0)$. See Fig. 32.

2.
$$x^2 - 10x + 25 = 0 \quad \textit{Original equation}$$
$$(x - 5)(x - 5) = 0 \quad \textit{Factor left side.}$$
$$x - 5 = 0 \quad \textit{Zero factor property}$$
$$x = 5$$

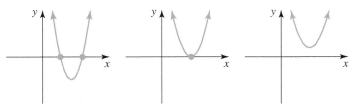

Zero
X=4.9999978   Y=0

Figure 33 Verify the work

Since using the zero factor property yields the *one* equation $x - 5 = 0$, there is one solution: 5. We use "zero" on a graphing calculator to check that the x-intercept of the graph of $f(x) = x^2 - 10x + 25$ is $(5, 0)$. See Fig. 33.

In Example 4, we found that the equation $4x^2 + 26x + 30 = 0$ has two solutions, whereas the equation $x^2 - 10x + 25 = 0$ has one solution. What are the possible numbers of solutions of a quadratic equation? To decide, note that the graph of a quadratic function can have two x-intercepts, one x-intercept, or no x-intercepts (see Fig. 34).

Figure 34 A quadratic function can have two, one, or no x-intercepts

Since the number of real-number solutions of an equation $ax^2 + bx + c = 0$ is equal to the number of x-intercepts of the graph of the function $f(x) = ax^2 + bx + c$, we conclude that **the solution set of a quadratic equation in one variable may contain two real numbers, one real number, or no real numbers.** We will solve quadratic equations that have no real-number solutions in Chapter 7.

In Example 4, both original equations had one side that was 0. If neither side of a quadratic equation in one variable is 0, we must first use properties of equality to get one side to be 0 so we can then apply the zero factor property.

▶ **Example 5** Solving a Quadratic Equation

Solve $2x^2 - 8x = 5x - 20$.

Solution

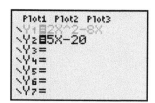

$$2x^2 - 8x = 5x - 20 \qquad \textit{Original equation}$$
$$2x^2 - 13x + 20 = 0 \qquad \textit{Write in } ax^2 + bx + c = 0 \textit{ form.}$$
$$(2x - 5)(x - 4) = 0 \qquad \textit{Factor left side.}$$
$$2x - 5 = 0 \quad \text{or} \quad x - 4 = 0 \qquad \textit{Zero factor property}$$
$$2x = 5 \quad \text{or} \quad x = 4$$
$$x = \frac{5}{2} \quad \text{or} \quad x = 4$$

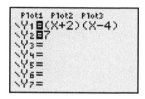

Figure 35 Verify the work

To verify that $\frac{5}{2}$ is a solution of $2x^2 - 8x = 5x - 20$, we can use a graphing calculator table to check that, for input $\frac{5}{2}$, the output for $y = 2x^2 - 8x$ is equal to the output for $y = 5x - 20$. We do similarly for input $x = 4$ (see Fig. 35).

▶

▶ **Example 6** Solving a Quadratic Equation

Solve $(x + 2)(x - 4) = 7$.

Solution

Although the left-hand side of $(x + 2)(x - 4) = 7$ is factored, the right-hand side is not zero. First, we find the product on the left-hand side of the equation:

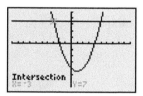

$$(x + 2)(x - 4) = 7 \qquad \textit{Original equation}$$
$$x^2 - 2x - 8 = 7 \qquad \textit{Find product on left side.}$$
$$x^2 - 2x - 15 = 0 \qquad \textit{Write in } ax^2 + bx + c = 0 \textit{ form.}$$
$$(x - 5)(x + 3) = 0 \qquad \textit{Factor left-hand side.}$$
$$x - 5 = 0 \quad \text{or} \quad x + 3 = 0 \qquad \textit{Zero factor property}$$
$$x = 5 \quad \text{or} \quad x = -3$$

Therefore, the solutions are -3 and 5. To verify the work, we can enter the equations $y = (x + 2)(x - 4)$ and $y = 7$ and use "intersect" to find the intersection points $(-3, 7)$ and $(5, 7)$. See Fig. 36. The x-coordinates of these points, -3 and 5, are the solutions of the original equation, which checks.

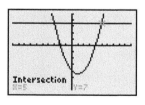

Figure 36 Verify the work

▶

▶ **Example 7** Solving a Quadratic Equation That Contains Fractions

Solve $\frac{1}{2}t^2 + \frac{1}{3} = \frac{5}{6}t$.

Solution

To clear the equation of fractions, we multiply both sides by the least common denominator (LCD), 6:

$$\frac{1}{2}t^2 + \frac{1}{3} = \frac{5}{6}t \qquad \textit{Original equation}$$
$$6 \cdot \frac{1}{2}t^2 + 6 \cdot \frac{1}{3} = 6 \cdot \frac{5}{6}t \qquad \textit{Multiply both sides by LCD, 6.}$$
$$3t^2 + 2 = 5t \qquad \textit{Simplify.}$$
$$3t^2 - 5t + 2 = 0 \qquad \textit{Write in } ax^2 + bx + c = 0 \textit{ form.}$$
$$(3t - 2)(t - 1) = 0 \qquad \textit{Factor left side.}$$
$$3t - 2 = 0 \quad \text{or} \quad t - 1 = 0 \qquad \textit{Zero factor property}$$
$$3t = 2 \quad \text{or} \quad t = 1$$
$$t = \frac{2}{3} \quad \text{or} \quad t = 1$$

▶

Now that we can solve some quadratic equations in one variable, we can find inputs of a quadratic function for some outputs.

▶ **Example 8**   Finding an Input and an Output of a Quadratic Function

Let $f(x) = x^2 - 3x - 23$.

1. Find $f(5)$.

2. Find x when $f(x) = 5$.

Solution

1. $f(5) = 5^2 - 3(5) - 23 = 25 - 15 - 23 = -13$

2. We substitute 5 for $f(x)$ in the equation $f(x) = x^2 - 3x - 23$:

$$5 = x^2 - 3x - 23 \qquad \textit{Substitute 5 for } f(x).$$
$$0 = x^2 - 3x - 28 \qquad \textit{Write in } 0 = ax^2 + bx + c \textit{ form.}$$
$$0 = (x - 7)(x + 4) \qquad \textit{Factor right-hand side.}$$
$$x - 7 = 0 \quad \text{or} \quad x + 4 = 0 \qquad \textit{Zero factor property}$$
$$x = 7 \quad \text{or} \qquad x = -4$$

Next, we verify that $f(7) = 5$ and $f(-4) = 5$:

Check that $f(7) = 5$

$$f(x) = x^2 - 3x - 23$$
$$f(7) = 7^2 - 3(7) - 23$$
$$= 5$$

Check that $f(-4) = 5$

$$f(x) = x^2 - 3x - 23$$
$$f(-4) = (-4)^2 - 3(-4) - 23$$
$$= 5$$

Or we can verify our work in Problems 1 and 2 by using a graphing calculator table (see Fig. 37).

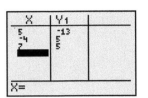

Figure 37 Verify the work

Recall from Section 5.2 that the inverse of a function g sends each output of g to its corresponding input(s). From Example 8, we see that the function $f(x) = x^2 - 3x - 23$ is not invertible, since the output 5 corresponds to not one input, but two: -4 and 7. It turns out that no quadratic function is invertible.

Cubic Equations in One Variable

So far in this section, we have solved quadratic equations. We will now solve some cubic equations, such as

$$4x^3 - 2x^2 - 36x + 18 = 0 \qquad 2x^3 = 42x + 8x^2$$

A **cubic equation in one variable** is an equation that can be put into the form

$$ax^3 + bx^2 + cx + d = 0$$

where $a, b, c,$ and d are constants and $a \neq 0$. We can solve some cubic equations by applying the zero factor property to three factors:

If $ABC = 0$, then $A = 0, B = 0,$ or $C = 0$.

▶ **Example 9**   Solving a Cubic Equation

Solve $2x^3 = 42x + 8x^2$.

Solution

$$2x^3 = 42x + 8x^2 \qquad \textit{Original equation}$$
$$2x^3 - 8x^2 - 42x = 0 \qquad \textit{Write in } ax^3 + bx^2 + cx + d = 0 \textit{ form.}$$
$$2x(x^2 - 4x - 21) = 0 \qquad \textit{Factor out GCF, 2x.}$$
$$2x(x - 7)(x + 3) = 0 \qquad \textit{Completely factor left side.}$$
$$2x = 0 \quad \text{or} \quad x - 7 = 0 \quad \text{or} \quad x + 3 = 0 \qquad \textit{Zero factor property}$$
$$x = 0 \quad \text{or} \qquad x = 7 \quad \text{or} \qquad x = -3$$

So, the solutions are $-3, 0,$ and 7.

Note that solving a cubic equation in one variable is similar to solving a quadratic equation in one variable. We now summarize the steps used to solve either type of equation.

> **Solving Quadratic or Cubic Equations by Factoring**
>
> If an equation can be solved by factoring, we solve it by the following steps:
> 1. Write the equation so one side of the equation is equal to zero.
> 2. Factor the nonzero side of the equation.
> 3. Apply the zero factor property.
> 4. Solve each equation that results from applying the zero factor property.

> **Example 10**   Finding *x*-Intercepts of the Graph of a Cubic Function

Find the *x*-intercepts of the graph of $f(x) = x^3 - 5x^2 - 4x + 20$.

Solution

We substitute 0 for $f(x)$ and solve for *x*:

$$x^3 - 5x^2 - 4x + 20 = 0 \qquad \text{Substitute 0 for } f(x).$$

$$\left.\begin{array}{r} x^2(x - 5) - 4(x - 5) = 0 \\ (x^2 - 4)(x - 5) = 0 \end{array}\right\} \qquad \text{Factor by grouping.}$$

$$(x + 2)(x - 2)(x - 5) = 0 \qquad A^2 - B^2 = (A + B)(A - B)$$

$$x + 2 = 0 \quad \text{or} \quad x - 2 = 0 \quad \text{or} \quad x - 5 = 0 \qquad \text{Zero factor property}$$

$$x = -2 \quad \text{or} \quad x = 2 \quad \text{or} \quad x = 5$$

So, the *x*-intercepts are $(-2, 0)$, $(2, 0)$, and $(5, 0)$. We use "zero" on a graphing calculator to verify our work (see Fig. 38).

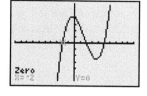
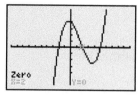
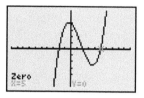

Figure 38 Verify the work

WARNING   It is a common error to try to apply the zero factor property to an equation such as $x^2(x - 5) - 4(x - 5) = 0$ and incorrectly conclude that the solutions are 0 and 5. The expression $x^2(x - 5) - 4(x - 5)$ is *not* factored, because it is a difference, not a product. Only after we factor the left side of the equation $x^2(x - 5) - 4(x - 5) = 0$ can we apply the zero factor property.

In Example 10, we worked with the cubic function $f(x) = x^3 - 5x^2 - 4x + 20$. Recall from Section 6.1 that a cubic function is a function whose equation can be put into the form $f(x) = ax^3 + bx^2 + cx + d$, where $a \neq 0$.

The cubic function sketched in graph (a) of Fig. 39 has exactly three *x*-intercepts, the cubic function sketched in graph (b) has exactly two *x*-intercepts, and cubic functions sketched in graphs (c) and (d) have exactly one *x*-intercept. It turns out the graph of any cubic function has exactly one, two, or three *x*-intercepts.

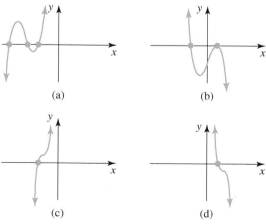

Figure 39 Graphs of typical cubic functions

The number of real-number solutions of a cubic equation $ax^3 + bx^2 + cx + d = 0$ is equal to the number of x-intercepts of the graph of the function $f(x) = ax^3 + bx^2 + cx + d$, so we conclude that **the solution set of a cubic equation in one variable may contain one, two, or three real numbers.**

Solving Polynomial Equations in One Variable by Graphing

Consider the equation $x^2 - x - 7 = -x^2$. If we add x^2 to both sides, the result is $2x^2 - x - 7 = 0$. Since the left side of the equation, $2x^2 - x - 7$, is prime (try it), we cannot solve the equation by factoring. However, we will show in Example 11 that we can solve it by graphing.

▶ **Example 11**   Using Graphing to Solve an Equation in One Variable

Use graphing to solve $x^2 - x - 7 = -x^2$.

Solution

We use "intersect" on a graphing calculator to find the solutions of the system

$$y = x^2 - x - 7$$
$$y = -x^2$$

See Fig. 40.

The approximate solutions of the system are $(-1.64, -2.68)$ and $(2.14, -4.57)$. The x-coordinates of these ordered pairs, -1.64 and 2.14, are the approximate solutions of the equation $x^2 - x - 7 = -x^2$. ▶

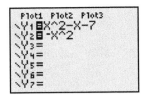
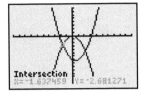
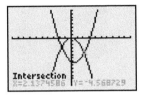

Figure 40 Solve the system

In Sections 7.4 and 7.5, we will discuss two symbolic methods that can be used to solve $x^2 - x - 7 = -x^2$.

Using a Quadratic Function to Model a Situation

In Sections 6.1 and 6.2, we used linear and quadratic functions to model authentic situations. Now we focus on using quadratic functions to perform modeling.

▶ **Definition**   Quadratic model

A **quadratic model** is a quadratic function, or its graph, that describes the relationship between two quantities in an authentic situation.

▶ **Example 12**   Modeling with a Quadratic Function

Annual revenues of restaurants are shown in Table 17 for various years. Let $f(t)$ be the annual revenue (in billions of dollars) of restaurants at t years since 1970. A model of the situation is $f(t) = \dfrac{1}{5}t^2 + 5t + 54$.

1. Use a graphing calculator to draw the graph of the model and, in the same viewing window, the scattergram of the data. Does the model fit the data well?
2. Predict the revenue in 2018.
3. Predict when the annual revenue was $84 billion.

Solution

1. The graph of the model and the scattergram of the data are shown in Fig. 41. The model appears to fit the data quite well.
2. To predict the revenue in 2018, we find $f(48)$:

$$f(48) = \frac{1}{5}(48)^2 + 5(48) + 54 = 754.8$$

The revenue in 2018 will be $754.8 billion, according to the model.

Table 17 Annual Revenue of Restaurants

Year	Annual Revenue (billions of dollars)
1970	42.8
1980	119.6
1990	239.3
2000	379.0
2012	631.8

Source: *National Restaurant Association*

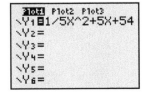
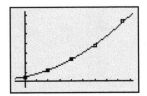

Figure 41 Check the fit

3. To estimate when the annual revenue was $84 billion, we substitute 84 for $f(t)$ in $f(t) = \dfrac{1}{5}t^2 + 5t + 54$ and solve for t:

$$84 = \frac{1}{5}t^2 + 5t + 54 \qquad \textit{Substitute 84 for } f(t).$$

$$0 = \frac{1}{5}t^2 + 5t - 30 \qquad \textit{Write in } 0 = at^2 + bt + c \textit{ form.}$$

$$0 = t^2 + 25t - 150 \qquad \textit{Multiply both sides by the LCD, 5.}$$

$$0 = (t - 5)(t + 30) \qquad \textit{Factor right-hand side.}$$

$$t - 5 = 0 \quad \text{or} \quad t + 30 = 0 \qquad \textit{Zero Factor Property}$$

$$t = 5 \quad \text{or} \qquad t = -30$$

The inputs -30 and 5 represent the years 1940 and 1975, respectively. The estimate of 1940 is an example of model breakdown, as a little research would show the revenue in 1940 was much less than $84 billion. Therefore, we estimate that it was 1975 when the revenue was $84 billion. We use a graphing calculator table to verify our work in Problems 2 and 3 (see Fig. 42).

X	Y₁
48	754.8
⁻30	84
5	84

X=48

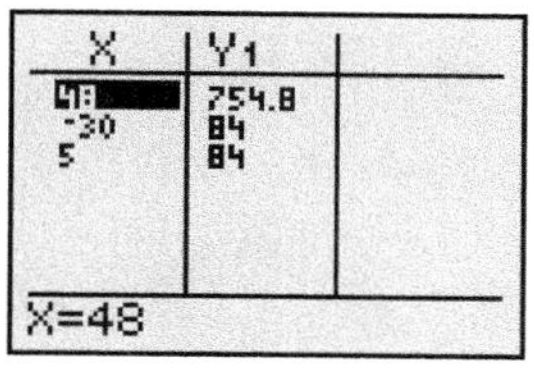

Figure 42 Verify the work

To make a prediction about the dependent variable of a quadratic model, we substitute the chosen value of the independent variable into the equation and solve for the dependent variable.

To make a prediction about the independent variable of a quadratic model, we substitute the chosen value of the dependent variable into the equation and solve for the independent variable. That involves writing the equation so one side is zero and factoring the nonzero side.

Area of Rectangular Objects

The area A of a rectangle is given by the formula $A = LW$, where L is the length of the rectangle and W is the width.

▶ **Example 13**   Solving an Area Problem

A person has a rectangular garden with a width of 9 feet and a length of 12 feet. She plans to place mulch outside of the garden to form a border of uniform width. If she has just enough mulch to cover 100 square feet of land, determine the width of the border.

Solution

We use the five-step problem-solving method of Section 3.4, but for step 2 we find an equation in one variable rather than a system of two equations in two variables (and solve the equation in step 3).

Step 1: Define each variable. Let x be the width (in feet) of the mulch border (see Fig. 43).

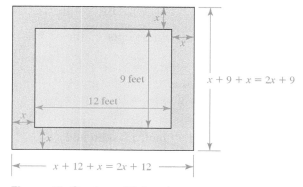

Figure 43 Garden with border

Step 2: Write an equation in one variable. For the outer rectangle (garden and border), the length is $2x + 12$ and the width is $2x + 9$ (see Fig. 43). We use the formula $A = LW$ to describe the area A (in square feet) of the outer rectangle:

$$\overset{\substack{\text{area of} \\ \text{outer rectangle}}}{\overbrace{A}} = \overset{\text{length}}{\overbrace{(2x + 12)}} \cdot \overset{\text{width}}{\overbrace{(2x + 9)}}$$

The area of the garden is $12 \cdot 9 = 108$ square feet, and the area of the border is given as 100 square feet. The area of the garden plus the area of the border is equal to the area of the outer rectangle:

$$\overset{\substack{\text{area of} \\ \text{garden}}}{\overbrace{108}} + \overset{\substack{\text{area of} \\ \text{border}}}{\overbrace{100}} = \overset{\substack{\text{area of} \\ \text{outer rectangle}}}{\overbrace{(2x + 12)(2x + 9)}}$$

$$208 = (2x + 12)(2x + 9)$$

Step 3: Solve the equation.

$$
\begin{aligned}
208 &= (2x + 12)(2x + 9) && \text{\textit{Equation from step 2}} \\
208 &= 4x^2 + 18x + 24x + 108 && \text{\textit{Find product on right side.}} \\
208 &= 4x^2 + 42x + 108 && \text{\textit{Combine like terms.}} \\
0 &= 4x^2 + 42x - 100 && \text{\textit{Write in } } 0 = ax^2 + bx + c \text{ \textit{form.}} \\
0 &= 2(2x^2 + 21x - 50) && \text{\textit{Factor out GCF, 2.}} \\
0 &= 2(2x + 25)(x - 2) && \text{\textit{Factor by trial and error.}}
\end{aligned}
$$

$$
\begin{aligned}
2x + 25 = 0 \quad &\text{or} \quad x - 2 = 0 && \text{\textit{Zero factor property}} \\
2x = -25 \quad &\text{or} \quad x = 2 \\
x = -\frac{25}{2} \quad &\text{or} \quad x = 2
\end{aligned}
$$

Step 4: Describe each result. For the result $x = -\dfrac{25}{2}$, the border width is negative. Model breakdown has occurred, because a width must be positive. The border width is 2 feet.

Step 5: Check. If the border width is 2 feet, then the outer rectangle has a width of 13 feet and a length of 16 feet. Therefore, the total area of the outer rectangle is $13 \cdot 16 = 208$ square feet. This checks with our calculation near the beginning of our work.

▶

▲▼ Group Exploration

Finding equations of quadratic functions

1. Use ZStandard to sketch graphs of the functions $f(x) = (x - 2)(x + 3)$, $g(x) = 2(x - 2)(x + 3)$, $h(x) = \frac{1}{2}(x - 2)(x + 3)$, and $k(x) = -(x - 2)(x + 3)$.

   a. What do you notice about the x-intercepts of the graphs of $f, g, h,$ and k?

   b. For a function of the form $y = a(x - 2)(x + 3)$, describe the effect the value of a has on the graph of the function. Sketch more graphs with varying values of a if you are unsure.

2. Find a possible equation of the function sketched in Fig. 44. Use a graphing calculator to verify your work.

3. Find an equation of the function sketched in Fig. 45. Use a graphing calculator to verify your work. [**Hint:** A point on the graph of an equation satisfies the equation.]

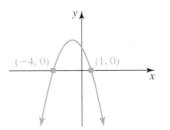

Figure 44 Find a possible equation (Problem 2)

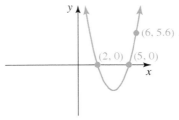

Figure 45 Find an equation (Problem 3)

Group Exploration

Looking ahead: Significance of a, h, and k for $y = a(x - h)^2 + k$

1. Use ZStandard followed by ZSquare to draw a graph of $y = x^2$.

2. Graph these equations of the form $y = x^2 + k$ in order, and describe, in terms of k, how you could "move" the graph of $y = x^2$ to get each graph:
$$y = x^2 + 1, \; y = x^2 + 2, \; y = x^2 + 3, \text{ and } y = x^2 + 4$$
Do the same with these equations:
$$y = x^2 - 1, \; y = x^2 - 2, \; y = x^2 - 3, \text{ and } y = x^2 - 4$$

3. Graph these equations of the form $y = (x - h)^2$ in order, and describe, in terms of h, how you could "move" the graph of $y = x^2$ to get each graph:
$$y = (x - 1)^2, \; y = (x - 2)^2, \; y = (x - 3)^2,$$
$$\text{and } y = (x - 4)^2$$
Do the same with these equations:
$$y = (x + 1)^2, \; y = (x + 2)^2, \; y = (x + 3)^2,$$
$$\text{and } y = (x + 4)^2$$

4. In this problem, you will explore the graphical significance of the constant a in functions of the form $y = ax^2$. From Problems 2 and 3, you should have an idea of how to go about it. Do this now and describe what you find. Don't forget to try negative values of a as well as values of a between 0 and 1.

5. a. Graph these equations in order, and explain how the graphs relate to your observations in Problems 2, 3, and 4:
$$y = x^2, y = 0.5x^2, y = -0.5x^2, y = -0.5(x + 1)^2,$$
$$\text{and } y = -0.5(x + 1)^2 - 6$$

   b. Using your graph of $y = -0.5(x + 1)^2 - 6$, find the coordinates of the vertex. Compare these coordinates with the equation $y = -0.5(x + 1)^2 - 6$. What do you notice?

6. Summarize your findings about a, h, and k in terms of how you could move or adjust the graph of $y = x^2$ to get the graph of $y = a(x - h)^2 + k$. Also, discuss how the coordinates of the vertex are related to a, h, and k. If you are unsure, continue exploring.

▶ **Tips for Success** **Scan Test Problems**

When you take a test, it is best to scan the test problems quickly, pick the problems with which you feel most comfortable, and complete those problems first. By doing so, you will warm up, gain confidence, and perhaps do better on the rest of the test. Also, you will probably have a better idea of how to allot your time on the remaining problems.

Homework 6.7

For extra help ▶ MyMathLab® Watch the videos in MyMathLab Download the MyDashboard App

Solve. Verify any results by checking that they satisfy the equation.

1. $(x + 4)(x - 7) = 0$
2. $(x + 3)(x - 9) = 0$
3. $w^2 + w - 12 = 0$
4. $r^2 + 3r - 28 = 0$
5. $x^2 - 8x + 15 = 0$
6. $x^2 - 6x + 5 = 0$
7. $14x + 49 + x^2 = 0$
8. $16 + x^2 + 8x = 0$
9. $-24 - 2t + t^2 = 0$
10. $-36 + y^2 - 5y = 0$
11. $25x^2 - 49 = 0$
12. $64x^2 - 9 = 0$
13. $6m^2 - 11m + 3 = 0$
14. $4p^2 - 3p - 10 = 0$
15. $3x^2 + 3x - 90 = 0$
16. $2x^2 + 6x - 80 = 0$
17. $8x^3 - 12x^2 - 20x = 0$
18. $12x^3 - 2x^2 - 2x = 0$

Solve. Use a graphing calculator table or graph to verify your work.

19. $x^2 = 5x + 14$
20. $x^2 = 11x + 12$
21. $4x^2 - 8x = 32$
22. $10x^2 - 30x = -20$

23. $12t - 36 = t^2$
24. $4w - 4 = w^2$
25. $16x^2 = 25$
26. $49x^2 = 4$
27. $6x^3 - 24x = 0$
28. $4x^3 - 100x = 0$
29. $3r^2 = 6r$
30. $5p^2 = 35p$
31. $9x = -2x^2 + 5$
32. $10x = -8x^2 - 3$
33. $2x^3 = 6x^2 + 36x$
34. $36x = 24x^2 - 4x^3$
35. $18y^3 + 3y^2 = 6y$
36. $8x^3 - 14x^2 = 4x$
37. $20x = -4x^2 - 25$
38. $24x = -9x^2 - 16$
39. $\frac{1}{4}x^2 - \frac{1}{2}x = 6$
40. $\frac{1}{8}x^2 - \frac{3}{4}x = 2$
41. $\frac{a^2}{2} - \frac{a}{6} = \frac{1}{3}$
42. $\frac{t^2}{5} - \frac{t}{2} = -\frac{1}{5}$
43. $x^2 - \frac{1}{25} = 0$
44. $x^2 - \frac{1}{49} = 0$

45. $(x + 2)(x + 5) = 40$ **46.** $(x + 3)(x - 2) = 24$

47. $4r^3 - 2r^2 - 36r + 18 = 0$ **48.** $y^3 + 3y^2 - 4y - 12 = 0$

49. $9x^3 - 12 = 4x - 27x^2$ **50.** $3x^2 - 4x = 12 - x^3$

51. $2x(x + 1) = 5x(x - 7)$ **52.** $x(x - 3) = 3x(x - 4)$

53. $4p(p - 1) - 24 = 3p(p - 2)$

54. $2w^2 + 2(w - 1) = w(1 - w)$

55. $(x^2 + 5x + 6)(x^2 - 5x - 24) = 0$

56. $(x^2 - 7x + 6)(x^2 + 3x - 4) = 0$

Find all x-intercepts. Verify your intercept(s) graphically by using a graphing calculator.

57. $f(x) = x^2 - 9x + 20$ **58.** $f(x) = x^2 - 4x - 21$

59. $f(x) = 36x^2 - 25$ **60.** $f(x) = 16x^2 - 81$

61. $f(x) = 24x^3 - 14x^2 - 20x$

62. $f(x) = 6x^3 + 15x^2 + 6x$

63. $f(x) = x^3 + 2x^2 - x - 2$

64. $f(x) = 4x^3 - 12x^2 - 9x + 27$

For Exercises 65–68, let $f(x) = x^2 - x - 6$.

65. Find $f(3)$.   **66.** Find $f(-4)$.

67. Find x when $f(x) = 14$.   **68.** Find x when $f(x) = 6$.

For Exercises 69–72, use the graph of $y = \frac{1}{2}x^2 + x - \frac{7}{2}$ shown in Fig. 46 to solve the given equation.

69. $\frac{1}{2}x^2 + x - \frac{7}{2} = 4$ **70.** $\frac{1}{2}x^2 + x - \frac{7}{2} = -2$

71. $\frac{1}{2}x^2 + x - \frac{7}{2} = -4$ **72.** $\frac{1}{2}x^2 + x - \frac{7}{2} = -5$

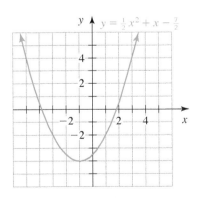

Figure 46 Exercises 69–72

For Exercises 73–76, use the graphs of $y = x^3 - 3x^2 + 1$ and $y = x - 2$ shown in Fig. 47 to solve the given equation or system.

73. $x^3 - 3x^2 + 1 = -3$ **74.** $x^3 - 3x^2 + 1 = 1$

75. $x^3 - 3x^2 + 1 = x - 2$ **76.** $y = x^3 - 3x^2 + 1$
$y = x - 2$

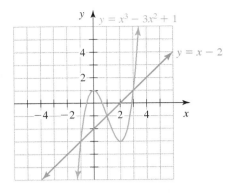

Figure 47 Exercises 73–76

Solve by using "intersect" on a graphing calculator. Round the solution(s) to the second decimal place.

77. $2x^2 - 5x - 3 = -x + 5$ **78.** $-x^2 + 2x + 4 = x - 1$

79. $-x^3 + 4x^2 - 2x = 4 - x$ **80.** $x^3 - 4x^2 + 5 = x - 5$

For Exercises 81–84, solve by referring to the values of the function $y = 3x^2 - 6x + 1$ shown in Table 18.

81. $3x^2 - 6x + 1 = 25$ **82.** $3x^2 - 6x + 1 = 1$

83. $3x^2 - 6x + 1 = -3$ **84.** $3x^2 - 6x + 1 = -2$

Table 18 Exercises 81–84

x	y
−2	25
−1	10
0	1
1	−2
2	1
3	10
4	25

85. The numbers of participants in the Ford Ironman World Championship in Hawaii are shown in Table 19 for various years. Participants attempt to swim 2.4 miles, bike 112 miles, and run 26.2 miles (a marathon).

Table 19 Numbers of Participants in the Ironman World Championship

Year	Number of Participants
1990	1387
1994	1405
1998	1487
2002	1607
2006	1786
2010	1927
2012	2039

Source: *Ford Ironman World Championship*

Let n be the number of participants at t years since 1990. A linear model of the situation is $n = L(t) = 31t + 1301$. An exponential model is $n = E(t) = 1325(1.019)^t$. A quadratic model is $n = Q(t) = t^2 + 8t + 1376$.

a. Use a graphing calculator to draw the graphs of all three models and, in the same viewing window, the scattergram of the data. Which model describes the situation best?

b. Use ZOOM OUT on a graphing calculator to help you determine which model predicts the largest participation for years between 2010 and 2020.

c. Find the n-intercept of each model. Which n-intercept describes the situation best?

d. Use Q to estimate when there were 1396 participants.

86. The numbers of U.S. households with VCRs are shown in Table 20 for various years.

Table 20 Numbers of U.S. Households with VCRs

Year	Number of Households with VCRs (millions)
2005	98.9
2006	97.7
2007	95.2
2008	88.8
2009	82.5
2010	74.3

Source: *The Nielsen Company*

Let $n = f(t)$ be the number (in millions) of U.S. households with VCRs at t years since 2000.

a. Use a graphing calculator to draw a scattergram to describe the data. Is it better to use a linear, exponential, or quadratic function to model the data? Explain.

b. Use a graphing calculator to draw the graph of the model $f(t) = -t^2 + 10t + 74$ and, in the same viewing window, the scattergram of the data. Does the model fit the data well?

c. What is the n-intercept? What does it mean in this situation?

d. Predict when only 18 million households will have VCRs.

87. Moody's Investors Service® evaluates the investment quality of companies. Although a B2 rating is six steps above Moody's worst rating, many companies rated B2 eventually default on their bonds (see Table 21).

Table 21 Percentage of Companies with a B2 Rating That Defaulted on Bonds

Years after Being Rated B2	Percent
2	12
4	24
6	32
8	36
10	41

Source: *Moody's Investors Service*

Let $f(t)$ be the percentage of companies with a B2 rating that defaulted on their bonds at t years since being rated B2. A model of the situation is $f(t) = -\dfrac{1}{3}t^2 + \dfrac{22}{3}t$.

a. Use a graphing calculator to draw the graph of the model and, in the same viewing window, the scattergram of the data. Does the model fit the data well?

b. Find $f(7)$. What does it mean in this situation?

c. Find t when $f(t) = 7$. What does it mean in this situation?

d. Find the t-intercepts. What do they mean in this situation?

88. The United State's annual coal exports are shown in Table 22 for various years.

Table 22 U.S. Coal Exports

Year	Coal Exports (million metric tons)
2004	23
2006	26
2008	39
2010	52
2011	63

Source: *Stifle, Nicolaus, and Co.*

Let $c = f(t)$ be U.S. annual coal exports (in million metric tons) at t years since 2000. A model of the situation is $f(t) = t^2 - 9t + 43$.

a. Use a graphing calculator to draw the graph of the model and, in the same viewing window, the scattergram of the data. Does the model fit the data well?

b. Find the c-intercept. What does it mean in this situation?

c. Find $f(17)$. What does it mean in this situation?

d. Find t when $f(t) = 79$. What does it mean in this situation?

e. In 2011, the United States imported 14 million metric tons of coal (Source: *U.S. Energy Information Administration*). Find the ratio of U.S. coal imports to U.S. coal exports in 2011. Assuming this ratio will be the same in 2018, predict the number of metric tons of coal that will be *imported* in 2018.

89. The percentages of Americans who think labor unions in the United States will become stronger are shown in Table 23 for various years.

Table 23 Percentages of Americans Who Think Labor Unions Will Become Stronger

Year	Percent
2004	21
2005	19
2007	19
2009	22
2011	25

Source: *The Gallup Organization*

Let $p = f(t)$ be the percentage of Americans at t years since 2000 who think labor unions in the United States will become stronger. A model of the situation is $f(t) = \dfrac{1}{4}t^2 - 3t + 28$.

a. Use a graphing calculator to draw the graph of the model and, in the same viewing window, the scattergram of the data. Does the model fit the data fairly well?

b. Find the p-intercept. What does it mean in this situation?

c. Predict the percentage of Americans in 2017 who will think labor unions will become stronger.

d. Predict when 44% of Americans will think labor unions will become stronger.

e. Let $f(t)$ be the percentage of private-sector workers who are in a union at t years since 2000. A reasonable model is $f(t) = -0.25t + 9.45$ (Source: *Bloomberg BNA*). Explain why it is surprising that the percentage of Americans who thought unions would become stronger increased from 2007 to 2011.

90. First-quarter (January through March) Internet advertising revenues are shown in Table 24 for various years.

Table 24 First-Quarter Internet Advertising Revenues

Year	First-Quarter Revenues (billions of dollars)
2000	2.0
2002	1.5
2004	2.2
2006	3.6
2008	5.7
2010	5.9
2012	8.4

Source: *Interactive Advertising Bureau*

Let $r = f(t)$ be first-quarter Internet advertising revenues (in billions of dollars) at t years since 2000. A model of the situation is $f(t) = \frac{1}{25}t^2 + \frac{2}{25}t + \frac{8}{5}$.

a. Use a graphing calculator to draw the graph of the model and, in the same viewing window, the scattergram of the data. Does the model fit the data well?

b. Find the r-intercept. What does it mean in this situation?

c. Predict the first-quarter Internet advertising revenues in 2018.

d. Estimate in which year first-quarter Internet advertising revenues were $3 billion.

91. The total attendance at Broadway shows in New York is shown in Table 25 for various years.

Table 25 Total Attendance at Broadway Shows

Year	Total Attendance (thousands)
2005	11,527
2006	12,003
2007	12,312
2008	12,267
2009	12,250
2010	11,890

Source: *National Arts Index 2012*

Let $f(t)$ be the total attendance (in thousands) at Broadway shows in the year that is t years since 2005. A model of the situation is $f(t) = -98t^2 + 561t + 11{,}536$.

a. Use a graphing calculator to draw the graph of the model and, in the same viewing window, the scattergram of the data. Does the model fit the data well?

b. Estimate the total attendance in 2012.

c. Estimate in which year(s) the total attendance was 11,536 thousand (11.536 million).

d. One possible reason for the decrease in attendance from 2008 to 2010 is that the economy performed poorly during that period. Assuming the economy improves and attendance increases in the future, will f model the situation well? Explain.

92. New-home sales rates (in thousands of homes per year) are shown in Table 26 for July of various years.

Table 26 New-Home Sales Rates in July

Year	Sales Rate (thousands of homes per year)
2005	1348
2006	1030
2007	800
2008	479
2009	402
2010	289
2011	300
2012	381

Source: *Commerce Department*

Let $f(t)$ be the new-home sales rate (in thousands of homes per year) in July at t years since 2005. A model of the situation is $f(t) = 34t^2 - 383t + 1370$.

a. Use a graphing calculator to draw the graph of the model and, in the same viewing window, the scattergram of the data. Does the model fit the data well?

b. Predict the sales rate in July 2017.

c. Predict in which year the sales rate in July will be 1370 thousand homes (1.37 million homes) per year.

d. The decrease in new-home sales rates in July from 2005 to 2010 is likely due to the high-risk home loans and poor economy during that period. Assuming the economy improves and new-home sales rates increase in the future, is it possible f will model the situation well? Explain.

93. A rectangular rug has an area of 60 square feet. If its length is 2 feet more than twice its width, find the dimensions of the rug.

94. A rectangular garden has an area of 65 square feet. If its length is 3 feet less than twice its width, find the dimensions of the garden.

95. The length of a rectangle is 4 centimeters more than the width. If both the width and length were doubled, the area would be 48 square centimeters. Find the dimensions of the original rectangle.

96. The length of a rectangle is 6 meters more than the width. If both the width and length were doubled, the area would be 108 square meters. Find the dimensions of the original rectangle.

97. A person has a rectangular garden with a width of 6 feet and a length of 10 feet. To form a border of uniform width, he plans to place mulch around the outside of the garden. If he has just enough mulch to cover 80 square feet of land, determine the width of the border.

98. A person has a rectangular garden with a width of 8 feet and a length of 12 feet. To form a border of uniform width, she plans to put sod around the outside of the garden. If she has just enough sod to cover 44 square feet of land, determine the width of the border.

99. A rectangular painting (not including the frame) has a width of 10 inches and a length of 14 inches. If the area of the frame (of uniform width) is 52 square inches, what is the width of the frame?

100. A rectangular painting (not including the frame) has a width of 9 inches and a length of 15 inches. If the area of the frame (of uniform width) is 112 square inches, what is the width of the frame?

Concepts

101. A student tries to solve the equation $x^2 = x$:

$$x^2 = x$$
$$\frac{x^2}{x} = \frac{x}{x}$$
$$x = 1$$

Describe any errors. Then solve the equation correctly.

102. A student tries to solve the equation $(x - 3)(x - 7) = 12$:

$$(x - 3)(x - 7) = 12$$
$$x - 3 = 2 \quad \text{or} \quad x - 7 = 6$$
$$x = 5 \quad \text{or} \quad x = 13$$

Describe any errors. Then solve the equation correctly.

103. A student tries to solve the equation $x^3 + 4x^2 - 9x - 36 = 0$:

$$x^3 + 4x^2 - 9x - 36 = 0$$
$$x^2(x + 4) - 9(x + 4) = 0$$
$$x + 4 = 0$$
$$x = -4$$

Describe any errors. Then solve the equation correctly.

104. A student tries to solve the equation $2x^2 - 18x + 36 = 0$:

$$2x^2 - 18x + 36 = 0$$
$$2\left(x^2 - 9x + 18\right) = 0$$
$$2(x - 3)(x - 6) = 0$$
$$x = 2, x = 3, \text{ or } x = 6$$

Describe any errors. Then solve the equation correctly.

105. Give an example of a function whose x-intercepts are $(-5, 0)$ and $(1, 0)$. Verify your work by using a graphing calculator.

106. Give three examples of quadratic functions for which each function's only x-intercept is $(2, 0)$.

107. Give an example of a cubic equation in one variable whose solutions are $-4, 0$, and 2.

108. Give an example of a quadratic equation in one variable that has 4 as its only solution.

109. The graph of a function h is sketched in Fig. 48. Find a possible equation of h. Verify your equation by using a graphing calculator.

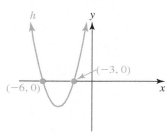

Figure 48 Exercise 109

110. The graph of a function g is sketched in Fig. 49. Find a possible equation of g. Verify your equation by using a graphing calculator.

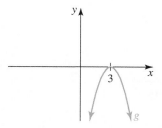

Figure 49 Exercise 110

111. Explain why a quadratic equation in one variable cannot have three solutions.

112. Explain how to solve a quadratic or cubic equation in one variable.

Related Review

Factor or solve, as appropriate.

113. $x^2 + 5x + 6$

114. $25x^2 - 64 = 0$

115. $x^2 + 5x + 6 = 0$

116. $25x^2 - 64$

117. $3p^3 + 8p^2 + 4p = 0$

118. $4w^3 - 20w^2 - 9w + 45$

119. $3p^3 + 8p^2 + 4p$

120. $4w^3 - 20w^2 - 9w + 45 = 0$

Solve. Round approximate solutions to the fourth decimal place.

121. $3x^2(x - 4) = 12x(x - 3)$

122. $4(3x - 5) - 2(5x + 1) = 20$

123. $3b^8 + 39 = 217$

124. $4w^3 - 20w^2 - w = -5$

125. $5(2)^t - 24 = 97$

126. $\log_4(r^3) = 5$

127. $\log(x + 3) + \log(x + 6) = 1$

128. $\log_2(2x + 3) + \log_2(x - 2) = 2$

Expressions, Equations, Functions, and Graphs

Give an example of the following. Then solve, simplify, or graph, as appropriate.

129. quadratic function

130. system of two linear equations in two variables

131. quadratic equation in one variable

132. linear function

133. exponential equation in one variable

134. difference of two logarithmic expressions with equal bases

Taking it to the Lab

Climate Change Lab (continued from Chapter 3)

Throughout our study of climate change, we have used the IPCC's yardstick that, by 2050, carbon dioxide emissions should be 0.9 metric ton per person per year. Yet it is difficult to imagine developed countries, with average annual carbon dioxide emissions of 10.2 metric tons per person today, reducing their emissions by 91% to meet the IPCC's recommendation. In particular, it is difficult to imagine that the United States will reduce its annual carbon dioxide emissions of 18.1 metric tons per person by 95% to reach that desired level.

Recall from the Climate Change Lab in Chapter 2 that the IPCC's yardstick is equivalent to recommending that 2050 carbon dioxide emissions be 60% less than the carbon dioxide emissions in 1990. We can reach this goal without reducing per-person carbon dioxide emissions at all—if we reduce world population.

Reducing world population seems impossible, because it is currently growing by leaps and bounds. The United Nations (U.N.) predicts that, from 2000 to 2050, world population will increase from 6.09 billion to 9.3 billion—a 53% increase (see Table 27).

Table 27 World Population

Year	Population (billions)	Year	Population (billions)
A.D. 1	0.17	1600	0.55
200	0.19	1800	0.81
400	0.19	2000	6.09
600	0.20	2025	7.9
800	0.22	2050	9.3
1000	0.25	2075	9.9
1200	0.36	2100	10.1
1400	0.35		

Source: *The Cambridge Factfinder*

Despite the large population growth in the first half of the century, the population will probably not grow nearly as quickly in the second half. The U.N. has predicted the population will increase from 9.3 billion in 2050 to 10.1 billion in 2100—a mere 9% increase. In fact, the U.N. has predicted the rate of change in 2100 will be very close to zero and might even be negative.

The U.N. uses a complicated model to make these predictions. A simpler model that matches well with the U.N. model for the years 2000 to 2100 is the quadratic function $f(t) = -0.00046t^2 + 0.086t + 6.08$, where $p = f(t)$ is world population (in billions) at t years since 2000.

Using the yardstick of 2050 carbon emissions at 60% less than the 21.6 billion metric tons of carbon dioxide emissions in 1990, we can calculate the largest carbon dioxide emissions that Earth can handle each year:

$$0.40(21.6) = 8.64 \text{ billion metric tons}$$

Next, we will consider two scenarios that stay within this limit.

For our first scenario, let's assume that in the future each person in the world emits 18.1 metric tons per year, the current per-person annual emissions rate for Americans (see Table 29). Then we could still be at the yearly limit of 8.64 billion metric tons of carbon dioxide if the world population were a mere 477 million. By modeling the data in Table 28, we could show that U.S. population alone will reach 477 million before 2080. Common sense dictates that countries would never voluntarily lower their populations enough to help reach this level.

Table 28 United States Population

Year	U.S. Population (billions)
1960	0.18
1970	0.21
1980	0.23
1990	0.25
2000	0.28
2010	0.31

Source: *U.S. Census Bureau; The Cambridge Factfinder*

For our second scenario, let's make an assumption about how low carbon dioxide emissions could be. Although 0.9 metric ton per person per year seems unreachable, perhaps 5.4 metric tons per person per year is attainable. After all, Sweden, Switzerland, and France already have per-person annual carbon dioxide emissions at or near 5.4 metric tons (see Table 29). If all countries annually produced 5.4 metric tons of carbon dioxide per person, Earth could handle 1.6 billion people.

Table 29 Gross Domestic Product (GDP) Ranks; Per-Person GDPs; and Per-Person Annual Carbon Emissions

Country	2010 GDP Rank	2010 Per-Person GDP (thousands of dollars)	2010 Per-Person Carbon Dioxide Emissions (metric tons)
Sweden	22	39.0	5.3
Switzerland	19	46.4	5.4
France	5	34.1	5.5
Italy	8	32.0	6.7
United Kingdom	6	35.7	7.9
Austria	25	40.0	8.1
Denmark	31	40.2	8.4
Japan	3	33.7	8.9
Germany	4	37.4	9.3
Belgium	21	37.6	9.9
Norway	23	57.2	10.5
Australia	15	38.2	16.0
United States	1	47.2	18.1
Netherlands	16	42.2	31.9

Source: *World Bank; Carbon Dioxide Information Analysis Center*

The first scenario reveals that we will not be able to get carbon dioxide emissions under control merely by reducing world population. Earlier, we observed that simply reducing per-person emissions will not be acceptable. So, as the second scenario suggests, it is only by reducing both world population and per-person emissions that we can reach the IPCC's goal.

Analyzing the Situation

1. Let w be world population (in billions of people) in the year t. For example, $t = 2005$ represents the year 2005.

   a. Use a graphing calculator to draw a scattergram of world population data.

   b. Calculate the changes in world population for every 200 (or 199) years up until 2000.

   c. When has world population grown most? Explain why it is surprising that world population will increase by only 0.2 billion from 2075 to 2100.

2. Now let w be world population (in billions of people) at t years *since 2000*.

   a. Create a scattergram for the years 2000–2100 that are listed in Table 27. In the same viewing window, draw a graph of the scattergram and the quadratic world population model f provided earlier.

   b. Use the quadratic model f to predict world population for the years 2000, 2025, 2050, 2075, and 2100.

   c. Does the quadratic model f make predictions that are similar to the U.N. predictions listed in Table 27? Explain.

3. In Problem 7 of the Climate Change Lab in Chapter 2, you found a model of the U.S. population (in billions) at t years since 1950. If you didn't find such an equation, find it now. Then use it to predict when the U.S. population will reach 477 million. Finally, compare your result with the claim that this will happen before 2080.

4. Perform a unit analysis for the estimate of the amount of carbon dioxide emissions (in billions of tons of carbon) that Earth can withstand each year:

$$0.40(21.6) = 8.64 \text{ billion metric tons}$$

   Explain why this computation gives the amount of carbon dioxide emissions that Earth can withstand each year.

5. Show the work for the claim that if everyone in the world emitted carbon dioxide as Americans do, then Earth could support only 477 million people.

6. Verify the claim that if worldwide annual carbon dioxide emissions were 5.4 tons of carbon dioxide per person, then Earth could support 1.6 billion people.

Projectile Lab

In this lab, you will estimate your vertical throwing speed.

Materials

You will need at least three people and the following items:

1. A baseball or other ball (a solid, heavy ball works best)

2. A digital stopwatch or some other timing device

Recording of Data

The first person should throw the ball straight up and say "Mark" at the moment the ball is released. The second person should hold his or her hand at the position of the ball's release and should say "Mark" when the ball returns to its initial height. The third person should begin timing when the first person says "Mark" and stop timing when the second person says "Mark."

Theory

Throughout this lab, we will use "height" to mean distance above the ground. Let h_0 be the ball's height (in feet) at the moment of its release. Let v_0 be the ball's speed (in feet per second) at that moment. We call h_0 the *initial height* and v_0 the *initial speed*. The ball's height h (in feet) is given by

$$h = -16t^2 + v_0 t + h_0$$

where t is the time (in seconds) since the ball was released. So, t and h are variables and v_0 and h_0 are constants.

Analyzing the Situation

1. Substitute 0 for t in the equation $h = -16t^2 + v_0 t + h_0$ and solve for h. Explain why your work shows that h_0 represents the initial height.

2. What was the actual initial height of the ball in your experiment? Substitute this value for h_0 in the equation $h = -16t^2 + v_0 t + h_0$.

3. How long did it take for the ball to return to its initial height? Substitute that time for t and the initial height for h in the equation you found in Problem 2. Then solve for v_0. What does your value for v_0 mean in this situation?

4. Substitute the value for v_0 that you found in Problem 3 into the equation you found in Problem 2. [**Hint:** Your equation should still have the variables t and h in it.]

5. Use a graphing calculator to draw a graph of your model. Use a pencil and paper to copy the graph.

6. What is the h-intercept of the model? What does it mean in this situation?

7. Use the model to estimate the height of the ball at 1 second.

Chapter Summary

Key Points of Chapter 6

Section 6.1   Adding and Subtracting Polynomial Expressions and Functions

Monomial	A **monomial** is a constant, a variable, or a product of a constant and one or more variables raised to *counting-number* powers.
Polynomial	A **polynomial,** or **polynomial expression,** is a monomial or a sum of monomials.
Degree	The **degree of a term** in one variable is the exponent on the variable. The degree of a term in two or more variables is the sum of the exponents on the variables. The **degree of a polynomial** is the highest degree of any nonzero term of the polynomial.
Like terms	**Like terms** either are constant terms or are variable terms that contain the same variable(s) raised to exactly the same power(s).
Combine like terms	To combine like terms, add the coefficients of the terms.
Add polynomials	To add polynomials, combine like terms.
Subtract polynomials	To subtract polynomials, first distribute -1; then combine like terms.
Quadratic function	A **quadratic function** is a function whose equation can be put into the form $$f(x) = ax^2 + bx + c$$ where $a \neq 0$. This form is called the **standard form.**
Cubic function	A **cubic function** is a function whose equation can be put into the form $$f(x) = ax^3 + bx^2 + cx + d$$ where $a \neq 0$.
Sum function and difference function	If f and g are functions and x is in the domain of both functions, then we can form the following functions: • **Sum function $f + g$,** where $(f + g)(x) = f(x) + g(x)$ • **Difference function $f - g$,** where $(f - g)(x) = f(x) - g(x)$
Meaning of a difference	If a difference $A - B$ is positive, then A is more than B. If a difference $A - B$ is negative, then A is less than B.

Section 6.2   Multiplying Polynomial Expressions and Functions

Multiply polynomials	To multiply two polynomials, multiply each term in the first polynomial by each term in the second polynomial. Then combine like terms if possible.
Square of a sum	$(A + B)^2 = A^2 + 2AB + B^2$
Square of a difference	$(A - B)^2 = A^2 - 2AB + B^2$
Product of binomial conjugates	$(A + B)(A - B) = A^2 - B^2$
Product function	If f and g are functions and x is in the domain of both functions, then we can form the **product function $f \cdot g$:** $(f \cdot g)(x) = f(x) \cdot g(x)$.

Section 6.3   Dividing Polynomials: Long Division and Synthetic Division

Dividing a polynomial by a monomial	To divide a polynomial by a monomial, use the property $\dfrac{A + C}{B} = \dfrac{A}{B} + \dfrac{C}{B}$, where B is nonzero, to divide each term of the polynomial by the monomial.

Section 6.3 Dividing Polynomials: Long Division and Synthetic Division (*Continued*)

Dividing a polynomial by a binomial	To divide a polynomial by a binomial, we can use long division.
Synthetic division	To perform synthetic division, the divisor must be of the form $x - a$. The first step is to write the dividend in descending order. Then we write a inside the ⌋ and write the coefficients of the dividend outside it.

Section 6.4 Factoring Trinomials of the Form $x^2 + bx + c$; Factoring Out the GCF

Factor	We **factor** a polynomial by writing it as a product.
Multiplying versus factoring	Multiplying and factoring are reverse processes.
Factoring $x^2 + bx + c$	To factor $x^2 + bx + c$, look for two integers p and q whose product is c and whose sum is b. That is, $pq = c$ and $p + q = b$. If such integers exist, the factored polynomial is $(x + p)(x + q)$.
Factoring $x^2 + bx + c$ with c positive	To factor a trinomial of the form $x^2 + bx + c$ with a positive constant term c, • If b is positive, look for two *positive* integers whose product is c and whose sum is b. • If b is negative, look for two *negative* integers whose product is c and whose sum is b.
Factoring $x^2 + bx + c$ with c negative	To factor a trinomial of the form $x^2 + bx + c$ with a negative constant term, c, look for two integers with *different* signs whose product is c and whose sum is b.
Prime polynomial	A polynomial that cannot be factored is called **prime.**
GCF	The **greatest common factor (GCF)** of two or more terms is the monomial with the largest coefficient and the highest degree that is a factor of all the terms.
Factor out GCF	When the leading coefficient of a polynomial is positive and the GCF is not 1, first factor out the GCF.
Completely factor	When factoring a polynomial, always *completely* factor it.
Factoring when the leading coefficient is negative	When the leading coefficient of a polynomial is negative, first factor out the opposite of the GCF.

Section 6.5 Factoring Polynomials

Factoring by grouping	For a polynomial with four terms, we **factor by grouping** (if it can be done) by **1.** Factoring the first two terms and the last two terms. **2.** Factoring out the binomial GCF.
Factoring $ax^2 + bx + c$ by trial and error	To **factor a trinomial** of the form $ax^2 + bx + c$ **by trial and error,** identify possible products by using the fact that if the trinomial can be factored as a product of two binomials, then the product of the coefficients of the first terms of the binomials is equal to a and the product of the last terms of the binomials is equal to c. To find the correct factored expression, multiply the possible products and identify those for which the coefficient of x is b.
Factoring $ax^2 + bx + c$ by grouping (*ac* method)	To **factor a trinomial** of the form $ax^2 + bx + c$ **by grouping** (if it can be done), **1.** Find pairs of numbers whose product is ac. **2.** Determine which of the pairs of numbers from step 1 has the sum b. Call this pair of numbers m and n. **3.** Write the bx term as $mx + nx$: $$ax^2 + bx + c = ax^2 + mx + nx + c$$ **4.** Factor $ax^2 + mx + nx + c$ by grouping. Another name for this technique is the ***ac* method.**

Section 6.6   Factoring Special Binomials; A Factoring Strategy

Difference of two squares

$$A^2 - B^2 = (A + B)(A - B)$$

Sum of squares

Except for factoring out the GCF, a sum of squares cannot be factored.

Sum of two cubes

$$A^3 + B^3 = (A + B)(A^2 - AB + B^2)$$

Difference of two cubes

$$A^3 - B^3 = (A - B)(A^2 + AB + B^2)$$

Factoring strategy

These five steps can be used to factor many polynomials (steps 2–4 can be applied to the entire polynomial or to a factor of the polynomial):

1. If the leading coefficient is positive and the GCF is not 1, factor out the GCF. If the leading coefficient is negative, factor out the opposite of the GCF.

2. For a binomial, try using one of the properties for the difference of two squares, the sum of two cubes, or the difference of two cubes.

3. For a trinomial of the form $ax^2 + bx + c$,
   a. If $a = 1$, try to find two integers whose product is c and whose sum is b.
   b. If $a \neq 1$, try to factor by using trial and error or by grouping.

4. For an expression with four terms, try factoring by grouping.

5. Continue applying steps 2–4 until the polynomial is completely factored.

Section 6.7   Using Factoring to Solve Polynomial Equations

Quadratic equation

A **quadratic equation in one variable** is an equation that can be put into the form $ax^2 + bx + c = 0$, where a, b, and c are constants and $a \neq 0$.

Zero factor property

Let A and B be real numbers. If $AB = 0$, then $A = 0$ or $B = 0$.

Connection between x-intercepts and solutions

Let f be a function. If k is a real-number solution of the equation $f(x) = 0$, then $(k, 0)$ is an x-intercept of the graph of the function f. Also, if $(k, 0)$ is an x-intercept of the graph of f, then k is a solution of $f(x) = 0$.

Number of solutions: quadratic equation

The solution set of a quadratic equation in one variable may contain two real numbers, one real number, or no real numbers.

Cubic equation

A **cubic equation in one variable** is an equation that can be put into the form

$$ax^3 + bx^2 + cx + d = 0$$

where a, b, c, and d are constants and $a \neq 0$.

Solving quadratic or cubic equations by factoring

If an equation can be solved by factoring, we solve it by the following steps:

1. Write the equation so one side of the equation is equal to zero.

2. Factor the nonzero side of the equation.

3. Apply the zero factor property.

4. Solve each equation that results from applying the zero factor property.

Number of solutions: cubic equation

The solution set of a cubic equation in one variable may contain one, two, or three real numbers.

Quadratic model

A **quadratic model** is a quadratic function, or its graph, that describes the relationship between two quantities in an authentic situation.

Area of a rectangle

The area A of a rectangle is given by the formula $A = LW$, where L is the length of the rectangle and W is the width.

Chapter 6 Review Exercises

For Exercises 1 and 2, perform the operation.

1. $\left(-7x^3 + 5x^2 - 9\right) + \left(2x^3 - 8x^2 + 3x\right)$

2. $\left(5a^3b - 2a^2b^2 + 9ab^3\right) - \left(8a^3b + 4a^2b^2 - ab^3\right)$

3. For $f(x) = 3x^2 - 5x + 2$, find $f(-2)$.

Values of a quadratic function f are listed in Table 30. For Exercises 4 and 5, refer to this table.

4. Find $f(2)$.

5. Find x when $f(x) = 9$.

Table 30 Some Values of a Quadratic Function f (Exercises 4 and 5)

x	y
0	1
1	6
2	9
3	10
4	9
5	6
6	1

For $f(x) = 3x^3 - 7x^2 - 4x + 2$ and $g(x) = -2x^3 + 5x^2 - 3x + 1$, find an equation of the given function; then evaluate the function at the indicated value.

6. $(f + g)(x)$, $(f + g)(2)$

7. $(f - g)(x)$, $(f - g)(-3)$

Find the product or simplify, as appropriate.

8. $(x - 7)(x + 7)$

9. $8a^2b\left(-5a^3b^5\right)$

10. $(4p + 9t)(2p - 5t)$

11. $(4x - 3)\left(5x^2 - 2x + 4\right)$

12. $(3x + 7y)^2$

13. $\left(6p^2 - 9t^3\right)\left(6p^2 + 9t^3\right)$

14. $-3rt^3\left(2r^2 - 5rt + 3t^2\right)$

15. $-4x(3x - 2)^2$

16. $\left(3m^2 - mp + 2p^2\right)\left(2m^2 + 3mp - 4p^2\right)$

For Exercises 17 and 18, if $f(x) = x^2 - 2x$, find the following.

17. $f(a - 4)$

18. $f(a + 3) - f(a)$

19. Write the function $f(x) = -2(x - 4)^2 + 3$ in standard form.

20. For $f(x) = 3x - 7$ and $g(x) = 2x^2 - 4x + 3$, find an equation of the product function $f \cdot g$. Then find $(f \cdot g)(3)$.

Divide.

21. $\dfrac{6x^5 - 2x^3 + 9x}{-3x^2}$

22. $\dfrac{20w^4p + 15w^3p^2 - 35w^2p^3}{5w^2p}$

Perform long division.

23. $\dfrac{8x^2 - 6x - 8}{2x + 1}$

24. $\dfrac{6x^3 - 16x^2 + 17x - 2}{3x - 2}$

25. $\dfrac{64b^3 - 27}{4b - 3}$

Perform synthetic division.

26. $\dfrac{2x^3 - 10x^2 + 15x - 4}{x - 3}$

27. $\dfrac{5y^2 - 8 + 3y^3 - 6y}{y + 2}$

28. $\dfrac{x^3 + x^2 + 16}{x + 3}$

Factor when possible.

29. $x^2 - 25$

30. $x^2 - 12x + 36$

31. $a^2 + 5ab - 36b^2$

32. $16a^5b^3 - 20a^3b^2$

33. $-11x - 24 + x^2$

34. $3w^2 - 5wy - 8y^2$

35. $81t^4 - 16w^4$

36. $6x^4 + 20x^3 - 16x^2$

37. $36x^2 + 49$

38. $x^2 - 3x - 54$

39. $2y^3 - 54$

40. $5r^2t + 30rt^2 + 45t^3$

41. $2ax - 10ay - 3bx + 15by$

For Exercises 42–48, solve.

42. $x^2 - 2x - 24 = 0$

43. $64t^2 = 9$

44. $3x(x + 10) = 6x^3$

45. $x^3 - 4x = 12 - 3x^2$

46. $\dfrac{m^2}{2} - \dfrac{7m}{6} + \dfrac{1}{3} = 0$

47. $32x^2 = 24x$

48. $4p(5p - 6) = (2p + 3)(2p - 3)$

49. Find all x-intercepts of the graph of $f(x) = 3x^3 + 3x^2 - 18x$.

For Exercises 50 and 51, use the graphs of $y = \dfrac{1}{2}x^2 + 2x - \dfrac{1}{2}$ and $y = x + 1$ shown in Fig. 50 to solve the given equation or system.

50. $\dfrac{1}{2}x^2 + 2x - \dfrac{1}{2} = 2$

51. $\dfrac{1}{2}x^2 + 2x - \dfrac{1}{2} = x + 1$

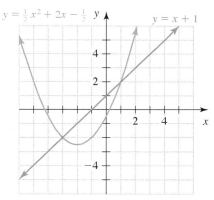

Figure 50 Exercises 50 and 51

52. The number (in thousands) of bank tellers is modeled by the function $B(t) = -2.42t^2 + 80.8t - 76$, where t is the number of years since 1990 (see Table 31). The number (in thousands) of ATMs is modeled by the function $A(t) = -2.29t^2 + 76.8t - 227$, where t is the number of years since 1990.

Table 31 Numbers of Bank Tellers and ATMs

Year	Number of Bank Tellers (thousands)	Number of ATMs (thousands)
1999	453	273
2001	533	352
2003	539	383
2005	599	395
2007	608	425
2009	577	402

Source: *American Bankers Association*

a. Find an equation of the sum function $B + A$.
b. Perform a unit analysis of the expression $B(t) + A(t)$.
c. Find $(B + A)(22)$. What does it mean in this situation?
d. Find an equation of the difference function $B - A$.
e. Find $(B - A)(22)$. What does it mean in this situation?

53. The total numbers of prescriptions of synthetic narcotics, morphine/opium derivatives, and codeine—all powerful and potentially addictive drugs—are shown in Table 32 for various years.

Table 32 Total Numbers of Prescriptions of Synthetic Narcotics, Morphine/Opium Derivatives, and Codeine

Year	Total Number of Prescriptions (millions)
2006	218
2007	233
2008	242
2009	247
2010	249
2011	245

Source: *IMS Health*

Let $f(t)$ be the total number (in millions) of prescriptions of synthetic narcotics, morphine/opium derivatives, and codeine in the year that is t years since 2005. A reasonable model is $f(t) = -2t^2 + 19t + 203$.

a. Use a graphing calculator to draw the graph of the model and, in the same viewing window, the scattergram of the data. Does the model fit the data well?
b. Estimate the total number of prescriptions of synthetic narcotics, morphine/opium derivatives, and codeine in 2012.
c. Predict in which year the total number of prescriptions of synthetic narcotics, morphine/opium derivatives, and codeine will be 193 million prescriptions.

54. The length of a rectangle is 8 meters more than the width. If both the width and length were doubled, the area would be 192 square meters. Find the dimensions of the original rectangle.

Chapter 6 Test

1. Find the sum:
$$\left(4a^3b - 9a^2b^2 - 2ab^3\right) + \left(-5a^3b + 4a^2b^2 + 3ab^3\right)$$

2. For $f(x) = 4x^2 + 5x - 9$ and $g(x) = 6x^2 - 3x + 7$, find an equation of the difference function $f - g$; then find $(f - g)(-2)$.

For Exercises 3–6, refer to Fig. 51.

3. Find $f(-3)$.
4. Find x when $f(x) = 3$.
5. Find x when $f(x) = 1$.
6. Find x when $f(x) = -3$.

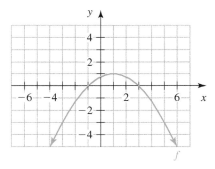

Figure 51 Exercises 3–6

For Exercises 7–12, find the product or simplify, as appropriate.

7. $-2xy^2\left(7x^2 - 3xy + 6y^2\right)$
8. $(4x - 7y)(3x + 5y)$
9. $(2w - 5t)\left(3w^2 - wt + 4t^2\right)$
10. $3x(2x + 3)^2$
11. $\left(3x^2 + x - 5\right)\left(2x^2 + 4x - 1\right)$
12. $\left(4x^2 + 9y^2\right)\left(4x^2 - 9y^2\right)$

13. For $f(x) = x^2 - 3x$, find $f(a - 5)$.
14. Write $f(x) = -3(x + 4)^2 - 7$ in standard form.
15. For $f(x) = 2x^2 - 5x + 4$ and $g(x) = 3x - 2$, find an equation of the product function $f \cdot g$; then find $(f \cdot g)(3)$.

16. Divide: $\dfrac{8a^4b - 12a^3b^2 - 20a^2b^3}{4ab^2}$

17. Perform long division: $\dfrac{14x - 18 + 8x^2}{4x - 3}$

18. Perform synthetic division: $\dfrac{4x^3 + 10x^2 - 5x + 1}{x + 3}$

Factor when possible.

19. $x^2 - 10x - 24$
20. $18x + 2x^3 - 12x^2$
21. $-16x^2 - 26x + 12$
22. $9m^2 - 64t^2$
23. $16a^4b - 36a^3b^2 + 18a^2b^3$
24. $54m^3 + 128p^3$

For Exercises 25–29, solve.

25. $25x^2 = 16$
26. $5w^3 - 15w^2 - 50w = 0$
27. $(2x - 7)(x - 3) = 10$
28. $2t^3 + 3t^2 = 18t + 27$
29. $3x(2x - 5) + 4x = 2(x - 3)$

30. Find all x-intercepts of the graph of $f(x) = 10x^2 - 19x + 6$.

31. Use "intersect" on a graphing calculator to solve the equation $\dfrac{1}{2}x^2 - \dfrac{2}{3}x - \dfrac{7}{4} = -\dfrac{3}{5}x + \dfrac{1}{2}$. Round your result(s) to the second decimal place.

32. The death rate from heart disease (number of deaths per 100,000 people) $R(t)$ in the United States is modeled by the function $R(t) = -7.8t + 564$, where t is the number of years since 1960 (see Table 33). The U.S. population (in 100,000s of people) $P(t)$ is modeled by the equation $P(t) = 26t + 1784$, where t is the number of years since 1960.

Table 33 Death Rates from Heart Disease; U.S. Population

Year	Death Rate (number of deaths per 100,000 people)	Population (in 100,000s)
1960	559	1807
1970	493	2051
1980	412	2277
1990	322	2501
2000	258	2824
2008	187	3048

Sources: *U.S. Center for Health Statistics; U.S. Census Bureau*

a. Check that the models fit the data well.
b. Find an equation of the product function $R \cdot P$.
c. Perform a unit analysis of the expression $R(t) \cdot P(t)$.
d. Find $(R \cdot P)(58)$. What does it mean in this situation?
e. Use a graphing calculator graph to determine whether the function $R \cdot P$ is increasing, decreasing, or neither for values of t between 5 and 60. What does your result mean in this situation? Explain how that is possible, given that U.S. population has been increasing.

33. Opium cultivations in Southeast Asia are shown in Table 34 for various years. A *hectare* is equal to 2.471 acres.

Table 34 Opium Cultivations in Southeast Asia

Year	Opium Cultivations (thousands of hectares)
2008	30
2009	34
2010	41
2011	47
2012	58

Source: *United Nations Office on Drugs and Crime*

Let $f(t)$ be the opium cultivation (in thousands of hectares) in Southeast Asia at t years since 2000. A reasonable model is $f(t) = t^2 - 13t + 70$.

a. Use a graphing calculator to draw the graph of the model and, in the same viewing window, the scattergram of the data. Does the model fit the data well?
b. Find $f(17)$. What does it mean in this situation?
c. Find t when $f(t) = 100$. What does it mean in this situation?

34. A rectangular painting (not including the frame) has a width of 11 inches and a length of 15 inches. If the area of the frame (of uniform width) is 120 square inches, what is the width of the frame?

Quadratic Functions

Would you say you are very happy, in general? The percentages of Americans who say they are "very happy" are shown in Table 1 for various years. Interestingly, the percentage decreased from 1990 to 2000, even though the economy performed quite well during that period. In Exercise 69 of Homework 7.3, we will predict the percentage of people who will say they are "very happy" in 2019.

In Chapter 6, we worked with polynomial expressions and equations. In this chapter, we will narrow our focus to quadratic expressions and equations. In particular, in Sections 7.1 and 7.2, we will graph quadratic functions. In Sections 7.3–7.5, we will discuss three nonfactoring methods of solving quadratic equations in one variable. In Sections 7.6 and 7.7, we will solve *systems of linear equations in three variables* to help us find equations of parabolas and quadratic models. Finally, in Section 7.8, we will use many of the skills learned earlier in this chapter to help us make estimates and predictions about authentic situations, such as the age at which Americans are most likely to forget to do something special for their significant other on Valentine's Day.

Table 1 Percentages of Americans Who Say They Are "Very Happy"

Year	Percent
1972	30
1980	35
1990	36
2000	34
2010	29

Source: *National Opinion Research Center*

▼7.1 Graphing Quadratic Functions in Vertex Form

Objectives

» Know the *vertex form* of a quadratic function.

» Graph a quadratic function in vertex form.

» Find the domain and range of a quadratic function.

» Find a quadratic model in vertex form.

In this section, we will work with parabolas. As we saw in Section 6.1, each parabola has a vertex and an axis of symmetry (see Figs. 1 and 2). Recall that the part of the parabola that lies to the left of the axis of symmetry is the mirror reflection of the part that lies to the right.

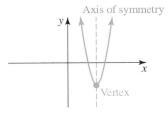

Figure 1 A parabola that opens upward

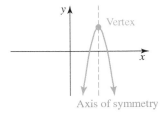

Figure 2 A parabola that opens downward

Vertex Form

Recall from Section 6.1 that a quadratic function is a function whose equation can be put into the standard form $f(x) = ax^2 + bx + c$, where $a \neq 0$, and that the graph of the function is a parabola. Here we will work with equations in another form, called *vertex form:* $f(x) = a(x - h)^2 + k$, where $a \neq 0$. Any equation in either of these two forms can be written in the other form. So, a function in vertex form is quadratic, and its graph is a parabola.

> **Vertex Form of a Quadratic Function**
>
> Let $f(x) = a(x - h)^2 + k$, where $a \neq 0$. Then f is a quadratic function, and its graph is a parabola. We say the equation is in **vertex form.**

Here are some quadratic functions in vertex form:

$$f(x) = 3(x - 5)^2 + 4 \qquad g(x) = -4(x + 9)^2 - 1 \qquad h(x) = 6x^2 - 8 \qquad k(x) = x^2$$

We will see later in this section that, for a quadratic function in vertex form, we can find the vertex quickly.

Graphs of Quadratic Functions of the Form $f(x) = ax^2$

To graph quadratic functions in vertex form $f(x) = a(x - h)^2 + k$, we begin by exploring graphs of equations of the form $f(x) = ax^2$ (where $h = 0$ and $k = 0$).

Table 2 Input–Output Pairs of $f(x) = x^2$ and $g(x) = 2x^2$

x	$f(x) = x^2$	$g(x) = 2x^2$
-3	9	18
-2	4	8
-1	1	2
0	0	0
1	1	2
2	4	8
3	9	18

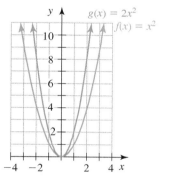

Figure 3 Graphs of $f(x) = x^2$ and $g(x) = 2x^2$

> **Example 1** Stretching a Graph Vertically

Compare the graph of $g(x) = 2x^2$ with the graph of $f(x) = x^2$.

Solution

We list input–output pairs of f and g in Table 2 and sketch the graphs of f and g in Fig. 3. For example, $g(-2) = 2(-2)^2 = 2(4) = 8$. Therefore, $(-2, 8)$ is a point on the graph of g.

For each value of x, the value of y is twice as large for $g(x) = 2x^2$ as it is for $f(x) = x^2$ (see Table 2). Therefore, the graph of g appears steeper (narrower) than the graph of f. Also, notice that the vertex for both functions is the point $(0, 0)$.

> **Example 2** Reflecting a Graph across the x-Axis

Compare the graph of $f(x) = \frac{1}{2}x^2$ with the graph of $g(x) = -\frac{1}{2}x^2$.

Solution

We list input–output pairs of f and g in Table 3 and sketch the graphs of f and g in Fig. 4.

Table 3 Input–Output Pairs of $f(x) = \frac{1}{2}x^2$ and $g(x) = -\frac{1}{2}x^2$

x	$f(x) = \frac{1}{2}x^2$	$g(x) = -\frac{1}{2}x^2$
-3	4.5	-4.5
-2	2	-2
-1	0.5	-0.5
0	0	0
1	0.5	-0.5
2	2	-2
3	4.5	-4.5

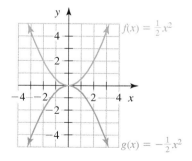

Figure 4 Graphs of $f(x) = \frac{1}{2}x^2$ and $g(x) = -\frac{1}{2}x^2$

The graph of $g(x) = -\frac{1}{2}x^2$ is the reflection across the x-axis of the graph of $f(x) = \frac{1}{2}x^2$. To see why, note that, for each value of x, the value of y for $g(x) = -\frac{1}{2}x^2$ is the opposite of the value of y for $f(x) = \frac{1}{2}x^2$ (see Table 3).

Our observations made in Examples 1 and 2 suggest the following properties.

> **Graphs of Quadratic Functions of the Form** $f(x) = ax^2$
>
> For a function of the form $f(x) = ax^2$,
> - The graph is a parabola with vertex $(0, 0)$.
> - If $|a|$ is a large number, then the parabola is steep. (It is narrow.)
> - If a is near zero, then the parabola is not steep. (It is wide.)
> - If $a > 0$, then the parabola opens upward.
> - If $a < 0$, then the parabola opens downward.
> - The graph of $y = -ax^2$ is the reflection of the graph of $f(x) = ax^2$ across the x-axis.

Translating Graphs

Next, we investigate graphs of functions of the form $f(x) = x^2 + k$.

> **Example 3**   Vertical Translation (Up–Down Shifts)

Compare the graphs of $f(x) = x^2 - 3$, $g(x) = x^2$, and $h(x) = x^2 + 3$.

Solution

We list input–output pairs of f, g, and h in Table 4 and sketch the graphs of the functions in Fig. 5.

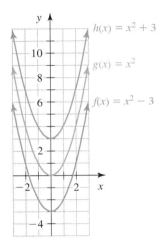

Figure 5 Graphs of
$f(x) = x^2 - 3$, $g(x) = x^2$,
and $h(x) = x^2 + 3$

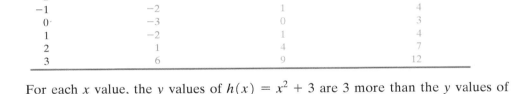

Table 4 Input–Output Pairs of $f(x) = x^2 - 3$, $g(x) = x^2$, and $h(x) = x^2 + 3$

x	$f(x) = x^2 - 3$	$g(x) = x^2$	$h(x) = x^2 + 3$
-3	6	9	12
-2	1	4	7
-1	-2	1	4
0	-3	0	3
1	-2	1	4
2	1	4	7
3	6	9	12

For each x value, the y values of $h(x) = x^2 + 3$ are 3 more than the y values of $g(x) = x^2$, which are 3 more than the y values of $f(x) = x^2 - 3$.

To sketch the graph of $h(x) = x^2 + 3$, we *translate* (move) the graph of $g(x) = x^2$ up by 3 units. To sketch the graph of $f(x) = x^2 - 3$, we translate the graph of $g(x) = x^2$ down by 3 units.

> **Example 4**   Horizontal Translation (Left–Right Shifts)

Compare the graph of $g(x) = (x - 5)^2$ with the graph of $f(x) = x^2$.

Solution

We list input–output pairs of g in Table 5 and sketch the graphs of f and g in Fig. 6.

Table 5 Input–Output Pairs
of $g(x) = (x - 5)^2$

x	$g(x)$
-1	36
0	25
1	16
2	9
3	4
4	1
5	0 ← Vertex
6	1
7	4
8	9

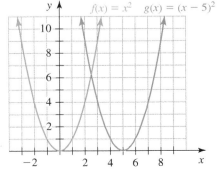

Figure 6 Graphs of $f(x) = x^2$ and
$g(x) = (x - 5)^2$

To graph $g(x) = (x - 5)^2$, we translate the graph of $f(x) = x^2$ to the *right* by 5 units.

▶ **Example 5**   Horizontal Translation (Left–Right Shifts)

Compare the graph of $g(x) = (x + 4)^2$ with the graph of $f(x) = x^2$.

Solution

We list input–output pairs of g in Table 6 and sketch the graphs of f and g in Fig. 7.

Table 6 Input–Output Pairs of $g(x) = (x + 4)^2$

x	$g(x)$
-8	16
-7	9
-6	4
-5	1
-4	0 ← Vertex
-3	1
-2	4
-1	9
0	16
1	25

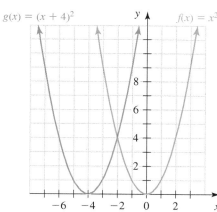

Figure 7 Graphs of $f(x) = x^2$ and $g(x) = (x + 4)^2$

To graph $g(x) = (x + 4)^2$, we translate the graph of $f(x) = x^2$ to the *left* by 4 units.

▶ **Three-Step Method of Graphing a Quadratic Function in Vertex Form**

To sketch the graph of $f(x) = a(x - h)^2 + k$, where $a \neq 0$,

1. Sketch the graph of $y = ax^2$.
2. Translate the graph from step 1 to the right by h units if $h > 0$ or to the left by $|h|$ units if $h < 0$.
3. Translate the graph from step 2 up by k units if $k > 0$ or down by $|k|$ units if $k < 0$.

▶ **Example 6**   Graphing a Quadratic Function

Sketch the graph of $f(x) = -(x - 4)^2$.

Solution

The equation of f is already in $f(x) = a(x - h)^2 + k$ form, with $a = -1, h = 4$, and $k = 0$. We follow the three-step graphing method:

Step 1. We sketch the graph of $y = -x^2$ in Fig. 8.

Step 2. Since $h = 4$, we translate the graph from step 1 to the right by 4 units.

Step 3. Since $k = 0$, there is no vertical translation.

Table 7 Input–Output Pairs of $f(x) = -(x - 4)^2$

x	$f(x)$
1	-9
2	-4
3	-1
4	0 ← Vertex
5	-1
6	-4
7	-9

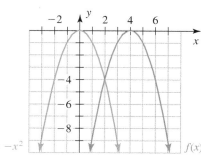

Figure 8 Graphs of $y = -x^2$ and $f(x) = -(x - 4)^2$

We check that the input–output pairs of f listed in Table 7 are points on our sketched parabola. We use integer inputs that are within 3 units of the x-coordinate of the vertex, 4. Also, we use a graphing calculator to verify our sketch (see Fig. 9).

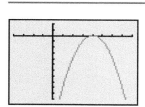

Figure 9 Graph of $f(x) = -(x - 4)^2$

▶ **Example 7**   Graphing a Quadratic Function

Sketch the graph of $f(x) = (x + 3)^2 + 1$.

Solution

First, we write the equation of f in $f(x) = a(x - h)^2 + k$ form:

$$f(x) = [x - (-3)]^2 + 1$$

Then we follow the three-step graphing method:

Step 1. We sketch the graph of $y = x^2$ in Fig. 10.

Step 2. Since $h = -3$, we translate the graph from step 1 to the left by 3 units.

Step 3. Since $k = 1$, we translate the graph from step 2 up by 1 unit.

We check that the input–output pairs of f listed in Table 8 are points on our sketched parabola. We use integer inputs that are within 3 units of the x-coordinate of the vertex, -3. Also, we can use a graphing calculator to verify our work (see Fig. 11).

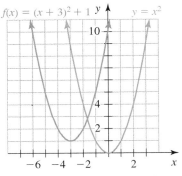

Figure 10 Graphs of $y = x^2$ and $f(x) = (x + 3)^2 + 1$

Table 8 Input–Output Pairs of $f(x) = (x + 3)^2 + 1$

x	$f(x)$
-6	10
-5	5
-4	2
-3	1 ← Vertex
-2	2
-1	5
0	10

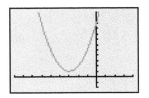

Figure 11 Graph of $f(x) = (x + 3)^2 + 1$

In Fig. 10, we see that the vertex of $f(x) = (x + 3)^2 + 1$ is the point $(-3, 1)$. This makes sense, since the vertex $(0, 0)$ of $y = x^2$ has been translated to the left by 3 units and up by 1 unit.

▶ **Vertex of a Quadratic Function**

The vertex of a quadratic function in vertex form, $f(x) = a(x - h)^2 + k$, is the point (h, k).

For example, the vertex of the function $f(x) = -3(x - 1)^2 + 5$ is $(1, 5)$. To find the vertex of the function $g(x) = 6(x + 2)^2 - 7$, we write the equation as $g(x) = 6[x - (-2)]^2 + (-7)$. So, the vertex is $(-2, -7)$.

Domain and Range of a Quadratic Function

Recall from Section 1.6 that the domain of a function is the set of values of x (the independent variable) and that the range of a function is the set of values of y (the dependent variable).

▶ **Example 8**   Graphing a Quadratic Function

Sketch the graph of $f(x) = -2(x + 6)^2 - 2$, and find the domain and range of f.

Solution

First, we write the equation of f in $f(x) = a(x - h)^2 + k$ form:

$$f(x) = -2[x - (-6)]^2 + (-2)$$

Then we follow the three-step graphing method:

Step 1. We sketch the graph of $y = -2x^2$ in Fig. 12.

Step 2. Since $h = -6$, we translate the graph from step 1 to the left by 6 units.

Step 3. Since $k = -2$, we translate the graph from step 2 down by 2 units.

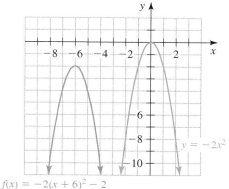

$f(x) = -2(x + 6)^2 - 2$

Figure 12 Graphs of $y = -2x^2$ and $f(x) = -2(x + 6)^2 - 2$

Table 9 Input–Output Pairs of $f(x) = -2(x + 6)^2 - 2$

x	$f(x)$
-8	-10
-7	-4
-6	-2 ← Vertex
-5	-4
-4	-10

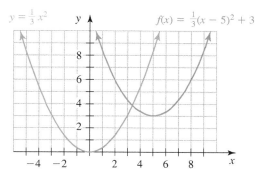

Figure 13 Graph of $f(x) = -2(x + 6)^2 - 2$

We check that the input–output pairs of f listed in Table 9 are points on our sketched parabola. Also, from the equation $f(x) = -2[x - (-6)]^2 + (-2)$, we see that the vertex is $(-6, -2)$, which matches our sketched parabola's vertex. Finally, we use a graphing calculator to verify our sketch (see Fig. 13).

Since we can compute a value of $-2(x + 6)^2 - 2$ for any real number x, the domain of $f(x) = -2(x + 6)^2 - 2$ is the set of all real numbers. From the graph of f, we see that the vertex $(-6, -2)$ is the maximum point and that values of y are less than or equal to -2. So, the range of f is the set of numbers y where $y \leq -2$.

▶ **Example 9** Graphing a Quadratic Function

Sketch the graph of $f(x) = \dfrac{1}{3}(x - 5)^2 + 3$, and find the domain and range of f.

Solution

We follow the three-step graphing method:

Step 1. We sketch the graph of $y = \dfrac{1}{3}x^2$ in Fig. 14.

Step 2. Since $h = 5$, we translate the graph from step 1 to the right by 5 units.

Step 3. Since $k = 3$, we translate the graph from step 2 up by 3 units.

Figure 14 Graphs of $y = \dfrac{1}{3}x^2$ and $f(x) = \dfrac{1}{3}(x - 5)^2 + 3$

Table 10 Input–Output Pairs
of $f(x) = \frac{1}{3}(x-5)^2 + 3$

x	f(x)
2	6
5	3 ← Vertex
8	6

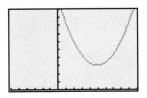

Figure 15 Graph of
$f(x) = \frac{1}{3}(x-5)^2 + 3$

Table 11 Percentages of
Women Between the Ages
of 25 Years and 54 Years
Who Work

Year	Percent
1980	64.0
1985	69.6
1990	74
1995	75.6
2000	76.7
2005	75.3
2010	75.1

Source: *Bureau of Labor Statistics*

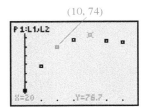

Figure 16 Working
women scattergram

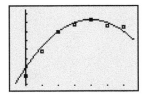

Figure 17 Check the fit

We check that the input–output pairs of f listed in Table 10 are points on our sketched parabola. Also, from the equation $f(x) = \frac{1}{3}(x-5)^2 + 3$, we see that the vertex is $(5, 3)$, which matches our sketched parabola's vertex. Finally, we use a graphing calculator to verify our work (see Fig. 15).

Since we can compute a value of $\frac{1}{3}(x-5)^2 + 3$ for any real number x, the domain of $f(x) = \frac{1}{3}(x-5)^2 + 3$ is the set of all real numbers. From the graph of f, we see that the vertex $(5, 3)$ is the minimum point and that values of y are greater than or equal to 3. So, the range of f is the set of numbers y where $y \geq 3$.

Find a Quadratic Model in Vertex Form

We can use our knowledge of graphing quadratic functions in vertex form to help us find an equation of a quadratic model.

▶ **Example 10**   Finding an Equation of a Quadratic Model

The percentages of women between the ages of 25 years and 54 years who work are shown in Table 11 for various calendar years. Let $f(t)$ be the percentage of women between the ages of 25 years and 54 years who work at t years since 1980.

1. Find an equation of f.
2. What is the vertex of the graph of f? What does it mean in this situation?
3. Use f to estimate the percentage of women between the ages of 25 years and 54 years who worked in 2008.

Solution

1. We use a graphing calculator to draw a scattergram of the data (see Fig. 16). It appears that a quadratic function would describe the situation much better than an exponential function or a linear function. We will find a quadratic function in vertex form, $f(t) = a(t - h)^2 + k$. Although it is not necessary to select the highest data point, $(20, 76.7)$, to be the vertex (see Fig. 16), it is convenient and satisfactory to do so. This means $h = 20$ and $k = 76.7$:

$$f(t) = a(t - 20)^2 + 76.7$$

Next, we imagine a parabola with vertex $(20, 76.7)$ that comes close to (or contains) the data points. Such a parabola might be the one that contains the data point $(10, 74)$. See Fig. 16. To find a, we substitute 10 for t and 74 for $f(t)$ in the equation $f(t) = a(t - 20)^2 + 76.7$ and solve for a:

$74 = a(10 - 20)^2 + 76.7$	*Substitute 10 for t and 74 for f(t).*
$74 = a(-10)^2 + 76.7$	*Subtract.*
$74 = 100a + 76.7$	*Simplify.*
$-2.7 = 100a$	*Subtract 76.7 from both sides.*
$-0.027 = a$	*Divide both sides by 100.*

The approximate equation is $f(t) = -0.027(t - 20)^2 + 76.7$. We check how well the model fits the data in Fig. 17. Since the graph appears to come close to (or contain) the data points, we conclude that f is a reasonable model of the situation.

2. The vertex of the graph of $f(t) = -0.027(t - 20)^2 + 76.7$ is $(20, 76.7)$, which means 76.7% of women between the ages of 25 years and 54 years worked in 2000. That is the highest percent in any year, according to the model.

3. We evaluate f at $t = 28$: $f(28) = -0.027(28 - 20)^2 + 76.7 = 74.972$. In 2008, about 75.0% of women between the ages of 25 years and 54 years worked, according to the model.

> **Finding a Quadratic Model in Vertex Form**
>
> To find a quadratic model in vertex form, given some data,
>
> 1. Create a scattergram of the data.
> 2. Imagine a parabola that comes close to (or contains) the data points, and select a point (h, k) to be the vertex. Although it is not necessary to select a data point, it is often convenient and satisfactory to do so.
> 3. Select a nonvertex point (not necessarily a data point) of the parabola, substitute the point's coordinates into the equation $f(t) = a(t - h)^2 + k$, and solve for a.
> 4. Substitute the result you found for a in step 3 into $f(t) = a(t - h)^2 + k$.

 **Group Exploration**

Drawing families of parabolas

1. On a graphing calculator, graph eight quadratic functions to make a design like the one in Fig. 18. List the equations of your parabolas.

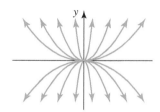

Figure 18 A family of parabolas

2. Now make a design like the one in Fig. 19. List the equations of your parabolas.

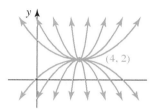

Figure 19 A family of parabolas with vertex $(4, 2)$

3. For a quadratic function of the form $f(x) = a(x - h)^2 + k$, summarize what you have learned about a, h, and k from this exploration and from the rest of this section.

> **Tips for Success** **Reread a Problem**
>
> After you think you have solved a problem, reread it to make sure you have answered its question(s). Also, reread the problem with the solution in mind. If what you read seems to make sense, then you've provided another check of your result(s).

 # Homework 7.1

For extra help ▶ MyMathLab°   Watch the videos in MyMathLab   Download the MyDashboard App

Graph the function by hand. Give the coordinates of the vertex. Then use a graphing calculator to verify your work.

1. $f(x) = 3x^2$
2. $f(x) = 2x^2$

3. $f(x) = -\dfrac{3}{2}x^2$
4. $f(x) = -\dfrac{2}{3}x^2$

5. $f(x) = -2x^2 + 5$
6. $f(x) = 2x^2 - 4$

7. $f(x) = (x - 1)^2$
8. $f(x) = (x + 3)^2$

9. $f(x) = -(x + 2)^2$
10. $f(x) = -3(x - 3)^2$

11. $f(x) = (x + 2)^2 - 6$
12. $f(x) = (x + 5)^2 - 7$

13. $f(x) = (x - 1)^2 + 3$
14. $f(x) = (x - 4)^2 + 2$

15. $f(x) = 2(x + 6)^2 - 6$
16. $f(x) = 3(x - 4)^2 + 1$

17. $f(x) = -3(x - 6)^2 - 2$
18. $f(x) = -(x + 1)^2 - 2$

19. $f(x) = \dfrac{1}{3}(x - 2)^2 + 3$
20. $f(x) = -\dfrac{1}{2}(x + 4)^2 - 2$

Graph the function by hand. Then use a graphing calculator to verify your work. Also, find the domain and range of the function.

21. $f(x) = x^2 - 4$
22. $f(x) = 2x^2 + 1$

23. $f(x) = -x^2 - 3$
24. $f(x) = -2x^2 + 5$

25. $f(x) = (x + 4)^2$

26. $f(x) = (x - 2)^2$

27. $f(x) = (x + 6)^2 + 2$

28. $f(x) = (x - 3)^2 + 1$

29. $f(x) = 2(x - 1)^2 - 4$

30. $f(x) = 3(x + 4)^2 - 7$

31. $f(x) = -(x - 5)^2 + 2$

32. $f(x) = -2(x + 2)^2 + 5$

33. U.S. Department of Defense spendings are shown in Table 12 for various years.

Table 12 U.S. Department of Defense Spendings

Year	Defense Spending (billions of dollars)
1992	298
1995	272
1998	268
2001	305
2004	456
2007	551
2010	720

Sources: *Department of Defense; Government Accountability Office*

Let $f(t)$ be the U.S. Department of Defense spending (in billions of dollars) in the year that is t years since 1990.

a. Find a quadratic equation of f in vertex form.

b. What is the vertex of the model? What does it mean in this situation?

c. Estimate defense spending in 2008.

d. In 2011, the federal government spent $68.3 billion on education. Estimate the ratio of federal spending on defense to federal spending on education in 2011.

34. The percentages of people living in the United States who are immigrants are shown in Table 13 for various years.

Table 13 Percentages of People Living in the United States Who Are Immigrants

Year	Percent
1930	12
1940	9
1950	7
1960	6
1970	5
1980	6
1990	8
2000	11
2010	13

Source: *U.S. Census Bureau*

Let $p = f(t)$ be the percentage of people living in the United States who are immigrants at t years since 1900.

a. Find a quadratic equation of f in vertex form.

b. What is the vertex of the model? What does it mean in this situation?

c. Predict the percentage of people living in the United States who will be immigrants in 2018.

d. Predict the *number* of immigrants in the United States in 2020. Assume the U.S. population will be 341.4 million in that year. Compare your result to 37.3 million, which is the current population of California, the most populous state in the United States.

35. The percentages of Americans who are obese are shown in Table 14 for various ages.

Table 14 Percentages of Americans Who Are Obese

Age Group (years)	Age Used to Represent Age Group (years)	Percent
under 25	18	11
25–34	29.5	25
35–44	39.5	28
45–54	49.5	30
55–64	59.5	30
65–74	69.5	27
75–84	79.5	19
over 84	90	8

Source: *The Gallup Organization*

Let $f(t)$ be the percentage of Americans who are obese at age t years.

a. Find a quadratic equation of f in vertex form.

b. What is the vertex of the model? What does it mean in this situation?

c. Estimate the percentage of Americans who are obese at age 73.

d. Use a graphing calculator to find the t-intercepts of the model. What do they mean in this situation? [**Hint:** First Zoom Out. Then see Appendix B.21 for graphing calculator instructions on how to use "zero."]

36. The pregnancy rates for American women are listed in Table 15 for various age groups.

Table 15 Pregnancy Rates for American Women

Age Group (years)	Age Used to Represent Age Group (years)	Pregnancy Rate (number of pregnancies per 1000 women)
15–17	16	42
18–19	18.5	119
20–24	22	164
25–29	27	169
30–34	32	135
35–39	37	76
40–44	42	17

Source: *National Center for Health Statistics*

Let $r = f(t)$ be the pregnancy rate (number of pregnancies per 1000 women) for women at age t years.

a. Find a quadratic equation of f in vertex form.

b. What is the vertex of the model? What does it mean in this situation?

c. Estimate the pregnancy rate for 20-year-old women.

d. Use a graphing calculator to find the t-intercepts of the model. What do they mean in this situation? [**Hint:** Zoom Out. Then see Appendix B.21 for graphing calculator instructions on how to use "zero."]

37. Recall that we can describe some or all of the input–output pairs of a function by means of an equation, a graph, a table, or words. Let $f(x) = 2(x - 1)^2 - 3$.

a. Describe the input–output pairs of f by using a graph.

b. Describe five input–output pairs of f by using a table.

c. Describe the input–output pairs of f by using words.

38. Recall that we can describe some or all of the input–output pairs of a function by means of an equation, a graph, a table, or words. Let $g(x) = -3(x + 4)^2 + 7$.

a. Describe the input–output pairs of g by using a graph.

b. Describe five input–output pairs of g by using a table.

c. Describe the input–output pairs of g by using words.

39. Let $f(x) = (x - 3)^2 + 2$.

a. Graph f by hand.

b. Find x when $f(x) = 3$.

c. Find x when $f(x) = 2$.

d. Find x when $f(x) = 1$.

40. Let $f(x) = -(x + 2)^2 + 5$.

a. Graph f by hand.

b. Find x when $f(x) = 6$.

c. Find x when $f(x) = 5$.

d. Find x when $f(x) = 4$.

Concepts

Write an equation of a parabola that meets the given criteria.

41. opens downward and has vertex $(-3, 4)$

42. opens upward and has vertex $(2, -5)$

43. Four functions of the form $y = a(x - h)^2 + k$ are graphed in Fig. 20. For each function, determine whether the constants $a, h,$ and k are positive, negative, or zero.

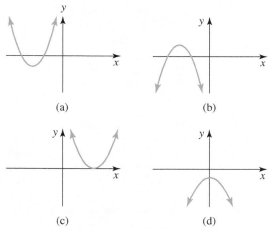

(a) (b)

(c) (d)

Figure 20 Exercise 43

44. For a quadratic function $f(x) = a(x - h)^2 + k$, for what values of $a, h,$ and k does the graph of f have a maximum point? a minimum point? Describe the maximum or minimum point in terms of $a, h,$ and k.

45. Use a graphing calculator to draw a family of parabolas similar to the family shown in Fig. 21. List the equations of your parabolas.

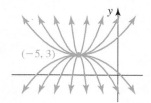

Figure 21 A family of parabolas with vertex $(-5, 3)$

46. Use a graphing calculator to draw a family of parabolas similar to the family shown in Fig. 22. List the equations of your parabolas.

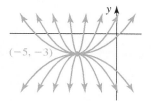

Figure 22 A family of parabolas with vertex $(-5, -3)$

47. Find an equation of the function f graphed in Fig. 23.

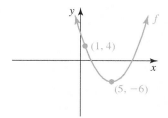

Figure 23 Exercise 47

48. The graph of the function $f(x) = 2.1(x - 2.73)^2 - 3.71$ is shown in Fig. 24. Find an equation of the function g, also graphed in Fig. 24.

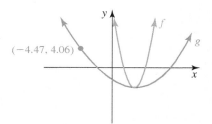

Figure 24 Exercise 48

49. The graph of the function $f(x) = 2.1(x - 2.73)^2 - 3.71$ is shown in Fig. 25. Find an equation of the function g, also graphed in Fig. 25. Assume the graphs of f and g have the same shape.

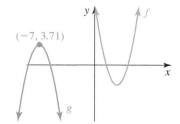

Figure 25 Exercise 49

50. Find equations of the four functions whose graphs produce the design shown in Fig. 26.

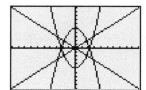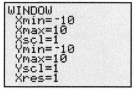

Figure 26 A design created by graphs of functions

For each exercise, decide whether it is possible for a parabola to have the indicated number of x-intercepts. If it is possible, find an equation of such a parabola. If it is not possible, explain why.

51. no *x*-intercepts   **52.** one *x*-intercept

53. two *x*-intercepts   **54.** three *x*-intercepts

55. Solve the system by finding ordered pairs that satisfy both equations. [**Hint:** Graph both equations on the same coordinate system.]

$$y = 2(x - 2)^2 + 5$$
$$y = -3(x - 2)^2 + 5$$

56. Use ZDecimal to draw the graph of $f(x) = 0.7x^2 + 2x - 1$. Then use TRACE to complete Table 16. Verify your table entries by using a graphing calculator table.

Table 16 Values of
$f(x) = 0.7x^2 + 2x - 1$

x	f(x)
−3	
−2	
−1	
0	
1	

57. Use a graphing calculator to graph $y = x^2$.
  a. Use the window settings displayed in Fig. 27. (You can get these settings by using ZDecimal.)
  b. Use the window settings displayed in Fig. 28. Compare what you see with what you saw in part (a).
  c. Use the window settings displayed in Fig. 29. Compare what you see with what you saw in part (a).
  d. Explain your results in parts (b) and (c).

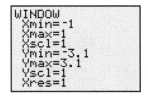

Figure 27 Window for Exercise 57a   **Figure 28** Window for Exercise 57b

Figure 29 Window for Exercise 57c

58. Use a graphing calculator to graph the function. Record window settings that allow you to see the graph, including the vertex, on the calculator screen.
  a. $f(x) = 1000x^2$
  b. $g(x) = 1000(x - 1000)^2$
  c. $h(x) = (x + 10,000)^2 + 10,000$

59. A student says that to graph $y = (x - 4)^2$, we translate the graph of $y = x^2$ to the left by 4 units. Is the student correct? Explain.

60. A student says the slope of the graph of $y = 2x^2$ is 2. Is the student correct? Explain.

61. A student uses ZStandard on a graphing calculator to graph $f(x) = 0.0001x^2 + 5$. He thought the graph should be a parabola, but the calculator displays a horizontal line. What would you tell him?

62. The vertex of a parabola is $(5, 3)$, and the parabola passes through the point $(8, 10)$. Find a third point that lies on the parabola.

63. Sketch, on the same coordinate system, the graph of the given function and the graph of $f(x) = a(x - h)^2 + k$ as shown in Fig. 30. Be sure to label which graph is which.
  a. $g(x) = a(x - 2h)^2 + k$ **b.** $p(x) = a(x - h)^2 + 2k$
  c. $q(x) = 2a(x - h)^2 + k$ **d.** $l(x) = 2a(x - 2h)^2 + 2k$

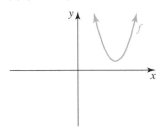

Figure 30 Exercise 63

64. Find two other quadratic functions that have the same domain and range as the function $f(x) = -2(x + 4)^2 + 7$.

65. Describe how to sketch the graph of a function of the form $f(x) = a(x - h)^2 + k, a \neq 0$. Include the effects that the values of *a*, *h*, and *k* have on the graph. (See page 4 for guidelines on writing a good response.)

66. To graph the quadratic function $y = a(x - h)^2 + k$, we translate the graph of $y = a(x - h)^2$ up by *k* units if $k > 0$ and down by $|k|$ units if $k < 0$. Explain. (See page 4 for guidelines on writing a good response.)

Related Review

67. a. Use a graphing calculator to graph the functions $f(x) = x^3$, $g(x) = (x - 4)^3$, and $h(x) = (x + 4)^3$ in the same viewing screen. Describe how to translate the graph of *f* to get the graph of *g* or the graph of *h*.
  b. Use a graphing calculator to graph the functions $f(x) = x^3$, $g(x) = x^3 - 4$, and $h(x) = x^3 + 4$ in the same viewing screen. Describe how to translate the graph of *f* to get the graph of *g* or the graph of *h*.
  c. Do the types of translation of $f(x) = x^3$ you performed in parts (a) and (b) match the types of translation we performed with $k(x) = x^2$ in this section? Explain.
  d. Graph $f(x) = 2^x$ by hand. Then translate this graph to graph the following functions.
    i. $g(x) = 2^{x+3}$ **ii.** $h(x) = 2^{x-4}$
    iii. $k(x) = 2^x + 2$ **iv.** $p(x) = 2^x - 1$

68. a. Use a graphing calculator to graph the functions $f(x) = 2^x$ and $g(x) = -2^x$ in the same viewing screen. Describe how to reflect the graph of *f* to get the graph of *g*.
  b. Use a graphing calculator to graph the functions $f(x) = x^4$ and $g(x) = -x^4$ in the same viewing screen. Describe how to reflect the graph of *f* to get the graph of *g*.
  c. Do the types of reflections you performed in parts (a) and (b) match the type of reflection we performed with $k(x) = x^2$ in this section? Explain.
  d. Graph $f(x) = x^3$ by hand. Then graph $g(x) = -x^3$ by hand.

Graph $y = 3^x$ by hand. Then use translations and reflections, as appropriate, to graph the given equation. Use a graphing calculator to verify your graph.

69. $f(x) = 3^{x+2} + 1$
71. $f(x) = -3^x + 4$

70. $f(x) = 3^{x-3} - 2$
72. $f(x) = -3^{x+3}$

Expressions, Equations, Functions, and Graphs

Perform the indicated instruction. Then use words such as linear, quadratic, cubic, exponential, logarithmic, polynomial, degree, function, one variable, *and* two variables *to describe the expression, equation, or system.*

73. Solve $\log_4(3x^2) + 2\log_4(2x^4) = 6$. Round any solutions to the fourth decimal place.

74. Solve:
$$y = -2x + 5$$
$$y = 4x + 23$$

75. Write as a single logarithm: $\log_4(3x^2) + 2\log_4(2x^4)$.

76. Solve $-2x + 5 = 4x + 23$.

77. Write as a single logarithm: $\log_4(3x^2) - 2\log_4(2x^4)$.

78. Graph $y = -2x + 5$ by hand.

▼ 7.2 Graphing Quadratic Functions in Standard Form

Objectives

» Graph a quadratic function in standard form by using two symmetric points to find the vertex.

» Graph a quadratic function in standard form by using the *vertex formula* to find the vertex.

» Find the *minimum value* or *maximum value* of a quantity.

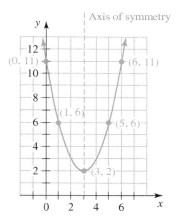

Figure 31 Locating symmetric points on a parabola

In Section 7.1, we graphed quadratic functions in vertex form, $f(x) = a(x - h)^2 + k$. In this section, we will discuss two methods of graphing quadratic functions in standard form, $f(x) = ax^2 + bx + c$. First, we will use two *symmetric points*. Then we will use the *vertex formula*. After discussing these methods, we will find the *minimum value* or *maximum value* of a quantity.

Method 1: Graphing by Using Two Symmetric Points to Find the Vertex

Recall from Section 6.1 that the part of the parabola that lies to the left of the axis of symmetry is the mirror reflection of the part that lies to the right (see Fig. 31). For any point on one side of the axis of symmetry, there is a point on the other side that is the "mirror reflection" of the first point. Such a pair of **symmetric points** corresponds to ordered pairs with equal y-coordinates.

For example, in Fig. 31, the point $(1, 6)$ and the point $(5, 6)$ are symmetric points. Since the vertex lies on the axis of symmetry, the x-coordinate of the vertex, 3, is equal to the average of the x-coordinates of the points $(1, 6)$ and $(5, 6)$:

$$\frac{1 + 5}{2} = 3$$

The average of the x-coordinates of *any* two symmetric points is equal to the x-coordinate of the vertex. As another example, we find the average of the x-coordinates of the y-intercept $(0, 11)$ and its symmetric point $(6, 11)$:

$$\frac{0 + 6}{2} = 3$$

The only point that does not have a symmetric point is the vertex, which lies on the axis of symmetry.

> ▶ **Using Two Symmetric Points to Find the Vertex**
>
> To find the vertex of a parabola in which (p, s) and (q, s) are symmetric points,
>
> **1.** Find the x-coordinate by using the formula
>
> $$x = \frac{p + q}{2}$$
>
> In words, the x-coordinate is the average of the x-coordinates of any two symmetric points.
>
> **2.** Find the y-coordinate by evaluating f at the value found in step 1. That is, find
>
> $$f\left(\frac{p + q}{2}\right)$$

In short, the vertex is $\left(\dfrac{p+q}{2}, f\left(\dfrac{p+q}{2}\right)\right)$.

▶ **Example 1** Finding the x-Coordinate of a Vertex

Find the x-coordinate of the vertex of the parabola sketched in the indicated figure.

1. Fig. 32   **2.** Fig. 33

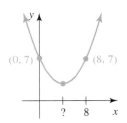

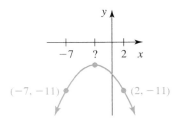

Figure 32 Problem 1   Figure 33 Problem 2

Solution

1. The x-coordinates of the symmetric points $(0, 7)$ and $(8, 7)$ are 0 and 8, respectively. Since $\dfrac{0+8}{2} = 4$, the x-coordinate of the vertex is 4.

2. The x-coordinates of the symmetric points $(-7, -11)$ and $(2, -11)$ are -7 and 2, respectively. Since $\dfrac{-7+2}{2} = -2.5$, the x-coordinate of the vertex is -2.5.

Averaging the x-coordinates of the y-intercept and its symmetric point to find the x-coordinate of the vertex is a key step in sketching the graph of a quadratic function in standard form.

▶ **Example 2** Graphing a Quadratic Function

Sketch the graph of $g(x) = x^2 - 4x + 7$.

Solution

First, we find the y-intercept of the graph of $g(x) = x^2 - 4x + 7$:

$$g(0) = 0^2 - 4(0) + 7 = 7$$

The y-intercept is $(0, 7)$. See Fig. 34.

Next, we find the symmetric point of the y-intercept. Since symmetric points have the same height, we know the y-coordinate of the symmetric point is 7. We find the x-coordinate by substituting 7 for y in the equation $g(x) = x^2 - 4x + 7$ and solving for x:

$$\begin{aligned}
7 &= x^2 - 4x + 7 &&\text{Substitute 7 for y.}\\
0 &= x^2 - 4x &&\text{Write in } 0 = ax^2 + bx \text{ form.}\\
0 &= x(x - 4) &&\text{Factor right-hand side.}\\
x &= 0 \quad\text{or}\quad x - 4 = 0 &&\text{Zero factor property}\\
x &= 0 \quad\text{or}\quad\quad x = 4
\end{aligned}$$

Therefore, the points that have height 7 are $(0, 7)$ and $(4, 7)$; these are symmetric points. To find the x-coordinate of the vertex, we average the x-coordinates of the symmetric points:

$$x\text{-coordinate of vertex} = \frac{0 + 4}{2} = 2$$

To find the y-coordinate of the vertex, we find $g(2)$:

$$g(2) = 2^2 - 4(2) + 7 = 4 - 8 + 7 = 3$$

So, the vertex is $(2, 3)$.

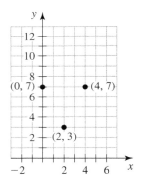

Figure 34 The vertex and two symmetric points

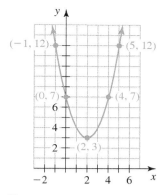

Figure 35 Graph of g

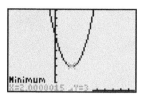

Figure 36 Verify the graph of g

We can find another pair of symmetric points on the graph by evaluating g at the values of x that are 3 units from $x = 2$ on either side—namely, at $x = -1$ and $x = 5$. At $x = 5$,

$$g(5) = 5^2 - 4(5) + 7 = 25 - 20 + 7 = 12$$

Thus, the graph passes through $(5, 12)$ and its symmetric point, $(-1, 12)$, We plot these points to assist us in sketching a graph of g (see Fig. 35).

We use a graphing calculator to verify our sketch (see Fig. 36). In particular, we check that the vertex (minimum point) is $(2, 3)$. The "minimum" choice on a graphing calculator will closely approximate the vertex (see Appendix B.19).

> **Using Symmetric Points to Graph a Quadratic Function in Standard Form (Method 1)**
>
> To sketch a graph of a quadratic function $f(x) = ax^2 + bx + c = 0$, where $b \neq 0$,
>
> 1. Find the y-intercept.
> 2. Find the y-intercept's symmetric point.
> 3. Average the x-coordinates of the two symmetric points to find the x-coordinate of the vertex.
> 4. Find the y-coordinate of the vertex.
> 5. Depending on how accurate your sketch is to be, find additional points on the parabola, as needed.
> 6. Sketch a parabola that contains the points found.

We use these steps to graph a quadratic function $f(x) = ax^2 + bx + c$, where $b \neq 0$. If $b = 0$, the y-intercept is the vertex and, therefore, does not have a symmetric point. In this case, however, $f(x) = ax^2 + 0x + c = ax^2 + c$ is in vertex form, and we can readily use the methods of Section 7.1 to sketch the graph.

▶ **Example 3** Graphing a Quadratic Function

Sketch the graph of $f(x) = -0.9x^2 - 5.8x - 5.7$.

Solution

We find the y-intercept by finding $f(0)$:

$$f(0) = -0.9(0)^2 - 5.8(0) - 5.7 = -5.7$$

So, the y-intercept is $(0, -5.7)$.

Next, we find the symmetric point of the y-intercept. We substitute -5.7 for $f(x)$ and solve for x:

$$\begin{aligned}
-5.7 &= -0.9x^2 - 5.8x - 5.7 && \text{Substitute } -5.7 \text{ for } f(x).\\
0 &= -0.9x^2 - 5.8x && \text{Write in } 0 = ax^2 + bx \text{ form.}\\
0 &= -x(0.9x + 5.8) && \text{Factor right-hand side.}\\
-x = 0 \quad &\text{or} \quad 0.9x + 5.8 = 0 && \text{Zero factor property}\\
x = 0 \quad &\text{or} \quad 0.9x = -5.8\\
x = 0 \quad &\text{or} \quad x = \frac{-5.8}{0.9}\\
&\approx -6.44
\end{aligned}$$

So, $(0, -5.7)$ and $(-6.44, -5.7)$ are approximate symmetric points. The approximate symmetric point of the y-intercept $(0, -5.7)$ is $(-6.44, -5.7)$.

We find the approximate x-coordinate of the vertex by averaging the x-coordinates of the points $(0, -5.7)$ and $(-6.44, -5.7)$:

$$\frac{0 + (-6.44)}{2} = -3.22$$

We find the approximate y-coordinate of the vertex by computing $f(-3.22)$:

$$f(-3.22) = -0.9(-3.22)^2 - 5.8(-3.22) - 5.7 \approx 3.64$$

So, the vertex is approximately $(-3.22, 3.64)$. See Fig. 37.

Although we could find and plot additional points, we can sketch a fairly accurate graph of f from the three points already found (see Fig. 38). We use a graphing calculator to verify our sketch (see Fig. 39). In particular, we check that the approximate vertex (maximum point) is $(-3.22, 3.64)$.

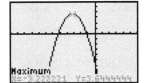

Figure 39 Verify the graph of f

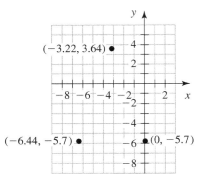

Figure 37 The vertex and two symmetric points

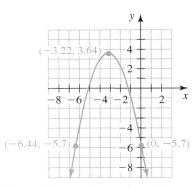

Figure 38 Graph of f from three points

Method 2: Graphing by Using the Vertex Formula to Find the Vertex

We can find a formula of the x-coordinate of the vertex of a parabola $f(x) = ax^2 + bx + c$, where $a \neq 0$. If $b = 0$, the vertex is the y-intercept, so the x-coordinate of the vertex is 0.

If $b \neq 0$, then we can find the x-coordinate of the vertex from the first three steps of the graphing method (method 1) we have been using in this section. To begin, we find the y-intercept by finding $f(0)$:

$$f(0) = a(0)^2 + b(0) + c = c$$

The y-intercept is $(0, c)$.

Next, we find the symmetric point of the y-intercept by substituting c for $f(x)$ and solving for x:

$c = ax^2 + bx + c$	Substitute c for f(x).
$0 = ax^2 + bx$	Subtract c from both sides.
$0 = x(ax + b)$	Factor right-hand side.
$x = 0$ or $ax + b = 0$	Zero factor property
$x = 0$ or $ax = -b$	Subtract b from both sides.
$x = 0$ or $x = -\dfrac{b}{a}$	Divide both sides by a.

The x-coordinate of the symmetric point is $-\dfrac{b}{a}$.

We find the *x*-coordinate of the vertex by averaging the *x*-coordinates of the *y*-intercept and symmetric point:

$$x = \frac{0 + \left(-\dfrac{b}{a}\right)}{2} = \frac{-\dfrac{b}{a}}{2} \qquad 0 + d = d$$

$$= -\frac{b}{a} \div 2 \qquad \frac{Q}{R} = Q \div R$$

$$= -\frac{b}{a} \cdot \frac{1}{2} \qquad \text{Multiply by reciprocal of 2, which is } \frac{1}{2}.$$

$$= -\frac{b}{2a} \qquad \text{Multiply numerators and multiply denominators.}$$

So, the formula of the *x*-coordinate of the vertex is $x = -\dfrac{b}{2a}$. If $b = 0$, this formula gives $x = -\dfrac{0}{2a} = 0$, which agrees with what we said earlier. So, the formula works for any value of *b*.

> ### Vertex Formula
>
> To find the vertex of the graph of a quadratic function $f(x) = ax^2 + bx + c$,
>
> **1.** Find the *x*-coordinate of the vertex by using the **vertex formula** $x = -\dfrac{b}{2a}$.
>
> **2.** Find the *y*-coordinate of the vertex by evaluating *f* at the value found in step 1. That is, find $f\left(-\dfrac{b}{2a}\right)$.

In short, the vertex is $\left(-\dfrac{b}{2a}, f\left(-\dfrac{b}{2a}\right)\right)$.

In Example 4, we use the vertex formula to find the vertex of the parabola we sketched in Example 2.

▶ **Example 4**   Using the Vertex Formula to Find the Vertex

Find the vertex of the graph of $g(x) = x^2 - 4x + 7$.

Solution

Comparing $g(x) = x^2 - 4x + 7$ with $f(x) = ax^2 + bx + c$, we see that $a = 1$ and $b = -4$. We substitute these values of *a* and *b* into the formula $x = -\dfrac{b}{2a}$:

$$x = -\frac{-4}{2(1)} = 2$$

The *x*-coordinate of the vertex is 2. To find the *y*-coordinate, we find $f(2)$:

$$f(2) = 2^2 - 4(2) + 7 = 3$$

So, the vertex is $(2, 3)$, as we saw in Example 2.

▶

In general, for any quadratic function of the form $f(x) = ax^2 + bx + c$, where $b \neq 0$, both methods we have discussed for finding the vertex give the same result.

Table 17 Input–Output Pairs
of $f(x) = 2x^2 + 10x + 7$

x	$f(x)$
-4	-1
-3	-5
-2	-5
-1	-1

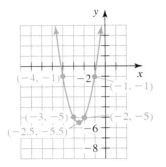

Figure 40 Graph of f from
five points

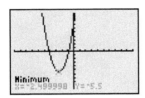

Figure 41 Verify the
graph of f

Table 18 Input–Output Pairs
of $f(x) = -2.2x^2 + 6.1x + 1.4$

x	$f(x)$
0	1.4
1	5.3
2	4.8
3	-0.1

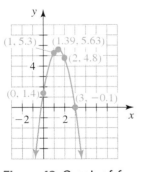

Figure 42 Graph of f
using five points

▶ **Example 5** Using the Vertex Formula to Graph a Quadratic Function

Sketch the graph of $f(x) = 2x^2 + 10x + 7$.

Solution

To find the x-coordinate of the vertex, we substitute 2 for a and 10 for b in the vertex formula $x = -\dfrac{b}{2a}$:

$$x = -\frac{10}{2(2)} = -2.5$$

The x-coordinate of the vertex is -2.5. To find the y-coordinate, we find $f(-2.5)$:

$$f(-2.5) = 2(-2.5)^2 + 10(-2.5) + 7 = -5.5$$

The vertex is $(-2.5, -5.5)$.

We find additional input–output pairs of f in Table 17. Notice that we select integer input values that are close to the vertex's x-coordinate, -2.5. We plot these found points and then sketch a parabola that contains them (see Fig. 40).

We use a graphing calculator to verify our sketch (see Fig. 41). In particular, we check that the approximate vertex (minimum point) is $(-2.5, -5.5)$. ▶

▶ **Example 6** Using the Vertex Formula to Graph a Quadratic Function

Sketch the graph of $f(x) = -2.2x^2 + 6.1x + 1.4$.

Solution

To find the x-coordinate of the vertex, we substitute -2.2 for a and 6.1 for b in the vertex formula $x = -\dfrac{b}{2a}$:

$$x = -\frac{6.1}{2(-2.2)} \approx 1.39$$

The x-coordinate of the vertex is about 1.39. To find the y-coordinate, we find $f(1.39)$:

$$f(1.39) = -2.2(1.39)^2 + 6.1(1.39) + 1.4 \approx 5.63$$

The approximate vertex is $(1.39, 5.63)$.

We find additional input–output pairs of f in Table 18. We plot these found points and then sketch a parabola that contains them (see Fig. 42). ▶

Minimum or Maximum Value

Earlier in this section, we located the vertex to help ourselves graph quadratic functions in standard form. Recall from Section 6.1 that the vertex is also the minimum or maximum point of the parabola. If the vertex is the maximum point, we call the y-coordinate of the vertex the **maximum value** of the function (see Fig. 43). If the vertex is the minimum point, we call the y-coordinate of the vertex the **minimum value** of the function (see Fig. 44).

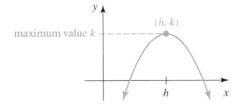

Figure 43 Quadratic function with a
maximum value k but no minimum value

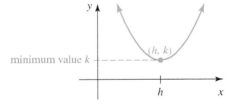

Figure 44 Quadratic function with a
minimum value k but no maximum value

If we convert a quadratic function in standard form, $f(x) = ax^2 + bx + c$, into vertex form, $f(x) = a(x - h)^2 + k$, the constant a has the same value for both forms.

So, what we have determined about the graphical significance of a for quadratic functions in vertex form also applies to quadratic functions in standard form.

> **Maximum or Minimum Value of a Function**
>
> For a quadratic function $f(x) = ax^2 + bx + c$ whose graph has vertex (h, k),
> - If $a < 0$, then the parabola opens downward and the maximum value of the function is k (see Fig. 43).
> - If $a > 0$, then the parabola opens upward and the minimum value of the function is k (see Fig. 44).

In Example 7, we estimate the maximum value of a quantity by finding the vertex of a quadratic model that opens downward.

> **Example 7** Finding the Maximum Value of a Quantity

A fireworks shell is launched into the air. The shell's height (in feet) $h = f(t)$ at time t seconds is modeled well by the function $f(t) = -16t^2 + 200t + 1$. When should the shell explode so it goes off at the maximum height? What is that height?

Solution

The function f is of the form $f(t) = at^2 + bt + c$, with $a = -16$ (a negative number), so the graph of f is a parabola that opens downward. Therefore, the vertex is the maximum point. We can find the time the shell will reach the maximum height by finding the vertex.

To find the t-coordinate of the vertex, we substitute $a = -16$ and $b = 200$ in the vertex formula $t = -\dfrac{b}{2a}$:

$$t = -\frac{200}{2(-16)} = 6.25$$

The t-coordinate is 6.25. To find the h-coordinate, we evaluate f at 6.25:

$$f(6.25) = -16(6.25)^2 + 200(6.25) + 1 = 626$$

So, the vertex is $(6.25, 626)$. We verify our work by using "maximum" on a graphing calculator (see Fig. 45). For graphing calculator instructions, see Appendix B.19.

A vertex of $(6.25, 626)$ means the shell will reach a maximum height of 626 feet at 6.25 seconds and should explode then.

The function $f(t) = -16t^2 + 200t + 1$ describes the shell's height in terms of time, *not* in terms of horizontal distance. So, the graph of f does *not* describe the path of the shell. Its path can be modeled by a quadratic function that describes the height in terms of horizontal distance.

Maximum
X=6.2499993 Y=626

Figure 45 Verify that the vertex is (6.25, 626)

> **Example 8** Finding the Maximum Value of a Quantity

A person plans to use 60 feet of fencing and the side of his house to enclose a rectangular garden (see Fig. 46). What dimensions of the rectangle would give the maximum area? What is that area?

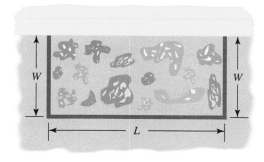

Figure 46 A garden

Solution

We use the five-step problem-solving method of Section 3.4, but in step 2 we use a system of equations to build a function and in step 3 we find the maximum point of the graph of the function.

Step 1: Define each variable. We let W be the width (in feet), L be the length (in feet), and A be the area (in square feet) of the rectangle (see Fig. 46).

Step 2: Use a system of two equations to build a function. No fencing is needed along the house, so the 60 feet of fencing can be used for the three sides of length W, W, and L:

$$W + W + L = 60$$

To obtain our first equation, we combine like terms on the left side:

$$2W + L = 60$$

We use the area formula, $A = LW$, as our second equation. The system is

$$2W + L = 60 \quad \textit{Equation (1)}$$
$$A = LW \quad \textit{Equation (2)}$$

Next, we will build a function that describes the area of the rectangle as a function of the width. To begin, we solve equation (1) for L:

$$2W + L = 60 \quad \textit{Equation (1)}$$
$$L = -2W + 60 \quad \textit{Subtract 2W from both sides.}$$

Then we substitute $-2W + 60$ for L in equation (2):

$$A = LW \quad \textit{Equation (2)}$$
$$A = (-2W + 60)W \quad \textit{Substitute} -2W + 60 \textit{ for L.}$$
$$A = -2W^2 + 60W \quad \textit{Distributive law}$$

Step 3: Find the maximum point of the graph of the function. The function $A = -2W^2 + 60W$ is of the form $A = aW^2 + bW + c$, where $a = -2$ (a negative number), so the graph is a parabola that opens downward (see Fig. 47). Therefore, the vertex is the maximum point. We can find the width of the rectangle with maximum area by finding the vertex.

To find the W-coordinate of the vertex, we substitute $a = -2$ and $b = 60$ in the vertex formula $W = -\dfrac{b}{2a}$:

$$W = -\frac{60}{2(-2)} = 15$$

To find the A-coordinate of the vertex, we substitute 15 for W in the equation $A = -2W^2 + 60W$:

$$A = -2(15)^2 + 60(15) = 450$$

To find the length of the rectangle, we substitute 15 for W in the equation $L = -2W + 60$:

$$L = -2(15) + 60 = 30$$

Step 4: Describe each result. The width is 15 feet, the length is 30 feet, and the area is 450 square feet.

Step 5: Check. The amount of fencing is $15 + 15 + 30 = 60$ feet, which checks. To check that the largest area is 450 square feet, we find the area of a couple of other rectangles that would involve 60 feet of fencing (see Fig. 48 on the next page).

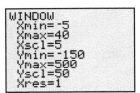

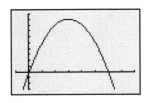

Figure 47 Graph of $A = -2W^2 + 60W$

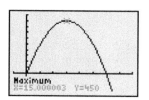

Figure 49 Verify that the maximum point is (15, 450)

$A = 250$	$W = 5$

$L = 50$

$A = 400$	$W = 10$

$L = 40$

Figure 48 Some other rectangles involving 60 feet of fencing

Since 450 square feet is larger than the area of either of the two rectangles in Fig. 48, it seems reasonable that our work is correct. Finally, we use "maximum" on a graphing calculator to check that the maximum point of the graph of $A = -2W^2 + 60W$ is $(15, 450)$. See Fig. 49.

Group Exploration

Comparing methods of graphing quadratic functions

1. a. Graph the function $f(x) = 2(x - 3)^2 - 5$ by using the method discussed in Section 7.1.

   b. Simplify the right-hand side of the equation $f(x) = 2(x - 3)^2 - 5$.

   c. Graph the equation you found in part (b) by using two symmetric points to find the vertex (method 1).

   d. Graph the equation you found in part (b) by using the vertex formula to find the vertex (method 2).

   e. Compare your graphs from parts (a), (c), and (d).

2. a. Graph the function $g(x) = x^2 + 10x + 25$ by using two symmetric points to find the vertex.

   b. Graph g by using the vertex formula to find the vertex.

   c. Factor the right-hand side of the equation $g(x) = x^2 + 10x + 25$.

   d. Use the method discussed in Section 7.1 to graph the equation you found in part (c).

   e. Compare your graphs from parts (a), (b), and (d).

Homework 7.2

For extra help ▶ **MyMathLab®**   ⊞ Watch the videos in MyMathLab   ⬤ Download the MyDashboard App

Find the x-coordinate of the vertex of the parabola sketched in the figure.

1. Fig. 50

2. Fig. 51

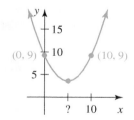

Figure 50 Exercise 1

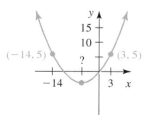

Figure 51 Exercise 2

Find the x-coordinate of the vertex of a parabola that passes through the given points. Round approximate results to the second decimal place.

3. $(0, 8)$ and $(6, 8)$

4. $(0, 5)$ and $(8, 5)$

5. $(0, -3)$ and $(-7, -3)$

6. $(0, -6)$ and $(-9, -6)$

7. $(0, 2)$ and $(7.29, 2)$

8. $(0, -7)$ and $(15.37, -7)$

A parabola has the given vertex and y-intercept. Find another point on the parabola.

9. vertex $(2, 5)$ and y-intercept $(0, 9)$

10. vertex $(-3, -8)$ and y-intercept $(0, 4)$

Graph the function by hand. Find the vertex; round approximate coordinates to the second decimal place. Verify your sketch by using a graphing calculator.

11. $y = x^2 - 6x + 7$

12. $y = x^2 - 4x + 5$

13. $y = x^2 + 8x + 9$

14. $y = x^2 + 2x - 7$

15. $y = -x^2 + 8x - 10$

16. $y = -2x^2 + 12x - 9$

17. $y = 3x^2 + 6x - 4$

18. $y = 2x^2 - 4x + 1$

19. $y = -3x^2 + 12x - 5$

20. $y = -2x^2 - 8x - 3$

21. $y = -4x^2 - 9x - 5$

22. $y = -2x^2 + 5x + 3$

23. $y = 2x^2 - 7x + 7$

24. $y = -3x^2 - 2x - 4$

25. $4x^2 - y + 6 = 8x$

26. $6x^2 = 3y - 24x - 15$

27. $y = 2.8x^2 - 8.7x + 4$

28. $y = -1.6x^2 - 4.8x + 3$

29. $y = 3.9x^2 + 6.9x - 3.4$

30. $y = -2.4x^2 + 6.1x - 7.8$

31. $3.6y - 26.3x = 8.3x^2 - 7.1$

32. $5.3 - 2.1y = 9.8x^2 - 3.4x + 8.3$

A parabola has the given x-intercepts. What is the x-coordinate of the vertex? Write your result in decimal form.

33. $(2, 0)$ and $(6, 0)$

34. $(-4, 0)$ and $(3, 0)$

35. $(-9, 0)$ and $(4, 0)$

36. $(-7, 0)$ and $(-3, 0)$

Find the x-intercepts and y-intercept. Next, find the vertex. Write the coordinates in decimal form. Then graph the function by hand. Verify your result by using a graphing calculator.

37. $y = 5x^2 - 10x$

38. $y = 2x^2 - 8x$

39. $y = -2x^2 + 6x$

40. $y = -3x^2 - 6x$

41. $y = x^2 - 10x + 24$

42. $y = x^2 - 4x - 5$

43. $y = x^2 - 8x + 7$

44. $y = x^2 - 10x + 16$

45. $y = x^2 - 9$

46. $y = x^2 - 1$

47. A batter hits a baseball. The ball's height (in feet) $h(t)$ after t seconds is given by $h(t) = -16t^2 + 140t + 3$.

    a. What is the ball's height when the batter makes contact with it?

    b. What is the maximum height of the ball? When does it reach that height?

    c. Graph h by hand.

48. A person on the edge of a cliff throws a stone so it hits the ground near the base of the cliff. The stone's height (in feet above the base) $h(t)$ after t seconds is given by $h(t) = -16t^2 + 30t + 200$.

    a. Find the vertex. What does it mean in this situation?

    b. Estimate the height of the cliff. State any assumptions you make.

    c. Did the person throw the stone upward or downward? Explain.

49. The percentages of households with outstanding student debt are shown in Table 19 for various years.

Table 19 Percentages of Households with Outstanding Student Debt

Year	Percent
1995	12
1998	11
2001	12
2004	13
2007	15
2010	19

Source: *Pew Research Center*

Let $f(t)$ be the percentage of households with outstanding student debt at t years since 1990.

    a. Use a graphing calculator to draw a scattergram to describe the data. Is it best to use a linear, an exponential, or a quadratic function to model the data? Explain.

    b. Use a graphing calculator to draw the graph of the model $f(t) = 0.058t^2 - 0.98t + 15.43$ and, in the same viewing window, the scattergram of the data. Does the model fit the data well?

    c. Predict the percentage of households that will have outstanding student debt in 2017.

    d. Estimate when the percentage of households with outstanding student debt was the least. What was that minimum percentage?

    e. In 2009, there were about 117 million households. Estimate the *number* of households that had outstanding student debt in 2009.

50. The numbers of people who died as a result of police action or while in police custody in South Africa are shown in Table 20 for various years.

Table 20 Numbers of People Who Died as a Result of Police Action or While in Police Custody in South Africa

Year	Number of Deaths
1998	552
2000	429
2002	328
2004	370
2006	408
2008	603
2010	799

Source: *Pew Research Center*

Let $f(t)$ be the number of people who died as a result of police action or while in police custody in South Africa in the year that is t years since 1990.

    a. Use a graphing calculator to draw a scattergram to describe the data. Is it best to use a linear, an exponential, or a quadratic function to model the data? Explain.

    b. Use a graphing calculator to draw the graph of the model $f(t) = 9.13t^2 - 235t + 1849$ and, in the same viewing window, the scattergram of the data. Does the model fit the data well?

    c. Estimate the number of people who died as a result of police action or while in police custody in 2012.

    d. Estimate when the number of people who died as a result of police action or while in police custody was the least. What was that number of people?

51. Americans' average annual expenditures are shown in Table 21 for various age groups.

Table 21 Americans' Average Annual Expenditures

Age Group (years)	Age Used to Represent Age Group (years)	Average Annual Expenditure (thousands of dollars)
under 25	20.0	24.3
25–34	29.5	40.3
35–44	39.5	48.3
45–54	49.5	48.7
55–64	59.5	44.3
65–74	69.5	32.2

Source: *Bureau of Labor Statistics, Consumer Expenditure Survey*

Let $f(t)$ be the average annual expenditure (in thousands of dollars) of Americans at age t years.

    a. Use a graphing calculator to draw a scattergram to describe the data. Is it best to use a linear, an exponential, or a quadratic function to model the data? Explain.

    b. Use a graphing calculator to draw the graph of the model $f(t) = -0.035t^2 + 3.25t - 26.34$ and, in the same viewing window, the scattergram of the data. Does the model fit the data well?

c. Estimate the average annual expenditure of 18-year-old Americans.

d. Estimate the age of Americans with the highest average annual expenditure. What is that expenditure?

52. The percentages of Americans who buy newspapers (print or online) are shown in Table 22 for various age groups.

Table 22 Percentages of Americans Who Buy Newspapers

Age Group (years)	Age Used to Represent Age Group (years)	Percent
25–34	29.5	33
35–44	39.5	43
45–54	49.5	48
55–64	59.5	53
over 65	70	51

Source: *Bureau of Labor Statistics*

Let $f(t)$ be the percentage of Americans at age t years who buy newspapers.

a. Use a graphing calculator to draw a scattergram to describe the data. Is it best to use a linear, an exponential, or a quadratic function to model the data? Explain.

b. Use a graphing calculator to draw the graph of the model $f(t) = -0.017t^2 + 2.15t - 15.57$ and, in the same viewing window, the scattergram of the data. Does the model fit the data well?

c. Estimate the percentage of 21-year-old Americans who buy newspapers.

d. Estimate the age of Americans who are most likely to buy newspapers. What percentage of these Americans buy newspapers?

e. In 2010, there were about 3.5 million 30-year-old Americans. Estimate the *number* of those Americans who bought newspapers.

53. Student-to-faculty ratios at Bates College are shown in Table 23 for various years.

Table 23 Student-to-Faculty Ratios at Bates College

Year	Student-to-Faculty Ratio
1985	13.8
1990	11.9
1995	11.0
2000	10.9
2004	10.7
2007	11.0

Source: *Bates College*

Let r be the student-to-faculty ratio at Bates College at t years since 1980. A linear model of the situation is $L(t) = -0.12t + 13.53$. An exponential model is $E(t) = 13.55(0.99)^t$. A quadratic model is $Q(t) = 0.0119t^2 - 0.5t + 15.9$.

a. Use a graphing calculator to draw the graphs of all three models and, in the same viewing window, the scattergram of the data. Which model best describes the situation?

b. Use Zoom Out on a graphing calculator to help you determine which model predicts the lowest student-to-faculty ratios for future years.

c. Use Q to predict when the student-to-faculty ratio will be 15.9.

d. Use Q to estimate when the student-to-faculty ratio was the least. What is that ratio?

e. The enrollment in 2011 was 1769 students. Use Q to estimate the *number of faculty* in that year.

54. The numbers of recreational boating fatalities are shown in Table 24 for various years.

Table 24 Numbers of Recreational Boating Fatalities

Year	Number of Fatalities
1980	1392
1985	1104
1990	880
1995	829
2000	701
2005	697
2011	758

Source: *U.S. Coast Guard*

Let n be the number of recreational boating fatalities in the year that is t years since 1980. A linear model of the situation is $L(t) = -20t + 1212$. An exponential model is $E(t) = 1204(0.98)^t$. A quadratic model is $Q(t) = 1.24t^2 - 58.18t + 1377$.

a. Use a graphing calculator to draw the graphs of all three models and, in the same viewing window, the scattergram of the data. Which model best describes the situation?

b. Use each of the three models to find three estimates of the number of fatalities in 2000. Which is the best estimate? Explain.

c. Use Zoom Out on a graphing calculator to help you determine which model predicts the lowest number of fatalities for any year beyond 2006.

d. Use Q to estimate in which year the number of recreational boating fatalities was the least. What is that number of fatalities?

55. A person plans to use 80 feet of fencing to enclose a rectangular garden. What dimensions of the rectangle would give the maximum area? What is that area?

56. A person plans to use 60 feet of fencing to enclose a rectangular patio. What dimensions of the rectangle would give the maximum area? What is that area?

57. A rancher plans to use 400 feet of fencing and a side of his barn to form a rectangular boundary for cattle (see Fig. 52). What dimensions of the rectangle would give the maximum area? What is that area?

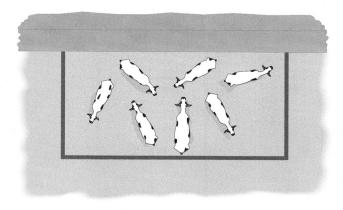

Figure 52 Exercise 57

58. A farmer plans to use 200 feet of fencing and a side of her barn to enclose a rectangular garden (see Fig. 53). What dimensions of the rectangle would give the maximum area? What is that area?

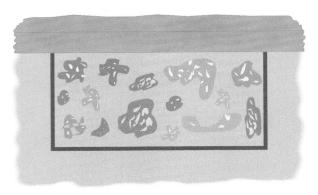

Figure 53 Exercise 58

59. Recall that we can describe some or all of the input–output pairs of a function by means of an equation, a graph, a table, or words. Let $f(x) = x^2 - 10x + 18$.
   a. Describe the input–output pairs of f by using a graph.
   b. Describe five input–output pairs of f by using a table.
   c. Describe the input–output pairs of f by using words.

60. Recall that we can describe some or all of the input–output pairs of a function by means of an equation, a graph, a table, or words. Let $g(x) = -2x^2 + 4x + 1$.
   a. Describe the input–output pairs of g by using a graph.
   b. Describe five input–output pairs of g by using a table.
   c. Describe the input–output pairs of g by using words.

For Exercises 61–68, refer to the graph sketched in Fig. 54.

61. Find $f(-5)$.
62. Find $f(-3)$.
63. Find x when $f(x) = 3$.
64. Find x when $f(x) = 4$.
65. Find x when $f(x) = 2$.
66. Find x when $f(x) = -1$.
67. Find the maximum value of f.
68. Find the vertex of the graph of f.

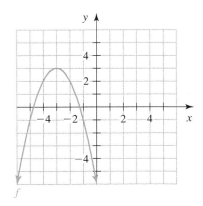

Figure 54 Exercises 61–68

Concepts

69. a. Find the x-coordinate of the vertex of the parabola $f(x) = x^2 + 4x - 12$ by averaging the x-coordinates of the y-intercept and its symmetric point.
   b. Find the x-coordinate of the vertex of the parabola $f(x) = x^2 + 4x - 12$ by averaging the x-coordinates of the x-intercepts.
   c. Compare the methods you used in parts (a) and (b). Are your results the same?
   d. Which method from parts (a) and (b) is easier to use to find the x-coordinate of the vertex of the parabola $g(x) = 54x^2 - 195x - 216$? Explain.
   e. Which method(s) can be used to find the x-coordinate of the vertex of the parabola $h(x) = x^2 + 4x + 6$? Explain.
   f. Summarize your findings in this exercise.

70. In this exercise, you will discover how to convert the standard form of a quadratic function to its vertex form.
   a. Find the vertex of the parabola $f(x) = 3x^2 - 6x + 7$.
   b. Recall that if (h, k) is the vertex of the graph of a quadratic function, then $f(x) = a(x - h)^2 + k$. Use your result from part (a) to determine h and k for $f(x) = 3x^2 - 6x + 7$.
   c. Substitute the values of h and k you found from part (b) in $f(x) = a(x - h)^2 + k$.
   d. Compare $f(x) = 3x^2 - 6x + 7$ with your result in part (c). Determine the value of a. [**Hint:** You may see this immediately. If not, write your result in part (c) in standard form and compare again with $f(x) = 3x^2 - 6x + 7$.]
   e. Substitute your value of a into your result from part (c).
   f. Verify your result graphically by comparing the graph of $f(x) = 3x^2 - 6x + 7$ with the graph of $f(x) = a(x - h)^2 + k$ for the values of a, h, and k you found.

71. Input–output pairs for four quadratic functions f, g, h, and k are listed in Table 25. For each function, decide whether $(3, 2)$ is the vertex. If $(3, 2)$ is not the vertex, estimate the coordinates of the vertex.

Table 25 Values of Four Quadratic Functions

x	$f(x)$	$g(x)$	$h(x)$	$k(x)$
1	10	8.2	19.3	11.6
2	4	2.9	7.3	4.4
3	2	2	2	2
4	4	5.5	3.4	4.4
5	10	13.4	11.5	11.6

72. Suppose that $f(x) = ax^2 + bx + c$, where $a > 0$ and g is a linear function. If $f(2) = g(2)$ and $f(5) = g(5)$, which is larger, $f(4)$ or $g(4)$? Explain. [**Hint:** Think graphically.]

73. Assume the graph of a quadratic function $f(x) = ax^2 + bx + c$ has vertex (h, k). If $a < 0$, then the maximum value of f is k. Explain.

74. Assume the graph of a quadratic function $f(x) = ax^2 + bx + c$ has vertex (h, k). If $a > 0$, then the minimum value of f is k. Explain.

75. Explain how to sketch the graph of a quadratic function $f(x) = ax^2 + bx + c$, where $b \neq 0$.

76. The x-coordinate of the vertex of the graph of a quadratic function is equal to the average of the x-coordinates of two symmetric points. Explain. Include a sketch of a graph of a quadratic function.

Related Review

Graph the equation by hand. Use a graphing calculator to verify your work.

77. $y = -3(x + 3)^2 + 5$

78. $y = -3x^2 - 6x + 5$

79. $y = -4\left(\dfrac{1}{2}\right)^x$

80. $y = -4 + \dfrac{1}{2}x$

81. We saw in Section 7.1 that the vertex of the graph of $f(x) = a(x - h)^2 + k$, where $a \neq 0$, is (h, k). In this exercise, we will show that this is true.

    a. Simplify the right-hand side of $f(x) = a(x - h)^2 + k$ to show that $f(x) = ax^2 - 2ahx + c$, where $c = ah^2 + k$.

    b. Use the vertex formula to show that the vertex of f is (h, k).

82. Consider the system

$$y = x^2 - x - 7$$
$$y = x + 1$$

    a. Use "intersect" on a graphing calculator to solve the system. [**Hint:** There are two solutions.]

    b. Use substitution to solve the system. [**Hint:** After finding the *x*-coordinates of the two solutions, don't forget to find the *y*-coordinates.]

Expressions, Equations, Functions, and Graphs

Perform the indicated instruction. Then use words such as linear, quadratic, cubic, exponential, logarithmic, polynomial, degree, function, one variable, *and* two variables *to describe the expression, equation, or system.*

83. Simplify $\dfrac{2b^{-2}c^4(3b^{-5}c^{-1})^2}{8b^{-6}c^{-4}}$.

84. Solve $x(3x - 5) + 2 = x^2 + 5$.

85. Graph $f(x) = -2(3)^x$ by hand.

86. Find the product $-2x(3x - 4)(5x - 2)$.

87. Solve $-2(3)^x = -200$. Round any solutions to the second decimal place.

88. Factor $6x^3 + 3x^2 - 18x$.

▼ 7.3 Using the Square Root Property to Solve Quadratic Equations

Objectives

» Know the *product property* and *quotient property* for square roots.

» Simplify expressions with square roots.

» *Rationalize the denominator* of a fraction.

» Use the *square root property* to solve quadratic equations.

» Make predictions with a quadratic function in vertex form.

» Know the meaning of *pure imaginary number, complex number,* and *imaginary number.*

In this section, we will discuss how to simplify expressions that have square roots. This skill will help us solve some equations that we cannot solve by factoring. We will then be able to make predictions about the dependent variable of a quadratic model in vertex form. Finally, we will define numbers that are not real numbers but can be solutions of quadratic equations.

Product Property for Square Roots

Recall from Section 4.2 that we can represent a principal *n*th root such as $k^{1/n}$ as $\sqrt[n]{k}$, where $k \geq 0$ if *n* is even. We call $\sqrt[n]{k}$ a *radical* and refer to k as the *radicand* of $\sqrt[n]{k}$. In this section, we restrict our study to principal square roots $\sqrt{k}$.

The radicand k must be nonnegative for the radical $\sqrt{k}$ to be a real number. For example, $\sqrt{-4}$ is not a real number.

For $k \geq 0$,

$$\sqrt{k} = k^{1/2}$$

We can use properties of exponents to prove the *product property for square roots*: $\sqrt{ab} = \sqrt{a}\sqrt{b}$, where $a \geq 0$ and $b \geq 0$. Here is the proof:

$$\sqrt{ab} = (ab)^{1/2} \quad \sqrt{k} = k^{1/2}$$
$$= a^{1/2}b^{1/2} \quad \text{Raise factors to nth power: } (ab)^n = a^n b^n$$
$$= \sqrt{a}\sqrt{b} \quad k^{1/2} = \sqrt{k}$$

So, $\sqrt{ab} = \sqrt{a}\sqrt{b}$.

▶ **Product Property for Square Roots**

For $a \geq 0$ and $b \geq 0$,

$$\sqrt{ab} = \sqrt{a}\sqrt{b}$$

In words, the square root of a product is the product of the square roots.

Table 26 Perfect Squares

x	Perfect Square x^2
0	0
1	1
2	4
3	9
4	16
5	25
6	36
7	49
8	64
9	81
10	100
11	121
12	144
13	169
14	196
15	225

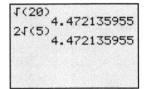

Figure 55 Verify that $\sqrt{20} = 2\sqrt{5}$

Simplifying Expressions with Square Roots

A **perfect square** is a number that has a square root that is rational. For example, 9 is a perfect square, because $\sqrt{9} = 3 = \dfrac{3}{1}$ is rational. By squaring the whole numbers from 0 to 15, we can find the integer perfect squares between 0 and 225, inclusive (see Table 26). Memorize the perfect squares shown in this table, because you will work with them again and again.

A radical $\sqrt{k}$ with a counting number k, where $k \geq 2$, is **simplified** if k does not have any perfect-square factors other than 1. We can use the product property for square roots to simplify expressions with square roots.

▶ **Example 1** Simplifying Radical Expressions

Simplify.

  1. $\sqrt{20}$ **2.** $\sqrt{32}$

Solution

  1. Note that 4 is the largest perfect-square factor of 20. We write 20 as a product of 4 and 5 and apply the product property for square roots:

$$\sqrt{20} = \sqrt{4 \cdot 5} \quad \text{\textit{4 is largest perfect-square factor.}}$$
$$= \sqrt{4}\sqrt{5} \quad \text{\textit{Product property:} } \sqrt{ab} = \sqrt{a}\sqrt{b}$$
$$= 2\sqrt{5} \quad \text{\textit{$\sqrt{4} = 2$}}$$

  We verify our work by using a graphing calculator (see Fig. 55). To compute $\sqrt{20}$, press 2nd x^2 **20**) ENTER .

  2. Both 4 and 16 are perfect-square factors of 32. Since 16 is the largest perfect-square factor, we write 32 as the product of 16 and 2 and apply the product property for square roots:

$$\sqrt{32} = \sqrt{16 \cdot 2} \quad \text{\textit{16 is largest perfect-square factor.}}$$
$$= \sqrt{16}\sqrt{2} \quad \text{\textit{Product property:} } \sqrt{ab} = \sqrt{a}\sqrt{b}$$
$$= 4\sqrt{2} \quad \text{\textit{$\sqrt{16} = 4$}}$$

In Problem 2 of Example 1, what would have happened if we had used the smaller perfect-square factor, 4, rather than the largest perfect-square factor, 16, to simplify $\sqrt{32}$?

$$\sqrt{32} = \sqrt{4 \cdot 8} = \sqrt{4}\sqrt{8} = 2\sqrt{8}$$

The radicand, 8, has a perfect-square factor of 4, so we continue to simplify:

$$\sqrt{32} = 2\sqrt{8} = 2\sqrt{4 \cdot 2} = 2\sqrt{4}\sqrt{2} = 2 \cdot 2\sqrt{2} = 4\sqrt{2}$$

The result is the same as our result in Example 1. This exploration suggests that

- The most efficient way to simplify a square root is to use the *largest* perfect-square factor of the radicand.
- If we don't use the largest perfect-square factor of the radicand, we can simplify the square root by continuing to use perfect-square factors until the radicand has no perfect-square factors other than 1.

▶ **Using the Product Property to Simplify Square Roots**

To use the product property to simplify a square root,

  1. Write the radicand as the product of the *largest* perfect-square factor and another number.

  2. Apply the product property for square roots.

Quotient Property for Square Roots

For the square root of a product, we often use the product property for square roots. What property can we use for the square root of a quotient?

> ### ▶ Quotient Property for Square Roots
>
> For $a \geq 0$ and $b > 0$,
>
> $$\sqrt{\frac{a}{b}} = \frac{\sqrt{a}}{\sqrt{b}}$$
>
> In words, the square root of a quotient is the quotient of the square roots.

You will prove the quotient property in Exercise 94.

If a square root has a fractional radicand, we **simplify the radical** by writing it as an expression whose radicand is not a fraction.

▶ Example 2 Simplifying a Radical Expression

Simplify $\sqrt{\dfrac{7}{64}}$.

Solution

$$\sqrt{\frac{7}{64}} = \frac{\sqrt{7}}{\sqrt{64}} \qquad \textit{Quotient property: } \sqrt{\frac{a}{b}} = \frac{\sqrt{a}}{\sqrt{b}}$$

$$= \frac{\sqrt{7}}{8} \qquad \sqrt{64} = 8$$

Rationalizing the Denominator of a Radical Expression

We simplify an expression of the form $\dfrac{p}{\sqrt{q}}$ by leaving no denominator as a radical expression. We call this process **rationalizing the denominator.**

▶ Example 3 Simplifying Radical Expressions

Simplify.

1. $\dfrac{2}{\sqrt{3}}$ **2.** $\sqrt{\dfrac{5}{18}}$

Solution

1. Since $\sqrt{3}\sqrt{3} = \sqrt{3 \cdot 3} = \sqrt{9} = 3$, we rationalize the denominator of $\dfrac{2}{\sqrt{3}}$ by multiplying by $\dfrac{\sqrt{3}}{\sqrt{3}}$:

$$\frac{2}{\sqrt{3}} = \frac{2}{\sqrt{3}} \cdot 1 \qquad a = a \cdot 1$$

$$= \frac{2}{\sqrt{3}} \cdot \frac{\sqrt{3}}{\sqrt{3}} \qquad \textit{Rationalize denominator: } \frac{\sqrt{3}}{\sqrt{3}} = 1$$

$$= \frac{2\sqrt{3}}{\sqrt{9}} \qquad \textit{Multiply numerators; multiply denominators;}$$
$$\qquad\qquad\qquad \textit{product property: } \sqrt{a}\sqrt{b} = \sqrt{ab}$$

$$= \frac{2\sqrt{3}}{3} \qquad \sqrt{9} = 3$$

2. $\sqrt{\dfrac{5}{18}} = \dfrac{\sqrt{5}}{\sqrt{18}}$ *Quotient property:* $\sqrt{\dfrac{a}{b}} = \dfrac{\sqrt{a}}{\sqrt{b}}$

$= \dfrac{\sqrt{5}}{3\sqrt{2}}$ $\sqrt{18} = \sqrt{9 \cdot 2} = \sqrt{9}\sqrt{2} = 3\sqrt{2}$

$= \dfrac{\sqrt{5}}{3\sqrt{2}} \cdot \dfrac{\sqrt{2}}{\sqrt{2}}$ *Rationalize denominator:* $\dfrac{\sqrt{2}}{\sqrt{2}} = 1$

$= \dfrac{\sqrt{10}}{3\sqrt{4}}$ *Multiply numerators; multiply denominators;*
                product property: $\sqrt{a}\sqrt{b} = \sqrt{ab}$

$= \dfrac{\sqrt{10}}{6}$ *Simplify.*

Figure 56 Verify the work

We verify our work by using a graphing calculator (see Fig. 56).

As Problem 1 of Example 3 shows, **to rationalize the denominator of a fraction of the form** $\dfrac{p}{\sqrt{q}}$**, where** q **is positive, we multiply the fraction by 1 in the form** $\dfrac{\sqrt{q}}{\sqrt{q}}$**.**

Summary of Simplifying a Radical Expression

We have discussed various ways to simplify a radical expression. What follows is a summary of those methods.

> ### Simplifying a Radical Expression
>
> To simplify a radical expression,
>
> 1. Use the quotient property for square roots so no radicand is a fraction.
> 2. Use the product property for square roots so no radicands have perfect-square factors other than 1.
> 3. Rationalize the denominators so no denominator is a radical expression.
> 4. Continue applying steps 1–3 until the radical expression is completely simplified.

Solving Quadratic Equations of the Form $x^2 = k$, where $k \geq 0$

We now turn our attention to solving quadratic equations of the form $x^2 = k$, where $k \geq 0$. From Section 4.4, we know that the solutions of the equation $x^2 = k$ are

$$\pm k^{1/2} = \pm\sqrt{k}$$

We call this relationship the **square root property.**

> ### Square Root Property
>
> Let k be a nonnegative constant. Then $x^2 = k$ is equivalent to
>
> $$x = \pm\sqrt{k}$$

We will discuss the case in which k is negative later in this section.

> ▶ **Example 4** Using the Square Root Property to Solve Equations

1. Solve $x^2 = 16$.   **2.** Solve $x^2 = 45$.

Solution

1.

$$x^2 = 16 \qquad \textit{Original equation}$$
$$x = \pm\sqrt{16} \quad \textit{Square root property}$$
$$x = \pm 4 \qquad \sqrt{16} = 4$$

2.

$$x^2 = 45 \qquad \textit{Original equation}$$
$$x = \pm\sqrt{45} \qquad \textit{Square root property}$$
$$x = \pm\sqrt{9 \cdot 5} \qquad \textit{9 is a perfect square.}$$
$$x = \pm 3\sqrt{5} \qquad \textit{Simplify.}$$

We use a graphing calculator to verify that $-3\sqrt{5} \approx -6.71$ and $3\sqrt{5} \approx 6.71$ are solutions (see Fig. 57).

WARNING

It is a common error to confuse solving an equation such as $x^2 = 16$ with computing a principal square root such as $\sqrt{16}$. In Problem 1 of Example 4, we found that the solutions of $x^2 = 16$ are the *two* numbers -4 and 4. Recall from Section 4.2 that $\sqrt{16}$ is the *one* number 4.

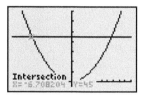

▶ **Example 5**   Using the Square Root Property to Solve an Equation

Solve $3x^2 - 5 = 6$.

Solution

$$3x^2 - 5 = 6 \qquad \textit{Original equation}$$
$$3x^2 = 11 \qquad \textit{Add 5 to both sides.}$$
$$x^2 = \frac{11}{3} \qquad \textit{Divide both sides by 3.}$$
$$x = \pm\sqrt{\frac{11}{3}} \qquad \textit{Square root property}$$
$$x = \pm\frac{\sqrt{11}}{\sqrt{3}} \qquad \textit{Quotient property: } \sqrt{\frac{a}{b}} = \frac{\sqrt{a}}{\sqrt{b}}$$
$$x = \pm\frac{\sqrt{11}}{\sqrt{3}} \cdot \frac{\sqrt{3}}{\sqrt{3}} \qquad \textit{Rationalize denominator.}$$
$$x = \pm\frac{\sqrt{33}}{3} \qquad \textit{Simplify.}$$

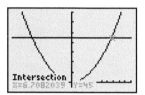

Figure 57 Verify the work

We enter $y = 3x^2 - 5$ into a graphing calculator and check that, for both inputs $-\dfrac{\sqrt{33}}{3}$ and $\dfrac{\sqrt{33}}{3}$, the output is 6 (see Fig. 58).

Solving Quadratic Equations of the Form $(px + q)^2 = k$

We can also use the square root property to solve equations that can be put into the form $(px + q)^2 = k$.

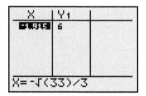

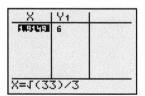

Figure 58 Verify the work

▶ **Example 6**   Using the Square Root Property to Solve an Equation

Solve $(3w - 4)^2 = 36$.

Solution

The base of $(3w - 4)^2$ is $3w - 4$. We can use the square root property to solve the equation $(3w - 4)^2 = 36$:

$$(3w - 4)^2 = 36 \qquad \textit{Original equation}$$
$$3w - 4 = \pm\sqrt{36} \qquad \textit{Square root property}$$
$$3w - 4 = \pm 6 \qquad \sqrt{36} = 6$$

$$3w - 4 = -6 \quad \text{or} \quad 3w - 4 = 6 \qquad \textit{Write as two equations.}$$
$$3w = -2 \quad \text{or} \quad 3w = 10$$
$$w = -\frac{2}{3} \quad \text{or} \quad w = \frac{10}{3}$$

▶ **Example 7**   Using the Square Root Property to Solve an Equation

Solve $\left(x + \dfrac{5}{2} \right)^2 = \dfrac{31}{4}$.

Solution

$$\left(x + \frac{5}{2} \right)^2 = \frac{31}{4} \qquad \text{\textit{Original equation}}$$

$$x + \frac{5}{2} = \pm\sqrt{\frac{31}{4}} \qquad \text{\textit{Square root property}}$$

$$x + \frac{5}{2} = \pm\frac{\sqrt{31}}{\sqrt{4}} \qquad \text{\textit{Quotient property:} } \sqrt{\frac{a}{b}} = \frac{\sqrt{a}}{\sqrt{b}}$$

$$x + \frac{5}{2} = \pm\frac{\sqrt{31}}{2} \qquad \sqrt{4} = 2$$

$$x = -\frac{5}{2} \pm \frac{\sqrt{31}}{2} \qquad \text{\textit{Subtract} } \frac{5}{2} \text{ \textit{from both sides.}}$$

$$x = \frac{-5 \pm \sqrt{31}}{2} \qquad \text{\textit{Add/subtract numerators and keep common}}$$
$$\text{\textit{denominator.}}$$

To verify our work, we store each result as x and check that $\left(x + \dfrac{5}{2} \right)^2$ is equal to $\dfrac{31}{4} = 7.75$ (see Fig. 59). See Appendix B.20 for graphing calculator instructions.

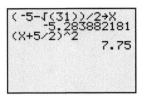

Figure 59 Verify the work

▶ **Example 8**   Solving a General Quadratic Equation

Solve $(px + q)^2 = k$ for x. Assume $k \geq 0$ and $p \neq 0$.

Solution

$$(px + q)^2 = k \qquad \text{\textit{Original equation}}$$

$$px + q = \pm\sqrt{k} \qquad \text{\textit{Square root property}}$$

$$px = -q \pm \sqrt{k} \qquad \text{\textit{Subtract q from both sides.}}$$

$$x = \frac{-q \pm \sqrt{k}}{p} \qquad \text{\textit{Divide both sides by p.}}$$

▶ **Example 9**   Finding x-Intercepts

Find the x-intercepts of the parabola $f(x) = -2(x - 7)^2 + 20$.

Solution

To find the x-intercepts, we substitute 0 for $f(x)$:

$$-2(x - 7)^2 + 20 = 0 \qquad \text{\textit{Substitute 0 for f(x).}}$$

$$-2(x - 7)^2 = -20 \qquad \text{\textit{Subtract 20 from both sides.}}$$

$$(x - 7)^2 = 10 \qquad \text{\textit{Divide both sides by} } -2.$$

$$x - 7 = \pm\sqrt{10} \qquad \text{\textit{Square root property}}$$

$$x = 7 \pm \sqrt{10} \qquad \text{\textit{Add 7 to both sides.}}$$

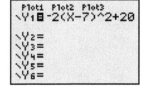

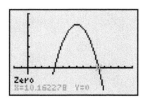

Figure 60 Verify the work

The x-intercepts are $(7 - \sqrt{10}, 0)$ and $(7 + \sqrt{10}, 0)$. In Fig. 60, we use "zero" on a graphing calculator to check that the approximate x-intercepts are $(3.84, 0)$ and $(10.16, 0)$. See Appendix B.21 for graphing calculator instructions.

Making Predictions with a Quadratic Model in Vertex Form

Our work in this section enables us to use a quadratic model in vertex form $f(t) = a(t - h)^2 + k$ to make predictions for the independent variable, t.

Table 27 Numbers of International Adoptions in the United States

Year	Number of Adoptions (thousands)
2000	18.9
2002	21.5
2004	23.0
2006	20.7
2008	17.5
2010	11.1
2011	9.3

Source: *U.S. Department of State*

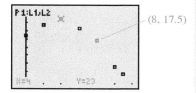

Figure 61 Scattergram of adoption data

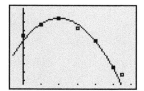

Figure 62 Check the fit

▶ **Example 10** Using a Quadratic Model to Make Predictions

The numbers of international adoptions in the United States are shown in Table 27 for various years. Let $f(t)$ be the number (in thousands) of international adoptions in the United States in the year that is t years since 2000.

1. Find an equation of f.
2. Estimate in which years there were 15 thousand international adoptions.

Solution

1. We use a graphing calculator to draw a scattergram of the data (see Fig. 61). It appears that a quadratic function will fit the data much better than an exponential model or a linear model. Recall from Section 7.1 that we can find a quadratic function in vertex form $f(t) = a(t - h)^2 + k$. To begin, we select the highest data point, $(4, 23)$, to be the vertex (see Fig. 61). Here, $h = 4$ and $k = 23$:

$$f(t) = a(t - 4)^2 + 23$$

Next, we imagine a parabola with vertex $(4, 23)$ that comes close to (or contains) the data points. Such a parabola might be the one that contains the data point $(8, 17.5)$. See Fig. 61. To find a, we substitute 8 for t and 17.5 for $f(t)$ in the equation $f(t) = a(t - 4)^2 + 23$:

$17.5 = a(8 - 4)^2 + 23$	*Substitute 8 for t and 17.5 for f(t).*
$17.5 = a(4)^2 + 23$	*Subtract.*
$17.5 = 16a + 23$	*Simplify.*
$-5.5 = 16a$	*Subtract 23 from both sides.*
$-0.34 \approx a$	*Divide both sides by 16.*

The approximate equation is $f(t) = -0.34(t - 4)^2 + 23$. The model fits the data well (see Fig. 62).

2. We substitute 15 for $f(t)$ in the equation $f(t) = -0.34(t - 4)^2 + 23$ and solve for t:

$-0.34(t - 4)^2 + 23 = 15$	*Substitute 15 for f(t).*
$-0.34(t - 4)^2 = -8$	*Subtract 23 from both sides.*
$(t - 4)^2 = \dfrac{-8}{-0.34}$	*Divide both sides by −0.34.*
$t - 4 = \pm\sqrt{\dfrac{8}{0.34}}$	*Square root property; simplify fraction.*
$t = 4 \pm \sqrt{\dfrac{8}{0.34}}$	*Add 4 to both sides.*

$t = 4 - \sqrt{\dfrac{8}{0.34}}$	or	$t = 4 + \sqrt{\dfrac{8}{0.34}}$	*Write as two equations.*
$t \approx 4 - 4.85$	or	$t \approx 4 + 4.85$	*Approximate square root.*
$t \approx -0.85$	or	$t \approx 8.85$	

The model estimates that there were 15 thousand international adoptions in the United States in both 1999 and 2009.

Complex Numbers

So far in this section, we have discussed equations of the form $x^2 = k$, where k is nonnegative. What happens when k is a negative number, such as -1?

From Section 4.4, we know that the equation $x^2 = -1$ has no real-number solutions. Now we define a number that is *not* a real number but *is* a solution of $x^2 = -1$.

We define $\sqrt{-1}$ to be a number whose square is -1. We represent this number as i.

▶ Definition   Imaginary unit *i*

The **imaginary unit,** written *i*, is the number whose square is −1. That is,

$$i^2 = -1 \quad \text{and} \quad i = \sqrt{-1}$$

Next, we define the square root of any negative number.

▶ Definition   Square root of a negative number

If *p* is a positive real number, then

$$\sqrt{-p} = i\sqrt{p}$$

If *b* is a nonzero real number, then we call an expression of the form *bi* a **pure imaginary number.**

▶ **Example 11**   Writing Numbers in *bi* Form

Write the number in *bi* form, where *b* is a real number. Simplify the result.

1. $\sqrt{-49}$ **2.** $-\sqrt{-24}$

Solution

1. $\sqrt{-49} = i\sqrt{49} = 7i$ **2.** $-\sqrt{-24} = -i\sqrt{24} = -i\sqrt{4 \cdot 6} = -2i\sqrt{6}$

▶

We can combine real numbers *a* and *b* with the imaginary unit *i* to form a *complex number* of the form

$$a + bi$$

▶ Definition   Complex number

A **complex number** is a number of the form

$$a + bi$$

where *a* and *b* are real numbers.

Here are some examples of complex numbers:

$$2 + 5i, \quad 3 - 4i, \quad 5 + 0i = 5, \quad 0 - 7i = -7i$$

Since $a = a + 0i$ and $bi = 0 + bi$, we see that all real numbers and all pure imaginary numbers are complex numbers.

A complex number that is not a real number is called an *imaginary number*.

▶ Definition   Imaginary number

An **imaginary number** is a number $a + bi$, where *a* and *b* are real numbers and $b \neq 0$.

The complex number $3 + 7i$ is an imaginary number, since $b = 7 \neq 0$. The complex number $4 = 4 + 0i$ is not an imaginary number, since $b = 0$.

We perform operations with complex numbers in much the same way that we perform operations with polynomials. Here we compare squaring the monomial $5x$ with squaring the pure imaginary number $5i$:

$$(5x)^2 = 5^2 x^2 = 25x^2 \qquad (5i)^2 = 5^2 i^2 = 25(-1) = -25$$

We use a graphing calculator to verify our work of squaring $5i$ (see Fig. 63). To compute $(5i)^2$, press ⎡(**5** ⎡2nd⎤□⎤ ⎤) ⎿△⏌ **2** ⎡ENTER⎤.

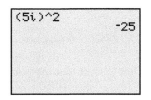

Figure 63 Check the work

Solving Quadratic Equations of the Form $x^2 = k$, where $k < 0$

We can extend the square root property to the case in which k is negative.

> **Square Root Property**
>
> Let k be a real-number constant. Then $x^2 = k$ is equivalent to
> $$x = \pm\sqrt{k}$$

▶ **Example 12**   Using the Square Root Property to Solve Equations

Solve.

1. $y^2 = -9$ **2.** $x^2 = -12$

Solution

1.

$$\begin{aligned} y^2 &= -9 && \textit{Original equation} \\ y &= \pm\sqrt{-9} && \textit{Square root property} \\ y &= \pm i\sqrt{9} && \sqrt{-p} = i\sqrt{p}, \textit{where } p > 0 \\ y &= \pm 3i && \sqrt{9} = 3 \end{aligned}$$

We check that both $-3i$ and $3i$ satisfy the original equation:

Check $y = -3i$	**Check $y = 3i$**
$y^2 = -9$	$y^2 = -9$
$(-3i)^2 \overset{?}{=} -9$	$(3i)^2 \overset{?}{=} -9$
$(-3)^2 i^2 \overset{?}{=} -9$	$3^2 i^2 \overset{?}{=} -9$
$9(-1) \overset{?}{=} -9$	$9(-1) \overset{?}{=} -9$
$-9 \overset{?}{=} -9$	$-9 \overset{?}{=} -9$
true	true

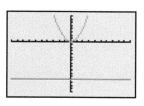

Figure 64 Check the work

2.

$$\begin{aligned} x^2 &= -12 && \textit{Original equation} \\ x &= \pm\sqrt{-12} && \textit{Square root property} \\ x &= \pm i\sqrt{12} && \sqrt{-p} = i\sqrt{p}, \textit{where } p > 0 \\ x &= \pm i(2\sqrt{3}) && \sqrt{12} = \sqrt{4 \cdot 3} = 2\sqrt{3} \\ x &= \pm 2i\sqrt{3} && \textit{Rearrange factors.} \end{aligned}$$

The graphical check in Fig. 64 shows that the graphs of $y = x^2$ and $y = -12$ do not intersect. This means that the equation $x^2 = -12$ has no real-number solutions. It *does* have the two imaginary-number solutions $\pm 2i\sqrt{3}$.

▶ **Example 13**   Using the Square Root Property to Solve an Equation

Solve $(x + 3)^2 = -28$.

Solution

$$\begin{aligned} (x + 3)^2 &= -28 && \textit{Original equation} \\ x + 3 &= \pm\sqrt{-28} && \textit{Square root property} \\ x + 3 &= \pm i\sqrt{28} && \sqrt{-p} = i\sqrt{p}, \textit{where } p > 0 \\ x + 3 &= \pm 2i\sqrt{7} && \sqrt{28} = \sqrt{4 \cdot 7} = 2\sqrt{7} \\ x &= -3 \pm 2i\sqrt{7} && \textit{Subtract 3 from both sides.} \end{aligned}$$

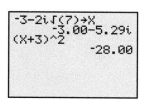

Figure 65 Verify the work

To verify our work, we store each result as x and check that $(x + 3)^2$ is equal to -28 (see Fig. 65). We press MODE and set FLOAT to 2, so the numbers in the result are rounded to the second decimal place.

Group Exploration

Deriving a formula for solving quadratic equations in $a(x - h)^2 + k = p$ form

1. Solve $2(x - 5)^2 + 7 = 10$.
2. Solve the equation $a(x - h)^2 + k = p$ for x. Assume $a \neq 0$ and $\dfrac{p - k}{a} \geq 0$. [**Hint:** Follow the same steps as in Problem 1.]

3. Use your result from Problem 2 to solve the equation $3(x - 4)^2 + 2 = 7$. [**Hint:** Substitute the appropriate values for a, h, k, and p into your formula from Problem 2.]

Group Exploration

Looking ahead: Perfect-square trinomials

1. Consider the true statement
$$(x + k)^2 = x^2 + (2k)x + k^2$$
For the trinomial on the right-hand side, the coefficient of x is $2k$ and the constant term is k^2. Describe how to use operations such as adding, subtracting, multiplying, dividing, and/or squaring to change $2k$ into k^2.

2. Show that your description in Problem 1 works for the true statement
$$(x + 3)^2 = x^2 + 6x + 9$$

3. Simplify $(x - k)^2$. Give a description similar to the one you made in Problem 1. Show that your description works for the true statement
$$(x - 4)^2 = x^2 - 8x + 16$$

4. Find a value of c such that the trinomial can be factored as the square of a binomial $(x + k)^2$ or $(x - k)^2$. Then factor the trinomial.

   a. $x^2 + 8x + c$ **b.** $x^2 + 10x + c$
   c. $x^2 - 14x + c$ **d.** $x^2 - 18x + c$

Homework 7.3

For extra help ▶ MyMathLab®   ▦ Watch the videos in MyMathLab   Download the MyDashboard App

Simplify.

1. $\sqrt{169}$
2. $\sqrt{196}$
3. $\sqrt{12}$
4. $\sqrt{75}$

5. $\sqrt{\dfrac{4}{9}}$
6. $\sqrt{\dfrac{25}{81}}$
7. $\sqrt{\dfrac{6}{49}}$
8. $\sqrt{\dfrac{13}{100}}$

9. $\dfrac{5}{\sqrt{2}}$
10. $\dfrac{4}{\sqrt{7}}$
11. $\dfrac{3}{\sqrt{32}}$
12. $\dfrac{8}{\sqrt{60}}$

13. $\sqrt{\dfrac{3}{2}}$
14. $\sqrt{\dfrac{7}{5}}$
15. $\sqrt{\dfrac{11}{20}}$
16. $\sqrt{\dfrac{7}{90}}$

Solve. All solutions are real numbers.

17. $x^2 = 25$
18. $x^2 = 64$
19. $x^2 - 3 = 0$
20. $x^2 - 19 = 0$
21. $t^2 = 32$
22. $r^2 = 24$
23. $5x^2 = 3$
24. $2x^2 = 13$
25. $3p^2 - 11 = 3$
26. $5w^2 - 28 = 5$
27. $(x + 4)^2 = 7$
28. $(x + 1)^2 = 3$
29. $(x - 5)^2 = 27$
30. $(x - 9)^2 = 75$
31. $(8y + 3)^2 = 36$
32. $(4m + 7)^2 = 81$
33. $(9x - 5)^2 = 0$
34. $(5x - 4)^2 = 0$

35. $\left(x + \dfrac{3}{4}\right)^2 = \dfrac{41}{16}$
36. $\left(x + \dfrac{5}{6}\right)^2 = \dfrac{51}{36}$
37. $\left(w - \dfrac{7}{3}\right)^2 = \dfrac{5}{9}$
38. $\left(p - \dfrac{2}{5}\right)^2 = \dfrac{17}{25}$
39. $5(x - 6)^2 + 3 = 33$
40. $2(x - 4)^2 + 5 = 27$
41. $-3(x + 1)^2 + 2 = -5$
42. $-7(x + 8)^2 + 4 = -1$

Find all x-intercepts.

43. $f(x) = x^2 - 17$
44. $f(x) = x^2 - 35$
45. $f(x) = 2(x - 3)^2 - 7$
46. $f(x) = 7(x - 6)^2 - 13$
47. $f(x) = -4(x - 2)^2 - 16$
48. $f(x) = -3(x - 5)^2 - 27$

Simplify.

49. $\sqrt{-36}$
50. $\sqrt{-25}$
51. $-\sqrt{-45}$
52. $-\sqrt{-40}$
53. $\sqrt{-\dfrac{5}{49}}$
54. $\sqrt{-\dfrac{7}{9}}$
55. $\sqrt{-\dfrac{13}{5}}$
56. $\sqrt{-\dfrac{2}{7}}$

Find all complex-number solutions.

57. $x^2 = -49$

58. $x^2 = -4$

59. $x^2 = -18$

60. $x^2 = -28$

61. $7x^2 + 26 = 5$

62. $4x^2 + 25 = 17$

63. $(m + 4)^2 = -8$

64. $(t + 8)^2 = -45$

65. $\left(x - \dfrac{5}{4}\right)^2 = -\dfrac{3}{16}$

66. $\left(x - \dfrac{1}{2}\right)^2 = -\dfrac{7}{4}$

67. $-2(y + 3)^2 + 1 = 9$

68. $-2(w + 1)^2 + 7 = 39$

69. The percentages of Americans who say they are "very happy" are shown in Table 28 for various years.

Table 28 Percentages of Americans Who Say They Are "Very Happy"

Year	Percent
1972	30
1980	35
1990	36
2000	34
2010	29

Source: *National Opinion Research Center*

Let $f(t)$ be the percentage of Americans who say they are "very happy" at t years since 1970.

a. Find a quadratic equation of f in vertex form.

b. Find $f(49)$. What does it mean in this situation?

c. Find t when $f(t) = 23$. What does it mean in this situation?

d. What is the vertex of the model? What does it mean in this situation?

70. The revenues from ringtones, ringbacks, and videos for cell phones are shown in Table 29 for various years.

Table 29 Revenues from Ringtones, Ringbacks, and Videos for Cell Phones

Year	Revenue (millions of dollars)
2005	422
2006	775
2007	879
2008	977
2009	729
2010	527

Source: *Recording Industry Association of America*

Let $f(t)$ be the annual revenue (in millions of dollars) from ringtones, ringbacks, and videos for cell phones at t years since 2000.

a. Find a quadratic equation of f in vertex form.

b. Use f to estimate the revenue in 2010. Find the error in your estimate.

c. Estimate when the annual revenue was $70 million.

d. What is the vertex of the model? What does it mean in this situation?

71. The revenues from U.S. adult mattresses are shown in Table 30 for various years.

Table 30 Revenues from U.S. Adult Mattresses

Year	Revenue (billions of dollars)
2007	5.2
2008	4.7
2009	4.4
2010	4.6
2011	5.0

Source: *International Sleep Products Association*

Let $f(t)$ be the annual revenue (in billions of dollars) at t years since 2000. A model of the situation is the following: $f(t) = 0.16(t - 9.15)^2 + 4.45$.

a. Use a graphing calculator to draw the graph of the model f and, in the same viewing window, the scattergram of the data. Does the model fit the data well?

b. What is the vertex? What does it mean in this situation?

c. Predict the revenue in 2017.

d. Predict when the annual revenue will be $10 billion.

72. The percentages of the U.S. federal debt owed to foreigners are shown in Table 31 for various years.

Table 31 Percentages of the U.S. Federal Debt Owed to Foreigners

Year	Percent
1985	15
1990	18
1995	22
2000	31
2005	45
2011	47

Source: *White House Office of Management and Budget*

Let $P(t)$ be the percentage of the U.S. federal debt owed to foreigners at t years since 1980. A model of the situation is $P(t) = 0.0157(t + 26.1)^2 - 1.7$

a. Use a graphing calculator to draw the graph of the model f and, in the same viewing window, the scattergram of the data. Does the model fit the data well?

b. Use P to predict the percentage of the federal debt owed to foreigners in 2018.

c. In Exercise 34 of Homework 4.5, you found an equation close to $f(t) = 222.15(1.085)^t$, where $f(t)$ is the federal debt (in billions of dollars) at t years since 1960. Use f to predict the federal debt in 2018. Then use your result in part (b) to predict the number of billions of dollars of that debt owed to foreigners in 2018.

d. Use P to predict when all of the debt will be owed to foreigners.

For Exercises 73–78, find approximate solutions of the given equation or system by referring to the graphs shown in Fig. 66. Round results or coordinates of results to the first decimal place.

73. $\dfrac{1}{2}(x - 2)^2 - 1 = -2(x - 3)^2 + 4$

74. $-2(x - 3)^2 + 4 = \dfrac{1}{2}x - 4$

75. $-2(x - 3)^2 + 4 = 2$ **76.** $\frac{1}{2}(x - 2)^2 - 1 = 0$

77. $y = -2(x - 3)^2 + 4$ **78.** $y = \frac{1}{2}(x - 2)^2 - 1$
$y = \frac{1}{2}x - 4$ $y = -2(x - 3)^2 + 4$

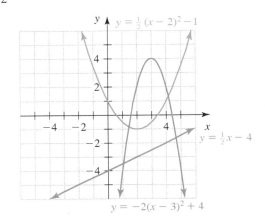

Figure 66 Exercises 73–78

For Exercises 79–86, solve for the specified variable. Assume the constants have values for which the equation has exactly two real-number solutions.

79. $a^2 + b^2 = c^2$, for a **80.** $\dfrac{r^2}{b} = c$, for r

81. $\dfrac{w^2}{r} + p = b$, for w **82.** $\dfrac{w^2 - k}{r} = b$, for w

83. $(x + b)^2 = k$, for x **84.** $(x - b)^2 - q = k$, for x

85. $(py + a)^2 + b = c$, for y **86.** $\dfrac{(py - a)^2}{b} = c$, for y

Concepts

87. A student tries to solve the equation $x^2 - 10x + 25 = 0$:

$$x^2 - 10x + 25 = 0$$
$$x^2 = 10x - 25$$
$$x = \pm\sqrt{10x - 25}$$

Describe any errors. Then solve the equation correctly.

88. A student tries to solve the equation $3(x - 5)^2 = 12$:

$$3(x - 5)^2 = 12$$
$$(x - 5)^2 = 4$$
$$x - 5 = 2$$
$$x = 7$$

Describe any errors. Then solve the equation correctly.

89. Let $f(x) = 2(x - 3)^2 + 5$.

  a. What is the vertex of the graph of f?
  b. Does the graph of f open upward or downward? Explain.
  c. How many real-number solutions does each of the equations that follow have? Explain how you can use your results from parts (a) and (b).
  i. $2(x - 3)^2 + 5 = 8$
  ii. $2(x - 3)^2 + 5 = 5$
  iii. $2(x - 3)^2 + 5 = 1$

90. Let $f(x) = -3(x + 2)^2 + 4$.
  a. What is the vertex of the graph of f?
  b. Does the graph of f open upward or downward? Explain.
  c. How many real-number solutions does each of the equations that follow have? Explain how you can use your results from parts (a) and (b).
  i. $-3(x + 2)^2 + 4 = 6$
  ii. $-3(x + 2)^2 + 4 = 4$
  iii. $-3(x + 2)^2 + 4 = 2$

91. a. Use factoring to solve the equation $25x^2 - 49 = 0$.
  b. Use the square root property to solve the equation $25x^2 - 49 = 0$.
  c. Compare your results for parts (a) and (b).
  d. Is it easier to solve $25x^2 - 49 = 0$ by factoring or by using the square root property? Explain.

92. a. Use factoring to solve the equation $(2x - 3)^2 = 16$.
  b. Use the square root property to solve the equation $(2x - 3)^2 = 16$.
  c. Compare your results for parts (a) and (b).
  d. Is it easier to solve $(2x - 3)^2 = 16$ by factoring or by using the square root property? Explain.

93. a. Can the equation $(x + 4)^2 = 5$ be solved with the square root property? If yes, do so.
  b. Can the equation $(x + 4)^2 = 5$ be solved by factoring? If yes, do so.
  c. Can all equations that can be solved with the square root property be solved by factoring? Explain.

94. Assume $a \geq 0$ and $b > 0$. Show that $\sqrt{\dfrac{a}{b}} = \dfrac{\sqrt{a}}{\sqrt{b}}$.

95. What forms of quadratic equations can you solve by using the square root property? By using factoring? For example, quadratic equations of the form $x^2 + 2bx + b^2 = 0$ can be solved by factoring. Include examples.

96. Give an example of a quadratic equation in one variable that has the given number and type of solutions. Then solve the equation.
  a. two real-number solutions
  b. one real-number solution
  c. two imaginary-number solutions

Related Review

Solve. Round any results to the fourth decimal place. Verify that they approximately satisfy the equation.

97. $x^6 = 142$ **98.** $x^4 = 83$
99. $(t - 4)^3 = 88$ **100.** $(p + 7)^5 = 61$
101. $3(x + 1)^5 - 4 = 44$ **102.** $4(x - 2)^3 + 7 = 79$

Expressions, Equations, Functions, and Graphs

Perform the indicated instruction. Then use words such as linear, quadratic, cubic, exponential, logarithmic, polynomial, degree, function, one variable, *and* two variables *to describe the expression, equation, or system.*

103. Factor $2w^3 + 3w^2 - 18w - 27$.
104. Solve $3(x - 4)^2 - 5 = -7$.
105. Solve $2w^3 + 3w^2 - 18w - 27 = 0$.
106. Simplify $3(x - 4)^2 - 5$.
107. Find the product $(5w^2 - 2)(4w + 3)$.
108. Graph $f(x) = 3(x - 4)^2 - 5$ by hand.

▼7.4 Solving Quadratic Equations by Completing the Square

Objectives

» Know the relationship between b and c in a perfect-square trinomial of the form $x^2 + bx + c$.

» Solve quadratic equations by *completing the square*.

» Know that any quadratic equation can be solved by completing the square.

So far, we have discussed how to solve quadratic equations by factoring and by using the square root property. In this section, we will discuss yet another way, called *completing the square*.

Perfect-Square Trinomials

To begin our study of completing the square, we simplify the square of a sum. For example,

$$(x + 3)^2 = x^2 + 6x + 9$$

So, $x^2 + 6x + 9$ is a perfect-square trinomial. Recall from Section 6.2 that a *perfect-square trinomial* is a trinomial that is equivalent to the square of a binomial.

For $x^2 + 6x + 9$, there is a special connection between the 6 and the 9. If we divide the 6 by 2 and then square the result, we get 9:

$$x^2 + 6x + 9$$

$$\left(\frac{6}{2}\right)^2 = 3^2 = 9$$

This is no coincidence. Consider simplifying $(x - 4)^2$: $(x - 4)^2 = x^2 - 8x + 16$. If we divide -8 by 2 and square the result, we get 16:

$$x^2 - 8x + 16$$

$$\left(\frac{-8}{2}\right)^2 = (-4)^2 = 16$$

For the general case, we simplify $(x + k)^2$, where k is a constant:

$$(x + k)^2 = x^2 + (2k)x + k^2$$

$$\left(\frac{2k}{2}\right)^2 = k^2$$

For $x^2 + (2k)x + k^2$, we see that if we divide the coefficient of x by 2 and square the result, we get the constant term k^2.

> ### ▶ Perfect-Square Trinomial Property
>
> For a perfect-square trinomial of the form $x^2 + bx + c$, dividing b by 2 and squaring the result gives c:
>
> $$x^2 + bx + c$$
>
> $$\left(\frac{b}{2}\right)^2 = c$$

▶ Example 1   Factoring Perfect-Square Trinomials

Find the value of c such that the expression is a perfect-square trinomial. Then factor the perfect-square trinomial.

1. $x^2 + 10x + c$ **2.** $x^2 - 9x + c$ **3.** $x^2 + \dfrac{5}{3}x + c$

Solution

1. We divide 10 by 2 and square the result:

$$\left(\frac{10}{2}\right)^2 = 5^2 = 25 = c$$

The expression is $x^2 + 10x + 25$, with factored form $(x + k)^2$ for some positive integer k. So, we have

$$x^2 + 10x + 25 = (x + k)^2 = x^2 + 2kx + k^2$$

The constant terms 25 and k^2 are equal.

Here $k^2 = 25$, or $k = 5$ (k is positive). So, the factored form of $x^2 + 10x + 25$ is $(x + 5)^2$.

2. We divide -9 by 2 and square the result:

$$\left(\frac{-9}{2}\right)^2 = \frac{81}{4} = c$$

The expression is $x^2 - 9x + \frac{81}{4}$, with factored form $(x - k)^2$ for some positive integer k. So, we have

$$x^2 - 9x + \frac{81}{4} = (x - k)^2 = x^2 - 2kx + k^2$$

The constant terms $\frac{81}{4}$ and k^2 are equal.

Here $k^2 = \frac{81}{4}$, or $k = \frac{9}{2}$ (k is positive). So, the factored form of $x^2 - 9x + \frac{81}{4}$ is $\left(x - \frac{9}{2}\right)^2$.

3. Dividing by 2 is the same as multiplying by $\frac{1}{2}$. So, we multiply $\frac{5}{3}$ by $\frac{1}{2}$ and square the result:

$$\left(\frac{5}{3} \cdot \frac{1}{2}\right)^2 = \left(\frac{5}{6}\right)^2 = \frac{25}{36} = c$$

The expression is $x^2 + \frac{5}{3}x + \frac{25}{36}$, with factored form $\left(x + \frac{5}{6}\right)^2$.

Solving $x^2 + bx + c = 0$ by Completing the Square

Now we can solve a quadratic equation by forming a perfect-square trinomial on one side of the equation.

▶ **Example 2**   Solving by Completing the Square

Solve $x^2 + 6x = -4$.

Solution

Since $\left(\frac{6}{2}\right)^2 = 3^2 = 9$, we add 9 to both sides of $x^2 + 6x = -4$ so the left side will be a perfect-square trinomial:

$$\begin{aligned}
x^2 + 6x &= -4 &&\textit{Original equation}\\
x^2 + 6x + 9 &= -4 + 9 &&\textit{Add 9 to both sides.}\\
(x + 3)^2 &= 5 &&\textit{Factor left side; simplify.}\\
x + 3 &= \pm\sqrt{5} &&\textit{Square root property}\\
x &= -3 \pm \sqrt{5} &&\textit{Subtract 3 from both sides.}
\end{aligned}$$

To check, we enter $y = x^2 + 6x$ in a graphing calculator and find that, for both inputs $-3 - \sqrt{5}$ and $-3 + \sqrt{5}$, the output is -4 (see Fig. 67).

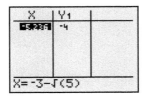

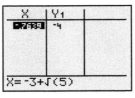

Figure 67 Verify the work

In Example 2, we added 9 to both sides of $x^2 + 6x = -4$ and factored the left side to get $(x + 3)^2$. By adding 9 to both sides of the equation, we say we *completed the square* for $x^2 + 6x$.

WARNING

When solving a quadratic equation such as $x^2 + 6x = -4$ by completing the square, it is a common error to add a number (in this case, 9) to only the left side of the equation. Remember to add the number to *both* sides of the equation.

▶ **Example 3** Solving by Completing the Square

Solve $t^2 - 5t + 1 = 0$.

Solution

To solve $t^2 - 5t + 1 = 0$, we first put the equation into the form $t^2 + bt = k$ before completing the square:

$$t^2 - 5t + 1 = 0 \qquad \text{\textit{Original equation}}$$

$$t^2 - 5t = -1 \qquad \text{\textit{Subtract 1 from both sides.}}$$

$$t^2 - 5t + \frac{25}{4} = -1 + \frac{25}{4} \qquad \text{\textit{Add} } \left(\frac{-5}{2}\right)^2 = \frac{25}{4} \text{ \textit{to both sides.}}$$

$$\left(t - \frac{5}{2}\right)^2 = -\frac{4}{4} + \frac{25}{4} \qquad \text{\textit{Factor left side; find LCD.}}$$

$$\left(t - \frac{5}{2}\right)^2 = \frac{21}{4} \qquad \begin{array}{l}\text{\textit{Add numerators and keep common}}\\ \text{\textit{denominator:} } \frac{a}{b} + \frac{c}{b} = \frac{a + c}{b}\end{array}$$

$$t - \frac{5}{2} = \pm\sqrt{\frac{21}{4}} \qquad \text{\textit{Square root property}}$$

$$t - \frac{5}{2} = \pm\frac{\sqrt{21}}{2} \qquad \text{\textit{Quotient property:} } \sqrt{\frac{a}{b}} = \frac{\sqrt{a}}{\sqrt{b}}$$

$$t = \frac{5}{2} \pm \frac{\sqrt{21}}{2} \qquad \text{\textit{Add} } \frac{5}{2} \text{ \textit{to both sides.}}$$

$$t = \frac{5 \pm \sqrt{21}}{2} \qquad \begin{array}{l}\text{\textit{Add/subtract numerators and keep}}\\ \text{\textit{common denominator.}}\end{array}$$

We use a graphing calculator to verify our work by storing an approximation of each solution as x and checking that $x^2 - 5x + 1$ is approximately 0 (see Fig. 68). For the calculator entry, the numerator of each fraction must be in parentheses. To store a value, see Appendix B.20.

Figure 68 Verify the work

▶

Solving $ax^2 + bx + c = 0$ by Completing the Square

So far, we have worked with trinomials only of the form $ax^2 + bx + c$, where $a = 1$. What do we do when $a \neq 1$? Consider simplifying $(2x + 5)^2$:

$$(2x + 5)^2 = 4x^2 + 20x + 25$$

Dividing $b = 20$ by 2 and squaring the result does *not* give 25:

$$\left(\frac{20}{2}\right)^2 = 10^2 = 100 \neq 25$$

So, the perfect-square trinomial property given for $ax^2 + bx + c$, where $a = 1$, does not extend to trinomials with $a \neq 1$. However, when solving a quadratic equation of the form $ax^2 + bx + c = 0$ with $a \neq 1$, we can first divide both sides by a to obtain an equation involving "$1x^2$"—an equation to which we *can* apply the property.

▶ **Example 4**   Solving by Completing the Square

Solve $2x^2 - 16x = -7$.

Solution

$$2x^2 - 16x = -7 \qquad \textit{Original equation}$$

$$x^2 - 8x = -\frac{7}{2} \qquad \textit{Divide both sides by 2.}$$

$$x^2 - 8x + 16 = -\frac{7}{2} + 16 \qquad \textit{Add } \left(\frac{-8}{2}\right)^2 = (-4)^2 = 16 \textit{ to both sides.}$$

$$(x - 4)^2 = -\frac{7}{2} + \frac{32}{2} \qquad \textit{Factor left side; find LCD.}$$

$$(x - 4)^2 = \frac{25}{2} \qquad \textit{Add numerators and keep common denominator: } \frac{a}{b} + \frac{c}{b} = \frac{a + c}{b}$$

$$x - 4 = \pm\sqrt{\frac{25}{2}} \qquad \textit{Square root property}$$

$$x - 4 = \pm\frac{5\sqrt{2}}{2} \qquad \sqrt{\frac{25}{2}} = \frac{\sqrt{25}}{\sqrt{2}} = \frac{5}{\sqrt{2}} \cdot \frac{\sqrt{2}}{\sqrt{2}} = \frac{5\sqrt{2}}{2}$$

$$x = 4 \pm \frac{5\sqrt{2}}{2} \qquad \textit{Add 4 to both sides.}$$

$$x = \frac{8}{2} \pm \frac{5\sqrt{2}}{2} \qquad \textit{Find LCD.}$$

$$x = \frac{8 \pm 5\sqrt{2}}{2} \qquad \textit{Add/subtract numerators and keep common denominator.}$$

▶

Any quadratic equation can be solved by completing the square. Here is a summary of this method.

▶ **Solving a Quadratic Equation by Completing the Square**

To solve a quadratic equation $ax^2 + bx + c = 0$ by **completing the square,**

1. If $a \neq 1$, divide both sides of the equation by a.
2. Write the equation in the form $x^2 + dx = k$, where d and k are constants.
3. Complete the square for the expression on the left side of the equation.
4. Solve the equation by using the square root property.

WARNING   To solve an equation of the form $ax^2 + bx = k$, where $a \neq 1$, we must divide both sides of the equation by a before completing the square on the left side of the equation.

▶ **Example 5**   Solving by Completing the Square

Solve $3x^2 + 7x - 5 = 0$.

Solution

$$3x^2 + 7x - 5 = 0 \qquad \textit{Original equation}$$

$$x^2 + \frac{7}{3}x - \frac{5}{3} = 0 \qquad \textit{Divide both sides by 3.}$$

$$x^2 + \frac{7}{3}x = \frac{5}{3} \qquad \textit{Add } \frac{5}{3} \textit{ to both sides.}$$

$$x^2 + \frac{7}{3}x + \frac{49}{36} = \frac{5}{3} + \frac{49}{36} \qquad \textit{Add } \left(\frac{7}{3} \cdot \frac{1}{2}\right)^2 = \left(\frac{7}{6}\right)^2 = \frac{49}{36} \textit{ to both sides.}$$

$$\left(x + \frac{7}{6}\right)^2 = \frac{60}{36} + \frac{49}{36} \qquad \textit{Factor left side; find LCD.}$$

$$\left(x + \frac{7}{6}\right)^2 = \frac{109}{36} \qquad \textit{Add numerators and keep common denominator: } \frac{a}{b} + \frac{c}{b} = \frac{a+c}{b}$$

$$x + \frac{7}{6} = \pm\sqrt{\frac{109}{36}} \qquad \textit{Square root property}$$

$$x + \frac{7}{6} = \pm\frac{\sqrt{109}}{6} \qquad \textit{Quotient property: } \sqrt{\frac{a}{b}} = \frac{\sqrt{a}}{\sqrt{b}}$$

$$x = -\frac{7}{6} \pm \frac{\sqrt{109}}{6} \qquad \textit{Subtract } \frac{7}{6} \textit{ from both sides.}$$

$$x = \frac{-7 \pm \sqrt{109}}{6} \qquad \textit{Add/subtract numerators and keep common denominator.}$$

Solving a Quadratic Equation That Has Imaginary-Number Solutions

In Example 6, we use completing the square to solve a quadratic equation that has imaginary-number solutions.

▶ **Example 6** Solving by Completing the Square

Solve $5x^2 - 10x + 45 = 0$.

Solution

Figure 69 Verify the work

$$5x^2 - 10x + 45 = 0 \qquad \textit{Original equation}$$

$$x^2 - 2x + 9 = 0 \qquad \textit{Divide both sides by 5.}$$

$$x^2 - 2x = -9 \qquad \textit{Subtract 9 from both sides.}$$

$$x^2 - 2x + 1 = -9 + 1 \qquad \textit{Add } \left(\frac{-2}{2}\right)^2 = (-1)^2 = 1 \textit{ to both sides.}$$

$$(x - 1)^2 = -8 \qquad \textit{Factor left side.}$$

$$x - 1 = \pm\sqrt{-8} \qquad \textit{Square root property}$$

$$x - 1 = \pm i\sqrt{8} \qquad \sqrt{-p} = i\sqrt{p}, \textit{ where } p > 0$$

$$x - 1 = \pm 2i\sqrt{2} \qquad \sqrt{8} = \sqrt{4 \cdot 2} = 2\sqrt{2}$$

$$x = 1 \pm 2i\sqrt{2} \qquad \textit{Add 1 to both sides.}$$

To verify our work, we store each result as x and check that $5x^2 - 10x + 45$ is equal to 0 (see Fig. 69).

▶

Group Exploration

Looking ahead: Deriving a formula for solving quadratic equations of the form $ax^2 + bx + c = 0$

1. Solve the equation $2x^2 + 9x + 3 = 0$.
2. Solve the quadratic equation $ax^2 + bx + c = 0$ for x. [**Hint:** Follow the same steps as in Problem 1.]

3. Use your result from Problem 2 to solve the equation $3x^2 + 11x + 5 = 0$. [**Hint:** Substitute the appropriate values of a, b, and c into your formula from Problem 2.]

▶ Tips for Success   Solve Problems

Although you can do many things to enhance your learning, there is no substitute for solving problems. Your mathematical ability will respond to solving problems in much the same way that your muscles respond to lifting weights. Muscles greatly increase in strength when you work out intensely, frequently, and consistently.

   To learn math, you must be an *active* participant. No amount of watching weight lifters lift, reading about weight-lifting techniques, or conditioning yourself psychologically can replace working out by lifting weights. Similarly, no amount of watching your instructor do problems, reading your text, or listening to a tutor can replace "working out" by solving problems.

Homework 7.4

For extra help ▶   **MyMathLab®**   ▦ Watch the videos in MyMathLab   ◉ Download the MyDashboard App

Find the value of c for which the expression is a perfect-square trinomial. Then factor the perfect-square trinomial.

1. $x^2 + 12x + c$

2. $x^2 + 20x + c$

3. $x^2 - 14x + c$

4. $x^2 - 18x + c$

5. $x^2 + 7x + c$

6. $x^2 + 11x + c$

7. $x^2 - 3x + c$

8. $x^2 - 5x + c$

9. $x^2 + \frac{1}{2}x + c$

10. $x^2 + \frac{1}{7}x + c$

11. $x^2 - \frac{4}{5}x + c$

12. $x^2 - \frac{3}{4}x + c$

Solve by completing the square. All solutions are real numbers.

13. $x^2 + 6x = 1$

14. $x^2 + 8x = 3$

15. $p^2 - 2p = 19$

16. $r^2 - 10r = 2$

17. $x^2 + 4x - 24 = 0$

18. $x^2 + 6x - 9 = 0$

19. $x^2 - 7x = 3$

20. $x^2 - 3x = 12$

21. $t^2 + 5t - 4 = 0$

22. $w^2 + 9w - 9 = 0$

23. $x^2 - \frac{5}{2}x = \frac{1}{2}$

24. $x^2 - \frac{4}{3}x = \frac{5}{3}$

25. $2x^2 + 8x = 3$

26. $3x^2 + 12x = 1$

27. $2r^2 - r - 7 = 0$

28. $3m^2 - m - 5 = 0$

29. $3x^2 + 4x - 5 = 0$

30. $5x^2 + 2x - 2 = 0$

31. $6x^2 - 8x = -1$

32. $4x^2 - 6x = 3$

33. $8w^2 + 4w - 3 = 0$

34. $6p^2 + 9p + 2 = 0$

Find all complex-number solutions by completing the square.

35. $x^2 + 2x = -7$

36. $x^2 + 10x = -28$

37. $x^2 - 6x + 17 = 0$

38. $x^2 - 8x + 36 = 0$

39. $k^2 + 3k + 4 = 0$

40. $m^2 + 5m + 7 = 0$

41. $x^2 + \frac{2}{3}x + \frac{7}{3} = 0$

42. $x^2 + \frac{5}{2}x + \frac{7}{2} = 0$

43. $4r^2 - 3r = -5$

44. $3t^2 - 2t = -6$

45. $4p^2 + 6p + 3 = 0$

46. $6w^2 + 3w + 3 = 0$

Find all x-intercepts.

47. $f(x) = x^2 - 8x + 3$

48. $g(x) = x^2 - 12x + 1$

49. $h(x) = 2x^2 - 5x - 4$

50. $f(x) = 3x^2 + 2x - 7$

51. $g(x) = x^2 + 10x + 25$

52. $h(x) = x^2 - 8x + 16$

53. A student tries to solve the equation $4x^2 + 6x = 1$ by completing the square:

$$4x^2 + 6x = 1$$
$$4x^2 + 6x + 9 = 1 + 9$$
$$(2x + 3)^2 = 10$$
$$2x + 3 = \pm\sqrt{10}$$
$$2x = -3 \pm \sqrt{10}$$
$$x = \frac{-3 \pm \sqrt{10}}{2}$$

Describe any errors. Then solve the equation correctly.

54. A student tries to solve the equation $x^2 + 8x - 3 = 0$:

$$x^2 - 8x - 3 = 0$$
$$x^2 - 8x = 3$$
$$x^2 - 8x + 16 = 3$$
$$(x - 4)^2 = 3$$
$$x - 4 = \pm\sqrt{3}$$
$$x = 4 \pm \sqrt{3}$$

Describe any errors. Then solve the equation correctly.

55. Let $f(x) = x^2 + 6x + 13$.
   a. Find x when $f(x) = 3$.   **b.** Find x when $f(x) = 4$.
   c. Find x when $f(x) = 6$.

56. Let $f(x) = 2x^2 - 8x + 9$.
   a. Find x when $f(x) = 2$.   **b.** Find x when $f(x) = 1$.
   c. Find x when $f(x) = 0$.

For Exercises 57–62, solve the given equation or system by referring to the solutions of the functions shown in Table 32.

57. $x^2 - 5x + 4 = -\frac{1}{2}x^2 + x - \frac{1}{2}$

58. $-\dfrac{1}{2}x^2 + x - \dfrac{1}{2} = -\dfrac{1}{4}x^2 - \dfrac{1}{4}x - \dfrac{1}{2}$

59. $x^2 - 5x + 4 = -2$

60. $-\dfrac{1}{2}x^2 + x - \dfrac{1}{2} = -\dfrac{1}{2}$

61. $y = -\dfrac{1}{2}x^2 + x - \dfrac{1}{2}$ **62.** $y = x^2 - 5x + 4$
    $y = -\dfrac{1}{4}x^2 - \dfrac{1}{4}x - \dfrac{1}{2}$ $y = -\dfrac{1}{2}x^2 + x - \dfrac{1}{2}$

Table 32 Some Solutions of Three Functions (Exercises 57–62)

x	0	1	2	3	4	5	6
$y = x^2 - 5x + 4$	4	0	−2	−2	0	4	10
$y = -\dfrac{1}{2}x^2 + x - \dfrac{1}{2}$	−0.5	0	−0.5	−2	−4.5	−8	−12.5
$y = -\dfrac{1}{4}x^2 - \dfrac{1}{4}x - \dfrac{1}{2}$	−0.5	−1	−2	−3.5	−5.5	−8	−11

Concepts

63. a. Simplify $(x + k)^2$.
 b. Consider the polynomial $x^2 + 2kx + k^2$, where k is a constant. Show that if you divide the coefficient of x by 2 and square the result, you get the constant term.

64. To solve $x^2 + 8x = 3$ by completing the square, we begin by computing $\left(\dfrac{8}{2}\right)^2 = 4^2 = 16$. Why must we add 16 to *both* sides of the equation $x^2 + 8x = 3$?

65. Find nonzero values of a, b, and c such that the equation $ax^2 + bx + c = 0$ has two imaginary-number solutions.

Your equation should be different from those in the text. [**Hint:** Begin with an appropriate equation of the form $(x - h)^2 = k$, and simplify the left side of the equation.]

66. Give an example of an equation that can be solved by factoring. Solve the equation by factoring; then solve it by completing the square. Which process was easier? Explain.

67. Compare the methods of solving a quadratic equation by factoring, by using the square root property, and by completing the square. Describe the methods, as well as their advantages and disadvantages.

68. Explain how to solve a quadratic equation by completing the square.

Related Review

69. Factor $w^2 - 10w + 25$.   **70.** Factor $t^2 + 14t + 49$.

71. Factor $x^2 + \dfrac{5}{3}x + \dfrac{25}{36}$.   **72.** Factor $x^2 - \dfrac{3}{2}x + \dfrac{9}{16}$.

Expressions, Equations, Functions, and Graphs

Perform the indicated instruction. Then use words such as linear, quadratic, cubic, exponential, logarithmic, polynomial, degree, function, one variable, *and* two variables *to describe the expression, equation, or system.*

73. Graph $f(x) = 2(3)^x$ by hand.

74. Solve $12x^3 - 27x = 0$.

75. Let $f(x) = 2(3)^x$. Find x when $f(x) = 65$. Round the result to the second decimal place.

76. Factor $12x^3 - 27x$.

77. Solve $\log_3(3x + 2) = 4$. Round the result to the second decimal place.

78. Find the product $(4x - 2)(3x^2 - 2x + 3)$.

7.5 Using the Quadratic Formula to Solve Quadratic Equations

Objectives

» Solve quadratic equations by using the *quadratic formula.*

» Use the *discriminant* to determine the number and type of solutions of a quadratic equation.

» Decide which method to use to solve a quadratic equation.

» Use the quadratic formula to make predictions with a quadratic model.

Any quadratic equation can be solved by completing the square. However, this method may be difficult to use on most quadratic equations. An easier option is to use an important equation called the *quadratic formula,* which can also be used to solve *any* quadratic equation.

The Quadratic Formula

To find the quadratic formula, we solve the general quadratic equation

$$ax^2 + bx + c = 0$$

by completing the square. For now, we assume a is positive:

$$ax^2 + bx + c = 0 \qquad \text{\textit{General quadratic equation}}$$

$$x^2 + \frac{b}{a}x + \frac{c}{a} = 0 \qquad \text{\textit{Divide both sides by a.}}$$

$$x^2 + \frac{b}{a}x = -\frac{c}{a} \qquad \text{\textit{Subtract }}\tfrac{c}{a}\text{\textit{ from both sides.}}$$

$$x^2 + \frac{b}{a}x + \frac{b^2}{4a^2} = -\frac{c}{a} + \frac{b^2}{4a^2} \qquad \text{\textit{Add }} \left(\frac{b}{a}\cdot\frac{1}{2}\right)^2 = \left(\frac{b}{2a}\right)^2 = \frac{b^2}{4a^2}$$

$$\text{\textit{to both sides.}}$$

$$\left(x + \frac{b}{2a}\right)^2 = -\frac{c}{a} \cdot \frac{4a}{4a} + \frac{b^2}{4a^2}$$ *Factor left side; find LCD.*

$$\left(x + \frac{b}{2a}\right)^2 = \frac{b^2 - 4ac}{4a^2}$$ *Add numerators and keep common denominator:* $\frac{A}{B} + \frac{C}{B} = \frac{A + C}{B}$

$$x + \frac{b}{2a} = \pm\sqrt{\frac{b^2 - 4ac}{4a^2}}$$ *Square root property*

$$x + \frac{b}{2a} = \pm\frac{\sqrt{b^2 - 4ac}}{2a}$$ *Quotient property:* $\sqrt{\frac{A}{B}} = \frac{\sqrt{A}}{\sqrt{B}}$

$$x = -\frac{b}{2a} \pm \frac{\sqrt{b^2 - 4ac}}{2a}$$ *Subtract* $\frac{b}{2a}$ *from both sides.*

$$x = \frac{-b \pm \sqrt{b^2 - 4ac}}{2a}$$ *Add/subtract numerators and keep common denominator.*

We have found a formula (the last line) for the solutions of a quadratic equation $ax^2 + bx + c = 0$, where a is positive. In a similar way, we could derive the same formula for a quadratic equation where a is negative.

> ### Quadratic Formula
>
> The solutions of a quadratic equation $ax^2 + bx + c = 0$ are given by the **quadratic formula:**
>
> $$x = \frac{-b \pm \sqrt{b^2 - 4ac}}{2a}$$

WARNING   For the fraction in the quadratic formula, notice that the term $-b$ is part of the numerator:

$$\frac{-b \pm \sqrt{b^2 - 4ac}}{2a} \leftarrow \text{Correct}$$

$$-b \pm \frac{\sqrt{b^2 - 4ac}}{2a} \leftarrow \text{Incorrect}$$

> ### Example 1   Solving by Using the Quadratic Formula

Solve $x^2 - 6x + 8 = 0$.

Solution

Comparing $x^2 - 6x + 8 = 0$ with $ax^2 + bx + c = 0$, we see $a = 1$, $b = -6$, and $c = 8$. We substitute these values for a, b, and c in the quadratic formula:

$$x = \frac{-(-6) \pm \sqrt{(-6)^2 - 4(1)(8)}}{2(1)}$$ *Substitute 1 for a, −6 for b, and 8 for c.*

$$x = \frac{6 \pm \sqrt{4}}{2}$$ *Simplify.*

$$x = \frac{6 \pm 2}{2}$$ $\sqrt{4} = 2$

$$x = \frac{6 - 2}{2} \quad \text{or} \quad x = \frac{6 + 2}{2}$$ *Write as two equations.*

$$x = 2 \quad \text{or} \quad x = 4$$

The solutions are 2 and 4.

Instead of using the quadratic formula, we could have solved $x^2 - 6x + 8 = 0$ by factoring:

$$x^2 - 6x + 8 = 0 \qquad \textit{Original equation}$$
$$(x - 2)(x - 4) = 0 \qquad \textit{Factor left side.}$$
$$x - 2 = 0 \quad \text{or} \quad x - 4 = 0 \qquad \textit{Zero factor property}$$
$$x = 2 \quad \text{or} \quad x = 4$$

A benefit of the quadratic formula is that we can use it to solve equations that are difficult or even impossible to solve by factoring. In Example 2, we solve an equation that is impossible to solve by factoring.

▶ **Example 2** Solving by Using the Quadratic Formula

Solve $2x^2 = 10x - 3$.

Solution

First, we write $2x^2 = 10x - 3$ in the form $ax^2 + bx + c = 0$:

$$2x^2 - 10x + 3 = 0$$

So, $a = 2$, $b = -10$, and $c = 3$. By the quadratic formula,

$$x = \frac{-(-10) \pm \sqrt{(-10)^2 - 4(2)(3)}}{2(2)} \qquad \textit{Substitute 2 for a, −10 for b, and 3 for c.}$$

$$x = \frac{10 \pm \sqrt{76}}{4} \qquad \textit{Simplify.}$$

$$x = \frac{10 \pm 2\sqrt{19}}{4} \qquad \sqrt{76} = \sqrt{4 \cdot 19} = \sqrt{4}\sqrt{19} = 2\sqrt{19}$$

$$x = \frac{10 - 2\sqrt{19}}{4} \quad \text{or} \quad x = \frac{10 + 2\sqrt{19}}{4} \qquad \textit{Write as two equations.}$$

$$x = \frac{2(5 - \sqrt{19})}{4} \quad \text{or} \quad x = \frac{2(5 + \sqrt{19})}{4} \qquad \textit{Factor out 2.}$$

$$x = \frac{5 - \sqrt{19}}{2} \quad \text{or} \quad x = \frac{5 + \sqrt{19}}{2} \qquad \textit{Simplify.}$$

The solutions are $\dfrac{5 \pm \sqrt{19}}{2}$.

▶

▶ **Example 3** Solving by Using the Quadratic Formula

Solve $\dfrac{1}{2}x^2 - \dfrac{5}{4}x = \dfrac{3}{2}$.

Solution

To begin, we clear the equation of fractions by multiplying both sides by the LCD, 4:

$$\frac{1}{2}x^2 - \frac{5}{4}x = \frac{3}{2} \qquad \textit{Original equation}$$

$$4 \cdot \frac{1}{2}x^2 - 4 \cdot \frac{5}{4}x = 4 \cdot \frac{3}{2} \qquad \textit{Multiply both sides by LCD, 4.}$$

$$2x^2 - 5x = 6 \qquad \textit{Simplify.}$$

$$2x^2 - 5x - 6 = 0 \qquad \textit{Subtract 6 from both sides.}$$

$$x = \frac{-(-5) \pm \sqrt{(-5)^2 - 4(2)(-6)}}{2(2)} \qquad \textit{Substitute a = 2, b = −5, and c = −6 in quadratic formula.}$$

$$x = \frac{5 \pm \sqrt{73}}{4} \qquad \textit{Simplify.}$$

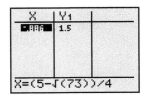

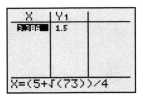

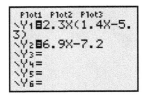

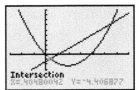

Figure 70 Verify the work

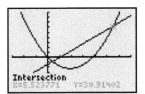

Figure 71 Verify the work

The solutions are $\dfrac{5 \pm \sqrt{73}}{4}$. We enter $y = \dfrac{1}{2}x^2 - \dfrac{5}{4}x$ in a graphing calculator and check that, for both inputs $\dfrac{5 \pm \sqrt{73}}{4}$, the output is $\dfrac{3}{2} = 1.5$ (see Fig. 70).

▶ **Example 4** Finding Approximate Solutions

Find approximate solutions of the equation $2.3x(1.4x - 5.3) = 6.9x - 7.2$.

Solution

First, we write the equation in the form $ax^2 + bx + c = 0$:

$$2.3x(1.4x - 5.3) = 6.9x - 7.2 \quad \textit{Original equation}$$
$$3.22x^2 - 12.19x = 6.9x - 7.2 \quad \textit{Distributive law}$$
$$3.22x^2 - 19.09x + 7.2 = 0 \quad \textit{Subtract 6.9x from both sides;}$$
$$\textit{add 7.2 to both sides.}$$

Then we substitute 3.22 for a, -19.09 for b, and 7.2 for c in the quadratic formula:

$$x = \frac{-(-19.09) \pm \sqrt{(-19.09)^2 - 4(3.22)(7.2)}}{2(3.22)} \quad \textit{Substitute into quadratic formula.}$$

$$x = \frac{19.09 \pm \sqrt{271.6921}}{6.44} \quad \textit{Simplify.}$$

$$x \approx \frac{19.09 \pm 16.48}{6.44} \quad \textit{Approximate square root.}$$

$$x \approx 0.41 \quad \text{or} \quad x \approx 5.52 \quad \textit{Compute.}$$

We use graphing calculator graphs to verify our work (see Fig. 71).

▶ **Example 5** Finding x-intercepts

Find the x-intercepts of the parabola $f(x) = 6x^2 + 3x - 2$.

Solution

First, we substitute 0 for $f(x)$. Then, we use the quadratic formula to solve for x:

$$0 = 6x^2 + 3x - 2 \quad \textit{Substitute 0 for f(x).}$$

$$x = \frac{-3 \pm \sqrt{3^2 - 4(6)(-2)}}{2(6)} \quad \textit{Substitute a = 6, b = 3, c = -2.}$$

$$x = \frac{-3 \pm \sqrt{57}}{12} \quad \textit{Simplify.}$$

The x-intercepts are $\left(\dfrac{-3 - \sqrt{57}}{12}, 0 \right)$ and $\left(\dfrac{-3 + \sqrt{57}}{12}, 0 \right)$. We use "zero" on a graphing calculator to verify that the approximate x-intercepts are $(-0.88, 0)$ and $(0.38, 0)$. See Fig. 72.

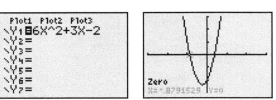

Figure 72 Verify the work

Solving a Quadratic Equation That Has Imaginary-Number Solutions

In Example 6, we use the quadratic formula to solve a quadratic equation that has imaginary-number solutions.

▶ **Example 6**   Solving by Using the Quadratic Formula

Solve $-3x^2 + 5x - 4 = 0$.

Solution

First, we multiply both sides of the equation by -1 so we can avoid having a negative denominator after we use the quadratic formula:

$$-3x^2 + 5x - 4 = 0 \quad \textit{Original equation}$$
$$3x^2 - 5x + 4 = 0 \quad \textit{Multiply both sides by } -1.$$

(Another benefit is that we have fewer negative numbers to substitute into the quadratic formula.) Then we substitute $a = 3$, $b = -5$, and $c = 4$ in the quadratic formula:

$$x = \frac{-(-5) \pm \sqrt{(-5)^2 - 4(3)(4)}}{2(3)} \quad \textit{Substitute into quadratic formula.}$$

$$x = \frac{5 \pm \sqrt{-23}}{6} \quad \textit{Simplify.}$$

$$x = \frac{5 \pm i\sqrt{23}}{6} \quad \sqrt{-p} = i\sqrt{p}, \textit{where } p > 0$$

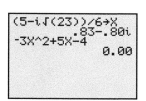

To verify our work, we store each result as x and check that $-3x^2 + 5x - 4$ is equal to 0 (see Fig. 73). We press $\boxed{\text{MODE}}$ and set FLOAT to 2 so the numbers in the result are rounded to the second decimal place.

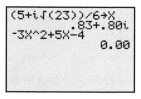

Figure 73 Verify the work

The graphical check in Fig. 74 shows that the graph of $y = -3x^2 + 5x - 4$ does not have any x-intercepts. This means the equation $-3x^2 + 5x - 4 = 0$ has no real-number solutions, which checks.

▶

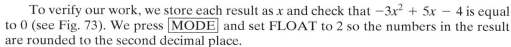

Figure 74 The graph of $y = -3x^2 + 5x - 4$ has no x-intercepts

Determining the Number of Real-Number Solutions

Recall from Section 6.7 that a quadratic equation can have two, one, or no real-number solutions. Let us see how this fact relates to the quadratic formula

$$x = \frac{-b \pm \sqrt{b^2 - 4ac}}{2a}$$

The answer lies with the number $b^2 - 4ac$, known as the *discriminant*. If the discriminant is positive, then there are two real-number solutions; see Example 4. If the discriminant is negative, then there are two imaginary-number solutions (and no real-number solutions); see Example 6. Finally, if the discriminant is 0, then the quadratic formula gives

$$x = \frac{-b \pm \sqrt{0}}{2a} = \frac{-b}{2a}$$

and therefore there is one real-number solution.

▶ **Determining the Number and Type of Solutions**

For the quadratic equation $ax^2 + bx + c = 0$, the **discriminant** is $b^2 - 4ac$. Also,

- If $b^2 - 4ac > 0$, there are two real-number solutions.
- If $b^2 - 4ac = 0$, there is one real-number solution.
- If $b^2 - 4ac < 0$, there are two imaginary-number solutions (and no real-number solutions).

▶ **Example 7**   Determining the Number and Type of Solutions

Determine the number and type of solutions of the equation $2x^2 - 3x + 5 = 0$.

Solution

Since $b^2 - 4ac = (-3)^2 - 4(2)(5) = -31 < 0$, we conclude that the quadratic equation $2x^2 - 3x + 5 = 0$ has two imaginary-number solutions (and no real-number solutions).

▶

We can also use the discriminant to determine the number of points on a parabola at a given height.

▶ **Example 8**   Finding the Number of Points at a Given Height

For $f(x) = x^2 - 6x + 12$, find the number of points that lie on the graph of f at the indicated height.

1. $y = 5$ **2.** $y = 3$ **3.** $y = 1$

Solution

1. We substitute 5 for $f(x)$ in the equation $f(x) = x^2 - 6x + 12$:

$$x^2 - 6x + 12 = 5 \quad \text{\small Substitute 5 for } f(x).$$
$$x^2 - 6x + 7 = 0 \quad \text{\small Subtract 5 from both sides.}$$

Since $b^2 - 4ac = (-6)^2 - 4(1)(7) = 8 > 0$, we conclude that there are two solutions of the equation $x^2 - 6x + 12 = 5$, which means two (symmetric) points have height $y = 5$.

2. We substitute 3 for $f(x)$:

$$x^2 - 6x + 12 = 3 \quad \text{\small Substitute 3 for } f(x).$$
$$x^2 - 6x + 9 = 0 \quad \text{\small Subtract 3 from both sides.}$$

Since $b^2 - 4ac = (-6)^2 - 4(1)(9) = 0$, we conclude that there is one solution of the equation $x^2 - 6x + 12 = 3$, which means one point has height $y = 3$. Since the point does not have a symmetric point, it must be the vertex of the parabola.

3. We substitute 1 for $f(x)$:

$$x^2 - 6x + 12 = 1 \quad \text{\small Substitute 1 for } f(x).$$
$$x^2 - 6x + 11 = 0 \quad \text{\small Subtract 1 from both sides.}$$

Since $b^2 - 4ac = (-6)^2 - 4(1)(11) = -8 < 0$, we conclude that there are no real-number solutions of the equation $x^2 - 6x + 12 = 1$, which means no points on the parabola have height $y = 1$.

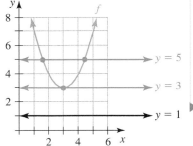

Figure 75 Graph of $f(x) = x^2 - 6x + 12$

In Example 8, we found that the parabola $f(x) = x^2 - 6x + 12$ has exactly two points at height $y = 5$, exactly one point at height $y = 3$, and no points at height $y = 1$. We indicate the three points on the graph of f in Fig. 75.

Deciding Which Method to Use to Solve a Quadratic Equation

In Chapter 6 and in this chapter, we have discussed four ways to solve quadratic equations: factoring, the square root property, completing the square, and the quadratic formula. How do we know which method to use?

Remember that **any quadratic equation can be solved by using the quadratic formula.** Although any equation can also be solved by completing the square, that method is much more difficult to use than the quadratic formula.

A low percentage of quadratic equations can be solved by factoring, because almost all polynomials are prime. However, if an equation *can* be solved by simple factoring techniques, then it is easier to solve by factoring than by any of the other three methods.

Here are some guidelines on deciding which method to use to solve a quadratic equation:

Method	When to Use
Factoring	For equations that can easily be put into the form $ax^2 + bx + c = 0$ and where $ax^2 + bx + c$ can easily be factored.
Square root property	For equations that can easily be put into the form $x^2 = k$ or $(x + p)^2 = k$.
Completing the square	When the directions require it.
Quadratic formula	For all equations except those that can easily be solved by factoring or by using the square root property.

▶ **Example 9**   Deciding Which Method to Use

Solve.

1. $w^2 - 3w - 54 = 0$ **2.** $(x + 3)^2 = 5$
3. $(x + 3)(x - 2) = 2(x + 1)$

Solution

1. The polynomial $w^2 - 3w - 54$ is factorable, so we solve the quadratic equation $w^2 - 3w - 54 = 0$ by factoring:

$$w^2 - 3w - 54 = 0 \qquad \text{\textit{Original equation}}$$
$$(w + 6)(w - 9) = 0 \qquad \text{\textit{Factor left side.}}$$
$$w + 6 = 0 \quad \text{or} \quad w - 9 = 0 \quad \text{\textit{Zero factor property}}$$
$$w = -6 \quad \text{or} \quad w = 9$$

2. The equation is of the form $(x + p)^2 = k$, so we solve it by using the square root property:

$$(x + 3)^2 = 5 \qquad \text{\textit{Original equation}}$$
$$x + 3 = \pm\sqrt{5} \qquad \text{\textit{Square root property}}$$
$$x = -3 \pm \sqrt{5}$$

3. First, we write the equation in $ax^2 + bx + c = 0$ form:

$$(x + 3)(x - 2) = 2(x + 1) \qquad \text{\textit{Original equation}}$$
$$x^2 + x - 6 = 2x + 2 \qquad \text{\textit{Multiply; distributive law}}$$
$$x^2 - x - 8 = 0 \qquad \text{\textit{Write in } ax^2 + bx + c = 0 \text{ form.}}$$

The polynomial $x^2 - x - 8$ is prime, so we can't solve the equation $x^2 - x - 8 = 0$ by factoring. The equation can't be put into the form $x^2 = k$, and it can't easily be put into the form $(x + p)^2 = k$, so we don't try to solve it by using the square root property. Instead, we substitute $a = 1, b = -1$, and $c = -8$ in the quadratic formula:

$$x = \frac{-(-1) \pm \sqrt{(-1)^2 - 4(1)(-8)}}{2(1)} \qquad \text{\textit{Substitute into quadratic formula.}}$$

$$x = \frac{1 \pm \sqrt{33}}{2} \qquad \text{\textit{Simplify.}}$$

Table 33 Bottled-Water Consumption

Year	Bottled-Water Consumption (billions of gallons)
1990	2.2
1995	3.1
2000	4.7
2005	7.5
2009	10.6

Source: *Beverage Marketing Corporation*

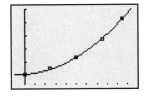

Figure 76 Check the fit

It just tastes better.

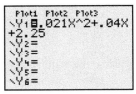

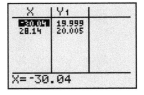

X= -30.04

Figure 77 Verify the results

Using a Quadratic Function to Model a Situation

We can use the quadratic formula to make a prediction about the independent variable of a quadratic model.

▶ **Example 10**   Modeling with a Quadratic Function

Annual consumption of bottled water in the United States has been increasing since 1990 (see Table 33). Let $f(t)$ be annual bottled-water consumption (in billions of gallons) at t years since 1990. A possible equation of f is

$$f(t) = 0.021t^2 + 0.04t + 2.25$$

1. Verify that f models the data well.
2. Predict when annual consumption will reach 20 billion gallons.

Solution

1. We draw the graph of f and the scattergram of the data in the same viewing window (see Fig. 76). It appears f is a reasonable model.
2. To predict when annual consumption will be 20 billion gallons, we substitute 20 for $f(t)$ and solve for t:

$$20 = 0.021t^2 + 0.04t + 2.25 \qquad \text{\textit{Substitute 20 for } f(t).}$$
$$0 = 0.021t^2 + 0.04t - 17.75 \qquad \text{\textit{Subtract 20 from both sides.}}$$
$$t = \frac{-0.04 \pm \sqrt{0.04^2 - 4(0.021)(-17.75)}}{2(0.021)} \qquad \text{\textit{Substitute into quadratic formula.}}$$
$$= \frac{-0.04 \pm \sqrt{1.4926}}{0.042} \qquad \text{\textit{Simplify.}}$$
$$\approx \frac{-0.04 \pm 1.2217}{0.042} \qquad \text{\textit{Approximate square root.}}$$
$$t \approx -30.04 \quad \text{or} \quad 28.14$$

We verify the results by entering $y = 0.021t^2 + 0.04t + 2.25$ in a graphing calculator and checking that the inputs -30.04 and 28.14 lead to outputs of about 20 (see Fig. 77).

The inputs -30.04 and 28.14 represent the years 1960 and 2018, respectively. The estimate of 1960 is a result of model breakdown, as a little research would show that bottled-water consumption in 1960 was much less than 20 billion gallons. Therefore, we predict it will be 2018 when bottled-water consumption reaches 20 billion gallons.

Recall from Section 6.7 that, to make a prediction about the dependent variable of a quadratic model, we substitute a value for the independent variable, then solve for the dependent variable. To make a prediction about the independent variable, we substitute a value for the dependent variable, then solve for the independent variable, usually by using the quadratic formula.

◢◣ Group Exploration

Comparing methods of solving quadratic equations

1. Solve the equation $x^2 + 5x + 6 = 0$ by factoring.
2. Solve the equation $x^2 + 5x + 6 = 0$ by completing the square.
3. Solve the equation $x^2 + 5x + 6 = 0$ by using the quadratic formula.
4. Compare your results from Problems 1, 2, and 3. Which method was easiest?
5. Repeat Problems 1–4 for the equation $x^2 + 4x - 7 = 0$.
6. Compare the methods of solving quadratic equations by factoring, by completing the square, and by using the quadratic formula. What are the advantages and disadvantages of each?

Group Exploration

Looking ahead: Finding an equation of a parabola

In this exploration, you will find an equation of the parabola that passes through the points $(1, 8)$, $(2, 15)$, and $(3, 24)$.

1. The point $(1, 8)$ lies on the parabola, so the ordered pair $(1, 8)$ should satisfy the equation $y = ax^2 + bx + c$. Find the equation that results from substituting 1 for x and 8 for y. This equation will be in terms of a, b, and c. Find another equation by using the ordered pair $(2, 15)$. Finally, find a third equation by using the ordered pair $(3, 24)$.

2. You should now have three equations, each in terms of a, b, and c. Choose any two of these equations and eliminate c. Then choose another pair of equations and again eliminate c.

3. You should now have two equations, both in terms of a and b, forming a system of two equations in two variables. Solve this system by substitution or elimination.

4. You should now know the values of a and b. Find c by substituting the values of a and b in one of the three equations found in Problem 1.

5. You should now know the values of a, b, and c. Substitute these values into the equation $y = ax^2 + bx + c$ to obtain an equation of the parabola.

6. Verify that the graph of your equation passes through the points $(1, 8)$, $(2, 15)$, and $(3, 24)$ by using a graphing calculator table or graph.

Homework 7.5

For extra help ▶ **MyMathLab®**   Watch the videos in MyMathLab   Download the MyDashboard App

Use the quadratic formula to solve the equation. All solutions are real numbers.

1. $2x^2 + 5x - 2 = 0$
2. $5x^2 + 5x - 1 = 0$
3. $3x^2 - 6x + 1 = 0$
4. $5x^2 - 4x - 3 = 0$
5. $t^2 = 4t + 3$
6. $w^2 = -2w + 5$
7. $-2x^2 + 5x = 3$
8. $-4x^2 + 7x = -2$
9. $3x^2 - 17 = 0$
10. $2x^2 - 15 = 0$
11. $2y^2 = -5y$
12. $5r^2 = -3r$
13. $\frac{2}{3}x^2 - \frac{5}{6}x = \frac{1}{3}$
14. $\frac{5}{8}x^2 + \frac{3}{4}x = \frac{1}{4}$
15. $(3x + 2)(x - 1) = 1$
16. $(4x - 3)(x - 1) = 4$

Find approximate solutions. Round any results to the second decimal place. All solutions are real numbers.

17. $2x^2 = 5x + 4$
18. $3x^2 = 9x + 2$
19. $2.85p^2 - 7.12p = 4.49$
20. $3.98r^2 - 2.17r = 3.68$
21. $-5.4x(x + 9.8) + 4.1 = 3.2 - 6.9x$
22. $7.1x(x - 4.9) - 7.1 = 2.5x + 6.3$

Find all x-intercepts.

23. $f(x) = 2x^2 - x - 7$
24. $f(x) = 3x^2 + 4x - 1$
25. $f(x) = 3x^2 + 2x + 5$
26. $f(x) = -5x^2 + 3x - 2$
27. $f(x) = x^2 + 2x - 5$
28. $f(x) = x^2 - 4x - 3$

Use the quadratic formula to find all complex-number solutions.

29. $x^2 - 3x + 8 = 0$
30. $x^2 - 3x + 15 = 0$

31. $-w^2 + 2w = 5$
32. $-r^2 + 4r = 7$
33. $\frac{1}{4}x^2 = 2x - \frac{9}{2}$
34. $\frac{5}{6}x^2 = 3x - \frac{7}{2}$
35. $3x(3x - 2) = -2$
36. $2x(5x - 2) = -1$
37. $3k^2 = 4k - 5$
38. $4y^2 = 2y - 1$

Solve by the method of your choice. All solutions are real numbers.

39. $4x^2 - 80 = 0$
40. $3x^2 - 36 = 0$
41. $5(w + 3)^2 + 2 = 8$
42. $3(w - 2)^2 - 1 = 6$
43. $m^2 = -12m - 36$
44. $t^2 = 14t - 49$
45. $-24x^2 + 18x = -60$
46. $-16x^2 + 20x = 4$
47. $\frac{1}{3}x^2 - \frac{3}{2}x = \frac{1}{6}$
48. $\frac{1}{8}x^2 - \frac{3}{4}x = \frac{1}{2}$
49. $(x - 5)(x + 2) = 3(x - 1) + 2$
50. $(x + 4)(x - 1) = 5(x + 2) - 1$
51. $25r^2 = 49$
52. $4p^2 = 81$
53. $(x - 1)^2 + (x + 2)^2 = 6$
54. $(x - 3)^2 + (x + 1)^2 = 17$

Use the method of your choice to find all complex-number solutions.

55. $4x^2 = -25$
56. $81x^2 = -49$
57. $-2t^2 + 5t = 6$
58. $-3w^2 + 4w = 2$
59. $(x - 6)^2 + 5 = -43$
60. $(x + 4)^2 - 3 = -66$
61. $(y - 2)(y - 5) = -4$
62. $(k + 3)(k - 2) = -25$

Determine the number and type of solutions.

63. $3x^2 + 4x - 5 = 0$ **64.** $x^2 - 5x - 8 = 0$

65. $2x^2 - 5x + 7 = 0$ **66.** $3x^2 - 2x + 5 = 0$

67. $4x^2 = 12x - 9$ **68.** $9x^2 = 6x - 1$

69. Let $f(x) = x^2 - 4x + 8$. Find the number of points that lie on the graph of f at the indicated height y.
  a. $y = 3$ **b.** $y = 4$ **c.** $y = 5$
  d. Use a graphing calculator to draw a graph of f, and sketch the graph on paper. Then explain why you found the number of points to be 0, 1, and 2 for parts (a), (b), and (c), respectively.

70. Let $g(x) = -x^2 + 6x - 2$. Find the number of points that lie on the graph of g at the indicated height y.
  a. $y = 6$ **b.** $y = 7$ **c.** $y = 8$
  d. Use a graphing calculator to draw a graph of g, and sketch the graph on paper. Then explain why you found the number of points to be 2, 1, and 0 for parts (a), (b), and (c), respectively.

71. Let $f(x) = x^2 - 6x + 7$. Find the coordinates of any points on the graph of f at height $y = 2$. Then find the vertex of the graph of f. Finally, sketch the graph of f.

72. Let $g(x) = x^2 + 8x + 6$. Find the approximate coordinates of any points on the graph of g at height $y = -5$. Then find the approximate vertex of the graph of g. Round all coordinates to the second decimal place. Finally, sketch the graph of g.

73. The *consumer confidence index* measures how optimistic consumers feel about the economy and their personal financial situation. The annual revenues from boats and accessories, new-home sales rates (in thousands of homes per year) in July, and the consumer confidence indexes in July are shown in Table 34 for various years.

Table 34 Annual Revenues from Boats and Accessories, July New-Home Sales Rates, and July Consumer Confidence Indexes

Year	Annual Revenue from Boats and Accessories (billions of dollars)	July New-Home Sales Rate (thousands of homes per year)	July Consumer Confidence Index
2007	37	800	106
2008	33	479	51
2009	31	402	48
2010	30	289	53
2011	32	300	59

Source: *National Marine Manufacturers Association*

Let $f(t)$ be the annual revenue from boats and accessories (in billions of dollars) at t years since 2005. A model of the situation is $f(t) = 0.929t^2 - 8.73t + 50.8$.
  a. Use a graphing calculator to draw the graph of the model f and, in the same viewing window, the scattergram of the data. Does the model fit the data well?
  b. Predict the revenue in 2014.
  c. Predict when the annual revenue will be \$55 billion.
  d. For the years shown in Table 34, determine in which year the revenue from boats and accessories was the least. Do the same for the July new-home sales rate and for the July

consumer confidence index. How much of a time lag does there seem to be between when consumers begin to feel better about the economy and when they begin to spend more?

74. The average state cigarette taxes per pack are listed in Table 35 for various years.

Table 35 Average State Cigarette Taxes per Pack

Year	Average State Cigarette Tax per pack (cents)
2001	43
2003	73
2005	93
2007	111
2009	134
2011	147
2012	149

Source: *Campaign for Tobacco-Free Kids*

Let $f(t)$ be the average state cigarette tax per pack (in cents) at t years since 2000. A model of the situation is $f(t) = -0.4t^2 + 14.97t + 29.22$.
  a. Use a graphing calculator to draw the graph of the model and, in the same viewing window, the scattergram of the data. Does the model fit the data well?
  b. Predict the average tax per pack in 2017.
  c. Predict when the average tax per pack will be 169 cents.
  d. About 14 billion packs of cigarettes were sold in 2010 (Source: *Federal Trade Commission*). Estimate *total* state cigarette taxes in 2010.

75. The percentages of police officers who are women are listed in Table 36 for various city populations.

Table 36 Percentages of Police Officers Who Are Women

City Population Group (in thousands)	Population Used to Represent City Population Group (in thousands)	Percent
0–9.999	5	8.3
10–24.999	17.5	7.5
25–49.999	37.5	8.5
50–99.999	75	9.4
100–249.999	175	11.7
250 or more	300	17.0

Source: *FBI Uniform Crime Report*

Let $f(n)$ be the percentage of police officers who are women in cities with populations of n thousand. A model of the situation is $f(n) = 0.00006n^2 + 0.012n + 7.88$.
  a. Use a graphing calculator to draw the graph of the model and, in the same viewing window, the scattergram of the data. Does the model fit the data well?
  b. Glen Ellyn, Illinois, has a population of 27.04 thousand. Estimate the percentage of police officers in Glen Ellyn who are women.
  c. Find n when $f(n) = 10$. What does it mean in this situation?

76. The average weights of mako sharks are listed in Table 37 for various lengths.

Table 37 Average Weights of Mako Sharks

Length (inches)	Weight (pounds)
53.5	41.2
60.0	59.6
70.8	101.7
80.5	153.7
90.1	221.4
100.9	317.8

Source: *National Marine Fisheries Service*

Let W be the average weight (in pounds) of a mako shark with length L inches. A quadratic model of the situation is $Q(L) = 0.0805L^2 - 6.64L + 167$. An exponential model is $E(L) = 4.48(1.044)^L$.

a. Compare how well the two models fit the data.

b. Find $Q(75)$. What does it mean in this situation?

c. Find L when $Q(L) = 75$. What does it mean in this situation?

d. Which of the two models describes the situation better for lengths less than 41 inches? [**Hint:** Zoom out.]

77. A person throws a stone into the air. The height (in feet) $h(t)$ after t seconds is given by $h(t) = -16t^2 + 52t + 4$.

a. What is the height of the stone after 3 seconds?

b. When is the stone at a height of 30 feet?

c. When does the stone reach the ground?

78. A baseball is hit by a batter. The height (in feet) $h(t)$ of the ball after t seconds is given by $h(t) = -16t^2 + 125t + 4$.

a. What is the height of the ball after 2 seconds?

b. When is the ball at a height of 200 feet?

c. When does the ball reach the ground?

For Exercises 79–84, find approximate solutions of the given equation or system by referring to the graphs shown in Fig. 78. Round results or coordinates of results to the first decimal place.

79. $\frac{1}{2}x^2 + 1 = -x^2 - x + 5$

80. $-x^2 - x + 5 = \frac{2}{5}x - 2$

81. $\frac{1}{2}x^2 + 1 = 4$

82. $-x^2 - x + 5 = 1$

83. $y = \frac{2}{5}x - 2$
$y = -x^2 - x + 5$

84. $y = \frac{1}{2}x^2 + 1$
$y = -x^2 - x + 5$

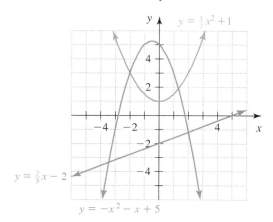

Figure 78 Exercises 79–84

Concepts

85. A student tries to solve $2x^2 + 5x = 1$:

$$x = \frac{-5 \pm \sqrt{5^2 - 4(2)(1)}}{2(2)}$$

$$x = \frac{-5 \pm \sqrt{17}}{4}$$

Describe any errors. Then solve the equation correctly.

86. A student tries to solve $3x^2 + 2x - 4 = 0$:

$$x = \frac{-2 \pm \sqrt{2^2 - 4(3)(-4)}}{2(3)}$$

$$x = \frac{-2 \pm \sqrt{52}}{6}$$

$$x = \frac{-2 \pm 2\sqrt{13}}{6}$$

$$x = \frac{-1 \pm 2\sqrt{13}}{3}$$

Describe any errors. Then solve the equation correctly.

87. A student tries to solve $5x^2 - 4x - 2 = 0$:

$$x = \frac{-(-4) \pm \sqrt{(-4)^2 - 4(5)(-2)}}{2(5)}$$

$$= \frac{4 \pm \sqrt{56}}{10}$$

Describe any errors. Then solve the equation correctly.

88. A student tries to solve $4x^2 + 3x - 2 = 0$:

$$x = -3 \pm \frac{\sqrt{3^2 - 4(4)(-2)}}{2(4)}$$

$$= -3 \pm \frac{\sqrt{41}}{8}$$

Describe any errors. Then solve the equation correctly.

89. The quadratic formula gives the solutions of any equation of the form $ax^2 + bx + c = 0$, where $a \neq 0$.

a. Find a "linear formula" that gives the solution of *any* equation of the form $mx + b = 0$, where $m \neq 0$.

b. Use your linear formula to solve $7x + 21 = 0$. Verify your result by solving $7x + 21 = 0$ in the usual way.

90. a. Use factoring to solve $3x^2 + 2x = 0$.

b. Use factoring to solve $ax^2 + bx = 0$ for x.

c. Use the formula you found in part (b) to solve the equation $3x^2 + 2x = 0$. Compare your results with your results from part (a).

d. Use the quadratic formula to solve $3x^2 + 2x = 0$. Compare your results with your results from part (a).

e. Use the quadratic formula to solve $ax^2 + bx = 0$ for x. Compare your results with your results from part (b).

f. Use the formula you found in part (e) to solve the equation $7x^2 - 3x = 0$.

91. Solve $x^2 - x - 20 = 0$ by factoring, by completing the square, and by using the quadratic formula. Compare your results.

92. Solve $3x^2 = 5x - 2$ by factoring, by completing the square, and by using the quadratic formula. Compare your results.

93. Explain how to determine whether to solve a quadratic equation by factoring, by using the square root property, by completing the square, or by using the quadratic formula. Give examples; for each example, describe the advantages of the method you chose and the disadvantages of the other methods.

94. Describe how to solve a quadratic equation by using the quadratic formula.

Related Review

Perform the indicated operations or solve, as appropriate.

95. $(x + 2)(x - 5)$

96. $2x(3x - 5) = 4$

97. $(x + 2)(x - 5) = 3$

98. $2x(3x - 5)$

99. $-4(x - 2)^2 + 3 = -1$

100. $(x + 3)^2$

101. $-4(x - 2)^2 + 3$

102. $(x + 3)^2 = 7$

Solve. Round approximate solutions to the fourth decimal place.

103. $4b^5 - 12 = 173$

104. $4r^2 = 8r - 3$

105. $4x - (7x - 5) = 3x + 1$

106. $2x^2 - 7x = 3$

107. $7(3)^t + 8 = 271$

108. $\log_3(x + 1) + \log_3(x + 3) = 2$

Expressions, Equations, Functions, and Graphs

Perform the indicated instruction. Then use words such as linear, quadratic, cubic, exponential, logarithmic, polynomial, degree, function, one variable, *and* two variables *to describe the expression, equation, or system.*

109. Factor $8x^2 - 18x + 9$.

110. Simplify $-3(x + 1)^2 + 4$.

111. Find $f(-2)$, where $f(x) = 8x^2 - 18x + 9$.

112. Solve $-3(x + 1)^2 + 4 = -20$.

113. Solve $8x^2 - 18x + 9 = 0$.

114. Graph $f(x) = -3(x + 1)^2 + 4$ by hand.

▼ 7.6 Solving Systems of Linear Equations in Three Variables; Finding Quadratic Functions

Objectives

» Know the meaning of *linear equation in three variables.*

» Solve a *system of linear equations in three variables.*

» Find a quadratic equation, in standard form, of a parabola that contains three given points.

In this section, we discuss how to solve a system of three equations. Then we will use this skill to help us find an equation of a parabola that contains three given points. In Section 7.7, we will use the skill to find an equation of a quadratic model.

Linear Equations in Three Variables

In Chapters 1–3, we worked with linear equations in *two* variables. Here we will work with linear equations in *three* variables.

▶ **Definition   Linear equation in three variables**

A **linear equation in three variables** is an equation that can be put into the form $Ax + By + Cz = D$, where A, B, C, and D are constants and A, B, and C are not all zero.

Here is an example of a linear equation in *three* variables:

$$3x - 5y + 2z = 8$$

An **ordered triple** (x, y, z) represents values of x, y, and z, just as an ordered pair (x, y) represents values of x and y. For example, the ordered triple $(2, -4, 7)$ represents the values $x = 2$, $y = -4$, and $z = 7$. An ordered triple (a, b, c) is a **solution** of an equation in terms of x, y, and z if the equation becomes a true statement when a, b, and c are substituted for x, y, and z, respectively. We say a solution **satisfies** the equation.

▶ **Example 1**   Identifying Solutions of a Linear Equation in Three Variables

Decide whether the given ordered triple is a solution of the equation $5x - 2y + 4z = 11$.

  1. $(-3, 1, 7)$ **2.** $(2, -9, 6)$

Solution

1. We substitute -3 for x, 1 for y, and 7 for z in $5x - 2y + 4z = 11$:

$$5(-3) - 2(1) + 4(7) \stackrel{?}{=} 11$$
$$11 \stackrel{?}{=} 11$$
$$\text{true}$$

The ordered triple $(-3, 1, 7)$ is a solution of the equation $5x - 2y + 4z = 11$.

2. We substitute 2 for x, -9 for y, and 6 for z in $5x - 2y + 4z = 11$:

$$5(2) - 2(-9) + 4(6) \stackrel{?}{=} 11$$
$$52 \stackrel{?}{=} 11$$
$$\text{false}$$

The ordered triple $(2, -9, 6)$ is not a solution of the equation $5x - 2y + 4z = 11$.

▶

Solving a System of Linear Equations in Three Variables

A **system of linear equations in three variables** consists of two or more linear equations in three variables. Here is an example of a system of linear equations in three variables:

$$2x - y + 3z = 4$$
$$x + 3y - 2z = -1$$
$$3x - 5y + z = 2$$

The **solution** of a system of linear equations in three variables is an ordered triple that satisfies *all* of the equations. We can use elimination to solve a system of equations in three variables.

▶ **Example 2**   Solving a System of Three Equations

Solve the system

$$x + y - z = -1 \quad \text{Equation (1)}$$
$$-4x - y + 2z = -7 \quad \text{Equation (2)}$$
$$2x - 2y - 5z = 7 \quad \text{Equation (3)}$$

Solution

By inspecting the coefficients of the nine variable terms, we see that it is easiest to eliminate y. We add the left sides and add the right sides of equations (1) and (2):

$$x + y - z = -1 \quad \text{Equation (1)}$$
$$\underline{-4x - y + 2z = -7} \quad \text{Equation (2)}$$
$$-3x \quad + z = -8 \quad \text{Equation (4)}$$

Next, we select equations (1) and (3) and eliminate y again. To do so, we multiply both sides of equation (1) by 2:

$$2x + 2y - 2z = -2 \quad \textit{Multiply both sides of equation (1) by 2.}$$
$$\underline{2x - 2y - 5z = 7} \quad \textit{Equation (3)}$$
$$4x \quad - 7z = 5 \quad \textit{Equation (5)}$$

Equations (4) and (5) form a system in two variables. To eliminate z, we multiply both sides of equation (4) by 7:

$$-21x + 7z = -56 \quad \textit{Multiply both sides of equation (4) by 7.}$$
$$\underline{4x - 7z = 5} \quad \textit{Equation (5)}$$
$$-17x \qquad = -51$$
$$x = 3$$

Next, we substitute 3 for x in equation (4) and solve for z:

$$-3(3) + z = -8 \quad \text{\textit{Substitute 3 for x in equation (4).}}$$
$$z = 1$$

Then we substitute 3 for x and 1 for z in equation (1) and solve for y:

$$3 + y - 1 = -1 \quad \text{\textit{Substitute 3 for x and 1 for z in equation (1).}}$$
$$y = -3$$

Therefore, $x = 3$, $y = -3$, and $z = 1$. So, the solution of the system is $(3, -3, 1)$. We check that the ordered triple satisfies *all three* original equations:

$x + y - z = -1$	$-4x - y + 2z = -7$	$2x - 2y - 5z = 7$
$3 + (-3) - 1 \overset{?}{=} -1$	$-4(3) - (-3) + 2(1) \overset{?}{=} -7$	$2(3) - 2(-3) - 5(1) \overset{?}{=} 7$
$-1 \overset{?}{=} -1$	$-7 \overset{?}{=} -7$	$7 \overset{?}{=} 7$
true	true	true

> **Solving a System of Three Linear Equations in Three Variables**
>
> To solve a system of three linear equations in three variables,
>
> 1. Select a pair of equations and eliminate a variable.
> 2. Select any other pair of equations and eliminate the *same variable* as in step 1.
> 3. The equations you found in steps 1 and 2 form a system of linear equations in *two* variables. Use elimination or substitution to solve this system.
> 4. Substitute the values of the two variables you found in step 3 into one of the original equations that contains the third variable. Solve for the third variable.
> 5. Write your solution as an ordered triple.

WARNING   Make sure you eliminate the *same* variable in steps 1 and 2. This way, your system in step 3 will be a system of equations in *two* variables (rather than three).

We can plot the point $(3, -3, 1)$ of Example 2 by using an x-axis, a y-axis, and a z-axis as shown in Fig. 79.

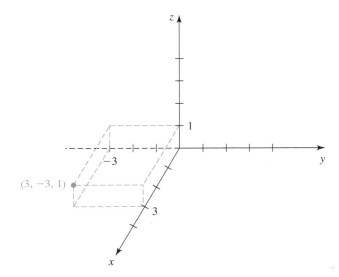

Figure 79 The point $(3, -3, 1)$

The graph of a linear equation in three variables is a plane. So, the graphs of equations (1), (2), and (3) of Example 2 are three planes that intersect at only the point $(3, -3, 1)$.

The intersection of three planes can be one point (see Fig. 80a), one line (see Fig. 80b), one plane (see Fig. 80c), or the empty set (see Fig. 80d). So, the solution set of a system of linear equations in three variables can contain exactly one ordered triple, an infinite number of ordered triples, or no ordered triples (the empty set). We will focus on systems whose solution set contains exactly one ordered triple.

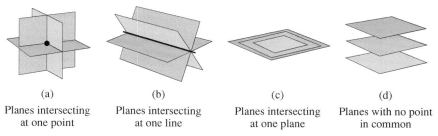

(a)	(b)	(c)	(d)
Planes intersecting at one point	Planes intersecting at one line	Planes intersecting at one plane	Planes with no point in common

Figure 80 Sketches of groups of three planes

It is difficult to graph linear equations in three variables, so we will not use graphing to solve systems of such equations.

▶ **Example 3** Solving a System of Three Equations

Solve the system

$$
\begin{aligned}
x + y + z &= 2 \quad \textit{Equation (1)} \\
10y - z &= 12 \quad \textit{Equation (2)} \\
2x - 3y &= 3 \quad \textit{Equation (3)}
\end{aligned}
$$

Solution

Equation (2) does not contain the variable x. To obtain a second equation that does not contain x, we select equations (1) and (3) and eliminate x. We begin by multiplying equation (1) by -2:

$$
\begin{aligned}
-2x - 2y - 2z &= -4 \quad \textit{Multiply both sides of equation (1) by } -2. \\
\underline{2x - 3y = 3} & \quad \textit{Equation (3)} \\
-5y - 2z &= -1 \quad \textit{Equation (4)}
\end{aligned}
$$

Equations (2) and (4) form a system in two variables. To eliminate y, we multiply both sides of equation (4) by 2:

$$
\begin{aligned}
10y - z &= 12 \quad \textit{Equation (2)} \\
\underline{-10y - 4z = -2} & \quad \textit{Multiply both sides of equation (4) by 2.} \\
-5z &= 10 \\
z &= -2
\end{aligned}
$$

Next, we substitute -2 for z in equation (2) and solve for y:

$$
\begin{aligned}
10y - (-2) &= 12 \quad \textit{Substitute } -2 \textit{ for z in equation (2).} \\
10y &= 10 \\
y &= 1
\end{aligned}
$$

Then we substitute 1 for y and -2 for z in equation (1) and solve for x:

$$
\begin{aligned}
x + 1 + (-2) &= 2 \quad \textit{Substitute 1 for y and } -2 \textit{ for z in equation (1).} \\
x &= 3
\end{aligned}
$$

Therefore, $x = 3$, $y = 1$, and $z = -2$. So, the solution of the system is $(3, 1, -2)$. We can check that the ordered triple satisfies all three original equations.

▶

Using Points That Are Not *y*-Intercepts to Find an Equation of a Parabola

Now that we know how to solve a system of linear equations in three variables, we can find an equation of a parabola that contains three given points. In Example 4, we find an equation of a parabola for which none of the given points are *y*-intercepts.

▶ **Example 4**   Finding an Equation of a Parabola

Find an equation of the parabola that contains the points $(1, 1)$, $(2, 3)$, and $(3, 9)$.

Solution

Our goal is to find values of the constants *a*, *b*, and *c* in the equation $y = ax^2 + bx + c$. Since the three given points lie on the parabola, each of the ordered pairs $(1, 1)$, $(2, 3)$, and $(3, 9)$ satisfies the equation $y = ax^2 + bx + c$:

$$1 = a(1)^2 + b(1) + c \quad \text{Substitute } (1, 1) \text{ into } y = ax^2 + bx + c.$$
$$3 = a(2)^2 + b(2) + c \quad \text{Substitute } (2, 3) \text{ into } y = ax^2 + bx + c.$$
$$9 = a(3)^2 + b(3) + c \quad \text{Substitute } (3, 9) \text{ into } y = ax^2 + bx + c.$$

We can simplify the right-hand sides of these equations:

$$a + b + c = 1 \quad \text{Equation (1)}$$
$$4a + 2b + c = 3 \quad \text{Equation (2)}$$
$$9a + 3b + c = 9 \quad \text{Equation (3)}$$

We select equations (1) and (2) and eliminate *c* by multiplying both sides of equation (1) by -1:

$$\begin{array}{rl} -a - b - c = -1 & \text{Multiply both sides of equation (1) by } -1. \\ \underline{4a + 2b + c = 3} & \text{Equation (2)} \\ 3a + b = 2 & \text{Equation (4)} \end{array}$$

Next, we select equations (1) and (3) and eliminate *c* again, once more multiplying both sides of equation (1) by -1:

$$\begin{array}{rl} -a - b - c = -1 & \text{Multiply both sides of equation (1) by } -1. \\ \underline{9a + 3b + c = 9} & \text{Equation (3)} \\ 8a + 2b = 8 & \text{Equation (5)} \end{array}$$

Then we divide both sides of Equation (5) by 2:

$$4a + b = 4 \quad \text{Equation (6)}$$

Equations (4) and (6) form a system in two variables. To eliminate *b*, we multiply both sides of equation (4) by -1:

$$\begin{array}{rl} -3a - b = -2 & \text{Multiply both sides of equation (4) by } -1. \\ \underline{4a + b = 4} & \text{Equation (6)} \\ a = 2 & \end{array}$$

Next, we substitute 2 for *a* in equation (4) and solve for *b*:

$$3(2) + b = 2$$
$$b = -4$$

Then we substitute 2 for *a* and -4 for *b* in equation (1) and solve for *c*:

$$2 + (-4) + c = 1 \quad \text{Substitute 2 for } a \text{ and } -4 \text{ for } b \text{ in equation (1).}$$
$$c = 3$$

Therefore, $a = 2$, $b = -4$, and $c = 3$, and the equation of the parabola is

$$y = 2x^2 - 4x + 3$$

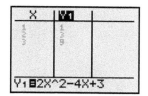

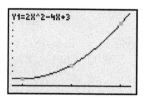

Figure 81 Verify the work

We use a graphing calculator table, as well as a scattergram and graph, to check that the parabola $y = 2x^2 - 4x + 3$ contains the points $(1, 1)$, $(2, 3)$, and $(3, 9)$. See Fig. 81.

To find a linear equation $y = mx + b$, we need *two* points to find the *two* constants m and b. To find an exponential equation $y = ab^x$, we need *two* points to find the *two* constants a and b. To find a quadratic equation in standard form, $y = ax^2 + bx + c$, we need *three* points to find the *three* constants a, b, and c.

> **Finding an Equation of a Parabola**
>
> To find an equation of a parabola that contains three given points,
>
> 1. Obtain a system of three linear equations in three variables by substituting the coordinates of each of the three given points into the general equation $y = ax^2 + bx + c$.
> 2. Solve the system you found in step 1.
> 3. Substitute the values of a, b, and c you found in step 2 into the equation $y = ax^2 + bx + c$.

Using the *y*-Intercept and Two Other Points

The process of finding an equation of a parabola is considerably easier if one of the three given points is the *y*-intercept, as we shall see in Example 5.

> **Example 5** Finding an Equation when One of the Given Points Is the *y*-Intercept

Find an equation of the parabola that contains the points $(0, 1)$, $(3, 7)$, and $(4, 5)$.

Solution

We begin by substituting the ordered pairs $(0, 1)$, $(3, 7)$, and $(4, 5)$, into $y = ax^2 + bx + c$:

$$1 = a(0)^2 + b(0) + c \quad \text{\textit{Substitute }} (0, 1) \textit{ into } y = ax^2 + bx + c.$$
$$7 = a(3)^2 + b(3) + c \quad \text{\textit{Substitute }} (3, 7) \textit{ into } y = ax^2 + bx + c.$$
$$5 = a(4)^2 + b(4) + c \quad \text{\textit{Substitute }} (4, 5) \textit{ into } y = ax^2 + bx + c.$$

Next, we simplify the right-hand sides of these equations:

$$c = 1 \quad \textit{Equation (1)}$$
$$9a + 3b + c = 7 \quad \textit{Equation (2)}$$
$$16a + 4b + c = 5 \quad \textit{Equation (3)}$$

Since $c = 1$, we substitute 1 for c in equations (2) and (3):

$$9a + 3b + 1 = 7 \quad \textit{Substitute 1 for c in equation (2).}$$
$$16a + 4b + 1 = 5 \quad \textit{Substitute 1 for c in equation (3).}$$

For each of these two equations, we subtract 1 on both sides:

$$9a + 3b = 6 \quad \textit{Equation (4)}$$
$$16a + 4b = 4 \quad \textit{Equation (5)}$$

To eliminate b, we multiply both sides of equation (4) by -4 and both sides of equation (5) by 3:

$$
\begin{aligned}
-36a - 12b &= -24 \quad \textit{Multiply both sides of equation (4) by } -4. \\
48a + 12b &= 12 \quad \textit{Multiply both sides of equation (5) by 3.} \\
\hline
12a &= -12 \\
a &= -1
\end{aligned}
$$

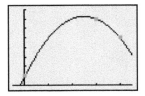

Figure 82 Verify the work

Next, we substitute -1 for a in equation (4) and solve for b:

$$9(-1) + 3b = 6 \quad \textit{Substitute } -1 \textit{ for a in equation (4).}$$
$$3b = 15$$
$$b = 5$$

Therefore, $a = -1$, $b = 5$, and $c = 1$, and the equation of the parabola is

$$y = -x^2 + 5x + 1$$

We use a graphing calculator table, as well as a scattergram and graph, to verify that the graph of $y = -x^2 + 5x + 1$ contains the points $(0, 1)$, $(3, 7)$, and $(4, 5)$. See Fig. 82.

In Example 5, we were able to find an equation of the desired parabola by using elimination once, rather than three times. We need to use elimination only once when one of the three given points is the y-intercept.

Group Exploration

For any three points, is there a quadratic function that contains them?

1. Find the values of a, b, and c of the function $f(x) = ax^2 + bx + c$, where the graph of f contains the points $(0, 1)$, $(1, 4)$, and $(2, 7)$. What type of function is f? Why did this happen?

2. Do the same for the points $(0, 1)$, $(0, 8)$, and $(1, 4)$. What happens? Is there a function $f(x) = ax^2 + bx + c$ whose graph contains these points? Explain.

3. What must be true of three points so there is a quadratic function whose graph contains the points? Give an example of three such points, plot them, and sketch the graph of the quadratic function that contains them. Then find an equation of the function and use a graphing calculator to view the graph. Compare the two graphs.

> ▶ Tips for Success   **Create an Example**
>
> When learning a definition or property, try to create an example. While studying the material in this section, you could select three points and determine whether there is a parabola that contains the chosen points, and if so, you could find an equation of the parabola. Creating examples will shed light on many details of a concept and will personalize the information.

Homework 7.6

For extra help ▶ MyMathLab®   Watch the videos in MyMathLab   Download the MyDashboard App

Solve the system.

1. $x + y + z = 0$
$x - y + z = 6$
$x + 2y - z = -7$

2. $x + y + z = 4$
$-x + y + 2z = 1$
$-x + y - 3z = -4$

3. $x + y - z = -1$
$2x - 2y + 3z = 8$
$2x - y + 2z = 9$

4. $2x - 3y + z = -9$
$-2x + y - 3z = 7$
$x - y + 2z = -5$

5. $3x - y + 2z = 0$
$2x + 3y + 8z = 8$
$x + y + 6z = 0$

6. $-x + y + z = 6$
$x - 2y + 3z = 5$
$-2x + y - 2z = -1$

7. $2x + y + z = 3$
$2x - y - z = 9$
$x + y - z = 0$

8. $x + y + z = 6$
$2x - y + z = 3$
$x + 2y - 3z = -4$

9. $2x + 2y + z = 1$
$-x + y + 2z = 3$
$x + 2y + 4z = 0$

10. $2x - 3y + z = 2$
$x - 5y + 5z = 3$
$3x + y - 3z = 5$

11. $2x - y + 2z = 6$
$3x + y - z = 5$
$x + 2y + z = 3$

12. $2x + y + z = -2$
$2x - y + 3z = 6$
$3x - 5y + 4z = 7$

13.
$$x \qquad - 3z = 6$$
$$y + 2z = 2$$
$$7x - 3y - 5z = 14$$

14.
$$2x + y \qquad = -2$$
$$3y - z = -14$$
$$x \qquad + 2z = 5$$

15.
$$2x - y \qquad = -8$$
$$y + 3z = 22$$
$$x \qquad - z = -8$$

16.
$$x + y \qquad = 1$$
$$y - 2z = 2$$
$$x \qquad - 3z = 14$$

Find an equation of the parabola that contains the given points. Use a graphing calculator to verify that the graph of your equation contains the points.

17. $(1, 6), (2, 11), (3, 18)$

18. $(1, 1), (2, 5), (3, 15)$

19. $(1, 9), (2, 7), (4, -15)$

20. $(1, 4), (2, 3), (3, 0)$

21. $(2, 2), (3, 11), (4, 24)$

22. $(2, 3), (3, -2), (4, -11)$

23. $(1, -3), (3, 9), (5, 29)$

24. $(2, -1), (4, 19), (5, 38)$

25. $(3, 7), (4, 0), (5, -11)$

26. $(2, 4), (4, 30), (5, 49)$

27. $(2, -5), (4, 3), (5, 13)$

28. $(1, 3), (2, 3), (4, -9)$

29. $(0, 4), (2, 8), (3, 1)$

30. $(0, 0), (1, 4), (2, 14)$

31. $(0, -1), (1, 3), (2, 13)$

32. $(0, 5), (2, 13), (3, 26)$

33. $(1, 1), (2, 4), (3, 9)$

34. $(1, -1), (2, -4), (3, -9)$

35. The graph of a quadratic function has y-intercept $(0, 4)$ and x-intercepts $(1, 0)$ and $(2, 0)$. Find an equation of the function.

36. The graph of a quadratic function has y-intercept $(0, 8)$ and x-intercepts $(-4, 0)$ and $(2, 0)$. Find an equation of the function.

Concepts

37. Find an equation of the parabola sketched in Fig. 83. [**Hint:** Choose three points whose coordinates appear to be integers.]

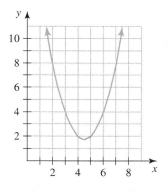

Figure 83 Exercise 37

38. Find an equation of the parabola sketched in Fig. 84. [**Hint:** Choose three points whose coordinates appear to be integers.]

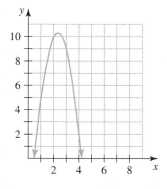

Figure 84 Exercise 38

39. Find an equation of the parabola sketched in Fig. 85.

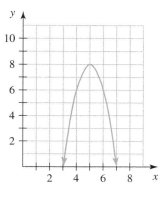

Figure 85 Exercise 39

40. Find an equation of the parabola sketched in Fig. 86.

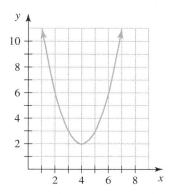

Figure 86 Exercise 40

41. In this exercise, you will show that two points do not determine a parabola.
   a. Plot the points $(1, 4)$ and $(3, 4)$ on a coordinate system.
   b. Sketch three parabolas, each of which contains both of the points $(1, 4)$ and $(3, 4)$. Find the vertex of each parabola.
   c. Write an equation of each of your three sketched parabolas. [**Hint:** You can use the vertex form $y = a(x - h)^2 + k$.]
   d. Explain why two points do not determine a parabola.

42. Find an equation of a parabola that is in quadrants I, III, and IV but not in quadrant II.

43. Choose three points that have different x-coordinates and do not all lie on a line. Find an equation of a parabola that contains the points. [**Hint:** To make the calculations easier, choose one of the points so it is the y-intercept.]

44. Create a system of three linear equations in three variables so $(2, 4, 3)$ is a solution.

45. Describe how to solve a system of three linear equations in three variables.

46. Describe how to find an equation of a parabola that contains three points that have different x-coordinates and do not all lie on a line.

Related Review

Find equations of a linear function, L, and an exponential function, E, such that the graph of each equation contains the given points. Round approximate constants to the second decimal place.

47. $(3, 13), (7, 85)$

48. $(2, 67), (5, 9)$

Find equations of a linear function, an exponential function, and a quadratic function such that the graph of each equation contains the given points. Use a graphing calculator to verify your work.

49. $(0, 2), (1, 4)$ **50.** $(0, 4), (2, 36)$

51. Find the values of *a, b,* and *c* of $f(x) = ax^2 + bx + c$, where the graph of *f* contains the points $(1, 1), (2, 2),$ and $(3, 3)$. What type of function is *f*?

52. Find the values of *a, b,* and *c* of $g(x) = ax^2 + bx + c$, where the graph of *g* contains the points $(1, 2), (2, 5),$ and $(3, 8)$. What type of function is *g*?

53. Find an equation of a parabola that has vertex $(5, -7)$ and contains the point $(8, 11)$.

54. Find an equation of a parabola that has vertex $(-5, 8)$ and contains the point $(-7, -4)$.

Expressions, Equations, Functions, and Graphs

Perform the indicated instruction. Then use words such as linear, quadratic, cubic, exponential, logarithmic, polynomial, degree, function, one variable, *and* two variables *to describe the expression, equation, or system.*

55. Solve $2x^2 - 10x + 7 = 0$.

56. Write $\log_3(t - 4) + \log_3(t + 1)$ as a single logarithm.

57. Find $f(2)$, where $f(x) = 2x^2 - 10x + 7$.

58. Solve $\log_3(t - 4) + \log_3(t + 1) = 2$.

59. Graph $f(x) = 2x^2 - 10x + 7$ by hand.

60. Solve $t^2 - 3t - 13 = 0$.

▼ 7.7 Finding Quadratic Models

Objectives

» Find an equation of a quadratic model in standard form.

» Determine whether a linear function, an exponential function, a quadratic function, or none of these can be used to model a situation.

In Section 7.6, we used three given points to find an equation of a parabola. In this section, we will use this skill to find an equation of a quadratic model. We will also discuss how to determine whether a linear model, an exponential model, a quadratic model, or none of these can be used to model an authentic situation.

Finding a Quadratic Model in Standard Form

In Example 1, we find an equation of a quadratic model.

▶ **Example 1**   Finding an Equation of a Quadratic Model

The percentages of adults ever diagnosed with high cholesterol are shown in Table 38 for various ages. Let $f(t)$ be the percentage of adults at age *t* years who have ever been diagnosed with high cholesterol. Find an equation of a model to describe the situation.

Table 38 Percentages of Adults Ever Diagnosed with High Cholesterol

Age (years)	Percent
50	29
60	43
70	50
80	47
90	39

Source: *The Gallup Organization*

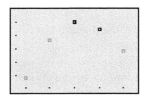

Figure 87 Cholesterol scattergram

Solution

We use a graphing calculator to draw a scattergram to describe the data (see Fig. 87). It looks like a parabola would fit the data well.

Through practice, we envision that the parabola containing the (blue) data points $(50, 29), (60, 43),$ and $(90, 39)$ may be close to the other data points. To find an equation of this parabola, we substitute the three ordered pairs $(50, 29), (60, 43),$ and $(90, 39)$ into the standard form $f(t) = at^2 + bt + c$:

$$29 = a(50)^2 + b(50) + c \quad \textit{Substitute } (50, 29) \textit{ into } f(t) = at^2 + bt + c.$$
$$43 = a(60)^2 + b(60) + c \quad \textit{Substitute } (60, 43) \textit{ into } f(t) = at^2 + bt + c.$$
$$39 = a(90)^2 + b(90) + c \quad \textit{Substitute } (90, 39) \textit{ into } f(t) = at^2 + bt + c.$$

We can simplify the right-hand sides of these equations:

$$2500a + 50b + c = 29 \quad \textit{Equation (1)}$$
$$3600a + 60b + c = 43 \quad \textit{Equation (2)}$$
$$8100a + 90b + c = 39 \quad \textit{Equation (3)}$$

We select equations (1) and (2) and eliminate *c* by multiplying both sides of equation (1) by -1:

$$-2500a - 50b - c = -29 \quad \textit{Multiply both sides of equation (1) by } -1.$$
$$\underline{3600a + 60b + c = 43} \quad \textit{Equation (2)}$$
$$1100a + 10b = 14 \quad \textit{Equation (4)}$$

Next, we select equations (2) and (3) and eliminate c again, this time multiplying both sides of equation (2) by -1:

$$\begin{array}{ll} -3600a - 60b - c = -43 & \textit{Multiply both sides of equation (2) by} -1.\\ \underline{8100a + 90b + c = 39} & \textit{Equation (3)}\\ 4500a + 30b = -4 & \textit{Equation (5)} \end{array}$$

Equations (4) and (5) form a system in two variables. To eliminate b, we multiply both sides of equation (4) by -3:

$$\begin{array}{ll} -3300a - 30b = -42 & \textit{Multiply both sides of equation (4) by} -3.\\ \underline{4500a + 30b = -4} & \textit{Equation (5)}\\ 1200a = -46\\ a \approx -0.03833 \end{array}$$

Next, we substitute -0.03833 for a in equation (4) and solve for b:

$$\begin{array}{ll} 1100(-0.03833) + 10b = 14 & \textit{Substitute} -0.03833 \textit{ for a in equation (4).}\\ -42.163 + 10b = 14\\ 10b = 56.163\\ b \approx 5.62 \end{array}$$

Then we substitute -0.03833 for a and 5.62 for b in equation (1) and solve for c:

$$\begin{array}{ll} 2500(-0.03833) + 50(5.62) + c = 29 & \textit{Substitute} -0.03833 \textit{ for a and 5.62}\\ 185.175 + c = 29 & \textit{for b in equation (1).}\\ c \approx -156.18 \end{array}$$

Finally, we substitute our approximate values of a, b, and c in the general equation $f(t) = at^2 + bt + c$ to obtain our quadratic model:

$$f(t) = -0.03833t^2 + 5.62t - 156.18$$

We verify the equation by observing that the graph of f appears to contain the points $(50, 29)$, $(60, 43)$, and $(90, 39)$. See Fig. 88. Since the graph appears to come close to the other data points, we conclude that f is a reasonable model of the situation.

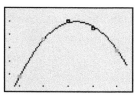

Figure 88 Check the fit

> ### Finding an Equation of a Quadratic Model
>
> To find an equation of a quadratic model, given some data,
>
> 1. Create a scattergram of the data.
> 2. Imagine a parabola that comes close to the data points, and choose three points (not necessarily data points) that lie on or close to the parabola.
> 3. Use the three points to find an equation of the parabola.
> 4. Use a graphing calculator to verify that the graph of the equation comes close to the points of the scattergram.

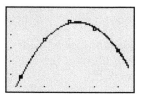

Figure 89 Compare the fit of models f and r

In Example 1, we could have used another procedure to find a quadratic model different from $f(t) = -0.03833t^2 + 5.62t - 156.18$. Instead of choosing three points and solving a system of equations, we could have used a graphing calculator's *quadratic regression*. Quadratic regression gives the model $r(t) = -0.03857t^2 + 5.64t - 156.49$. In Fig. 89, the graphs of the models f and r are so similar that ZoomStat appears to show just one curve. For graphing calculator instructions, see Appendix B.16.

We call the equation $r(t) = -0.03857t^2 + 5.64t - 156.49$ the **quadratic regression equation** for the given data. We refer to its graph as a **quadratic regression curve**.

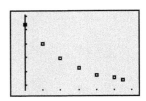

Figure 90 Bicycle store scattergram

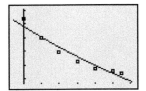

Figure 91 Exponential regression model

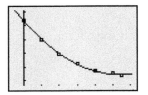

Figure 92 Quadratic regression model

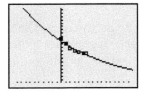

Figure 93 Exponential regression model

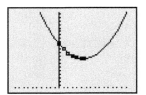

Figure 94 Quadratic regression model

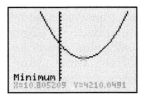

Figure 95 The vertex of the graph of Q

Determining Which Type of Model to Use

In Example 2, we will compare how well a linear model, an exponential model, and a quadratic model describe an authentic situation.

▶ **Example 2** Determining Which Model to Use

The numbers of specialty bicycle stores are shown in Table 39 for various years.

Table 39 Numbers of Specialty Bicycle Stores

Year	Number of Stores
2000	6195
2002	5505
2004	4982
2006	4600
2008	4349
2010	4256
2011	4178

Source: *The Bike Shop List*

Let n be the number of specialty bicycle stores at t years since 2000. Find an equation of a model to describe the situation.

Solution

First, we use a graphing calculator to draw a scattergram to describe the data (see Fig. 90). Since the points suggest a curve that "bends," we will not use a linear function to model the data. To decide between an exponential model and a quadratic model, we use a graphing calculator to find the exponential regression equation and the quadratic regression equation:

$$E(t) = 5914(0.966)^t \qquad \textit{Exponential regression equation}$$
$$Q(t) = 16.89t^2 - 365t + 6182 \qquad \textit{Quadratic regression equation}$$

Next, we see how well both regression models fit the data (see Figs. 91 and 92).

It appears Q fits the data better than E does. So, for most years between 2000 and 2011, inclusive, Q estimates the number of specialty bicycle stores better than E does. This suggests Q estimates the number of stores better than E does for at least a few years before 2000.

Does Q predict the number of stores better than E does for years after 2011? To see, we use Zoom Out on a graphing calculator (see Figs. 93 and 94).

It will also help to use "minimum" on a graphing calculator to find the approximate vertex of the graph of Q, which is $(10.81, 4210)$. See Fig. 95. So, Q predicts that the number of specialty bicycle stores has increased since 2011, which is not consistent with the decrease in the number of stores from 2000 to 2011. The decrease in the number of stores is likely to continue due to increasing online bicycle sales. The model E predicts that the number of stores will continue to decrease, which will most likely prove to be true. So, E is probably the best model for the years after 2011.

▶

Our work in Example 2 suggests two criteria for selecting a model.

▶ **Selecting a Model**

When performing step 1 of the modeling process, we must decide whether a linear function, an exponential function, a quadratic function, or none of these is suitable for modeling the situation. Here are the criteria for selecting a model:

- The graph of the model should fit the points well.
- The model should make sense within the context of the authentic situation.

In Example 2, we used the criterion of fit to determine that Q is the best model for the years between 2000 and 2011, inclusive. Using this same criterion, we assumed Q best estimates the number of specialty bicycle stores for at least a few years before 2000. We used the criterion of context (the number of stores has generally been decreasing over time) to determine E likely best predicts the number of stores for at least a few years after 2011.

Here, we outline the four-step modeling process again.

> ### Four-Step Modeling Process
>
> To find a model and make estimates and predictions,
>
> 1. Create a scattergram of the data. Decide whether a line, an exponential curve, a parabola, or none of these comes close to the points.
> 2. Find an equation of your model.
> 3. Verify that your equation has a graph that comes close to the points in the scattergram. If it doesn't, check for calculation errors or use different points to find the equation. An alternative is to reconsider your choice of model in step 1.
> 4. Use your equation of the model to draw conclusions, make estimates, and/or make predictions.

We will perform activities from step 4 in Section 7.8.

Group Exploration

Choosing three "good" points to find a quadratic model

Table 40 lists the average numbers of paid vacation days and holidays for full-time workers at medium-to-large companies for various years of experience. Let D be the average number of paid vacation days and holidays in one year for someone who has worked at a company for t years.

Table 40 Paid Vacation Days and Holidays

Years of Service	Days Off
1	9.4
3	11.2
5	13.6
10	16.6
15	18.8
20	20.4
25	21.6
30	21.9

Source: USA Today

1. Use a graphing calculator to create a scattergram of the vacation data. Does a linear function, an exponential function, or a quadratic function seem to model the data best? Explain.

2. Use the three data points $(1, 9.4)$, $(15, 18.8)$, and $(30, 21.9)$ to find an equation $D = at^2 + bt + c$ of the parabola that comes close to the data points in your scattergram.

3. Draw the graph of your quadratic model and your scattergram in the same viewing window to verify that the parabola passes through the points $(1, 9.4)$, $(15, 18.8)$, and $(30, 21.9)$. Does your quadratic function seem to be a reasonable model of the vacation data?

4. The first three rows in Table 40 give the data points $(1, 9.4)$, $(3, 11.2)$, and $(5, 13.6)$. Had you used these three points, you would have found the equation $D = 0.075t^2 + 0.60t + 8.73$. Compare its graph with the graph you drew in Problem 3. Explain why the graphs look so different.

5. In the future, you will encounter other data sets that can be modeled well by using a quadratic function. Describe a general "game plan" for deciding which three points to use to find a quadratic model.

Homework 7.7

For extra help ▶   MyMathLab°   Watch the videos in MyMathLab   Download the MyDashboard App

1. Four scattergrams of data are sketched in Fig. 96. Decide whether a linear function, an exponential function, a quadratic function, or none of these types of functions would be reasonable for modeling the data.

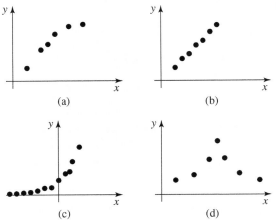

Figure 96 Scattergrams of data, Exercise 1

2. Make a sketch of each scattergram in Fig. 96. Then sketch the graph of the function you would use to model the data.

3. The percentages of teenagers who smoked cigarettes in the past month are shown in Table 41 for various ages.

Table 41 Percentages of Teenagers Who Smoked Cigarettes in the Past Month

Age (years)	Percent
12	1.7
13	3.3
14	8.4
15	13.6
16	20.1
17	26.4

Source: *National Household Survey on Drug Abuse*

Let $f(t)$ be the percentage of teenagers at age t years who smoked cigarettes in the past month. Find an equation of f by hand, and find a regression equation of f by using a graphing calculator. Compare the graphs of the two models.

4. Domestic airline fuel prices are shown in Table 42 for various years.

Table 42 Domestic Airline Fuel Prices

Year	Domestic Airline Fuel Price (cents per gallon)
2000	80
2001	78
2002	71
2003	84
2004	115
2005	165
2006	195
2007	209
2008	310

Source: *Bureau of Transportation Statistics*

Let $f(t)$ be the domestic airline fuel price (in cents per gallon) at t years since 2000. Find an equation of f by hand, and find a regression equation of f by using a graphing calculator. Compare the graphs of the two models.

5. The prices of an ounce of gold are listed in Table 43 for various years.

Table 43 Prices of an Ounce of Gold

Year	Price of an Ounce of Gold (dollars)
2001	271
2002	310
2003	363
2004	410
2005	445
2006	603
2007	695
2008	872
2009	972
2010	1116
2011	1572
2012	1669

Source: *Kitco, Inc.*

Let $f(t)$ be the price (in dollars) of an ounce of gold at t years since 2000.

a. Use the data for the years 2002, 2007, and 2012 to find a quadratic equation of f.
b. The data for the years 2005, 2006, and 2007 lead to the equation $f(t) = -33t^2 + 521t - 1335$. The data for the years 2010, 2011, and 2012 lead to the equation $f(t) = -179.5t^2 + 4226t - 23189$. In part (a), you found yet another equation of f. Use a graphing calculator to determine which of these triples of years gives the best model of the data. Could you have guessed this before you found the equations? If so, explain how.

6. July is the most popular month for Americans to take vacations (see Table 44).

Table 44 Percentages of Americans Who Vacation, by Month

Month	Number of Months since July t	Percent
July	0	43
August	1	34
September	2	21
October	3	15
November	4	11
December	5	11
January	6	3
February	7	3
March	8	4
April	9	8
May	10	20
June	11	30

Source: *2001 American Express Leisure Travel Index*

Let $f(t)$ be the percentage of Americans who take a vacation in the month that is t months since July.

a. Use the data for August, October, and May to find a quadratic equation of f.

b. The data for July, August, and September lead to the equation $f(t) = -2t^2 - 7t + 43$. The data for November, December, and January lead to the equation $f(t) = -4t^2 + 36t - 69$. The data for December, March, and May lead to $f(t) = 2.07t^2 - 29.2t + 105.33$. In part (a), you found yet another equation of f. Use a graphing calculator to determine which of these four triples of months gives the best model of the data. Could you have guessed this before you found the equations? If so, explain how.

7. The U.S. population is shown in Table 45 for various years.

Table 45 U.S. Population

Year	Population (millions)	Year	Population (millions)
1790	3.9	1910	92.2
1800	5.3	1920	106.0
1810	7.2	1930	123.2
1820	9.6	1940	132.2
1830	12.9	1950	151.3
1840	17.1	1960	179.3
1850	23.2	1970	203.3
1860	31.4	1980	226.5
1870	39.8	1990	248.7
1880	50.2	2000	281.4
1890	63.0	2010	308.7
1900	76.2		

Source: *U.S. Census Bureau*

a. Let $f(t)$ be the U.S. population (in millions) at t years since 1790. Find and verify an equation of f.

b. The U.S. population is shown in Table 46 for various years since 1990. An equation of a linear model for these years is $L(t) = 2.99t - 346.55$, where $L(t)$ represents the U.S. population (in millions) at t years since 1790.

Table 46 U.S. Population

Year	Population (millions)
1990	248.7
1993	259.9
1996	269.4
1999	279.0
2002	287.8
2005	295.8
2008	304.4
2010	308.7

Source: *U.S. Census Bureau*

i. Use a graphing calculator to draw the graphs of f and L and, in the same viewing window, the scattergram of the data *for the years shown in Table 45.* Which function describes the population better for these years? Explain.

ii. Use a graphing calculator to draw the graphs of f and L and, in the same viewing window, the scattergram of the data *for the years shown in Table 46.* Which function describes the population better for these years? Explain.

iii. How can one function be a better model for the period 1790–2010 but the other function be a better model for part of that period?

iv. Does the portion of the graph of f you viewed in part (ii) for the years from 1990 to 2010 appear to be linear, quadratic, or exponential? How is this possible?

8. The percentages of Americans who say they do volunteer work are listed in Table 47 for various age groups.

Table 47 Percentages of Americans Who Say They Volunteer

Age Group (years)	Age Used to Represent Age Group (years)	Percent
18–24	21.0	38
25–34	29.5	51
35–54	44.5	55
55–64	59.5	48
65–74	69.5	45
over 74	80.0	34

Source: *The Gallup Organization*

Let $f(A)$ be the percentage of Americans at age A years who say they volunteer. Find and verify an equation of f.

9. China has manufactured so many solar panels that it has created an enormous oversupply. The numbers of gigawatts of solar panels manufactured in China and the numbers of gigawatts of solar panels installed in the world are shown in Table 48 for various years.

Table 48 Solar Panels Manufactured in China and Worldwide Solar Panel Installations

Year	Solar Panels Manufactured in China (gigawatts)	Worldwide Solar Panel Installations (gigawatts)
2007	2	3
2008	3	6
2009	8	7
2010	16	18
2011	38	27
2012	50	31

Source: *GTM Research*

a. Let $f(t)$ be the number of gigawatts of solar panels manufactured in China and let $g(t)$ be the number of gigawatts of solar panels installed in the world, both in the year that is t years since 2000. Find a quadratic equation of f and a linear equation of g.

b. Use "intersect" on a graphing calculator to find the intersection points of the graphs of f and g. What do these points mean in this situation?

10. The percentages of California's population who are foreign born and the percentages who were born in other U.S. states are listed in Table 49 for various years.

a. Let $f(t)$ and $g(t)$ be the percentages of California's population that are foreign born and born in other U.S. states, respectively, at t years since 1900. Find and verify regression equations of f and g.

b. Use "intersect" on a graphing calculator to find the intersection points of the graphs of f and g. What do these points mean in this situation?

Table 49 Californians Not Originally from California

	Percent	
Year	Foreign Born	Born in Other U.S. States
1970	8.8	47.9
1980	15.1	39.5
1990	21.7	31.8
2000	25.9	23.5
2010	27.2	18.0

Source: *William Frey analysis of U.S. Census Bureau sources*

Concepts

11. A student believes the data listed in Table 50 suggest a quadratic relationship, because the values of y increase and then decrease. What would you tell the student?

Table 50 Is There a Quadratic Relationship? (Exercise 11)

x	y
0	3
1	4
2	7
3	12
4	20
5	35
6	20
7	12
8	7
9	4
10	3

12. A student uses the points $(2, 2.5)$, $(3, 4.1)$, and $(4, 6.4)$ to find an equation of a quadratic function to model the data in Table 51. Did the student make a good selection of points? If so, explain; then find the equation of those points. If not, explain; then make a better choice of points and find an equation.

Table 51 A Student Models Some Data (Exercise 12)

x	y
2	2.5
3	4.1
4	6.4
5	7.5
6	8.0
7	7.8
8	7.1
9	5.8
10	3.9
11	1.4
12	−1.7

13. Describe how to find an equation of a quadratic function that can be used to model data whose scattergram suggests a quadratic relationship.

14. Describe how to determine whether a linear function, an exponential function, a quadratic function, or none of these can be used to model an authentic situation. Discuss at least two criteria you can use to help you select a type of model.

Related Review

15. The percentages of American college students who are minorities are listed in Table 52 for various years.

Table 52 Percentages of American College Students Who Are Minorities

Year	Percent
1976	15
1980	16
1990	20
2000	28
2010	39

Source: *Department of Education*

Let $f(t)$ be the percentage of American college students who are minorities at t years since 1970.
a. Find a linear equation, an exponential equation, and a quadratic equation of f. Compare how well the models fit the data.
b. For years before 1976, which of the three models likely gives the best estimates of the percentages of American college students who are minorities? [**Hint:** Use a graphing calculator to sketch the graphs of the three equations. If you used ZoomStat to form your window, now use Zoom Out.]

16. The amounts (in terabytes) of digital data stored on devices in a typical U.S. household are listed in Table 53 for various years.

Table 53 Amounts of Digital Data Stored in a U.S. Household

Year	Amount of Digital Data Stored on Devices in a Typical U.S. Household (terabytes)
2006	0.58
2007	1.01
2008	1.58
2009	2.37
2010	3.46

Source: *Coughlin Associates*

Let $f(t)$ be the amount (in terabytes) of digital data stored on devices in a typical U.S. household at t years since 2000.
a. Find a linear equation, an exponential equation, and a quadratic equation of f. Compare how well the models fit the data.
b. For years before 2006, which of the three models likely gives the best estimates of the amount of digital data stored on devices in a typical U.S. household? [**Hint:** Use a graphing calculator to sketch the graphs of the three equations. If you used ZoomStat to form your window, now use Zoom Out.]
c. Use each of the three models to predict the amount of digital data that will be stored on devices in a typical household in 2014. Coughlin Associates predicts that 11.55 terabytes will be stored. Which of your three results is closest to this value?

Expressions, Equations, Functions, and Graphs

Perform the indicated instruction. Then use words such as lin-ear, quadratic, cubic, exponential, logarithmic, polynomial, degree, function, one variable, *and* two variables *to describe the expression, equation, or system.*

17. Solve:

$$\frac{1}{2}x - \frac{2}{3}y = 2$$
$$\frac{4}{3}x + \frac{5}{2}y = 31$$

18. Solve $3x(x - 2) = 5 - 2x^2$.

19. Graph $\frac{1}{2}x - \frac{2}{3}y = 2$ by hand.

20. Find the product $(4x - 5)(2x^2 + x - 3)$.

21. Find an equation of a line that contains the points $(-5, -2)$ and $(-2, -7)$.

22. Simplify $\left(\frac{8b^{-2}c^{-4}}{27b^7c^{-10}}\right)^{-1/3}$.

▼ 7.8 Modeling with Quadratic Functions

Objectives

» Use a quadratic model to make estimates and predictions.

» Estimate the maximum or minimum value of a quantity.

» Use a system of a quadratic model and another model to make estimates and predictions.

» Find the maximum revenue of a business venture.

In Section 7.7, we discussed how to find an equation of a quadratic model. In this section, we will use such an equation to make estimates and predictions about an authentic situation. We will also use a system of a quadratic model and another model to make predictions.

Using a Quadratic Function to Make Predictions

In Example 1, we use a quadratic model to make some predictions.

▶ **Example 1**   Using a Quadratic Model to Make Predictions

The revenues of Microsoft are shown in Table 54 for various years. Let r be the annual revenue (in billions of dollars) at t years since 1990.

1. Find a model to describe the situation.
2. In what years is there model breakdown for certain?
3. Predict the revenue in 2018.
4. Predict when the annual revenue will be $100 billion.

Table 54 Revenues of Microsoft

Year	Revenue (billions of dollars)
1992	2.8
1995	5.9
2000	23.0
2005	39.8
2010	62.5
2012	73.7

Source: *Microsoft*

Solution

1. First, we use a graphing calculator to draw a scattergram to describe the data (see Fig. 97). Since the points suggest a curve that "bends," we will not use a linear func-tion to model the data. To decide between an exponential model and a quadratic model, we use a graphing calculator to find the exponential regression equation and the quadratic regression equation:

$$E(t) = 2.81(1.17)^t \qquad \textit{Exponential regression equation}$$
$$Q(t) = 0.092t^2 + 1.36t - 1.25 \qquad \textit{Quadratic regression equation}$$

Next, we see how well each regression model fits the data (see Figs. 98 and 99).

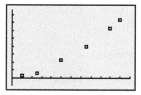

Figure 97 Microsoft scattergram

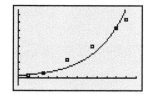

Figure 98 Exponential regression model

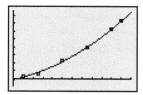

Figure 99 Quadratic regression model

It appears Q fits the data points better than E does. Since it is likely that Q will give better predictions than E, we will use $Q(t) = 0.092t^2 + 1.36t - 1.25$ as our model.

2. The part of the parabola in Fig. 100 (see next page) that lies below the t-axis suggests the revenue was negative in those years, which is false—the revenue of a company is

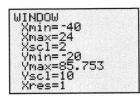

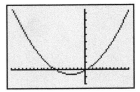

Figure 100 Part of the parabola lies below the *t*-axis

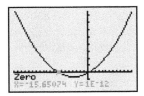

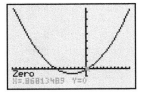

Figure 101 Verify the *t*-intercepts are approximately $(-15.65, 0)$ and $(0.87, 0)$

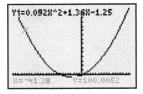

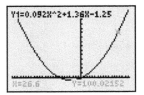

Figure 102 Verify that $t \approx -41.38$ and $t \approx 26.60$

always nonnegative. So, model breakdown occurs for the part of the model between the *t*-intercepts.

To find the *t*-intercepts, we substitute 0 for $Q(t)$ in the equation $Q(t) = 0.092t^2 + 1.36t - 1.25$ and solve for *t*:

$$0 = 0.092t^2 + 1.36t - 1.25 \qquad \textit{Substitute 0 for } Q(t).$$

$$t = \frac{-1.36 \pm \sqrt{1.36^2 - 4(0.092)(-1.25)}}{2(0.092)} \qquad \begin{array}{l}\textit{Substitute } a = 0.092, b = 1.36, \\ \textit{and } c = -1.25 \textit{ in quadratic formula.}\end{array}$$

$$t \approx -15.65 \quad \text{or} \quad t \approx 0.87 \qquad \textit{Compute.}$$

The *t*-intercepts are approximately $(-15.65, 0)$ and $(0.87, 0)$. To verify our work, we use "zero" on a graphing calculator (see Fig. 101). See Appendix B.21 for graphing calculator instructions.

We conclude that model breakdown occurs for the years between 1974 and 1991. Model breakdown also occurs for the years up until 1974, because the company started in 1975. Therefore, model breakdown occurs for the years before 1991.

3. To find the revenue in 2018, we evaluate *Q* at 28:

$$Q(28) = 0.092(28)^2 + 1.36(28) - 1.25 \approx 108.96$$

So, the revenue will be about \$109 billion in 2018, according to the model.

4. To find when the revenue will be \$100 billion, we substitute 100 for $Q(t)$ and solve for *t*:

$$100 = 0.092t^2 + 1.36t - 1.25 \qquad \textit{Substitute 100 for } Q(t).$$

$$0 = 0.092t^2 + 1.36t - 101.25 \qquad \textit{Subtract 100 from both sides.}$$

$$t = \frac{-1.36 \pm \sqrt{1.36^2 - 4(0.092)(-101.25)}}{2(0.092)} \qquad \begin{array}{l}\textit{Substitute } a = 0.092, b = 1.36, \textit{and} \\ c = -101.25 \textit{ in quadratic formula.}\end{array}$$

$$t \approx -41.38 \quad \text{or} \quad t \approx 26.60 \qquad \textit{Compute.}$$

We can use a graphing calculator to verify our work (see Fig. 102). The values of *t* we found represent the years 1949 and 2017. Model breakdown occurs for 1949, because the company began in 1975. In Problem 2, we decided model breakdown occurs for years before 2001, which checks. So, we predict the revenue will be \$100 billion in 2017.

In Example 1, we used a quadratic model to make predictions. Recall from Section 6.7 that, to make a prediction about the dependent variable, we substitute a value for the independent variable and solve for the dependent variable. To make a prediction about the independent variable, we substitute a value for the dependent variable and solve for the independent variable, usually by using the quadratic formula.

Finding the Maximum or Minimum Value of a Quantity

In Example 2, we find the vertex of a quadratic function to help us determine the maximum value of the function.

▶ **Example 2**   Making Estimates

Table 55 on the next page lists the percentages of workers who use computers on the job, by age groups. Let $p = f(t)$ be the percentage of workers who use computers at age *t* years.

1. Find an equation of *f*.
2. Use *f* to estimate the percentage of 22-year-old workers who use computers on the job.
3. Estimate the age(s) at which half of workers use computers on the job.
4. Estimate the age of workers who are *most likely* to use computers on the job (the maximum percentage). What is that maximum percentage?
5. Find the *t*-intercepts. What do they mean in this situation?

Table 55 Workers Who Use Computers on the Job

Age Group (years)	Age Used to Represent Age Group (years)	Percent
18–25	21.5	34.4
25–29	27.0	48.3
30–39	34.5	50.7
40–49	44.5	51.3
50–59	54.5	43.9
over 59	62.5	27.2

Source: *National Center for Education Statistics*

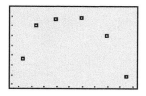

Figure 103 Computer worker scattergram

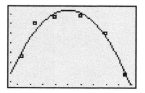

Figure 104 Verify computer worker model

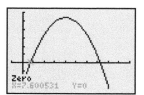

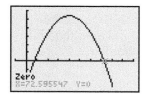

Figure 105 Verify the intercepts

Solution

1. We begin by drawing a scattergram of the data (see Fig. 103). It looks like a parabola would fit the data well. We can use a graphing calculator to find the quadratic regression model:

$$f(t) = -0.051t^2 + 4.09t - 28.14$$

To verify this result, we draw the scattergram and the graph of f in the same viewing window (see Fig. 104). It appears f is a reasonable model of the data.

2. Since

$$f(22) = -0.051(22)^2 + 4.09(22) - 28.14 \approx 37.16$$

we estimate that about 37.2% of 22-year-old workers use computers at work. We can verify this computation by using a graphing calculator table or graph.

3. Half of all workers is 50%, so we substitute 50 for $f(t)$ in the equation $f(t) = -0.051t^2 + 4.09t - 28.14$:

$$50 = -0.051t^2 + 4.09t - 28.14$$

Next, we write the equation in $at^2 + bt + c = 0$ form:

$$-0.051t^2 + 4.09t - 78.14 = 0$$

Then we apply the quadratic formula:

$$t = \frac{-4.09 \pm \sqrt{4.09^2 - 4(-0.051)(-78.14)}}{2(-0.051)}$$ *Substitute $a = -0.051$, $b = 4.09$, and $c = -78.14$ in quadratic formula.*

$$t \approx 48.80 \quad \text{or} \quad t \approx 31.40$$ *Compute.*

So, according to our model, half of 31-year-old workers and half of 49-year-old workers use computers on the job. We can verify these results by using a graphing calculator table or graph.

4. The function f is of the form $f(t) = at^2 + bt + c$, with $a = -0.051 < 0$, so the graph of f is a parabola that opens downward (see Fig. 104). Therefore, the vertex is the maximum point. We can find the age when workers are most likely to use computers by finding the vertex.

 To find the t-coordinate of the vertex, we substitute $a = -0.051$ and $b = 4.09$ in the vertex formula $t = -\dfrac{b}{2a}$:

$$t = -\frac{4.09}{2(-0.051)} \approx 40.10$$

The t-coordinate is about 40. To find the p-coordinate, we evaluate f at 40:

$$f(40) = -0.051(40)^2 + 4.09(40) - 28.14 = 53.86$$

The vertex is about $(40, 53.9)$. So, according to our model, about 53.9% of 40-year-old workers use computers on the job—the highest percentage for any age group. We can verify our computations by using "maximum" on a graphing calculator.

5. To find the t-intercepts, we substitute 0 for $f(t)$ in the quadratic equation $f(t) = -0.051t^2 + 4.09t - 28.14$ and solve for t:

$$0 = -0.051t^2 + 4.09t - 28.14$$ *Substitute 0 for $f(t)$.*

$$t = \frac{-4.09 \pm \sqrt{4.09^2 - 4(-0.051)(-28.14)}}{2(-0.051)}$$ *Substitute $a = -0.051$, $b = 4.09$, and $c = -28.14$ in quadratic formula.*

$$t \approx 72.60 \quad \text{or} \quad t \approx 7.60$$ *Compute.*

The t-intercepts are approximately $(7.6, 0)$ and $(72.6, 0)$. We use "zero" on a graphing calculator to verify our work (see Fig. 105). See Appendix B.21 for graphing calculator instructions.

The model estimates that no 8-year-old workers use computers on the job; this is correct but only because, legally, 8-year-old children cannot work. The model also estimates that no 73-year-old workers use computers on the job. Model breakdown has occurred, because some 73-year-old workers do use computers.

Modeling with a System of a Quadratic Equation and Another Equation

In Example 3, we make an estimate by working with a system of a quadratic model and a linear model.

▶ **Example 3**   Modeling with a System of a Quadratic Equation and a Linear Equation

In Exercise 78 of Homework 6.1, the market shares of world manufacturing output $U(t)$ and $C(t)$ of the United States and China, respectively, are modeled by the system

$$p = U(t) = -0.47t + 24.68$$
$$p = C(t) = 0.13t^2 - 0.54t + 11.24$$

where t is the number of years since 2000 (see Table 56).

Table 56 United States' and China's Market Shares of Manufacturing Output

| Year | Market Share (Percent) | |
	United States	China
2004	22.8	11.1
2005	22.5	11.9
2006	21.7	12.8
2007	21.4	13.9
2008	20.8	15.0
2009	20.6	17.2
2010	20.0	18.9

Source: *United Nations*

Estimate in which year(s) the market share of world manufacturing output of the United States was equal to that of China.

Solution

We substitute $0.13t^2 - 0.54t + 11.24$ for p in the equation $p = -0.47t + 24.68$:

$$0.13t^2 - 0.54t + 11.24 = -0.47t + 24.68 \quad \text{Substitute } 0.13t^2 - 0.54t + 11.24 \text{ for } p.$$
$$0.13t^2 - 0.07t - 13.44 = 0 \quad \text{Write in } at^2 + bt + c = 0 \text{ form.}$$

The quadratic formula gives

$$t = \frac{-(-0.07) \pm \sqrt{(-0.07)^2 - 4(0.13)(-13.44)}}{2(0.13)}$$

$$t \approx -9.90 \quad \text{or} \quad t \approx 10.44$$

The values of t we found represent 1990 and 2010. However, a little research would show that China's market share of world manufacturing output was much less than the United States' in 1990. So, the market shares of the two countries were approximately equal in 2010, according to the models. Even though the 2010 market shares shown in Table 56 are not equal, the models suggest China's market share overtook the United States' by 2011 (see Fig. 106). We conclude the two countries' market shares were equal at some time in 2010.

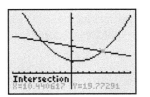

Figure 106 China's market share overtook the United States' in 2011

In Example 3, we used substitution with a system of a quadratic equation and a linear equation, both in two variables. **We can solve such a system as well as a system of two quadratic equations if at least one quadratic equation is in standard form $y = ax^2 + bx + c$.**

Maximum Revenue

Recall from Section 3.4 that if each of n objects has value v, then their total value T is given by $T = vn$. In Example 4, we will find the maximum value of the revenue of a chartered flight.

▶ Example 4   Finding the Maximum Value of a Quantity

A group charters a flight that normally costs $800 per person. A group discount reduces the fare by $10 for each ticket sold; the more tickets sold, the lower the per-person fare. There are 60 seats on the plane, including 4 seats for the crew. What size of group would maximize the airline's revenue?

Solution

We use the five-step problem-solving method of Section 3.4, but in step 2 we use a system of equations to build a function and in step 3 we find the maximum point of the graph of the function.

Step 1. Define each variable. We let n be the number of people in the group, p be the price (in dollars per person), and R be the revenue (in dollars).

Step 2. Use a system of two equations to build a function. A group of 3 people would be charged $800 - 3(10) = 770$ dollars per person. A group of 4 people would be charged $800 - 4(10) = 760$ dollars per person. So, a group of n people would be charged $800 - n(10)$ dollars per person. Our first equation is

$$p = -10n + 800$$

For our second equation, the revenue is equal to the price of one ticket times the number of tickets sold:

$$\underset{\text{revenue}}{R} = \underset{\substack{\text{dollars} \\ \text{ticket}}}{p} \cdot \underset{\text{tickets}}{n}$$

So, our system is

$$p = -10n + 800 \quad \textit{Equation (1)}$$
$$R = pn \quad\quad\quad\quad \textit{Equation (2)}$$

Next, we will build a revenue function whose independent variable is n. To begin, we substitute $-10n + 800$ for p in equation (2):

$$R = pn \quad\quad\quad\quad\quad\quad \textit{Equation (2)}$$
$$R = (-10n + 800)n \quad \textit{Substitute} -10n + 800 \textit{ for p.}$$
$$R = -10n^2 + 800n \quad\quad \textit{Distributive law}$$

Step 3. Find the maximum point of the graph of the function. The graph of the function $R = -10n^2 + 800n$ is a parabola that opens downward (see Fig. 107). So, the parabola has a maximum point (at the vertex).

To find the n-coordinate of the vertex, we use the vertex formula $n = -\dfrac{b}{2a}$:

$$n = -\frac{800}{2(-10)} = 40$$

To find the R-coordinate of the vertex, we substitute 40 for n in the revenue equation $R = -10n^2 + 800n$:

$$R = -10(40)^2 + 800(40) = 16{,}000$$

To find the price, we substitute 40 for n in the equation $p = -10n + 800$:

$$p = -10(40) + 800 = 400$$

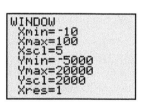

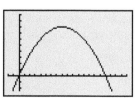

Figure 107 Graph of
$R = -10n^2 + 800n$

Step 4. Describe each result. The revenue is greatest if there are 40 people in a group. The price is then $400 per person, and the revenue is $16,000.

Step 5. Check. The revenue from 40 people, each paying $400, is $40 \cdot 400 = 16,000$ dollars, which checks. To check that the largest revenue is $16,000 dollars, we find the revenue for groups with 1 person fewer or 1 person more than 40 people.

39 people in group

price is $800 - 39(10) = 410$ dollars

revenue is $410 \cdot 39 = 15{,}990$ dollars

41 people in group

price is $800 - 41(10) = 390$ dollars

revenue is $390 \cdot 41 = 15{,}990$ dollars

Since a revenue of $16,000 is more than either of these (equal) revenues of $15,990, it seems reasonable that our work is correct. Finally, we use "maximum" on a graphing calculator to check that the maximum point of the parabola $R = -10n^2 + 800n$ is $(40, 16{,}000)$. See Fig. 108.

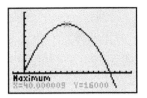

Figure 108 Verify that the maximum point is (40, 16,000)

 Group Exploration ————————————————————————————

Modeling differences of quantities

Refer to Example 3 for background information on the market shares of world manufacturing output of the United States and China.

1. Complete Table 57.

Table 57 Differences in United States' and China's Market Shares of Manufacturing Output

Year	Market Share (Percent)		Difference in Market Shares of the United States and China
	United States	China	
2004	22.8	11.1	22.8 − 11.1 = 11.7
2005	22.5	11.9	
2006	21.7	12.8	
2007	21.4	13.9	
2008	20.8	15.0	
2009	20.6	17.2	
2010	20.0	18.9	

2. Let $D(t)$ be the difference in market shares of the manufacturing output of the United States and China

at t years since 2000. Find a regression equation of D. Remember to use a graphing calculator to draw a scattergram of the data first.

3. Which of the statements that follow is correct? Explain.

$$D(t) = (U + C)(t) \qquad D(t) = (U - C)(t)$$
$$D(t) = (C - U)(t)$$

4. In Example 3, we used the following equations of U and C:

$$p = U(t) = -0.47t + 24.68$$
$$p = C(t) = 0.13t^2 - 0.54t + 11.24$$

Substitute $-0.47t + 24.68$ for $U(t)$ and substitute $0.13t^2 - 0.54t + 11.24$ for $C(t)$ in the equation $D(t) = U(t) - C(t)$ to find an equation of D. Simplify the right-hand side of your equation and compare the result with the equation you found in Problem 2.

5. Find t when $D(t) = 0$. What does your result mean in this situation? Compare your result with the result in Example 3.

▶ Tips for Success   Form a Study Group to Prepare for the Final Exam

To prepare for the final exam, it may be helpful to form a study group. The group could list important concepts of the course and discuss the meanings of these concepts and how to apply them. You could also list important techniques learned in the course and practice those techniques. Set aside some solo study time after the group study session to make sure you can do the mathematics without the help of other members of the study group.

Homework 7.8

For extra help ▶   Watch the videos in MyMathLab   Download the MyDashboard App

1. In Exercise 49 of Homework 7.2, you worked with the model $f(t) = 0.058t^2 - 0.98t + 15.43$, where $p = f(t)$ is the percentage of households with outstanding student debt at t years since 1990 (see Table 58).

Table 58 Percentages of Households with Outstanding Student Debt

Year	Percent
1995	12
1998	11
2001	12
2004	13
2007	15
2010	19

Source: *Pew Research Center*

a. Find the p-intercept. What does it mean in this situation?
b. Estimate the percentage of households that had outstanding student debt in 2009. Did you perform interpolation or extrapolation? Explain.
c. Predict the percentage of households that will have outstanding student debt in 2018. Did you perform interpolation or extrapolation? Explain.
d. Predict when 36% of households will have outstanding student debt.

2. In Exercise 8 of Homework 7.7, you found an equation close to $f(A) = -0.0197A^2 + 1.86A + 9.90$, where $f(A)$ is the percentage of Americans at age A years who say they do volunteer work (see Table 59).

Table 59 Percentages of Americans Who Say They Volunteer

Age Group (years)	Age Used to Represent Age Group (years)	Percent
18–24	21.0	38
25–34	29.5	51
35–54	44.5	55
55–64	59.5	48
65–74	69.5	45
over 74	80.0	34

Source: *The Gallup Organization*

a. Estimate the percentage of 25-year-old Americans who say they volunteer. Did you perform interpolation or extrapolation?
b. Estimate the percentage of 16-year-old Americans who say they volunteer. Did you perform interpolation or extrapolation?
c. For what age do half of Americans say they volunteer?
d. For what age is the percentage who say they volunteer the greatest? What is that maximum percentage?

3. A householder is the person in whose name a house, condominium, or apartment is owned or rented. The percentages of householders who own a home are shown in Table 60 for various age groups.

Table 60 Percentages of Householders Who Own a Home

Age Group (years)	Age Used to Represent Age Group (years)	Percent Who Own a Home
15–24	19.5	18
25–34	29.5	46
35–44	39.5	66
45–54	49.5	75
55–64	59.5	80
65–74	69.5	81
75–84	79.5	77

Source: *U.S. Census Bureau*

Let $f(a)$ be the percentage of householders who own a home at age a years.
a. Find an equation of f.
b. Find the a-intercepts. What do they mean in this situation?
c. For what values of a is there model breakdown for certain? Which ages are represented by these values?
d. Estimate the age of householders who are most likely to own a home. What percentage of householders at this age own a home?
e. Estimate all ages at which half of householders own homes.

4. A tennis ball is tossed upward, and its heights at various times are recorded (see Table 61).

Table 61 Heights of a Tennis Ball

Time (seconds)	Height (feet)
0.00	1.93
0.06	2.25
0.12	2.51
0.18	2.69
0.24	2.70
0.30	2.54
0.36	2.37

Source: *J. Lehmann*

Let $f(t)$ be the height (in feet) of the tennis ball at t seconds.
a. Find an equation of f.
b. Find the t-intercepts. What do they mean in this situation?
c. For what values of t is there model breakdown for certain? Explain.
d. Estimate the maximum height of the tennis ball. When did it reach this height?
e. Assume that, after the toss, the tennis ball bounces on the ground several times. Sketch a qualitative graph that describes the relationship between the height of the tennis ball and the time until the tennis ball comes to rest.

5. In Exercise 7 of Homework 7.7, you found an equation close to $P = f(t) = 0.0068t^2 - 0.13t + 6.49$, where $f(t)$ is the U.S. population (in millions) at t years since 1790 (see Table 62).

Table 62 U.S. Population

Year	Population (millions)	Year	Population (millions)
1790	3.9	1910	92.2
1800	5.3	1920	106.0
1810	7.2	1930	123.2
1820	9.6	1940	132.2
1830	12.9	1950	151.3
1840	17.1	1960	179.3
1850	23.2	1970	203.3
1860	31.4	1980	226.5
1870	39.8	1990	248.7
1880	50.2	2000	281.4
1890	63.0	2010	308.7
1900	76.2		

Source: *U.S. Census Bureau*

a. Find $f(228)$. What does it mean in this situation?

b. Find t, where $f(t) = 335$. What does your result mean in this situation?

c. Graph f by hand.

d. For what values of t is there model breakdown? Which years are represented by these values?

e. Sketch a qualitative graph that describes the relationship between t and P for all time, past and future.

6. A *filibuster* is an action such as a prolonged speech or raising an objection that is used to delay the debate of a bill in the Senate. The numbers of filibusters are shown in Table 63 for various years.

Table 63 Numbers of Filibusters

Year	Number of Filibusters
1962	4
1972	24
1982	31
1992	60
2002	71
2012	110

Source: *U.S. Senate*

Let $n = f(t)$ be the number of filibusters in the year that is t years since 1950.

a. Find a quadratic equation of f.

b. Find $f(67)$. What does it mean in this situation?

c. Find t when $f(t) = 67$. What does it mean in this situation?

d. Find the t-intercepts of the model. What do they mean in this situation?

e. Assuming that the number of filibusters has increased throughout time, find the years in the past when model breakdown occurred for certain.

7. The numbers of career home runs hit by Barry Bonds are shown in Table 64 for various years. Let $f(t)$ be the number of career home runs hit by Barry Bonds at t years since 1980.

a. Find an equation of f.

b. Use f to estimate when Barry Bonds tied Hank Aaron's record of 755 lifetime home runs.

c. Due to injury, Bonds hit only 5 home runs in 2005. Find $f(25)$ and $f(26)$. Then find the difference $f(26) - f(25)$. Does your result suggest Bonds tied Aaron's record in 2006? Explain.

d. Bonds turned 42 years old on July 24, 2006. Discuss any assumptions you made in part (c), and explain why Bonds may not have tied Aaron's record in 2006.

Table 64 Numbers of Career Home Runs Hit by Barry Bonds

Year	Number of Career Home Runs
1986	16
1990	117
1995	292
2000	494
2004	703

Source: *Baseball-reference.com*

8. The percentages of Americans who say they've forgotten to do something special for their significant other on Valentine's Day are shown in Table 65 for various ages.

Table 65 Percentages of Americans Who Forgot to Do Something Special on Valentine's Day

Age Group (years)	Age Used to Represent Age Group (years)	Percent
25–34	29.5	11
35–44	39.5	17
45–54	49.5	24
55–64	59.5	27
over 64	70.0	29

Source: *CARAVAN for DHL*

Let $f(a)$ be the percentage of Americans at age a years who say they've forgotten to do something special for their significant other on Valentine's Day.

a. Find an equation of f.

b. Find the a-intercepts. What do they mean in this situation?

c. Find the vertex. What does it mean in this situation?

d. Estimate the percentage of 21-year-old Americans who say they've forgotten to do something special for their significant other on Valentine's Day. The actual percentage is 19%. Has model breakdown occurred? Explain.

e. For what values of a is there model breakdown for certain? Which years are represented by these values? Are there other values of a for which it is likely there is model breakdown? If so, find those values of a and the years represented by them.

9. In Exercise 9 of Homework 7.7 you found a system close to

$$n = f(t) = 2.20t^2 - 31.65t + 115.51$$
$$n = g(t) = 6.11t - 42.75$$

where $f(t)$ is the number of gigawatts of solar panels manufactured in China and $g(t)$ is the number of gigawatts of solar panels installed in the world, both in the year that is t years since 2000 (see Table 66). Use substitution to estimate in which years the number of gigawatts of solar panels manufactured in China was equal to the number of gigawatts of solar panels installed in the world.

Table 66 Solar Panels Manufactured in China and Worldwide Solar Panel Installations

Year	Solar Panels Manufactured in China (gigawatts)	Worldwide Solar Panel Installations (gigawatts)
2007	2	3
2008	3	6
2009	8	7
2010	16	18
2011	38	27
2012	50	31

Source: *GTM Research*

10. Women tend to be younger than men in their first marriage. The median ages at which women and men were first married are shown in Table 67 for various years.

Table 67 Median Ages at First Marriages

Year	Median Age Women (years)	Median Age Men (years)
1975	21.1	23.5
1980	22.0	24.7
1985	23.3	25.5
1990	23.9	26.1
2000	24.5	26.9
2005	25.1	26.8
2010	25.5	27.0

Source: *U.S. Census Bureau*

Let $W(t)$ be the median age (in years) at which women were first married and $M(t)$ be the median age (in years) at which men were first married, both at t years since 1900.

a. Find a regression equation of women's median marrying age and another regression equation of men's median marrying age.

b. Predict when the median age or ages at which women and men first marry will be equal, if ever.

11. In the 2000 presidential election, the race between George W. Bush and Al Gore was so close that there was concern about the accuracy of vote-counting systems, including punch cards, lever machines, and paper ballots. Punch cards and lever systems are gradually being replaced with optical scan or other modern electronic vote-counting systems (see Table 68).

Table 68 Vote-Counting Systems

Year	Percent of Registered Voters Punch Card or Lever Machine	Percent of Registered Voters Optical Scan or Other Modern Electronic System
1990	71.7	13.5
1992	69.4	16.5
1994	63.1	25.8
1996	58.0	32.3
1998	52.9	36.4
2002	35.7	54.3
2004	26.0	65.0
2008	11.0	80.0

Source: *Federal Election Commission*

a. Let $f(t)$ be the percentage of voters using punch cards or lever machines and $g(t)$ be the percentage of voters using optical scan or other modern electronic systems, both at t years since 1990. Find regression equations of f and g.

b. Use substitution to estimate when the percentage of voters using optical scan or other modern electronic systems equaled the percentage of voters using punch cards or lever machines. Is your result a major (even-numbered) election year (congressional or presidential)? If not, in which even-numbered year were the percentages closest?

c. There are three other ways to vote: DataVote (punch holes in ballots that haven't been perforated), paper (count hand-marked ballots manually), and mixed systems. Let $h(t)$ be the percentage of voters using any of these three ways to vote at t years since 1990. Which of the statements that follow is correct? Explain.

$$h(t) = (f + g)(t) \quad h(t) = 100 - (f + g)(t)$$
$$h(t) = (f - g)(t) \quad h(t) = 100 - (f - g)(t)$$

d. Find an equation of h.

e. Find $h(17)$. What does it mean in this situation?

12. In Exercise 10 of Homework 7.7, the percentages of California's population $f(t)$ and $g(t)$ who are foreign born and born in other U.S. states, respectively, are modeled by the system

$$p = f(t) = -0.0089t^2 + 2.07t - 93.07$$
$$p = g(t) = 0.0037t^2 - 1.43t + 129.70$$

where t is the number of years since 1900 (see Table 69).

Table 69 Californians Not Originally from California

Year	Percent Foreign Born	Percent Born in Other U.S. States
1970	8.8	47.9
1980	15.1	39.5
1990	21.7	31.8
2000	25.9	23.5
2010	27.2	18.0

Source: *William Frey analysis of U.S. Census Bureau sources*

a. Use substitution to estimate when the percentages of foreign born and those born in other U.S. states were equal. What is that percentage? That year, what percentage of California's population was originally from California?

b. Let $h(t)$ be the percentage of California's population that was originally from California at t years since 1900. Which of the statements that follow is correct? Explain.

$$h(t) = 100 - (f - g)(t) \quad h(t) = (f - g)(t)$$
$$h(t) = 100 - (f + g)(t) \quad h(t) = (f + g)(t)$$

c. Find an equation of h.

d. Find $h(118)$. What does it mean in this situation?

e. Use a graphing calculator to sketch a graph of h. Is the curve increasing or decreasing for $t \geq 62$? What does it mean in this situation?

13. A ski club charters a bus that normally costs $250 per person. A group discount reduces the fare by $5 for each ticket sold; the more tickets sold, the lower is the per-person fare. There are 31 seats on the bus, including 1 seat for the driver. What size of group would maximize the bus company's revenue?

14. A company charters a party boat that normally costs $60 per person. A group discount reduces the fare by $0.50 for each ticket sold; the more tickets sold, the lower is the per-person fare. The maximum capacity of the boat is 80 people, including the crew of 10 people. What size of group would maximize the boat company's revenue?

15. Some students reserve the buffet room in a restaurant for a graduation party. The buffet dinner normally costs $28 per person. A group discount reduces the price by $0.20 for each student who attends; the more dinners sold, the lower is the per-person price. The room's maximum capacity is 80 people. What size of party would maximize the restaurant's revenue?

16. A group charters a flight that normally costs $900 per person. A group discount reduces the fare by $15 for each ticket sold; the more tickets sold, the lower is the per-person fare. There are 40 seats on the plane, including 4 seats for the crew. What size of group would maximize the airline's revenue?

17. A person plans to use 160 feet of fencing to enclose a rectangular play area. What dimensions of the rectangle would maximize the area? What is that area?

18. A rancher plans to use 1200 feet of fencing and the side of her barn to form a rectangular boundary for cattle (see Fig. 109). What dimensions of the rectangle would maximize the area? What is that area?

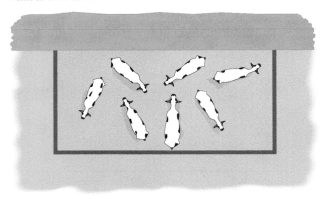

Figure 109 Boundary for cattle

Concepts

19. Assume the quadratic function $f(t) = at^2 + bt + c$ is a model of a situation where t is the number of years since 2000 and the vertex is (h, k). Explain why there is sometimes model breakdown for either $t < h$ or for $t > h$. Include a graph of f in your explanation.

20. Assume the quadratic function $f(t) = at^2 + bt + c$ is a model of a situation where t is the number of years since 2000 and $(2, 0)$ and $(18, 0)$ are t-intercepts. Explain why there is sometimes model breakdown for $t < 2$ and $t > 18$. Include a graph of f in your explanation.

21. For a quadratic model, discuss how to find intercepts, the vertex, and the maximum or minimum value; how to make predictions for the dependent or independent variable; and how to determine values of the independent variable where model breakdown occurs.

22. Describe how you can find a system of two quadratic equations in two variables to model an authentic situation. Explain how you can use the system to make an estimate or a prediction about the situation.

Related Review

23. Harnessing wind energy is much more affordable and cleaner than processing oil or coal. Table 70 lists worldwide wind-generating capacities in thousands of megawatts (thousand MW) for various years.

Table 70 Worldwide Wind-Generating Capacities

Year	Wind-Generating Capacity (thousand MW)
1994	3.7
1997	7.6
2000	17.4
2003	39.4
2006	74.1
2009	158.9
2011	238.4

Source: *World Wind Energy Association*

Let $f(t)$ be the wind-generating capacity (in thousand MW) at t years since 1990.

a. Find a linear regression equation, an exponential regression equation, and a quadratic regression equation of f. Compare how well the models fit the data.

b. For the years before 1994, which equation likely best models the situation?

c. One MW of wind-generating capacity meets the electricity needs of about 1000 people in an industrialized country. Use your exponential model to predict when wind energy could meet the electricity needs of the entire world. Assume world population is 7.0 billion. [**Hint:** Note that the units of $f(t)$ are *thousands* of megawatts.]

d. Now use your quadratic model to predict when wind energy could meet the electricity needs of the entire world.

e. Explain why the year you predicted in part (d) is so much later than the year you predicted in part (c).

OK, Timmy, trim the sails, we're approaching the freeway!

24. The numbers of coal miners employed are shown in Table 71 for various years.

Table 71 Numbers of Coal Miners Employed

Year	Number of Coal Miners (thousands)
1923	705
1933	419
1943	416
1953	293
1963	142
1973	148
1983	176
1993	101
2003	71
2011	86

Source: *National Mining Association*

Let $f(t)$ be the number (in thousands) of coal miners employed at t years since 1900.

a. Find a linear regression equation, an exponential regression equation, and a quadratic regression equation of f. Compare how well the models fit the data.

b. Assuming that the number of coal miners will generally decrease, which equation will best model the situation for the years after 2011?

c. Note that the number of coal miners increased from 2003 to 2011. If the number of coal miners employed continues to increase, which equation will best model the situation for the years after 2011?

d. Use the exponential model to predict when 60 thousand coal miners will be employed.

e. What is the base b of the exponential model $f(t) = ab^t$? What does it mean in this situation?

Expressions, Equations, Functions, and Graphs

Give an example of the following. Then solve, simplify, or graph, as appropriate.

25. exponential function

26. linear function

27. quadratic equation in one variable

28. system of two linear equations in two variables

29. quadratic function

30. logarithmic function

31. exponential equation in one variable

32. logarithmic equation in one variable

Taking it to the Lab

Climate Change Lab (continued from Chapter 6)

Some developing countries' carbon dioxide emissions are increasing greatly as their economies continue to grow. In particular, China's future carbon dioxide emissions will affect the planet considerably, because of that country's large population, large population growth, and increasing per-person carbon dioxide emissions (see Table 72). Unless China takes measures to slow the growth of carbon dioxide emissions, its per-person emissions in 2050 could reach 41.5 metric tons—about 21 times the 1990 per-person emissions.

Table 72 China's Population and Carbon Dioxide Emissions

Year	Population (billions)	Per-Person Carbon Emissions (metric tons per person)
1990	1.15	1.98
1995	1.21	2.38
2000	1.27	2.86
2005	1.31	4.21
2010	1.34	6.15

Source: *U.S. Census Bureau; U.S. Energy Information Administration*

Although the United States has the largest gross domestic product (GDP) in the world, China's GDP is likely to surpass U.S. GDP as early as 2020.* So, it is not surprising China has large carbon dioxide emissions. In fact, China has already overtaken the United States as the top emitter of carbon dioxide in the world; in 2010, China's emissions were 8.2 billion metric tons and U.S. emissions were 5.6 billion metric tons.[†]

Even though China has larger carbon dioxide emissions than the United States, its per-person emissions are about one-third of the United States' (see Tables 72 and 73). If U.S. per-person emissions were to hold steady at 18.1 metric tons, China's per-person emissions could reach that level as early as 2029.

Table 73 U.S. Population and Carbon Dioxide Emissions

Year	Population (billions)	Per-Person Carbon Emissions (metric tons per person)
1950	0.15	16.0
1960	0.18	16.1
1970	0.21	20.5
1980	0.23	20.9
1990	0.25	20.0
2000	0.28	21.1
2010	0.31	18.1

Source: *U.S. Census Bureau; The Cambridge Factfinder*

*The New York Times.
[†]Carbon Dioxide Information Analysis Center

Recall from the Climate Change Lab in Chapter 6 that if world population were to decline to 1.6 billion, then the IPCC's 2050 carbon dioxide emissions goal could be met if carbon dioxide emissions were limited to 5.4 metric tons per person each year. This per-person limit would create room for most developing countries to expand their economies.

Such a population–emissions strategy would require some developing countries to learn to expand their economies in new ways that would not increase per-person carbon dioxide emissions so much. Other developing countries such as China and oil-rich countries such as Qatar would actually have to reduce their per-person emissions. It would also require developed countries to learn to maintain their economies while reducing their per-person carbon dioxide emissions. Finally, it would require that world population be reduced by 77% from its 2010 level of 6.85 billion. All requirements would be great challenges.

Analyzing the Situation

1. Assume that China's *per-person* annual carbon dioxide emissions are increasing linearly. Let $L(t)$ be China's per-person annual carbon emissions (in metric tons per person) at t years since 1950. Find the linear regression equation of L.

2. Now assume that China's *per-person* annual carbon emissions are increasing quadratically. Let $Q(t)$ be China's per-person annual carbon emissions (in metric tons per person) at t years since 1950. Find the quadratic regression equation of Q.

3. Find $L(70)$ and $Q(70)$. What do they mean in this situation? Compare your results with the claim that China's per-person emissions in 2050 could be as high as 41.5 metric tons of carbon dioxide per person.

4. Let $P(t)$ be China's population (in billions) at t years since 1950. Create a scattergram for China's population data. Find the linear regression equation of P.

5. Find an equation of $Q \cdot P$. Perform a unit analysis of the equation. Find $(Q \cdot P)(70)$. What does it mean in this situation?

6. In Problem 8 of the Climate Change Lab in Chapter 2, you found a model of U.S. annual carbon dioxide emissions (in billions of metric tons) $h(t)$ at t years since 1950. If, however, you didn't find such an equation, find it now. Then use h, $Q \cdot P$, and "intersect" on a graphing calculator to estimate when China and the United States had the same annual amount of carbon dioxide emissions. What is that annual amount of carbon dioxide emissions?

7. Use Q to verify the claim that China's *per-person* annual carbon dioxide emissions could reach the United States' 2010 level of 18.1 metric tons of carbon dioxide per person as early as 2029.

8. Explain why the year you found in Problem 6 is so much earlier than the year you found in Problem 7.

Projectile Lab (continued from Chapter 6)

In the Projectile Lab in Chapter 6, you found an equation of a quadratic model that describes the times and heights of a ball that you threw straight up. In this lab, you will analyze that situation further.

Analyzing the Situation

1. What model did you work with in the Projectile Lab in Chapter 6? Provide the equation and define the variables.

2. Use the model to estimate both times when the ball was at a height of 8 feet.

3. Find the average of the two times you found in Problem 2.

4. Use the model to estimate the height of the ball at the time you found in Problem 3.

5. Use a graphing calculator to draw a graph of the model. Copy the graph, and indicate on the graph the two points that represent when the ball was at a height of 8 feet and the point that represents when the ball was at the height you found in Problem 4.

6. By referring to your graph in Problem 5, explain why your result in Problem 4 is the maximum height of the ball.

7. Use "maximum" on a graphing calculator to estimate the maximum height of the ball. Compare this result with your result from Problem 4.

8. Find the average speed of the ball on its way up. That is, find the ball's average speed from the moment it was released to the moment it reached its maximum height.

9. Explain why it makes sense that your result in Problem 8 is less than the initial speed you found in the Projectile Lab in Chapter 6.

Projectile Lab (Using a CBR or CBL)

In this lab, you will toss a softball vertically into the air and record the softball's height at various times. If your instructor prefers, use the data listed in Table 74.

Table 74 Heights of a Softball

Time (seconds)	Height (feet)	Time (seconds)	Height (feet)
0.00	3.3994	0.32	4.4545
0.02	3.5650	0.34	4.4077
0.04	3.7271	0.36	4.3393
0.06	1.5000	0.38	4.2925
0.08	4.0620	0.40	4.2024
0.10	4.1340	0.42	4.0980
0.12	4.1916	0.44	3.9900
0.14	4.2709	0.46	3.8711
0.16	4.3429	0.48	3.7379
0.18	4.4005	0.50	3.5903
0.20	4.4473	0.52	3.4354
0.22	4.4797	0.54	3.2662
0.24	4.4977	0.56	3.0861
0.26	4.5049	0.58	2.9061
0.28	4.5013	0.60	2.7044
0.30	4.4797		

Source: *J. Lehmann*

Materials

If you are going to perform your own experiment, you will need the following materials:

1. a softball (or some other object)

2. a CBR data collection device, or a CBL data collection system with a Vernier motion detector probe

Analyzing the Data

1. If you collected your own softball data, display these data in a table. If not, use the data in Table 74.

2. Let $h = f(t)$ be the height (in feet) of the softball at t seconds. Use a graphing calculator to draw a scattergram of the softball data.

3. If you are using the data in Table 74, should the graph of your model come close to (0.06, 1.5), which is described in the table? If you performed your own experiment, should the graph of your model come close to all of your data points? Explain.

4. Find an equation of f.

5. Use a graphing calculator to draw a graph of your model and the scattergram in the same viewing window. Also, graph the model and scattergram by hand. How well does f model the data?

6. Use your equation of f to estimate when the softball reached the ground.

7. What is the h-intercept of your model? What does it mean in this situation?

8. Use your model to estimate the height of the softball at 0.7 second.

9. Use your model to estimate the height of the softball at 10 seconds.

10. For what values of t is there model breakdown? Explain.

11. Use your model to estimate when the softball reached its maximum height. What was the maximum height?

Water Flow Lab

In this experiment, you will fill a cylinder with water and allow the water to flow out of a small hole near the bottom. The point of the experiment is to explore the relationship between the volume of water that flows out of the hole and the time elapsed.

If your instructor prefers, use the data listed in Table 75.

Table 75 Heights of Water in a Cylinder with Radius 1.5 Inches

Time (seconds)	Height (inches)
0	30
9	25
18	20
29	15
42	10
58	5
79	1

Source: *J. Lehmann*

Materials

If you are going to perform your own experiment, you will need at least three people and the following items:

1. a timing device, a tape measure or ruler, and a marker

2. a transparent cylinder with a closed bottom. Near the bottom, there should be a hole that is large enough so that water flows out rather than drips out. The cylinder should be large enough and the hole small enough so that it takes at least a minute for the full cylinder to drain. For example, a cylinder that is 4 feet long with a diameter of 3 inches works well with a hole that has a diameter of about $\frac{1}{8}$ inch.

3. a bucket to catch the water that flows out of the cylinder

Preparation

Make about eight equally spaced marks along the cylinder. Fill the cylinder with water, keeping the hole near the bottom sealed until you are ready to begin timing. While two people are preparing the cylinder and water, the third person should prepare to record the times it takes for the water level to reach the various marks on the cylinder.

Recording of Data

Record the height of each mark, the amount of time (from the start of the experiment) it takes for the water level to reach each mark, and the radius of the cylinder.

Analyzing the Data

1. If you collect your own water-flow data, display these data in a table. If not, then use the data in Table 75.

2. Let $H = f(t)$ be the height (in inches) of the water at t seconds after the water begins to flow out of the cylinder. Use a graphing calculator to draw a scattergram of your data.

3. Find an equation of f. The water flow is likely to be a bit erratic at the end, so it's probably best to avoid using a data point that corresponds to a water level of zero.

4. Use a graphing calculator to graph your model and the scattergram in the same viewing window. Graph your model and the scattergram by hand. How well does f model the data?

5. Find the H-intercept of your model. What does it mean in this situation? Does model breakdown occur before the H-intercept, after the H-intercept, or neither? Explain.

6. Find the t-intercept(s) of your model. What does such a point mean in this situation? Does model breakdown occur before the t-intercept, after the t-intercept, both, or neither? Explain. If there are not any t-intercepts, what does your model imply?

7. Find the vertex of your model. Does model breakdown occur before the vertex, after the vertex, or neither? Explain.

8. Use your model to estimate the height of the water at 20 seconds.

9. Use your model to estimate how many seconds it took for the water level to reach a height of 7 inches.

Taking It One Step Further

10. For a cylinder of radius R and height H, the volume of the cylinder can be described by the equation $V = \pi R^2 H$. If R and H are in inches, then V is in cubic inches. Substitute your value of R into the equation $V = \pi R^2 H$.

11. You have $H = at^2 + bt + c$ and $V = \pi R^2 H$, where a, b, c, and R are known constants. Substitute $at^2 + bt + c$ for H into the equation $V = \pi R^2 H$ to find an equation that describes the volume of water in terms of the time elapsed since the start of the experiment.

12. Use your result from Part 11 to estimate the volume of water in the cylinder at $t = 10$ seconds.

13. How much water has flowed out of the cylinder during the time span from $t = 10$ to $t = 20$? From $t = 20$ to $t = 30$? Explain why the two amounts are not equal.

Quadratic Lab: Topic of Your Choice

Your objective in this lab is to find a quadratic function to model an authentic situation. Your function should model a situation that has not been discussed in this text. You must first find some data. Almanacs, newspapers, magazines, scientific journals, and the Internet are good resources for data. Or conduct an experiment to obtain your data.

Analyzing the Data

1. What two variables did you explore? [**Hint:** Describe the units of the variables.]

2. Does it makes sense that a quadratic function models your situation best? Explain.

3. Which variable is the dependent variable? Which variable is the independent variable?

4. State the source of your data. If you conducted an experiment, provide a careful description with specific details of how you ran your experiment.

5. Include a table of your data.

6. Use a graphing calculator to draw a scattergram of your data.

7. Find an equation of a quadratic model to describe the data.

8. Use a graphing calculator to graph your quadratic model and the scattergram in the same viewing window. Graph your model and the scattergram by hand. How well does the model fit the data?

9. Find all intercepts of your quadratic model. What do they mean in this situation? Has model breakdown occurred at the intercepts?

10. Find the vertex of your model. What does it mean in this situation? Has model breakdown occurred at the vertex?

11. Choose an input of your model. Find the output that comes from the chosen input. What does your result mean in this situation?

12. Choose an output of your model. Find the input that originates from the chosen output. What does your result mean in this situation?

13. Comment on your lab experience. For example,
    a. Address whether this lab was enjoyable, insightful, and so on.
    b. Were you surprised by any of your findings? If so, which ones?
    c. How would you improve your procedure for this lab if you did it again?
    d. How would you improve your procedure if you had more time and money?

Chapter Summary

Key Points of Chapter 7

Section 7.1   Graphing Quadratic Functions in Vertex Form

Vertex form of a quadratic function	Let $f(x) = a(x - h)^2 + k$, where $a \neq 0$. Then f is a quadratic function, and its graph is a parabola with vertex (h, k). We say the equation is in **vertex form.**
Graphs of quadratic functions of the form $f(x) = ax^2$	For a function of the form $f(x) = ax^2$, • The graph is a parabola with vertex $(0, 0)$. • If $|a|$ is a large number, then the parabola is steep. (It is narrow.) • If a is near zero, then the parabola is not steep. (It is wide.) • If $a > 0$, then the parabola opens upward. • If $a < 0$, then the parabola opens downward. • The graph of $y = -ax^2$ is the reflection of the graph of $f(x) = ax^2$ across the x-axis.

Section 7.1   Graphing Quadratic Functions in Vertex Form (*Continued*)

Three-step method of graphing a quadratic function in vertex form	To sketch the graph of $f(x) = a(x - h)^2 + k$, where $a \neq 0$, 1. Sketch the graph of $y = ax^2$. 2. Translate the graph from step 1 to the right by h units if $h > 0$ or to the left by $\lvert h \rvert$ units if $h < 0$. 3. Translate the graph from step 2 up by k units if $k > 0$ or down by $\lvert k \rvert$ units if $k < 0$.
Finding a quadratic model in vertex form	To find a quadratic model in vertex form, given some data, 1. Create a scattergram of the data. 2. Imagine a parabola that comes close to (or contains) the data points, and select a point (h, k) to be the vertex. Although it is not necessary to select a data point, it is often convenient and satisfactory to do so. 3. Select a nonvertex point (not necessarily a data point) of the parabola, substitute the point's coordinates into the equation $f(t) = a(t - h)^2 + k$, and solve for a. 4. Substitute the result you found for a in step 3 into $f(t) = a(t - h)^2 + k$.

Section 7.2   Graphing Quadratic Functions in Standard Form

Using two symmetric points to find the vertex	To find the vertex of a parabola in which (p, s) and (q, s) are symmetric points, 1. Find the x-coordinate by using the formula $x = \dfrac{p + q}{2}$. In words, the x-coordinate is the average of the x-coordinates of any two symmetric points. 2. Find the y-coordinate by evaluating f at the value found in step 1. That is, find $f\left(\dfrac{p + q}{2}\right)$.
Using symmetric points to graph a quadratic function in standard form (method 1)	To sketch a graph of a quadratic function $f(x) = ax^2 + bx + c$, where $b \neq 0$, 1. Find the y-intercept. 2. Find the y-intercept's symmetric point. 3. Average the x-coordinates of the two symmetric points to find the x-coordinate of the vertex. 4. Find the y-coordinate of the vertex. 5. Depending on how accurate your sketch is to be, find additional points on the parabola, as needed. 6. Sketch a parabola that contains the points found.
Vertex formula	To find the vertex of the graph of a quadratic function $f(x) = ax^2 + bx + c$, 1. Find the x-coordinate of the vertex by using the **vertex formula** $x = -\dfrac{b}{2a}$. 2. Find the y-coordinate of the vertex by evaluating f at the value found in step 1. That is, find $f\left(-\dfrac{b}{2a}\right)$.
Maximum or minimum value of a function	For a quadratic function $f(x) = ax^2 + bx + c$ whose graph has vertex (h, k), • If $a < 0$, then the parabola opens downward and the maximum value of the function is k. • If $a > 0$, then the parabola opens upward and the minimum value of the function is k.

Section 7.3   Using the Square Root Property to Solve Quadratic Equations

Product property for square roots	For $a \geq 0$ and $b \geq 0$, $\sqrt{ab} = \sqrt{a}\sqrt{b}$.
Using the product property to simplify square roots	To use the product property to simplify a square root, 1. Write the radicand as the product of the *largest* perfect-square factor and another number. 2. Apply the product property for square roots.

Section 7.3   Using the Square Root Property to Solve Quadratic Equations (*Continued*)

Quotient property for square roots	For $a \geq 0$ and $b > 0$, $\sqrt{\dfrac{a}{b}} = \dfrac{\sqrt{a}}{\sqrt{b}}$.
Rationalize the denominator	To rationalize the denominator of a fraction of the form $\dfrac{p}{\sqrt{q}}$, where q is positive, multiply the fraction by 1 in the form $\dfrac{\sqrt{q}}{\sqrt{q}}$.
Simplifying a radical expression	To simplify a radical expression, 1. Use the quotient property for square roots so no radicand is a fraction. 2. Use the product property for square roots so no radicands have perfect-square factors other than 1. 3. Rationalize the denominators so no denominator is a radical expression. 4. Continue applying steps 1–3 until the radical expression is completely simplified.
Square root property	Let k be a real-number constant. Then $x^2 = k$ is equivalent to $x = \pm\sqrt{k}$.
Imaginary unit i	The **imaginary unit,** written i, is the number whose square is -1. That is, $i^2 = -1$ and $i = \sqrt{-1}$.
Square root of a negative number	If p is a positive real number, then $\sqrt{-p} = i\sqrt{p}$.
Complex number	A **complex number** is a number of the form $a + bi$, where a and b are real numbers.
Imaginary number	An **imaginary number** is a number $a + bi$, where a and b are real numbers and $b \neq 0$.

Section 7.4   Solving Quadratic Equations by Completing the Square

Perfect-square trinomial property	For a perfect-square trinomial of the form $x^2 + bx + c$, dividing b by 2 and squaring the result gives c: $$x^2 + bx + c$$ $$\left(\frac{b}{2}\right)^2 = c$$
When completing the square can be used	Any quadratic equation can be solved by completing the square.
Solving a quadratic equation by completing the square	To solve a quadratic equation $ax^2 + bx + c = 0$ by **completing the square,** 1. If $a \neq 1$, divide both sides of the equation by a. 2. Write the equation in the form $x^2 + dx = k$, where d and k are constants. 3. Complete the square for the expression on the left side of the equation. 4. Solve the equation by using the square root property.

Section 7.5   Using the Quadratic Formula to Solve Quadratic Equations

Quadratic formula	The solutions of a quadratic equation $ax^2 + bx + c = 0$ are given by the **quadratic formula:** $$x = \frac{-b \pm \sqrt{b^2 - 4ac}}{2a}$$
Determining the number and type of solutions	For the quadratic equation $ax^2 + bx + c = 0$, the **discriminant** is $b^2 - 4ac$. Also, • If $b^2 - 4ac > 0$, there are two real-number solutions. • If $b^2 - 4ac = 0$, there is one real-number solution. • If $b^2 - 4ac < 0$, there are two imaginary-number solutions (and no real-number solutions).

Section 7.5   Using the Quadratic Formula to Solve Quadratic Equations (*Continued*)

When the quadratic formula can be used	Any quadratic equation can be solved by using the quadratic formula.
Guidelines on solving quadratic equations	Here are some guidelines on deciding which method to use to solve a quadratic equation:

Method	When to Use
Factoring	For equations that can easily be put into the form $ax^2 + bx + c = 0$ and where $ax^2 + bx + c$ can easily be factored.
Square root property	For equations that can easily be put into the form $x^2 = k$ or $(x + p)^2 = k$.
Completing the square	When the directions require it.
Quadratic formula	For all equations except those that can easily be solved by factoring or by using the square root property.

Section 7.6   Solving Systems of Linear Equations in Three Variables; Finding Quadratic Functions

Linear equation in three variables	A **linear equation in three variables** is an equation that can be put into the form $Ax + By + Cz = D$, where A, B, C, and D are constants and A, B, and C are not all zero.
System of linear equations in three variables	A **system of linear equations in three variables** consists of two or more linear equations in three variables.
Solution	The **solution** of a system of linear equations in three variables is an ordered triple that satisfies *all* of the equations.

Solving a system of three linear equations in three variables	To solve a system of three linear equations in three variables,

1. Select a pair of equations and eliminate a variable.
2. Select any other pair of equations and eliminate the *same variable* as in step 1.
3. The equations you found in steps 1 and 2 form a system of linear equations in *two* variables. Use elimination or substitution to solve this system.
4. Substitute the values of the two variables you found in step 3 into one of the original equations that contains the third variable. Solve for the third variable.
5. Write your solution as an ordered triple.

Finding an equation of a parabola	To find an equation of a parabola that contains three given points,

1. Obtain a system of three linear equations in three variables by substituting the coordinates of each of the three given points into the general equation $y = ax^2 + bx + c$.
2. Solve the system you found in step 1.
3. Substitute the values of a, b, and c you found in step 2 into the equation $y = ax^2 + bx + c$.

Section 7.7   Finding Quadratic Models

Finding an equation of a quadratic model	To find an equation of a quadratic model, given some data,

1. Create a scattergram of the data.
2. Imagine a parabola that comes close to the data points, and choose three points (not necessarily data points) that lie on or close to the parabola.
3. Use the three points to find an equation of the parabola.
4. Use a graphing calculator to verify that the graph of the equation comes close to the points of the scattergram.

Section 7.7   Finding Quadratic Models (*Continued*)

Selecting a model   When performing step 1 of the modeling process, we must decide whether a linear function, an exponential function, a quadratic function, or none of these is suitable for modeling the situation. Here are the criteria for selecting a model:

- The graph of the model should fit the points well.
- The model should make sense within the context of the authentic situation.

Four-step modeling process   To find a model and make estimates and predictions,

1. Create a scattergram of the data. Decide whether a line, an exponential curve, a parabola, or none of these comes close to the points.
2. Find an equation of your model.
3. Verify that your equation has a graph that comes close to the points in the scattergram. If it doesn't, check for calculation errors or use different points to find the equation. An alternative is to reconsider your choice of model in step 1.
4. Use your equation of the model to draw conclusions, make estimates, and/or make predictions.

Section 7.8   Modeling with Quadratic Functions

Solving a system of quadratic equations   We can use substitution to solve any system of two quadratic equations if at least one equation is in standard form $y = ax^2 + bx + c$.

Chapter 7 Review Exercises

Sketch the graph of the function by hand.

1. $y = -3x^2$
2. $y = 3(x + 1)^2 - 4$
3. $y = -2(x - 3)^2 + 5$
4. $y = \frac{1}{2}(x + 4)^2 - 2$
5. A function of the form $y = a(x - h)^2 + k$ has been sketched in Fig. 110. Describe the signs of the constants a, h, and k.

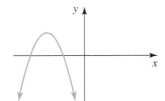

Figure 110 Exercise 5

Graph the function. Find the vertex; round coordinates to the second decimal place.

6. $y = 3x^2 - 12x + 7$
7. $y = -2x^2 + 8x + 5$
8. $1.7x + 2.6x^2 + y = 6.7x^2 - 10x + 2.1$

Simplify.

9. $\sqrt{72}$
10. $\sqrt{\frac{49}{100}}$

Solve. All solutions are real numbers.

11. $3x^2 - 2x - 2 = 0$
12. $5x^2 = 7$
13. $5(p - 3)^2 + 4 = 7$
14. $(t + 1)(t - 7) = 4$
15. $2x^2 = 4 - 5x$
16. $4x - x^2 = 1$
17. $5x^2 - 6x = 2$
18. $7x^2 - 20 = 0$
19. $(x + 2)^2 + (x - 3)^2 = 15$
20. $5(5x^2 - 8) = 9$
21. $\frac{3}{2}x^2 - \frac{3}{4}x = \frac{1}{2}$

Find approximate solutions. Round the results to the second decimal place.

22. $2.7x^2 - 5.1x = 9.8$
23. $1.7(x^2 - 2.3) = 3.4 - 2.8x$

Find all complex-number solutions.

24. $-2(x + 4)^2 = 9$
25. $2x^2 = 4x - 7$

Solve by completing the square. All solutions are real numbers.

26. $x^2 + 6x - 4 = 0$
27. $2t^2 = -3t + 6$

Find all x-intercepts.

28. $h(x) = 3x^2 + 2x - 2$
29. $k(x) = -5x^2 + 3x - 1$
30. Solve $x^2 - 2x - 8 = 0$ by factoring, completing the square, and using the quadratic formula.
31. Find the number and type of solutions of the equation $3x^2 - 5x + 4 = 0$.
32. Let $f(x) = 3x^2 - 6x + 7$.
    a. Find x when $f(x) = 3$.
    b. Find x when $f(x) = 4$.
    c. Find x when $f(x) = 5$.
    d. Discuss, in terms of the graph of f, why you found zero, one, and two values of x for parts (a), (b), and (c), respectively.

For Exercises 33–35, find approximate solutions of the equation or system by referring to the graphs shown in Fig. 111. Round results or coordinates of results to the first decimal place.

33. $-\frac{1}{4}(x - 1)^2 + 1 = x^2$
34. $-\frac{1}{4}(x - 1)^2 + 1 = -3$
35. $y = -\frac{1}{4}(x - 1)^2 + 1$
    $y = -\frac{1}{3}x - 2$

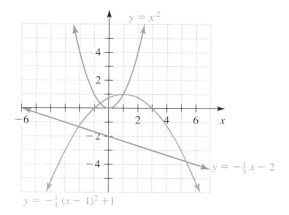

Figure 111 Exercises 33–35

Solve the system.

36. $x + 2y - 3z = -4$
$2x - y + z = 3$
$3x + 2y + z = 10$

37. $2x - 3z = -4$
$3x + y = 0$
$x - 4y + 2z = 17$

For Exercises 38 and 39, find an equation of the parabola that passes through the three given points.

38. $(2, 9), (3, 18), (5, 48)$

39. $(0, 5), (2, 3), (4, -15)$

40. Find equations of a linear function, an exponential function, and a quadratic function such that the graph of each function contains both of the points $(0, 4)$ and $(1, 2)$.

41. Find an equation of the parabola sketched in Fig. 112.

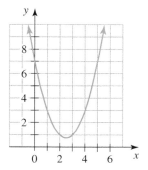

Figure 112 Exercise 41

42. A batter hits a baseball into the air. The height (in feet) $h(t)$ of the baseball after t seconds is given by

$$h(t) = -16t^2 + 100t + 3$$

a. Find the maximum height of the baseball. When does it reach that height?

b. A fielder catches the ball at a height of 3 feet. How many seconds after the batter hit the ball did the fielder have to get into position to catch the ball?

c. Graph h by hand.

43. A farmer plans to use 180 feet of fencing and a side of his barn to enclose a rectangular garden (see Fig. 113). What

should the dimensions of the rectangle be so the area is as large as possible? What is that area?

Figure 113 Exercise 43

44. The percentages of military personnel in the Iraq and Afghanistan wars who have done more than one tour of duty are listed in Table 76 for various years.

Table 76 Percentages of Military Personnel Who Have Done More than One Tour of Duty

Year	Percent
2001	7
2003	18
2005	28
2007	33
2010	38

Source: *Department of Defense*

Let $p = f(t)$ be the percentage of military personnel in the Iraq and Afghanistan wars who have done more than one tour of duty at t years since 2000.

a. Find an equation of f.

b. Find the vertex. What does it mean in this situation?

c. Estimate when 37% of military personnel had done more than one tour of duty.

d. Estimate the percentage of military personnel in 2006 who had done more than one tour of duty.

45. The percentages of Americans who get their news every day from newspapers and the percentages of Americans who get their news every day on the Internet are shown in Table 77 for various years.

Table 77 Percentages of Americans Who Get Their News Every Day from Newspapers and from the Internet

Year	Percent from Newspapers	Year	Percent from Internet
1996	50	1998	6
1998	48	1999	8
2000	47	2002	15
2002	41	2004	20
2004	42	2006	23
2006	40	2008	29
2008	34	2010	34
2010	31	2012	39
2012	29		

Source: *Pew Research Center*

Let $f(t)$ be the percentage of Americans who get their news every day from newspapers, and let $g(t)$ be the percentage of Americans who get their news on the Internet, both at t years since 1990.

a. Find a quadratic regression equation of f and a linear regression equation of g.

b. Use f and g to estimate when the percentage of Americans who get their news every day from newspapers was equal to the percentage of Americans who get their news every day on the Internet. What was that percent?

Chapter 7 Test

1. Graph the function $f(x) = -2(x + 5)^2 - 1$ by hand.

2. What can you say about the values of $a, h,$ and k if the equation of the parabola shown in Fig. 114 is $y = a(x - h)^2 + k$?

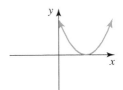

Figure 114 Exercise 2

3. Give an example of a quadratic function that has vertex $(2, -7)$ and no x-intercepts.

4. Graph $f(x) = -2x^2 - 4x + 3$ by hand. Find the vertex.

5. Let $f(x) = x^2 - 2x - 8$.
   a. Find the x-intercepts.
   b. Find the vertex.
   c. Graph f by hand. Indicate the x-intercepts and vertex on the graph.

Simplify.

6. $\sqrt{32}$

7. $\sqrt{\dfrac{20}{75}}$

For Exercises 8–14, solve. All solutions are real numbers.

8. $x^2 - 3x - 10 = 0$

9. $6x^2 = 100$

10. $4(r - 3)^2 + 1 = 7$

11. $\dfrac{5}{6}x^2 - \dfrac{1}{2}x = \dfrac{2}{3}$

12. $(x - 3)(x + 5) = 6$

13. $2x(x + 5) = 4x - 3$

14. $3x^2 - 6x = 1$

15. Find approximate solutions of $3.7x^2 = 2.4 - 5.9x$. Round your results to the second decimal place.

Find all complex-number solutions.

16. $3x^2 - 6x = -5$

17. $-2(p + 4)^2 = 24$

For Exercises 18 and 19, solve by completing the square.

18. $x^2 - 8x - 2 = 0$

19. $2(x^2 - 4) = -3x$

20. Find the x-intercepts of the graph of $f(x) = 3x^2 - 8x + 1$.

21. Find the x-intercepts and vertex of the graph of $f(x) = -2(x - 3)^2 + 5$. Round the coordinates to the second decimal place. Then graph f by hand.

22. Find the nonzero value(s) of a such that the equation $ax^2 - 4x + 4a = 0$ has exactly one solution.

23. Find an equation of the parabola that passes through the points $(1, 4), (2, 9),$ and $(3, 16)$.

24. Find an equation of the parabola that has vertex $(5, 3)$ and that contains the point $(3, 11)$.

25. Let $f(x) = x^2 - 6x + 11$. Find the number of points that lie on the graph of f at the indicated height.
   a. $y = 1$ **b.** $y = 2$ **c.** $y = 3$

Solve the system.

26. $x + 4y + 3z = 2$
        $2x + y + z = 10$
        $-x + y + 2z = 8$

27. $2x - 3y = 4$
        $3y + 2z = 2$
        $x - z = -5$

28. Let $f(t)$ be the height (in feet) of a baseball at t seconds after a batter has hit the ball. A reasonable equation of f is $f(t) = -16t^2 + 80t + 3$. At what time is the ball at its maximum height? What is that height?

29. The percentages of Americans who feel they are taking a great risk by entering personal information into a pop-up ad are shown in Table 78 for various age groups.

Table 78 Percentages of Americans Who Feel They Are Taking a Great Risk by Entering Personal Information into a Pop-Up Ad

Age Group (years)	Age Used to Represent Age Group (years)	Percent
18–24	21.0	27
25–34	29.5	33
35–44	39.5	37
45–54	49.5	44
55–64	59.5	39
over 64	70.0	23

Source: *Wells Fargo*

Let $f(t)$ be the percentage of Americans at age t years who feel they are taking a great risk by entering personal information into a pop-up ad.
   a. Find an equation of f.
   b. Find $f(31)$. What does it mean in this situation?
   c. Find t when $f(t) = 31$. What does it mean in this situation?
   d. Find the t-intercepts. What do they mean in this situation?
   e. Find the vertex. What does it mean in this situation?

30. A company charters a party boat that normally costs $40 per person. A group discount reduces the fare by $0.25 for each ticket sold; the more tickets sold, the lower is the per-person fare. The maximum capacity of the boat is 90 people, including the crew of 5 people. What size of group would maximize the boat owner's revenue?

Cumulative Review of Chapters 1–7

Solve. All solutions are real numbers.

1. $81x^2 - 49 = 0$

2. $\log_4(m + 3) = 2$

3. $5x^2 - 2x = 4$

4. $2(3t^2 - 10) = -7t$

5. $(2p - 5)(3p + 4) = 5p - 2$

6. $2(5x + 2) - 1 = 9(x - 3) - (3x - 8)$

7. $2x(3x - 4) + 5 = 4 - x^2$

For Exercises 8–13, solve. All solutions are real numbers. Round any results to the fourth decimal place.

8. $3\ln(2w) + 2\ln(3w) = 8$

9. $5b^6 + 4 = 82$

10. $3(2)^{4x-5} = 95$

11. $\log_b(65) = 4$

12. $3e^x - 5 = 49$

13. $3\log_2(x^4) - 2\log_2(4x) = 5$

14. Find all complex-number solutions of $2x^2 - 6x = -5$.

15. Solve $2x^2 + 3x - 6 = 0$ by completing the square.

Solve the system.

16. $y = 3x - 1$
$2x - 3y = -11$

17. $\dfrac{1}{2}x - y = \dfrac{5}{2}$
$\dfrac{2}{5}x - \dfrac{3}{5}y = \dfrac{6}{5}$

18. $2x - y + 3z = 1$
$3x + 2y - z = -6$
$4x - 3y + 2z = -7$

19. Solve the inequality $2(3x - 4) < 5 - 3(6x + 5)$. Describe the solution set as an inequality, in interval notation, and in a graph.

Simplify.

20. $\left(2b^4c^{-5}\right)^3\left(3b^{-1}c^{-2}\right)^4$

21. $\left(\dfrac{6b^8c^{-3}}{8b^{-4}c^{-1}}\right)^3$

Simplify. Write your result as a single logarithm with a coefficient of 1.

22. $3\log_b(4x) - 4\log_b(x^3)$

23. $3\ln(x^7) + 2\ln(x^5)$

For Exercises 24–27, perform the indicated operation.

24. $(3x - 4y)^2$

25. $(5p - 7q)(5p + 7q)$

26. $-3x(x^2 - 5)(x^3 + 8)$

27. $(x^2 - 3x - 4)(x^2 + 4x - 5)$

28. Write $f(x) = -2(x - 5)^2 + 3$ in standard form.

For Exercises 29–32, let $f(x) = 2x^2 - 3x + 4$, $g(x) = 3x^2 - 5x - 2$, $h(x) = 4x - 2$, and $k(x) = x - 3$. Find the equation of the given function; then evaluate the function at the indicated value.

29. $f + g, (f + g)(2)$

30. $f - g, (f - g)(-3)$

31. $g \cdot h, (g \cdot h)(-1)$

32. $g \circ k, (g \circ k)(5)$

33. Perform long division: $\dfrac{6x^3 - 11x^2 + 7x - 10}{2x - 3}$.

34. Perform synthetic division: $\dfrac{2x^3 + 5x^2 - 14x - 9}{x + 4}$.

Factor.

35. $m^4 - 16n^4$

36. $x^3 - 13x^2 + 40x$

37. $8p^2 + 22pq - 21q^2$

38. $x^3 + 4x^2 - 9x - 36$

For Exercises 39–44, refer to Table 79.

39. Find a possible equation of f.

40. Find a possible equation of g.

41. Find the slope of the graph of k.

42. Find x when $g(x) = 4$.

43. Find $(f \circ k)(3)$.

44. Find $h^{-1}(7)$.

Table 79 Values of Four Functions (Exercises 39–44)

x	$f(x)$	x	$g(x)$	x	$h(x)$	x	$k(x)$
0	20	1	4	4	7	0	−8
1	17	2	12	5	14	1	−4
2	14	3	36	6	28	2	0
3	11	4	108	7	56	3	4
4	8	5	324	8	112	4	8
5	5	6	972	9	224	5	12

Sketch the graph of the function.

45. $y = -2(x + 4)^2 + 3$

46. $y = \log_3(x)$

47. $2x - 5y = 20$

48. $y = 2(3)^x$

49. $y = x^2 + 4x - 5$

50. $y = 8\left(\dfrac{1}{4}\right)^x$

51. Use the graph of the relation in Fig. 115 to determine the domain and range. Is the relation a function?

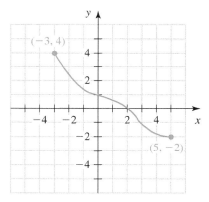

Figure 115 Exercise 51

52. Find the equation of the line that contains the point $(-2, 6)$ and is perpendicular to the line $3x - 4y = 5$.

53. Find an approximate equation $y = ab^x$ of an exponential curve that contains the points $(2, 27)$ and $(5, 83)$. Round a and b to the second decimal place.

54. Find an equation of a parabola that contains the points $(1, -1), (2, 4)$, and $(4, 20)$.

55. Let f be the linear function, g be the exponential function, and h be a quadratic function whose graphs contain the points $(0, 3)$ and $(1, 6)$.
   a. Find possible equations of f, g, and h.
   b. Use a graphing calculator to draw the graphs of f, g, and h in the same viewing window.

For Exercises 56–58, let $f(x) = -x^2 + 6x - 5$.

56. Find x when $f(x) = 3$.

57. Find the x-intercepts.

58. Graph f by hand.

For Exercises 59 and 60, find the logarithm.

59. $\log_2(16)$

60. $\log_5\left(\dfrac{1}{25}\right)$

61. The graph of a function f is sketched in Fig. 116. Sketch the graph of f^{-1}.

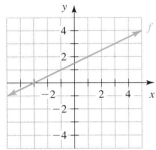

Figure 116 Exercise 61

For Exercises 62 and 63, (a) find the inverse of the given function; (b) show that $(f^{-1} \circ f)(x) = x$; (c) show that $(f \circ f^{-1})(x) = x$.

62. $f(x) = 3^x$

63. $f(x) = \dfrac{2}{5}x + 1$

64. A person plans to invest a total of \$12,000. She will invest in both a First Funds TN Tax-Free I account at 6% annual interest and a W & R International Growth C account at 11% annual interest. How much should she invest in each account to earn \$845 total interest in one year?

65. The numbers of cases of HIV acquired at birth, by year of diagnosis, in the United States has decayed approximately exponentially from 480 cases in 1996 to 151 cases in 2010 (Source: *Centers for Disease Control and Prevention*). Predict in which year there will be 80 cases of HIV acquired at birth in the United States.

66. Although opioid is an effective painkiller used in Vicodin, OxyContin, and Percocet, it is also highly addictive. About 16,500 people die of overdoses annually, which is more than all illegal drugs combined (Source: *The Wall Street Journal, December 15–16, 2012*). The rates of admission for treatment of opioid addiction are shown in Table 80 for various years.

Table 80 Rates of Admission for Treatment of Opioid Addiction

Year	Number of Admissions per 100,000 People
2000	1.0
2002	1.7
2004	2.1
2006	2.8
2008	4.0
2010	5.4

Source: *National Vital Statistics*

Let $r = f(t)$ be the admission rate (number of admissions per 100,000 people) for treatment of opioid addiction in the year that is t years since 2000.

a. Find a linear regression equation, an exponential regression equation, and a quadratic regression equation of f. Compare how well the models fit the data.

b. Find the vertex of the graph of your quadratic model. What does it mean in this situation?

c. For years before 1998, which of the models likely best describes the situation? Explain.

d. Use the exponential model to predict when the admission rate for opioid addiction will be 18 admissions per 100,000 people.

e. Use the quadratic model to predict when the admission rate for opioid addiction will be 18 admissions per 100,000 people.

f. Explain why the year you predicted in part (e) is later than the year you predicted in part (d). [**Hint:** It may help to Zoom Out.]

67. As unions have attracted an increasing number of workers in the service industries, the percentage of union members who work in manufacturing has declined (see Table 81).

Table 81 Percentages of Union Members Who Work in Manufacturing

Year	Percent
1985	29
1990	25
1995	21
2000	17
2005	13
2010	13

Source: *Bureau of Labor Statistics*

Let $p = f(t)$ be the percentage of union members who work in manufacturing at t years since 1980.

a. Find an equation of f.

b. Find $f(37)$. What does it mean in this situation?

c. Find t when $f(t) = 5$. What does it mean in this situation?

d. Find an equation of f^{-1}.

e. Find $f^{-1}(100)$. What does it mean in this situation?

f. Find the t-intercept of the graph of f. What does it mean in this situation?

g. For what values of t is there model breakdown for certain?

68. The average ages of light trucks and passenger cars are shown in Table 82 for various years.

Table 82 Average Ages of Light Trucks and Passenger Cars

Year	Average Age (years)	
	Light Trucks	Passenger Cars
2007	9.0	10.4
2008	9.3	10.6
2009	9.8	10.8
2010	10.1	11.0
2011	10.4	11.1

Source: *R.L. Polk & Co.*

Let $f(t)$ and $g(t)$ be the average ages (in years) of light trucks and passenger cars, respectively, both at t years since 2000.

a. Find linear equations of f and g.

b. Find $f(17)$ and $g(17)$. What do they mean in this situation?

c. Predict when the average age of light trucks will be equal to the average age of passenger cars. What is that average age?

d. Predict when the average age of light trucks will be greater than the average age of passenger cars.

e. Find an equation of $f - g$. Then find $(f - g)(18)$. What does it mean in this situation?

f. Find $\dfrac{f(18) + g(18)}{2}$. Give at least two reasons why your result may *not* turn out to be the average age (in years) of all light trucks and passenger cars in 2018.

Rational Functions

If you drive a car, how much did you pay for gasoline last year? In Exercise 8 of Homework 8.6, you will find a model that you will use to predict how much an American will pay, on average, for gasoline in 2018 (see Table 1).

In Chapters 6 and 7, we worked with polynomial functions. In this chapter, we will discuss how to divide these functions to form new ones called *rational functions*. We will also work with *rational expressions* and discuss how to simplify them and perform operations with them. We will solve *rational equations,* which will help us use rational functions to make predictions about authentic situations. For example, we will use a rational function to estimate the percentage of revenue that was from downloaded music in 2011.

Table 1 Average Prices of Gasoline; Vehicle Fuel Consumption

Year	Price of Gasoline (dollars per gallon)	Year	Amount of Fuel Consumed (millions of gallons)
1995	1.21	1975	108,900
1997	1.29	1980	115,000
1999	1.22	1985	121,300
2001	1.53	1990	130,800
2003	1.64	1995	143,800
2005	2.34	2000	162,600
2007	2.85	2005	174,800
2009	2.40	2010	169,700
2010	2.84		

Source: *Federal Highway Administration*

▼ 8.1 Finding the Domains of Rational Functions and Simplifying Rational Expressions

Objectives

» Know the meaning of *rational function* and *vertical asymptote.*

» Find the domain of a rational function.

» Simplify a *rational expression.*

» Know the connection between vertical asymptotes and domains of rational functions.

» Form *quotient functions.*

» Use a *rational model* to describe the percentage of a quantity.

In this section, we will discuss the meaning of a *rational function* and how to find its domain. We will simplify *rational expressions.* We will also discuss how to use a *rational model* to make estimates about authentic situations.

Meaning of a Rational Function

In Chapters 6 and 7, we worked with polynomials. If P and Q are polynomials, where Q is nonzero, we call the ratio $\dfrac{P}{Q}$ a **rational expression.** The name "rational" refers to "ratio." Here are some examples:

$$\frac{x^3 - 3x + 6}{x^7 - 8} \qquad \frac{-2x^2 + 17}{5x - 1} \qquad -\frac{2}{7x^3} \qquad \frac{3x^2 + 5x - 4}{2x^2 - x + 9}$$

A rational expression is part of an equation of a rational function.

479

▶ Definition   Rational function

A **rational function** is a function whose equation can be put into the form

$$f(x) = \frac{P(x)}{Q(x)}$$

where $P(x)$ and $Q(x)$ are polynomials and $Q(x)$ is nonzero.

In Example 1, we evaluate a rational function at some input values.

▶ Example 1   Evaluating a Rational Function

Evaluate the function $f(x) = \dfrac{x - 5}{x^2 - 4}$ at the indicated values.

1. $f(6)$ **2.** $f(-3)$

Solution

1. $f(6) = \dfrac{6 - 5}{6^2 - 4} = \dfrac{1}{32}$ **2.** $f(-3) = \dfrac{-3 - 5}{(-3)^2 - 4} = \dfrac{-8}{5} = -\dfrac{8}{5}$

We use a graphing calculator table to check that $f(6) = \dfrac{1}{32} = 0.03125$ and $f(-3) = -\dfrac{8}{5} = -1.6$ (see Fig. 1).

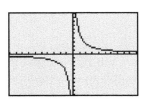

Figure 1 Verify the work

WARNING   To enter a rational function such as $\dfrac{x - 5}{x^2 - 4}$ into a graphing calculator, we enclose both the numerator and the denominator in parentheses (see Fig. 1).

Domain of a Rational Function

Our work in Example 1 shows that the numbers 6 and -3 are in the domain of the function $f(x) = \dfrac{x - 5}{x^2 - 4}$. Are all real numbers in the domain of f? We will explore this issue in Example 2.

To learn about the domain of a rational function, it will help to consider the simpler rational function $f(x) = \dfrac{5}{x}$ first. Note that $f(0)$ is undefined, since $\dfrac{5}{0}$ is undefined. (We cannot divide by 0.) So, 0 is *not* in the domain of f. Since division by nonzero numbers *is* defined, the domain of f is the set of real numbers except 0.

Figure 2 displays a graphing calculator graph of $f(x) = \dfrac{5}{x}$. The x-axis appears to be a horizontal asymptote of the graph of f; that is, in fact, true. The graph of f also appears to get arbitrarily close to, but never intersect, the y-axis; that is also true. We say the y-axis is a **vertical asymptote** of the graph of f. Just as with a horizontal asymptote, a vertical asymptote is *not* part of the graph of a function.

Figure 2 Graph of $f(x) = \dfrac{5}{x}$

▶ Example 2   Finding the Domain of a Rational Function

Find the domain of the function.

1. $f(x) = \dfrac{2}{x - 3}$ **2.** $g(x) = \dfrac{x - 5}{x^2 - 4}$

Solution

1. For $f(x) = \dfrac{2}{x - 3}$, the number 3 is not in the domain, because $\dfrac{2}{3 - 3}$ involves a division by zero. No other value of x leads to a division by 0, so the domain is the set

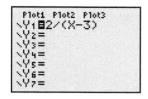

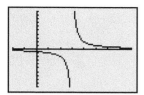

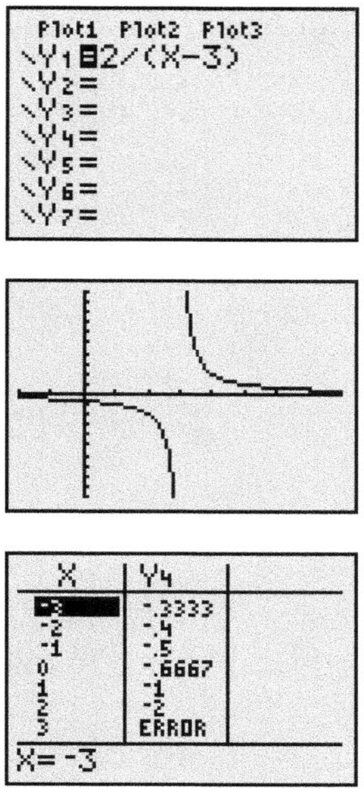

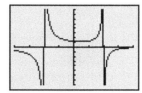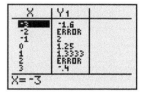

Figure 3 The graph of f has a vertical asymptote at $x = 3$, and 3 is not in the domain of f

of real numbers except 3. In Fig. 3, we draw a graph of f and build a table of input–output pairs of f.

From Fig. 3, it appears the graph of f has a vertical asymptote at $x = 3$; that is true. The "ERROR" message across from $x = 3$ in the table supports the idea that the value 3 for x leads to division by 0. (The TI-83 and TI-84 display either "ERROR" or "ERR:.")

2. To find which values of x lead to a division by 0, we set the denominator of $\dfrac{x - 5}{x^2 - 4}$ equal to 0 and solve for x:

$$x^2 - 4 = 0 \qquad \textit{Set denominator equal to 0.}$$
$$(x + 2)(x - 2) = 0 \qquad \textit{Factor left side.}$$
$$x + 2 = 0 \quad \text{or} \quad x - 2 = 0 \quad \textit{Zero factor property}$$
$$x = -2 \quad \text{or} \qquad x = 2$$

The numbers -2 and 2 are *not* in the domain, since each value of x leads to a division by zero. The domain of g is the set of real numbers except -2 and 2. In Fig. 4, we draw a graph of g and build a table of input–output pairs of g. A graphing calculator approximates graphs by plotting many points and connecting the points with curves. The steep lines that are "almost" the lines $x = -2$ and $x = 2$ are *not* part of the graph. Some TI graphing calculators do not show these lines.

Figure 4 The graph of g has vertical asymptotes at $x = -2$ and $x = 2$, and -2 and 2 are not in the domain of g

From Fig. 4, it appears the graph of g has vertical asymptotes at $x = -2$ and $x = 2$; that is true. The "ERROR" messages across from $x = -2$ and $x = 2$ in the table support the idea that each of the values -2 and 2 for x lead to a division by zero.

Our work in Problem 2 of Example 2 suggests the following property.

Domain of a Rational Function

The domain of a rational function $f(x) = \dfrac{P(x)}{Q(x)}$ is the set of real numbers except for those numbers that, when substituted for x, give $Q(x) = 0$.

Example 3   Finding the Domain of a Rational Function

Find the domain of the function.

1. $f(x) = \dfrac{x - 4}{x^2 + 5x + 2}$ **2.** $g(x) = \dfrac{x^2 - 5x + 1}{x^2 + 10}$

Solution

1. We set the denominator of the right-hand side of $f(x) = \dfrac{x - 4}{x^2 + 5x + 2}$ equal to 0:

$$x^2 + 5x + 2 = 0$$

Then we substitute $a = 1, b = 5,$ and $c = 2$ in the quadratic formula:

$$x = \frac{-5 \pm \sqrt{5^2 - 4(1)(2)}}{2(1)} \qquad \text{\textit{Substitute into quadratic formula.}}$$

$$= \frac{-5 \pm \sqrt{17}}{2} \qquad\qquad \text{\textit{Simplify.}}$$

The domain of f is the set of real numbers except $\dfrac{-5 - \sqrt{17}}{2}$ and $\dfrac{-5 + \sqrt{17}}{2}$.

2. We set the denominator of the right-hand side of $g(x) = \dfrac{x^2 - 5x + 1}{x^2 + 10}$ equal to 0 and solve:

$$x^2 + 10 = 0$$
$$x^2 = -10$$

Since a real number squared is nonnegative, we conclude there are no real-number solutions of $x^2 + 10 = 0$. Therefore, for the function g, no values of x lead to division by 0. So, the domain of g is the set of (all) real numbers.

▶

In Problem 1 of Example 2, we found that substituting 3 in the expression $\dfrac{2}{x - 3}$ leads to a division by 0. We call the number 3 an excluded value of the expression.

▶ Definition   Excluded value

A number is an **excluded value** of a rational expression if substituting the number into the expression leads to a division by 0.

For instance, 5 is an excluded value of the expression $\dfrac{7}{x - 5}$. This means 5 is *not* in the domain of the function $f(x) = \dfrac{7}{x - 5}$.

Simplifying Rational Expressions

To simplify a fraction, we factor the numerator and the denominator and use the property $\dfrac{a}{a} = 1$, where $a \neq 0$. Here we use these steps to simplify $\dfrac{8}{12}$:

$$\frac{8}{12} = \frac{4(2)}{4(3)} = \frac{4}{4} \cdot \frac{2}{3} = 1 \cdot \frac{2}{3} = \frac{2}{3}$$

We simplify the rational expression $\dfrac{2x + 6}{x^2 - 9}$ in a similar manner:

$$\frac{2x + 6}{x^2 - 9} = \frac{2(x + 3)}{(x - 3)(x + 3)} \qquad \text{\textit{Factor numerator and denominator.}}$$

$$= \frac{2}{x - 3} \cdot \frac{x + 3}{x + 3} \qquad \text{\textit{x + 3 is a factor of both numerator and denominator.}}$$

$$= \frac{2}{x - 3} \cdot 1 \qquad\qquad \text{\textit{Simplify:}} \frac{x + 3}{x + 3} = 1$$

$$= \frac{2}{x - 3} \qquad\qquad\quad a \cdot 1 = a$$

The number 3 is the only excluded value of our result, $\dfrac{2}{x - 3}$. The numbers -3 and 3 are the only excluded values of the original expression, $\dfrac{2x + 6}{x^2 - 9}$. (Try it.) When we write

$$\frac{2x + 6}{x^2 - 9} = \frac{2}{x - 3}$$

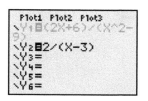

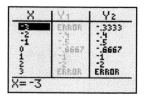

Figure 5 Verify the work

we mean the two expressions give the same result for each real number substituted for x, except for any excluded values (-3 and 3) of either expression. In Fig. 5, we use a graphing calculator table to verify our work.

A rational expression is in **lowest terms** if the numerator and denominator have no common factors other than 1 or -1. We **simplify a rational expression** by writing it in lowest terms. We also write the numerator and the denominator in factored form.

> ▶ **Simplifying a Rational Expression**
>
> To simplify a rational expression,
>
> **1.** Factor the numerator and the denominator.
>
> **2.** Use the property
>
> $$\frac{AB}{AC} = \frac{A}{A} \cdot \frac{B}{C} = 1 \cdot \frac{B}{C} = \frac{B}{C}$$
>
> where A and C are nonzero, so the expression is in lowest terms.

Throughout the rest of this chapter, you may assume the form $\frac{A}{B}$ represents a rational expression.

In the expression $\frac{AB}{AC}$, note that the polynomial A is a factor of both the numerator and the denominator. The expression $\frac{3x}{7x}$ can be simplified to $\frac{3}{7}$ when $x \neq 0$, because x is a factor of both the numerator and the denominator.

WARNING   The expression

$$\frac{3x + 2}{7x}$$

is in lowest terms already. Although x is a factor of the term $7x$, it is not a factor of $3x + 2$, the (entire) numerator. Likewise, the expression

$$\frac{(x + 4)(x + 6) + 5}{3(x + 4)}$$

is in lowest terms already. The expression $x + 4$ is not a factor of $(x + 4)(x + 6) + 5$, the (entire) numerator. To see that the rational expression is in lowest terms, we simplify the numerator to get $\dfrac{x^2 + 10x + 29}{3(x + 4)}$. (Try it.)

▶ **Example 4** Simplify the Right-Hand Side of an Equation

Simplify the right-hand side of the equation $f(x) = \dfrac{2x^2 - 6x - 20}{2x^2 - 50}$.

Solution

$$f(x) = \frac{2x^2 - 6x - 20}{2x^2 - 50} \qquad \textit{Original equation}$$

$$= \frac{2(x^2 - 3x - 10)}{2(x^2 - 25)}$$

$$= \frac{2(x - 5)(x + 2)}{2(x - 5)(x + 5)} \quad \left. \right\} \textit{Factor numerator and denominator.}$$

$$= \frac{x + 2}{x + 5} \qquad \textit{Simplify: } \frac{2(x - 5)}{2(x - 5)} = 1$$

So, we can describe f by the equation $f(x) = \dfrac{x + 2}{x + 5}$, where the domain is all real numbers except -5 and 5.

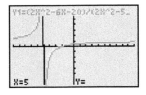

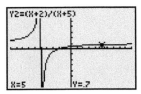

Figure 6 Verify the work

To check, we substitute a value—say, 3—for x in both of the expressions

$\dfrac{2x^2 - 6x - 20}{2x^2 - 50}$ and $\dfrac{x + 2}{x + 5}$ and check that the results are equal:

$$\frac{2(3)^2 - 6(3) - 20}{2(3)^2 - 50} = \frac{-20}{-32} = \frac{5}{8}, \qquad \frac{3 + 2}{3 + 5} = \frac{5}{8}$$

We perform a more convincing check by comparing graphing calculator graphs for the functions $y = \dfrac{2x^2 - 6x - 20}{2x^2 - 50}$ and $y = \dfrac{x + 2}{x + 5}$. See Fig. 6. To hand-sketch a graph of $f(x) = \dfrac{2x^2 - 6x - 20}{2x^2 - 50}$, we use an open circle at the point $(5, 0.7)$ to indicate that the point is not part of the graph.

The graphs of the functions are the same for $x \neq -5$ and $x \neq 5$.

Connection Between Vertical Asymptotes and Domains

Example 2 suggests that if the graph of a rational function has a vertical asymptote at $x = k$, then k is not in the domain of the function, which is true.

In Example 4, we wrote f in the form

$$f(x) = \frac{2(x - 5)(x + 2)}{2(x - 5)(x + 5)}$$

by factoring the numerator and the denominator of the right-hand side of the original equation of f. From this form, we see that the domain of f is the set of real numbers except -5 and 5. Yet, $x = -5$ is the only vertical asymptote of the graph of f (see Fig. 6). The reason $x = 5$ is not a vertical asymptote has to do with the fact that both the numerator and the denominator of f contain the factor $x - 5$.

> **Vertical Asymptotes and Domains of Rational Functions**
>
> If the graph of a rational function f has a vertical asymptote $x = k$, then k is not in the domain of f. If k is not in the domain of a rational function g, then $x = k$ may or may not be a vertical asymptote of the graph of g.

> **Example 5**   Simplifying the Right-Hand Side of an Equation

Simplify the right-hand side of the equation $f(x) = \dfrac{x^3 - 5x^2 + 6x}{x^3 - 2x^2 - 9x + 18}$.

Solution

$$\begin{aligned}
f(x) &= \frac{x^3 - 5x^2 + 6x}{x^3 - 2x^2 - 9x + 18} && \textit{Original equation} \\[2mm]
&= \frac{x(x^2 - 5x + 6)}{x^2(x - 2) - 9(x - 2)} \\[2mm]
&= \frac{x(x - 3)(x - 2)}{(x^2 - 9)(x - 2)} && \textit{Factor numerator and denominator.} \\[2mm]
&= \frac{x(x - 3)(x - 2)}{(x + 3)(x - 3)(x - 2)} \\[2mm]
&= \frac{x}{x + 3} && \textit{Simplify: } \frac{(x - 3)(x - 2)}{(x - 3)(x - 2)} = 1
\end{aligned}$$

▶ **Example 6**   Simplifying the Right-Hand Side of an Equation

Simplify the right-hand side of the equation $f(x) = \dfrac{x^2 - x - 12}{4 - x}$.

Solution

$$f(x) = \frac{x^2 - x - 12}{4 - x} \qquad \textit{Original equation}$$

$$= \frac{x^2 - x - 12}{-x + 4} \qquad \textit{Write denominator in descending order.}$$

$$= \frac{(x - 4)(x + 3)}{-1(x - 4)} \qquad \textit{Factor numerator and denominator.}$$

$$= \frac{x + 3}{-1} \qquad \textit{Simplify:} \frac{x - 4}{x - 4} = 1$$

$$= -x - 3 \qquad \frac{x + 3}{-1} = -\frac{x + 3}{1} = -(x + 3) = -x - 3$$

In Example 7, we will simplify a rational expression in two variables.

▶ **Example 7**   Simplifying a Rational Expression in Two Variables

Simplify $\dfrac{x^2 - 8xy + 16y^2}{x^2 - 16y^2}$.

Solution

$$\frac{x^2 - 8xy + 16y^2}{x^2 - 16y^2} = \frac{(x - 4y)(x - 4y)}{(x + 4y)(x - 4y)} \qquad \textit{Factor numerator and denominator.}$$

$$= \frac{x - 4y}{x + 4y} \qquad \textit{Simplify:} \frac{x - 4y}{x - 4y} = 1$$

Quotient Function

In Sections 6.1 and 6.2, we worked with sum, difference, and product functions. Now we will work with *quotient functions*.

▶ **Definition**   Quotient function

If f and g are functions, x is in the domain of both functions, and $g(x)$ is nonzero, then we can form the **quotient function** $\dfrac{f}{g}$:

$$\left(\frac{f}{g}\right)(x) = \frac{f(x)}{g(x)}$$

For example, if $f(x) = 3^x$ and $g(x) = x + 5$, then $\left(\dfrac{f}{g}\right)(x) = \dfrac{f(x)}{g(x)} = \dfrac{3^x}{x + 5}$.

▶ **Example 8**   Quotient Functions

Let $f(x) = 8x^3 - 125$ and $g(x) = 4x^2 - 25$.

1. Find an equation of $\dfrac{f}{g}$. Simplify the right-hand side of the equation.

2. Find $\left(\dfrac{f}{g}\right)(3)$.

Solution

1. $\left(\dfrac{f}{g}\right)(x) = \dfrac{f(x)}{g(x)}$ *Definition of quotient function*

$= \dfrac{8x^3 - 125}{4x^2 - 25}$ *Substitute $8x^3 - 125$ for $f(x)$ and*
$\qquad\qquad\qquad$ *$4x^2 - 25$ for $g(x)$.*

$= \dfrac{(2x - 5)(4x^2 + 10x + 25)}{(2x - 5)(2x + 5)}$ *Factor numerator and denominator.*

$= \dfrac{4x^2 + 10x + 25}{2x + 5}$ *Simplify:* $\dfrac{2x-5}{2x-5} = 1$

2. $\left(\dfrac{f}{g}\right)(3) = \dfrac{4(3)^2 + 10(3) + 25}{2(3) + 5} = \dfrac{91}{11}$

By the definition of a rational function, we see that if P and Q are polynomial functions, then the quotient function $\dfrac{P}{Q}$ is rational.

Use a Rational Model to Describe the Percentage of a Quantity

A **rational model** is a rational function, or its graph, that describes an authentic situation. In this section, we will focus on using a rational model to describe the percentage of a quantity.

Suppose a student takes a quiz and answers 6 out of 8 questions correctly. To compute the percentage of questions answered correctly, we divide the number of questions answered correctly by the total number of questions and multiply the result by 100:

$$\text{Percentage of correct answers} = \dfrac{6}{8} \cdot 100\% = 75\%$$

We take similar steps to calculate a percentage in general.

> **Percentage Formula**
>
> If m items out of n items have a certain attribute, then the percentage p (written $p\%$) of the n items that have the attribute is
>
> $$p = \dfrac{m}{n} \cdot 100$$
>
> We call this equation the **percentage formula.**

We will use the percentage formula to form a rational model in Example 9.

Table 2 Numbers of Internet Users in the United States

Year	Number of Internet Users (millions)
2006	204
2007	212
2008	220
2009	228
2010	240

Source: *The Nielsen Company*

▶ **Example 9**   Using a Rational Model to Make a Prediction

In Exercise 5 of Homework 2.1, you modeled the number of Internet users in the United States (see Table 2). A reasonable model is $I(t) = 8.8t + 150.4$, where $I(t)$ is the number of Internet users (in millions) at t years since 2000. In Exercise 7 of Homework 7.7, you modeled the U.S. population. A reasonable model is $U(t) = 0.0068t^2 + 2.71t + 277.89$, where $U(t)$ is the U.S. population (in millions) at t years since 2000.

1. Let $P(t)$ be the percentage of Americans who are Internet users at t years since 2000. Find an equation of P.
2. Use P to estimate the percentage of Americans who were Internet users in 2010. Then compute the actual percentage by referring to Table 2 and using the 2010 U.S. population as 308.7 million. Is your result from using the model an underestimate or an overestimate?
3. Find $P(18)$. What does it mean in this situation?

Isn't the Internet great? You can shop without leaving home. I used it to send all of my gifts this year.

That's nothing– last week I went on a virtual vacation and never had to board a plane!

Solution

1. To find the percentage of Americans who are Internet users, we divide the number of Internet users by the number of Americans and multiply the result by 100:

$$P(t) = \frac{I(t)}{U(t)} \cdot 100 \qquad \text{\textit{Percentage formula: }} p = \frac{m}{n} \cdot 100$$

$$= \frac{8.8t + 150.4}{0.0068t^2 + 2.71t + 277.89} \cdot \frac{100}{1} \qquad \begin{array}{l}\textit{Substitute } 8.8t + 150.4 \textit{ for } I(t) \textit{ and}\\ 0.0068t^2 + 2.71t + 277.89 \textit{ for } U(t).\end{array}$$

$$= \frac{880t + 15{,}040}{0.0068t^2 + 2.71t + 277.89} \qquad \textit{Multiply numerators; multiply denominators.}$$

2. $P(10) = \dfrac{880(10) + 15{,}040}{0.0068(10)^2 + 2.71(10) + 277.89} \approx 77.99$

The model estimates that about 78.0% of Americans were Internet users in 2010. To find the actual percentage, we divide the number of Internet users in 2010 (from Table 2) by the U.S. population (given) and multiply the result by 100:

$$\frac{240{,}000{,}000}{308{,}700{,}000} \cdot 100\% \approx 77.75\%$$

Our result from using the model is a slight overestimate.

3. $P(18) = \dfrac{880(18) + 15{,}040}{0.0068(18)^2 + 2.71(18) + 277.89} \approx 93.90$

The model estimates that about 93.9% of Americans will be Internet users in 2018.

Group Exploration

Connection between the domain and vertical asymptotes

1. Find the domain of $f(x) = \dfrac{6}{x}$. Use ZStandard to graph f. Explain why it makes sense that the graph does not have a y-intercept. Find any vertical asymptotes.

2. Use ZStandard to graph $f(x) = \dfrac{6}{x}$ and $g(x) = \dfrac{6}{x - 4}$ on the same viewing screen. Describe how you can translate the graph of f to get the graph of g.

3. What is the vertical asymptote of the graph of $g(x) = \dfrac{6}{x - 4}$? What do you observe about the connection between the vertical asymptote and the domain of g?

4. Use ZStandard to graph $h(x) = \dfrac{7x - 7}{x^2 + 2x - 8}$. What is (are) the vertical asymptote(s)? What is the connection between the vertical asymptote(s) and the domain of h?

5. Find the domain of the function $f(x) = \dfrac{x - 2}{2 - x}$. Use ZDecimal to graph f. Explain why the graph is so different from the graphs you drew in Problems 1, 2, and 4. [**Hint:** Simplify the right-hand side of the equation of f.] Describe what happens when you use TRACE to try to find the value of y when $x = 2$. Explain.

6. Describe the connection between the vertical asymptote(s) of the graph of the function $g(x) = \dfrac{5x - 10}{x^2 - 7x + 10}$ and the domain of g. [**Hint:** Simplify the right-hand side of the equation of g.]

7. True or False? Explain.
   a. If the graph of a rational function f has a vertical asymptote $x = k$, then k is not in the domain of f.
   b. If k is not in the domain of a rational function g, then $x = k$ is a vertical asymptote of the graph of g.

▶ **Tips for Success**   **Stick with It**

If you are having difficulty doing an exercise, don't panic! Reread the exercise and reflect on what you have already sorted out about the problem—what you know and where you need to go. Your solution to the problem may be just around the corner.

Homework 8.1

For extra help ▶ MyMathLab°   Watch the videos in MyMathLab   Download the MyDashboard App

Evaluate the function at the indicated values if possible. If an indicated value is not in the domain, say so.

1. $f(x) = \dfrac{x + 1}{x^2 - 9}; f(-1), f(2), f(3)$

2. $f(x) = \dfrac{x - 2}{x^2 - 1}; f(-3), f(1), f(2)$

3. $f(x) = \dfrac{x^3 - 8}{2x^2 + 3x - 1}; f(-1), f(0), f(3)$

4. $f(x) = \dfrac{x^3 + 5}{3x^2 - x - 6}; f(-2), f(0), f(1)$

Find the domain of the function. Verify your result with a graphing calculator table or graph.

5. $f(x) = \dfrac{8}{x}$

6. $f(x) = \dfrac{9}{x}$

7. $f(x) = \dfrac{x}{2}$

8. $f(x) = \dfrac{x}{5}$

9. $f(x) = \dfrac{x - 5}{x + 3}$

10. $f(x) = \dfrac{x + 4}{x - 9}$

11. $f(x) = \dfrac{x - 3}{2x + 1}$

12. $f(x) = \dfrac{x + 4}{5x - 7}$

13. $f(x) = \dfrac{x - 9}{x^2 - 3x - 10}$

14. $f(x) = \dfrac{x - 1}{x^2 + 5x - 24}$

15. $f(x) = -\dfrac{2}{4x^2 - 25}$

16. $f(x) = -\dfrac{7}{81x^2 - 49}$

17. $f(x) = \dfrac{x + 3}{x^2 + 1}$

18. $f(x) = \dfrac{x + 8}{x^2 + 4}$

19. $f(x) = \dfrac{x - 10}{2x^2 - 7x - 15}$

20. $f(x) = \dfrac{x - 3}{6x^2 + 7x - 20}$

21. $f(x) = -\dfrac{x + 3}{x^2 - 3x + 6}$

22. $f(x) = -\dfrac{x + 6}{3x^2 - x + 4}$

23. $f(x) = \dfrac{x^2 + 5x - 1}{3x^2 - 2x - 7}$

24. $f(x) = \dfrac{x^2 - x + 3}{6x^2 + 4x - 1}$

25. $f(x) = \dfrac{2x - 14}{4x^3 - 8x^2 - 9x + 18}$

26. $f(x) = \dfrac{5x + 10}{x^3 + 5x^2 - 4x - 20}$

Simplify the right-hand side of the equation of f. Use a graphing calculator table to verify your work.

27. $f(x) = \dfrac{20x^7}{15x^4}$

28. $f(x) = \dfrac{12x^3}{16x^{10}}$

29. $f(x) = \dfrac{4x - 28}{5x - 35}$

30. $f(x) = \dfrac{-4x - 20}{6x + 30}$

31. $f(x) = \dfrac{x^2 + 7x + 10}{x^2 - 7x - 18}$

32. $f(x) = \dfrac{x^2 + 8x + 12}{x^2 + 9x + 18}$

33. $f(x) = \dfrac{x^2 - 49}{x^2 - 14x + 49}$

34. $f(x) = \dfrac{x^2 - 25}{x^2 + 10x + 25}$

35. $f(x) = \dfrac{16x^2 - 25}{8x^2 - 22x + 15}$

36. $f(x) = \dfrac{9x^2 - 4}{3x^2 - 17x + 10}$

37. $f(x) = \dfrac{x - 5}{5 - x}$

38. $f(x) = \dfrac{2 - x}{x - 2}$

39. $f(x) = \dfrac{4x - 12}{18 - 6x}$

40. $f(x) = \dfrac{-2x + 10}{4x - 20}$

41. $f(x) = \dfrac{6x - 18}{9 - x^2}$

42. $f(x) = \dfrac{9 - x}{x^2 - 81}$

43. $f(x) = \dfrac{x^2 + 2x - 35}{-x^2 + 3x + 10}$

44. $f(x) = \dfrac{x^2 + x - 20}{-x^2 + 11x - 28}$

45. $f(x) = \dfrac{3x^3 + 21x^2 + 36x}{x^2 - 9}$

46. $f(x) = \dfrac{x^2 - 49}{2x^3 - 8x^2 - 42x}$

47. $f(x) = \dfrac{x^2 - 2x - 8}{4x^3 + 8x^2 - 9x - 18}$

48. $f(x) = \dfrac{25x^3 - 75x^2 - 4x + 12}{x^2 - 4x + 3}$

49. $f(x) = \dfrac{x^3 + 8}{x^2 - 4}$

50. $f(x) = \dfrac{x^3 + 27}{x^2 - 9}$

51. $f(x) = \dfrac{3x^2 + 7x - 6}{27x^3 - 8}$

52. $f(x) = \dfrac{4x^2 - 11x + 6}{64x^3 - 27}$

Simplify.

53. $\dfrac{x^2 - 6xy + 9y^2}{x^2 - 3xy}$

54. $\dfrac{x^2 + 10xy + 25y^2}{xy + 5y^2}$

55. $\dfrac{6a^2 + ab - 2b^2}{3a^2 - 7ab - 6b^2}$

56. $\dfrac{2p^2 - 9pt + 10t^2}{8p^2 - 18pt - 5t^2}$

57. $\dfrac{p^3 - q^3}{p^2 - q^2}$

58. $\dfrac{mn + n^2}{m^3 + n^3}$

For the functions $f(x) = x^2 + 2x - 8$, $g(x) = x^2 - 8x + 12$, $h(x) = 3x^2 + 17x + 20$, and $k(x) = 3x^2 - 13x - 30$, find an equation of the given quotient function. Evaluate the quotient function at the indicated value.

59. $\dfrac{f}{g}, \left(\dfrac{f}{g}\right)(3)$

60. $\dfrac{g}{k}, \left(\dfrac{g}{k}\right)(2)$

61. $\dfrac{h}{f}, \left(\dfrac{h}{f}\right)(4)$

62. $\dfrac{k}{h}, \left(\dfrac{k}{h}\right)(3)$

For $f(x) = 3x^3 - x^2$, $g(x) = 18x^3 + 12x^2 + 2x$, $h(x) = 9x^2 - 1$, and $k(x) = 27x^3 + 1$, find an equation of the given quotient function. Evaluate the quotient function at the indicated value.

63. $\dfrac{f}{h}, \left(\dfrac{f}{h}\right)(-2)$

64. $\dfrac{g}{f}, \left(\dfrac{g}{f}\right)(-1)$

65. $\dfrac{k}{g}, \left(\dfrac{k}{g}\right)(-1)$

66. $\dfrac{h}{k}, \left(\dfrac{h}{k}\right)(0)$

67. Levels of participation in the Supplemental Nutrition Assistance Program (SNAP) in August are shown in Table 3 for various years. Let $F(t)$ be the participation (in millions) in August of the year that is t years since 2000. A reasonable model is $F(t) = -1.03t^2 + 25.09t - 105.88$. In Exercise 7 of Homework 7.7, you modeled the U.S. population. A reasonable model is $U(t) = 0.0068t^2 + 2.71t + 277.9$, where $U(t)$ is the U.S. population (in millions) at t years since 2000.

Table 3 Levels of Participation in August in SNAP

Year	Participation (millions)
2008	29.2
2009	36.2
2010	42.4
2011	45.8
2012	47.0

Source: *U.S. Department of Agriculture*

a. Let $P(t)$ be the percentage of Americans who participated in SNAP in August of the year that is t years since 2000. Find an equation of P.

b. Use P to estimate the percentage of Americans who participated in SNAP in August of 2012. Then compute the actual percentage by referring to Table 3 and using the 2012 U.S. population as 314.5 million. Is your result from using the model an underestimate or an overestimate?

c. Find $P(16)$. What does it mean in this situation?

68. In Exercise 47 of Homework 3.5, you found an equation close to $D(t) = 0.34t + 0.56$, where $D(t)$ is the annual revenue (in billions of dollars) from downloaded music at t years since 2005 (see Table 4). The annual revenue (in billions of dollars) from all music (downloaded and CDs) $A(t)$ is given by $A(t) = -1.18t + 11.13$, where t is the number of years since 2005.

Table 4 Annual Revenues from Downloaded Music and All Music

Year	Downloads	All Music
2006	0.86	10.25
2007	1.23	8.70
2008	1.67	7.15
2009	1.98	6.26
2010	2.20	5.57

Annual Revenue (billions of dollars)

Source: *Recording Industry Association of America*

a. Let $P(t)$ be the percentage of the annual revenue from all music that is from downloaded music at t years since 2005. Find an equation of P.

b. Use P to estimate the percentage of the annual revenue from all music that was from downloaded music in 2010. Then compute the actual percentage. Is your result an underestimate or an overestimate?

c. Find $P(6)$. What does it mean in this situation?

69. The numbers of Latinos who are registered to vote and the numbers of them who are eligible to vote are shown in Table 5.

a. Let $R(t)$ be the number (in millions) of Latinos who are registered to vote at t years since 1980. Find a quadratic equation of R.

b. Let $E(t)$ be the number (in millions) of Latinos who are eligible to vote at t years since 1980. Find a quadratic equation of E.

c. Let $P(t)$ be the percentage of voter-eligible Latinos who are registered to vote at t years since 1980. Find an equation of P.

Table 5 Numbers of Latinos Who Are Registered to Vote and Eligible to Vote

Year	Registered to Vote	Eligible to Vote
1988	4.6	7.7
1992	5.1	8.3
1996	6.6	11.2
2000	7.5	13.2
2004	9.3	16.1
2008	11.6	19.5
2010	11.0	21.3

Millions of Latinos

Source: *Pew Hispanic Center*

d. Find the percentage of voter-eligible Latinos who will be registered to vote in 2017.

e. Use the window settings in Fig. 7 to draw a graph of P. Then use "maximum" to find the maximum point of the graph of P for values of t between 0 and 40. What does it mean in this situation?

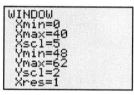

Figure 7 Window settings for Exercise 69e

f. Has the percentage of voter-eligible Latinos who are registered to vote been increasing, decreasing, or neither since 1996? How is this possible, given that the number of Latinos who were registered to vote grew by over 75% from 1996 to 2008?

70. The enrollments of men and of all students at U.S. colleges are shown in Table 6 for various years. In Example 10 of Section 6.1, we found the equation $M(t) = 0.012t^2 - 0.12t + 6.65$, where $M(t)$ is the enrollment (in millions) of men at t years since 1990.

Table 6 College Enrollments

Year	Men	All Students
1995	6.3	14.2
2000	6.7	15.3
2005	7.5	17.5
2008	8.2	19.1
2010	9.1	21.2

Enrollment (millions)

Source: *National Center for Education Statistics*

a. Let $A(t)$ be the enrollment (in millions) of all college students at t years since 1990. Find an equation of A.

b. Let $P(t)$ be the percentage of college students who are men at t years since 1990. Find an equation of P.

c. Find the percentage of college students who will be men in 2017.

d. Use the window settings in Fig. 8 to draw a graph of P. Is P increasing, decreasing, or neither for the values of t between 5 and 20? What does that mean in this situation? How is this possible, given that the college enrollment of men has been increasing since 1995?

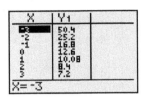

Figure 8 Window settings for Exercise 70d

Concepts

71. Give examples of three rational functions, each of whose domains are the set of real numbers except -3 and 3.

72. Give examples of three rational functions, each of whose domains are the set of real numbers except $\frac{1}{2}$ and $\frac{1}{3}$.

73. A graphing calculator table for a rational function is shown in Fig. 9. List seven members of the domain. List seven members of the range.

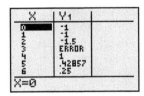

Figure 9 Exercise 73

74. A student decides that the domain of the function

$$f(x) = \frac{6}{x(x-3) + 2(x-3)}$$

is the set of real numbers except 3. After viewing the table shown in Fig. 10, the student believes his work is correct. What would you tell this student?

X	Y1
0	-1
1	-1
2	-1.5
3	ERROR
4	1
5	.42857
6	.25

X=0

Figure 10 Exercise 74

75. A student states that the domain of the function

$$f(x) = \frac{(x-2)(x-4)}{(x-5)(x-1)}$$

is the set of real numbers except 1, 2, 4, and 5. Is the student correct? Explain.

76. It is a common error to think 0 is not in the domain of the function $f(x) = \frac{7}{x+4}$. Evaluate f at 0 to show that 0 is in the domain of f.

77. A student tries to simplify the expression $\frac{2(x+4)+3}{(x+4)(x-1)}$:

$$\frac{2(x+4)+3}{(x+4)(x-1)} = \frac{2+3}{x-1} = \frac{5}{x-1}$$

Substitute 3 for x in the original expression and in the student's result. What can you conclude about the student's work, based on the results of your substitutions? Explain.

78. A student tries to simplify the expression $\frac{(x-2)(x-1)}{4(x-2)+5}$:

$$\frac{(x-2)(x-1)}{4(x-2)+5} = \frac{x-1}{4+5} = \frac{x-1}{9}$$

Next, she substitutes 3 for x in the original expression and in her result:

$$\frac{(3-2)(3-1)}{4(3-2)+5} = \frac{2}{9}; \quad \frac{3-1}{9} = \frac{2}{9}$$

The student concludes that the result $\frac{x-1}{9}$ is correct. What would you tell her?

79. A person plans to drive at a constant speed from San Francisco to Los Angeles. The driving time (in hours) $T(s)$ is given by the equation

$$T(s) = \frac{420}{s}$$

where s is the constant speed (in miles per hour).
   a. Find $T(50)$. What does it mean in this situation?
   b. Find $T(55)$, $T(60)$, $T(65)$, and $T(70)$.
   c. Is T an increasing function or a decreasing function for $s > 0$? Explain why that makes sense in this situation. Use ZStandard and then Zoom Out once or twice to verify your answer.

80. Some students agree to share equally in the expense of renting a beach house for $1200 during spring break.
   a. What is the per-student expense if 10 students rent it?
   b. What is the per-student expense if 12 students rent it?
   c. Let $p(n)$ be the per-student expense (in dollars) for n students to rent the house. Find an equation of p. [**Hint:** Reflect on your work in parts (a) and (b).]
   d. Use ZStandard and then Zoom Out twice to draw a graph of p. Is p a decreasing function or an increasing function for $n > 0$? Explain why that makes sense in this situation.
   e. Find $p(15)$. What does it mean in this situation?

81. Describe how to find the domain of a rational function. If you believe a number is not in the domain, describe how you can verify that belief. (See page 4 for guidelines on writing a good response.)

82. Describe how to simplify a rational expression. Explain how you can check that the result and the original expression are equivalent. (See page 4 for guidelines on writing a good response.)

Related Review

For Exercises 83–86, find the domain.

83. $f(x) = 4x - 8$ **84.** $f(x) = 3(2)^x$

85. $f(x) = 2(x-4)^2 - 5$ **86.** $f(x) = \frac{x-3}{x^2 - 49}$

87. **a.** Use factoring to simplify $\frac{x^2 + 5x + 6}{x + 3}$.

   b. Use long division or synthetic division to simplify $\frac{x^2 + 5x + 6}{x + 3}$.

   c. Which method from parts (a) and (b) is easier to use to simplify $\frac{x^2 + 5x + 6}{x + 3}$? Explain.

88. **a.** Use factoring to simplify $\frac{4x^3 + 8x^2 - 9x - 18}{2x^2 + x - 6}$.

   b. Use long division to simplify $\frac{4x^3 + 8x^2 - 9x - 18}{2x^2 + x - 6}$.

   c. Which method from parts (a) and (b) is easier to use to simplify $\frac{4x^3 + 8x^2 - 9x - 18}{2x^2 + x - 6}$? Explain.

Expressions, Equations, Functions, and Graphs

Perform the indicated instruction. Then use words such as linear, quadratic, cubic, exponential, logarithmic, rational, polynomial, degree, function, one variable, *and* two variables *to describe the expression, equation, or system.*

89. Find the domain of $f(x) = \dfrac{x-5}{x^2 - 4x - 21}$.

90. Solve $-2x^2 - 4x + 3 = 0$.

91. Solve $3x^3 + 5x^2 = 12x + 20$.

92. Graph $f(x) = -2x^2 - 4x + 3$ by hand.

93. Factor $8x^3 - 125$.

94. Find an equation of a parabola that contains the points $(2, 6)$, $(3, 1)$, and $(4, -8)$.

▼8.2 Multiplying and Dividing Rational Expressions; Converting Units

Objectives

» Multiply and divide rational expressions.

» Convert units of quantities.

In this section, we will multiply and divide rational expressions. Then we will use these skills to convert units of quantities.

Multiplication of Rational Expressions

At times in this course, we have multiplied fractions by using the property $\dfrac{a}{b} \cdot \dfrac{c}{d} = \dfrac{ac}{bd}$, where b and d are nonzero. For example,

$$\frac{2}{3} \cdot \frac{5}{7} = \frac{2 \cdot 5}{3 \cdot 7} = \frac{10}{21}$$

We multiply more complicated rational expressions in a similar way.

> **Multiplying Rational Expressions**
>
> If $\dfrac{A}{B}$ and $\dfrac{C}{D}$ are rational expressions and B and D are nonzero, then
>
> $$\frac{A}{B} \cdot \frac{C}{D} = \frac{AC}{BD}$$
>
> In words, to multiply two rational expressions, write the numerators as a product and write the denominators as a product.

▶ **Example 1**   Multiplying Rational Expressions

Find the product $\dfrac{4x^3}{7x - 1} \cdot \dfrac{3x + 5}{2x}$. Simplify the result.

Solution

$$\frac{4x^3}{7x - 1} \cdot \frac{3x + 5}{2x} = \frac{4x^3 \cdot (3x + 5)}{(7x - 1) \cdot 2x}$$
Multiply numerators and multiply denominators: $\dfrac{A}{B} \cdot \dfrac{C}{D} = \dfrac{AC}{BD}$

$$= \frac{2 \cdot 2 \cdot x \cdot x \cdot x \cdot (3x + 5)}{(7x - 1) \cdot 2 \cdot x}$$
Factor numerator and denominator.

$$= \frac{2x^2(3x + 5)}{7x - 1}$$
Simplify: $\dfrac{2x}{2x} = 1$

We verify our work by creating a graphing calculator table for $y = \dfrac{4x^3}{7x - 1} \cdot \dfrac{3x + 5}{2x}$ and $y = \dfrac{2x^2(3x + 5)}{7x - 1}$. See Fig. 11. (To enter an equation by using Y_n references, see Appendix B.25.) In the table, $x = 0$ gives an "ERROR" message, because 0 is an excluded value of the original expression.

Figure 11 Verify the work

▶

To find the product of rational expressions, we usually begin by factoring the numerators and the denominators if possible. That will put us in a good position to simplify after we have found the product.

▶ **Example 2**   Multiplying Rational Expressions

Find the product $\dfrac{k^2 - 9}{2k^2 - k - 10} \cdot \dfrac{4k^2 - 25}{k^2 + 4k - 21}$. Simplify the result.

Solution

We begin by factoring the numerators and denominators:

$$\dfrac{k^2 - 9}{2k^2 - k - 10} \cdot \dfrac{4k^2 - 25}{k^2 + 4k - 21} = \dfrac{(k - 3)(k + 3)}{(2k - 5)(k + 2)} \cdot \dfrac{(2k - 5)(2k + 5)}{(k - 3)(k + 7)}$$ *Factor numerators and denominators.*

$$= \dfrac{(k - 3)(k + 3)(2k - 5)(2k + 5)}{(2k - 5)(k + 2)(k - 3)(k + 7)}$$ *Multiply numerators; multiply denominators.*

$$= \dfrac{(k + 3)(2k + 5)}{(k + 2)(k + 7)}$$ *Simplify:* $\dfrac{(k - 3)(2k - 5)}{(k - 3)(2k - 5)} = 1$

▶ **How to Multiply Rational Expressions**

To multiply two rational expressions,

1. Factor the numerators and the denominators.
2. Multiply by using the property $\dfrac{A}{B} \cdot \dfrac{C}{D} = \dfrac{AC}{BD}$, where B and D are nonzero.
3. Simplify the result.

▶ **Example 3**   Finding a Product Function

Let $f(x) = \dfrac{35x^2 - 25x}{x^2 - 36}$ and $g(x) = \dfrac{6 - x}{15x^4}$.

1. Find an equation of the product function $f \cdot g$.
2. Find $(f \cdot g)(2)$.

Solution

1. $(f \cdot g)(x) = f(x) \cdot g(x)$ *Definition of $f \cdot g$*

$$= \dfrac{35x^2 - 25x}{x^2 - 36} \cdot \dfrac{6 - x}{15x^4}$$ *Substitute $\dfrac{35x^2 - 25x}{x^2 - 36}$ for $f(x)$ and $\dfrac{6 - x}{15x^4}$ for $g(x)$.*

$$= \dfrac{5x(7x - 5)}{(x - 6)(x + 6)} \cdot \dfrac{-(x - 6)}{3 \cdot 5x^4}$$ *Factor numerators and denominators; $6 - x = -x + 6 = -(x - 6)$*

$$= -\dfrac{5x(7x - 5)(x - 6)}{(x - 6)(x + 6) \cdot 3 \cdot 5 \cdot x^4}$$ *Multiply numerators; multiply denominators;* $\dfrac{-a}{b} = -\dfrac{a}{b}$

$$= -\dfrac{7x - 5}{3x^3(x + 6)}$$ *Simplify:* $\dfrac{5x(x - 6)}{5x(x - 6)} = 1$

2. $(f \cdot g)(2) = -\dfrac{7(2) - 5}{3(2)^3(2 + 6)} = -\dfrac{9}{192} = -\dfrac{3}{64}$

Division of Rational Expressions

How do we divide two rational expressions? We will need to find the reciprocal of a rational expression to divide rational expressions. The **reciprocal** of $\dfrac{A}{B}$ is $\dfrac{B}{A}$. For example, the reciprocal of $\dfrac{x+2}{9}$ is $\dfrac{9}{x+2}$.

At times in this course, we have divided fractions by using the property $\dfrac{a}{b} \div \dfrac{c}{d} = \dfrac{a}{b} \cdot \dfrac{d}{c}$, where b, c, and d are nonzero. For example,

$$\frac{2}{3} \div \frac{5}{7} = \frac{2}{3} \cdot \frac{7}{5} = \frac{14}{15}$$

Dividing by $\dfrac{5}{7}$ is the same as multiplying by the reciprocal of $\dfrac{5}{7}$, which is $\dfrac{7}{5}$. We divide more complicated rational expressions in a similar way.

> **Dividing Rational Expressions**
>
> If $\dfrac{A}{B}$ and $\dfrac{C}{D}$ are rational expressions and B, C, and D are nonzero, then
>
> $$\frac{A}{B} \div \frac{C}{D} = \frac{A}{B} \cdot \frac{D}{C}$$
>
> In words, to divide by a rational expression, multiply by its reciprocal.

▶ **Example 4** Dividing Two Rational Expressions

Find the quotient $\dfrac{6x^2}{x-3} \div \dfrac{4x^7}{x+1}$.

Solution

$$\frac{6x^2}{x-3} \div \frac{4x^7}{x+1} = \frac{6x^2}{x-3} \cdot \frac{x+1}{4x^7} \qquad \text{\textit{Multiply by reciprocal of } } \frac{4x^7}{x+1}, \text{\textit{which is }} \frac{x+1}{4x^7}.$$

$$= \frac{2 \cdot 3 \cdot x^2}{x-3} \cdot \frac{x+1}{2 \cdot 2 \cdot x^7} \qquad \text{\textit{Factor numerators and denominators.}}$$

$$= \frac{2 \cdot 3 \cdot x^2(x+1)}{(x-3) \cdot 2 \cdot 2 \cdot x^7} \qquad \text{\textit{Multiply numerators; multiply denominators.}}$$

$$= \frac{3(x+1)}{2x^5(x-3)} \qquad \text{\textit{Simplify: }} \frac{2x^2}{2x^2} = 1$$

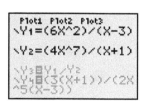

Figure 12 Verify the work

We verify our work by creating a graphing calculator table for $y = \dfrac{6x^2}{x-3} \div \dfrac{4x^7}{x+1}$ and $y = \dfrac{3(x+1)}{2x^5(x-3)}$. See Fig. 12. The values $x = -1$, $x = 0$, and $x = 3$ give "ERROR" messages, because each of these values is an excluded value of either the original expression or our result (why?).

▶

> **How to Divide Rational Expressions**
>
> To divide two rational expressions,
>
> 1. Write the quotient as a product by using the property $\dfrac{A}{B} \div \dfrac{C}{D} = \dfrac{A}{B} \cdot \dfrac{D}{C}$, where B, C, and D are nonzero.
> 2. Find the product.
> 3. Simplify.

▶ **Example 5**   Dividing Two Rational Expressions

Find the quotient $\dfrac{x^3 - y^3}{9x^2 - y^2} \div \dfrac{x^3 + x^2y + xy^2}{6x^2 - xy - y^2}$.

Solution

$$\dfrac{x^3 - y^3}{9x^2 - y^2} \div \dfrac{x^3 + x^2y + xy^2}{6x^2 - xy - y^2} = \dfrac{x^3 - y^3}{9x^2 - y^2} \cdot \dfrac{6x^2 - xy - y^2}{x^3 + x^2y + xy^2}$$

Multiply by reciprocal of $\dfrac{x^3 + x^2y + xy^2}{6x^2 - xy - y^2}$.

$$= \dfrac{(x - y)\left(x^2 + xy + y^2\right)}{(3x + y)(3x - y)} \cdot \dfrac{(2x - y)(3x + y)}{x\left(x^2 + xy + y^2\right)}$$

Factor numerators and denominators.

$$= \dfrac{(x - y)\left(x^2 + xy + y^2\right)(2x - y)(3x + y)}{(3x + y)(3x - y) \cdot x\left(x^2 + xy + y^2\right)}$$

Multiply numerators; multiply denominators.

$$= \dfrac{(x - y)(2x - y)}{x(3x - y)}$$

Simplify:
$\dfrac{\left(x^2 + xy + y^2\right)(3x + y)}{\left(x^2 + xy + y^2\right)(3x + y)} = 1$

Since our result is in lowest terms, we are done.

▶

▶ **Example 6**   Finding a Quotient Function

Let $f(x) = \dfrac{81x^2 - 49}{3x^2 + 16x + 5}$ and $g(x) = \dfrac{7 - 9x}{18x + 6}$.

1. Find an equation of the quotient function $\dfrac{f}{g}$.   **2.** Find $\left(\dfrac{f}{g}\right)(3)$.

Solution

1. $\dfrac{f}{g}(x) = \dfrac{f(x)}{g(x)}$

Definition of $\dfrac{f}{g}$

$$= f(x) \div g(x)$$

$\dfrac{R}{S} = R \div S$

$$= \dfrac{81x^2 - 49}{3x^2 + 16x + 5} \div \dfrac{7 - 9x}{18x + 6}$$

Substitute $\dfrac{81x^2 - 49}{3x^2 + 16x + 5}$ for $f(x)$ and $\dfrac{7 - 9x}{18x + 6}$ for $g(x)$.

$$= \dfrac{81x^2 - 49}{3x^2 + 16x + 5} \cdot \dfrac{18x + 6}{7 - 9x}$$

Multiply by reciprocal of $\dfrac{7 - 9x}{18x + 6}$.

$$= \dfrac{(9x - 7)(9x + 7)}{(3x + 1)(x + 5)} \cdot \dfrac{6(3x + 1)}{-(9x - 7)}$$

Factor numerators and denominators;
$7 - 9x = -9x + 7 = -(9x - 7)$

$$= -\dfrac{(9x - 7)(9x + 7) \cdot 6(3x + 1)}{(3x + 1)(x + 5)(9x - 7)}$$

Multiply numerators; multiply denominators; $\dfrac{a}{-b} = -\dfrac{a}{b}$

$$= -\dfrac{6(9x + 7)}{x + 5}$$

Simplify: $\dfrac{(9x - 7)(3x + 1)}{(9x - 7)(3x + 1)} = 1$

2. $\left(\dfrac{f}{g}\right)(3) = -\dfrac{6[9(3) + 7]}{3 + 5} = -\dfrac{204}{8} = -\dfrac{51}{2}$

▶

In Example 7, we will combine three rational expressions by using two operations.

▶ **Example 7**   Combining Three Rational Expressions

Perform the indicated operations:

$$\left(\dfrac{x^2 - 2x - 48}{x^2 + 8x + 16} \div \dfrac{3x^2 - 9x}{x^2 - 16}\right) \cdot \dfrac{6x + 24}{5x + 30}$$

Solution

$$\left(\frac{x^2 - 2x - 48}{x^2 + 8x + 16} \div \frac{3x^2 - 9x}{x^2 - 16}\right) \cdot \frac{6x + 24}{5x + 30} = \left(\frac{x^2 - 2x - 48}{x^2 + 8x + 16} \cdot \frac{x^2 - 16}{3x^2 - 9x}\right) \cdot \frac{6x + 24}{5x + 30}$$

$$= \left(\frac{(x-8)(x+6)}{(x+4)^2} \cdot \frac{(x-4)(x+4)}{3x(x-3)}\right) \cdot \frac{2 \cdot 3 \cdot (x+4)}{5(x+6)}$$

$$= \frac{2 \cdot 3 \cdot (x-8)(x+6)(x-4)(x+4)^2}{3 \cdot 5 \cdot x \cdot (x+4)^2(x-3)(x+6)}$$

$$= \frac{2(x-8)(x-4)}{5x(x-3)}$$

▶

Converting Units of Quantities

Suppose we're ordering a rug measured in feet, but we measured the width and the length of the floor in inches. There is no need to remeasure: We can convert the units of a quantity to equivalent units by multiplying by ratios of units, where each ratio is equal to 1. For example, since there are 12 inches in 1 foot, the following ratio is equal to 1:

$$\frac{12 \text{ inches}}{1 \text{ foot}} = 1$$

The reciprocal is also equal to 1:

$$\frac{1 \text{ foot}}{12 \text{ inches}} = 1$$

Suppose that the width of a floor is 130 inches. Here we convert from units of inches to feet:

$$\frac{130 \text{ inches}}{1} \cdot \frac{1 \text{ foot}}{12 \text{ inches}} \approx 10.8 \text{ feet}$$

When converting, we can eliminate "inches," because $\frac{\text{inches}}{\text{inches}} = 1$.

We can eliminate a pair of the same units even if one is in singular form and the other is in plural form. For example, $\frac{\text{feet}}{\text{foot}} = 1$. However, $\frac{\text{inch}^2}{\text{inch}} = \text{inch}$, not 1.

Some equivalent units are shown in the margin.

Equivalent Units

Length

1 inch = 2.54 centimeters
1 foot = 12 inches
1 yard = 3 feet
1 yard ≈ 0.914 meter
1 mile = 5280 feet
1 mile ≈ 1.61 kilometers
1 kilometer = 1000 meters

Volume

1 cup = 8 ounces
1 quart = 4 cups
1 quart ≈ 0.946 liter
1 gallon = 4 quarts

Weight

1 gram = 1000 milligrams
1 pound = 16 ounces

Time

1 year ≈ 365 days

▶ **Example 8** Converting Units

Make the indicated unit conversions. Round the results to the second decimal place for Problems 2 and 4.

1. The official width of a football field is 160 feet. What is its width in yards?
2. A Burgundy-style barrel holds 228 liters of wine. What is that volume in quarts?
3. A person drives a car at 50 miles per hour. What is that speed in feet per minute?
4. Americans consume an average of 18.5 gallons of coffee per year (Source: *Beverage Marketing Corporation*). What is that consumption in cups per day?

Solution

1. Since there are 3 feet in one yard, we can multiply 160 feet by $\frac{1 \text{ yard}}{3 \text{ feet}}$. By doing so, we can eliminate "feet," because $\frac{\text{feet}}{\text{feet}} = 1$:

$$\frac{160 \text{ feet}}{1} \cdot \frac{1 \text{ yard}}{3 \text{ feet}} = \frac{160}{3} \text{ yards}$$

The official width is $53\frac{1}{3}$ yards.

2. Since there is approximately 0.946 liter in 1 quart, we multiply 228 liters by $\dfrac{1 \text{ quart}}{0.946 \text{ liter}} \approx 1$ so the liters are eliminated:

$$\frac{228 \text{ liters}}{1} \cdot \frac{1 \text{ quart}}{0.946 \text{ liter}} \approx 241.01 \text{ quarts}$$

The barrel holds approximately 241.01 quarts of wine.

3. There are 60 minutes in 1 hour and 5280 feet in one mile. To convert, we multiply by ratios equal to 1. We arrange the ratios so the units we want to eliminate appear in one numerator and one denominator:

$$\frac{50 \text{ miles}}{1 \text{ hour}} \cdot \frac{1 \text{ hour}}{60 \text{ minutes}} \cdot \frac{5280 \text{ feet}}{1 \text{ mile}} = 4400 \, \frac{\text{feet}}{\text{minute}}$$

So, the person is traveling at 4400 feet per minute.

4. There are 4 quarts in 1 gallon, 4 cups in 1 quart, and approximately 365 days in 1 year. To convert, we multiply by ratios equal to 1 or approximately equal to 1. Again, we arrange the ratios so the units we want to eliminate appear in one numerator and one denominator:

$$\frac{18.5 \text{ gallons}}{1 \text{ year}} \cdot \frac{4 \text{ quarts}}{1 \text{ gallon}} \cdot \frac{4 \text{ cups}}{1 \text{ quart}} \cdot \frac{1 \text{ year}}{365 \text{ days}} \approx 0.81 \text{ cup per day}$$

On average, Americans consume about 0.81 cup of coffee per day.

▶ **Converting Units**

To convert the units of a quantity,

1. Write the quantity in the original units.
2. Multiply by fractions equal to 1 so the units you want to eliminate appear in one numerator and one denominator.

Group Exploration

Looking ahead: Adding and subtracting rational expressions

1. Compare graphing calculator tables for $y = \dfrac{2}{x} + \dfrac{3}{x}$ and $y = \dfrac{5}{x}$. What does this comparison suggest about finding the sum $\dfrac{A}{B} + \dfrac{C}{B}$?

2. Compare graphing calculator tables for $y = \dfrac{5}{x} - \dfrac{2}{x}$ and $y = \dfrac{3}{x}$. What does this comparison suggest about finding the difference $\dfrac{A}{B} - \dfrac{C}{B}$?

3. Use a graphing calculator table to find outputs of the function $y = \dfrac{x}{5} - \dfrac{x+10}{5}$. What do you notice about

the outputs? Explain why it makes sense that the outputs are what they are.

4. Compare graphing calculator tables for $y = \dfrac{2}{x} + \dfrac{x}{3}$ and $y = \dfrac{2+x}{x+3}$. Is the statement

$$\frac{A}{B} + \frac{C}{D} = \frac{A + C}{B + D}, \quad \begin{array}{l} \text{where } B, D, \text{ and} \\ B + D \text{ are nonzero} \end{array}$$

true or false, in general? Explain. [**Hint:** In what way is this sum different from the sum and differences in Problems 1–3?]

5. State any concepts suggested by this exploration.

Homework 8.2

Perform the indicated operation. Simplify the result.

1. $\dfrac{5}{x} \cdot \dfrac{2}{x}$

2. $\dfrac{x}{9} \cdot \dfrac{3}{x}$

3. $\dfrac{7x^5}{2} \div \dfrac{5x^3}{6}$

4. $\dfrac{14}{8x^9} \div \dfrac{21}{6x^5}$

5. $\dfrac{5p^3}{4p - 8} \cdot \dfrac{3p - 6}{10p^8}$

6. $\dfrac{5m - 20}{21m^6} \cdot \dfrac{7m^2}{3m^2 - 12m}$

7. $\dfrac{6x - 18}{5x^5} \div \dfrac{5x - 15}{x^3}$

8. $\dfrac{20x^6}{7x - 14} \div \dfrac{50x^8}{2x - 4}$

9. $\dfrac{4a^3}{9b^2} \cdot \dfrac{3b^5}{8a}$

10. $\dfrac{3a^2}{10b^4} \cdot \dfrac{15b}{7a^5}$

11. $\dfrac{3y^5}{2x^4} \div \dfrac{15y^9}{16x^7}$

12. $\dfrac{7x^4}{8y^2} \div \dfrac{21x^3}{16y^4}$

13. $\dfrac{r^2 + 10r + 21}{r - 9} \cdot \dfrac{2r - 18}{r^2 - 9}$

14. $\dfrac{w^2 - 3w - 28}{w - 5} \cdot \dfrac{5w - 25}{w^2 - 49}$

15. $\dfrac{x^2 + 3x + 2}{3x - 3} \div \dfrac{x^2 - x - 6}{6x - 6}$

16. $\dfrac{x^2 + 9x + 20}{8x - 16} \div \dfrac{x^2 - 2x - 35}{4x - 8}$

17. $\dfrac{2x - 12}{x + 1} \cdot \dfrac{4x + 4}{18 - 3x}$

18. $\dfrac{2x + 4}{4x - 20} \cdot \dfrac{12 - 3x}{x + 2}$

19. $\dfrac{2k^2 - 32}{k^2 - 2k - 24} \div \dfrac{k + 6}{k^2 - 7k + 6}$

20. $\dfrac{3b^2 - 27}{b^2 - 12b + 35} \div \dfrac{b + 3}{b^2 - b - 20}$

21. $\dfrac{2a^2 + 3ab}{3a - 6b} \cdot \dfrac{a^2 - 4b^2}{2ab + 3b^2}$

22. $\dfrac{2a + 10b}{3a^2 + ab} \cdot \dfrac{9a^2 - b^2}{ab + 5b^2}$

23. $\dfrac{4 - x}{x^2 + 10x + 25} \div \dfrac{3x^2 - 9x - 12}{25 - x^2}$

24. $\dfrac{6 - x}{x^2 + 8x + 16} \div \dfrac{4x^2 - 16x - 48}{16 - x^2}$

25. $\dfrac{t^2 - 8t + 16}{t^2 - 2t - 3} \cdot \dfrac{3 - t}{t^2 - 16}$

26. $\dfrac{p^2 - 3p - 10}{p^2 - 4p - 12} \cdot \dfrac{6 - p}{p^2 - 25}$

27. $\dfrac{-x^2 + 7x - 10}{2x^2 + 5x - 12} \div \dfrac{-x^2 + 4}{8x^2 - 18}$

28. $\dfrac{-x^2 - 5x + 14}{3x^2 - 5x - 12} \div \dfrac{-x^2 + 4}{5x^2 - 45}$

29. $\dfrac{-4x - 6}{36 - x^2} \cdot \dfrac{4x + 24}{6x^2 + x - 12}$

30. $\dfrac{-6x - 15}{9 - x^2} \cdot \dfrac{6x + 18}{4x^2 + 4x - 15}$

31. $\dfrac{9x^2 - 16}{x + 2} \div \left(3x^2 + 5x - 12\right)$

32. $\dfrac{16x^2 - 25}{x + 3} \div \left(4x^2 - 13x + 10\right)$

33. $\dfrac{6m^2 - 17m - 14}{m^2 + 6m + 9} \cdot \dfrac{9 - m^2}{4m^2 - 49}$

34. $\dfrac{3r^2 + 7r - 20}{r^2 + 4r + 4} \cdot \dfrac{4 - r^2}{9r^2 - 25}$

35. $\dfrac{x^2 - 4x - 32}{x^2 + 7x + 12} \div \dfrac{x^2 - 2x - 48}{x^2 + 3x - 4}$

36. $\dfrac{x^2 - 6x + 8}{x^2 - 9x + 14} \div \dfrac{x^2 - x - 12}{x^2 + x - 56}$

37. $\dfrac{p^2 + 4pt - 12t^2}{p^2 + pt - 12t^2} \cdot \dfrac{p^2 + 7pt + 12t^2}{p^2 - 7pt + 10t^2}$

38. $\dfrac{m^2 - 6mn + 9n^2}{m^2 + 3mn - 10n^2} \cdot \dfrac{m^2 + 10mn + 25n^2}{m^2 - 4mn + 3n^2}$

39. $\dfrac{2x^2 - xy - 3y^2}{3xy - 5y^2} \div \dfrac{4x^2 - 9y^2}{3x^2 - 14xy + 15y^2}$

40. $\dfrac{4t^2 - 9tw + 2w^2}{9t^2 - 4w^2} \div \dfrac{4t^2 - 5tw + w^2}{6tw - 4w^2}$

41. $\dfrac{3x^3 - 15x^2 + 18x}{x^2 + 16x + 64} \cdot \dfrac{x^2 - 64}{4x^4 - 28x^3 + 40x^2}$

42. $\dfrac{6x^3 + 6x^2 - 12x}{x^2 - 9} \cdot \dfrac{x^2 - 6x + 9}{2x^4 + 10x^3 - 12x^2}$

43. $\dfrac{w^2 - 2w - 8}{12w^4 + 32w^3 - 12w^2} \div \dfrac{w^2 - 9w + 20}{12w^3 + 54w^2 + 54w}$

44. $\dfrac{t^2 + 9t + 18}{6t^4 - 8t^3 - 8t^2} \div \dfrac{t^2 - 5t - 24}{12t^3 + 20t^2 + 8t}$

45. $\dfrac{x^2 + 4x - 5}{x^3 + 6x^2 - 4x - 24} \cdot \dfrac{x^2 + 8x + 12}{x^2 + 10x + 25}$

46. $\dfrac{x^2 - 3x - 10}{x^2 - 12x + 36} \cdot \dfrac{x^2 - 3x - 18}{x^3 + 2x^2 - 25x - 50}$

47. $\dfrac{18x^3 + 27x^2 - 8x - 12}{3x^2 - x - 2} \div \left(6x^2 + 5x - 6\right)$

48. $\dfrac{4x^3 - 8x^2 - x + 2}{2x^2 - 11x + 5} \div \left(2x^2 - 3x - 2\right)$

49. $\dfrac{k^3 - 8}{k^3 + 27} \cdot \dfrac{k^2 - 9}{k^2 - 4}$

50. $\dfrac{y^3 - 1}{y^2 - 4} \cdot \dfrac{y^3 - 8}{y^2 - 1}$

51. $\dfrac{8x^3 - 27}{3x^2 - 6x + 12} \div \dfrac{8x^2 + 12x + 18}{6x^3 + 48}$

52. $\dfrac{64x^3 + 125}{3x^2 - 3x + 3} \div \dfrac{32x^2 - 40x + 50}{6x^3 + 6}$

53. $\dfrac{a^2 + ab - 2b^2}{a^3 + b^3} \cdot \dfrac{a^2 + 2ab + b^2}{a^2 - b^2}$

54. $\dfrac{6p + 4q}{4p^2 + 2pq + q^2} \cdot \dfrac{8p^3 - q^3}{3p^2 + 2pq}$

For $f(x) = \dfrac{x^2 - 6x - 16}{x^2 + 3x - 40}$ and $g(x) = \dfrac{x^2 - 64}{x^2 - 3x - 10}$, find an equation of the given function. Evaluate the function at the indicated value.

55. $f \cdot g, (f \cdot g)(6)$

56. $\dfrac{f}{g}, \left(\dfrac{f}{g}\right)(9)$

57. $\dfrac{g}{f}, \left(\dfrac{g}{f}\right)(7)$

For $f(x) = \dfrac{1 - x^2}{x^2 - 3x - 28}$ and $g(x) = \dfrac{x^2 - 8x + 7}{x^2 + 5x + 4}$, find an equation of the given function. Evaluate the function at the indicated value.

58. $f \cdot g, (f \cdot g)(2)$

59. $\dfrac{f}{g}, \left(\dfrac{f}{g}\right)(4)$

60. $\dfrac{g}{f}, \left(\dfrac{g}{f}\right)(3)$

Perform the indicated operations. Simplify the result.

61. $\left(\dfrac{20x^7}{x^2 - 9} \div \dfrac{x^2 - 14x + 24}{5x - 15}\right) \cdot \dfrac{x^2 + x - 6}{8x^{13}}$

62. $\left(\dfrac{8x^2 + 10x - 3}{-2x^2 - 8x} \cdot \dfrac{x^2 + x}{16x^2 - 1}\right) \div \dfrac{-10x - 15}{8x^5}$

63. $\dfrac{12k^3}{k^2 - 4} \div \left(\dfrac{22k^6}{-6k + 12} \cdot \dfrac{k}{11k + 22}\right)$

64. $\dfrac{3 - p}{20p^5} \div \left(\dfrac{p^2 - 9}{30p^2} \div \dfrac{8p^2 + 6p}{3p}\right)$

65. $\left(\left(\dfrac{x - 4}{x + 5}\right)^2 \cdot \left(\dfrac{x + 5}{x - 1}\right)^2\right) \div \left(\dfrac{x - 4}{x - 1}\right)^2$

66. $\dfrac{3x + 6}{4x + 20} \div \left(\dfrac{x^2 - 4}{x^2 - 25} \div \dfrac{x - 2}{x - 5}\right)^2$

For Exercises 67–76, round approximate results to the second decimal place. Refer to the list of equivalent units in the margin of p. 495 as needed.

67. The average height of a woman in the United States is 63.8 inches. What is that height in feet?

68. A German stein is 23 centimeters tall. What is the mug's height in inches?

69. A person buys 15 gallons of gasoline. How many liters of gasoline is that?

70. The speed limit on motorways in England is 113 kilometers per hour. What is the speed limit in miles per hour?

71. In Trader Giotto's Roasted Garlic Spaghetti Sauce, there are approximately 1.63 grams of salt in 1 pound of sauce. How many milligrams of salt are there in 1 ounce of sauce?

72. In Barbara's Puffins Cinnamon Cereal, there are 42.5 milligrams of potassium in 1 ounce of cereal. How many grams of potassium are there in 1 pound of the cereal?

73. DairyCo, a UK dairy company, reports that the 2011 average yield of one of their cows is 7533 liters of milk per year. What is that yield in gallons per day?

74. A Volkswagen Golf BlueMotion has gas mileage equal to 100 kilometers per 3.2 liters. What is the car's gas mileage in miles per gallon?

75. A person drives at a speed of 67 miles per hour. How fast is the person traveling in feet per second?

76. A person drives at a speed of 25 meters per second. How fast is the person traveling in miles per hour?

Concepts

77. A student tries to find the quotient $\dfrac{x - 2}{x + 8} \div \dfrac{x + 8}{x - 5}$:

$$\dfrac{x - 2}{x + 8} \div \dfrac{x + 8}{x - 5} = \dfrac{x - 2}{x - 5}$$

Find a value to substitute for x to show that the student's work is incorrect. Then find the quotient correctly. Use a graphing calculator table to verify your result.

78. A student tries to find the product $\dfrac{x + 2}{x + 5} \cdot \dfrac{x + 2}{x - 5}$:

$$\dfrac{x + 2}{x + 5} \cdot \dfrac{x + 2}{x - 5} = \dfrac{x^2 + 4}{x^2 - 25}$$

Find a value to substitute for x to show that the student's work is incorrect. Then find the product correctly. Use a graphing calculator table to verify your result.

79. Perform the indicated operations.

a. $\dfrac{1}{x} \div \dfrac{1}{x}$

b. $\dfrac{1}{x} \div \left(\dfrac{1}{x} \div \dfrac{1}{x}\right)$

c. $\dfrac{1}{x} \div \left(\dfrac{1}{x} \div \left(\dfrac{1}{x} \div \dfrac{1}{x}\right)\right)$

d. $\dfrac{1}{x} \div \left(\dfrac{1}{x} \div \left(\dfrac{1}{x} \div \left(\dfrac{1}{x} \div \dfrac{1}{x}\right)\right)\right)$

e. $\underbrace{\dfrac{1}{x} \div \left(\dfrac{1}{x} \div \left(\dfrac{1}{x} \div \cdots \div \left(\dfrac{1}{x} \div \left(\dfrac{1}{x} \div \dfrac{1}{x}\right)\right)\cdots\right)\right)}_{n \text{ division symbols}}$

80. Explain how dividing rational expressions is similar to dividing rational numbers.

81. When converting units, why can we only multiply by ratios equal to 1?

82. Describe how to multiply two rational expressions, and describe how to divide two rational expressions.

Related Review

Find equations of $f \cdot g$ and $\dfrac{f}{g}$. $\left[\textbf{\textit{Hint:}} \; b^n c^n = (bc)^n, \dfrac{b^n}{c^n} = \left(\dfrac{b}{c}\right)^n \right]$

83. $f(x) = 8^x, g(x) = 2^x$ **84.** $f(x) = 6^x, g(x) = 3^x$

85. $f(x) = 12(6)^x, g(x) = 3(2)^x$

86. $f(x) = 10(8)^x, g(x) = 2(4)^x$

For Exercises 87 and 88, refer to the list of equivalent units in the margin of p. 495 as needed.

87. The width of a picture is 2.5 yards.
 a. Use ratios equal to 1 to find the width in inches.
 b. Let $f(w)$ be the number of inches in w feet, and let $g(x)$ be the number of feet in x yards.
  i. Find equations of f and g.
  ii. Find an equation of $f \circ g$.
  iii. Find $(f \circ g)(2.5)$. What does it mean in this situation? Compare the result with your result in part (a).

88. A bowl contains 3.5 quarts of punch.
 a. Use ratios equal to 1 to describe the volume of punch in ounces.

b. Let $f(C)$ be the number of ounces in C cups, and let $g(Q)$ be the number of cups in Q quarts.
  i. Find equations of f and g.
  ii. Find an equation of $f \circ g$.
  iii. Find $(f \circ g)(3.5)$. What does it mean in this situation? Compare the result with your result in part (a).

Expressions, Equations, Functions, and Graphs

Perform the indicated instruction. Then use words such as linear, quadratic, cubic, exponential, logarithmic, rational, polynomial, degree, function, one variable, *and* two variables *to describe the expression, equation, or system.*

89. Write $4 \log_b(2x^2) - 2 \log_b(3x^3)$ as a single logarithm.

90. Find the product $(5t - 3)(4t - 6)$.

91. Solve $\log_2(x - 3) + \log_2(x - 2) = 3$. Round any solutions to the fourth decimal place.

92. Factor $6t^2 - 19t + 10$.

93. Solve $5(4)^x - 23 = 81$. Round any solutions to the fourth decimal place.

94. Solve $6t^2 - 19t + 10 = 0$.

▼ 8.3 Adding and Subtracting Rational Expressions

Objective

» Add and subtract rational expressions.

In Section 8.2, we multiplied and divided rational expressions. How do we add and subtract rational expressions?

Addition of Rational Expressions

At times in this course, we have added fractions by using the property $\dfrac{a}{b} + \dfrac{c}{b} = \dfrac{a + c}{b}$, where b is nonzero. For example,

$$\frac{3}{13} + \frac{5}{13} = \frac{8}{13}$$

We add more complicated rational expressions that have a common denominator in a similar way.

> **Adding Rational Expressions That Have a Common Denominator**

If $\dfrac{A}{B}$ and $\dfrac{C}{B}$ are rational expressions and B is nonzero, then

$$\frac{A}{B} + \frac{C}{B} = \frac{A + C}{B}$$

In words, to add two rational expressions that have a common denominator, add the numerators and keep the common denominator.

After adding two rational expressions, it may be possible to simplify the result.

▶ **Example 1** Adding Two Rational Expressions That Have a Common Denominator

Find the sum $\dfrac{x^2 + 5x}{x^2 - 9} + \dfrac{6}{x^2 - 9}$.

Solution

$$\frac{x^2 + 5x}{x^2 - 9} + \frac{6}{x^2 - 9} = \frac{x^2 + 5x + 6}{x^2 - 9}$$ *Add numerators and keep common denominator:* $\frac{A}{B} + \frac{C}{B} = \frac{A + C}{B}$

$$= \frac{(x + 2)(x + 3)}{(x - 3)(x + 3)}$$ *Factor numerator and denominator.*

$$= \frac{x + 2}{x - 3}$$ *Simplify:* $\frac{x + 3}{x + 3} = 1$

Suppose two brothers, John and Paul, own the following numbers and types of musical instruments:

John	Paul
3 guitars	1 guitar
1 bass guitar	2 bass guitars
1 sitar	1 sitar

The brothers will not give their instruments to each other, but each brother wants to own the same number and types of musical instruments as the other brother has.

Since Paul has one more bass guitar than John has, John wants one more bass guitar. Since John has two more guitars than Paul has, Paul wants two more guitars. John and Paul have the same number of sitars, so neither brother wants another sitar.

Let's compare this situation with finding the least common denominator (LCD) for the sum $\frac{3}{40} + \frac{7}{50}$. First, we find the prime factorization of each denominator:

$$40 = 2 \cdot 2 \cdot 2 \cdot 5$$
$$50 = 2 \cdot 5 \cdot 5$$

What factors do each of the denominators need so the denominators can become the same? Since 50 has one more 5 factor than 40 has, the denominator 40 needs one 5 factor. Since 40 has two more 2 factors than 50 has, the denominator 50 needs two 2 factors.

We use the fact that $\frac{A}{A} = 1$ when $A \neq 0$ to introduce the one 5 factor for 40 and the two 2 factors for 50:

$$\frac{3}{40} + \frac{7}{50} = \frac{3}{2 \cdot 2 \cdot 2 \cdot 5} + \frac{7}{2 \cdot 5 \cdot 5}$$ *Find prime factorization of each denominator.*

$$= \frac{3}{2 \cdot 2 \cdot 2 \cdot 5} \cdot \frac{5}{5} + \frac{7}{2 \cdot 5 \cdot 5} \cdot \frac{2 \cdot 2}{2 \cdot 2}$$ *Introduce missing factors.*

$$= \frac{3 \cdot 5}{2 \cdot 2 \cdot 2 \cdot 5 \cdot 5} + \frac{7 \cdot 2 \cdot 2}{2 \cdot 5 \cdot 5 \cdot 2 \cdot 2}$$ *Find products.*

$$= \frac{15}{200} + \frac{28}{200}$$ *Simplify.*

$$= \frac{43}{200}$$ *Add numerators and keep common denominator:* $\frac{A}{B} + \frac{C}{B} = \frac{A + C}{B}$

This method not only helps us find the LCD, but also suggests what forms of $\frac{A}{A}$ to use to introduce missing factors.

▶ **Example 2**   Adding Two Rational Expressions That Have Different Denominators

Find the sum $\frac{5}{6x} + \frac{9}{4x^3}$.

Solution

We begin by factoring the denominators:

$$6x = 2 \cdot 3 \cdot x$$
$$4x^3 = 2 \cdot 2 \cdot x \cdot x \cdot x$$

Since $4x^3$ has one more 2 factor and two more x factors than $6x$ has, the denominator $6x$ needs one more 2 factor and two more x factors. Since $6x$ has a 3 factor and $4x^3$ does not, the denominator $4x^3$ needs a 3 factor.

We use the fact that $\dfrac{A}{A} = 1$, where A is nonzero, to introduce the missing factors:

$$\frac{5}{6x} + \frac{9}{4x^3} = \frac{5}{2 \cdot 3 \cdot x} + \frac{9}{2 \cdot 2 \cdot x \cdot x \cdot x} \qquad \textit{Factor denominators.}$$

$$= \frac{5}{2 \cdot 3 \cdot x} \cdot \frac{2 \cdot x \cdot x}{2 \cdot x \cdot x} + \frac{9}{2 \cdot 2 \cdot x \cdot x \cdot x} \cdot \frac{3}{3} \qquad \textit{Introduce missing factors.}$$

$$= \frac{10x^2}{12x^3} + \frac{27}{12x^3} \qquad \textit{Find products.}$$

$$= \frac{10x^2 + 27}{12x^3} \qquad \textit{Add numerators and keep common denominator.}$$

The result is in lowest terms. We use a graphing calculator table to verify our work (see Fig. 13). There are "ERROR" messages across from $x = 0$ in the table, because both the original expression and our result are not defined at 0 (why?).

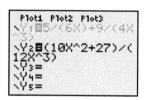

Figure 13 Verify the work

▶ **Example 3** Adding Two Rational Expressions That Have Different Denominators

Find the sum $\dfrac{2}{p + 3} + \dfrac{4}{p - 5}$.

Solution

The denominator $p + 3$ needs a $p - 5$ factor, and the denominator $p - 5$ needs a $p + 3$ factor. We use the fact that $\dfrac{A}{A} = 1$, where A is nonzero, to introduce the missing factors:

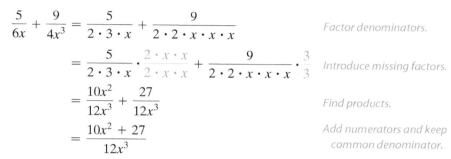

$$\frac{2}{p + 3} + \frac{4}{p - 5} = \frac{2}{p + 3} \cdot \frac{p - 5}{p - 5} + \frac{4}{p - 5} \cdot \frac{p + 3}{p + 3} \qquad \textit{Introduce missing factors.}$$

$$= \frac{2(p - 5)}{(p + 3)(p - 5)} + \frac{4(p + 3)}{(p - 5)(p + 3)} \qquad \textit{Find products.}$$

$$= \frac{2(p - 5) + 4(p + 3)}{(p + 3)(p - 5)} \qquad \textit{Add numerators and keep common denominator: } \frac{A}{B} + \frac{C}{B} = \frac{A + C}{B}$$

$$= \frac{2p - 10 + 4p + 12}{(p + 3)(p - 5)} \qquad \textit{Distributive law}$$

$$= \frac{6p + 2}{(p + 3)(p - 5)} \qquad \textit{Combine like terms.}$$

$$= \frac{2(3p + 1)}{(p + 3)(p - 5)} \qquad \textit{Factor numerator.}$$

The result is in lowest terms.

▶

For the sum of two expressions with different denominators, we first factor the denominators, if possible, to help us find the LCD.

▶ **Example 4**   Adding Two Rational Expressions That Have Different
Denominators

Find the sum $\dfrac{3x}{x^2 + 2xy + y^2} + \dfrac{2y}{x^2 - y^2}$.

Solution

First, we factor the denominators:

$$x^2 + 2xy + y^2 = (x + y)(x + y)$$
$$x^2 - y^2 = (x + y)(x - y)$$

Since $x^2 - y^2$ has an $x - y$ factor but $x^2 + 2xy + y^2$ does not, the denominator $x^2 + 2xy + y^2$ needs an $x - y$ factor. Since $x^2 + 2xy + y^2$ has one more $x + y$ factor than $x^2 - y^2$ has, the denominator $x^2 - y^2$ needs an $x + y$ factor:

$$\dfrac{3x}{x^2 + 2xy + y^2} + \dfrac{2y}{x^2 - y^2} = \dfrac{3x}{(x + y)(x + y)} + \dfrac{2y}{(x + y)(x - y)}$$ *Factor denominators.*

$$= \dfrac{3x}{(x + y)(x + y)} \cdot \dfrac{x - y}{x - y} + \dfrac{2y}{(x + y)(x - y)} \cdot \dfrac{x + y}{x + y}$$ *Introduce missing factors.*

$$= \dfrac{3x(x - y)}{(x + y)(x + y)(x - y)} + \dfrac{2y(x + y)}{(x + y)(x + y)(x - y)}$$ *Find products.*

$$= \dfrac{3x(x - y) + 2y(x + y)}{(x + y)(x + y)(x - y)}$$ *Add numerators and keep common denominator.*

$$= \dfrac{3x^2 - 3xy + 2xy + 2y^2}{(x + y)^2(x - y)}$$ *Distributive law*

$$= \dfrac{3x^2 - xy + 2y^2}{(x + y)^2(x - y)}$$ *Combine like terms.*

The result is in lowest terms.

▶

▶ **How to Add Two Rational Expressions That Have Different Denominators**

To add two rational expression with different denominators,

1. Factor the denominators of the expressions if possible. Determine which factors are missing.

2. Use the property $\dfrac{A}{A} = 1$, where A is nonzero, to introduce missing factors.

3. Add the expressions by using the property $\dfrac{A}{B} + \dfrac{C}{B} = \dfrac{A + C}{B}$, where B is nonzero.

4. Simplify.

▶ **Example 5**   Finding a Sum Function

Let $f(x) = \dfrac{3}{12x^3 - 22x^2 + 6x}$ and $g(x) = \dfrac{x + 1}{30x^2 - 10x}$.

1. Find an equation of $f + g$.
2. Find $(f + g)(2)$.

Solution

1. To start, we use the definition of $f + g$:

$$(f + g)(x) = f(x) + g(x) \qquad \text{\textit{Definition of} } f + g$$

$$= \frac{3}{12x^3 - 22x^2 + 6x} + \frac{x + 1}{30x^2 - 10x} \qquad \textit{Substitute } \frac{3}{12x^3 - 22x^2 + 6x} \textit{ for }$$

$$\qquad\qquad f(x) \textit{ and } \frac{x+1}{30x^2 - 10x} \textit{ for } g(x).$$

Next, we factor the denominators:

$$12x^3 - 22x^2 + 6x = 2x(6x^2 - 11x + 3) = 2 \cdot x \cdot (3x - 1)(2x - 3)$$
$$30x^2 - 10x = 10x(3x - 1) = 2 \cdot 5 \cdot x \cdot (3x - 1)$$

Since $30x^2 - 10x$ has a 5 factor but $12x^3 - 22x^2 + 6x$ does not, the denominator $12x^3 - 22x^2 + 6x$ needs a 5 factor. Since $12x^3 - 22x^2 + 6x$ has a $2x - 3$ factor but $30x^2 - 10x$ does not, the denominator $30x^2 - 10x$ needs a $2x - 3$ factor:

$$(f + g)(x) = \frac{3}{2 \cdot x \cdot (3x - 1)(2x - 3)} + \frac{x + 1}{2 \cdot 5 \cdot x \cdot (3x - 1)} \qquad \textit{Factor denominators.}$$

$$= \frac{3}{2 \cdot x \cdot (3x - 1)(2x - 3)} \cdot \frac{5}{5} + \frac{x + 1}{2 \cdot 5 \cdot x \cdot (3x - 1)} \cdot \frac{2x - 3}{2x - 3} \qquad \begin{array}{l}\textit{Introduce missing}\\ \textit{factors.}\end{array}$$

$$= \frac{15}{10x(3x - 1)(2x - 3)} + \frac{(x + 1)(2x - 3)}{10x(3x - 1)(2x - 3)} \qquad \textit{Find products.}$$

$$= \frac{15 + (x + 1)(2x - 3)}{10x(3x - 1)(2x - 3)} \qquad \begin{array}{l}\textit{Add numerators and keep}\\ \textit{common denominator.}\end{array}$$

$$= \frac{15 + 2x^2 - x - 3}{10x(3x - 1)(2x - 3)} \qquad \textit{Find product.}$$

$$= \frac{2x^2 - x + 12}{10x(3x - 1)(2x - 3)} \qquad \textit{Combine like terms.}$$

The result is in lowest terms.

2. $(f + g)(2) = \dfrac{2(2)^2 - (2) + 12}{10(2)[3(2) - 1][2(2) - 3]} = \dfrac{18}{100} = \dfrac{9}{50}$

Subtraction of Rational Expressions

At times in this course, we have subtracted fractions by using the property $\dfrac{a}{b} - \dfrac{c}{b} = \dfrac{a - c}{b}$, where b is nonzero. For example,

$$\frac{6}{11} - \frac{4}{11} = \frac{2}{11}$$

We subtract more complicated rational expressions that have a common denominator in a similar way.

> **Subtracting Rational Expressions That Have a Common Denominator**
>
> If $\dfrac{A}{B}$ and $\dfrac{C}{B}$ are rational expressions and B is nonzero, then
>
> $$\frac{A}{B} - \frac{C}{B} = \frac{A - C}{B}$$
>
> In words, to subtract two rational expressions that have a common denominator, subtract the numerators and keep the common denominator.

▶ **Example 6** Subtracting Two Rational Expressions

Find the difference $\dfrac{x^2}{x+1} - \dfrac{x+2}{x+1}$.

Solution

$$\frac{x^2}{x+1} - \frac{x+2}{x+1} = \frac{x^2 - (x+2)}{x+1}$$

Subtract numerators and keep common denominator: $\dfrac{A}{B} - \dfrac{C}{B} = \dfrac{A-C}{B}$

$$= \frac{x^2 - x - 2}{x+1}$$ *Simplify.*

$$= \frac{(x-2)(x+1)}{x+1}$$ *Factor numerator.*

$$= x - 2$$ *Simplify:* $\dfrac{x+1}{x+1} = 1$

▶

WARNING   It is a common error to write

$$\frac{x^2}{x+1} - \frac{x+2}{x+1} = \frac{x^2 - x + 2}{x+1}$$ *Incorrect*

This work is incorrect. **When subtracting rational expressions, be sure to subtract the *entire* numerator:**

$$\frac{x^2}{x+1} - \frac{x+2}{x+1} = \frac{x^2 - (x+2)}{x+1} = \frac{x^2 - x - 2}{x+1}$$

(See Example 6 for the rest of the work.)

When subtracting rational expressions with different denominators, we use the method discussed earlier in this section to find the LCD.

▶ **Example 7** Subtracting Two Rational Expressions That Have Different Denominators

Find the difference $\dfrac{5}{4ab^2} - \dfrac{3}{2a^3b}$.

Solution

We begin by factoring the denominators:

$$4ab^2 = 2 \cdot 2 \cdot a \cdot b \cdot b$$
$$2a^3b = 2 \cdot a \cdot a \cdot a \cdot b$$

Since $2a^3b$ has two more a factors than $4ab^2$ has, the denominator $4ab^2$ needs two more a factors. Since $4ab^2$ has one more 2 factor and one more b factor than $2a^3b$ has, the denominator $2a^3b$ needs one 2 factor and one b factor:

$$\frac{5}{4ab^2} - \frac{3}{2a^3b} = \frac{5}{2 \cdot 2 \cdot a \cdot b \cdot b} - \frac{3}{2 \cdot a \cdot a \cdot a \cdot b}$$ *Factor denominators.*

$$= \frac{5}{2 \cdot 2 \cdot a \cdot b \cdot b} \cdot \frac{a \cdot a}{a \cdot a} - \frac{3}{2 \cdot a \cdot a \cdot a \cdot b} \cdot \frac{2 \cdot b}{2 \cdot b}$$ *Introduce missing factors.*

$$= \frac{5a^2}{4a^3b^2} - \frac{6b}{4a^3b^2}$$ *Find products.*

$$= \frac{5a^2 - 6b}{4a^3b^2}$$ *Subtract numerators and keep common denominator.*

The result is in lowest terms.

▶

The steps we take to subtract two rational expressions are similar to the steps we take to add two rational expressions.

> ▶ **How to Subtract Two Rational Expressions That Have Different Denominators**
>
> To subtract two rational expressions that have different denominators,
>
> 1. Factor the denominators of the expressions if possible. Determine which factors are missing.
> 2. Use the property $\dfrac{A}{A} = 1$, where A is nonzero, to introduce missing factors.
> 3. Subtract the expressions by using the property $\dfrac{A}{B} - \dfrac{C}{B} = \dfrac{A - C}{B}$, where B is nonzero.
> 4. Simplify.

▶ **Example 8** Subtracting Two Rational Expressions That Have Different Denominators

Find the difference $\dfrac{3x - 1}{2x^2 - 7x - 4} - \dfrac{5}{x^2 - 8x + 16}$.

Solution

$$\frac{3x - 1}{2x^2 - 7x - 4} - \frac{5}{x^2 - 8x + 16} = \frac{3x - 1}{(2x + 1)(x - 4)} - \frac{5}{(x - 4)(x - 4)}$$ *Factor denominators.*

$$= \frac{3x - 1}{(2x + 1)(x - 4)} \cdot \frac{x - 4}{x - 4} - \frac{5}{(x - 4)(x - 4)} \cdot \frac{2x + 1}{2x + 1}$$ *Introduce missing factors.*

$$= \frac{(3x - 1)(x - 4) - 5(2x + 1)}{(2x + 1)(x - 4)(x - 4)}$$ *Find products; subtract numerators and keep common denominator.*

$$= \frac{3x^2 - 13x + 4 - 10x - 5}{(2x + 1)(x - 4)^2}$$ *Find products.*

$$= \frac{3x^2 - 23x - 1}{(2x + 1)(x - 4)^2}$$ *Combine like terms.*

The result is in lowest terms.

▶

▶ **Example 9** Subtracting Two Rational Expressions That Have Different Denominators

Find the difference $\dfrac{y}{y - 2} - \dfrac{3}{2 - y}$.

Solution

$$\frac{y}{y - 2} - \frac{3}{2 - y} = \frac{y}{y - 2} - \frac{3}{-(y - 2)}$$ $2 - y = -y + 2 = -(y - 2)$

$$= \frac{y}{y - 2} - \left(-\frac{3}{y - 2} \right)$$ $\dfrac{A}{-B} = -\dfrac{A}{B}$

$$= \frac{y}{y - 2} + \frac{3}{y - 2}$$ $A - (-B) = A + B$

$$= \frac{y + 3}{y - 2}$$ *Add numerators and keep common denominator:* $\dfrac{A}{B} + \dfrac{C}{B} = \dfrac{A + C}{B}$

▶

WARNING   The work in Example 9 shows that, to find the difference $\dfrac{y}{y-2} - \dfrac{3}{2-y}$, it is *not* necessary to introduce the factor $2-y$ into the denominator $y-2$ or to introduce the factor $y-2$ into the denominator $2-y$. This method applies to any sum or difference of two rational expressions in which the denominators are of the form $A-B$ and $B-A$.

In Example 10, we combine three rational expressions by performing two operations.

▶ **Example 10**   Performing Operations with Three Rational Expressions

Perform the indicated operations: $\left(\dfrac{x+2}{x^2-x} - \dfrac{6}{x^2-1} \right) + \dfrac{3}{x^2+x}$.

Solution

$\left(\dfrac{x+2}{x^2-x} - \dfrac{6}{x^2-1} \right) + \dfrac{3}{x^2+x}$

$= \left(\dfrac{x+2}{x(x-1)} - \dfrac{6}{(x-1)(x+1)} \right) + \dfrac{3}{x(x+1)}$ *Factor denominators.*

$= \left(\dfrac{x+2}{x(x-1)} \cdot \dfrac{x+1}{x+1} - \dfrac{6}{(x-1)(x+1)} \cdot \dfrac{x}{x} \right) + \dfrac{3}{x(x+1)} \cdot \dfrac{x-1}{x-1}$ *Introduce missing factors.*

$= \dfrac{(x+2)(x+1) - 6x}{x(x-1)(x+1)} + \dfrac{3(x-1)}{x(x-1)(x+1)}$ *Find products; subtract numerators.*

$= \dfrac{(x+2)(x+1) - 6x + 3(x-1)}{x(x-1)(x+1)}$ *Add numerators.*

$= \dfrac{x^2 + 3x + 2 - 6x + 3x - 3}{x(x-1)(x+1)}$ *Find products.*

$= \dfrac{x^2 - 1}{x(x-1)(x+1)}$ *Combine like terms.*

$= \dfrac{(x-1)(x+1)}{x(x-1)(x+1)}$ *Factor numerator.*

$= \dfrac{1}{x}$ *Simplify.*

▶ **Example 11**   Finding a Difference Function

Let $f(x) = \dfrac{x-1}{x+1}$ and $g(x) = \dfrac{x+1}{x-1}$.

1. Find an equation of $f - g$.
2. Find $(f-g)(5)$.

Solution

1. $(f-g)(x) = f(x) - g(x)$ *Definition of $f-g$*

$= \dfrac{x-1}{x+1} - \dfrac{x+1}{x-1}$ *Substitute $\dfrac{x-1}{x+1}$ for $f(x)$ and $\dfrac{x+1}{x-1}$ for $g(x)$.*

$= \dfrac{x-1}{x+1} \cdot \dfrac{x-1}{x-1} - \dfrac{x+1}{x-1} \cdot \dfrac{x+1}{x+1}$ *Introduce missing factors.*

$= \dfrac{(x-1)(x-1) - (x+1)(x+1)}{(x-1)(x+1)}$ *Find products; subtract numerators and keep common denominator: $\dfrac{A}{B} - \dfrac{C}{B} = \dfrac{A-C}{B}$*

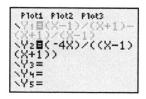

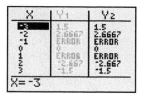

Figure 14 Verify the work

$$= \frac{x^2 - 2x + 1 - (x^2 + 2x + 1)}{(x - 1)(x + 1)} \qquad \textit{Find products.}$$

$$= \frac{x^2 - 2x + 1 - x^2 - 2x - 1}{(x - 1)(x + 1)} \qquad \textit{Subtract trinomial.}$$

$$= \frac{-4x}{(x - 1)(x + 1)} \qquad \textit{Combine like terms.}$$

The result is in lowest terms. We use a graphing calculator table to verify our work (see Fig. 14). The values $x = -1$ and $x = 1$ give "ERROR" messages, because -1 and 1 are not in the domain of either the function $y = \frac{x - 1}{x + 1} - \frac{x + 1}{x - 1}$ or the function $y = \frac{-4x}{(x - 1)(x + 1)}$ (why?).

2. $(f - g)(5) = \frac{-4(5)}{(5 - 1)(5 + 1)} = \frac{-20}{24} = -\frac{5}{6}$

Group Exploration

Adding and subtracting rational expressions

In Problems 1–3, a student tries to perform an operation and simplify the result. If the work is correct, decide whether there is a more efficient way to do the problem. If the work is incorrect, describe any errors and do the problem correctly.

1. Find the sum $\frac{5}{x + 1} + \frac{2}{x + 3}$. Simplify the result.

$$\frac{5}{x + 1} + \frac{2}{x + 3} = \left(\frac{5}{x + 1} + \frac{2}{x + 3} \right) \cdot (x + 1)(x + 3)$$

$$= \frac{5}{x + 1} \cdot (x + 1)(x + 3)$$

$$\quad + \frac{2}{x + 3} \cdot (x + 1)(x + 3)$$

$$= 5(x + 3) + 2(x + 1)$$

$$= 7x + 17$$

2. Find the difference $\frac{5x}{x - 7} - \frac{3x + 4}{x - 7}$. Simplify the result.

$$\frac{5x}{x - 7} - \frac{3x + 4}{x - 7} = \frac{5x - 3x + 4}{x - 7}$$

$$= \frac{2x + 4}{x - 7}$$

3. Find the sum $\frac{4}{(x - 2)(x + 3)} + \frac{1}{x - 2}$. Simplify the result.

$$\frac{4}{(x - 2)(x + 3)} + \frac{1}{x - 2}$$

$$= \frac{4}{(x - 2)(x + 3)} \cdot \frac{x - 2}{x - 2} + \frac{1}{x - 2} \cdot \frac{(x - 2)(x + 3)}{(x - 2)(x + 3)}$$

$$= \frac{4(x - 2) + (x - 2)(x + 3)}{(x - 2)(x - 2)(x + 3)}$$

$$= \frac{4x - 8 + x^2 + x - 6}{(x - 2)^2(x + 3)}$$

$$= \frac{x^2 + 5x - 14}{(x - 2)^2(x + 3)}$$

$$= \frac{(x - 2)(x + 7)}{(x - 2)^2(x + 3)}$$

$$= \frac{x + 7}{(x - 2)(x + 3)}$$

▶ **Tips for Success   Write a Summary**

After each class meeting, consider writing a summary of what you have learned. Your summaries will increase your understanding, as well as your memory, of concepts and procedures. They will also serve as good references for quizzes and exams.

Homework 8.3

Perform the indicated operation. Simplify the result.

1. $\dfrac{5}{x} + \dfrac{2}{x}$

2. $\dfrac{3}{x^2} + \dfrac{6}{x^2}$

3. $\dfrac{x}{x^2 - 9} + \dfrac{3}{x^2 - 9}$

4. $\dfrac{x}{x^2 - 4} + \dfrac{2}{x^2 - 4}$

5. $\dfrac{6m^2}{m^2 - 4m + 3} - \dfrac{4m^2 + 6m}{m^2 - 4m + 3}$

6. $\dfrac{7c^2}{c^2 + c - 6} - \dfrac{2c^2 + 10c}{c^2 + c - 6}$

7. $\dfrac{3x^2 + 9x}{x^2 + 10x + 21} - \dfrac{2x^2 + x - 15}{x^2 + 10x + 21}$

8. $\dfrac{2x^2 - 4x}{3x^2 - 6x} - \dfrac{x^2 + x - 6}{3x^2 - 6x}$

9. $\dfrac{2}{x^6} - \dfrac{4}{x^2}$

10. $\dfrac{4}{x^5} - \dfrac{7}{x^3}$

11. $\dfrac{3}{10x^6} + \dfrac{5}{12x^4}$

12. $\dfrac{3}{14x^2} + \dfrac{4}{21x^9}$

13. $\dfrac{7}{4a^2b} - \dfrac{5}{6ab^3}$

14. $\dfrac{5}{6ab^3} - \dfrac{2}{9a^4b^2}$

15. $\dfrac{3}{x + 1} + \dfrac{4}{x - 2}$

16. $\dfrac{3}{x - 2} + \dfrac{2}{x + 3}$

17. $\dfrac{6}{(x + 4)(x - 6)} - \dfrac{4}{(x - 1)(x + 4)}$

18. $\dfrac{2}{(x + 1)(x - 2)} - \dfrac{3}{(x - 2)(x + 3)}$

19. $\dfrac{5}{3t - 6} - \dfrac{2}{5t + 15}$

20. $\dfrac{b}{8b - 4} - \dfrac{2}{3b - 6}$

21. $\dfrac{3}{x^2 - 25} + \dfrac{5}{x^2 - 5x}$

22. $\dfrac{-2}{x^2 - 2x - 3} + \dfrac{3}{x^2 - 9}$

23. $\dfrac{2}{x^2 - 9} + \dfrac{3}{x^2 - 7x + 12}$

24. $\dfrac{4}{x^2 - 2x} + \dfrac{1}{x^2 - 5x + 6}$

25. $2 + \dfrac{k - 3}{k + 1}$

26. $\dfrac{w + 2}{w - 5} + 3$

27. $2 - \dfrac{2x + 4}{x^2 + 3x + 2}$

28. $\dfrac{6x^2 + 2x - 4}{x^2 - 1} - 5$

29. $\dfrac{8}{x - 6} - \dfrac{4}{6 - x}$

30. $\dfrac{x}{x - 3} - \dfrac{2}{3 - x}$

31. $\dfrac{2x + 1}{x^2 - 4x - 21} + \dfrac{3}{14 - 2x}$

32. $\dfrac{4x + 5}{x^2 + 3x - 40} + \dfrac{2}{15 - 3x}$

33. $\dfrac{-2c}{7 - 2c} - \dfrac{c + 1}{4c^2 - 49}$

34. $\dfrac{-5m}{5 - 3m} - \dfrac{m + 2}{9m^2 - 25}$

35. $\dfrac{2b}{a^2 - b^2} + \dfrac{a}{ab - b^2}$

36. $\dfrac{n}{m^2 + 3mn} + \dfrac{3m}{2mn + 6n^2}$

37. $\dfrac{x}{x^2 + 5x + 6} - \dfrac{3}{x^2 + 7x + 12}$

38. $\dfrac{x}{x^2 + 11x + 30} - \dfrac{5}{x^2 + 9x + 20}$

39. $\dfrac{x - 1}{x + 2} + \dfrac{x + 2}{x - 1}$

40. $\dfrac{x + 4}{x - 6} + \dfrac{x - 6}{x + 4}$

41. $\dfrac{y - 5}{y - 3} - \dfrac{y + 3}{y + 5}$

42. $\dfrac{k + 2}{k - 1} - \dfrac{k + 1}{k - 2}$

43. $\dfrac{x + 4}{x^2 - 7x + 10} - \dfrac{5}{x^2 - 25}$

44. $\dfrac{x - 2}{x^2 - x - 2} - \dfrac{4}{x^2 - 1}$

45. $\dfrac{x + 2}{(x - 4)(x + 3)^2} + \dfrac{x - 1}{(x - 4)(x + 1)(x + 3)}$

46. $\dfrac{x + 1}{(x + 2)^2(x + 3)} + \dfrac{x + 5}{(x + 2)(x + 3)(x + 4)}$

47. $\dfrac{c + 2}{c^2 - 4} + \dfrac{3c}{c^2 - 2c}$

48. $\dfrac{w + 5}{w^2 - 25} + \dfrac{4w}{w^2 - 5w}$

49. $\dfrac{x - 1}{4x^2 + 20x + 25} - \dfrac{x + 4}{6x^2 + 17x + 5}$

50. $\dfrac{x - 3}{2x^2 + 11x - 6} - \dfrac{x + 2}{2x^2 + 7x - 4}$

51. $\dfrac{3x - 1}{x^2 + 4x + 4} + \dfrac{2x + 1}{3x^2 + 5x - 2}$

52. $\dfrac{x - 3}{3x^2 - x - 4} + \dfrac{2x + 5}{6x^2 + x - 12}$

53. $\dfrac{3p}{p^2 - 2pq - 24q^2} - \dfrac{2q}{p^2 - 3pq - 18q^2}$

54. $\dfrac{2x}{x^2 - 6xy + 8y^2} - \dfrac{5y}{x^2 + 3xy - 10y^2}$

55. $\dfrac{x - 1}{6x^2 - 24x} + \dfrac{5}{3x^3 - 6x^2 - 24x}$

56. $\dfrac{3}{2x^3 + 14x^2 + 20x} + \dfrac{x + 2}{14x^2 + 28x}$

Perform the indicated operations. Simplify your result.

57. $\left(\dfrac{2}{x^2 - 4} + \dfrac{3}{x + 2}\right) - \dfrac{1}{2x - 4}$

58. $\left(\dfrac{5}{3x - 9} - \dfrac{2x - 1}{x^2 - 9}\right) + \dfrac{4}{x + 3}$

59. $\dfrac{3}{t + 1} - \left(\dfrac{2t - 3}{t^2 + 6t + 5} + \dfrac{2}{t + 5}\right)$

60. $\dfrac{2k + 11}{k^2 + k - 6} - \left(\dfrac{2}{k + 3} + \dfrac{3}{2 - k}\right)$

Let $f(x) = \dfrac{x + 3}{x - 4}$ and $g(x) = \dfrac{x + 4}{x - 3}$. Find an equation of the given function.

61. $f + g$ **62.** $f - g$ **63.** $g - f$

Let $f(x) = \dfrac{x - 2}{x^2 - 2x - 8}$ and $g(x) = \dfrac{x + 1}{3x + 6}$. Find an equation of the given function.

64. $f + g$ **65.** $f - g$ **66.** $g - f$

Concepts

67. A student tries to find the sum $\dfrac{2}{x + 1} + \dfrac{3}{x + 2}$:

$$\dfrac{2}{x + 1} + \dfrac{3}{x + 2} = \dfrac{2}{x + 1} \cdot \dfrac{1}{x + 2} + \dfrac{3}{x + 2} \cdot \dfrac{1}{x + 1}$$

$$= \dfrac{2}{(x + 1)(x + 2)} + \dfrac{3}{(x + 2)(x + 1)}$$

$$= \dfrac{5}{(x + 1)(x + 2)}$$

Describe any errors. Then find the sum correctly.

68. A student tries to find the difference $\dfrac{6x}{x + 4} - \dfrac{3x + 2}{x + 4}$:

$$\dfrac{6x}{x + 4} - \dfrac{3x + 2}{x + 4} = \dfrac{6x - (3x + 2)}{x + 4}$$

$$= \dfrac{6x - 3x + 2}{x + 4}$$

$$= \dfrac{3x + 2}{x + 4}$$

Describe any errors. Then find the difference correctly.

69. A student tries to find the difference $\dfrac{9x}{x - 3} - \dfrac{5x + 1}{x - 3}$:

$$\dfrac{9x}{x - 3} - \dfrac{5x + 1}{x - 3} = \dfrac{9x - 5x + 1}{x - 3}$$

$$= \dfrac{4x + 1}{x - 3}$$

Find any errors. Then find the difference correctly.

70. Two students try to find the sum $\dfrac{3}{x - 4} + \dfrac{2}{4 - x}$:

Student A's Work

$$\dfrac{3}{x - 4} + \dfrac{2}{4 - x} = \dfrac{3}{x - 4} + \dfrac{2}{-(x - 4)}$$

$$= \dfrac{3}{x - 4} - \dfrac{2}{x - 4}$$

$$= \dfrac{1}{x - 4}$$

Student B's Work

$$\dfrac{3}{x - 4} + \dfrac{2}{4 - x} = \dfrac{3}{x - 4} \cdot \dfrac{4 - x}{4 - x} + \dfrac{2}{4 - x} \cdot \dfrac{x - 4}{x - 4}$$

$$= \dfrac{3(4 - x) + 2(x - 4)}{(x - 4)(4 - x)}$$

$$= \dfrac{12 - 3x + 2x - 8}{(x - 4)(4 - x)}$$

$$= \dfrac{4 - x}{(x - 4)(4 - x)}$$

$$= \dfrac{1}{x - 4}$$

Compare the two methods. Are both correct? Explain. Discuss why student A's method is shorter.

71. Describe how to add two rational expressions that have different denominators. Then describe how to subtract two such expressions.

72. When subtracting rational expressions, we subtract the *entire* numerator. Give an example to show how to do this and what can go wrong if we subtract only part of the numerator.

Related Review

Find equations of $f + g$ and $f - g$.

73. $f(x) = 6x^2 - 4x + 3, g(x) = 2x^2 - 7x - 5$
74. $f(x) = 3x^2 + 8x - 2, g(x) = -5x^2 - 3x + 4$
75. $f(x) = 2(5)^x, g(x) = -3(5)^x$
76. $f(x) = 4(3)^x, g(x) = 7(3)^x$

Perform the indicated operations. Simplify your result.

77. $\dfrac{4x + 5}{x + 2} + \left(\dfrac{3x + 15}{x^2 - 4} \cdot \dfrac{x^2 - 2x}{x^2 + 7x + 10}\right)$

78. $\dfrac{2x - 7}{x - 5} - \left(\dfrac{2x + 10}{x^2 + 9x + 20} \div \dfrac{x^2 - 25}{3x + 12}\right)$

79. $\dfrac{5x + 5}{3x + 6} \cdot \left(\dfrac{x^2 + 4x}{x^2 + 2x + 1} + \dfrac{4}{x^2 + 2x + 1}\right)$

80. $\dfrac{x^2 - 16}{2x - 12} \div \left(\dfrac{x^2}{x^2 - 36} - \dfrac{2x + 8}{x^2 - 36}\right)$

Expressions, Equations, Functions, and Graphs

Perform the indicated instruction. Then use words such as linear, quadratic, cubic, exponential, logarithmic, rational, polynomial, degree, function, one variable, and two variables to describe the expression, equation, or system.

81. Graph $f(x) = 3\left(\dfrac{1}{3}\right)^x$ by hand.

82. Find the product $(3p - 2)(9p^2 + 6p + 4)$.

83. Find all real-number solutions of $5b^4 = 66$. Round any results to the fourth decimal place.

84. Factor $64p^3 - 27$.

85. Find an approximate equation $y = ab^x$ of an exponential curve that contains the points $(3, 95)$ and $(7, 2)$. Round the values of a and b to the second decimal place.

86. Solve $6p^3 + 21p^2 = 12p$.

▼ 8.4 Simplifying Complex Rational Expressions

Objective

» Simplify *complex rational expressions.*

In this section, we will work with complex rational expressions. A **complex rational expression** is a rational expression whose numerator or denominator (or both) is a rational expression. Here are some examples of such expressions:

$$\frac{\dfrac{x^2}{2}-\dfrac{3}{x^3}}{\dfrac{x}{6}+\dfrac{7}{x^2}} \qquad \frac{\dfrac{3x}{x-1}}{\dfrac{x^3}{x-2}} \qquad \frac{\dfrac{5x}{x^2-2x+1}}{x+4}$$

Here we find the values of two numerical complex rational expressions:

$$\frac{2}{\dfrac{2}{2}}=\frac{2}{1}=2 \qquad \frac{\dfrac{2}{2}}{2}=\frac{1}{2}$$

From these two examples, we see that it is important to keep track of the main fraction bar (the longest one, in bold) of the complex fraction.

We will discuss two methods for simplifying complex rational expressions. Ask your instructor whether you are required to know method 1, method 2, or both methods. If the choice is yours, compare the use of method 1 in Examples 1 and 2 with the use of method 2 in Examples 3 and 4. The complex rational expressions in these examples are simplified by both methods so you can get a sense of the advantages and disadvantages of each.

Method 1: Writing a Complex Rational Expression as a Quotient of Two Rational Expressions

An expression in the form $\dfrac{R}{S}$, where R and S are themselves expressions, can be written in the form $R \div S$. We use this fact to help simplify a complex rational expression:

$$\frac{\dfrac{5}{3}}{\dfrac{7}{2}}=\frac{5}{3} \div \frac{7}{2} \qquad \frac{R}{S}=R \div S$$

$$=\frac{5}{3} \cdot \frac{2}{7} \qquad \textit{Multiply by reciprocal of } \frac{7}{2}.$$

$$=\frac{10}{21} \qquad \textit{Multiply numerators; multiply denominators.}$$

We **simplify a complex rational expression** by writing it as a rational expression $\dfrac{P}{Q}$, with $\dfrac{P}{Q}$ in lowest terms.

▶ **Example 1**   Simplifying a Complex Rational Expression by Method 1

Simplify by method 1.

1. $\dfrac{\dfrac{12}{x}}{\dfrac{8}{x^3}}$
    2. $\dfrac{\dfrac{x^2-9}{x^2+2x+1}}{\dfrac{2x-6}{4x+4}}$

Solution

1. $\dfrac{\dfrac{12}{x}}{\dfrac{8}{x^3}} = \dfrac{12}{x} \div \dfrac{8}{x^3}$ $\dfrac{R}{S} = R \div S$

$= \dfrac{12}{x} \cdot \dfrac{x^3}{8}$ *Multiply by reciprocal of $\dfrac{8}{x^3}$, which is $\dfrac{x^3}{8}$.*

$= \dfrac{2 \cdot 2 \cdot 3}{x} \cdot \dfrac{x^3}{2 \cdot 2 \cdot 2}$ *Factor numerator and denominator.*

$= \dfrac{2 \cdot 2 \cdot 3 \cdot x^3}{x \cdot 2 \cdot 2 \cdot 2}$ *Multiply numerators; multiply denominators.*

$= \dfrac{3x^2}{2}$ *Simplify: $\dfrac{2 \cdot 2 \cdot x}{2 \cdot 2 \cdot x} = 1$*

Figure 15 Verify the work

We use a graphing calculator table to verify our work (see Fig. 15). The value $x = 0$ gives an "ERROR" message, because 0 is an excluded value of the numerator (and the denominator) of the original expression.

2. $\dfrac{\dfrac{x^2 - 9}{x^2 + 2x + 1}}{\dfrac{2x - 6}{4x + 4}} = \dfrac{x^2 - 9}{x^2 + 2x + 1} \div \dfrac{2x - 6}{4x + 4}$ $\dfrac{R}{S} = R \div S$

$= \dfrac{x^2 - 9}{x^2 + 2x + 1} \cdot \dfrac{4x + 4}{2x - 6}$ *Multiply by reciprocal of $\dfrac{2x - 6}{4x + 4}$.*

$= \dfrac{(x - 3)(x + 3)}{(x + 1)(x + 1)} \cdot \dfrac{2 \cdot 2(x + 1)}{2(x - 3)}$ *Factor numerators and denominators.*

$= \dfrac{(x - 3)(x + 3) \cdot 2 \cdot 2 \cdot (x + 1)}{(x + 1)(x + 1) \cdot 2(x - 3)}$ *Multiply numerators; multiply denominators.*

$= \dfrac{2(x + 3)}{x + 1}$ *Simplify: $\dfrac{2(x - 3)(x + 1)}{2(x - 3)(x + 1)} = 1$*

Next, we use method 1 to simplify a complex rational expression that has two rational expressions in the numerator and two rational expressions in the denominator.

▶ **Example 2** Simplifying a Complex Rational Expression by Method 1

Simplify $\dfrac{\dfrac{1}{y^2} + \dfrac{3}{2x}}{\dfrac{2}{y} - \dfrac{1}{3x}}$.

Solution

We write both the numerator and the denominator as fractions and simplify as before:

$$\dfrac{\dfrac{1}{y^2} + \dfrac{3}{2x}}{\dfrac{2}{y} - \dfrac{1}{3x}} = \dfrac{\dfrac{1}{y^2} \cdot \dfrac{2x}{2x} + \dfrac{3}{2x} \cdot \dfrac{y^2}{y^2}}{\dfrac{2}{y} \cdot \dfrac{3x}{3x} - \dfrac{1}{3x} \cdot \dfrac{y}{y}}$$

} *Introduce missing factors to get a common denominator, $2xy^2$.*

} *Introduce missing factors to get a common denominator, $3xy$.*

$$= \dfrac{\dfrac{2x}{2xy^2} + \dfrac{3y^2}{2xy^2}}{\dfrac{6x}{3xy} - \dfrac{y}{3xy}}$$ *Find products.*

$$= \dfrac{\dfrac{2x + 3y^2}{2xy^2}}{\dfrac{6x - y}{3xy}}$$ *Add numerators and keep common denominator.*

Subtract numerators and keep common denominator.

$$= \dfrac{2x + 3y^2}{2xy^2} \div \dfrac{6x - y}{3xy}$$ $\dfrac{R}{S} = R \div S$

$$= \dfrac{2x + 3y^2}{2xy^2} \cdot \dfrac{3xy}{6x - y}$$ *Multiply by reciprocal of $\dfrac{6x - y}{3xy}$.*

$$= \dfrac{\left(2x + 3y^2\right) \cdot 3xy}{2xy^2(6x - y)}$$ *Multiply numerators; multiply denominators.*

$$= \dfrac{3\left(2x + 3y^2\right)}{2y(6x - y)}$$ *Simplify: $\dfrac{xy}{xy} = 1$*

Since our result is in lowest terms, we are done.

▶

▶ **Using Method 1 to Simplify a Complex Rational Expression**

To simplify a complex rational expression by method 1,

1. Write both the numerator and the denominator as fractions.
2. Write the complex rational expression as the quotient of two rational expressions:

$$\dfrac{\dfrac{A}{B}}{\dfrac{C}{D}} = \dfrac{A}{B} \div \dfrac{C}{D}, \quad \text{where } B, C, \text{ and } D \text{ are nonzero.}$$

3. Divide the rational expressions.

Method 2: Multiplying by $\dfrac{\text{LCD}}{\text{LCD}}$

Alternatively, we can simplify a complex rational expression by first finding the LCD of all of the fractions in the numerator and denominator. Then, we multiply by 1 in the form $\dfrac{\text{LCD}}{\text{LCD}}$.

In Example 3, we simplify the same complex rational expressions that we simplified in Example 1, but now we use method 2.

▶ **Example 3**   Simplifying a Complex Rational Expression by Method 2

Simplify by method 2.

1. $\dfrac{\dfrac{12}{x}}{\dfrac{8}{x^3}}$

2. $\dfrac{\dfrac{x^2 - 9}{x^2 + 2x + 1}}{\dfrac{2x - 6}{4x + 4}}$

Solution

1. The LCD of $\dfrac{12}{x}$ and $\dfrac{8}{x^3}$ is x^3. So, we multiply the complex rational expression by 1 in the form $\dfrac{x^3}{x^3}$:

$$\frac{\dfrac{12}{x}}{\dfrac{8}{x^3}} = \frac{\dfrac{12}{x} \cdot \dfrac{x^3}{1}}{\dfrac{8}{x^3} \cdot \dfrac{x^3}{1}} \qquad \textit{Multiply by } \frac{\text{LCD}}{\text{LCD}}; \frac{x^3}{x^3} = 1.$$

$$= \frac{\dfrac{12x^3}{x}}{\dfrac{8x^3}{x^3}} \qquad \textit{Simplify.}$$

$$= \frac{12x^2}{8} \qquad \textit{Simplify fractions in numerator and in denominator.}$$

$$= \frac{2 \cdot 2 \cdot 3 \cdot x^2}{2 \cdot 2 \cdot 2} \qquad \textit{Factor numerator and denominator.}$$

$$= \frac{3x^2}{2} \qquad \textit{Simplify: } \frac{2 \cdot 2}{2 \cdot 2} = 1$$

The result is the same as our result in Problem 1 of Example 1.

2. $\dfrac{\dfrac{x^2 - 9}{x^2 + 2x + 1}}{\dfrac{2x - 6}{4x + 4}} = \dfrac{\dfrac{(x - 3)(x + 3)}{(x + 1)(x + 1)}}{\dfrac{2(x - 3)}{4(x + 1)}}$ *Factor numerators and denominators of fractions.*

$$= \frac{\dfrac{(x - 3)(x + 3)}{(x + 1)(x + 1)} \cdot \dfrac{4(x + 1)(x + 1)}{1}}{\dfrac{2(x - 3)}{4(x + 1)} \cdot \dfrac{4(x + 1)(x + 1)}{1}} \qquad \begin{array}{l}\textit{Multiply by } \frac{\text{LCD}}{\text{LCD}}; \\[4pt] \frac{4(x+1)(x+1)}{4(x+1)(x+1)} = 1.\end{array}$$

$$= \frac{\dfrac{(x - 3)(x + 3) \cdot 4(x + 1)(x + 1)}{(x + 1)(x + 1)}}{\dfrac{2(x - 3) \cdot 4(x + 1)(x + 1)}{4(x + 1)}} \qquad \begin{array}{l}\textit{Multiply numerators;} \\ \textit{multiply denominators.}\end{array}$$

$$= \frac{2 \cdot 2(x - 3)(x + 3)}{2(x - 3)(x + 1)} \qquad \begin{array}{l}\textit{Simplify numerator and} \\ \textit{denominator.}\end{array}$$

$$= \frac{2(x + 3)}{x + 1} \qquad \textit{Simplify: } \frac{2(x - 3)}{2(x - 3)} = 1$$

The result is the same as our result in Problem 2 of Example 1.

►

    In comparing our work in Examples 1 and 3, we see that methods 1 and 2 required about the same number of steps. One advantage that method 1 has over method 2 for *these* complex rational expressions is that method 1 does not require us to find an LCD.

    In Example 4, we simplify the same expression as in Example 2, but now we use method 2.

▶ **Example 4**   Simplifying a Complex Rational Expression by Method 2

Simplify $\dfrac{\dfrac{1}{y^2} + \dfrac{3}{2x}}{\dfrac{2}{y} - \dfrac{1}{3x}}$ by method 2.

Solution

The LCD of the rational expressions in the numerator and the denominator is $6xy^2$. To simplify, we multiply by $\dfrac{6xy^2}{6xy^2}$:

$$\dfrac{\dfrac{1}{y^2} + \dfrac{3}{2x}}{\dfrac{2}{y} - \dfrac{1}{3x}} = \dfrac{\dfrac{1}{y^2} + \dfrac{3}{2x}}{\dfrac{2}{y} - \dfrac{1}{3x}} \cdot \dfrac{6xy^2}{6xy^2} \qquad \text{Multiply by } \dfrac{\text{LCD}}{\text{LCD}}, \dfrac{6xy^2}{6xy^2}.$$

$$= \dfrac{\dfrac{1}{y^2} \cdot \dfrac{6xy^2}{1} + \dfrac{3}{2x} \cdot \dfrac{6xy^2}{1}}{\dfrac{2}{y} \cdot \dfrac{6xy^2}{1} - \dfrac{1}{3x} \cdot \dfrac{6xy^2}{1}} \qquad \text{Distributive law}$$

$$= \dfrac{6x + 9y^2}{12xy - 2y^2} \qquad \text{Simplify.}$$

$$= \dfrac{3(2x + 3y^2)}{2y(6x - y)} \qquad \text{Factor numerator and denominator.}$$

The result is the same as our result in Example 2.

▶

WARNING   For the first step in Example 4, it would be incorrect to multiply by the fraction

$$\dfrac{\text{LCD of the numerator}}{\text{LCD of the denominator}} = \dfrac{2xy^2}{3xy}:$$

$$\dfrac{\dfrac{1}{y^2} + \dfrac{3}{2x}}{\dfrac{2}{y} - \dfrac{1}{3x}} = \dfrac{\dfrac{1}{y^2} + \dfrac{3}{2x}}{\dfrac{2}{y} - \dfrac{1}{3x}} \cdot \dfrac{2xy^2}{3xy} \qquad \text{Incorrect}$$

This is incorrect because the expression $\dfrac{2xy^2}{3xy}$ is not equivalent to 1. It *is* correct to multiply by $\dfrac{6xy^2}{6xy^2} = 1$.

In comparing our work in Examples 2 and 4, we see that method 2 required fewer steps than method 1 did. In general, when the numerator, denominator, or both contain two rational expressions, method 2 is usually easier to use.

▶ **Using Method 2 to Simplify a Complex Rational Expression**

To simplify a rational expression by method 2,

1. Find the LCD of all of the fractions in the numerator and denominator.
2. Multiply by 1 in the form $\dfrac{\text{LCD}}{\text{LCD}}$.
3. Simplify the numerator and the denominator to polynomials.
4. Simplify the rational expression.

In Example 5, we form the quotient function of two rational functions.

> **Example 5** Finding a Quotient Function by Method 2

Let $f(x) = 2 - \dfrac{5}{x + 2}$ and $g(x) = \dfrac{x}{x + 2} + \dfrac{x + 1}{x^2 - 4x - 12}$.

1. Find an equation of $\dfrac{f}{g}$.   **2.** Find $\left(\dfrac{f}{g}\right)(4)$.

Solution

1. $\left(\dfrac{f}{g}\right)(x) = \dfrac{f(x)}{g(x)}$ *Definition of* $\dfrac{f}{g}$

$$= \dfrac{2 - \dfrac{5}{x + 2}}{\dfrac{x}{x + 2} + \dfrac{x + 1}{x^2 - 4x - 12}}$$ *Substitute for $f(x)$ and $g(x)$.*

Since the denominator (and the numerator) contains two rational expressions, method 2 should be easier to use than method 1:

$$\left(\dfrac{f}{g}\right)(x) = \dfrac{2 - \dfrac{5}{x + 2}}{\dfrac{x}{x + 2} + \dfrac{x + 1}{(x - 6)(x + 2)}}$$ *Factor $x^2 - 4x - 12$.*

$$= \dfrac{2 - \dfrac{5}{x + 2}}{\dfrac{x}{x + 2} + \dfrac{x + 1}{(x - 6)(x + 2)}} \cdot \dfrac{(x - 6)(x + 2)}{(x - 6)(x + 2)}$$ *Multiply by $\dfrac{LCD}{LCD}$.*

$$= \dfrac{2(x - 6)(x + 2) - \dfrac{5}{x + 2} \cdot \dfrac{(x - 6)(x + 2)}{1}}{\dfrac{x}{x + 2} \cdot \dfrac{(x - 6)(x + 2)}{1} + \dfrac{x + 1}{(x - 6)(x + 2)} \cdot \dfrac{(x - 6)(x + 2)}{1}}$$ *Distributive law*

$$= \dfrac{2(x - 6)(x + 2) - 5(x - 6)}{x(x - 6) + (x + 1)}$$ *Simplify.*

$$= \dfrac{2x^2 - 8x - 24 - 5x + 30}{x^2 - 6x + x + 1}$$ *Find products.*

$$= \dfrac{2x^2 - 13x + 6}{x^2 - 5x + 1}$$ *Combine like terms.*

$$= \dfrac{(2x - 1)(x - 6)}{x^2 - 5x + 1}$$ *Factor numerator.*

We use a graphing calculator table to verify our work (see Fig. 16). The value $x = -2$ gives an "ERROR" message, because -2 is not in the domain of $\dfrac{f}{g}$.

2. $\left(\dfrac{f}{g}\right)(4) = \dfrac{[2(4) - 1][4 - 6]}{(4)^2 - 5(4) + 1} = \dfrac{-14}{-3} = \dfrac{14}{3}$

Figure 16 Verify the work

Our work in Example 5 suggests that if two expressions R and S are rational, then the quotient $\dfrac{R}{S}$ is rational. This is, indeed, true if the numerator of S is nonzero.

Group Exploration

Looking ahead: Solving rational equations

1. Solve $\dfrac{1}{2} + \dfrac{x}{3} = \dfrac{5}{6}$.

2. Solve $\dfrac{1}{x-2} + \dfrac{2}{3} = \dfrac{5}{x-2}$. [**Hint:** Multiply both sides by the LCD of all three fractions.]

3. Solve $\dfrac{x}{x-2} - 5 = \dfrac{2}{x-2}$. Check whether your result satisfies the equation. What is the solution set? Explain.

4. The equations in Problems 1–3 are called *rational equations in one variable*. What does your work in Problem 3 suggest you should always do when solving a rational equation in one variable?

Homework 8.4

Simplify.

1. $\dfrac{\dfrac{2}{x}}{\dfrac{3}{x}}$

2. $\dfrac{\dfrac{x}{8}}{\dfrac{x}{6}}$

3. $\dfrac{\dfrac{7}{x^2}}{\dfrac{21}{x^5}}$

4. $\dfrac{\dfrac{8}{x^8}}{\dfrac{24}{x^2}}$

5. $\dfrac{\dfrac{4a^2}{5b}}{\dfrac{6a}{15b^3}}$

6. $\dfrac{\dfrac{9b^3}{8a}}{\dfrac{3b}{20a^4}}$

7. $\dfrac{\dfrac{3x-3}{2x+10}}{\dfrac{6x^2-6}{4x+20}}$

8. $\dfrac{\dfrac{6x-12}{5x-5}}{\dfrac{3x^2-12}{2x-6}}$

9. $\dfrac{\dfrac{x^2-49}{3x^2-9x}}{\dfrac{x^2-5x-14}{7x-21}}$

10. $\dfrac{\dfrac{x^2-25}{5x-30}}{\dfrac{x^2+x-30}{2x^2-12x}}$

11. $\dfrac{\dfrac{25x^2-4}{9x^2-16}}{\dfrac{25x^2-20x+4}{9x^2-24x+16}}$

12. $\dfrac{\dfrac{25x^2-30x+9}{4x^2-49}}{\dfrac{25x^2-9}{}}$

13. $\dfrac{\dfrac{2}{x^3} - \dfrac{3}{x}}{\dfrac{5}{x^3} + \dfrac{4}{x^2}}$

14. $\dfrac{\dfrac{3}{x} - \dfrac{1}{x^2}}{\dfrac{3}{x^2} - \dfrac{1}{x^3}}$

15. $\dfrac{4 + \dfrac{3}{x}}{\dfrac{2}{x} - 3}$

16. $\dfrac{\dfrac{3}{x} + 5}{\dfrac{2}{x} + 4}$

17. $\dfrac{\dfrac{5}{2x^3} - 4}{\dfrac{1}{6x^3} - 3}$

18. $\dfrac{\dfrac{3}{4x^2} - 2}{4 - \dfrac{5}{8x^2}}$

19. $\dfrac{\dfrac{a^2}{b} - b}{\dfrac{1}{b} - \dfrac{1}{a}}$

20. $\dfrac{\dfrac{m^2}{9n} - n}{\dfrac{1}{n} + \dfrac{3}{m}}$

21. $\dfrac{\dfrac{1}{x} - \dfrac{8}{x^2} + \dfrac{15}{x^3}}{\dfrac{1}{x} - \dfrac{5}{x^2}}$

22. $\dfrac{\dfrac{4}{x} - \dfrac{1}{x^2} + \dfrac{3}{x^3}}{\dfrac{2}{x} - \dfrac{5}{x^2}}$

23. $\dfrac{\dfrac{x}{x-4} - \dfrac{2x}{x+1}}{\dfrac{x}{x+1} - \dfrac{2x}{x-4}}$

24. $\dfrac{\dfrac{2}{x-3} + \dfrac{5}{x-2}}{\dfrac{3}{x-2} - \dfrac{4}{x-3}}$

25. $\dfrac{p + \dfrac{2}{p-4}}{p - \dfrac{3}{p-4}}$

26. $\dfrac{\dfrac{3}{w+1} + 2}{4 - \dfrac{5}{w-1}}$

27. $\dfrac{\dfrac{1}{x+3} - \dfrac{1}{x}}{3}$

28. $\dfrac{\dfrac{2}{x+4} - \dfrac{2}{x}}{4}$

29. $\dfrac{\dfrac{3}{a+b} - \dfrac{3}{a-b}}{2ab}$

30. $\dfrac{\dfrac{4}{2a-b} - \dfrac{2}{a-3b}}{5ab^2}$

31. $\dfrac{\dfrac{1}{(x+2)^2} - \dfrac{1}{x^2}}{2}$

32. $\dfrac{\dfrac{5}{(x+3)^2} - \dfrac{5}{x^2}}{3}$

33. $\dfrac{\dfrac{6}{2x-8} + \dfrac{10}{x^2-4x}}{\dfrac{1}{x^2-x-12} - \dfrac{2}{x^2-16}}$

34. $\dfrac{\dfrac{4}{3x-9} - \dfrac{1}{x^2-3x}}{\dfrac{2}{x^2-2x-15} + \dfrac{5}{x^2-9}}$

35. $\dfrac{\dfrac{x+7}{x^2+7x+10} - \dfrac{6}{x^2+2x}}{\dfrac{x+1}{x^2+7x+10} + \dfrac{6}{x^2+5x}}$

36. $\dfrac{\dfrac{x-1}{x^2+x-12} + \dfrac{2}{x^2-3x}}{\dfrac{x+2}{x^2+x-12} - \dfrac{3}{x^2+4x}}$

Use the given functions to find an equation of $\dfrac{f}{g}$.

37. $f(x) = \dfrac{5x + 10}{x^2 - 6x + 9}$ and $g(x) = \dfrac{4x + 8}{x^2 - 4x + 3}$

38. $f(x) = \dfrac{5x - 10}{2x^2 + x - 15}$ and $g(x) = \dfrac{7x - 14}{x^2 + 5x + 6}$

39. $f(x) = \dfrac{x}{2} - \dfrac{2}{x}$ and $g(x) = \dfrac{3}{2} + \dfrac{3}{x}$

40. $f(x) = \dfrac{x}{5} - \dfrac{5}{x}$ and $g(x) = \dfrac{8}{5} - \dfrac{8}{x}$

41. $f(x) = \dfrac{2x}{x^2 - 25} + \dfrac{x + 5}{x - 5}$ and $g(x) = \dfrac{x - 5}{x + 5} + \dfrac{3x}{x^2 - 25}$

42. $f(x) = \dfrac{6x}{x^2 - 9} + \dfrac{x - 3}{x + 3}$ and $g(x) = \dfrac{x + 3}{x - 3} - \dfrac{6x}{x^2 - 9}$

Concepts

43. A student tries to simplify the complex rational expression $\dfrac{x}{\dfrac{1}{x} + \dfrac{1}{2}}$:

$$\dfrac{x}{\dfrac{1}{x} + \dfrac{1}{2}} = x \div \left(\dfrac{1}{x} + \dfrac{1}{2}\right)$$

$$= x\left(\dfrac{x}{1} + \dfrac{2}{1}\right)$$

$$= x \cdot (x + 2)$$

$$= x^2 + 2x$$

Describe any errors. Then simplify the expression correctly.

44. A student tries to simplify the complex rational expression $\dfrac{\dfrac{5}{2} + \dfrac{3}{x}}{\dfrac{7}{x} + \dfrac{4}{x^2}}$:

$$\dfrac{\dfrac{5}{2} + \dfrac{3}{x}}{\dfrac{7}{x} + \dfrac{4}{x^2}} = \dfrac{\dfrac{5}{2} + \dfrac{3}{x}}{\dfrac{7}{x} + \dfrac{4}{x^2}} \cdot \dfrac{2x}{x^2}$$

$$= \dfrac{\dfrac{5}{2} \cdot \dfrac{2x}{1} + \dfrac{3}{x} \cdot \dfrac{2x}{1}}{\dfrac{7}{x} \cdot \dfrac{x^2}{1} + \dfrac{4}{x^2} \cdot \dfrac{x^2}{1}}$$

$$= \dfrac{5x + 6}{7x + 4}$$

Describe any errors. Then simplify the expression correctly.

45. Simplify the given expression by method 1; then simplify it again by method 2. Decide which method you prefer for this expression. Explain.

$$\dfrac{\dfrac{6}{x^2} - \dfrac{5}{x}}{\dfrac{2}{x^2} + \dfrac{3}{2x}}$$

46. Simplify the given expression by method 1; then simplify it again by method 2. Decide which method you prefer for this expression. Explain.

$$\dfrac{\dfrac{x^2 - 3x - 28}{3x - 6}}{\dfrac{x^2 - 14x + 49}{6x - 12}}$$

47. The equation $\dfrac{8}{4} = 2$ implies that $2 \cdot 4 = 8$. What does the equation $\dfrac{2}{\frac{1}{3}} = 6$ imply? Is your result true?

48. Let $f(x) = \dfrac{x}{x + 2}$. Find an equation of a function g so $\left(\dfrac{f}{g}\right)(x) = x + 3$.

49. Describe a complex rational expression. Give an example. Then simplify it.

50. Describe how to simplify a complex rational expression.

Related Review

Simplify.

51. $\dfrac{8x^{-2}y^5}{6x^{-7}y^8}$

52. $\dfrac{6x^4y^{-5}}{15x^{-3}y^{-2}}$

53. $\dfrac{x^{-1} + x^{-2}}{x^{-2} - x^{-1}}$ [**Hint:** First write as a complex rational expression.]

54. $\dfrac{x^{-3} - x^{-1}}{x^{-1} + x^{-2}}$ [**Hint:** First write as a complex rational expression.]

55. $\dfrac{2b^{-2} - 4b}{8b^{-1} - 6b}$

56. $\dfrac{3y + 2y^{-1}}{6y - 4y^{-3}}$

For $f(x) = \dfrac{x + 2}{3 - x}$ and $g(x) = \dfrac{x}{x - 1}$, find an equation of the given composite function.

57. $f \circ g$

58. $g \circ f$

59. When a patient is treated with a radioactive element, the element decreases in amount exponentially from both radioactive (physical) decay and biological means, such as urination. The effective half-life of an element is given by

$$H_e = \dfrac{1}{\dfrac{1}{H_p} + \dfrac{1}{H_b}}$$

where H_p and H_b are the physical and biological half-lives, respectively.

a. Simplify the right-hand side of the formula.

b. Use the result you found in part (a) to find the effective half-life of sulfur-35, which has a physical half-life of 87.4 days and a biological half-life of 623 days.

60. a. Solve the equation $b^{mx+c} = k$ for x.

b. Students A and B try to solve the equation in part (a). Student A's result is $\dfrac{\log(k) - c \log(b)}{m \log(b)}$. Student B's result is $\dfrac{\dfrac{\log(k)}{\log(b)} - c}{m}$. Simplify student B's result. Are the students' results equivalent?

Expressions, Equations, Functions, and Graphs

Perform the indicated instruction. Then use words such as linear, quadratic, cubic, exponential, logarithmic, rational, polynomial, degree, function, one variable, *and* two variables *to describe the expression, equation, or system.*

61. Find the sum $\dfrac{x-2}{x^2-2x-24} + \dfrac{x+4}{x^2-8x+12}$.

62. Solve:
$$y = -\frac{3}{2}x + 4$$
$$\frac{3}{4}x - \frac{1}{2}y = 4$$

63. Find the product $\dfrac{x-2}{x^2-2x-24} \cdot \dfrac{x+4}{x^2-8x+12}$.

64. Graph $f(x) = -\dfrac{3}{2}x + 4$ by hand.

65. Find the domain of $f(x) = \dfrac{2x-1}{x^2-2x-24}$.

66. Find the inverse of $f(x) = -\dfrac{3}{2}x + 4$.

▼ 8.5 Solving Rational Equations

Objectives

» Solve *rational equations in one variable.*

» Solve formulas involving rational expressions.

» Compare solving rational equations with simplifying rational expressions.

» Use a rational model to make estimates and predictions about the independent variable.

In Sections 8.1–8.4, we worked mostly with rational expressions. In this section, we will solve rational *equations* in one variable.

Solving Rational Equations in One Variable

A **rational equation in one variable** is an equation in one variable in which both sides can be written as rational expressions. Here are some examples of rational equations in one variable:

$$\frac{3x}{x-4} + \frac{x-2}{5x+3} = 2 \qquad \frac{5}{x} = 9 \qquad \frac{x}{x-3} + \frac{3}{x^2-6x+9} = \frac{x-5}{x-3}$$

As we have done in earlier sections, we will clear an equation of fractions by multiplying both sides of the equation by the LCD.

With rational equations, it is possible to take the usual steps for solving equations, yet arrive at x values that are excluded values for one or more of the fractions in the equation. These values of x are *not* solutions. We call such values **extraneous solutions.**

▶ **Example 1** Solving a Rational Equation

Solve the equation $\dfrac{2}{p} + 5 = \dfrac{8}{p} - 1$.

Solution

We note that 0 is an excluded value. We clear the equation of fractions by multiplying both sides of the equation by p, which is the LCD of the fractions $\dfrac{2}{p}$ and $\dfrac{8}{p}$:

$$\frac{2}{p} + 5 = \frac{8}{p} - 1 \qquad \textit{Original equation}$$

$$p\left(\frac{2}{p} + 5\right) = p\left(\frac{8}{p} - 1\right) \qquad \textit{Multiply both sides by LCD, p.}$$

$$p \cdot \frac{2}{p} + p \cdot 5 = p \cdot \frac{8}{p} - p \cdot 1 \qquad \textit{Distributive law}$$

$$2 + 5p = 8 - p \qquad \textit{Simplify.}$$

$$6p = 6$$

$$p = 1$$

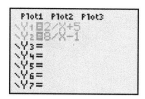

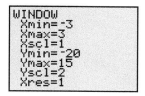

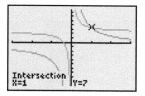

Figure 17 Verify the work

Since 1 is not an excluded value, we conclude that 1 is the solution of the equation. We check that 1 satisfies the original equation:

$$\frac{2}{p} + 5 = \frac{8}{p} - 1 \qquad \textit{Original equation}$$

$$\frac{2}{1} + 5 \overset{?}{=} \frac{8}{1} - 1 \qquad \textit{Substitute 1 for p.}$$

$$7 \overset{?}{=} 7 \qquad \textit{Simplify.}$$

$$\text{true}$$

We also check our work by using "intersect" on a graphing calculator (see Fig. 17).

▶ **Example 2** Solving a Rational Equation

Solve $2 - \dfrac{1}{x-2} = \dfrac{x-3}{x-2}$.

Solution

We note that 2 is an excluded value, because $x - 2$ is in the denominator. We clear the equation of fractions by multiplying both sides of the equation by $x - 2$, which is the LCD of the fractions $\dfrac{1}{x-2}$ and $\dfrac{x-3}{x-2}$:

$$2 - \frac{1}{x-2} = \frac{x-3}{x-2} \qquad \textit{Original equation}$$

$$(x-2)\left(2 - \frac{1}{x-2}\right) = (x-2) \cdot \frac{x-3}{x-2} \qquad \textit{Multiply both sides by LCD, } x-2.$$

$$(x-2) \cdot 2 - (x-2) \cdot \frac{1}{x-2} = (x-2) \cdot \frac{x-3}{x-2} \qquad \textit{Distributive law}$$

$$(x-2) \cdot 2 - 1 = x - 3 \qquad \textit{Simplify.}$$

$$2x - 4 - 1 = x - 3 \qquad \textit{Distributive law}$$

$$x = 2$$

Our result, 2, is *not* a solution, because 2 is an excluded value. Since the only possibility, 2, is not a solution of the original equation, we conclude that no number is a solution. We say the solution set is the *empty set*.

▶ To see where we introduced the extraneous solution 2 in Example 2, notice that 2 does not satisfy the equation

$$(x-2) \cdot 2 - (x-2) \cdot \frac{1}{x-2} = (x-2) \cdot \frac{x-3}{x-2}$$

because 2 is an excluded value of the expression $(x-2) \cdot \dfrac{x-3}{x-2}$. However, 2 does satisfy the next equation, $(x-2) \cdot 2 - 1 = x - 3$:

$$(x-2) \cdot 2 - 1 = x - 3$$

$$(2-2) \cdot 2 - 1 \overset{?}{=} 2 - 3$$

$$-1 \overset{?}{=} -1$$

$$\text{true}$$

Since multiplying both sides of a rational equation by the LCD and then simplifying both sides may introduce extraneous solutions, we must always check that any proposed solution is not an excluded value.

To solve a rational equation, we factor the denominators of fractions to help us determine any excluded values, to find the LCD, and, later, to help us simplify rational expressions.

▶ **Example 3**   Solving a Rational Equation

Solve $\dfrac{x}{x + 2} - \dfrac{7}{5 - x} = \dfrac{14}{x^2 - 3x - 10}$.

Solution

We begin by factoring the denominators:

$$\dfrac{x}{x + 2} - \dfrac{7}{5 - x} = \dfrac{14}{x^2 - 3x - 10} \qquad \textit{Original equation}$$

$$\dfrac{x}{x + 2} - \dfrac{7}{-(x - 5)} = \dfrac{14}{(x - 5)(x + 2)} \qquad \begin{array}{l}\textit{Factor denominators;}\\ 5 - x = -x + 5 = -(x - 5)\end{array}$$

$$\dfrac{x}{x + 2} + \dfrac{7}{(x - 5)} = \dfrac{14}{(x - 5)(x + 2)} \qquad \dfrac{a}{-b} = -\dfrac{a}{b}$$

The excluded values are -2 and 5. Next, we clear the equation of fractions by multiplying both sides by the LCD, $(x - 5)(x + 2)$:

$$(x - 5)(x + 2)\left(\dfrac{x}{x + 2} + \dfrac{7}{x - 5}\right) = (x - 5)(x + 2) \cdot \dfrac{14}{(x - 5)(x + 2)} \qquad \begin{array}{l}\textit{Multiply}\\ \textit{both sides}\\ \textit{by LCD.}\end{array}$$

On the left-hand side, we use the distributive law. On the right-hand side, we simplify:

$$(x - 5)(x + 2) \cdot \dfrac{x}{x + 2} + (x - 5)(x + 2) \cdot \dfrac{7}{x - 5} = 14 \qquad \textit{Distributive law; simplify.}$$

$$(x - 5) \cdot x + (x + 2) \cdot 7 = 14 \qquad \textit{Simplify.}$$

$$x^2 - 5x + 7x + 14 = 14 \qquad \textit{Distributive law}$$

$$x^2 + 2x + 14 = 14 \qquad \textit{Combine like terms.}$$

$$x^2 + 2x = 0 \qquad \textit{Subtract 14 from both sides.}$$

$$x(x + 2) = 0 \qquad \textit{Factor left-hand side.}$$

$$x = 0 \quad \text{or} \quad x + 2 = 0 \qquad \textit{Zero factor property}$$

$$x = 0 \quad \text{or} \qquad x = -2$$

Since -2 is an excluded value, it is *not* a solution. The only solution is 0. We use a graphing calculator table to check our work (see Fig. 18).

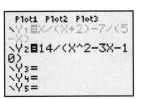

Figure 18 Verify the work

▶ **Solving a Rational Equation in One Variable**

To solve a rational equation in one variable,

1. Factor the denominator(s) if possible.
2. Identify any excluded values.
3. Find the LCD of all of the fractions.
4. Multiply both sides of the equation by the LCD, which gives a simpler equation to solve.
5. Solve the simpler equation.
6. Discard any proposed solutions that are excluded values.

▶ **Example 4**   Finding an Input Value of a Rational Function

Let $f(x) = \dfrac{x + 1}{x - 3} - \dfrac{x - 2}{x + 3}$. Find x when $f(x) = 1$.

Solution

We note that the domain of f is the set of real numbers except -3 and 3. We substitute 1 for $f(x)$ in the equation $f(x) = \dfrac{x + 1}{x - 3} - \dfrac{x - 2}{x + 3}$ and solve for x:

$$1 = \frac{x+1}{x-3} - \frac{x-2}{x+3}$$

$$(x-3)(x+3) \cdot 1 = (x-3)(x+3)\left(\frac{x+1}{x-3} - \frac{x-2}{x+3}\right)$$

$$(x-3)(x+3) = (x-3)(x+3) \cdot \frac{x+1}{x-3} - (x-3)(x+3) \cdot \frac{x-2}{x+3}$$

$$(x-3)(x+3) = (x+3)(x+1) - (x-3)(x-2) \quad \text{Simplify.}$$

$$x^2 - 9 = x^2 + 4x + 3 - (x^2 - 5x + 6) \quad \text{Find products.}$$

$$x^2 - 9 = x^2 + 4x + 3 - x^2 + 5x - 6 \quad \text{Subtract trinomial.}$$

$$x^2 - 9 = 9x - 3 \quad \text{Combine like terms.}$$

$$x^2 - 9x - 6 = 0 \quad \text{Write in } ax^2 + bx + c = 0 \text{ form.}$$

$$x = \frac{-(-9) \pm \sqrt{(-9)^2 - 4(1)(-6)}}{2(1)} \quad \text{Substitute into quadratic formula.}$$

$$x = \frac{9 \pm \sqrt{105}}{2} \quad \text{Simplify.}$$

Since both of our results are in the domain of f, we conclude that if $f(x) = 1$, then $x = \frac{9 - \sqrt{105}}{2}$ or $x = \frac{9 + \sqrt{105}}{2}$.

We enter $y = \frac{x+1}{x-3} - \frac{x-2}{x+3}$ in a graphing calculator and check that, for both inputs $\frac{9 - \sqrt{105}}{2}$ and $\frac{9 + \sqrt{105}}{2}$, the output is 1 (see Fig. 19).

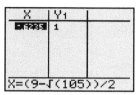

Figure 19 Verify the work

Solving Formulas Involving Rational Expressions

Formulas that contain rational expressions are useful in many fields, such as finance, physics, meteorology, mathematics, electronics, and chemistry. It can be helpful to solve such a formula for one of its variables.

▶ **Example 5** Solving a Formula Involving a Rational Expression

The following formula is useful in electronics:

$$I = \frac{\mathcal{E}}{R + r}$$

Here I is the current in an electrical circuit, $\mathcal{E}$ is the electromotive force, R is the circuit's resistance, and r is the battery's resistance. Solve the formula for the variable R.

Solution

To begin, we multiply both sides of the equation by the LCD, $R + r$:

$$I = \frac{\mathcal{E}}{R + r} \quad \text{Original formula}$$

$$(R + r) \cdot I = (R + r) \cdot \frac{\mathcal{E}}{R + r} \quad \text{Multiply both sides by LCD, } R + r.$$

$$RI + rI = \mathcal{E} \quad \text{Distributive law; simplify.}$$

$$RI = \mathcal{E} - rI \quad \text{Subtract } rI \text{ from both sides.}$$

$$\frac{RI}{I} = \frac{\mathcal{E} - rI}{I} \quad \text{Divide both sides by } I.$$

$$R = \frac{\mathcal{E} - rI}{I} \quad \text{Simplify.}$$

Solving Rational Equations versus Simplifying Rational Expressions

Throughout this course, we have solved equations and simplified expressions. In solving an equation, our objective is to find any *numbers* that satisfy the equation. In simplifying an expression, our objective is to find a simpler, yet equivalent, *expression*.

> ### ▶ Solving a Rational Equation versus Simplifying a Rational Expression
>
> To solve a rational equation, clear the fractions in it by multiplying both sides of the equation by the LCD. To simplify a rational expression, do *not* multiply it by the LCD—the only multiplication permissible is multiplication by 1, usually in the form $\frac{A}{A}$, where A is a nonzero polynomial.

Here we compare solving a rational equation with simplifying a rational expression:

Solving the Equation $\frac{2}{3} = \frac{4}{x}$

The number 0 is an excluded value.

$$\frac{2}{3} = \frac{4}{x} \qquad \textit{Original equation}$$

$$3x \cdot \frac{2}{3} = 3x \cdot \frac{4}{x} \qquad \begin{array}{l}\textit{Multiply both sides by}\\ \textit{LCD, 3x.}\end{array}$$

$$2x = 12 \qquad \textit{Simplify.}$$

$$x = 6$$

The result is a number.

Simplifying the Expression $\frac{2}{3} + \frac{4}{x}$

$$\frac{2}{3} + \frac{4}{x} = \frac{2}{3} \cdot \frac{x}{x} + \frac{4}{x} \cdot \frac{3}{3} \quad \begin{array}{l}\textit{Introduce missing}\\ \textit{factors.}\end{array}$$

$$= \frac{2x}{3x} + \frac{12}{3x} \qquad \textit{Find products.}$$

$$= \frac{2x + 12}{3x} \qquad \frac{A}{B} + \frac{C}{B} = \frac{A + C}{B}$$

The result is an expression.

For the equation $\frac{2}{3} = \frac{4}{x}$, the solution is the *number* 6. We simplify the expression $\frac{2}{3} + \frac{4}{x}$ by writing it as the *expression* $\frac{2x + 12}{3x}$. In general, **the result of solving a rational equation is the empty set or a set of one or more numbers. The result of simplifying a rational expression is an expression.**

Using a Rational Model to Make Predictions about the Independent Variable

In Section 8.1, we modeled the percentage of a quantity by means of a rational model, which we used to make a prediction about the dependent variable. Now that we know how to solve a rational equation in one variable, we can use such a model to make a prediction about the independent variable.

Table 7 Numbers of Internet Users

Year	Number of Internet Users (millions)
2006	204
2007	212
2008	220
2009	228
2010	240

Source: *The Nielsen Company*

▶ Example 6   Using a Rational Model to Make a Prediction

In Example 9 of Section 8.1, we found the model $P(t) = \dfrac{880t + 15{,}040}{0.0068t^2 + 2.71t + 277.89}$, where $P(t)$ is the percentage of Americans who are Internet users at t years since 2000 (see Table 7). Predict when 92% of Americans will be Internet users.

Solution

We substitute 92 for $P(t)$ in the equation of P and solve for t:

$$92 = \frac{880t + 15{,}040}{0.0068t^2 + 2.71t + 277.89}$$

$$(0.0068t^2 + 2.71t + 277.89) \cdot 92 = (0.0068t^2 + 2.71t + 277.89) \cdot \frac{880t + 15{,}040}{0.0068t^2 + 2.71t + 277.89}$$

$$0.6256t^2 + 249.32t + 25{,}565.88 = 880t + 15{,}040$$

$$0.6256t^2 - 630.68t + 10{,}525.88 = 0$$

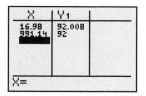

Figure 20 Verify the work

Now we substitute $a = 0.6256$, $b = -630.68$, and $c = 10{,}525.88$ in the quadratic formula:

$$t = \frac{-(-630.68) \pm \sqrt{(-630.68)^2 - 4(0.6256)(10{,}525.88)}}{2(0.6256)} \quad \text{Substitute into quadratic formula.}$$

$$t \approx 16.98 \quad \text{or} \quad t \approx 991.14 \qquad \text{Compute.}$$

We verify the results by entering $y = \dfrac{880t + 15{,}040}{0.0068t^2 + 2.71t + 277.89}$ in a graphing calculator and checking that the inputs 16.98 and 991.14 lead to outputs of about 92 (see Fig. 20).

The inputs 16.98 and 991.14 represent the years 2017 and 2991, respectively. Model breakdown has occurred for the prediction 2991: The year is too far into the future for us to have any faith in this prediction! Therefore, we predict 92% of Americans will be Internet users in 2017.

Group Exploration

Simplifying versus solving

1. Two students tried to solve $4 = \dfrac{5}{x} + \dfrac{3}{x}$. Did one, both, or neither of these students solve the equation correctly? Explain.

Student A

$$4 = \frac{5}{x} + \frac{3}{x}$$

$$4x = x\left(\frac{5}{x} + \frac{3}{x}\right)$$

$$4x = x \cdot \frac{5}{x} + x \cdot \frac{3}{x}$$

$$4x = 5 + 3$$

$$4x = 8$$

$$x = 2$$

Student B

$$4 = \frac{5}{x} + \frac{3}{x}$$

$$= \frac{5}{x} + \frac{3}{x} - 4$$

$$= \frac{8}{x} - 4$$

$$= \frac{8}{x} - 4 \cdot \frac{x}{x}$$

$$= \frac{8}{x} - \frac{4x}{x}$$

$$= \frac{-4x + 8}{x}$$

Student C

$$4 + \frac{5}{x} + \frac{3}{x} = x\left(4 + \frac{5}{x} + \frac{3}{x}\right)$$

$$= 4x + x \cdot \frac{5}{x} + x \cdot \frac{3}{x}$$

$$= 4x + 5 + 3$$

$$= 4x + 8$$

Student D

$$4 + \frac{5}{x} + \frac{3}{x} = 4 \cdot \frac{x}{x} + \frac{5}{x} + \frac{3}{x}$$

$$= \frac{4x}{x} + \frac{5}{x} + \frac{3}{x}$$

$$= \frac{4x + 8}{x}$$

Student E

$$4 + \frac{5}{x} + \frac{3}{x} = 0$$

$$x\left(4 + \frac{5}{x} + \frac{3}{x}\right) = x \cdot 0$$

$$4x + 5 + 3 = 0$$

$$4x = -8$$

$$x = -2$$

2. Three students tried to simplify $4 + \dfrac{5}{x} + \dfrac{3}{x}$. Which students, if any, simplified the expression correctly? Explain.

3. a. What is the difference in your goals in solving a rational equation versus simplifying a rational expression?

b. Explain how that difference relates to the techniques you use to solve an equation versus simplify an expression.

Homework 8.5

For extra help ▶ **MyMathLab®**   Watch the videos in MyMathLab   Download the MyDashboard App

Solve. All solutions are real numbers.

1. $\dfrac{7}{x} = \dfrac{2}{x} + 1$

2. $\dfrac{8}{x} = \dfrac{5}{x} + 3$

5. $\dfrac{x - 2}{x - 7} = \dfrac{5}{x - 7}$

6. $\dfrac{-1}{x - 5} = \dfrac{x - 6}{x - 5}$

3. $\dfrac{7}{4x} - \dfrac{5}{6} = \dfrac{1}{12x}$

4. $\dfrac{5}{8x} - \dfrac{7}{4} = \dfrac{3}{2x}$

7. $\dfrac{5}{4p - 7} = \dfrac{2}{2p + 3}$

8. $\dfrac{3}{2y - 9} = \dfrac{4}{3y + 5}$

9. $\dfrac{3}{x+1} + \dfrac{2}{5} = 1$

10. $\dfrac{2}{3} = \dfrac{7}{x-5} + 2$

11. $\dfrac{1}{x-2} + \dfrac{1}{x+2} = \dfrac{4}{x^2-4}$

12. $\dfrac{3}{x-5} + \dfrac{2}{x+5} = \dfrac{30}{x^2-25}$

13. $2 + \dfrac{4}{k-2} = \dfrac{8}{k^2-2k}$

14. $1 + \dfrac{4}{m-5} = \dfrac{2}{m^2-5m}$

15. $\dfrac{-48}{x^2-2x-15} - \dfrac{6}{x+3} = \dfrac{7}{x-5}$

16. $\dfrac{-36}{x^2+x-20} - \dfrac{2}{x-4} = \dfrac{4}{x+5}$

17. $\dfrac{x^2-23}{2x^2-5x-3} + \dfrac{2}{x-3} = \dfrac{-1}{2x+1}$

18. $\dfrac{4x^2-24x}{3x^2-x-2} + \dfrac{3}{3x+2} = \dfrac{-4}{x-1}$

19. $\dfrac{w+7}{w^2-9} = \dfrac{-w+2}{w-3}$

20. $\dfrac{t-6}{t^2-4} = \dfrac{-t+1}{t-2}$

21. $3 + \dfrac{2}{x} = \dfrac{4}{x^2}$

22. $\dfrac{5}{x} = \dfrac{3}{x^2} - 4$

23. $\dfrac{5}{r^2-3r+2} - \dfrac{1}{r-2} = \dfrac{r+6}{3r-3}$

24. $\dfrac{3}{p^2-6p+9} + \dfrac{p-2}{3p-9} = \dfrac{p}{2p-6}$

25. $\dfrac{2x}{x+1} - \dfrac{3}{2} = \dfrac{-2}{x+2}$

26. $-\dfrac{1}{2} + \dfrac{x}{x-1} = \dfrac{-1}{x+3}$

27. $\dfrac{x-4}{x^2-7x+12} - \dfrac{x+2}{x-3} = 0$

28. $\dfrac{x+2}{x^2+x-30} - \dfrac{x+3}{x-5} = 0$

29. $\dfrac{t}{t-3} = 2 - \dfrac{5}{3-t}$

30. $4 - \dfrac{k}{k-5} = \dfrac{1}{5-k}$

31. $\dfrac{12}{9-x^2} + \dfrac{3}{x+3} = \dfrac{-2}{x-3}$

32. $\dfrac{-2}{x+5} + \dfrac{3}{x-5} = \dfrac{-20}{25-x^2}$

33. $\dfrac{x+2}{x-3} - \dfrac{x-3}{x+2} = \dfrac{5x}{x^2-x-6}$

34. $\dfrac{x-4}{x+1} + \dfrac{x+1}{x-4} = \dfrac{13x}{x^2-3x-4}$

35. $\dfrac{2y}{y-2} - \dfrac{2y-5}{y^2-7y+10} = \dfrac{-4}{y-5}$

36. $\dfrac{3p}{p+1} - \dfrac{4p-1}{p^2-2p-3} = \dfrac{-2}{p-3}$

37. $\dfrac{x-2}{x^2-2x-3} + \dfrac{x+5}{x^2-1} = \dfrac{x+3}{x^2-4x+3}$

38. $\dfrac{x+4}{x^2+x-2} + \dfrac{x+1}{x^2-4} = \dfrac{x-3}{x^2-3x+2}$

Find all complex-number solutions.

39. $\dfrac{5}{x} - \dfrac{2}{x^2} = 4$

40. $\dfrac{7}{x} + 5 = -\dfrac{6}{x^2}$

41. $\dfrac{2}{t-5} - \dfrac{3t}{t+5} = \dfrac{35}{t^2-25}$

42. $\dfrac{3}{k+4} - \dfrac{2k}{k-4} = \dfrac{2}{k^2-16}$

43. $\dfrac{x-1}{3x-12} + \dfrac{-x+1}{x-5} = \dfrac{4x}{x^2-9x+20}$

44. $\dfrac{-x+6}{2x-6} + \dfrac{x-1}{x+4} = \dfrac{2x}{x^2+x-12}$

Find x when y is equal to the indicated value.

45. $f(x) = \dfrac{3}{x-5}, y = 4$

46. $g(x) = \dfrac{7}{x+4}, y = 3$

47. $f(x) = \dfrac{5}{x-1} + \dfrac{3}{x+1}, y = -1$

48. $g(x) = \dfrac{2}{x+1} - \dfrac{4}{x-2}, y = -1$

Find all x-intercepts.

49. $f(x) = \dfrac{x-1}{x-5} - \dfrac{x+2}{x+3}$

50. $g(x) = \dfrac{x+4}{x-2} - \dfrac{x-3}{x+6}$

For Exercises 51–56, solve for the specified variable.

51. $F = \dfrac{mv^2}{r}$, for r

52. $P = \dfrac{nrT}{V}$, for V

53. $F = -\dfrac{GMm}{r^2}$, for M

54. $\dfrac{P_1V_1}{T_1} = \dfrac{P_2V_2}{T_2}$, for P_1

55. $P = \dfrac{A}{1+rt}$, for t

56. $P = \dfrac{A}{1+rt}$, for r

57. In Exercise 69 of Homework 8.1, you found the rational model $P(t) = \dfrac{0.48t^2 + 14t + 295}{0.015t^2 + 0.055t + 6.05}$, where $P(t)$ is the percentage of voter-eligible Latinos who are registered to vote at t years since 1980 (see Table 8).

Table 8 Numbers of Latinos Who Are Registered to Vote and Eligible to Vote

	Millions of Latinos	
Year	Registered to Vote	Eligible to Vote
1988	4.6	7.7
1992	5.1	8.3
1996	6.6	11.2
2000	7.5	13.2
2004	9.3	16.1
2008	11.6	19.5
2010	11.0	21.3

Source: *Pew Hispanic Center*

Predict when exactly half of voter-eligible Latinos will be registered to vote.

58. In Exercise 70 of Homework 8.1, you found the rational model $P(t) = \dfrac{1.2t^2 - 12t + 665}{0.026t^2 - 0.2t + 14.6}$, where $P(t)$ is the percentage of college students who are men at t years since 1990 (see Table 9).

Table 9 College Enrollments

| Year | Enrollment (millions) | |
	Men	All Students
1995	6.3	14.2
2000	6.7	15.3
2005	7.5	17.5
2008	8.2	19.1
2010	9.1	21.2

Source: *National Center for Education Statistics*

Predict when 43.2% of college students will be men.

59. The amounts employees pay for health insurance and the total costs (paid by employees and employers) are shown in Table 10 for various years.

Table 10 Health Insurance Costs

| Year | Health Insurance Cost (thousands of dollars) | |
	Employee Cost	Total Cost
2007	1.98	8.6
2008	2.22	9.23
2009	2.27	9.78
2010	2.38	10.39
2011	2.53	10.98

Source: *TW/NBGH Value Purchasing Survey*

a. Let $E(t)$ be the amount (in thousands of dollars) paid by employees for health insurance in the year that is t years since 2000. Find a linear equation of E.
b. Let $C(t)$ be the total cost (in thousands of dollars) of health insurance in the year that is t years since 2000. Find an equation of C.
c. Let $P(t)$ be the percentage of the total cost of health insurance paid by employees in the year that is t years since 2000. Find an equation of P.
d. Find $P(17)$. What does it mean in this situation?
e. Find t when $P(t) = 23$. What does it mean in this situation?
f. Use the window settings in Fig. 21 to graph P. Is P increasing, decreasing, or neither for the values of t between 7 and 20? What does that mean in this situation? How is this possible, given that the amount employees pay for health insurance has been increasing since 2007?

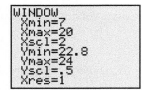

Figure 21 Window settings for Exercise 59f

60. The numbers of prisoners and the numbers of releases from prison are shown in Table 11 for various years.

Table 11 Prisoners and Releases from Prisons

Year	Numbers of Prisoners Released from Prison (thousands)	Total Number of Prisoners (thousands)
2000	605	1391
2002	630	1440
2004	672	1497
2006	713	1570
2008	735	1610
2009	729	1614

Source: *Bureau of Justice Statistics*

a. Let $r(t)$ be the number (in thousands) of releases from prison in the year that is t years since 2000. Find a linear equation of r.
b. Let $n(t)$ be the total number (in thousands) of prisoners at t years since 2000. Find a linear equation of n.
c. Let $P(t)$ be the percentage of prisoners who are released in the year that is t years since 2000. Find an equation of P.
d. Find $P(11)$. What does it mean in this situation?
e. Find t when $P(t) = 47$. What does it mean in this situation?
f. Use the window settings in Fig. 22 to graph P. Is P increasing, decreasing, or neither for the values of t between 0 and 20? What does that mean in this situation?

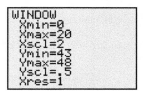

Figure 22 Window settings for Exercise 60f

For Exercises 61–66, find approximate solutions of the given equation or system by referring to the graphs shown in Fig. 23. Round results or coordinates of results to the first decimal place.

61. $\dfrac{5}{x - 2} = x^2 - 6x + 10$

62. $\dfrac{5}{x - 2} = -x^2 + x - 1$

63. $\dfrac{5}{x - 2} = 4$

64. $\dfrac{5}{x - 2} = -1$

65. $y = \dfrac{5}{x - 2}$
$y = -x^2 + x - 1$

66. $y = \dfrac{5}{x - 2}$
$y = x^2 - 6x + 10$

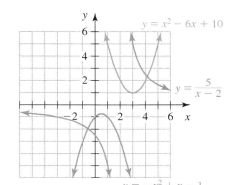

Figure 23
Exercises 61–66

67. Let $f(x) = \dfrac{x + a}{x + b}$. Find values of a and b such that $f(0) = 2$ and $f(1) = \dfrac{5}{2}$.

68. Let $f(x) = \dfrac{x + a}{x + b}$. Find values of a and b such that $f(1) = -2$ and $f(3) = -8$.

Concepts

69. A student tries to solve the equation $\dfrac{4}{x + 2} - \dfrac{2}{x} = \dfrac{1}{x + 2}$:

$$\frac{4}{x + 2} - \frac{2}{x} = \frac{1}{x + 2}$$

$$\frac{4}{x + 2} \cdot \frac{x}{x} - \frac{2}{x} \cdot \frac{x + 2}{x + 2} = \frac{1}{x + 2} \cdot \frac{x}{x}$$

$$\frac{4x - 2(x + 2)}{x(x + 2)} = \frac{x}{x(x + 2)}$$

$$\frac{4x - 2x - 4}{x(x + 2)} = \frac{x}{x(x + 2)}$$

$$\frac{2x - 4}{x(x + 2)} = \frac{x}{x(x + 2)}$$

$$2x - 4 = x$$

$$x = 4$$

Describe a more efficient way to solve the equation.

70. A student tries to simplify the expression $\dfrac{3}{x + 1} + \dfrac{3}{x - 1}$:

$$\frac{3}{x + 1} + \frac{3}{x - 1}$$

$$= (x - 1)(x + 1)\left(\frac{3}{x + 1} + \frac{3}{x - 1}\right)$$

$$= (x - 1)(x + 1) \cdot \frac{3}{x + 1} + (x - 1)(x + 1) \cdot \frac{3}{x - 1}$$

$$= 3(x - 1) + 3(x + 1)$$

$$= 3x - 3 + 3x + 3$$

$$= 6x$$

Describe any errors. Then simplify the expression correctly.

71. When simplifying a rational expression, can we multiply it by the LCD? Explain. When solving a rational equation, can we multiply both sides of the equation by the LCD? Explain.

72. Why must we check that any proposed solution of a rational equation is an excluded value?

73. A student tries to solve a rational equation in one variable. The result is $\dfrac{x - 2}{x^2 - 4x + 1}$. What would you tell the student?

74. Describe how to solve a rational equation in one variable.

Related Review

Solve or simplify, as appropriate. For equations, all solutions are real numbers.

75. $\dfrac{5}{x} + \dfrac{4}{x + 1} - \dfrac{3}{x}$

76. $\dfrac{2}{k + 3} + \dfrac{k}{k - 3} + \dfrac{-10}{k^2 - 9}$

77. $\dfrac{5}{x} + \dfrac{4}{x + 1} = \dfrac{3}{x}$

78. $\dfrac{2}{k + 3} + \dfrac{k}{k - 3} = \dfrac{-10}{k^2 - 9}$

79. $\dfrac{x + 2}{x^2 - 5x + 6} - \dfrac{x + 1}{x^2 - 4} = \dfrac{4}{x^2 - x - 6}$

80. $\dfrac{3}{x^2 - 4x - 12} - \dfrac{x - 3}{x^2 - 7x + 6}$

81. $\dfrac{x + 2}{x^2 - 5x + 6} - \dfrac{x + 1}{x^2 - 4} + \dfrac{4}{x^2 - x - 6}$

82. $\dfrac{3}{x^2 - 4x - 12} - \dfrac{x - 3}{x^2 - 7x + 6} = \dfrac{x}{x^2 + x - 2}$

Solve. All solutions are real numbers. Round approximate solutions to the fourth decimal place.

83. $2p^3 - p^2 = 8p - 4$

84. $2(2m^2 - m) = 1 - 3m$

85. $2(4)^x + 3 = 106$

86. $\dfrac{3}{x^2 - 9} - \dfrac{x - 2}{x^2 - x - 12} = \dfrac{-1}{x - 4}$

87. $\log_3(5x - 4) - \log_3(2x - 3) = 2$

88. $2\log_2(x + 2) - \log_2(x + 3) = 1$

Expressions, Equations, Functions, and Graphs

Perform the indicated instruction. Then use words such as linear, quadratic, cubic, exponential, logarithmic, rational, polynomial, degree, function, one variable, *and* two variables *to describe the expression, equation, or system.*

89. Graph $f(x) = -2(x + 2)^2 + 3$ by hand.

90. Solve $\log_5(2x^4) = 3$. Round any solutions to the fourth decimal place.

91. Solve $-2(x + 2)^2 + 3 = -15$.

92. Graph $f(x) = \log_2(x)$ by hand.

93. Simplify $-2(x + 2)^2 + 3$.

94. Simplify $\log_b(b^3)$.

▼ 8.6 Modeling with Rational Functions

Objectives

» Use a rational function to model the *mean* of a quantity.

» Model the percentage of a quantity.

» Use a rational function to model the time it takes to travel a given distance at a constant speed.

In this section, we will use rational functions to model authentic situations.

Modeling the Mean of a Quantity

To begin, suppose four students go on a road trip during spring break. The total cost for gas is $20. Consider the following possibilities:

A. Each person pays $5 for gas.

B. The amounts contributed for gas are $4, $4, $6, and $6.

C. One student pays $20, and the other three students ride for free.

We compute the *mean* amount of money each student spent for gas by dividing the total spent by the number of students:

$$\text{mean amount spent per student} = \frac{\text{total amount spent for gas}}{\text{number of students}}$$

$$= \frac{20\ \text{dollars}}{4\ \text{students}} = 5\ \text{dollars per student}$$

So, the mean amount of money spent per student is $5. We also say the *average* amount of money spent per student is $5.

For scenarios A, B, and C, we make the following observations:

A. The mean gives the (exact) per-person amount if all students pay an equal amount.

B. The mean gives a reasonable estimate of the per-person amount if the students pay nearly the same amount.

C. The mean gives a poor estimate of the per-person amount if the students pay very different amounts.

> **Computing the Mean**
>
> If a quantity Q is divided into n parts, the **mean** amount M of the quantity per part is given by
>
> $$M = \frac{Q}{n}$$

As another example, if a student makes 21 phone calls in 7 days, the mean number of calls he makes per day is $\frac{21}{7} = 3$ calls. The mean is a fairly good estimate of the number of calls on a given day, provided the student made about the same number of calls each day.

> **Example 1**   Modeling the Mean of a Quantity

The underground band Melted Zipper wants to make and sell a CD of its original songs. It costs about $1000 to record the music onto a digital audiotape (DAT), $100 to rearrange the music and improve the sound quality, $350 for artwork for the cover and inside leaflet, and $350 to set up production. In addition, it will cost $2.50 for each CD manufactured.

1. What is the total cost of making 300 CDs?
2. Let $C(n)$ be the total cost (in dollars) of making n CDs. Find an equation of C.
3. Let $P(n)$ be the price (in dollars) the band should set for each CD so it breaks even by making and selling n CDs. Find an equation of P.
4. Find $P(300)$. What does it mean in this situation?
5. Find n when $P(n) = 10$. What does it mean in this situation?
6. Describe the values of $P(n)$ for large values of n.

Solution

1. First, we compute the total *fixed costs*—the costs that do not depend on how many CDs are manufactured:

$$1000 + 100 + 350 + 350 = 1800\ \text{dollars}$$

The band must also pay $2.50 per CD manufactured. If the band manufactures 300 CDs, this cost, called the *variable cost*, is $2.50(300) = 750$ dollars.

To find the total cost, we add the variable cost and the fixed costs:

$$2.50(300) + 1800 = 2550\ \text{dollars}$$

2. The total cost is equal to $2.50 times the number of CDs, plus the fixed cost of $1800:

$$C(n) = 2.50n + 1800$$

Jay   Jim   Steve

Melted Zipper

3. If the band makes and sells n CDs, it can break even by selling the CD for the amount found by dividing the total cost into n parts. This amount is the mean cost per CD:

$$
\begin{aligned}
P(n) &= \text{mean cost per CD} \\
&= \frac{\text{total cost}}{\text{number of CDs manufactured}} \\
&= \frac{2.50n + 1800}{n}
\end{aligned}
$$

4. $P(300) = \dfrac{2.50(300) + 1800}{300} = 8.50$

If the band makes and sells 300 CDs, it must sell each CD for \$8.50 to break even.

5. We substitute 10 for $P(n)$ in the equation of P and solve for n:

$$
\begin{aligned}
10 &= \frac{2.50n + 1800}{n} && \textit{Substitute 10 for P(n).} \\
n \cdot 10 &= n \cdot \frac{2.50n + 1800}{n} && \textit{Multiply both sides by LCD, n.} \\
10n &= 2.50n + 1800 && \textit{Simplify.} \\
7.5n &= 1800 \\
n &= 240
\end{aligned}
$$

If the band can sell each CD for \$10, then it must make 240 CDs to break even.

6. First, we use graphing calculator tables to display input–output pairs of P (see Figs. 24, 25, and 26).

Figure 24 Enter the function

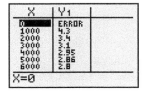

Figure 25 Inputs increasing by 1000

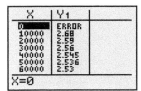

Figure 26 Inputs increasing by 10,000

From the tables, we see that as n increases, the mean price required to break even decreases. This happens because, as the number of CDs manufactured increases, the more the fixed cost is spread out, so the smaller the fixed cost that each sale has to cover. In fact, if we continue to scroll down a table for larger and larger inputs n, the outputs $P(n)$ approach 2.50, the variable cost in dollars per CD.

We can also study a graphing calculator graph to observe that the break-even CD price approaches \$2.50 for large manufacturing runs (see Figs. 27, 28, and 29). It appears that, for large inputs, the height of the graph of P gets close to 2.50.

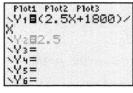

Figure 27 Enter the functions; Y_2 is the variable cost per disc

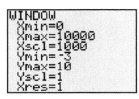

Figure 28 Set up the window to allow for large n

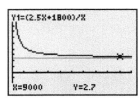

Figure 29 Graph the functions

This means that if the band could sell tens of thousands of CDs, it could price them at a few cents above the \$2.50 cost and still break even.

Table 12 Bottled-Water Consumption

Year	Bottled-Water Consumption (millions of gallons)
1990	2200
1995	3100
2000	4700
2005	7500
2009	10,600

Source: *Beverage Marketing Corporation*

▶ **Example 2** Modeling the Mean of a Quantity

In Example 10 of Section 7.5, we modeled the annual U.S. consumption of bottled water. A reasonable model is $B(t) = 21t^2 + 42t + 2250$, where $B(t)$ is the annual U.S. bottled-water consumption (in millions of gallons) at t years since 1990 (see Table 12).

In Exercise 7 of Homework 7.7, you modeled the U.S. population. A reasonable model is $U(t) = 0.0068t^2 + 2.58t + 251.4$, where $U(t)$ is the U.S. population (in millions) at t years since 1990.

1. Let $M(t)$ be the annual mean consumption of bottled water per person (in gallons per person) at t years since 1990. Find an equation of M.
2. Perform a unit analysis of the equation of M.
3. Find $M(27)$. What does it mean in this situation?
4. Find t when $M(t) = 60$. What does it mean in this situation?

Solution

1. The annual mean consumption of bottled water per person is equal to the total annual consumption divided by the U.S. population:

$$M(t) = \frac{B(t)}{U(t)} = \frac{21t^2 + 42t + 2250}{0.0068t^2 + 2.58t + 251.4}$$

2. Here is a unit analysis of the equation of M:

gallons per person $\rightarrow M(t) = \dfrac{B(t)}{U(t)} = \dfrac{21t^2 + 42t + 2250}{0.0068t^2 + 2.58t + 251.4}$ ← millions of gallons ← millions of people

The units on both sides of the equation are gallons per person, which suggests the equation is correct.

3. $M(27) = \dfrac{21(27)^2 + 42(27) + 2250}{0.0068(27)^2 + 2.58(27) + 251.4} \approx 57.34$

The annual mean consumption of bottled water will be about 57.3 gallons per person in 2017, according to the model.

4. To begin, we substitute 60 for $M(t)$ in the equation of M:

$$60 = \frac{21t^2 + 42t + 2250}{0.0068t^2 + 2.58t + 251.4}$$

$$(0.0068t^2 + 2.58t + 251.4) \cdot 60 = (0.0068t^2 + 2.58t + 251.4) \cdot \frac{21t^2 + 42t + 2250}{0.0068t^2 + 2.58t + 251.4}$$

$$0.408t^2 + 154.8t + 15,084 = 21t^2 + 42t + 2250$$

$$0 = 20.592t^2 - 112.8t - 12,834$$

Now we substitute $a = 20.592$, $b = -112.8$, and $c = -12,834$ in the quadratic formula and solve for t:

$$t = \frac{-(-112.8) \pm \sqrt{(-112.8)^2 - 4(20.592)(-12,834)}}{2(20.592)}$$ *Substitute into quadratic formula.*

$$t \approx -22.38 \quad \text{or} \quad t \approx 27.85$$ *Compute.*

We verify the results by entering $y = \dfrac{21t^2 + 42t + 2250}{0.0068t^2 + 2.58t + 251.4}$ in a graphing calculator and checking that the inputs -22.38 and 27.85 lead to outputs of about 60 (see Fig. 30).

The inputs -22.38 and 27.85 represent the years 1968 and 2018, respectively. The 1968 estimate indicates model breakdown: Research would show that the annual mean consumption of bottled water in 1968 was much less than 60 gallons per person. Therefore, we predict it will be 2018 when the annual mean consumption of bottled water reaches 60 gallons per person.

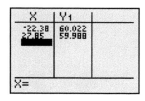

Figure 30 Verify the work

Modeling the Percentage of a Quantity

In Sections 8.1 and 8.5, we modeled the percentage of a quantity. In Example 3, we will first find a sum function that will help us find another function that describes the percentage of a quantity.

Table 13 Numbers of Broadband Cable and DSL and Fiber Optic Subscribers

	Number of Subscribers (millions)	
Year	Broadband Cable	DSL and Fiber Optic
2003	13	6
2005	22	13
2007	32	22
2009	40	27
2011	44	31

Source: *Kagan*

Table 14 Numbers of Households

Year	Number of Households (millions)
1995	99.0
1997	101.0
1999	103.6
2001	108.2
2003	111.3
2005	111.3
2007	116.0
2009	117.2
2010	117.5

Source: *U.S. Census Bureau*

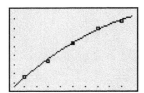

Figure 33 Broadband cable model

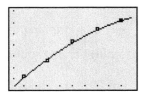

Figure 34 DSL and fiber optic model

▶ **Example 3**   Modeling the Percentage of a Quantity

The numbers of broadband cable subscribers and the numbers of DSL and fiber optic subscribers in the United States are shown in Table 13 for various years. Let $B(t)$ be the number of broadband cable subscribers and $D(t)$ be the number of DSL and fiber optic subscribers, both in millions, at t years since 1990.

1. Find equations of B and D.
2. Find an equation of the sum function $B + D$. What do the inputs and outputs of $B + D$ mean in this situation?
3. The numbers of U.S. households are shown in Table 14 for various years. A reasonable model is $H(t) = 1.3t + 92.7$, where $H(t)$ is the total number (in millions) of U.S. households at t years since 1990. Let $P(t)$ be the percentage of U.S. households that are broadband cable, DSL, or fiber optic subscribers. Find an equation of P. Assume no household subscribes to both services.
4. Find t when $P(t) = 68$. What does it mean in this situation?

Solution

1. Scattergrams of the data suggest we use a quadratic function to model both the number of broadband cable subscribers and the number of DSL and fiber optic subscribers (see Figs. 31 and 32). The quadratic regression equation of B and the quadratic regression equation of D are, respectively,

$$B(t) = -0.214t^2 + 11.29t - 98$$
$$D(t) = -0.179t^2 + 9.27t - 85$$

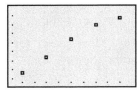

Figure 31 Broadband cable scattergram

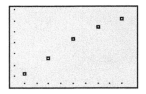

Figure 32 DSL and fiber optic scattergram

The models fit the points in the scattergrams of the two data sets quite well (see Figs. 33 and 34).

2. $(B + D)(t) = B(t) + D(t)$ *Definition of sum function*

      $= (-0.214t^2 + 11.29t - 98)$

       $+ (-0.179t^2 + 9.27t - 85)$ *Substitute.*

      $= -0.393t^2 + 20.56t - 183$ *Combine like terms.*

The inputs of $B + D$ are the numbers of years since 1990, and the outputs are the total numbers of subscribers (in millions).

3. To find the percentage of households that subscribe, we divide the total number of subscribers by the number of households and multiply the result by 100:

$$P(t) = \frac{(B + D)(t)}{H(t)} \cdot 100 \qquad \text{\textit{Percent formula: } } p = \frac{m}{n} \cdot 100$$

$$= \frac{-0.393t^2 + 20.56t - 183}{1.3t + 92.7} \cdot \frac{100}{1} \qquad \begin{array}{l}\textit{Substitute } -0.393t^2 + 20.56t - 183 \textit{ for}\\ (B + D)(t) \textit{ and } 1.3t + 92.7 \textit{ for } H(t).\end{array}$$

$$= \frac{-39.3t^2 + 2056t - 18{,}300}{1.3t + 92.7} \qquad \begin{array}{l}\textit{Multiply numerators;}\\ \textit{multiply denominators.}\end{array}$$

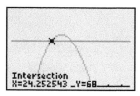

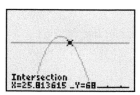

Figure 35 Verify the work

4. We substitute 68 for $P(t)$ in the equation of P:

$$68 = \frac{-39.3t^2 + 2056t - 18,300}{1.3t + 92.7}$$

$$(1.3t + 92.7) \cdot 68 = (1.3t + 92.7) \cdot \frac{-39.3t^2 + 2056t - 18,300}{1.3t + 92.7}$$

$$88.4t + 6303.6 = -39.3t^2 + 2056t - 18,300$$

$$39.3t^2 - 1967.6t + 24,603.6 = 0$$

Now we substitute $a = 39.3$, $b = -1967.6$, and $c = 24,603.6$ in the quadratic formula:

$$t = \frac{-(-1967.6) \pm \sqrt{(-1967.6)^2 - 4(39.3)(24,603.6)}}{2(39.3)} \quad \text{\textit{Substitute into quadratic formula.}}$$

$$t \approx 24.25 \quad \text{or} \quad t \approx 25.81 \quad\quad \text{\textit{Compute.}}$$

To verify the results, we can enter the equations $y = \dfrac{-39.3t^2 + 2056t - 18,300}{1.3t + 92.7}$ and $y = 68$ and use "intersect" to find the intersection points, which are approximately $(24.25, 68)$ and $(25.81, 68)$. See Fig. 35.

The t-coordinates 24.25 and 25.81 represent the years 2014 and 2016, respectively. The 2016 prediction most likely indicates model breakdown: It is unlikely the percentage will decline and return to the 2014 level (see Fig. 35). Therefore, we predict 68% of households will be broadband cable, DSL, or fiber optic subscribers in 2014.

Distance-Speed-Time Applications

How do we model the distance traveled by an object moving at a constant speed? For instance, if a car is driven at 50 mph for 2 hours, it will travel 50 miles in the first hour and 50 miles in the second hour, for a total distance of $50 \cdot 2 = 100$ miles. If a car is driven at 60 miles per hour for 3 hours, it will travel $60 \cdot 3 = 180$ miles.

In general, the (constant) speed of a car multiplied by the amount of time the car is in motion gives the distance traveled.

▶ Distance-Speed-Time Relationship

If an object is moving at a constant speed s for an amount of time t, then the distance d traveled is given by

$$d = st$$

and the time t is given by

$$t = \frac{d}{s}$$

▶ Example 4 Distance-Speed-Time Relationship

A person plans to drive a steady 55 mph on an 80-mile trip. Compute the driving time.

Solution

Since the person is traveling at a constant speed, we use the equation

$$t = \frac{d}{s}$$

We substitute 80 for d and 55 for s in the equation:

$$t = \frac{80}{55} \approx 1.45$$

So, the driving time will be about 1.5 hours.

▶ **Example 5**   Modeling Driving Time

A student at Seattle Central Community College plans to drive from Seattle, Washington, to Eugene, Oregon. The speed limit is 70 mph in Washington and 65 mph in Oregon. She will drive 164 miles in Washington, then 121 miles in Oregon.

1. If the student drives steadily at the speed limits, compute the driving time.
2. If the student exceeds the speed limits, let $T(a)$ be the driving time (in hours) at a mph above the speed limits. Find an equation of T.
3. Find $T(0)$. Compare this result with the result in Problem 1.
4. If the student drives 5 mph over the speed limits, compute the driving time.
5. If the student wants the driving time to be 4 hours, how much over the speed limits would she have to drive?

Solution

1. Since the student drives at a constant speed in Washington, we can use the equation $t = \dfrac{d}{s}$ to compute the time (in hours) spent driving in Washington:

$$t = \frac{\text{distance in Washington}}{\text{speed in Washington}}$$

$$= \frac{164}{70}$$

We can also compute the time (in hours) spent driving in Oregon:

$$t = \frac{\text{distance in Oregon}}{\text{speed in Oregon}}$$

$$= \frac{121}{65}$$

The total driving time is the sum of our two computed times:

$$\frac{164}{70} + \frac{121}{65} \approx 4.2 \text{ hours}$$

2. If the student drives, say, 5 mph over the speed limits, then she will drive $5 + 70 = 75$ mph in Washington and $5 + 65 = 70$ mph in Oregon. If she drives a miles per hour over the speed limits, she will drive $(a + 70)$ mph in Washington and $(a + 65)$ mph in Oregon. We use these expressions for speeds to find an equation of T:

$$T(a) = \frac{\text{distance in Washington}}{\text{speed in Washington}} + \frac{\text{distance in Oregon}}{\text{speed in Oregon}}$$

$$= \frac{164}{a + 70} + \frac{121}{a + 65}$$

3. $T(0) = \dfrac{164}{0 + 70} + \dfrac{121}{0 + 65} \approx 4.2$

The driving time will be about 4.2 hours if the student drives at the speed limits. We found the same result in Problem 1.

4. If the student drives 5 mph over the speed limits, then $a = 5$:

$$T(5) = \frac{164}{5 + 70} + \frac{121}{5 + 65} \approx 3.9$$

The driving time will be about 3.9 hours.

5. If the trip is to take 4 hours, then $T(a) = 4$:

$$4 = \frac{164}{a + 70} + \frac{121}{a + 65}$$

$$(a + 65)(a + 70) \cdot 4 = (a + 65)(a + 70) \cdot \left(\frac{164}{a + 70} + \frac{121}{a + 65} \right)$$

$$(a^2 + 135a + 4550) \cdot 4 = (a + 65)(a + 70) \cdot \frac{164}{a + 70} + (a + 65)(a + 70) \cdot \frac{121}{a + 65}$$

$$4a^2 + 540a + 18{,}200 = (a + 65) \cdot 164 + (a + 70) \cdot 121$$

$$4a^2 + 540a + 18{,}200 = 164a + 10{,}660 + 121a + 8470$$

$$4a^2 + 540a + 18{,}200 = 285a + 19{,}130$$

$$4a^2 + 255a - 930 = 0$$

$$a = \frac{-255 \pm \sqrt{255^2 - 4(4)(-930)}}{2(4)}$$

$$a \approx -67.2 \quad \text{or} \quad a \approx 3.5$$

The value $a = -67.2$ represents driving under the speed limits by 67.2 mph—model breakdown has occurred. So, the student would have to drive about 3.5 mph over the speed limits for the driving time to be 4 hours.

▶

Group Exploration

Looking ahead: Inverse variation

Suppose you intend to drive 100 miles. Let $f(s)$ be the time (in hours) it will take you to drive 100 miles if you drive at a constant speed of s miles per hour.

1. Find an equation of f.

2. Find $f(50)$, $f(55)$, $f(60)$, and $f(70)$. What do your results mean in this situation?

3. Consider completing the 100-mile trip several times, each time at a higher constant speed than the last. What happens to the travel time as the speed gets extremely high? Use a graphing calculator table and graph to

verify your answer. (Recall from Section 4.3 that when a function behaves like this, we say the horizontal axis is a *horizontal asymptote* of the graph of the function.)

4. Consider completing the 100-mile trip several times, each time at a *lower* constant speed than the last. What happens to the travel time as the speed gets extremely close to 0? Use a graphing calculator table and graph to verify your answer.

5. Does the graph of f have a vertical asymptote? If so, what is it? How does your answer relate to Problem 4?

Homework 8.6

For extra help ▶ **MyMathLab®** ▦ Watch the videos in MyMathLab ● Download the MyDashboard App

1. The ski club at a community college plans to spend $1250 to charter a bus for a ski trip. The cost will be split evenly among the students who sign up for the trip. Each student will also pay $350 for food, lodging, and ski lift tickets.
  a. Let $C(n)$ be the total cost (in dollars) for n students going on the trip. Find an equation of C.
  b. Let $M(n)$ be the mean cost per student (in dollars per student) if n students go on the trip. Find an equation of M.
  c. What is the mean cost per student if 30 students go?
  d. The ski trip will be cancelled unless the mean cost per student is $400 or less. What is the minimum number of students needed to go on the trip?

2. Manhattan is one of the most densely populated regions in the United States. This borough consists of 660,700,000 square feet of land. Let $f(P)$ be the number of square feet of Manhattan each resident would own if Manhattan were divided equally among its P residents.
  a. Find an equation of f.
  b. Use f to estimate the amount of land per Manhattanite if 1.6 million people live in Manhattan.
  c. If the land in the United States were divided equally among U.S. residents, each resident would own about 437,000 square feet of land. How many people could live in Manhattan if each resident owned 437,000 square feet

of Manhattan? Compare your answer with the number of people given in part (b).

3. For a five-year high school reunion, graduates rent out a restaurant that charges a flat fee of $500 for a band, plus $50 per person for food and two drinks.

   a. Let $T(n)$ be the total cost (in dollars) for n people to attend the reunion. Find an equation of T.

   b. Let $M(n)$ be the mean cost per person (in dollars per person) if n people attend the reunion. Find an equation of M.

   c. Find $M(270)$. What does it mean in this situation?

   d. Find n when $M(n) = 60$. What does it mean in this situation?

   e. Complete Table 15 by using a graphing calculator table.

Table 15 Mean Cost per Person for the Reunion

Number of People n	Mean Cost per Person $M(n)$
100	
200	
300	
400	
500	

   f. What do the values of $M(n)$ get close to as the values of n get very large? What does the result mean in this situation?

4. A student agrees to throw a party, provided that each guest shares the expenses equally with him. A four-person local band will play for $200 and free drinks and snacks. The student estimates the mean cost of drinks and snacks will be $3 per person.

   a. Suppose n people (including the host and band members) attend the party. Let $C(n)$ be the party's total cost (in dollars). Find an equation of C.

   b. Let $P(n)$ be the equal share of expenses (in dollars) each guest and host contributes. Find an equation of P. [**Hint:** Recall that band members get free drinks and snacks.]

   c. If the host and guests are willing to pay at most $5 each, how many guests must attend to cover expenses?

   d. What do the values of $P(n)$ get close to as the values of n get very large? What does the result mean in this situation?

   e. If the host and guests are willing to pay only $2 each, how many guests must attend to cover expenses? Explain why this makes sense.

5. Leasing expenses, equipment maintenance, salaries, electricity, and marketing cost a car manufacturer an average of $90,000 per day to produce a certain type of car. Materials, invoices, and shipping cost the manufacturer an average of $7000 per car.

   a. Suppose the car manufacturer produces and sells n cars of that type per day. Let $C(n)$ be the total daily cost (in dollars). Find an equation of C.

   b. Suppose the car manufacturer produces and sells n cars of that type per day. Let $B(n)$ be the amount (in dollars) the manufacturer should charge per car to break even by selling n cars. Find an equation of B.

   c. Suppose the car manufacturer produces and sells n cars of that type per day. Let $P(n)$ be the amount (in dollars) the manufacturer should charge per car to make a profit of $2000 per car. Find an equation of P. [**Hint:** Build on your equation from part (b) to find an equation of P.]

   d. Find $P(40)$. What does it mean in this situation?

   e. What do the values of $P(n)$ get close to as the values of n get very large? What does that mean in this situation?

6. In Example 1 of this section, we found the rational function

$$P = f(n) = \frac{2.50n + 1800}{n}$$

where $f(n)$ models the price (in dollars) the band Melted Zipper should set for its CD to break even by making and selling n CDs. [**Note:** We use different notation than in Example 1. Here we use f for the name of the function and P for the name of the dependent variable.]

   a. If Melted Zipper sets the CD's price at $7, how many CDs must be made and sold for the band to break even?

   b. Find an equation of f^{-1}. [**Hint:** Perform steps similar to those in part (a), but do not substitute a value for P. After a couple of steps, factor out n on one side of the equation.]

   c. Find $f^{-1}(7)$. Compare this result with that in part (a).

7. The total income of all U.S. households and the numbers of U.S. households are shown in Table 16 for various years.

Table 16 Total Annual Income of All Households; Numbers of Households

Year	Total Annual Income of All Households (billions of dollars)	Number of Households (billions)
1995	6201	0.0990
1997	6937	0.1010
1999	7787	0.1036
2001	8685	0.1082
2003	9164	0.1113
2005	10,486	0.1133
2007	11,912	0.1160
2009	12,175	0.1172
2010	12,547	0.1175

Source: *U.S. Census Bureau*

   a. Let $I(t)$ be the total annual income (in billions of dollars) of all households at t years since 1990. Find an equation of I.

   b. In Example 3 of this section, we modeled the number of U.S. households. A reasonable model is $H(t) = 0.0013t + 0.093$, where $H(t)$ is the number (in billions) of U.S. households at t years since 1990. Let $M(t)$ be the mean annual income per household (in dollars per household) at t years since 1990. Find an equation of M.

c. Perform a unit analysis of your equation of *M*.

d. Predict when the mean annual income per household will be $125,000.

e. Use the window settings in Fig. 36 to graph *M*. Is *M* increasing, decreasing, or neither for values of *t* between 5 and 30? What does that mean in this situation?

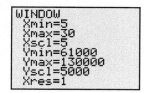

Figure 36 Window settings for Exercise 7e

8. Fuel consumption (in millions of gallons) by vehicles in the United States is listed in Table 17 for various years.

Table 17 Vehicle Fuel Consumption

Year	Amount of Fuel Consumed (millions of gallons)
1975	108,900
1980	115,000
1985	121,300
1990	130,800
1995	143,800
2000	162,600
2005	174,800
2010	169,700

Source: *Federal Highway Administration*

a. Let *F*(*t*) be the total amount of fuel (in millions of gallons) used during the year that is *t* years since 1970. Find a regression equation of *F*.

b. In Exercise 7 of Homework 7.7, you modeled the U.S. population. A good model is $U(t) = 0.0068t^2 + 2.31t + 202.61$, where $U(t)$ is the U.S. population (in millions) at *t* years since 1970. Let $M(t)$ be the mean amount of fuel used per person (in gallons per person) during the year that is *t* years since 1970. Find an equation of *M*.

c. Find *t* when $M(t) = 591$. What does it mean in this situation?

d. Use the window settings in Fig. 37 to graph *M*. Is *M* increasing; decreasing; or neither for values of *t* between −5 and 50? What does that mean in this situation?

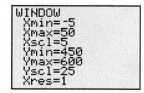

Figure 37 Per-person fuel consumption

e. Let $P(t)$ be the average price (in dollars per gallon) of gasoline at *t* years since 1970 (see Table 18). The quadratic regression model is $P(t) = 0.0036t^2 − 0.12t + 1.79$. Find $(P \cdot M)(48)$. What does it mean in this situation?

Table 18 Average Prices of Gasoline

Year	Price (dollars per gallon)
1995	1.21
1997	1.29
1999	1.22
2001	1.53
2003	1.64
2005	2.34
2007	2.85
2009	2.40
2010	2.84

Source: *Department of Energy*

f. Is $M(t)$ an underestimate or an overestimate of the mean amount of fuel used per *driver*? Explain.

9. Textbook revenues are shown in Table 19 for various years.

Table 19 Textbook Revenues

Year	Revenue (millions of dollars)
2004	9198
2005	9977
2006	10,126
2007	10,697
2008	11,162

Source: *U.S. Census Bureau*

a. Let $R(t)$ be the annual revenue (in millions of dollars) from textbooks at *t* years since 1990. Find a linear equation of *R*.

b. In Exercise 70 of Homework 8.1, you found an equation close to $E(t) = 0.026t^2 − 0.2t + 14.61$, where $E(t)$ is the college enrollment (in millions) at *t* years since 1990 (see Table 20). Let $A(t)$ be the mean amount of money spent on textbooks per student (in dollars per student) during the year that is *t* years since 1990. Find an equation of *A*.

Table 20 College Enrollments

Year	Enrollment (millions)
1995	14.2
2000	15.3
2005	17.5
2008	19.1
2010	21.2

Source: *U.S. Census Bureau*

c. Predict the mean amount of money per student that will be spent on textbooks in 2018.

d. During which year will the mean amount of money students spend on textbooks be $525 per student?

10. The numbers of colleges are shown in Table 21 for various years.

a. Let $N(t)$ be the total number (in thousands) of colleges at *t* years since 1980. Find a linear equation of *N*.

Table 21 Number of Colleges

Year	Number of Colleges (thousands)
1980	3.231
1985	3.340
1990	3.559
1995	3.706
2000	4.182
2005	4.276
2010	4.495

Source: *National Center for Education Statistics*

  b. College enrollment (in *thousands*), $E(t)$, can be modeled by the equation $E(t) = 26t^2 - 726t + 19{,}257$, where t is the number of years since 1980 (see Table 20). Let $M(t)$ be the mean enrollment per college at t years since 1980. Find an equation of M.

  c. Predict when the mean enrollment will be 5800 students per college.

  d. Use the window settings shown in Fig. 38 to graph M. Then use "minimum" on a graphing calculator to find when the mean enrollment was the lowest. What was that enrollment?

```
WINDOW
 Xmin=0
 Xmax=40
 Xscl=5
 Ymin=3000
 Ymax=7000
 Yscl=500
 Xres=1
```

Figure 38 Window settings for Exercise 10d

11. The numbers of morning daily newspapers and evening daily newspapers are shown in Table 22 for various years.

Table 22 Numbers of Morning Dailies and Evening Dailies

Year	Morning	Evening
	Number of Daily Newspapers	
1980	387	1388
1985	482	1220
1990	559	1084
1995	656	891
2000	766	727
2005	817	645
2009	869	528

Source: *Editor & Publisher Co.*

  a. Let $M(t)$ be the number of morning daily newspapers and $E(t)$ be the number of evening daily newspapers, both at t years since 1980. Find linear equations of M and E.

  b. Find an equation of the sum function $M + E$. What do the inputs and outputs of $M + E$ mean in this situation?

  c. Let $P(t)$ be the percentage of newspapers that are morning dailies at t years since 1980. Find an equation of P.

  d. Find $P(36)$. What does it mean in this situation?

  e. Find t when $P(t) = 80$. What does it mean in this situation?

12. The numbers of women and men who live alone are shown in Table 23 for various years.

Table 23 Numbers of Women and Men Who Live Alone

Year	Number Living Alone (millions)	
	Women	Men
1980	11.3	7.0
1985	12.7	7.9
1990	14.0	9.0
1995	14.6	10.1
2000	15.6	11.2
2005	17.3	12.8
2010	17.4	14.0

Source: *U.S. Census Bureau*

  a. Let $W(t)$ be the number of women who live alone and $M(t)$ be the number of men who live alone, both in millions, at t years since 1980. Find linear equations of W and M.

  b. Find an equation of the sum function $W + M$. What do the inputs and outputs of $W + M$ mean in this situation?

  c. Let $P(t)$ be the percentage of people living alone who are women at t years since 1980. Find an equation of P.

  d. Predict in which year 55% of people who live alone will be women.

  e. Use the window settings shown in Fig. 39 to graph P. Is P increasing, decreasing, or neither for values of t between 0 and 40? How is this possible, given that the number of women who live alone has been increasing since 1980?

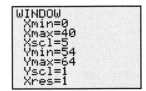

```
WINDOW
 Xmin=0
 Xmax=40
 Xscl=5
 Ymin=54
 Ymax=64
 Yscl=1
 Xres=1
```

Figure 39 Window settings for Exercise 12e

13. The numbers of U.S. women and men who earned a bachelor's degree are listed in Table 24 for various years.

Table 24 Women and Men Who Earned a Bachelor's Degree

Year	Number of People Who Earned a Bachelor's Degree (thousands)	
	Women	Men
1980	456	474
1985	497	483
1990	560	492
1995	634	526
2000	708	530
2005	826	613
2009	916	685

Source: *National Center for Education Statistics*

a. Let $W(t)$ be the number of women and $M(t)$ be the number of men, both in thousands, who earned a bachelor's degree in the year that is t years since 1980. Find quadratic equations of W and M.

b. Find an equation of the sum function $W + M$. What do the inputs and outputs of $W + M$ mean in this situation?

c. Among people who earned a bachelor's degree at t years since 1980, let $P(t)$ be the percentage who are men. Find an equation of P.

d. Estimate in which year 42.1% of people who earn a bachelor's degree will be men.

e. Use the window settings shown in Fig. 40 to graph P. Is P increasing, decreasing, or neither for values of t between 0 and 35? How is this possible, given that the number of bachelor's degrees earned by men has been increasing since 1980?

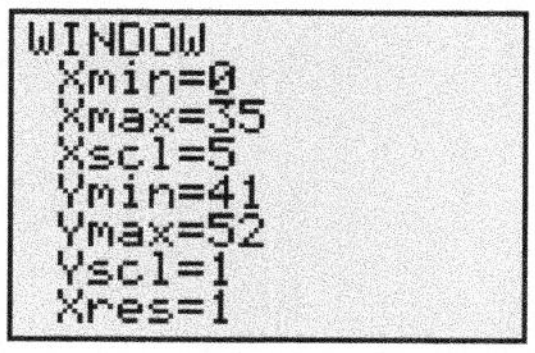

```
WINDOW
 Xmin=0
 Xmax=35
 Xscl=5
 Ymin=41
 Ymax=52
 Yscl=1
 Xres=1
```

Figure 40 Window settings for Exercise 13e

14. In Exercise 48 of Homework 3.5, you found the system

$$W(t) = -0.53t + 62.09$$
$$L(t) = 0.24t - 10.35$$

where $W(t)$ is the annual consumption of whole milk and $L(t)$ is the annual consumption of lower fat and skim milk, both in gallons per person, at t years since 1900 (see Table 25).

Table 25 Annual U.S. Per-Person Consumptions of Whole Milk, Lower Fat and Skim Milk

	Annual Consumption (gallons per person)	
Year	Whole Milk	Lower Fat and Skim Milk
1955	33.5	2.9
1965	28.8	3.7
1975	21.7	8.1
1985	14.3	12.3
1995	8.6	15.3
2005	7.0	14.1
2010	5.6	14.8

Source: *USDA/Economic Research Service*

a. Find an equation of the sum function $W + L$. What do the inputs and outputs of $W + L$ mean in this situation?

b. Let $P(t)$ be the percentage of milk consumed that is whole milk in the year that is t years since 1900. Find an equation of P.

c. Predict the percentage of milk consumed in 2016 that will be whole milk.

d. Predict in which year 6% of the milk consumed will be whole milk.

15. A person drives 60 mph for 85 miles. Compute the driving time.

16. A person drives at a constant speed for 100 miles in 1.7 hours. What is that speed?

17. A student plans to drive from Cuyahoga Community College in Cleveland, Ohio, to Pittsburgh, Pennsylvania. He will drive 85 miles in Ohio, then 53 miles in Pennsylvania. The speed limit is 70 mph in Ohio and 65 mph in Pennsylvania.

a. Let $T(a)$ be the driving time (in hours) if the student drives a mph above the speed limits. Find an equation of T.

b. If he drives 5 mph over the speed limits, compute the driving time.

c. By how much would he have to exceed the speed limits for the driving time to be 1.8 hours? Verify your answer by using a graphing calculator table.

18. A student plans to drive from Oklahoma City, Oklahoma, to Little Rock, Arkansas. She will drive 183 miles in Oklahoma, then 161 miles in Arkansas. The speed limit is 75 mph in Oklahoma and 70 mph in Arkansas.

a. Let $T(a)$ be the driving time (in hours) if the student drives a mph above the speed limits. Find an equation of T.

b. If she drives 5 mph over the speed limits, compute the driving time.

c. By how much would she have to exceed the speed limits for the driving time to be 4 hours? Verify your answer by using a graphing calculator table.

19. A student plans to drive from Ivy Tech Community College in Indianapolis, Indiana, to the University of Illinois in Champaign–Urbana, Illinois. She will drive 83 miles in Indiana, then 37 miles in Illinois. The speed limit is 70 mph in Indiana and 65 mph in Illinois.

a. Let $T(a)$ be the driving time (in hours) if the student drives a mph above the speed limits. Find an equation of T.

b. Find $T(0)$ and $T(10)$. What do they mean in this situation?

c. Find $T(0) - T(10)$. What does it mean in this situation?

d. Find a when $T(a) = 1.6$. What does it mean in this situation?

20. A student plans to drive from Madison Area Technical College in Madison, Wisconsin, to Fergus Falls, Minnesota. He will drive 204 miles in Wisconsin, then 240 miles in Minnesota. The speed limit is 65 mph in Wisconsin and 70 mph in Minnesota.

a. Let $T(a)$ be the driving time (in hours) if the student drives a mph above the speed limits. Find an equation of T.

b. Find $T(0)$ and $T(5)$. What do they mean in this situation?

c. Find $T(0) - T(5)$. What does it mean in this situation?

d. Find a when $T(a) = 6$. What does it mean in this situation?

21. In Example 5 of this section, we found the equation

$$T(a) = \frac{164}{a + 70} + \frac{121}{a + 65}$$

where $T(a)$ is the driving time (in hours) for a student to drive from Seattle, Washington, to Eugene, Oregon, at a mph above the speed limits.

a. Perform the addition on the right side of the equation of T.

b. Use your result in part (a) to find the driving time if the student drives 10 mph over the speed limits.

Concepts

22. If a person is traveling at 0 miles per hour, how long will it take the person to travel 5 miles? Explain why this suggests we cannot divide by 0 by referring to the formula $t = \dfrac{d}{s}$, where t is the number of hours it takes to travel d miles at s miles per hour.

23. a. Describe a situation where the mean salary of a group of people estimates the salaries of the people well.

b. Describe a situation where the mean salary of a group of people does not estimate the salaries of the people well.

24. Describe how to use two or more models to form a function that models the mean of a quantity. Compare this process with using two or more models to form a function that models the percentage of a quantity. For both types of modeling, give an example that is different from those in this textbook.

Related Review

25. The risk of having shingles (a painful rash related to chicken pox) increases with age (see Table 26). Let $f(t)$ be the percentage of Americans who have shingles at age t years.

Table 26 Percentages of Americans Who Have Shingles

Age (years)	Percent
10	0.5
20	1.3
30	2.7
40	4.8
50	7.5
60	11.9
70	19.7
80	31.8
90	46.1

Source: *J. C. Donahue et al.*, Archives of Internal Medicine, *1995*

a. Find a linear equation, an exponential equation, and a quadratic equation of f. Compare how well the models fit the data.

b. For ages less than 23 years, explain why there is model breakdown for both the linear model and the quadratic model. How well does the exponential model fit the data for these ages?

c. Use the exponential model to estimate at what age 25% of Americans have shingles.

d. What is the base b of the exponential model $f(t) = ab^t$? What does it mean in this situation?

e. A study showed that a new vaccine can reduce the number of shingles cases by 51%. If the vaccine is approved and all 85-year-old Americans receive it, use the exponential model to predict the percentage of 85-year-old Americans who will have shingles.

26. World land speed records are shown in Table 27 for various years.

Table 27 Land Speed Records

Year	Record (mph)
1904	91
1914	124
1927	175
1935	301
1947	394
1960	407
1970	622
1983	633
1997	763

Source: *Fédération Internationale de l'Automobile*

Let $r = f(t)$ be the land speed record (in miles per hour) at t years since 1900.

a. Use a graphing calculator to draw a scattergram of the data. Which type of function would best model the data—linear, exponential, or quadratic? Explain.

b. Find an equation of a linear model to describe the data.

c. What is the slope? What does it mean in this situation?

d. The speed of sound is about 748 mph. Use the model you found in part (b) to estimate when a car first broke the sound barrier (i.e., exceeded 748 mph). For which year(s) shown in Table 27 did a car actually break the barrier?

e. Find an equation of f^{-1}.

f. Find $f^{-1}(1000)$. What does it mean in this situation?

Expressions, Equations, Functions, and Graphs

Perform the indicated instruction. Then use words such as linear, quadratic, cubic, exponential, logarithmic, rational, polynomial, degree, function, one variable, *and* two variables *to describe the expression, equation, or system.*

27. Factor $75x^3 - 50x^2 - 12x + 8$.

28. Solve $2x^2 + 12x + 13 = 0$.

29. Solve $75x^3 - 50x^2 = 12x - 8$.

30. Find the vertex of the graph of $f(x) = 2x^2 + 12x + 13$.

31. Find the product $(x^2 + 2x - 3)(3x^2 - x - 4)$.

32. Graph $f(x) = 2x^2 + 12x + 13$ by hand.

▼ 8.7 Variation

Objectives

» Know the meaning of *direct variation* and *inverse variation*.

» In direct variation and inverse variation, know how a change in the independent variable affects the value of the dependent variable.

» Use a single point to find a *direct variation equation* or an *inverse variation equation*.

» Use direct variation models and inverse variation models to make estimates.

» Use ratios to find a direct variation constant, and use products to find an inverse variation constant.

Table 28 Drop and Bounce Heights of a Golf Ball

Drop Height (inches)	Bounce Height (inches)
6	4.8
12	10.0
18	15.0
24	20.3
30	26.4
36	31.0
42	37.5
48	44.5
54	47.3
60	52.0

Source: *J. Lehmann*

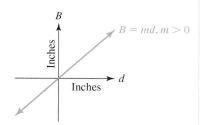

Figure 44 The graph of $B = md$ with $m > 0$

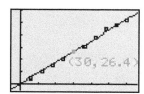

Figure 45 A line that contains the origin and the data point (30, 26.4)

In this section, we will discuss two simple, yet important, types of equations in two variables: *direct variation equations* and *inverse variation equations*.

Direct Variation

In Example 1, we model a situation by using a direct variation equation.

▶ **Example 1** Using a Direct Variation Equation to Model Data

A golf ball is dropped from various heights, and the bounce height is recorded each time (see Table 28). Let B be the bounce height (in inches) of the golf ball after it was dropped from an initial height of d inches. Find an equation of a function that models the situation well.

Solution

We begin by drawing a scattergram of the data (see Fig. 41). It appears the variables d and B are approximately linearly related. The linear regression equation is

$$B = 0.90d - 0.77$$

Although this model fits the data very well (see Fig. 42), it estimates that very small drop heights will have *negative* bounce heights (see Fig. 43). Model breakdown has occurred. Also, as the drop heights get closer to 0 inches, the bounce heights should get close to 0 inches. However, the model estimates that as the drop heights get close to 0, the bounce heights will get close to -0.77 inch.

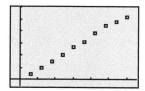

Figure 41 A scattergram of the data

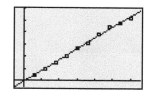

Figure 42 Regression line fits the data well

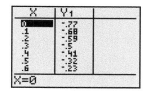

Figure 43 Regression line estimates negative bounce heights

It would be better to find a model of the form $B = md$, where $m > 0$ (see Fig. 44). Such a model estimates a *positive* bounce height for any drop height, including small ones. It also estimates that as drop heights get close to 0 inches, the bounce heights will get close to 0 inches.

If we imagine the line that contains the origin $(0, 0)$ and the data point $(30, 26.4)$, it appears the line might come close to the other data points (see Fig. 45). To find a slope m for the model $B = md$, we substitute the coordinates of the data point $(30, 26.4)$ into the equation $B = md$:

$$26.4 = m(30) \quad \text{\small Substitute 30 for d and 26.4 for B.}$$
$$\frac{26.4}{30} = m \quad \text{\small Divide both sides by 30.}$$
$$m = 0.88$$

The equation is $B = 0.88d$. The model fits the data quite well (see Fig. 45).

In Example 1, we found the model $B = 0.88d$. This equation is an example of a direct variation equation.

▶ **Definition** Direct variation

If $y = kx$ for some nonzero constant k, we say **y varies directly as x** or that **y is proportional to x.** We call k the **variation constant** or the **constant of proportionality.** The equation $y = kx$ is called a **direct variation equation.**

For $y = 5x$, we say y varies directly as x with variation constant 5. For $p = 2t$, we say p varies directly as t with variation constant 2.

Changes in Values for Direct Variation

The graph of a direct variation equation $y = kx$ is a line with slope k and y-intercept $(0, 0)$.

In Fig. 46, we sketch three such lines, where $k = \dfrac{1}{2}$, $k = 1$, and $k = 2$.

If k is positive (positive slope), then $y = kx$ is an increasing function. So, if the value of x increases, the value of y increases.

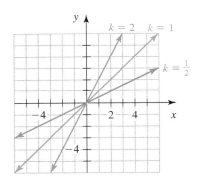

Figure 46 Graphs of $y = kx$,

where $k = \dfrac{1}{2}$, $k = 1$, and $k = 2$

Changes in Values of Variables for Direct Variation

Assume y varies directly as x with some positive variation constant k:

- If the value of x increases, then the value of y increases.
- If the value of x decreases, then the value of y decreases.

For example, consider the golf ball model $B = 0.88d$ in Example 1. As drop heights increase, so do the bounce heights. As drop heights decrease, so do the bounce heights.

Using One Point to Find a Direct Variation Equation

If one variable varies directly as another variable and we know one point that lies on the graph, we can find the variation constant k as well as the direct variation equation.

▶ Example 2   Finding a Direct Variation Equation

The variable y varies directly as x with positive variation constant k.
1. What happens to the value of y as the value of x increases?
2. If $y = 5$ when $x = 3$, find an equation for x and y.

Solution
1. Since y varies directly as x with positive variation constant k, the value of y must increase as the value of x increases.
2. The equation is of the form $y = kx$. We find the constant k by substituting 3 for x and 5 for y:

$$y = kx \qquad \text{\textit{y varies directly as x.}}$$
$$5 = k(3) \qquad \text{\textit{Substitute 3 for x and 5 for y.}}$$
$$\frac{5}{3} = k \qquad \text{\textit{Divide both sides by 3.}}$$

The equation is $y = \dfrac{5}{3}x$. We use a graphing calculator graph to check that the curve

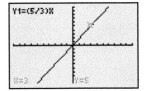

Figure 47 Verify the work

$y = \dfrac{5}{3}x$ contains the point $(3, 5)$. See Fig. 47.

▶ Example 3   Using a Direct Variation Equation

The variable w varies directly as t. If $w = 7$ when $t = 2$, find the value of t when $w = 9$.

Solution

Since w varies directly as t, we can describe the relationship between t and w by the equation $w = kt$. We find the constant k by substituting 2 for t and 7 for w:

$$w = kt \qquad \textit{w varies directly as t.}$$
$$7 = k(2) \qquad \textit{Substitute 2 for t and 7 for w.}$$
$$\frac{7}{2} = k \qquad \textit{Divide both sides by 2.}$$

The equation is $w = \frac{7}{2}t$. We find the value of t when $w = 9$ by substituting 9 for w in the equation $w = \frac{7}{2}t$ and solving for t:

$$9 = \frac{7}{2}t \qquad \textit{Substitute 9 for w.}$$
$$18 = 7t \qquad \textit{Multiply both sides by LCD, 2.}$$
$$\frac{18}{7} = t \qquad \textit{Divide both sides by 7.}$$

So, $t = \frac{18}{7}$ when $w = 9$.

In Example 1, we used the function $B = 0.88d$ to model bounce heights of a golf ball. In Exercise 46, you will show that the function $B = 0.80d$ reasonably models bounce heights of a racquetball. Since B varies directly as d for a golf ball and a racquetball, it is a reasonable conjecture that B varies directly as d for another type of ball similar in construction, such as another golf ball, another racquetball, or perhaps even a tennis ball.

▶ **Example 4**   Finding a Direct Variation Model

Assume the bounce height B (in inches) of a tennis ball varies directly as the drop height d (in inches). The bounce height of the tennis ball is 20 inches when the ball is dropped from an initial height of 30 inches.

1. Find an equation of B and d.
2. Estimate the bounce height if the drop height is 50 inches.

Solution

1. The equation is of the form $B = kd$. We substitute 30 for d and 20 for B to find the constant k:

$$20 = k(30) \qquad \textit{Substitute 30 for d and 20 for B.}$$
$$\frac{20}{30} = k \qquad \textit{Divide both sides by 30.}$$
$$k \approx 0.67$$

The equation is $B = 0.67d$.

2. We substitute 50 for d in the equation $B = 0.67d$:

$$B = 0.67(50) \qquad \textit{Substitute 50 for d.}$$
$$B = 33.5$$

The bounce height will be 33.5 inches, according to the model.

▶ **Finding and Using a Direct Variation Model**

Assume a quantity p varies directly as a quantity t. To make estimates about an authentic situation,

1. Substitute the values of a data point into the equation $p = kt$; then solve for k.
2. Substitute the value of k into the equation $p = kt$.
3. Use the equation from step 2 to make estimates of quantity t or p.

In Example 4, we did not run an experiment and perform the usual modeling steps to find the tennis ball model $B = 0.67d$. Instead, we assumed the model was of the form $B = kd$ because that is the form of our models of the golf ball and the racquetball. The tennis ball model may or may not be accurate. The only way to know for sure is to run an experiment.

Next, we take a closer look at the significance of $k = 0.88$ for the golf ball model $B = 0.88d$. This equation $B = 0.88d$ tells us the bounce height is equal to 88% of the drop height. We list the values of k and their meanings for the three balls we have investigated:

Type of Ball	Model	Value of k	Height of Bounce
Golf ball	$B = 0.88d$	0.88	88% of drop height
Racquetball	$B = 0.80d$	0.80	80% of drop height
Tennis ball	$B = 0.67d$	0.67	67% of drop height

The value of k takes into account how "bouncy" the ball is.

A Variable Varying Directly as an Expression

So far we have described functions in which the dependent variable varies directly as the independent *variable*. Now, for nonzero constant k, we list some examples of functions in which the dependent variable varies directly as an *expression*:

$$y = kx^2 \qquad \text{\textit{y varies directly as } } x^2.$$
$$p = k\sqrt{t} \qquad \text{\textit{p varies directly as } } \sqrt{t}.$$
$$F = k\log(r) \qquad \text{\textit{F varies directly as } } \log(r).$$

So, we use "varies directly" to mean the dependent variable is equal to a constant times an expression containing the independent variable.

Inverse Variation

In Sections 8.1, 8.5, and 8.6, we worked with rational equations in two variables. Now we will focus on a very simple type of rational equation in two variables: an inverse variation equation.

▶ **Definition   Inverse variation**

If $y = \dfrac{k}{x}$ for some nonzero constant k, we say **y varies inversely as x** or that **y is inversely proportional to x.** We call k the **variation constant** or the **constant of proportionality.** The equation $y = \dfrac{k}{x}$ is called an **inverse variation equation.**

For $y = \dfrac{5}{x}$, we say y varies inversely as x with variation constant 5. For $B = \dfrac{8}{v}$, we say B varies inversely as v with variation constant 8.

Changes in Values for Inverse Variation

In Fig. 48, we graph three equations of the form $y = \dfrac{k}{x}$, where $k = 1$, $k = 2$, and $k = 4$.

If k is positive, then the function $y = \dfrac{k}{x}$ is decreasing for positive values of x. So, if the value of x increases, the value of y decreases.

▶ **Changes in Values of Variables for Inverse Variation**

Assume y varies inversely as x with some positive variation constant k. For positive values of x,

• If the value of x increases, then the value of y decreases.
• If the value of x decreases, then the value of y increases.

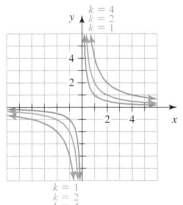

Figure 48 Graphs of $y = \dfrac{k}{x}$, where $k = 1$, $k = 2$, and $k = 4$

Use One Point to Find an Inverse Variation Equation

If one variable varies inversely as another variable and we know one point that lies on the graph, we can find the variation constant k as well as the inverse variation equation.

▶ **Example 5** Finding an Inverse Variation Equation

The variable y varies inversely as x with the positive variation constant k.

  1. For positive values of x, what happens to the value of y as the value of x increases?
  2. If $y = 4$ when $x = 2$, find an equation for x and y.

Solution

  1. Since y varies inversely as x with positive variation constant k, and since the values of x are positive, the value of y must decrease as the value of x increases.
  2. The equation is of the form $y = \dfrac{k}{x}$. We find the constant k by substituting 2 for x and 4 for y in the equation $y = \dfrac{k}{x}$:

$$y = \frac{k}{x} \quad \textit{y varies inversely as x.}$$

$$4 = \frac{k}{2} \quad \textit{Substitute 2 for x and 4 for y.}$$

$$8 = k \quad \textit{Multiply both sides by LCD, 2.}$$

The equation is $y = \dfrac{8}{x}$. We use a graphing calculator graph to check that the curve $y = \dfrac{8}{x}$ contains the point $(2, 4)$. See Fig. 49.

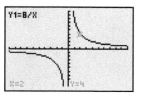

Figure 49 Verify the work

▶ **Example 6** Using an Inverse Variation Equation

The variable G varies inversely as r. If $G = 8$ when $r = 3$, find the value of r when $G = 4$.

Solution

Since G varies inversely as r, we can describe the relationship between r and G by the equation $G = \dfrac{k}{r}$. We find the constant k by substituting 3 for r and 8 for G:

$$G = \frac{k}{r} \quad \textit{G varies inversely as r.}$$

$$8 = \frac{k}{3} \quad \textit{Substitute 3 for r and 8 for G.}$$

$$24 = k \quad \textit{Multiply both sides by LCD, 3.}$$

The equation is $G = \dfrac{24}{r}$. We find the value of r when $G = 4$ by substituting 4 for G in the equation $G = \dfrac{24}{r}$ and then solving for r:

$$4 = \frac{24}{r} \quad \textit{Substitute 4 for G.}$$

$$4r = 24 \quad \textit{Multiply both sides by LCD, r.}$$

$$r = 6 \quad \textit{Divide both sides by 4.}$$

So, $r = 6$ when $G = 4$.

Table 29 Volumes and Pressures in a Syringe

Volume (cm³)	Pressure (atm)
3	2.23
4	1.76
5	1.46
6	1.23
7	1.05
8	0.93
9	0.83
10	0.74
11	0.67
12	0.60
13	0.56
14	0.52
15	0.48
16	0.44
17	0.42
18	0.39
19	0.37
20	0.35

Source: *J. Lehmann*

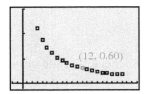

Figure 50 Scattergram of the data

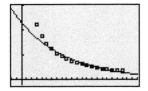

Figure 51 Exponential regression model

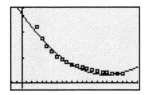

Figure 52 Quadratic regression model

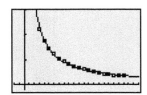

Figure 53 Inverse variation model

▶ **Example 7**   Finding an Inverse Variation Model

The more you squeeze a sealed syringe filled with air, the harder it gets to squeeze it farther. Some air volumes in cubic centimeters (cm³) and corresponding pressures in atmospheres (atm) in a sealed syringe are given in Table 29.

Let P be the pressure (in atm) in the syringe at air volume V (in cm³).

1. Find an equation for V and P.
2. As the value of V increases, what happens to the value of P, according to the model? What does that pattern mean in this situation?
3. Estimate at what volume the pressure will be 5 atm.

Solution

1. We draw a scattergram of the data in Fig. 50. Since the points suggest a curve that "bends," we will not use a linear function to model the data. To decide among an exponential function, a quadratic function, and an inverse variation function, we find equations of each.

   First, we find an inverse variation equation of the form $P = \dfrac{k}{V}$. If we imagine an inverse variation curve that contains the data point $(12, 0.60)$, it appears the curve might come close to the other data points (see Fig. 50). To find k, we substitute the data point $(12, 0.60)$ in the equation $P = \dfrac{k}{V}$:

   $$0.60 = \frac{k}{12} \quad \text{\textit{Substitute 12 for V and 0.60 for P.}}$$

   $$7.2 = k \quad \text{\textit{Multiply both sides by LCD, 12.}}$$

   The variation equation is $P = \dfrac{7.2}{V}$. Next, we use a graphing calculator to find the exponential regression equation and the quadratic regression equation:

   $$P = 2.32(0.90)^V \quad \text{\textit{Exponential regression equation}}$$
   $$P = 0.0086V^2 - 0.29V + 2.77 \quad \text{\textit{Quadratic regression equation}}$$
   $$P = \frac{7.2}{V} \quad \text{\textit{Inverse variation equation}}$$

   Now we see how well each model fits the data (see Figs. 51, 52, and 53). It appears the inverse variation model $P = \dfrac{7.2}{V}$ fits the data better than the other two models do.

2. The variable P varies inversely as V, according to our model. So, as the value of V increases, the value of P decreases. The larger the volume of air, the less the pressure will be.

3. We substitute 5 for P in the equation $P = \dfrac{7.2}{V}$ and solve for V:

   $$5 = \frac{7.2}{V} \quad \text{\textit{Substitute 5 for P.}}$$
   $$5V = 7.2 \quad \text{\textit{Multiply both sides by LCD, V.}}$$
   $$V = 1.44 \quad \text{\textit{Divide both sides by 5.}}$$

The pressure is 5 atm when the air volume is 1.44 cubic centimeters.

The equation $P = \dfrac{k}{V}$ is an excellent model for many situations, as long as the temperature and number of molecules in the container are constant. This equation is a form of **Boyle's law.** The constant k takes into account the temperature and the number of molecules.

▶ **Finding and Using an Inverse Variation Model**

Assume a quantity p varies inversely as a quantity t. To make estimates about an authentic situation,

1. Substitute the values of a data point into the equation $p = \dfrac{k}{t}$; then solve for k.

2. Substitute the value of k into the equation $p = \dfrac{k}{t}$.

3. Use the equation from step 2 to make estimates of quantity t or p.

A Variable Varying Inversely as an Expression

For nonzero constant k, we list some examples of functions in which the dependent variable varies inversely as an *expression*:

$$y = \frac{k}{x^3} \qquad \text{\textit{y varies inversely as } } x^3.$$

$$A = \frac{k}{r-5} \qquad \text{\textit{A varies inversely as } } r - 5.$$

$$w = \frac{k}{2^t} \qquad \text{\textit{w varies inversely as } } 2^t.$$

So, we use "varies inversely" to mean that the dependent variable is equal to a constant divided by an expression containing the independent variable.

▶ **Example 8** Finding an Inverse Variation Model

The weight of an object varies inversely as the square of its distance from the center of Earth. An astronaut weighs 180 pounds at sea level (about 4 thousand miles from Earth's center). How much does the astronaut weigh 2 thousand miles above Earth's surface?

Solution

We let w be the weight (in pounds) of the astronaut d thousand miles from the center of Earth. Our desired model has the form

$$w = \frac{k}{d^2}$$

The denominator of the fraction on the right-hand side is d^2, because weight varies inversely as the *square* of distance d.

Next, we substitute 4 for d and 180 for w in the equation $w = \dfrac{k}{d^2}$ and solve for k:

$$180 = \frac{k}{4^2} \qquad \text{\textit{Substitute 4 for d and 180 for w.}}$$

$$180 = \frac{k}{16} \qquad \text{\textit{4}}^2 = 16$$

$$2880 = k \qquad \text{\textit{Multiply both sides by LCD, 16.}}$$

The model is $w = \dfrac{2880}{d^2}$. We see from Fig. 54 that when the astronaut is 2 thousand miles above Earth's surface, the astronaut is $4 + 2 = 6$ thousand miles from the center of Earth.

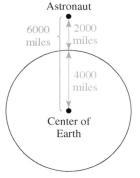

Figure 54 The astronaut is 6000 miles from Earth's center

To find w, we substitute 6 for d in the equation $w = \dfrac{2880}{d^2}$:

$$w = \frac{2880}{6^2} = 80$$

The astronaut weighs 80 pounds 2 thousand miles above Earth's surface.

Using Ratios and Products to Find Variation Constants

First, we will discuss another way to find a direct variation constant. Then we will discuss another way to find an inverse variation constant.

Using Ratios to Find a Direct Variation Constant

In Example 9, we use ratios to find a direct variation constant.

▶ **Example 9** Finding a Direct Variation Constant by Using Ratios

Use ratios of bounce heights and drop heights to find a model of the golf ball data shown in Example 1.

Solution

From our work in Example 1, we know we want an equation of the form $B = kd$. To find k, we begin by solving the equation $B = kd$ for k:

$$k = \frac{B}{d}$$

Next, we use the first two columns of Table 30 to calculate the approximate ratios $\dfrac{B}{d}$ for the third column.

Table 30 Ratios of Drop and Bounce Heights of a Golf Ball

Drop Height d (inches)	Bounce Height B (inches)	$\dfrac{B}{d}$
6	4.8	0.80
12	10.0	0.83
18	15.0	0.83
24	20.3	0.85
30	26.4	0.88
36	31.0	0.86
42	37.5	0.89
48	44.5	0.93
54	47.3	0.88
60	52.0	0.87

According to our model $B = kd$, the ratios $\dfrac{B}{d}$ should be equal to a constant k. The reason the ratios vary a bit is most likely due to errors in measuring the drop and bounce heights. Or there might be imperfections in the golf ball or the surface of the floor.

Next, we find the mean of the ratios $\dfrac{B}{d}$ in the third column:

$$\frac{0.80 + 0.83 + 0.83 + 0.85 + 0.88 + 0.86 + 0.89 + 0.93 + 0.88 + 0.87}{10} \approx 0.86$$

Finally, we substitute 0.86 for k in the equation $B = kd$:

$$B = 0.86d$$

The model fits the data reasonably well (see Fig. 55). However, it appears the model we found in Example 1 fits the data slightly better (see Fig. 56).

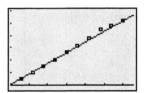

Figure 55 The model $B = 0.86d$

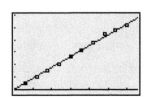

Figure 56 The model $B = 0.88d$

We now have two ways to find a direct variation model. The method shown in Example 1 requires few calculations, but finding a good value of k depends on a good selection of an ordered pair. The method shown in Example 9 requires more calculations, but it is not necessary to select an ordered pair to find k.

Using Products to Find an Inverse Variation Constant

In Example 10, we use products to find an inverse variation constant.

▶ **Example 10**   Finding an Inverse Variation Constant by Using Products

Use products of volumes and pressures to find a model of the syringe data shown in Example 7.

Solution

From our work in Example 7, we know we want an equation of the form $P = \dfrac{k}{V}$. To find k, we begin by solving the equation $P = \dfrac{k}{V}$ for k:

$$k = VP$$

Next, we use the values of V and P in the first two columns and fourth and fifth columns of Table 31 to calculate the products VP for the third and sixth columns, respectively.

Table 31 Products of Volumes and Pressures in a Syringe

Volume V (cm^3)	Pressure P (atm)	VP	Volume V (cm^3)	Pressure P (atm)	VP
3	2.23	6.69	12	0.60	7.20
4	1.76	7.04	13	0.56	7.28
5	1.46	7.30	14	0.52	7.28
6	1.23	7.38	15	0.48	7.20
7	1.05	7.35	16	0.44	7.04
8	0.93	7.44	17	0.42	7.14
9	0.83	7.47	18	0.39	7.02
10	0.74	7.40	19	0.37	7.03
11	0.67	7.37	20	0.35	7.00

According to our model $P = \dfrac{k}{V}$, the products VP should be equal to a constant k.

The reason the products vary a bit is most likely due to errors in measuring the volumes and pressures. Or there might be imperfections in the syringe.

Next, we find the mean of the products PV in the third and sixth columns:

$$\frac{6.69 + 7.04 + 7.30 + 7.38 + 7.35 + \cdots + 7.00}{18} \approx 7.20$$

Finally, we substitute 7.20 for k in the equation $P = \dfrac{k}{V}$:

$$P = \frac{7.20}{V}$$

This is the same equation we found in Example 7.

▶

We now have two ways to find an inverse variation model. The method shown in Example 7 requires few calculations, but finding a good value of k depends on a good selection of an ordered pair. The method shown in Example 10 requires more calculations, but it is not necessary to select an ordered pair to find k.

Group Exploration

Looking ahead: Simplifying radical expressions

Recall from Section 4.2 that $\sqrt[n]{a} = a^{1/n}$. So,

$$\sqrt[5]{a^3} = \left(a^3\right)^{1/5} = a^{3 \cdot \frac{1}{5}} = a^{3/5}$$

We say $\sqrt[5]{a^3}$ is in *radical form* and the expression $a^{3/5}$ is in *exponential form*.

1. Write $\sqrt[7]{a^4}$ in exponential form.
2. Write $\sqrt[9]{a^2}$ in exponential form.
3. Write $\sqrt{a^7}$ in exponential form. [**Hint:** $\sqrt{a}$ is shorthand for $\sqrt[2]{a}$.]

4. Write $\sqrt[n]{a^m}$ in exponential form.
5. Write each of the following in exponential form and simplify.
   a. $\sqrt{a^2}$, $\sqrt{a^4}$, $\sqrt{a^6}$, $\sqrt{a^8}$
   b. $\sqrt[3]{a^3}$, $\sqrt[3]{a^6}$, $\sqrt[3]{a^9}$, $\sqrt[3]{a^{12}}$
6. Simplify $\sqrt{x^7}$. [**Hint:** $x^7 = x^6 \cdot x$]
7. Simplify $\sqrt{x^{13}}$.

▶ Tips for Success   **Plan for the Final Exam**

Don't wait until the last minute to begin studying for your final exam. Look at your finals schedule and decide how you will allocate your time to prepare for each final.

It is important that you are well rested so you can fully concentrate during your final exam. Plan to do some fun activities that involve exercise—a great way to neutralize stress.

Homework 8.7

For extra help ▶ MyMathLab°   Watch the videos in MyMathLab   Download the MyDashboard App

Translate the sentence into an equation.

1. I varies directly as t.
2. z varies inversely as d.
3. w varies inversely as $x + 4$.
4. V varies directly as r cubed.

Translate the equation into a sentence by using the phrase "varies directly" or "varies inversely."

5. $w = \dfrac{k}{r}$

6. $d = kt$

7. $T = k\sqrt{w}$

8. $y = \dfrac{k}{2^x}$

Find an equation that meets the given conditions.

9. c varies directly as u, and $c = 12$ when $u = 3$.
10. p varies inversely as d, and $p = 3$ when $d = 5$.
11. w varies inversely as $\sqrt{t}$, and $w = 3$ when $t = 16$.
12. A varies directly as r^2, and $A = 4\pi$ when $r = 2$.

For Exercises 13–20, find the requested value of the variable.

13. If y varies directly as x, and $y = 12$ when $x = 4$, find y when $x = 9$.
14. If p varies directly as t, and $p = 18$ when $t = 3$, find p when $t = 5$.

15. If G varies inversely as r, and $G = 8$ when $r = 3$, find G when $r = 4$.
16. If W varies inversely as u, and $W = 15$ when $u = 2$, find W when $u = 6$.
17. If p varies directly as x^2, and $p = 6$ when $x = 2$, find x when $p = 24$.
18. If y varies directly as w^2, and $y = 6$ when $w = 3$, find w when $y = 54$.
19. If I varies inversely as $r + 2$, and $I = 9$ when $r = 3$, find r when $I = 7$.
20. If D varies inversely as $t + 3$, and $D = 5$ when $t = 4$, find t when $D = 9$.
21. The variable B varies directly as w with positive variation constant k. Describe what happens to the value of B as the value of w increases.
22. The variable y varies directly as t with positive variation constant k. Describe what happens to the value of y as the value of t decreases.
23. The variable w varies inversely as p with positive variation constant k. For positive values of p, what happens to the value of w as the value of p increases?
24. The variable F varies inversely as r with positive variation constant k. For positive values of r, what happens to the value of F as the value of r decreases?
25. The transaction demand is the amount of money demanded in an immediate exchange for goods and services. The

transaction demand varies directly as the gross domestic product (GDP). If the GDP increases, what happens to the transaction demand?

26. A training apparatus for improving the performance of swimmers produces a pulsating signal whose frequency varies directly as the swimmer's speed. If a swimmer's speed decreases, what happens to the frequency of the signal?

27. Nerve conduction in muscles varies inversely as a person's height. Will a tall person have more or less nerve conduction than a short person?

28. The frequency of a vibrating guitar string varies inversely with the diameter of the string. Will a large-diameter string have a higher or lower frequency than a small-diameter string?

29. Bernice Fitz-Gibbon, U.S. advertising executive, said, "Creativity varies inversely with the number of cooks involved in the broth." What did she mean?

30. Craig Bruce said, "Time is a resource whose supply is inversely proportional to its demand." What did he mean?

31. For a Montgomery County (Maryland) resident, the cost of tuition at Montgomery College varies directly as the number of credit hours taken. For spring 2013, the cost of 15 credit hours was $1680. What did 12 credit hours cost?

32. For a Jackson County (Michigan) resident, the cost of tuition at Jackson Community College varies directly as the number of billing contact hours taken. For academic year 2012–2013, the cost of 13 billing contact hours was $1378. What did 15 billing contact hours cost?

33. When a stone is tied to a string and whirled in a circle at constant speed, the tension in the string varies inversely as the radius of the circle. If the radius is 60 centimeters, the tension is 80 newtons. Find the tension if the radius is 50 centimeters.

34. The current flowing in an electrical circuit at a constant potential varies inversely as the resistance of the circuit. If the current is 25 amperes when the resistance is 4 ohms, what is the current when the resistance is 5 ohms?

35. The distance that an object falls varies directly as the square of the time the object is in motion. If an object falls for 3 seconds, it will fall 144.9 feet. To estimate the height of a cliff, a person drops a stone at the edge of the cliff and measures how long it takes the stone to reach the base. If it takes 3.4 seconds, what is the height of the cliff?

36. A car is traveling at speed s (in mph) on a dry asphalt road, and the brakes are suddenly applied. The braking distance d (in feet) varies directly as the square of the speed s. If a car traveling at 60 mph has a braking distance of 226.8 feet, what is the braking distance of a car traveling at 70 mph?

37. The intensity of the radiation used to treat a tumor varies inversely as the square of the distance from the machine that emits the radiation. If the intensity is 90 milliroentgens per hour (mr/hr) at a distance of 2.5 meters, at what distance is the intensity 45 mr/hr?

38. The volume of a sphere varies directly as the cube of its radius. A sphere with a 3-foot radius has a volume of 36π cubic feet. How much air is required to fill a beach ball with radius 1.6 feet?

39. The force F (in pounds) required to push a sofa across a floor varies directly as the weight w (in pounds) of the sofa.

a. A person can push a 120-pound sofa across a wood floor by pushing with a force of 50 pounds. Find an equation that describes the relationship between w and F.

b. How much force is required to push a 150-pound sofa across a wood floor?

c. How would an equation of a model for a *carpeted* floor compare with the model you found in part (a)? In particular, how would the variation constants compare?

40. The distance d (in miles) that a student travels by car varies directly as the travel time t (in hours). The student travels 93 miles in 1.5 hours.

a. Is the student traveling at a constant speed? Explain.

b. Find an equation that describes the relationship between time and distance.

c. How far will the student travel in 2 hours?

41. The time T (in seconds) it takes to hear thunder after you see lightning varies directly as the distance d (in feet) from the lightning if the temperature does not vary much during the storm. In a certain storm, it takes 3 seconds to hear thunder when lightning is seen 3313 feet away.

a. Find an equation that describes the relationship between d and T for the storm.

b. If it takes 4 seconds for you to hear thunder after you see lightning, how far away is the lightning?

c. What does the constant k represent in this situation? Explain. [**Hint:** Recall that slope is the rate of change of the *dependent* variable with respect to the *independent* variable.]

d. There is a rule of thumb that the number of seconds it takes you to hear thunder after you see lightning is equal to the number of miles that you are from the lightning. Is this rule of thumb a good approximation? If yes, explain. If no, find a better rule of thumb. [**Hint:** There are 5280 feet in 1 mile.]

42. The force F (in pounds) you must exert on a wrench handle to loosen a bolt on a bike varies inversely as the length L (in inches) of the handle. A force of 40 pounds is needed when the handle is 6 inches long.

a. Find an equation that describes the relationship between handle length and force.

b. If you use an 8-inch-long wrench to loosen the bolt, how much force do you need to apply to the handle?

c. Is it easier to use a wrench with a short or long handle? Explain in terms of the equation you found in part (a).

43. The weight (in pounds) $w = f(d)$ of an object varies inversely as the square of its distance (in thousands of miles) d from the center of Earth.

a. An astronaut weighs 200 pounds at sea level (about 4 thousand miles from Earth's center). Find an equation of f.

b. How much would the astronaut weigh 1 thousand miles above Earth's surface?

c. At what distance from the center of Earth would the astronaut weigh 1 pound?

d. Use f to estimate how much the astronaut would weigh on the surface of the Moon. The Moon is a mean distance of about 239 thousand miles from Earth. Has model breakdown occurred? Explain.

e. Without finding an equation, discuss how an equation of a model for a 190-pound astronaut would compare with the equation you found in part (a). Discuss how the variation constants would compare.

44. The intensity (in watts per square meter, W/m^2) $I = f(d)$ of a television signal varies inversely as the square of the distance d (in kilometers) from the transmitter. The intensity of a television signal is 30 W/m^2 at a distance of 2.6 km.
  a. Find an equation of f.
  b. Find $f(1), f(2), f(3)$, and $f(4)$. What do they mean in this situation?
  c. Use a graphing calculator to draw a graph of f. What happens to the value of I as the value of d increases, for $d > 0$? What does that mean in this situation?
  d. What can you say about the value of $f(d)$ for an extremely large value of d? Explain. What does that mean in this situation?

45. When a guitarist picks the second-thickest string on a six-string guitar (the "open 'A' string"), the string vibrates at a frequency of 110 hertz—that is, 110 times a second. By firmly pressing the "A" string against the fret board, the guitarist shortens the effective length of the string. As a result, the frequency increases (and so does the pitch of the note). See Fig. 57.

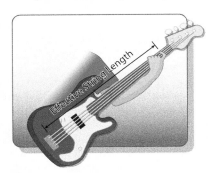

Figure 57 Exercise 45

We use some of the letters of the alphabet, sometimes in conjunction with the "sharp" symbol, ♯, to refer to these notes. The frequencies for the open "A" string and the next 12 notes are listed in Table 32.

Table 32 Effective Lengths and Frequencies of 13 Notes on the "A" String

Note	Effective Length of "A" String (inches)	Frequency (hertz)
A	25.50	110.0
A♯	24.07	116.6
B	22.72	123.5
C	21.44	130.8
C♯	20.24	138.6
D	19.10	146.9
D♯	18.03	155.6
E	17.02	164.8
F	16.06	174.6
F♯	15.16	185.0
G	14.31	196.0
G♯	13.51	207.7
A	12.75	220.0

Sources: Math and Music, *Garland and Kahn; J. Lehmann*

  a. Let F be the frequency (in hertz) of the "A" string when the string's effective length is L inches. Use a graphing calculator to draw a scattergram of the data.

  b. Find an equation of a reasonable model to describe the data. Does your model fit the data well?
  c. In a sentence that uses the phrase "varies directly" or "varies inversely," describe how the effective length and frequency of the "A" string are related.
  d. When the "A" string is vibrating, what is its frequency if the effective length is 7.58 inches?
  e. Use your equation from part (b) to show that if you halve any effective length of the "A" string, the frequency will double. [**Hint:** First, substitute a for L in your model's equation. Then substitute $\frac{1}{2}a$ for L.]

46. A racquetball is dropped from various heights, and the bounce height is recorded each time (see Table 33).

Table 33 Drop and Bounce Heights of a Racquetball

Drop Height (inches)	Bounce Height (inches)
6	5.0
12	9.3
18	15.0
24	19.6
30	24.0
36	27.6
42	32.8
48	38.0

Source: *J. Lehmann*

Let $B = f(d)$ be the bounce height (in inches) of the racquetball after it is dropped from an initial height of d inches.
  a. Use a graphing calculator to draw a scattergram of the data.
  b. Find an equation of f.
  c. In a sentence using the phrase "varies directly" or "varies inversely," describe how the initial and bounce heights of the racquetball are related.
  d. What is the slope of the graph of f? What does it mean in this situation?
  e. What is the B-intercept? What does it mean in this situation?

47. As you move away from an object, it appears to decrease in height. To describe this relationship, a math professor stood 10 feet from his garage, held a yardstick 1 foot away, and measured the image of his garage. The image of the garage had an *apparent height* of 16.0 inches. He collected apparent heights of the garage at various distances from it (see Table 34).

Table 34 Apparent Heights of a Car Garage

Distance from Garage (feet)	Apparent Height of Garage (inches)
10	16.0
20	7.3
30	4.8
40	3.8
50	3.0
60	2.5
70	2.0

Source: *J. Lehmann*

Let $a = f(d)$ be the apparent height (in inches) of the garage when the professor was d feet from the garage.

a. Use a graphing calculator to draw a scattergram of the data.

b. Find an equation of f.

c. In a sentence using the phrase "varies directly" or "varies inversely," describe how the distance from the garage and the apparent height of the garage are related.

d. Your model f is a decreasing function for $d > 0$. Explain why that makes sense in this situation.

e. Find the apparent height from a distance of 100 feet.

f. Estimate the actual height of the garage. [**Hint:** Think about how the apparent heights were recorded.]

48. A pizza with diameter 12 inches (a "12-inch pizza") and three toppings weighs 36 ounces at Toto's Restaurant and Pizzeria in San Bruno, California. The weight of a three-topping pizza varies directly as the square of the pizza's diameter.

a. Let $W(d)$ be the weight (in ounces) of a three-topping pizza with diameter d inches. Find an equation of W.

b. Table 35 lists the prices for various sizes of three-topping pizzas at Toto's Restaurant and Pizzeria. Let $P(d)$ be the price (in dollars) of a three-topping pizza with diameter d inches. Find an equation of P.

Table 35 Prices of Pizzas

Diameter (inches)	Price (dollars)
12	18.75
14	20.75
16	24.25
18	26.25

Source: *Toto's Restaurant and Pizzeria*

c. In a sentence using the phrase "varies directly", "varies linearly," or "varies inversely," describe how the diameter and price of the pizza are related.

d. Let $C(d)$ be the cost per ounce (in dollars per ounce) of a three-topping pizza with diameter d inches. Find an equation of C.

e. Find the value of d where $C(d) = 0.372$. What does it mean in this situation?

f. Use a graphing calculator to draw a graph of C. Is C increasing or decreasing for $d > 0$? What does that mean in this situation?

49. A *pendulum* is an object hanging from a lightweight cord. A pendulum can be made by tying one end of some thread to a weight—say, a washer—and attaching the other end of the thread to a surface so that the weight is suspended and can swing freely. The *period* of the pendulum is the amount of time it takes for the weight to swing forward and backward once. Let T be the period (in seconds) of a pendulum and L be the length (in centimeters) of the thread. Some values of L and T generated from an experiment are shown in Table 36.

a. The period of a pendulum varies directly as the square root of the length of the thread. Write an equation involving L, T, and the variation constant k.

b. Solve the equation you found in part (a) for k.

c. Use the first two columns of Table 36 to complete the third column. What is a reasonable value of k? How did you find this value?

Table 36 Periods of a Pendulum

Length L (cm)	Period T (seconds)	k
5.0	0.50	
10.0	0.63	
15.0	0.88	
20.0	1.00	
25.0	1.13	
32.5	1.25	
45.0	1.50	
60.0	1.75	
85.0	2.00	
110.0	2.25	

Source: *J. Lehmann*

d. Substitute your value of k into your equation from part (a).

e. Draw the graph of your model and a scattergram of the data in the same viewing window. Does your model fit the data well?

f. Estimate the period if the thread is 130 inches long.

50. The illumination from a light bulb decreases as the distance from the bulb increases. Let I be the illumination in milliwatts per square centimeter (mW/cm^2) at d centimeters from a 25-watt light bulb. Some values of d and I generated by an experiment are shown in Table 37.

Table 37 Illumination from a Light Bulb

Distance d (cm)	Illumination I (mW/cm^2)	k
70	0.845	
80	0.677	
90	0.546	
100	0.435	
110	0.349	
120	0.293	
130	0.260	
140	0.214	

Source: *J. Lehmann*

a. The illumination from a light source varies inversely as the square of the distance from the source. Write an equation involving d, I, and the variation constant k.

b. Solve the equation you found in part (a) for k.

c. Use the first two columns of Table 37 to complete the third column. What is a reasonable value of k? How did you find this value?

d. Substitute your value of k into your equation from part (a) to find an equation of a model.

e. Draw the graph of your model and a scattergram of the data in the same viewing window. Does your model fit the data well?

f. Estimate the illumination at 160 centimeters from the bulb.

g. How would an equation of a model for a 50-watt bulb compare with the model you found in part (d)? How would the variation constants compare?

Concepts

For Exercises 51–56, write a variation equation in the given variables. State the value of the variation constant k.

51. Let $f(L)$ be the area (in square inches) of a rectangle with width 5 inches and length L (in inches).

52. Let $f(s)$ be the area (in square meters) of a square with sides of length s (in meters).

53. A group of n people wins a total of $2 million from a state lottery drawing. Let $f(n)$ be each person's share (in millions of dollars).

54. Let $f(s)$ be the time (in hours) it takes a person to drive 100 miles at a constant speed s (in mph).

55. Let $f(r)$ be the circumference (in inches) of a circle with radius r (in inches).

56. Let $f(r)$ be the area (in square feet) of a circle with radius r (in feet).

57. Suppose the latest Foster the People album is about to be released. Let $n = f(a)$ be the number of albums (in millions) that will be sold, where a is the advertising budget (in thousands of dollars). A graph of f is sketched in Fig. 58.

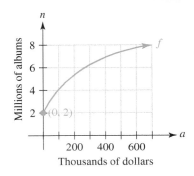

Figure 58 Advertising budget and album sales

   a. Is f an increasing function? Explain.
   b. Does the number of albums sold vary directly as the amount of money spent on advertising? Explain.
   c. Compare the meanings of these two statements: "One quantity varies directly as another quantity." "One quantity will increase if the other quantity increases."

58. For a direct variation equation $y = kx$, where k is positive, we know that as the value of x increases, the value of y increases. If k is negative for $y = kx$, what happens to the value of y as the value of x increases? Explain. [**Hint:** Sketch a graph.]

For Exercises 59–62, decide whether the statement is true or false. Explain.

59. The height of a person varies directly as the person's age.

60. The area of a circle varies directly as the radius of the circle.

61. The temperature of hot coffee varies inversely as the time since it was poured into a cup.

62. The height of a baseball hit straight up varies inversely as the time since it was hit.

63. Assume y varies directly as x and that the variation constant is k. Does it follow that x varies directly as y? If yes, what is the variation constant? If no, explain. [**Hint:** Solve the equation $y = kx$ for x.]

64. Assume y varies inversely as x and that the variation constant is k. Does it follow that x varies inversely as y? If yes, what is the variation constant? If no, explain. [**Hint:** Solve the equation $y = \dfrac{k}{x}$ for x.]

65. Five miles is approximately the same distance as 8.05 kilometers. One student finds the model $y = 1.61x$, and another student finds the model $y = 0.62x$. Even though their results are different, both students are correct. How is this possible? What does 1.61 of the model $y = 1.61x$ represent? What does 0.62 of the equation $y = 0.62x$ represent?

66. Describe the meanings of *direct variation equation* and *inverse variation equation*. Compare these two types of equations. Compare some properties of these types of equations.

Related Review

67. a. If y varies directly as x, are x and y linearly related? Explain.
   b. If w and t are linearly related, does w vary directly as t? Explain.

68. a. If a quantity y varies directly as a quantity x, how many data points do you need to find an equation to describe the situation?
   b. If the quantities w and t are linearly related, how many data points do you need to find an equation to describe the situation?

69. The number n of words a typist can type varies directly as the amount of time t (in minutes) he types. He can type 310 words in 5 minutes. What is the slope of the model that describes this situation? What does it mean in this situation?

70. The total cost c (in dollars) of some 5-inch $\times$ 7-inch school photos shot by Lifetouch® varies directly as the number n of photos that are purchased. It costs $27.96 for 4 such photos. What is the slope of the model that describes this situation? What does it mean in this situation?

Expressions, Equations, Functions, and Graphs

Give an example of the following. Then solve, simplify, or graph, as appropriate.

71. system of two linear equations in two variables

72. linear equation in one variable

73. difference of two rational expressions

74. quadratic equation in one variable

75. quadratic function

76. rational equation in one variable

77. exponential function

78. the sum of two logarithmic expressions with the same base

Taking it to the Lab

Climate Change Lab (continued from Chapter 7)

In previous Climate Change Labs, we found various models related to carbon dioxide emissions and human populations. We can use these models to find meaningful ratios and percentages of quantities.

Analyzing the Situation

1. Let $u(t)$ be the U.S. population and $w(t)$ be the world population (both in billions), both at t years since 1950. Here are some reasonable models:

$$u(t) = 0.0025t + 0.155$$
$$w(t) = -0.00046t^2 + 0.132t + 0.63$$

Recall from the Climate Change Lab in Chapter 6 that the world population model works well only for the years 2000–2100. Find a model of the percentage $p(t)$ of the world population that is in the United States at t years since 1950.

2. Use a graphing calculator table to find $p(50)$, $p(60)$, $p(70)$, $p(80)$, $p(90)$, and $p(100)$. What do your results tell you about this situation?

3. Let $f(t)$ be U.S. carbon dioxide emissions and $g(t)$ be world carbon dioxide emissions (both in billions of metric tons), both in the year that is t years since 1950. Here are some reasonable models:

$$f(t) = 0.06t + 2.61$$
$$g(t) = 0.4t + 5.75$$

Find a model of the percentage $h(t)$ of worldwide carbon dioxide emissions emitted in the United States in the year that is t years since 1950.

4. Use a graphing calculator table to find $h(50)$, $h(60)$, $h(70)$, $h(80)$, $h(90)$, and $h(100)$. What do your results tell you about this situation?

5. A model of U.S. carbon dioxide emissions $c(t)$ (in billions of metric tons) in the year that is t years since 1950 is $f(t) = 0.06t + 2.61$. A model of the U.S. population $u(t)$ (in billions) at t years since 1950 is $u(t) = 0.0025t + 0.155$. Find a model of the U.S. per-person carbon dioxide emissions $r(t)$ (in metric tons per person) in the year that is t years since 1950.

6. Use a graphing calculator table to find $r(50)$, $r(60)$, $r(70)$, $r(80)$, $r(90)$, and $r(100)$. What do your results tell you about this situation?

7. Explain how it is possible for the U.S. share of annual worldwide carbon dioxide emissions to decline even if U.S. per-person annual carbon dioxide emissions increase. [**Hint:** There may be two reasons. Consider your result in Problem 1. Consider also what is happening in developing countries.]

Illumination Lab

The illumination from a light bulb decreases as the distance from the bulb increases. Illumination can be measured in milliwatts per square centimeter (MW/cm²). In this experiment, you will study the relationship between the illumination I (in MW/cm²) of a 25-watt light bulb and the distance d (in cm) from the bulb.

Materials

You will need the following materials:
1. a 25-watt light bulb
2. a metric tape measure or a meterstick
3. a light sensor probe. (A Texas Instruments CBL unit and light sensor probe used in conjunction with a TI-83, TI-84, TI-86, or TI-Nspire graphing calculator works well.)

Preparation

It is best to perform this experiment at night in a room with all lights other than the 25-watt bulb turned off, the shades or curtains closed, and all doors shut. Place the meterstick so that you can measure horizontal distances from the center of the light bulb.

Recording of Data

Record the intensity of the light at distances of 70 cm, 80 cm, 90 cm, and every 10 centimeters thereafter until you reach 140 cm.

Analyzing the Data

1. Adjust your illumination readings for any small amount of light in the room due to sources other than the 25-watt light bulb. If you are using the CBL unit, an initial step will allow you to input the illumination of the room with the bulb off. The unit will subtract this value from your illumination readings. Otherwise, you will have to subtract this small amount of "background" illumination from your illumination readings.

2. Complete the second column of Table 38.

Table 38 Illumination by a Light Bulb

Distance d (cm)	Illumination I (MW/cm²)	d^2I
70		
80		
90		
100		
110		
120		
130		
140		

Source: *J. Lehmann*

3. Use a graphing calculator to draw a scattergram of your light data.

4. The illumination from a light bulb varies inversely as the distance squared. Write an equation involving d, I, and k.

5. Solve your equation from Part 4 for k. Use the first two columns of Table 38 to complete the third column. What is a reasonable value of k? How did you find this value?

6. Substitute your value of k into your equation from Part 4. Let $f(d) = I$. Write your equation with the function name f.

7. Use a graphing calculator to graph your model and the scattergram in the same viewing window. Graph your model and the scattergram by hand. How well does f model the data?

8. Use your model to estimate the illumination from the bulb at a distance of 150 centimeters.

9. Use your model to estimate the distance at which the illumination from the bulb is 0.1 MW/cm^2.

10. For what values of d is there model breakdown?

11. Explain why it makes sense in this situation that f is a decreasing function for positive values of d.

Boyle's Law Lab

The more you squeeze a sealed syringe filled with air, the harder it gets to squeeze it farther. That's because, as the volume of air in the syringe decreases, the pressure of the air inside the syringe increases. In this experiment, you will study the relationship between the pressure P in atmospheres (atm) of the air inside a syringe and the volume V in cubic centimeters (cm^3) of the air in the syringe.

Materials
To do this lab, you will need the following materials:
1. a Texas Instruments CBL unit
2. a TI-83, TI-84, TI-86, or TI-Nspire graphing calculator with graph link cable
3. a syringe apparatus (made by the Vernier Company)
4. a CBL-DIN adapter (made by the Vernier Company; Vernier offers the syringe apparatus and CBL-DIN adapter as a package.)

Preparation
Follow the instructions that come with the syringe apparatus to set up the equipment. An initial "at-rest" volume setting of around 8 cm^3 works well. You will have to enter a pressure-gathering program into your CBL unit. (The code for the program is included in the syringe/CBL-DIN package.)

Recording of Data
Record the pressures of the air at volumes 3 cm^3, 4 cm^3, 5 cm^3, and so on until you reach 20 cm^3. Take one pressure reading with each run of the pressure-gathering program.

Analyzing the Data
1. Complete the second and fifth columns of Table 39.

Table 39 Pressures and Volumes in a Syringe

Volume V (cm^3)	Pressure P (atm)	PV	V (cm^3)	P (atm)	PV
3			12		
4			13		
5			14		
6			15		
7			16		
8			17		
9			18		
10			19		
11			20		

Source: *J. Lehmann*

2. Use a graphing calculator to draw a scattergram of the data.

3. The pressure of air inside a syringe varies inversely as the volume of that air. Write an equation involving V, P, and k.

4. Solve your equation from Part 3 for k. Use the first two columns and the fourth and fifth columns of Table 39 to complete the third and sixth columns, respectively. What is a reasonable value of k? How did you find this value?

5. Substitute your value of k into your equation from Part 3. Let $f(V) = P$. Write your equation with the function name f.

6. Use a graphing calculator to graph your model and the scattergram in the same viewing window. Graph your model and the scattergram by hand. How well does f model the data?

7. Use your model to estimate the air pressure in the syringe if the volume is 2 cm^3.

8. Use your model to estimate the volume in the syringe at which the air pressure would be 4 atm.

9. Use your model to predict what the air pressure would be if all the air were squeezed out of the syringe. Do you think this could be done in reality? Explain.

Chapter Summary

Key Points of Chapter 8

Section 8.1   Finding the Domains of Rational Functions and Simplifying Rational Expressions

Throughout these key points, assume A, B, C, and D are polynomials.

Rational function

A **rational function** is a function whose equation can be put into the form $f(x) = \dfrac{P(x)}{Q(x)}$, where $P(x)$ and $Q(x)$ are polynomials and $Q(x)$ is nonzero.

Domain of a rational function

The domain of a rational function $f(x) = \dfrac{P(x)}{Q(x)}$ is the set of all real numbers except for those numbers that, when substituted for x, give $Q(x) = 0$.

Excluded value

A number is an **excluded value** of a rational expression if substituting the number into the expression leads to a division by 0.

Simplify a rational expression

To simplify a rational expression,

1. Factor the numerator and the denominator.

2. Use the property $\dfrac{AB}{AC} = \dfrac{A}{A} \cdot \dfrac{B}{C} = 1 \cdot \dfrac{B}{C} = \dfrac{B}{C}$, where A and C are nonzero, so the expression is in lowest terms.

Vertical asymptotes and domains of rational functions

If the graph of a rational function f has a vertical asymptote $x = k$, then k is not in the domain of f. If k is not in the domain of a rational function g, then $x = k$ may or may not be a vertical asymptote of the graph of g.

Quotient function

If f and g are functions, x is in the domain of both functions, and $g(x)$ is nonzero, then we can form the **quotient function** $\dfrac{f}{g}$: $\left(\dfrac{f}{g}\right)(x) = \dfrac{f(x)}{g(x)}$.

Rational model

A **rational model** is a rational function, or its graph, that describes an authentic situation.

Percentage formula

If m items out of n items have a certain attribute, then the percentage p (written $p\%$) of the n items that have the attribute is $p = \dfrac{m}{n} \cdot 100$. We call this equation the **percentage formula.**

Section 8.2   Multiplying and Dividing Rational Expressions; Converting Units

Multiplying rational expressions

If $\dfrac{A}{B}$ and $\dfrac{C}{D}$ are rational expressions and B and D are nonzero, then $\dfrac{A}{B} \cdot \dfrac{C}{D} = \dfrac{AC}{BD}$.

How to multiply rational expressions

To multiply two rational expressions,

1. Factor the numerators and the denominators.

2. Multiply by using the property $\dfrac{A}{B} \cdot \dfrac{C}{D} = \dfrac{AC}{BD}$, where B and D are nonzero.

3. Simplify the result.

Dividing rational expressions

If $\dfrac{A}{B}$ and $\dfrac{C}{D}$ are rational expressions and B, C, and D are nonzero, then $\dfrac{A}{B} \div \dfrac{C}{D} = \dfrac{A}{B} \cdot \dfrac{D}{C}$.

How to divide rational expressions

To divide two rational expressions,

1. Write the quotient as a product by using the property $\dfrac{A}{B} \div \dfrac{C}{D} = \dfrac{A}{B} \cdot \dfrac{D}{C}$, where B, C, and D are nonzero.

2. Find the product.

3. Simplify.

Section 8.2   Multiplying and Dividing Rational Expressions; Converting Units (*Continued*)

Converting units   To convert the units of a quantity,

1. Write the quantity in the original units.
2. Multiply by fractions equal to 1 so the units you want to eliminate appear in one numerator and one denominator.

Section 8.3   Adding and Subtracting Rational Expressions

Adding rational expressions that have a common denominator   If $\dfrac{A}{B}$ and $\dfrac{C}{B}$ are rational expressions and B is nonzero, then $\dfrac{A}{B} + \dfrac{C}{B} = \dfrac{A + C}{B}$.

Subtracting rational expressions that have a common denominator   If $\dfrac{A}{B}$ and $\dfrac{C}{B}$ are rational expressions and B is nonzero, then $\dfrac{A}{B} - \dfrac{C}{B} = \dfrac{A - C}{B}$.

Subtract entire numerator   When subtracting rational expressions, be sure to subtract the *entire* numerator.

How to add or subtract two rational expressions that have different denominators   To add or subtract two rational expressions that have different denominators,

1. Factor the denominators of the expressions if possible. Determine which factors are missing.
2. Use the property $\dfrac{A}{A} = 1$, where A is nonzero, to introduce missing factors.
3. Add the expressions by using the property $\dfrac{A}{B} + \dfrac{C}{B} = \dfrac{A + C}{B}$, where B is nonzero; or

   subtract the expressions by using the property $\dfrac{A}{B} - \dfrac{C}{B} = \dfrac{A - C}{B}$, where B is nonzero.
4. Simplify.

Section 8.4   Simplifying Complex Rational Expressions

Complex rational expression   A **complex rational expression** is a rational expression whose numerator or denominator (or both) is a rational expression.

Using method 1 to simplify a complex rational expression   To simplify a complex rational expression by method 1,

1. Write both the numerator and the denominator as fractions.
2. Write the complex rational expression as the quotient of two rational expressions:

$$\frac{\dfrac{A}{B}}{\dfrac{C}{D}} = \frac{A}{B} \div \frac{C}{D}, \text{where } B, C, \text{ and } D \text{ are nonzero.}$$

3. Divide the rational expressions.

Using method 2 to simplify a complex rational expression   To simplify a complex rational expression by method 2,

1. Find the LCD of all of the fractions in the numerator and denominator.
2. Multiply by 1 in the form $\dfrac{\text{LCD}}{\text{LCD}}$.
3. Simplify the numerator and the denominator to polynomials.
4. Simplify the rational expression.

Section 8.5   Solving Rational Equations

Rational equation in one variable   A **rational equation in one variable** is an equation in one variable in which both sides can be written as rational expressions.

Check proposed solutions   Since multiplying both sides of a rational equation by the LCD and then simplifying both sides may introduce extraneous solutions, we must always check that any proposed solution is not an excluded value.

Section 8.5   Solving Rational Equations (*Continued*)

Solving a rational equation in one variable	To solve a rational equation in one variable, **1.** Factor the denominator(s) if possible. **2.** Identify any excluded values. **3.** Find the LCD of all of the fractions. **4.** Multiply both sides of the equation by the LCD, which gives a simpler equation to solve. **5.** Solve the simpler equation. **6.** Discard any proposed solutions that are excluded values.
Solving a rational equation versus simplifying a rational expression	To solve a rational equation, clear the fractions in it by multiplying both sides of the equation by the LCD. To simplify a rational expression, do *not* multiply it by the LCD — the only multiplication permissible is multiplication by 1, usually in the form $\dfrac{A}{A}$, where A is a nonzero polynomial.
Results of solving rational equations and simplifying rational expressions	The result of solving a rational equation is the empty set or a set of one or more numbers. The result of simplifying a rational expression is an expression.

Section 8.6   Modeling with Rational Functions

Mean	If a quantity Q is divided into n parts, the **mean** amount M of the quantity per part is given by $M = \dfrac{Q}{n}$.
Distance-speed-time relationship	If an object is moving at a constant speed s for an amount of time t, then the distance d traveled is given by $d = st$ and the time t is given by $t = \dfrac{d}{s}$.

Section 8.7   Variation

Direct variation	If $y = kx$ for some nonzero constant k, we say that **y varies directly as x** or that **y is proportional to x.** We call k the **variation constant** or the **constant of proportionality.** The equation $y = kx$ is called a **direct variation equation.**
Changes in values of variables for direct variation	Assume y varies directly as x with some positive variation constant k: • If the value of x increases, then the value of y increases. • If the value of x decreases, then the value of y decreases.
Finding and using a direct variation model	Assume a quantity p varies directly as a quantity t. To make estimates about an authentic situation, **1.** Substitute the values of a data point into the equation $p = kt$; then solve for k. **2.** Substitute the value of k into the equation $p = kt$. **3.** Use the equation from step 2 to make estimates of quantity t or p.
Inverse variation	If $y = \dfrac{k}{x}$ for some nonzero constant k, we say that **y varies inversely as x** or that **y is inversely proportional to x.** We call k the **variation constant** or the **constant of proportionality.** The equation $y = \dfrac{k}{x}$ is called an **inverse variation equation.**
Changes in values of variables for inverse variation	Assume y varies inversely as x with some positive variation constant k. For positive values of x, • If the value of x increases, then the value of y decreases. • If the value of x decreases, then the value of y increases.
Finding and using an inverse variation model	Assume a quantity p varies inversely as a quantity t. To make estimates about an authentic situation, **1.** Substitute the values of a data point into the equation $p = \dfrac{k}{t}$; then solve for k. **2.** Substitute the value of k into the equation $p = \dfrac{k}{t}$. **3.** Use the equation from step 2 to make estimates of quantity t or p.

Chapter 8 Review Exercises

1. For $f(x) = \dfrac{5x - 3}{2x^2 - 3x + 1}$, find $f(0)$ and $f(2)$.

Find the domain of the rational function.

2. $f(x) = \dfrac{5}{4x^2 - 49}$

3. $f(x) = \dfrac{x^2 - 4}{12x^2 + 13x - 35}$

4. $f(x) = \dfrac{3x + 7}{9x^3 + 18x^2 - x - 2}$

For Exercises 5–7, simplify the right-hand side of the equation.

5. $f(x) = \dfrac{3x - 12}{x^2 - 6x + 8}$

6. $f(x) = \dfrac{16 - x^2}{2x^3 - 16x^2 + 32x}$

7. $f(x) = \dfrac{x + 2}{x^3 + 8}$

8. Simplify $\dfrac{6a^2 - 17ab + 5b^2}{3a^2 - 4ab + b^2}$.

9. For $f(x) = x^2 + 3x - 28$ and $g(x) = x^3 - x^2 - 12x$, find an equation of $\dfrac{f}{g}$. Then find $\dfrac{f}{g}(-2)$.

Perform the indicated operation(s).

10. $\dfrac{3x + 6}{2x - 4} \cdot \dfrac{5x - 10}{6x + 12}$

11. $\dfrac{x^2 - 49}{9 - x^2} \cdot \dfrac{2x^3 + 8x^2 - 42x}{5x - 35}$

12. $\dfrac{p^3 - t^3}{p^2 - t^2} \cdot \dfrac{p^2 + 6pt + 5t^2}{p^2t + pt^2 + t^3}$

13. $\dfrac{x^2 - 4}{x^2 + 3x + 2} \div \dfrac{4x^2 - 24x + 32}{x^2 - 5x + 4}$

14. $\dfrac{4 - x}{4x} \div \dfrac{16 - x^2}{16x^2}$

15. $\dfrac{8x^3 + 4x^2 - 18x - 9}{x^2 - 6x + 9} \div \dfrac{4x^2 + 8x + 3}{x^2 - 9}$

16. $\dfrac{w}{w^2 - 5w + 6} + \dfrac{3}{3 - w}$

17. $\dfrac{x}{2x^3 - 3x^2 - 5x} + \dfrac{2}{x^3 - x}$

18. $\dfrac{x - 1}{x^2 - 4} + \dfrac{x + 3}{x^2 - 4x + 4}$

19. $\dfrac{3}{4k - 12} - \dfrac{k}{k^2 - 2k - 3}$

20. $\dfrac{x + 1}{25 - x^2} - \dfrac{x - 4}{2x^2 - 14x + 20}$

21. $\dfrac{2m}{m^2 - 3mn - 10n^2} - \dfrac{4n}{m^2 + 8mn + 12n^2}$

22. $\dfrac{2}{x - 5} - \left(\dfrac{x^2 + 5x + 6}{3x^2 - 75} \div \dfrac{x^2 + 2x}{3x + 15} \right)$

Let $f(x) = \dfrac{x^2 - x - 2}{x^2 + 5x + 6}$ and $g(x) = \dfrac{x + 3}{x + 2}$. *Find an equation of the given function.*

23. $f \cdot g$ **24.** $f \div g$ **25.** $f + g$ **26.** $f - g$

For Exercises 27 and 28, round approximate results to the second decimal place. Refer to the list of equivalent units in the margin of p. 495 as needed.

27. For international soccer matches, the minimum length of the field allowed is 100 meters and the maximum length allowed is 110 meters. What are these lengths in yards?

28. Water leaks into a boat at a rate of 8 gallons per hour. Describe this rate in cups per minute.

Simplify.

29. $\dfrac{\dfrac{x - 2}{x^2 - 9}}{\dfrac{x^2 - 4}{x + 3}}$

30. $\dfrac{\dfrac{4}{3x^4} - \dfrac{2}{6x^2}}{\dfrac{1}{2x} + \dfrac{1}{4}}$

For Exercises 31–34, solve. All solutions are real numbers.

31. $\dfrac{1}{x + 5} - \dfrac{2}{x - 2} = \dfrac{-14}{x^2 + 3x - 10}$

32. $\dfrac{x}{x + 2} + \dfrac{3}{x + 4} = \dfrac{14}{x^2 + 6x + 8}$

33. $\dfrac{5}{x} + 3 = \dfrac{4}{x^2}$

34. $\dfrac{x - 3}{2x^2 - 7x - 4} - \dfrac{5}{2x^2 + 3x + 1} = \dfrac{x - 1}{x^2 - 3x - 4}$

35. Find all complex-number solutions of the equation $\dfrac{2x}{x + 6} - \dfrac{4}{x - 3} = \dfrac{-37}{x^2 + 3x - 18}$.

36. Find the x-intercept(s) of the graph of $f(x) = \dfrac{x - 7}{x + 1} - \dfrac{x + 3}{x - 4}$.

37. Solve the formula $S = \dfrac{a}{1 - r}$ for r.

Translate the equation with nonzero constant k by using the phrase "varies directly" or "varies inversely" in a sentence.

38. $H = ku^2$ **39.** $w = \dfrac{k}{\log(t)}$

For Exercises 40 and 41, find an equation that meets the given conditions.

40. y varies directly as $\sqrt{x}$, and $y = 2$ when $x = 49$.

41. B varies inversely as r^3, and $B = 9$ when $r = 2$.

42. The number of inches of water varies directly as the number of inches of snow. If 20 inches of snow will melt to 2.24 inches of water, 37 inches of snow will melt to how many inches of water?

43. Let m be the mass (in grams) of a ball bearing with radius r (in cm). Table 40 shows values of r and m for ball bearings of various sizes.

Table 40 Radii and Masses of Ball Bearings

Radius r (cm)	Mass m (grams)	k
1.0	17.1	
1.2	29.4	
1.4	46.7	
1.6	69.6	
1.8	99.1	
2.0	135.9	

 a. The mass of a ball bearing is directly proportional to the radius cubed. Write an equation involving r, m, and k.
 b. Solve the equation that you found in part (a) for k.
 c. Use the first two columns of Table 40 to complete the third column. What is a reasonable value of k? How did you find this value?
 d. Substitute your value of k into your equation from part (a) to find an equation of a model.
 e. Draw the graph of your model and a scattergram of the data in the same viewing window. Does your model fit the data well?
 f. What is the mass of a ball bearing with radius 2.3 cm?

44. A hotel offers a one-day rental of a conference room (capacity 300) for a flat fee of $600, plus a per-person charge of $40 for lunch.
 a. Let $C(n)$ be the total cost (in dollars) of renting the room if n people use the room for one day. Find an equation of C.
 b. Let $M(n)$ be the mean cost per person (in dollars per person) if n people use the room for one day. Find an equation of M.
 c. Find $M(270)$. What does it mean in this situation?
 d. Find n when $M(n) = 50$. What does it mean in this situation?

45. In Exercise 28 of Homework 3.1, the average annual U.S. per-person consumption (in pounds per person) $C(t)$ and

$R(t)$ of chicken and red meat, respectively, are modeled by the system

$$C(t) = 1.13t + 39.29$$
$$R(t) = -0.94t + 144.88$$

where t is the number of years since 1970 (see Table 41).

Table 41 Average Annual U.S. Per-Person Consumption of Chicken and Red Meat

Year	Average Annual Consumption (pounds per person)	
	Chicken	Red Meat
1970	40.3	145.8
1980	48.0	136.8
1990	61.5	120.0
2000	78.0	120.7
2010	83.7	108.7
2011	84.2	104.3

Source: *U.S. Department of Agriculture*

 a. Find an equation of the sum function $C + R$. What do the inputs and outputs of $C + R$ mean in this situation?
 b. Let $P(t)$ be the percentage of chicken and red meat consumed that is chicken at t years since 1970. Find an equation of P.
 c. Use P to estimate the percentage of chicken and red meat consumed that was chicken in 2011. Then compute the actual percentage. Is your result from using the model an underestimate or an overestimate?
 d. Find $P(47)$. What does it mean in this situation?
 e. Predict the year when half of the chicken and red meat consumed will be chicken.

46. A student plans to drive 75 miles on an undivided highway and another 40 miles on a divided highway. The speed limits are 50 mph for the undivided highway and 65 mph for the divided highway.
 a. Let $T(a)$ be the driving time (in hours) if the student drives a mph above the speed limits. Find an equation of T.
 b. Find $T(5)$. What does it mean in this situation?
 c. By how much over the speed limits would the student need to drive for the driving time to be 2 hours? Use a graphing calculator table to verify your result.

Chapter 8 Test

For Exercises 1–3, find the domain of the function.

1. $f(x) = \dfrac{5}{6x^2 + 11x - 10}$

2. $g(x) = \dfrac{2}{72 - 2x^2}$ **3.** $h(x) = \dfrac{x}{3}$

4. Give examples of three functions, each with a domain that is the set of real numbers except -3 and 7.

Simplify the right-hand side of the equation.

5. $f(x) = \dfrac{6 - 3x}{x^2 - 5x + 6}$ **6.** $f(x) = \dfrac{9x^2 - 1}{18x^3 - 12x^2 + 2x}$

For Exercises 7–10, perform the indicated operation.

7. $\dfrac{5x^4}{3x^2 + 6x + 12} \cdot \dfrac{x^3 - 8}{15x^7}$

8. $\dfrac{p^2 - 4t^2}{p^2 + 6pt + 9t^2} \div \dfrac{p^2 - 3pt + 2t^2}{p^2 + 3pt}$

9. $\dfrac{5x + 12}{-2x^2 - 8x} - \dfrac{2x + 1}{x^2 + 2x - 8}$

10. $\dfrac{x + 2}{x^2 - 9} + \dfrac{3}{x^2 + 11x + 24}$

11. Perform the indicated operations:

$$\frac{3}{x^2 - 2x} \div \left(\frac{x}{5x - 10} - \frac{x - 1}{x^2 - 4} \right)$$

12. Let $f(x) = \dfrac{x + 1}{x - 5}$ and $g(x) = \dfrac{x - 2}{x + 4}$. Find an equation of $f - g$. Then find $(f - g)(0)$.

13. One ounce of Hormel Turkey Chili with Beans, contains 83.33 milligrams of sodium. How many grams of sodium are there in 1 pound of the chili? Round you answer to the second decimal place. Refer to the list of equivalent units in the margin of p. 495 as needed.

14. Simplify $\dfrac{5 + \dfrac{2}{x}}{3 - \dfrac{4}{x - 1}}$.

For Exercises 15 and 16, solve.

15. $\dfrac{2}{x - 1} - \dfrac{5}{x + 1} = \dfrac{4x}{x^2 - 1}$

16. $\dfrac{5}{w - 3} = \dfrac{w}{w - 2} + \dfrac{w}{w^2 - 5w + 6}$

17. Let $f(x) = \dfrac{2}{x - 4} + \dfrac{3}{x + 1}$. Find x when $f(x) = 5$.

For Exercises 18–20, let $f(x) = \dfrac{(x - 5)(x + 2)}{(x - 1)(x + 3)}$.

18. Find $f(-2)$.

19. Find $f(1)$.

20. Find x when $y = 0$.

For Exercises 21 and 22, find an equation that meets the given conditions.

21. W varies directly as t^2, and $W = 3$ when $t = 7$.

22. y varies inversely as $\sqrt{x}$, and $y = 8$ when $x = 25$.

23. It costs a bike manufacturer about $200 per bike for the materials to manufacture a line of mountain bikes. It also costs $10,000 each month for the manufacturing plant's lease, electricity, salaries, and so on.
  a. Let $C(n)$ be the total monthly cost (in dollars) if n bikes are manufactured in a certain month. Find an equation of C.
  b. Let $B(n)$ be the price (in dollars) the manufacturer should charge for each bike to break even by making and selling n bikes in a month. Find an equation of B.
  c. Let $P(n)$ be the price (in dollars) the manufacturer should charge for each bike to earn a profit of $150 per bike by making and selling n bikes in a month. Find an equation of P.
  d. Find $P(100)$. What does it mean in this situation?

24. A student plans to drive from San Francisco, California, to Salt Lake City, Utah. She will drive 400 miles in California, then 920 miles in Nevada and Utah. The speed limit is 70 mph in California and 75 mph in Nevada and Utah.
  a. Let $T(a)$ be the driving time (in hours) if the student drives a mph above the speed limits. Find an equation of T.
  b. Find $T(5)$. What does it mean in this situation?
  c. Find a when $T(a) = 17$. What does your result mean in this situation?

25. The frequency $g(L) = F$ (in hertz) of a tuning fork varies inversely as the square of the length L (in cm) of the prongs. The frequency is 50 hertz when the prong length is 8 cm.
  a. Find an equation of g.
  b. Find the frequency if the prong length is 6 cm.
  c. What is the prong length if the frequency is 200 hertz?
  d. Is g increasing or decreasing for $L > 0$? What does that mean in this situation?

26. Community centers provide health care to millions of mostly poor people. The numbers of such centers and the numbers of patients served are shown in Table 42 for various years.

Table 42 Numbers of Community Health Centers and Patients

Year	Number of Centers (thousands)	Number of Patients (thousands)
2001	0.76	10,000
2003	0.88	12,000
2005	0.96	14,000
2007	1.06	16,000
2009	1.15	18,000
2011	1.14	20,000

Source: *National Association of Community Health Centers*

  a. Let $C(t)$ be the number (in thousands) of community centers at t years since 2000. Find an equation of C.
  b. Let $P(t)$ be the number (in thousands) of patients at community centers at t years since 2000. Find an equation of P.
  c. Let $M(t)$ be the mean number of patients per community center at t years since 2000. Find an equation of M.
  d. Predict the mean number of patients per community center in 2017.
  e. Predict when the mean number of patients per community center will be 21,000 patients.

Radical Functions

How much spam do you receive? The percentage of e-mail that is spam has more than quadrupled since 1999 (see Table 1). In Exercise 75 of Homework 9.5, you will predict when 95% of e-mail will be spam.

In previous chapters, we worked with linear, exponential, logarithmic, polynomial, and rational functions. In Section 7.3, we worked with radical expressions. In this chapter, we will discuss how to simplify more types of radical expressions, as well as how to perform operations with them. We will also solve *radical equations in one variable*. Finally, we will use *square root functions* to make predictions, such as when the average credit card debt per household will be $13 thousand.

Table 1 Percentages of E-Mail That Is Spam

Year	Percent
1999	21
2002	56
2004	68
2006	80
2008	81
2010	85

Source: *IronPort*

9.1 Simplifying Radical Expressions

Objectives

» Convert expressions in radical form to exponential form and vice versa.

» Know the *product property for radicals* and the *power property for radicals.*

» Simplify radical expressions.

» Know the meaning of *radical function, square root function, radical model,* and *square root model.*

» Use a radical model to make an estimate or prediction.

In this section, we will discuss the meaning of a *radical expression* and how to use properties to simplify such an expression.

Radical Expressions

Recall from Section 4.2 that we can represent a principal nth root such as $x^{1/n}$ as $\sqrt[n]{x}$, where n is a counting number greater than 1. We say n is the **index** and the symbol $\sqrt{}$ is the **radical sign.** The notation for the principal square root of x, $\sqrt{x}$, is shorthand for $\sqrt[2]{x}$. An expression under the radical sign is called a **radicand.** In $\sqrt[5]{3x+6}$, the radicand is $3x + 6$. A radical sign together with an index and a radicand is called a **radical.** Here we label the radical sign, index, and radicand for the radical $\sqrt[4]{2x-7}$:

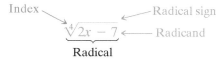

Some more radicals are $\sqrt[3]{21}$, $\sqrt{x}$, $\sqrt[3]{x^4}$, $\sqrt{5x-8}$, and $\sqrt[4]{(x+1)^3}$.

An expression that contains a radical is called a **radical expression.** Here are some radical expressions:

$$\sqrt[4]{85}, \quad \sqrt{x}, \quad \sqrt[3]{4x+9}, \quad 2\sqrt[3]{2x}+5\sqrt[4]{7}, \quad \left(8\sqrt{x}-5\right)\left(3\sqrt[3]{x}+4\right), \quad \frac{2\sqrt{x}-7}{6\sqrt{x}-4}$$

Recall from Section 4.2 that, for nonnegative a, $\sqrt[n]{a}$ is the nonnegative number whose nth power is a. If a is negative and n is odd, then $\sqrt[n]{a}$ is the (negative) number whose nth power is a. If a is negative and n is even, then $\sqrt[n]{a}$ is not a real number.

561

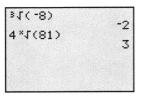

Figure 1 Verify the work

▶ **Example 1** Evaluating Radicals

Evaluate the radical.

1. $\sqrt[3]{-8}$

2. $\sqrt[4]{81}$

Solution

1. $\sqrt[3]{-8} = -2$, since $(-2)^3 = -8$.
2. $\sqrt[4]{81} = 3$, since $3^4 = 81$.

We use a graphing calculator to verify our work (see Fig. 1). To enter $\sqrt[3]{-8}$, press $\boxed{\text{MATH}}$ **4** $\boxed{(-)}$ **8** $\boxed{)}$ $\boxed{\text{ENTER}}$. To enter $\sqrt[4]{81}$, press **4** $\boxed{\text{MATH}}$ **5** $\boxed{(}$ **81** $\boxed{)}$ $\boxed{\text{ENTER}}$.

▶

Recall from Section 7.3 that a number that has a square root that is rational is called a *perfect square*. More generally, a number that has an nth root that is rational is called a **perfect nth power.** For example, -8 is a perfect 3rd power, or **perfect cube,** because $\sqrt[3]{-8} = -2 = \dfrac{-2}{1}$ is rational. The number 81 is a perfect 4th power, because $\sqrt[4]{81} = 3 = \dfrac{3}{1}$ is rational.

Recall from Section 4.2 that if $a^{1/n}$ is defined, then
$$a^{m/n} = \left(a^{1/n}\right)^m = \left(a^m\right)^{1/n}$$
or we can write
$$a^{m/n} = \left(\sqrt[n]{a}\right)^m = \sqrt[n]{a^m}$$
For example, $x^{3/5} = \left(\sqrt[5]{x}\right)^3 = \sqrt[5]{x^3}$. We say the expressions $\left(\sqrt[n]{x}\right)^m$ and $\sqrt[n]{x^m}$ are in *radical form* and the expression $x^{m/n}$ is in *exponential form*.

▶ **Example 2** Writing Exponential and Radical Forms

If the expression is in exponential form, write it in radical form. If it is in radical form, write it in exponential form.

1. $x^{3/7}$ 2. $\sqrt{x^5}$ 3. $(3w + 1)^{4/5}$ 4. $\sqrt[8]{(2x + 5)^3}$

Solution

1. $x^{3/7} = \sqrt[7]{x^3}$
2. $\sqrt{x^5}$ is shorthand for $\sqrt[2]{x^5}$. So, $\sqrt{x^5} = x^{5/2}$.
3. $(3w + 1)^{4/5} = \sqrt[5]{(3w + 1)^4}$
4. $\sqrt[8]{(2x + 5)^3} = (2x + 5)^{3/8}$

▶

Simplifying Radical Expressions

It will be helpful, at times, to write a radical expression in exponential form and use exponential properties to simplify the result.

▶ **Example 3** Simplifying Radical Expressions

Write the expression in exponential form; then simplify the result.

1. $\sqrt[3]{x^3}$ 2. $\sqrt[3]{x^{12}}$ 3. $\sqrt[3]{x^{21}}$

Solution

1. $\sqrt[3]{x^3} = x^{3/3} = x^1 = x$
2. $\sqrt[3]{x^{12}} = x^{12/3} = x^4$
3. $\sqrt[3]{x^{21}} = x^{21/3} = x^7$

▶

In addition to the numbers that are perfect nth powers, some variable expressions are perfect nth powers. As in Example 3, we can eliminate the radical sign from expressions of the form $\sqrt[3]{x^k}$ when k is a multiple of 3. In general, if $\sqrt[n]{x}$ is defined, we can eliminate the radical sign from $\sqrt[n]{x^k}$ when k is a multiple of the index n. If n is a counting number greater than 1 and k is a multiple of n, we say x^k is a **perfect nth power.**

Here are perfect nth powers for $n = 2$, $n = 3$, and $n = 4$:

Value of n	Name	Examples	Description of Exponents
2	perfect square	$x^2, x^4, x^6, x^8, \ldots$	multiples of 2
3	perfect cube	$x^3, x^6, x^9, x^{12}, \ldots$	multiples of 3
4	perfect 4th power	$x^4, x^8, x^{12}, x^{16}, \ldots$	multiples of 4

The base of a perfect nth power can be any variable expression. For example, $(7x + 2)^{15}$ is a perfect 5th power; furthermore, we can find the 5th root of it:

$$\sqrt[5]{(7x + 2)^{15}} = (7x + 2)^{15/5} = (7x + 2)^3$$

In Section 7.3, we studied the product property for square roots,

$$\sqrt{ab} = \sqrt{a}\sqrt{b}$$

where $a \geq 0$ and $b \geq 0$. The more general product property for radicals,

$$\sqrt[n]{ab} = \sqrt[n]{a}\sqrt[n]{b}$$

is true for any counting-number index n greater than 1 where $\sqrt[n]{a}$ and $\sqrt[n]{b}$ are defined. Here is the proof:

$$\sqrt[n]{ab} = (ab)^{1/n} \quad \textit{Write in exponential form.}$$
$$= a^{1/n}b^{1/n} \quad \textit{$(ab)^m = a^m b^m$}$$
$$= \sqrt[n]{a}\sqrt[n]{b} \quad \textit{Write in radical form.}$$

> **Product Property for Radicals**
>
> If $\sqrt[n]{a}$ and $\sqrt[n]{b}$ are defined, then
>
> $$\sqrt[n]{ab} = \sqrt[n]{a}\sqrt[n]{b}$$
>
> In words, the nth root of a product is the product of the nth roots.

A radical with index n is **simplified** when the radicand does not have any factors that are perfect nth powers (other than -1 or 1) and the index is as small as possible. We will discuss how to find the smallest possible index later in this section.

Here we use the product property for radicals to simplify $\sqrt{25x^6}$:

$$\sqrt{25x^6} = \sqrt{25}\sqrt{x^6} \quad \textit{Product property: $\sqrt[n]{ab} = \sqrt[n]{a}\sqrt[n]{b}$}$$
$$= 5x^3 \quad \textit{$\sqrt{25} = 5$; $\sqrt{x^6} = x^3$ for $x \geq 0$}$$

Notice that the radicand $25x^6$ is the product of the perfect squares 25 and x^6. We can use the product property to simplify any radical with index n whose radicand is a product of nth powers.

We can also use the product property to simplify some radicals with index n whose radicand is *not* a product of perfect nth powers only. For those radicals, we write the radicand as a product of one or more perfect nth powers and another expression with no factors that are perfect nth powers. Then we apply the product property.

▶ **Example 4** Simplifying Radical Expressions

Simplify. Assume x is nonnegative.

1. $\sqrt{200}$ **2.** $\sqrt{x^7}$ **3.** $\sqrt{12w^{11}}$

Solution

1. The numbers 4, 25, and 100 are all perfect-square factors of 200. Recall from Section 7.3 that it is most efficient to work with the largest one, which is 100. So, we write 200 as $100 \cdot 2$ and apply the product property for radicals:

$$\sqrt{200} = \sqrt{100 \cdot 2} \quad \text{\textit{100 is largest perfect-square factor.}}$$
$$= \sqrt{100}\sqrt{2} \quad \text{\textit{Product property: }} \sqrt[n]{ab} = \sqrt[n]{a}\sqrt[n]{b}$$
$$= 10\sqrt{2} \quad \text{\textit{$\sqrt{100} = 10$}}$$

2. The powers x^2, x^4, and x^6 are all perfect-square factors of x^7. Since x^6 is the perfect-square factor with the largest exponent, we write x^7 as $x^6 \cdot x$ and apply the product property for radicals:

$$\sqrt{x^7} = \sqrt{x^6 \cdot x} \quad \text{\textit{x^6 is perfect-square factor with largest exponent.}}$$
$$= \sqrt{x^6}\sqrt{x} \quad \text{\textit{Product property: }} \sqrt[n]{ab} = \sqrt[n]{a}\sqrt[n]{b}$$
$$= x^3\sqrt{x} \quad \text{\textit{$\sqrt{x^6} = x^3$ for $x \geq 0$}}$$

3. The number 4 is the largest perfect-square factor of 12, and the power w^{10} is the perfect-square factor of w^{11} with the largest exponent:

$$\sqrt{12w^{11}} = \sqrt{4 \cdot 3 \cdot w^{10} \cdot w} \quad \text{\textit{4 and w^{10} are perfect squares.}}$$
$$= \sqrt{4 \cdot w^{10} \cdot 3w} \quad \text{\textit{Rearrange factors.}}$$
$$= \sqrt{4}\sqrt{w^{10}}\sqrt{3w} \quad \text{\textit{Product property: }} \sqrt[n]{ab} = \sqrt[n]{a}\sqrt[n]{b}$$
$$= 2w^5\sqrt{3w} \quad \text{\textit{$\sqrt{4} = 2$; $\sqrt{w^{10}} = w^5$ for $w \geq 0$}}$$

In Example 4, we had to decide which perfect nth powers to use to factor the radicands. Our work in Example 4 suggests two guidelines:

- **If the radicand has more than one numerical factor that is a perfect nth power, select the largest one.**
- **If the radicand has more than one factor that is a perfect nth power with the same variable base, select the one with the largest exponent.**

▶ **Example 5**   Simplifying Radical Expressions

Simplify. Assume all variables are nonnegative.

1. $\sqrt{48x^4y^{13}}$ 2. $\sqrt{(5x + 3)^9}$

Solution

1. $$\sqrt{48x^4y^{13}} = \sqrt{16 \cdot 3 \cdot x^4 \cdot y^{12} \cdot y} \quad \text{\textit{16, x^4, and y^{12} are perfect squares.}}$$
$$= \sqrt{16 \cdot x^4 \cdot y^{12} \cdot 3y} \quad \text{\textit{Rearrange factors.}}$$
$$= \sqrt{16}\sqrt{x^4}\sqrt{y^{12}}\sqrt{3y} \quad \text{\textit{Product property: }} \sqrt[n]{ab} = \sqrt[n]{a}\sqrt[n]{b}$$
$$= 4x^2y^6\sqrt{3y} \quad \text{\textit{$\sqrt{16} = 4$; $\sqrt{x^4} = x^2$ for $x \geq 0$; $\sqrt{y^{12}} = y^6$ for $y \geq 0$}}$$

2. $$\sqrt{(5x + 3)^9} = \sqrt{(5x + 3)^8(5x + 3)} \quad \text{\textit{$(5x + 3)^8$ is a perfect-square factor.}}$$
$$= \sqrt{(5x + 3)^8}\sqrt{5x + 3} \quad \text{\textit{Product property: }} \sqrt[n]{ab} = \sqrt[n]{a}\sqrt[n]{b}$$
$$= (5x + 3)^4\sqrt{5x + 3} \quad \text{\textit{$\sqrt{(5x + 3)^8} = (5x + 3)^4$ for $5x + 3 \geq 0$}}$$

We use a graphing calculator table to verify our work (see Fig. 2).

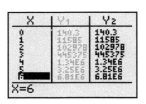

Figure 2 Verify the work

In Example 5, we simplified square root expressions. In Example 6, we simplify radical expressions with index n greater than 2.

▶ **Example 6** Simplifying Radical Expressions

Simplify. Assume all variables are nonnegative.

1. $\sqrt[3]{40x^{17}}$ **2.** $\sqrt[4]{80x^{20}y^{15}}$ **3.** $\sqrt[5]{(2x+7)^{34}}$

Solution

1. $\sqrt[3]{40x^{17}} = \sqrt[3]{8\cdot 5\cdot x^{15}\cdot x^2}$ *8 and x^{15} are perfect 3rd powers (perfect cubes).*

$\qquad\qquad = \sqrt[3]{8\cdot x^{15}\cdot 5x^2}$ *Rearrange factors.*

$\qquad\qquad = \sqrt[3]{8}\sqrt[3]{x^{15}}\sqrt[3]{5x^2}$ $\sqrt[n]{ab} = \sqrt[n]{a}\sqrt[n]{b}$

$\qquad\qquad = 2x^5\sqrt[3]{5x^2}$ $\sqrt[3]{8}=2;\ \sqrt[3]{x^{15}}=x^5$

2. $\sqrt[4]{80x^{20}y^{15}} = \sqrt[4]{16\cdot 5\cdot x^{20}\cdot y^{12}\cdot y^3}$ *16, x^{20}, and y^{12} are perfect 4th powers.*

$\qquad\qquad = \sqrt[4]{16\cdot x^{20}\cdot y^{12}\cdot 5y^3}$ *Rearrange factors.*

$\qquad\qquad = \sqrt[4]{16}\sqrt[4]{x^{20}}\sqrt[4]{y^{12}}\sqrt[4]{5y^3}$ $\sqrt[n]{ab} = \sqrt[n]{a}\sqrt[n]{b}$

$\qquad\qquad = 2x^5y^3\sqrt[4]{5y^3}$ $\sqrt[4]{16}=2;\ \sqrt[4]{x^{20}}=x^5$ *for $x\ge 0$;* $\sqrt[4]{y^{12}}=y^3$ *for $y\ge 0$*

3. $\sqrt[5]{(2x+7)^{34}} = \sqrt[5]{(2x+7)^{30}(2x+7)^4}$ *$(2x+7)^{30}$ is a perfect 5th power.*

$\qquad\qquad = \sqrt[5]{(2x+7)^{30}}\sqrt[5]{(2x+7)^4}$ $\sqrt[n]{ab} = \sqrt[n]{a}\sqrt[n]{b}$

$\qquad\qquad = (2x+7)^6\sqrt[5]{(2x+7)^4}$ $\sqrt[5]{(2x+7)^{30}} = (2x+7)^6$

Consider the radical expression $\sqrt[8]{x^6}$, $x\ge 0$. Although the radicand x^6 does not have factors that are perfect 8th powers, we can write the radical with a smaller index:

$$\sqrt[8]{x^6} = x^{6/8} = x^{3/4} = \sqrt[4]{x^3}$$

If $\sqrt[n]{x}$ is defined and the fraction $\dfrac{m}{n}$ can be simplified, then we can decrease the index of $\sqrt[n]{x^m}$ by writing $\sqrt[n]{x^m} = x^{m/n}$ and simplifying the exponent $\dfrac{m}{n}$.

Simplifying a radical expression includes writing the result with as small an index as possible.

▶ **Example 7** Simplifying Radical Expressions

Simplify. Assume $x\ge 0$.

1. $\sqrt[12]{(3x+7)^8}$ **2.** $\sqrt[10]{4}$ **3.** $\sqrt[4]{81x^6}$ **4.** $\sqrt[3]{\sqrt{t}}$

Solution

1. $\sqrt[12]{(3x+7)^8} = (3x+7)^{8/12}$ *Write in exponential form.*

$\qquad\qquad = (3x+7)^{2/3}$ *Simplify exponent.*

$\qquad\qquad = \sqrt[3]{(3x+7)^2}$ *Write in radical form.*

2. $\sqrt[10]{4} = \sqrt[10]{2^2}$ $4 = 2^2$

$\qquad = 2^{2/10}$ *Write in exponential form.*

$\qquad = 2^{1/5}$ *Simplify exponent.*

$\qquad = \sqrt[5]{2}$ *Write in radical form.*

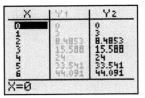

Figure 3 Verify the work

3. $\sqrt[4]{81x^6} = \sqrt[4]{81 \cdot x^4 \cdot x^2}$ *81 and x^4 are perfect 4th powers.*

$\qquad = \sqrt[4]{81}\,\sqrt[4]{x^4}\,\sqrt[4]{x^2}$ *$\sqrt[n]{ab} = \sqrt[n]{a}\sqrt[n]{b}$*

$\qquad = 3x\sqrt[4]{x^2}$ *$\sqrt[4]{81} = 3$; $\sqrt[4]{x^4} = x$ for $x \geq 0$*

$\qquad = 3x \cdot x^{2/4}$ *Write in exponential form.*

$\qquad = 3x \cdot x^{1/2}$ *Simplify exponent.*

$\qquad = 3x\sqrt{x}$ *Write in radical form.*

We verify our work by comparing graphing calculator tables for $y = \sqrt[4]{81x^6}$ and $y = 3x\sqrt{x}$ for $x \geq 0$ (see Fig. 3).

4. $\sqrt[3]{\sqrt{t}} = \left(t^{1/2}\right)^{1/3}$ *Write in exponential form.*

$\qquad = t^{\frac{1}{2} \cdot \frac{1}{3}}$ *Multiply exponents: $(b^m)^n = b^{mn}$*

$\qquad = t^{1/6}$ *Multiply numerators; multiply denominators.*

$\qquad = \sqrt[6]{t}$ *Write in radical form.*

▶ **Simplifying a Radical Expression**

To simplify a radical expression with index n,

1. Find perfect nth-power factors of the radicand.
2. Apply the product property for radicals.
3. Find the nth root of each perfect nth power.
4. Write the radical with as small an index as possible.

Here we consider the expression $\sqrt[n]{x^n}$, where x is negative. First, we compare $\sqrt{x^2}$ for $x = -4$ and for $x = 4$:

$$\sqrt{(-4)^2} = \sqrt{16} = 4 \qquad \sqrt{4^2} = \sqrt{16} = 4$$

So, when -4 or 4 is substituted for x in the expression $\sqrt{x^2}$, we get the same result: 4. This is precisely what happens if we substitute -4 or 4 in the absolute value (Section A.3) expression $|x|$:

$$|-4| = 4 \qquad |4| = 4$$

These examples suggest that $\sqrt{x^2} = |x|$. It turns out that $\sqrt[n]{x^n} = |x|$ for any even index n.

Here are some examples where n is odd:

$$\sqrt[3]{4^3} = \sqrt[3]{64} = 4 \qquad\qquad \sqrt[5]{2^5} = \sqrt[5]{32} = 2$$
$$\sqrt[3]{(-4)^3} = \sqrt[3]{-64} = -4 \qquad \sqrt[5]{(-2)^5} = \sqrt[5]{-32} = -2$$

These examples suggest that $\sqrt[n]{x^n} = x$ if n is odd.

▶ **Power Property for Radicals**

Let n be a counting number greater than 1:

- If n is even, then $\sqrt[n]{x^n} = |x|$.
- If n is odd, then $\sqrt[n]{x^n} = x$.

For example, $\sqrt[8]{(-5)^8} = |-5| = 5$ and $\sqrt[7]{(-3)^7} = -3$.

Radical Functions

A **radical function** is a function whose equation contains a radical with a variable in the radicand. Here are some examples of radical functions:

$$f(x) = \sqrt[4]{x} \qquad g(x) = 8\sqrt{x} - 3 \qquad h(x) = 6\sqrt[3]{(x+7)^2} \qquad k(x) = \frac{\sqrt[3]{x} - 5}{\sqrt{x} + 1}$$

▶ **Example 8** Evaluating Radical Functions

For $f(x) = \sqrt[3]{2x - 1}$ and $g(x) = -3\sqrt{x} + 7$, find the following.

1. $f(14)$ **2.** $f(6)$ **3.** $g(16)$

Solution

1. $f(14) = \sqrt[3]{2(14) - 1} = \sqrt[3]{27} = 3$

2. $f(6) = \sqrt[3]{2(6) - 1} = \sqrt[3]{11}$

3. $g(16) = -3\sqrt{16} + 7 = -3(4) + 7 = -5$

A **square root function** is a radical function in which any radicals are square root radicals. For example, the function $h(x) = 9\sqrt{x - 3} + 4$ is a square root function. In Example 9, we graph the square root function $f(x) = \sqrt{x}$.

▶ **Example 9** Graphing a Square Root Function

Sketch the graph of $f(x) = \sqrt{x}$.

Solution

We list some input–output pairs in Table 2. We choose perfect-square inputs because we can find their outputs mentally. Since the radicand of $\sqrt{x}$ must be nonnegative, we cannot choose any negative numbers as inputs. Then we sketch the graph of f (see Fig. 4).

Table 2 Input–Output Pairs of $f(x) = \sqrt{x}$

x	y
0	0
1	1
4	2
9	3
16	4

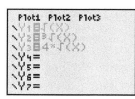

Figure 4 Graph of $f(x) = \sqrt{x}$

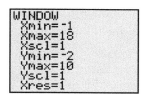

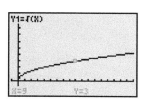

Figure 5 Verify the graph of $f(x) = \sqrt{x}$

We use a graphing calculator to verify our graph (see Fig. 5).

We use a graphing calculator to draw the graphs of $y = \sqrt{x}$, $y = \sqrt[3]{x}$, and $y = \sqrt[4]{x}$ (see Fig. 6).

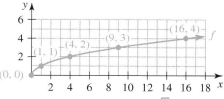

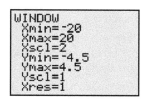

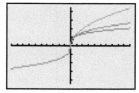

Figure 6 Graphs of $y = \sqrt{x}$, $y = \sqrt[3]{x}$, and $y = \sqrt[4]{x}$

Radical Model

A **radical model** is a radical function, or its graph, that describes an authentic situation. Radical functions can model a variety of situations, including the rise in temperature of an enclosed car, the period of a planet, the length of a braking car's skid marks, and the percentage of e-mail that is spam.

Table 3 Percentages of Foundations That Compensate All of Their Board Members

Asset Group (millions of dollars)	Asset Used to Represent Asset Group (millions of dollars)	Percent
0–5	2.5	4
5–10	7.5	8
10–25	17.5	10
25–50	37.5	15
50–100	75	20
100–250	175	21
250–500	375	32

Source: *New York Times*

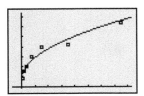

Figure 7 Check the fit

A **square root model** is a square root function, or its graph, that describes an authentic situation. We will work with such a model in Example 10.

▶ **Example 10**   Using a Square Root Model to Make a Prediction

The percentages of foundations that compensate all of their board members are shown in Table 3 for various assets. Let $f(a)$ be the percentage of foundations with assets of a million dollars that compensate all of their board members. A model of the situation is $f(a) = 1.5\sqrt{a} + 4$.

1. Use a graphing calculator to draw the graph of f and, in the same viewing window, the scattergram of the data. Does the graph of f fit the data well?
2. Estimate the percentage of foundations with assets of $30 million that compensate all of their board members.

Solution

1. The graph of f and the scattergram of the data are shown in Fig. 7. The model appears to fit the data well.
2. We evaluate f at 30:

$$f(30) = 1.5\sqrt{30} + 4 \approx 12.22$$

About 12.2% of foundations with assets of $30 million compensate all of their board members, according to the model.

Group Exploration

Index property for radicals

Assume $x \geq 0$.

1. Write the expression with as small an index as possible. [**Hint:** First write the expression in exponential form.]

   a. $\sqrt[8]{x^6}$ **b.** $\sqrt[6]{x^4}$

   c. $\sqrt[16]{x^{10}}$ **d.** $\sqrt[9]{x^3}$

   e. $\sqrt[22]{x^4}$ **f.** $\sqrt[30]{x^{25}}$

2. Let k, m, and n be counting numbers, where m and n have no common factors. Write the expression $\sqrt[kn]{x^{km}}$ with as small an index as possible. Include the exponential form of the expression $\sqrt[kn]{x^{km}}$.

3. Describe what your result from Problem 2 tells you about simplifying a radical expression. Use this observation to simplify $\sqrt[20]{x^{16}}$ in one step.

▶ **Tips for Success**   **Use 3-by-5 Cards**

Do you have trouble memorizing definitions and properties? If so, try writing a word or phrase on one side of a 3-by-5 card. On the other side, put its definition or state a property and how it can be applied. For example, you could write "product property for radicals" on one side of a card and "$\sqrt[n]{ab} = \sqrt[n]{a}\sqrt[n]{b}$, where n is a counting number and $\sqrt[n]{a}$ and $\sqrt[n]{b}$ are defined" on the other side. You could also describe, in your own words, the meaning of the property and how you can apply it. Once you have completed a card for each definition and property, shuffle the cards and quiz yourself until you are confident you know the definitions and properties and how to apply them. Quiz yourself again later to make sure you have retained the information.

In addition to memorizing definitions and properties, it is important you continue to strive to understand their meanings and how to apply them.

Homework 9.1

For extra help ▶ **MyMathLab®** 🔲 Watch the videos in MyMathLab 🔵 Download the MyDashboard App

If the expression is in exponential form, write it in radical form. If it is in radical form, write it in exponential form.

1. $x^{2/5}$
2. $x^{3/8}$
3. $\sqrt[4]{x^3}$
4. $\sqrt[9]{x^5}$
5. $\sqrt{w}$
6. $\sqrt[3]{t}$
7. $(2x + 9)^{3/7}$
8. $(5x + 1)^{5/6}$
9. $\sqrt{(3k + 2)^4}$
10. $\sqrt[6]{8m + 3}$

Simplify. Assume each variable is nonnegative.

11. $\sqrt{50}$
12. $\sqrt{20}$
13. $\sqrt{x^8}$
14. $\sqrt{x^{18}}$
15. $\sqrt{36x^6}$
16. $\sqrt{4x^4}$
17. $\sqrt{5a^2b^{12}}$
18. $\sqrt{7a^{10}b^{14}}$
19. $\sqrt{x^9}$
20. $\sqrt{x^{15}}$
21. $\sqrt{24x^5}$
22. $\sqrt{12x^{13}}$
23. $\sqrt{80x^3y^8}$
24. $\sqrt{27x^{10}y^7}$
25. $\sqrt{200a^3b^5}$
26. $\sqrt{75a^{15}b^9}$
27. $\sqrt{(2x + 5)^8}$
28. $\sqrt{(3x + 4)^2}$
29. $\sqrt{(6t + 3)^5}$
30. $\sqrt{(7w + 1)^{13}}$
31. $\sqrt[3]{27}$
32. $\sqrt[5]{32}$
33. $\sqrt[6]{x^6}$
34. $\sqrt[9]{x^9}$
35. $\sqrt[3]{8x^3}$
36. $\sqrt[4]{16x^4}$
37. $\sqrt[5]{-32x^{20}}$
38. $\sqrt[3]{-27x^{18}}$
39. $\sqrt[4]{81a^{12}b^{28}}$
40. $\sqrt[5]{32a^{15}b^{30}}$
41. $\sqrt[6]{x^{17}}$
42. $\sqrt[8]{x^{25}}$
43. $\sqrt[3]{-125a^{17}b^{12}}$
44. $\sqrt[3]{-8a^{21}b^{29}}$
45. $\sqrt[5]{64x^{39}y^7}$
46. $\sqrt[4]{32x^{19}y^{13}}$
47. $\sqrt[3]{(6xy)^5}$
48. $\sqrt[7]{(4x^2y)^7}$
49. $\sqrt[4]{(3x + 6)^4}$
50. $\sqrt[8]{(5x + 2)^8}$
51. $\sqrt[5]{(4p + 7)^{20}}$
52. $\sqrt[3]{(3k + 5)^{12}}$
53. $\sqrt[6]{(2x + 9)^{31}}$
54. $\sqrt[5]{(4x + 5)^{43}}$

Simplify. (Write your result with as small an index n as possible.) Assume each variable is nonnegative.

55. $\sqrt[8]{x^6}$
56. $\sqrt[6]{x^3}$
57. $\sqrt[6]{x^4}$
58. $\sqrt[9]{x^6}$
59. $\sqrt[12]{(2m + 7)^{10}}$
60. $\sqrt[21]{(3r + 5)^{14}}$
61. $\sqrt[6]{x^{14}}$
62. $\sqrt[8]{x^{22}}$
63. $\sqrt[6]{27}$
64. $\sqrt[8]{25}$
65. $\sqrt[4]{\sqrt[3]{p}}$
66. $\sqrt[5]{\sqrt{t}}$
67. $\sqrt[10]{16x^8}$
68. $\sqrt[12]{125x^9}$
69. $\sqrt[4]{\sqrt{ab}}$
70. $\sqrt[3]{\sqrt[5]{3w}}$

For $f(x) = \sqrt[5]{x}$, $g(x) = \sqrt[3]{3x + 2}$, and $h(x) = 2\sqrt{x} - 5$, find the following.

71. $f(-32)$
72. $f(32)$
73. $g(2)$
74. $g(-22)$
75. $g(-7)$
76. $g(5)$
77. $h(49)$
78. $h(25)$

79. Graph $f(x) = 2\sqrt[3]{x}$ by hand. [**Hint:** Evaluate *f* at some perfect cubes.]

80. Graph $g(x) = 3\sqrt[4]{x}$ by hand. [**Hint:** Evaluate *g* at some perfect 4th powers.]

81. The average temperature rises above the *ambient temperature* (outside temperature) in an enclosed vehicle are shown in Table 4 for various elapsed times.

Table 4 Average Temperature Rises in an Enclosed Vehicle (for Ambient Temperatures between 72°F and 96°F)

Elapsed Time (minutes)	Average Temperature Rise (°F)
0	0
10	19
20	29
30	34
40	38
50	41
60	43

Source: *Jan Null, Department of Geosciences, San Francisco State University*

Let $f(t)$ be the average temperature rise (°F) in a vehicle at *t* minutes after the vehicle is enclosed. ("Cracking" the windows had little effect on the data.) A model of the situation is $f(t) = 8.5\sqrt[5]{t^2}$.

a. Use a graphing calculator to draw the graph of the model and, in the same viewing window, the scattergram of the data. Does the model fit the data well?

b. Estimate the average temperature rise 24 minutes after the vehicle is enclosed if the ambient temperature is 85°F.

c. Estimate the *temperature* inside the car 45 minutes after the vehicle is enclosed if the ambient temperature is 90°F.

d. Since 1998, more than 300 children have died of hyperthermia after being left inside a hot vehicle. A body core temperature of 107°F is usually fatal. Use TRACE to estimate how long it would take for the temperature in an enclosed vehicle to reach 107°F if the ambient temperature is 80°F.

82. The *Beaufort wind scale*, which ranges from 0 to 12, describes wind intensities. Some of the even-numbered *Beaufort numbers* and the corresponding wind speeds and weather conditions are shown in Table 5.

Table 5 Beaufort Numbers, Wind Speeds, and Weather Conditions

Beaufort Number	Wind Speed Group (miles per hour)	Wind Speed Used to Represent Wind Speed Group (miles per hour)	Weather Conditions
0	0	0	calm
2	4–7	5.5	light breeze
4	13–18	15.5	moderate breeze
6	25–31	28.0	strong breeze
8	39–46	42.5	gale
10	55–63	59.0	storm

Source: Stormfax® Weather Almanac

Let $V = f(B)$ be the wind speed (in miles per hour) that corresponds to the Beaufort number B. A model of the situation is $f(B) = 1.87\sqrt{B^3}$.

a. Use a graphing calculator to draw the graph of the model and, in the same viewing window, the scattergram of the data. Does the model fit the data well?

b. The U.S. Coast Guard issues a small-craft advisory when the Beaufort number is 6 or 7. Estimate the wind speed of a near gale, which has Beaufort number 7.

c. Estimate the wind speed in a violent storm, which has Beaufort number 11.

d. The quadratic function $Q(B) = 0.33B^2 + 2.72B - 0.46$ is a model of the situation. Does Q fit the data well? Which model, f or Q, describes the wind speed better when the weather is calm? Explain.

83. A *tsunami* is a fast-moving sea wave typically caused by an underwater earthquake. An earthquake in the Indian Ocean in 2004 caused tsunamis that killed more than 265,000 people. The speed (in meters per second) $f(d)$ of a tsunami can be modeled by the function $f(d) = \sqrt{gd}$, where g is a constant approximately equal to 9.8 and d is the average depth (in meters) of the water.

a. The Indian Ocean has an average depth of 3890 meters. Estimate the speed in meters per second of a tsunami in the Indian Ocean.

b. Find $f(1000)$, $f(2000)$, and $f(3000)$. Is f an increasing or a decreasing function? What does that mean in this situation?

c. As a tsunami slows down, it gets taller. As a tsunami approaches the shore, what happens to the speed and height of the tsunami?

d. Convert your result in part (a) to units of miles per hour. (One mile is approximately 1609 meters.)

84. Suppose a driver traveling on a dry road slams on the brakes. Let D be the distance (in feet) that the car will skid and S be the speed (in miles per hour) before braking. The relationship between D and S is described by the model $S = \sqrt{30FD}$, where F is a drag factor—a measure of the roughness of the road surface. The drag factor on new concrete is 0.95; on polished concrete or asphalt, it is 0.75.

a. A motorist involved in an accident claims that he was driving at the speed limit, 50 miles per hour. The car's skid marks on the new concrete road are 120 feet long. Assuming the motorist applied the brakes suddenly, estimate his speed before braking.

b. If the motorist first applied the brakes lightly, then forcefully applied them after a few seconds, explain why your result in part (a) is an underestimate of his speed before braking.

Concepts

85. A student says $\sqrt{x^{16}}$ is equal to x^4, since $\sqrt{16} = 4$. What would you tell this student?

86. Is the statement $\sqrt[n]{a + b} = \sqrt[n]{a} + \sqrt[n]{b}$ true or false for all values of a and b where $\sqrt[n]{a}$ and $\sqrt[n]{b}$ are defined? [**Hint:** Substitute values of a, b, and n in the two expressions and compare the results.]

87. A student tries to solve $\sqrt[6]{x^3}$:

$$\sqrt[6]{x^3} = x^{6/3}$$
$$= x^2$$

Describe any errors. Then simplify the expression correctly.

88. A student tries to simplify $\sqrt[3]{(a + b)^3}$:

$$\sqrt[3]{(a + b)^3} = \sqrt[3]{a^3 + b^3}$$
$$= \sqrt[3]{a^3} + \sqrt[3]{b^3}$$
$$= a + b$$

Describe any errors. Then simplify the expression correctly.

89. Write the expression $\sqrt[n]{\sqrt[n]{x}}$ with one radical sign. [**Hint:** Write the expression in exponential form.]

90. a. Use a graphing calculator to draw a graph of the given function. What do you notice about the graph?

    i. $y = \sqrt[3]{x^3}$

    ii. $y = \sqrt[5]{x^5}$

    iii. $y = \sqrt[7]{x^7}$

b. Compare your graphs in part (a) with the graph of $y = x$. Explain how your observation relates to the power property for radicals.

c. Use a graphing calculator to draw a graph of the given function. What do you notice about the graph?

    i. $y = \sqrt{x^2}$ **ii.** $y = \sqrt[4]{x^4}$ **iii.** $y = \sqrt[6]{x^6}$

d. Compare your graphs in part (c) with the graph of $y = |x|$. Explain how your observation relates to the power property for radicals. [***Graphing Calculator:*** The absolute value choice "abs(" is located in the "NUM" menu. ("NUM" is in the "MATH" menu.)]

91. In this exercise, you will explore another version of the power property. Simplify.

    a. $\left(\sqrt{x}\right)^2$ **b.** $\left(\sqrt[3]{x}\right)^3$ **c.** $\left(\sqrt[n]{x}\right)^n$

92. Describe how to simplify a radical expression. (See page 4 for guidelines on writing a good response.)

Related Review

Assume each variable is nonnegative.

93. a. Simplify $\sqrt{16x^4y^6}$ by using the product property for radicals.

b. Simplify $\sqrt{16x^4y^6}$ first by writing the expression in exponential form, then by using properties of exponents.

c. Compare the results that you found in parts (a) and (b).

94. a. Simplify $\sqrt[3]{8x^6y^9}$ by using the product property for radicals.

b. Simplify $\sqrt[3]{8x^6y^9}$ first by writing the expression in exponential form, then by using properties of exponents.

c. Compare the results you found in parts (a) and (b).

Expressions, Equations, Functions, and Graphs

Perform the indicated instruction. Then use words such as linear, quadratic, cubic, exponential, logarithmic, rational, radical, polynomial, degree, function, one variable, *and* two variables *to describe the expression, equation, or system.*

95. Solve $\dfrac{2x}{x^2 + x - 6} - \dfrac{3x - 1}{x^2 + 6x + 9} = \dfrac{-3}{x + 3}$.

96. Solve $2x^2 - 4x - 3 = 0$ by completing the square.

97. Find the difference $\dfrac{2x}{x^2 + x - 6} - \dfrac{3x - 1}{x^2 + 6x + 9}$.

98. Graph $f(x) = 2x^2 - 4x - 3$ by hand.

99. Find the domain of $f(x) = \dfrac{2x}{x^2 + x - 6}$.

100. Solve $4(2x - 5)^2 = 48$.

▼9.2 Adding, Subtracting, and Multiplying Radical Expressions

Objectives

» Add, subtract, and multiply radical expressions.

» Know another version of the power property for radicals.

» Simplify the square of a radical expression with two terms.

In this section, we add, subtract, and multiply radical expressions. We also simplify the square of a radical with two terms.

Adding and Subtracting Radical Expressions

We can use the distributive law to add like terms, such as $2x$ and $7x$:

$$2x + 7x = (2 + 7)x = 9x$$

How do we add (or subtract) radical expressions? We can again use the distributive law if the radicals are like radicals. We say $2\sqrt[3]{x}$ and $7\sqrt[3]{x}$ are like radicals, because they have the same index *and* the same radicand. In general, radicals that have the same index and the same radicand are called **like radicals.**

We add the like radicals $2\sqrt[3]{x}$ and $7\sqrt[3]{x}$ as follows:

$$2\sqrt[3]{x} + 7\sqrt[3]{x} = (2 + 7)\sqrt[3]{x} = 9\sqrt[3]{x}$$

To add or subtract like radicals, we use the distributive law. When we add or subtract like radicals, we say we *combine like radicals.*

▶ **Example 1**   Combining Like Radicals

Combine like radicals.

1. $3\sqrt{x} + 6\sqrt{x}$

2. $4\sqrt[5]{3xy^2} - 2\sqrt[5]{3xy^2}$

3. $4\sqrt[3]{x} + 5\sqrt[6]{x}$

4. $3\sqrt[4]{x} - 2\sqrt[4]{x} + 1$

Solution

1. $3\sqrt{x} + 6\sqrt{x} = (3 + 6)\sqrt{x}$ *Distributive law*

$\qquad\qquad\quad = 9\sqrt{x}$ *Add.*

2. $4\sqrt[5]{3xy^2} - 2\sqrt[5]{3xy^2} = (4 - 2)\sqrt[5]{3xy^2}$ *Distributive law*

$\qquad\qquad\qquad\qquad = 2\sqrt[5]{3xy^2}$ *Subtract.*

3. Since the radicals $4\sqrt[3]{x}$ and $5\sqrt[6]{x}$ have different indexes, we cannot use the distributive law. The expression $4\sqrt[3]{x} + 5\sqrt[6]{x}$ is already in simplified form.

4. Since the radicals $3\sqrt[4]{x}$ and $2\sqrt[4]{x} + 1$ have different radicands, we cannot use the distributive law. The expression $3\sqrt[4]{x} - 2\sqrt[4]{x} + 1$ is already in simplified form.

▶ **Example 2**   Performing Operations with Radical Expressions

Perform the indicated operations.

1. $3\sqrt[4]{x} + 4\sqrt{x} + 2\sqrt[4]{x} + 7\sqrt{x}$

2. $3(5\sqrt[3]{x+1} - 2) - 4\sqrt[3]{x+1}$

Solution

1. $3\sqrt[4]{x} + 4\sqrt{x} + 2\sqrt[4]{x} + 7\sqrt{x} = (4\sqrt{x} + 7\sqrt{x}) + (3\sqrt[4]{x} + 2\sqrt[4]{x})$ *Group like radicals.*

$\qquad\qquad\qquad\qquad\qquad = (4 + 7)\sqrt{x} + (3 + 2)\sqrt[4]{x}$ *Distributive law*

$\qquad\qquad\qquad\qquad\qquad = 11\sqrt{x} + 5\sqrt[4]{x}$ *Add.*

2. $3(5\sqrt[3]{x+1} - 2) - 4\sqrt[3]{x+1} = 3 \cdot 5\sqrt[3]{x+1} - 3 \cdot 2 - 4\sqrt[3]{x+1}$ *Distributive law*

$\qquad\qquad\qquad\qquad\qquad = 15\sqrt[3]{x+1} - 4\sqrt[3]{x+1} - 6$ *Group like radicals.*

$\qquad\qquad\qquad\qquad\qquad = (15 - 4)\sqrt[3]{x+1} - 6$ *Distributive law*

$\qquad\qquad\qquad\qquad\qquad = 11\sqrt[3]{x+1} - 6$ *Subtract.*

Sometimes, simplifying radicals will allow us to combine like radicals.

▶ **Example 3**   Adding or Subtracting Radical Expressions

Perform the indicated operation.

1. $\sqrt{45w} + \sqrt{20w}$ **2.** $5b\sqrt{3a^3} - a\sqrt{12ab^2}$

Solution

1.
$$\sqrt{45w} + \sqrt{20w} = \sqrt{9 \cdot 5w} + \sqrt{4 \cdot 5w} \qquad \text{\textit{9 and 4 are perfect squares.}}$$
$$= \sqrt{9}\sqrt{5w} + \sqrt{4}\sqrt{5w} \qquad \sqrt[n]{ab} = \sqrt[n]{a}\sqrt[n]{b}$$
$$= 3\sqrt{5w} + 2\sqrt{5w} \qquad \sqrt{9} = 3; \sqrt{4} = 2$$
$$= (3 + 2)\sqrt{5w} \qquad \text{\textit{Distributive law}}$$
$$= 5\sqrt{5w} \qquad \text{\textit{Add.}}$$

2.
$$5b\sqrt{3a^3} - a\sqrt{12ab^2} = 5b\sqrt{a^2 \cdot 3a} - a\sqrt{4 \cdot b^2 \cdot 3a} \qquad \text{\textit{a^2, 4, and b^2 are perfect squares.}}$$
$$= 5b\sqrt{a^2}\sqrt{3a} - a\sqrt{4}\sqrt{b^2}\sqrt{3a} \qquad \sqrt[n]{ab} = \sqrt[n]{a}\sqrt[n]{b}$$
$$= 5b \cdot a \cdot \sqrt{3a} - a \cdot 2 \cdot b \cdot \sqrt{3a} \qquad \text{\textit{$\sqrt{a^2} = a$ for $a \geq 0$; $\sqrt{4} = 2$; $\sqrt{b^2} = b$ for $b \geq 0$}}$$
$$= 5ab\sqrt{3a} - 2ab\sqrt{3a} \qquad \text{\textit{Rearrange factors.}}$$
$$= (5ab - 2ab)\sqrt{3a} \qquad \text{\textit{Distributive law}}$$
$$= 3ab\sqrt{3a} \qquad \text{\textit{Combine like terms.}}$$

▶ **Example 4**   Subtracting Radical Expressions

Find the difference $2\sqrt[3]{16x^4} - 4x\sqrt[3]{54x}$.

Solution
$$2\sqrt[3]{16x^4} - 4x\sqrt[3]{54x} = 2\sqrt[3]{8 \cdot x^3 \cdot 2x} - 4x\sqrt[3]{27 \cdot 2x} \qquad \text{\textit{8, x^3, and 27 are perfect cubes.}}$$
$$= 2\sqrt[3]{8}\sqrt[3]{x^3}\sqrt[3]{2x} - 4x\sqrt[3]{27}\sqrt[3]{2x} \qquad \sqrt[n]{ab} = \sqrt[n]{a}\sqrt[n]{b}$$
$$= 2 \cdot 2 \cdot x \cdot \sqrt[3]{2x} - 4x \cdot 3 \cdot \sqrt[3]{2x} \qquad \text{\textit{$\sqrt[3]{8} = 2$, $\sqrt[3]{x^3} = x$, $\sqrt[3]{27} = 3$}}$$
$$= 4x\sqrt[3]{2x} - 12x\sqrt[3]{2x} \qquad \text{\textit{Multiply.}}$$
$$= (4x - 12x)\sqrt[3]{2x} \qquad \text{\textit{Distributive law}}$$
$$= -8x\sqrt[3]{2x} \qquad \text{\textit{Combine like terms.}}$$

Multiplying Radical Expressions

Next, we multiply radical expressions. We will use the product property

$$\sqrt[n]{ab} = \sqrt[n]{a}\sqrt[n]{b}, \qquad \text{where } \sqrt[n]{a} \text{ and } \sqrt[n]{b} \text{ are defined}$$

Here we multiply $5\sqrt{2x}$ and $4\sqrt{3}$ and simplify the result:

$$5\sqrt{2x} \cdot 4\sqrt{3} = 5 \cdot 4 \cdot \sqrt{2x} \cdot \sqrt{3} \qquad \text{\textit{Rearrange factors.}}$$
$$= 5 \cdot 4 \cdot \sqrt{2x \cdot 3} \qquad \text{\textit{Product property}}$$
$$= 20\sqrt{6x} \qquad \text{\textit{Multiply.}}$$

It is good practice to check whether the product of radical expressions can be simplified.

▶ **Example 5**   Finding Products of Radical Expressions

Find the product.

1. $2\sqrt{6x} \cdot 5\sqrt{2x}$ **2.** $3\sqrt{5x}\left(4\sqrt{x} - \sqrt{5}\right)$

Figure 8 Verify the work

Solution

1. $2\sqrt{6x} \cdot 5\sqrt{2x} = 2 \cdot 5\sqrt{6x} \cdot \sqrt{2x}$ *Rearrange factors.*

$\qquad\qquad\qquad = 2 \cdot 5 \cdot \sqrt{6x \cdot 2x}$ *Product property*

$\qquad\qquad\qquad = 10 \cdot \sqrt{12x^2}$ *Multiply.*

$\qquad\qquad\qquad = 10 \cdot \sqrt{4 \cdot x^2 \cdot 3}$ *4 and x^2 are perfect squares.*

$\qquad\qquad\qquad = 10 \cdot 2x\sqrt{3}$ *$\sqrt{4} = 2, \sqrt{x^2} = x$ for $x \geq 0$*

$\qquad\qquad\qquad = 20x\sqrt{3}$ *Multiply.*

We verify our work by comparing graphing calculator tables for $y = 2\sqrt{6x} \cdot 5\sqrt{2x}$ and $y = 20x\sqrt{3}$, for $x \geq 0$ (see Fig. 8).

2. $3\sqrt{5x}\left(4\sqrt{x} - \sqrt{5}\right) = 3\sqrt{5x} \cdot 4\sqrt{x} - 3\sqrt{5x} \cdot \sqrt{5}$ *Distributive law*

$\qquad\qquad\qquad\qquad = 3 \cdot 4 \cdot \sqrt{5x}\sqrt{x} - 3\sqrt{5x}\sqrt{5}$ *Rearrange factors.*

$\qquad\qquad\qquad\qquad = 12\sqrt{5x \cdot x} - 3\sqrt{5x \cdot 5}$ *Product property*

$\qquad\qquad\qquad\qquad = 12\sqrt{x^2 \cdot 5} - 3\sqrt{25x}$ *x^2 and 25 are perfect squares.*

$\qquad\qquad\qquad\qquad = 12 \cdot x \cdot \sqrt{5} - 3 \cdot 5 \cdot \sqrt{x}$ *$\sqrt{x^2} = x$ for $x \geq 0, \sqrt{25} = 5$*

$\qquad\qquad\qquad\qquad = 12x\sqrt{5} - 15\sqrt{x}$ *Multiply.*

Note that if $\sqrt[n]{x}$ is defined, then

$$\left(\sqrt[n]{x}\right)^n = x^{n/n} = x^1 = x$$

This property is helpful in simplifying powers or products of radical expressions.

> **Another Version of the Power Property for Radicals**
>
> If $\sqrt[n]{x}$ is defined, then
>
> $$\left(\sqrt[n]{x}\right)^n = x$$
>
> In words, the nth power of the nth root of a number is that number.

In particular, we have $\left(\sqrt{x}\right)^2 = x$ if $x \geq 0$.

▶ **Example 6**   **Simplifying Radical Expressions**

Simplify.

1. $\left(2\sqrt{x} - 7\right)\left(3\sqrt{x} + 4\right)$ **2.** $\left(2\sqrt{3x} + 5\right)\left(2\sqrt{3x} - 5\right)$

Solution

1. Multiply each term of the first factor by each term of the second factor, and combine like radicals:

$\left(2\sqrt{x} - 7\right)\left(3\sqrt{x} + 4\right) = 2\sqrt{x} \cdot 3\sqrt{x} + 2\sqrt{x} \cdot 4 - 7 \cdot 3\sqrt{x} - 7 \cdot 4$ *Multiply pairs of terms.*

$\qquad\qquad\qquad\qquad\quad = 6\sqrt{x^2} + 8\sqrt{x} - 21\sqrt{x} - 28$ *Simplify.*

$\qquad\qquad\qquad\qquad\quad = 6x - 13\sqrt{x} - 28$ *$\left(\sqrt[n]{x}\right)^n = x$; combine like radicals.*

2. We use the property $(A + B)(A - B) = A^2 - B^2$:

$$(2\sqrt{3x} + 5)(2\sqrt{3x} - 5) = (2\sqrt{3x})^2 - 5^2 \quad (A + B)(A - B) = A^2 - B^2$$
$$= 2^2(\sqrt{3x})^2 - 5^2 \quad (AB)^2 = A^2B^2$$
$$= 4(3x) - 25 \quad \text{Simplify.}$$
$$= 12x - 25 \quad \text{Multiply.}$$

We can verify our result by comparing tables for $y = (2\sqrt{3x} + 5)(2\sqrt{3x} - 5)$ and $y = 12x - 25$ for $x \geq 0$.

▶

▶ **Example 7**   Simplifying the Square of a Radical Expression with Two Terms

Simplify $(x - \sqrt{3})^2$.

Solution

To begin, we substitute x for A and $\sqrt{3}$ for B in the property for the square of a difference:

$$(A - B)^2 = A^2 - 2\ A\ \ B + \ B^2$$
$$\downarrow \quad \downarrow \quad \quad \downarrow \quad \downarrow\downarrow \quad \downarrow \quad \quad \downarrow$$
$$(x - \sqrt{3})^2 = x^2 - 2(x)\sqrt{3} + (\sqrt{3})^2 \quad \text{Substitute x for A and } \sqrt{3} \text{ for B.}$$
$$= x^2 - 2x\sqrt{3} + 3 \quad (\sqrt{x})^2 = x \text{ for } x \geq 0$$

Another way to simplify $(x - \sqrt{3})^2$ is to use the fact that $C^2 = CC$ and multiply pairs of terms:

$$(x - \sqrt{3})^2 = (x - \sqrt{3})(x - \sqrt{3}) \quad C^2 = CC$$
$$= x^2 - x\sqrt{3} - x\sqrt{3} + \sqrt{3}\sqrt{3} \quad \text{Multiply pairs of terms.}$$
$$= x^2 - 2x\sqrt{3} + 3 \quad \text{Combine like radicals; } \sqrt{x}\sqrt{x} = x \text{ for } x \geq 0$$

▶

WARNING

When we simplify $(x + k)^2$, it is important to remember the middle term of $x^2 + 2kx + k^2$. Likewise, when we simplify $(x - k)^2$, it is important to remember the middle term of $x^2 - 2kx + k^2$. Do not make the following typical error in simplifying $(\sqrt{x} + \sqrt{5})^2$:

$$(\sqrt{x} + \sqrt{5})^2 = (\sqrt{x})^2 + (\sqrt{5})^2 = x + 5 \quad \text{Incorrect}$$
$$(\sqrt{x} + \sqrt{5})^2 = (\sqrt{x})^2 + 2\sqrt{5}\sqrt{x} + (\sqrt{5})^2 = x + 2\sqrt{5x} + 5 \quad \text{Correct}$$

▶ **Example 8**   Simplifying the Square of a Radical Expression with Two Terms

Simplify $(\sqrt{a} + 3\sqrt{b})^2$.

Solution

We use the property for the square of a sum:

$$(\sqrt{a} + 3\sqrt{b})^2 = (\sqrt{a})^2 + 2 \cdot \sqrt{a} \cdot 3\sqrt{b} + (3\sqrt{b})^2 \quad (A + B)^2 = A^2 + 2AB + B^2$$
$$= (\sqrt{a})^2 + 6\sqrt{ab} + 3^2(\sqrt{b})^2 \quad \sqrt[n]{a}\sqrt[n]{b} = \sqrt[n]{ab}; (xy)^n = x^ny^n$$
$$= a + 6\sqrt{ab} + 9b \quad (\sqrt{x})^2 = x \text{ for } x \geq 0; 3^2 = 9$$

▶

In Example 9, we find products of radical expressions with indexes other than $n = 2$.

▶ **Example 9**   Multiplying Radical Expressions

Find the product.

1. $(2\sqrt[5]{x^2})(7\sqrt[5]{x^4})$

2. $(\sqrt[4]{x^3} + 5)(\sqrt[4]{x^3} - 6)$

Solution

1. $\left(2\sqrt[5]{x^2}\right)\left(7\sqrt[5]{x^4}\right) = 2 \cdot 7 \cdot \sqrt[5]{x^2}\sqrt[5]{x^4}$ *Rearrange factors.*

$= 2 \cdot 7\sqrt[5]{x^2 \cdot x^4}$ $\sqrt[n]{a}\sqrt[n]{b} = \sqrt[n]{ab}$

$= 14\sqrt[5]{x^6}$ $b^m b^n = b^{m+n}$

$= 14x\sqrt[5]{x}$ $\sqrt[5]{x^6} = \sqrt[5]{x^5 x^1} = x\sqrt[5]{x}$

2. $\left(\sqrt[4]{x^3} + 5\right)\left(\sqrt[4]{x^3} - 6\right)$

$= \sqrt[4]{x^3}\sqrt[4]{x^3} - \sqrt[4]{x^3} \cdot 6 + 5 \cdot \sqrt[4]{x^3} - 5 \cdot 6$ *Multiply pairs of terms.*

$= \sqrt[4]{x^3 \cdot x^3} - 6\sqrt[4]{x^3} + 5\sqrt[4]{x^3} - 30$ *Product property*

$= \sqrt[4]{x^6} - \sqrt[4]{x^3} - 30$ *Multiply; combine like radicals.*

$= x\sqrt[4]{x^2} - \sqrt[4]{x^3} - 30$ $\sqrt[4]{x^6} = \sqrt[4]{x^4 \cdot x^2} = x\sqrt[4]{x^2}$
                                             for $x \geq 0$

$= x\sqrt{x} - \sqrt[4]{x^3} - 30$ $\sqrt[4]{x^2} = x^{2/4} = x^{1/2} = \sqrt{x}$
                                             for $x \geq 0$

We cannot combine the radicals $x\sqrt{x}$ and $-\sqrt[4]{x^3}$, since the indexes (and the radicands) are different. So, we are done.

▶

To multiply two radicals that have the same index, we use the product property.

How do we multiply two radicals with *different* indexes? Here we find the product $\sqrt[3]{x} \cdot \sqrt[4]{x}$:

$\sqrt[3]{x} \cdot \sqrt[4]{x} = x^{\frac{1}{3}} \cdot x^{\frac{1}{4}}$ *Write in exponential form.*

$= x^{\frac{1}{3} + \frac{1}{4}}$ $a^m a^n = a^{m+n}$

$= x^{\frac{4}{12} + \frac{3}{12}}$ *Get a common denominator.*

$= x^{\frac{7}{12}}$ *Add numerators; keep common denominator.*

$= \sqrt[12]{x^7}$ *Write in radical form.*

▶ **Multiplying Two Radicals That Have Different Indexes but the Same Radicand**

To multiply two radicals that have different indexes but the same radicand,

1. Write the radicals in exponential form.
2. Use exponential properties to simplify the expression involving exponents.
3. Write the simplified expression in radical form.

▶ **Example 10** Simplifying Radical Expressions

Perform the operations. Assume $x \geq 0$.

1. $2\sqrt{x}\left(\sqrt[3]{x} - 5\right)$ **2.** $\left(\sqrt[3]{x} + 3\sqrt[5]{x^2}\right)^2$

Solution

1. $2\sqrt{x}\left(\sqrt[3]{x} - 5\right) = 2\sqrt{x}\sqrt[3]{x} - 2\sqrt{x} \cdot 5$ *Distributive law*

$= 2x^{\frac{1}{2}}x^{\frac{1}{3}} - 10\sqrt{x}$ *Write in exponential form.*

$= 2x^{\frac{1}{2} + \frac{1}{3}} - 10\sqrt{x}$ $a^m a^n = a^{m+n}$

$= 2x^{\frac{3}{6} + \frac{2}{6}} - 10\sqrt{x}$ *Get a common denominator.*

$= 2x^{\frac{5}{6}} - 10\sqrt{x}$ *Add numerators; keep common denominator.*

$= 2\sqrt[6]{x^5} - 10\sqrt{x}$ *Write in radical form.*

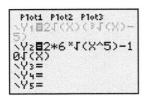

Figure 9 Verify the work

We can verify our result by comparing tables for $y = 2\sqrt{x}\left(\sqrt[3]{x} - 5\right)$ and $y = 2\sqrt[6]{x^5} - 10\sqrt{x}$, for $x \geq 0$ (see Fig. 9).

2. $\left(\sqrt[3]{x} + 3\sqrt[5]{x^2}\right)^2$

$$= \left(\sqrt[3]{x}\right)^2 + 2\left(\sqrt[3]{x}\right)\left(3\sqrt[5]{x^2}\right) + \left(3\sqrt[5]{x^2}\right)^2 \qquad (A + B)^2 = A^2 + 2AB + B^2$$

$$= \left(\sqrt[3]{x}\right)^2 + 6x^{\frac{1}{3}}x^{\frac{2}{5}} + 3^2\left(\sqrt[5]{x^2}\right)^2 \qquad \textit{Write in exponential form.}$$

$$= \sqrt[3]{x^2} + 6x^{\frac{1}{3} + \frac{2}{5}} + 9\sqrt[5]{\left(x^2\right)^2} \qquad \left(\sqrt[n]{x}\right)^m = \sqrt[n]{x^m}$$

$$= \sqrt[3]{x^2} + 6x^{\frac{5}{15} + \frac{6}{15}} + 9\sqrt[5]{x^4} \qquad \textit{Get a common denominator.}$$

$$= \sqrt[3]{x^2} + 6x^{\frac{11}{15}} + 9\sqrt[5]{x^4} \qquad \textit{Add numerators; keep}$$
$$\qquad\qquad\qquad\qquad\qquad\qquad\qquad \textit{common denominator.}$$

$$= \sqrt[3]{x^2} + 6\sqrt[15]{x^{11}} + 9\sqrt[5]{x^4} \qquad \textit{Write in radical form.}$$

Another way to simplify $\left(\sqrt[3]{x} + 3\sqrt[5]{x^2}\right)^2$ is to use the fact that $C^2 = CC$ and multiply pairs of terms. (Try it.)

▶ **Simplifying a Radical Expression**

To simplify a radical expression,

1. Perform any indicated multiplications.

2. Combine like radicals.

3. For any radical with index n, write the radicand as a product of one or more perfect nth powers and another expression that has no factors that are perfect nth powers. Then apply the product property for radicals.

4. Write any radicals with as small an index as possible.

Depending on the radical expression, we may need to perform these steps in a different order or return to a step at a later stage in the process of simplifying the expression. We will discuss more ways to simplify radical expressions in Section 9.3.

◣◥◢ Group Exploration

Looking ahead: Rationalizing the denominator

In Section 7.3, you "rationalized the denominator" of fractions of the form $\dfrac{1}{\sqrt{a}}$ by finding an equivalent expression that does not have a radical in any denominator. Here you will explore how to rationalize the denominator of a fraction with a denominator that is a sum or a difference involving radicals.

1. Perform the indicated multiplication.

    a. $\left(x - \sqrt{2}\right)\left(x + \sqrt{2}\right)$ **b.** $\left(x + \sqrt{5}\right)\left(x - \sqrt{5}\right)$

    c. $\left(\sqrt{x} - 4\right)\left(\sqrt{x} + 4\right)$ **d.** $\left(\sqrt{x} + 3\right)\left(\sqrt{x} - 3\right)$

2. What patterns do you notice from your work in Problem 1?

3. Rationalize the denominator of $\dfrac{1}{\sqrt{x} - 7}$ by performing the multiplication

$$\frac{1}{\sqrt{x} - 7} \cdot \frac{\sqrt{x} + 7}{\sqrt{x} + 7}$$

Use graphing calculator tables to verify your work.

4. Rationalize the denominator of the expression $\dfrac{1}{\sqrt{x} + 5}$.

5. Describe how to rationalize the denominator of a radical expression.

Homework 9.2

For extra help ▶ **MyMathLab**° Watch the videos in MyMathLab Download the MyDashboard App

Simplify. Use a graphing calculator table to compare your result with the original expression when possible. Assume each variable is nonnegative.

1. $4\sqrt{x} + 5\sqrt{x}$ **2.** $8\sqrt{x} - 4\sqrt{x}$

3. $2\sqrt[3]{5x^2y} - 6\sqrt[3]{5x^2y}$ **4.** $5\sqrt[4]{2xy^3} - 7\sqrt[4]{2xy^3}$

5. $3\sqrt{5a} + 2\sqrt{3b} - 6\sqrt{3b} + 7\sqrt{5a}$

6. $4\sqrt{7b} - \sqrt{2a} - 4\sqrt{2a} + 9\sqrt{7b}$

7. $2\sqrt{x} + 5 - 7\sqrt[3]{x} - 9 + 5\sqrt[3]{x}$

8. $4 - 6\sqrt[4]{x} + 3\sqrt[3]{x} - 1 - 8\sqrt[4]{x}$

9. $6\sqrt[3]{x-1} - 3\sqrt[3]{x-1} - 2\sqrt{x-1}$

10. $4\sqrt[3]{3x+1} + 3\sqrt[3]{3x+1} - 5\sqrt[3]{3x+1}$

11. $3.7\sqrt[4]{x} - 1.1\sqrt[4]{x} - 4.2\sqrt[6]{x} + 4.2\sqrt[6]{x}$

12. $4.1\sqrt{x} - 2.9\sqrt[3]{x} - 5.8\sqrt[3]{x} + 2.3\sqrt{x}$

13. $3(7 - \sqrt{x} + 2) - (\sqrt{x} + 2)$

14. $4(1 - 3\sqrt{x} - 8) - (5\sqrt{x} - 3)$

15. $7(\sqrt[3]{x} + 1) - 7(\sqrt[3]{x} - 1)$ **16.** $5(\sqrt[4]{a} - 2) + 5(2 - \sqrt[4]{a})$

17. $\sqrt{12b} + \sqrt{75b}$ **18.** $\sqrt{8x} - \sqrt{18x}$

19. $\sqrt{18x^5} + 2x\sqrt{50x^3}$ **20.** $\sqrt{27x^7} + 2x^2\sqrt{12x^3}$

21. $5\sqrt{4x^3} - x\sqrt{36x}$ **22.** $2\sqrt{9x^3} - x\sqrt{49x}$

23. $3\sqrt{81x^2} - 2\sqrt{100x^2}$ **24.** $2\sqrt{36x^2} + 5\sqrt{16x^2}$

25. $a\sqrt{12b^3} + b\sqrt{75ba^2}$ **26.** $b\sqrt{20a^5} - a\sqrt{45a^3b^2}$

27. $\sqrt[3]{27x^5} - x\sqrt[3]{8x^2}$ **28.** $\sqrt[3]{54x^7} - x\sqrt[3]{16x^4}$

29. $y\sqrt[4]{16x^{11}y^4} - 3x\sqrt[4]{x^7y^8}$

30. $7x^2\sqrt[5]{x^3y^{10}} + 3y\sqrt[5]{32x^{13}y^5}$

Simplify. Use a graphing calculator table to verify your result when possible. Assume each variable is nonnegative.

31. $3\sqrt{x} \cdot 2\sqrt{x}$ **32.** $-5\sqrt{x} \cdot 4\sqrt{x}$

33. $-2\sqrt{5x} \cdot 4\sqrt{3x}$ **34.** $-3\sqrt{10x} \cdot 2\sqrt{5x}$

35. $2\sqrt{7t}(\sqrt{7t} - \sqrt{2t})$ **36.** $4\sqrt{2k}(\sqrt{8} - 3\sqrt{k})$

37. $(2\sqrt{x} + 6)(5\sqrt{x} + 4)$ **38.** $(3\sqrt{x} + 7)(2\sqrt{x} + 5)$

39. $(4\sqrt{x} + \sqrt{3})(2\sqrt{x} - \sqrt{5})$

40. $(5\sqrt{x} - \sqrt{2})(3\sqrt{x} - \sqrt{3})$

41. $(5\sqrt{a} + \sqrt{b})(\sqrt{a} - 2\sqrt{b})$

42. $(2\sqrt{a} + \sqrt{b})(\sqrt{a} - \sqrt{b})$

43. $(1 - \sqrt{w})(1 + \sqrt{w})$ **44.** $(2 + 3\sqrt{p})(2 - 3\sqrt{p})$

45. $(7x + \sqrt{5})(7x - \sqrt{5})$

46. $(4\sqrt{x} + \sqrt{3})(4\sqrt{x} - \sqrt{3})$

47. $(2\sqrt{a} - \sqrt{b})(2\sqrt{a} + \sqrt{b})$

48. $(3\sqrt{a} - \sqrt{b})(3\sqrt{a} + \sqrt{b})$

49. $(5 + 6\sqrt{x})^2$ **50.** $(3\sqrt{x} + 2)^2$

51. $(4\sqrt{x} - \sqrt{5})^2$ **52.** $(2\sqrt{x} - \sqrt{7})^2$

53. $(\sqrt{a} + 2\sqrt{b})^2$ **54.** $(3\sqrt{a} - \sqrt{b})^2$

55. $(\sqrt{2x-5} + 3)^2$ **56.** $(\sqrt{3x+4} - 5)^2$

57. $\sqrt{x}\sqrt[5]{x}$ **58.** $\sqrt[4]{x}\sqrt[6]{x}$

59. $\sqrt[5]{x^4}\sqrt[5]{x^3}$ **60.** $\sqrt[4]{3x^2}\sqrt[4]{3x^2}$

61. $-5\sqrt{m}(\sqrt[4]{2m} - 4)$ **62.** $-4\sqrt[3]{t}(\sqrt[4]{t} + 3)$

63. $(\sqrt[3]{x} + 1)^2$ **64.** $(\sqrt[4]{x} - 5)^2$

65. $(\sqrt[4]{k} - \sqrt[3]{k})^2$ **66.** $(2\sqrt[5]{r} + \sqrt{r})^2$

67. $(2\sqrt{x} - 6)(3\sqrt[3]{x} + 1)$

68. $(4\sqrt[3]{x^2} + 1)(5\sqrt[4]{x^2} + 2)$

69. $(3\sqrt[4]{x} + 5)(3\sqrt[4]{x} - 5)$

70. $(2\sqrt[5]{x} + 1)(3\sqrt[5]{x} - 2)$

71. The flow rate r (in gallons per minute) of water from the nozzle of a firefighter's hose can be modeled by the formula $r = 30d^2\sqrt{P}$, where d is the nozzle diameter (in inches) and P is the nozzle pressure (in pounds per square inch). The flow rates of solid bore nozzles are shown in Table 6 for various nozzle pressures and diameters.

Table 6 Flow Rates of Solid Bore Nozzles (gallons per minute)

Nozzle Pressure (pounds per square inch)	Nozzle Diameter (inches)				
	0.5	1.0	1.5	2.0	2.5
40	47	188	423	752	1174
60	58	230	518	921	1438
80	66	266	598	1063	1661
100	74	297	668	1188	1857
120	81	325	732	1302	2034
140	88	352	791	1406	2197
175	98	393	884	1572	2456
200	105	420	945	1681	2626

Source: *Firetactics.com*

a. If the value of P is constant and the value of d is increased, what happens to the value of r? Explain how you can tell this from Table 6, the model's equation, and thinking about the situation.

b. i. If the nozzle pressure is 100 pounds per square inch, use the model to estimate the flow rates of water for nozzle diameters of 0.5 inch, 1 inch, 1.5 inches, 2 inches, and 2.5 inches.

ii. Which estimate in part (i) has the largest error? What is that error?

iii. Which estimate in part (i) has the largest percentage error? What is that percentage error? [**Hint:** To find each percentage error, divide the error by the actual amount and multiply the result by 100.]

c. In Virginia, the flow rate of water for firefighting must be at least 500 gallons per minute for one- and two-family dwellings that do not exceed 3600 square feet in area. Use the model to determine whether the requirement will be met if a 1.75-inch-diameter nozzle has 45 pounds per square inch of pressure. What is the estimated flow rate?

72. The time it takes for a planet to make one revolution around the Sun is the planet's *period*. The period $f(d)$ (in years) of a planet whose average distance from the Sun is d million kilometers is modeled by the equation

$$f(d) = 0.0005443\sqrt{d^3}$$

a. What is the period of Neptune, whose average distance from the Sun is 4498 million kilometers?

b. Use a graphing calculator table to find Earth's average distance from the Sun.

c. Suppose in the future we colonize Mars, whose average distance from the Sun is 228 million kilometers. What is the period of Mars? If a person is 20 years old in "Earth years," how old is the person in "Mars years"?

Concepts

73. A student tries to simplify $(x + \sqrt{7})^2$:

$$(x + \sqrt{7})^2 = x^2 + (\sqrt{7})^2 = x^2 + 7$$

Describe any errors. Then simplify the expression correctly.

74. A student tries to simplify $(x - \sqrt{3})^2$:

$$(x - \sqrt{3})^2 = x^2 - (\sqrt{3})^2 = x^2 - 3$$

Describe any errors. Then simplify the expression correctly.

75. A student tries to find the product $7(2\sqrt{3})$:

$$7(2\sqrt{3}) = 14\sqrt{21}$$

Describe any errors. Then find the product correctly.

76. A student tries to find the product $(3\sqrt{5})(4\sqrt{5})$:

$$(3\sqrt{5})(4\sqrt{5}) = 12\sqrt{5}$$

Describe any errors. Then find the product correctly.

For Exercises 77 and 78, write the expression as a single radical. [**Hint:** *Write the expression in exponential form.*]

77. $\dfrac{\sqrt{x}}{\sqrt[3]{x}}$

78. $\sqrt[3]{\sqrt{x}}$

79. a. Write the expression $\sqrt[4]{x}\sqrt[5]{x}$ as a single radical.

b. Write the expression $\sqrt[m]{x}\sqrt[n]{x}$ as a single radical. [**Hint:** Perform steps similar to your work in part (a).]

c. Use your result from part (b) to find the product $\sqrt[4]{x}\sqrt[5]{x}$. Compare your result with your result from part (a).

d. Use your result from part (b) to find the product $\sqrt[3]{x}\sqrt[7]{x}$.

80. We cannot factor $x^2 - 3$ over the integers. We *can* factor $x^2 - 3$ over the real numbers:

$$x^2 - 3 = (x - \sqrt{3})(x + \sqrt{3})$$

a. Factor $x^2 - 2$ over the real numbers.

b. Factor $x^2 - 5$ over the real numbers.

c. Simplify $\dfrac{x^2 - 2}{x - \sqrt{2}}$.

d. Simplify $\dfrac{x^2 - 7}{x + \sqrt{7}}$.

81. a. Let n be a counting number. Decide whether each of the following is true or false:

  i. $\sqrt[n]{ab} = \sqrt[n]{a}\sqrt[n]{b}$

  ii. $\sqrt[n]{a + b} = \sqrt[n]{a} + \sqrt[n]{b}$

  iii. $(ab)^n = a^n b^n$

  iv. $(a + b)^n = a^n + b^n$

  v. $\dfrac{1}{ab} = a^{-1}b^{-1}$

  vi. $\dfrac{1}{a + b} = a^{-1} + b^{-1}$

b. Compare the types of equations that are true and the types of equations that are false in part (a). What patterns do you notice?

82. Why can we write the product of $\sqrt[5]{2}$ and $\sqrt[5]{3}$ as one radical but we cannot write the sum of $\sqrt[5]{2}$ and $\sqrt[5]{3}$ as one radical?

83. Describe how to multiply two radical expressions. Include a discussion of various types of formulas, laws, and techniques you can use to find such products.

84. Find two radical expressions whose sum is $9\sqrt{x} + 7$ and whose difference is $\sqrt{x} + 3$.

Related Review

Simplify. Assume $x \geq 0$.

85. $3\sqrt{x} - 5\sqrt{x}$

86. $(3\sqrt{x})^2$

87. $(3\sqrt{x})(-5\sqrt{x})$

88. $(3 + \sqrt{x})^2$

Expressions, Equations, Functions, and Graphs

Perform the indicated instruction. Then use words such as linear, quadratic, cubic, exponential, logarithmic, rational, radical, polynomial, degree, function, one variable, *and* two variables *to describe the expression, equation, or system.*

89. Write $\log_b(x^2 + 3x - 40) - \log_b(x^2 - 64)$ as a single logarithm.

90. Factor $2x^2 + 5x - 12$.

91. Solve $\log_2(3x - 4) - \log_2(2x - 3) = 3$.

92. Solve $2x(2x - 3) = 15 - 2x$.

93. Solve $2(3)^{5x-1} = 35$. Round any solutions to the fourth decimal place.

94. Let $f(x) = 2x^2 + 5x - 12$. Find x when $f(x) = -5$.

▼ 9.3 Rationalizing Denominators and Simplifying Quotients of Radical Expressions

Objectives

» Rationalize the denominator of a radical expression.

» Know the *quotient property for radicals*.

» Use the quotient property to simplify radical expressions.

» Use a *radical conjugate* to rationalize the denominator of a radical expression.

In Section 9.2, we discussed how to add, subtract, and multiply radical expressions. How do we simplify quotients of radical expressions?

Rationalizing Denominators of Radical Expressions

Recall from Section 7.3 that we simplify an expression of the form $\dfrac{p}{\sqrt{q}}$ by leaving no denominator as a radical expression and that we call this process *rationalizing the denominator*. For example, to rationalize the denominator of $\dfrac{2}{\sqrt{5}}$, we multiply by $1 = \dfrac{\sqrt{5}}{\sqrt{5}}$:

$$\frac{2}{\sqrt{5}} = \frac{2}{\sqrt{5}} \cdot \frac{\sqrt{5}}{\sqrt{5}}$$

$$= \frac{2\sqrt{5}}{5}$$

In this section, we will rationalize the denominator of each of the following radical expressions:

$$\frac{4}{5\sqrt{3x}} \qquad \frac{3y}{\sqrt[5]{8x^2}} \qquad \frac{5}{3 + \sqrt{x}} \qquad \frac{\sqrt{x} + 4}{3\sqrt{x} - \sqrt{2}}$$

That is, we will write each expression so that no denominator is a radical expression.

▶ **Example 1**   Rationalizing a Denominator

Simplify $\dfrac{4}{5\sqrt{3x}}$.

Solution

Since $\sqrt{3x} \cdot \sqrt{3x} = 3x$ where $x \geq 0$, we rationalize the denominator of $\dfrac{4}{5\sqrt{3x}}$ by multiplying by $\dfrac{\sqrt{3x}}{\sqrt{3x}}$:

$$\frac{4}{5\sqrt{3x}} = \frac{4}{5\sqrt{3x}} \cdot \frac{\sqrt{3x}}{\sqrt{3x}} \qquad \textit{Rationalize denominator.}$$

$$= \frac{4\sqrt{3x}}{5\left(\sqrt{3x}\right)^2} \qquad \textit{Multiply numerators; multiply denominators.}$$

$$= \frac{4\sqrt{3x}}{5(3x)} \qquad \left(\sqrt{x}\right)^2 = x \textit{ for } x \geq 0$$

$$= \frac{4\sqrt{3x}}{15x} \qquad \textit{Multiply.}$$

We use a graphing calculator table to verify our work (see Fig. 10). The table has "ERROR" messages across from $x = 0$, because the original expression and our result are not defined at 0 (why?).

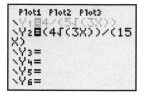

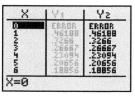

Figure 10 Verify the work

In Example 2, we will rationalize the denominator for indexes other than 2. With any index n, our intermediate goal is the same: to write the denominator so that the radicand of its radical is a perfect nth power.

▶ **Example 2**   Rationalizing Denominators

Simplify.

1. $\dfrac{1}{\sqrt[3]{x}}$

2. $\dfrac{3y}{\sqrt[5]{8x^2}}$

Solution

1. For the radicand to be a perfect cube, x must be multiplied by $x \cdot x = x^2$. So, we multiply $\dfrac{1}{\sqrt[3]{x}}$ by $\dfrac{\sqrt[3]{x^2}}{\sqrt[3]{x^2}}$:

$$\dfrac{1}{\sqrt[3]{x}} = \dfrac{1}{\sqrt[3]{x}} \cdot \dfrac{\sqrt[3]{x^2}}{\sqrt[3]{x^2}} \qquad \textit{Rationalize denominator.}$$

$$= \dfrac{\sqrt[3]{x^2}}{\sqrt[3]{x^3}} \qquad \textit{Multiply numerators; multiply denominators.}$$

$$= \dfrac{\sqrt[3]{x^2}}{x} \qquad \sqrt[3]{x^3} = x$$

2. To become a perfect 5th power, the radicand $8x^2 = 2 \cdot 2 \cdot 2 \cdot x \cdot x$ must be multiplied by $2 \cdot 2 \cdot x \cdot x \cdot x = 4x^3$:

$$\dfrac{3y}{\sqrt[5]{8x^2}} = \dfrac{3y}{\sqrt[5]{8x^2}} \cdot \dfrac{\sqrt[5]{4x^3}}{\sqrt[5]{4x^3}} \qquad \textit{Rationalize denominator.}$$

$$= \dfrac{3y\sqrt[5]{4x^3}}{\sqrt[5]{8x^2 \cdot 4x^3}} \qquad \textit{Multiply numerators; multiply denominators.}$$

$$= \dfrac{3y\sqrt[5]{4x^3}}{\sqrt[5]{32x^5}} \qquad \textit{Multiply.}$$

$$= \dfrac{3y\sqrt[5]{4x^3}}{\sqrt[5]{32}\,\sqrt[5]{x^5}} \qquad \sqrt[n]{ab} = \sqrt[n]{a}\,\sqrt[n]{b}$$

$$= \dfrac{3y\sqrt[5]{4x^3}}{2x} \qquad \sqrt[5]{32} = 2, \ \sqrt[5]{x^5} = x$$

▶

As shown in Example 2, **to rationalize the denominator of a radical expression of the form $\dfrac{A}{\sqrt[n]{x^m}}$, we multiply the expression by a fraction of the form $\dfrac{\sqrt[n]{x^k}}{\sqrt[n]{x^k}}$ so the radical in the denominator has a perfect nth-power radicand.**

Quotient Property

In Section 7.3, we worked with the quotient property for square roots:

$$\sqrt{\dfrac{a}{b}} = \dfrac{\sqrt{a}}{\sqrt{b}}, \quad \text{where } a \geq 0 \text{ and } b > 0$$

Next, we describe the quotient property for any index n.

> ▶ **Quotient Property for Radicals**
>
> If $\sqrt[n]{a}$ and $\sqrt[n]{b}$ are defined and b is nonzero, then
>
> $$\sqrt[n]{\dfrac{a}{b}} = \dfrac{\sqrt[n]{a}}{\sqrt[n]{b}}$$
>
> In words, the nth root of a quotient is the quotient of the nth roots.

For example, $\sqrt[3]{\dfrac{8}{27}} = \dfrac{\sqrt[3]{8}}{\sqrt[3]{27}} = \dfrac{2}{3}$.

You will prove the quotient property for radicals in Exercise 74.

Using the Quotient Property to Simplify Radical Expressions

If a radical expression has a fractional radicand, we simplify the expression by writing it as an expression in which no radicand is a fraction. We can use the quotient property to help us do this.

▶ **Example 3**   Simplifying Radical Expressions

Simplify.

1. $\sqrt{\dfrac{5}{k}}$

2. $\sqrt[3]{\dfrac{7y}{2x^2}}$

Solution

1. $\sqrt{\dfrac{5}{k}} = \dfrac{\sqrt{5}}{\sqrt{k}}$ *Quotient property*

$= \dfrac{\sqrt{5}}{\sqrt{k}} \cdot \dfrac{\sqrt{k}}{\sqrt{k}}$ *Rationalize denominator.*

$= \dfrac{\sqrt{5k}}{k}$ *Multiply numerators; multiply denominators.*

2. $\sqrt[3]{\dfrac{7y}{2x^2}} = \dfrac{\sqrt[3]{7y}}{\sqrt[3]{2x^2}}$ *Quotient property*

$= \dfrac{\sqrt[3]{7y}}{\sqrt[3]{2x^2}} \cdot \dfrac{\sqrt[3]{4x}}{\sqrt[3]{4x}}$ *To become a perfect cube, $2x^2 = 2 \cdot x \cdot x$ must be multiplied by $2 \cdot 2 \cdot x = 4x$.*

$= \dfrac{\sqrt[3]{28xy}}{\sqrt[3]{8x^3}}$ *Multiply numerators; multiply denominators.*

$= \dfrac{\sqrt[3]{28xy}}{2x}$ $\sqrt[3]{8} = 2, \sqrt[3]{x^3} = x$

Using Radical Conjugates to Rationalize Denominators

Recall from Section 6.2 that we call binomials such as $5x + 2$ and $5x - 2$ binomial conjugates of each other. Similarly, we call the radical expressions $\sqrt{5} + \sqrt{2}$ and $\sqrt{5} - \sqrt{2}$ radical conjugates of each other. We say the sum of two radicals and the difference of the same two radicals are **radical conjugates** of each other.

What happens when we find the product of two radical conjugates? Here we use the property $(A + B)(A - B) = A^2 - B^2$ to find the product $(\sqrt{5} + \sqrt{2})(\sqrt{5} - \sqrt{2})$:

$$(\sqrt{5} + \sqrt{2})(\sqrt{5} - \sqrt{2}) = (\sqrt{5})^2 - (\sqrt{2})^2 \quad (A + B)(A - B) = A^2 - B^2$$
$$= 5 - 2 \quad (\sqrt{x})^2 = x \text{ for } x \geq 0$$
$$= 3 \quad \text{Subtract.}$$

The result contains no radicals. We next list a few expressions, their conjugates, and the products of the expressions and their conjugates:

Expression	Conjugate	Product
$4 - \sqrt{x}$	$4 + \sqrt{x}$	$16 - x$
$7 + 3\sqrt{x}$	$7 - 3\sqrt{x}$	$49 - 9x$
$2\sqrt{x} - 3\sqrt{5}$	$2\sqrt{x} + 3\sqrt{5}$	$4x - 45$

Just as before, we notice that the products of the conjugates contain no radicals. We will use this observation to help us rationalize a denominator in Example 4.

▶ **Example 4** Rationalizing a Denominator

Simplify $\dfrac{5}{3 + \sqrt{x}}$.

Solution

The conjugate of the denominator is $3 - \sqrt{x}$. We can rationalize the denominator of $\dfrac{5}{3 + \sqrt{x}}$ by multiplying by $\dfrac{\text{conjugate}}{\text{conjugate}} = \dfrac{3 - \sqrt{x}}{3 - \sqrt{x}}$:

$$\dfrac{5}{3 + \sqrt{x}} = \dfrac{5}{3 + \sqrt{x}} \cdot \dfrac{3 - \sqrt{x}}{3 - \sqrt{x}} \qquad \textit{Multiply by } \dfrac{3 - \sqrt{x}}{3 - \sqrt{x}}.$$

$$= \dfrac{5(3 - \sqrt{x})}{(3 + \sqrt{x})(3 - \sqrt{x})} \qquad \textit{Multiply numerators; multiply denominators.}$$

$$= \dfrac{5(3 - \sqrt{x})}{3^2 - (\sqrt{x})^2} \qquad (A + B)(A - B) = A^2 - B^2$$

$$= \dfrac{15 - 5\sqrt{x}}{9 - x} \qquad \textit{Distributive law; } (\sqrt{x})^2 = x \textit{ for } x \geq 0$$

We use a graphing calculator table to verify our work (see Fig. 11).

Figure 11 Verify the work

WARNING

When we try to rationalize the denominator of $\dfrac{5}{3 + \sqrt{x}}$, it is *not* helpful to multiply the fraction by $\dfrac{\sqrt{x}}{\sqrt{x}}$:

$$\dfrac{5}{3 + \sqrt{x}} = \dfrac{5}{3 + \sqrt{x}} \cdot \dfrac{\sqrt{x}}{\sqrt{x}} = \dfrac{5\sqrt{x}}{3\sqrt{x} + x}$$

Rather, the conjugate of the denominator is $3 - \sqrt{x}$, so we multiply the fraction by $\dfrac{\text{conjugate}}{\text{conjugate}} = \dfrac{3 - \sqrt{x}}{3 - \sqrt{x}}$, as shown in Example 4.

▶ **Rationalizing a Denominator by Using a Radical Conjugate**

To rationalize the denominator of a square root expression if the denominator is a sum or difference involving radicals,

1. Determine the radical conjugate of the denominator.

2. Multiply the original fraction by the fraction $\dfrac{\text{conjugate}}{\text{conjugate}}$.

3. Find the product of the denominators by using $(A + B)(A - B) = A^2 - B^2$.

▶ **Example 5** Rationalizing a Denominator

Simplify $\dfrac{\sqrt{x} + 4}{3\sqrt{x} - \sqrt{2}}$.

Solution

$$\frac{\sqrt{x}+4}{3\sqrt{x}-\sqrt{2}} = \frac{\sqrt{x}+4}{3\sqrt{x}-\sqrt{2}} \cdot \frac{3\sqrt{x}+\sqrt{2}}{3\sqrt{x}+\sqrt{2}}$$

Conjugate of $3\sqrt{x}-\sqrt{2}$ is $3\sqrt{x}+\sqrt{2}$.

$$= \frac{\left(\sqrt{x}+4\right)\left(3\sqrt{x}+\sqrt{2}\right)}{\left(3\sqrt{x}-\sqrt{2}\right)\left(3\sqrt{x}+\sqrt{2}\right)}$$

Multiply numerators; multiply denominators.

$$= \frac{3\sqrt{x}\sqrt{x}+\sqrt{x}\sqrt{2}+4\cdot3\sqrt{x}+4\sqrt{2}}{\left(3\sqrt{x}\right)^2-\left(\sqrt{2}\right)^2}$$

Multiply pairs of terms; $(A-B)(A+B)=A^2-B^2$

$$= \frac{3x+\sqrt{2x}+12\sqrt{x}+4\sqrt{2}}{9x-2}$$

Simplify.

▶

▶ **Example 6** Rationalizing a Denominator

Simplify $\dfrac{\sqrt{a}+\sqrt{b}}{\sqrt{a}-\sqrt{b}}$.

Solution

$$\frac{\sqrt{a}+\sqrt{b}}{\sqrt{a}-\sqrt{b}} = \frac{\sqrt{a}+\sqrt{b}}{\sqrt{a}-\sqrt{b}} \cdot \frac{\sqrt{a}+\sqrt{b}}{\sqrt{a}+\sqrt{b}}$$

Conjugate of $\sqrt{a}-\sqrt{b}$ is $\sqrt{a}+\sqrt{b}$.

$$= \frac{\left(\sqrt{a}+\sqrt{b}\right)\left(\sqrt{a}+\sqrt{b}\right)}{\left(\sqrt{a}-\sqrt{b}\right)\left(\sqrt{a}+\sqrt{b}\right)}$$

Multiply numerators; multiply denominators.

$$= \frac{\left(\sqrt{a}+\sqrt{b}\right)^2}{\left(\sqrt{a}\right)^2-\left(\sqrt{b}\right)^2}$$

$CC=C^2$; $(A-B)(A+B)=A^2-B^2$

$$= \frac{\left(\sqrt{a}\right)^2+2\sqrt{a}\sqrt{b}+\left(\sqrt{b}\right)^2}{\left(\sqrt{a}\right)^2-\left(\sqrt{b}\right)^2}$$

$(A+B)^2=A^2+2AB+B^2$

$$= \frac{a+2\sqrt{ab}+b}{a-b}$$

$\left(\sqrt{x}\right)^2=x$ for $x\geq0$; $\sqrt[n]{a}\sqrt[n]{b}=\sqrt[n]{ab}$

▶

Group Exploration

Looking ahead: Sketching graphs of square root functions

1. Use a graphing calculator to draw a graph of $y=\sqrt{x}$.

2. Use a graphing calculator to compare graphs of $y=0.5\sqrt{x}$, $y=\sqrt{x}$, $y=2\sqrt{x}$, and $y=-2\sqrt{x}$. Describe the effect a has on the graph of $y=a\sqrt{x}$, where $a\neq0$.

3. Use a graphing calculator to compare graphs of $y=\sqrt{x}-2$, $y=\sqrt{x}$, and $y=\sqrt{x}+4$. Describe the effect h has on the graph of $y=\sqrt{x}-h$.

4. Use a graphing calculator to compare graphs of $y=\sqrt{x}-2$, $y=\sqrt{x}$, and $y=\sqrt{x}+4$. Describe the effect k has on the graph of $y=\sqrt{x}+k$.

5. Use a graphing calculator to graph

$$y=\sqrt{x}, \quad y=0.5\sqrt{x}, \quad y=0.5\sqrt{x}+3, \quad \text{and}$$
$$y=0.5\sqrt{x}+3-2$$

in order, and explain how these graphs relate to your observations in Problems 2, 3, and 4.

6. Sketch the graph of $y=2\sqrt{x}-3+1$. Use a graphing calculator to verify your sketch.

7. Describe how a, h, and k affect the graph of $f(x)=a\sqrt{x}-h+k$, where $a\neq0$. Compare their effects for this function with their effects for the quadratic function $g(x)=a(x-h)^2+k$.

▶ Tips for Success   Retake Quizzes and Exams

To study for your final exam, consider retaking your quizzes and other exams. These quizzes and exams can reveal your weak areas. If you have difficulty with a certain concept, you can refer to Homework exercises that address this concept. Reflect on *why* you are having such difficulty, rather than just doing more Homework exercises that address the concept.

Homework 9.3

For extra help ▶ MyMathLab®   Watch the videos in MyMathLab   Download the MyDashboard App

Simplify. Use a graphing calculator table to verify your result when possible. Assume each variable is nonnegative.

1. $\dfrac{8}{\sqrt{x}}$

2. $\dfrac{2}{\sqrt{x}}$

3. $\dfrac{3}{\sqrt{5p}}$

4. $\dfrac{2}{\sqrt{7r}}$

5. $\dfrac{4}{3\sqrt{2x}}$

6. $\dfrac{7}{6\sqrt{3x}}$

7. $\dfrac{10}{\sqrt{8k}}$

8. $\dfrac{6}{\sqrt{27t}}$

9. $\sqrt{\dfrac{4}{x}}$

10. $\sqrt{\dfrac{25}{x}}$

11. $\sqrt{\dfrac{7}{2}}$

12. $\sqrt{\dfrac{5}{3}}$

13. $\sqrt{\dfrac{2y}{x}}$

14. $\sqrt{\dfrac{11y}{x}}$

15. $\sqrt{\dfrac{x}{12y}}$

16. $\sqrt{\dfrac{x}{18y}}$

17. $\dfrac{3}{\sqrt{x-4}}$

18. $\dfrac{5}{\sqrt{2x+1}}$

19. $\dfrac{\sqrt{2a^3}}{\sqrt{3b}}$

20. $\dfrac{\sqrt{5b^5}}{\sqrt{7a}}$

21. $\dfrac{2}{\sqrt[3]{5}}$

22. $\dfrac{5}{\sqrt[3]{2}}$

23. $\dfrac{5}{\sqrt[3]{4}}$

24. $\dfrac{1}{\sqrt[3]{25}}$

25. $\dfrac{4}{5\sqrt[3]{x}}$

26. $\dfrac{7}{4\sqrt[3]{x^2}}$

27. $\dfrac{6}{\sqrt[3]{2x^2}}$

28. $\dfrac{1}{\sqrt[3]{9x}}$

29. $\dfrac{7t}{\sqrt[4]{4t^3}}$

30. $\dfrac{2w}{\sqrt[5]{16w^2}}$

31. $\dfrac{\sqrt[3]{x}}{\sqrt{x}}$

32. $\dfrac{\sqrt[5]{x}}{\sqrt[4]{2x}}$

33. $\sqrt[5]{\dfrac{2}{x^3}}$

34. $\sqrt[3]{\dfrac{4}{x^2}}$

35. $\sqrt[4]{\dfrac{4}{9x^2}}$

36. $\sqrt[3]{\dfrac{7}{25x}}$

37. $\sqrt[5]{\dfrac{3w}{4x^4y^2}}$

38. $\sqrt[6]{\dfrac{5w}{8x^2y^3}}$

Simplify. Use a graphing calculator to verify your result when possible.

39. $\dfrac{1}{5+\sqrt{3}}$

40. $\dfrac{1}{1+\sqrt{5}}$

41. $\dfrac{2}{\sqrt{3}+\sqrt{7}}$

42. $\dfrac{4}{\sqrt{2}+\sqrt{5}}$

43. $\dfrac{1}{3\sqrt{r}-7}$

44. $\dfrac{6}{5\sqrt{t}-2}$

45. $\dfrac{\sqrt{x}}{\sqrt{x}-1}$

46. $\dfrac{\sqrt{x}}{\sqrt{x}+1}$

47. $\dfrac{3\sqrt{x}}{4\sqrt{x}-\sqrt{5}}$

48. $\dfrac{4\sqrt{x}}{2\sqrt{x}+\sqrt{6}}$

49. $\dfrac{\sqrt{x}}{\sqrt{x}-y}$

50. $\dfrac{\sqrt{y}}{x-2\sqrt{y}}$

51. $\dfrac{\sqrt{x}-5}{\sqrt{x}+5}$

52. $\dfrac{\sqrt{x}+9}{\sqrt{x}+9}$

53. $\dfrac{2\sqrt{x}+5}{3\sqrt{x}+1}$

54. $\dfrac{4\sqrt{x}-3}{2\sqrt{x}+5}$

55. $\dfrac{6\sqrt{x}+\sqrt{5}}{3\sqrt{x}-\sqrt{7}}$

56. $\dfrac{8\sqrt{x}-\sqrt{3}}{4\sqrt{x}-\sqrt{2}}$

57. $\dfrac{\sqrt{x}-\sqrt{y}}{\sqrt{x}+\sqrt{y}}$

58. $\dfrac{2\sqrt{x}-\sqrt{y}}{3\sqrt{x}-\sqrt{y}}$

59. $\dfrac{1}{\sqrt{x+1}-\sqrt{x}}$

60. $\dfrac{2}{\sqrt{x+3}+\sqrt{x}}$

61. The distance (in miles) $f(h)$ to the horizon at an altitude h feet above sea level is given by the equation

$$f(h) = \sqrt{\dfrac{3h}{2}}$$

   a. Simplify the right-hand side of the horizon–distance equation.

   b. The Willis Tower in Chicago is 1450 feet tall. What would be the distance to the horizon from the top of this skyscraper? Assume the base of the building is at sea level.

   c. If an airplane flies at an altitude of 30,000 feet above sea level, what is the distance to the horizon from the airplane?

62. The time (in seconds) $f(d)$ that it takes for an object to fall d feet can be modeled by the equation

$$f(d) = \sqrt{\dfrac{2d}{g}}$$

   where g is the constant 32.2 feet per second squared.

   a. Simplify the right-hand side of the model's equation.

   b. Find $f(100)$. What does it mean in this situation?

   c. In 2002, sky divers jumped off the 1483-foot-tall Petronas Towers (in Malaysia), the tallest habitable buildings in the world. Estimate how long a sky diver was in free fall by finding the time it would take to fall 1483 feet with a closed parachute. Ideally, the parachute opens. If so, is your estimate an underestimate or an overestimate? Explain.

   d. Is f an increasing or a decreasing function? Explain why that makes sense in this situation.

63. In the ISO paper-size system, the length-to-width ratio of all pages is $\dfrac{\sqrt{2}}{1}$ (see Fig. 12).

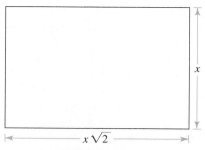

Figure 12 ISO-sized paper

a. Show that if you cut a piece of ISO-sized paper parallel to its shorter side to form two pieces with equal area, each piece will also have a length-to-width ratio of $\dfrac{\sqrt{2}}{1}$ (see Fig. 13). (This property allows two ISO pages of equal size to be photocopied onto one page by setting the magnification factor on a copying machine to $\sqrt{\dfrac{1}{2}} \approx 0.71 = 71\%$.)

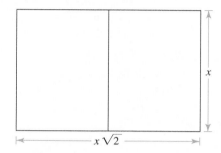

Figure 13 ISO-sized paper cut in two

b. The largest ISO paper size has an area of 1 square meter. Find the (exact) width of a page of this size. Then round your result to the third decimal place.

64. *Escape velocity* is the initial velocity that an object needs in order to break free of a planet's or moon's gravitational pull. If we ignore the effects of air resistance and the rotation of the planet or moon and assume there is no continued propulsion, as by a rocket, the escape velocity v (in meters per second) is given by $v = \sqrt{\dfrac{2GM}{r}}$, where G is a constant equal to 6.67×10^{-11}, M is the mass (in kilograms) of the planet or moon, and r is the object's distance (in meters) from the center of the planet or moon.

a. Simplify the right-hand side of the model's equation.

b. Use Table 7 to find the escape velocity on the planet's or moon's surface at the equator. Round your result to the first decimal place.
  i. Earth   **ii.** the Moon   **iii.** Jupiter

Table 7 Masses and Equatorial Radii of Earth, the Moon, and Jupiter

Planet/Moon	Mass of Planet/Moon (kilograms)	Radius of Planet/Moon (meters)
Earth	5.976×10^{24}	6.378×10^{6}
The Moon	7.349×10^{22}	1.737×10^{6}
Jupiter	1.899×10^{27}	7.149×10^{7}

c. In terms of blastoffs, would a round trip to Jupiter or the Moon require more fuel?

d. Convert your result of part (b, i) to units of miles per hour. (There are approximately 1609.3 meters in 1 mile.)

Concepts

65. Two students try to rationalize the denominator of the expression $\dfrac{2}{\sqrt{x}}$:

Student 1's work	**Student 2's work**
$\dfrac{2}{\sqrt{x}} = \dfrac{2}{\sqrt{x}} \cdot \dfrac{\sqrt{x}}{\sqrt{x}}$	$\dfrac{2}{\sqrt{x}} = \left(\dfrac{2}{\sqrt{x}}\right)^2$
$= \dfrac{2\sqrt{x}}{\sqrt{x}\sqrt{x}}$	$= \dfrac{2^2}{\left(\sqrt{x}\right)^2}$
$= \dfrac{2\sqrt{x}}{x}$	$= \dfrac{4}{x}$

Did one, both, or neither of these students rationalize the denominator correctly? Describe any errors and where they occurred.

66. Two students try to rationalize the denominator of $\dfrac{3}{\sqrt{x^3}}$:

Student 1's work	**Student 2's work**
$\dfrac{3}{\sqrt{x^3}} = \dfrac{3}{\sqrt{x^3}} \cdot \dfrac{\sqrt{x^3}}{\sqrt{x^3}}$	$\dfrac{3}{\sqrt{x^3}} = \dfrac{3}{x\sqrt{x}}$
$= \dfrac{3\sqrt{x^3}}{\sqrt{x^3}\sqrt{x^3}}$	$= \dfrac{3}{x\sqrt{x}} \cdot \dfrac{\sqrt{x}}{\sqrt{x}}$
$= \dfrac{3(x\sqrt{x})}{x^3}$	$= \dfrac{3\sqrt{x}}{x \cdot x}$
$= \dfrac{3\sqrt{x}}{x^2}$	$= \dfrac{3\sqrt{x}}{x^2}$

Did one, both, or neither of the students rationalize the denominator correctly? Explain.

67. A student tries to rationalize the denominator of $\dfrac{5}{\sqrt[3]{x}}$:

$$\dfrac{5}{\sqrt[3]{x}} = \dfrac{5}{\sqrt[3]{x}} \cdot \dfrac{\sqrt[3]{x}}{\sqrt[3]{x}}$$
$$= \dfrac{5\sqrt[3]{x}}{x}$$

Describe any errors. Then rationalize the denominator correctly.

68. Two students try to rationalize the denominator of the expression $\dfrac{4}{2 + \sqrt{x}}$:

Student 1's work	**Student 2's work**
$\dfrac{4}{2 + \sqrt{x}} = \dfrac{4}{2 + \sqrt{x}} \cdot \dfrac{\sqrt{x}}{\sqrt{x}}$	$\dfrac{4}{2 + \sqrt{x}} = \dfrac{4}{2 + \sqrt{x}} \cdot \dfrac{2 - \sqrt{x}}{2 - \sqrt{x}}$
$= \dfrac{4\sqrt{x}}{2 + \sqrt{x}\sqrt{x}}$	$= \dfrac{8 - 4\sqrt{x}}{2^2 - \left(\sqrt{x}\right)^2}$
$= \dfrac{4\sqrt{x}}{2 + x}$	$= \dfrac{8 - 4\sqrt{x}}{4 - x}$

Did one, both, or neither of these students rationalize the denominator correctly? Describe any errors and where they occurred.

We rationalize the numerator of a radical expression by finding an equivalent expression whose numerator contains no radicals. For Exercises 69–72, rationalize the numerator of the given expression.

69. $\dfrac{\sqrt{x}}{3}$

70. $\dfrac{\sqrt{x}}{\sqrt{2}}$

71. $\dfrac{\sqrt{x+2}-\sqrt{x}}{2}$

72. $\dfrac{\sqrt{x+3}+\sqrt{x}}{3}$

73. Simplify the expression.

$$\frac{\dfrac{1}{\sqrt{x}}-\dfrac{3}{x}}{\dfrac{2}{\sqrt{x}}+\dfrac{1}{x}}$$

74. Prove the quotient property for radicals—that is,

$$\sqrt[n]{\frac{a}{b}}=\frac{\sqrt[n]{a}}{\sqrt[n]{b}}$$

where $\sqrt[n]{a}$ and $\sqrt[n]{b}$ are defined and b is nonzero.

75. Find and simplify the exact solution of $x\sqrt{2}+3\sqrt{5}=9\sqrt{5}$.

76. Find the exact solution of $x^2\sqrt{2}+x\sqrt{17}+\sqrt{2}=0$. Simplify your result. [**Hint:** Use the quadratic formula.]

77. Describe how to rationalize the denominator of a radical expression in which the denominator is a radical.

78. Describe how to rationalize the denominator of a radical expression in which the denominator is a sum or difference involving radicals.

Related Review

79. a. Factor A^3+B^3.
   b. Find the product $(A+B)(A^2-AB+B^2)$. Explain how your work is related to your work in part (a).
   c. Find the product $(x+2)(x^2-2x+4)$. Explain how your work is related to the result you found in part (b).

d. Find the product $(\sqrt[3]{x}+\sqrt[3]{2})(\sqrt[3]{x^2}-\sqrt[3]{2x}+\sqrt[3]{4})$. Explain how your work is related to the result you found in part (b).
   e. Rationalize the denominator of $\dfrac{1}{\sqrt[3]{x}+\sqrt[3]{2}}$. [**Hint:** Multiply by 1. See part (d).]

80. a. Factor A^3-B^3.
   b. Find the product $(A-B)(A^2+AB+B^2)$. Explain how your work is related to your work in part (a).
   c. Find the product $(x-2)(x^2+2x+4)$. Explain how your work is related to the result you found in part (b).
   d. Find the product $(\sqrt[3]{x}-\sqrt[3]{2})(\sqrt[3]{x^2}+\sqrt[3]{2x}+\sqrt[3]{4})$. Explain how your work is related to the result you found in part (b).
   e. Rationalize the denominator of $\dfrac{1}{\sqrt[3]{x}-\sqrt[3]{2}}$. [**Hint:** Multiply by 1. See part (d).]

Expressions, Equations, Functions, and Graphs

Perform the indicated instruction. Then use words such as linear, quadratic, cubic, exponential, logarithmic, rational, radical, polynomial, degree, function, one variable, *and* two variables *to describe the expression, equation, or system.*

81. Find the product $(5x-4)(3x^2-2x-1)$.

82. Graph $f(x)=-4(3)^x$ by hand.

83. Factor $24x^3-3000$.

84. Simplify $\dfrac{(16b^{2/3}c^3)^{1/4}}{(27b^{3/4}c^{-5})^{2/3}}$.

85. Solve $5x^2-3=4x-1$.

86. Find any real-number solutions of $5b^4-43=76$. Round any results to the fourth decimal place.

▼ 9.4 Graphing and Combining Square Root Functions

Objectives

» Know the graphical significance of a, h, and k for a square root function of the form $y=a\sqrt{x-h}+k$.

» Sketch graphs of square root functions.

» Find the domain and range of a square root function.

» Find the sum function, difference function, product function, and quotient function of two square root functions.

In this section, we will graph square root functions and perform operations with square root functions.

Graphing Square Root Functions

Recall from Section 7.1 that, to graph a function such as $h(x)=(x-3)^2$, we translate the graph of $k(x)=x^2$ to the right by 3 units. Can we graph the square root function $g(x)=\sqrt{x-3}$ by translating the function $f(x)=\sqrt{x}$ in some way? We will explore this question in Example 1.

▶ **Example 1**   Translating a Graph Horizontally

Compare the graph of $g(x)=\sqrt{x-3}$ with the graph of $f(x)=\sqrt{x}$.

Solution

We list input–output pairs of g in Table 8. We choose inputs that lead to easily found outputs. Then we sketch graphs of g and f (see Fig. 14).

Table 8 Input–Output
Pairs of $g(x) = \sqrt{x-3}$

x	y
3	0
4	1
7	2
12	3
19	4

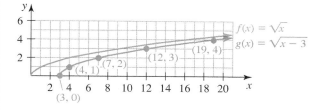

Figure 14 Graphs of
$g(x) = \sqrt{x-3}$ and $f(x) = \sqrt{x}$

The graph of $g(x) = \sqrt{x-3}$ is the translation of the graph of $f(x) = \sqrt{x}$ to the right by 3 units. To see why this makes sense, we solve both equations for x:

$$
\begin{aligned}
f(x) &= \sqrt{x} \\
y &= \sqrt{x} \\
\sqrt{x} &= y \\
\left(\sqrt{x}\right)^2 &= y^2 \\
x &= y^2
\end{aligned}
\qquad\qquad
\begin{aligned}
g(x) &= \sqrt{x-3} \\
y &= \sqrt{x-3} \\
\sqrt{x-3} &= y \\
\left(\sqrt{x-3}\right)^2 &= y^2 \\
x - 3 &= y^2 \\
x &= y^2 + 3
\end{aligned}
$$

For each positive value of y, the input value of x for g is 3 more than the input value of x for f. Therefore, the graph of $g(x) = \sqrt{x-3}$ lies 3 units to the right of the graph of $f(x) = \sqrt{x}$.

In Example 1, we found that, to graph $g(x) = \sqrt{x-3}$, we translate the graph of $f(x) = \sqrt{x}$ to the right by 3 units. This is the same pattern we observed with quadratic functions: To graph the quadratic function $g(x) = (x-3)^2$, we translate the graph of $f(x) = x^2$ to the right by 3 units.

In fact, the values of a, h, and k have similar effects on a square root function $g(x) = a\sqrt{x-h} + k$, where $a \neq 0$, as on a quadratic function $Q(x) = a(x-h)^2 + k$. Here are some examples of how we can translate the graph of $y = \sqrt{x}$ to obtain the graph of an equation of the form $y = \sqrt{x-h} + k$:

Function	To graph the function $g(x) = \sqrt{x-h} + k$,
$g(x) = \sqrt{x-2}$	translate the graph of $y = \sqrt{x}$ to the right by 2 units.
$g(x) = \sqrt{x+2}$	translate the graph of $y = \sqrt{x}$ to the left by 2 units.
$g(x) = \sqrt{x} - 2$	translate the graph of $y = \sqrt{x}$ down by 2 units.
$g(x) = \sqrt{x} + 2$	translate the graph of $y = \sqrt{x}$ up by 2 units.

The graphs of $f(x) = -a\sqrt{x}$ and $g(x) = a\sqrt{x}$ are reflections of each other across the x-axis (see Fig. 15).

If $a > 0$, then $g(x) = a\sqrt{x-h} + k$ is an increasing function and (h, k) is the minimum point (see Fig. 16). **If $a < 0$, then g is a decreasing function and (h, k) is the maximum point** (see Fig. 17).

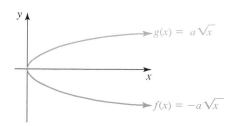

Figure 15 Typical graphs of
$f(x) = -a\sqrt{x}$ and $g(x) = a\sqrt{x}$,
where $a > 0$

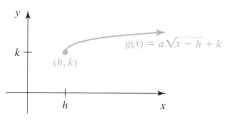

Figure 16 If $a > 0$, then g is increasing
with minimum point (h, k)

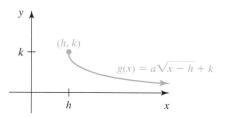

Figure 17 If $a < 0$, then g is decreasing
with maximum point (h, k)

If $a > 1$, then the graph of $g(x) = a\sqrt{x - h} + k$ **rises more quickly than the graph of** $y = \sqrt{x - h} + k$. **If** $0 < a < 1$, **then the graph rises more slowly.**

> **Three-Step Method for Graphing a Square Root Function**
>
> To sketch the graph of $f(x) = a\sqrt{x - h} + k$, where $a \neq 0$,
>
> 1. Sketch the graph of $y = a\sqrt{x}$.
> 2. Translate the graph sketched in step 1 to the right by h units if $h > 0$ and to the left by $|h|$ units if $h < 0$.
> 3. Translate the graph sketched in step 2 up by k units if $k > 0$ and down by $|k|$ units if $k < 0$.

The graph of a square root function is called a **square root curve**.

▶ **Example 2**   Graphing a Square Root Function

Sketch the graph of $g(x) = -2\sqrt{x + 4} - 1$. Find the domain and range of g.

Solution

First, we sketch the graph of $y = -2\sqrt{x}$ in Fig. 18. Next, we translate the graph to the left by 4 units and down by 1 unit.

   We check that the solutions of g listed in Table 9 lie on our sketch of the graph of g. Also, we use a graphing calculator to verify our sketch (see Fig. 19).

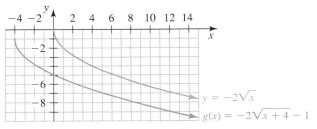

Figure 18 Graphs of $y = -2\sqrt{x}$ and $g(x) = -2\sqrt{x + 4} - 1$

Table 9 Input–Output Pairs of $g(x) = -2\sqrt{x + 4} - 1$

x	$g(x)$
-4	-1
-3	-3
0	-5
5	-7
12	-9

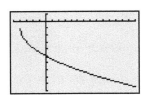

Figure 19 Verify the graph of $g(x) = -2\sqrt{x + 4} - 1$

   From the graph of g, we see that the values of x are greater than or equal to -4. So, the domain is the set of numbers x where $x \geq -4$. We can also find the domain by using the fact that the radicand $x + 4$ must be nonnegative:

$$x + 4 \geq 0 \qquad \textit{Radicand must be nonnegative.}$$
$$x + 4 - 4 \geq 0 - 4 \qquad \textit{Subtract 4 from both sides.}$$
$$x \geq -4$$

   From the graph of g, we see that the maximum point is $(-4, -1)$, so the values of y are less than or equal to -1. Therefore, the range is the set of numbers y where $y \leq -1$.

▶ **Example 3**   Graphing a Square Root Function

Sketch the graph of $f(x) = 2\sqrt{x - 3} + 5$. Find the domain and range of f.

Solution

First, we sketch the graph of $y = 2\sqrt{x}$ in Fig. 20. Next, we translate the graph to the right by 3 units and up by 5 units.

We check that the solutions of f listed in Table 10 lie on our sketch of the graph of f. Also, we use a graphing calculator to verify our sketch (see Fig. 21).

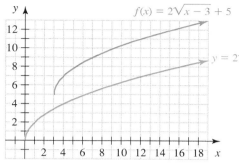

Figure 20 Graphs of $y = 2\sqrt{x}$ and $f(x) = 2\sqrt{x-3} + 5$

Table 10 Input–Output Pairs of $f(x) = 2\sqrt{x-3} + 5$	
x	$f(x)$
3	5
4	7
7	9
12	11
19	13

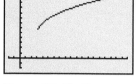

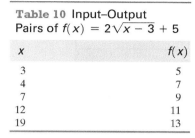

Figure 21 Verify the graph of $f(x) = 2\sqrt{x-3} + 5$

From the graph of f, we see that the values of x are greater than or equal to 3. So, the domain is the set of numbers x where $x \geq 3$. We can also find the domain by using the fact that the radicand $x - 3$ must be nonnegative:

$$x - 3 \geq 0 \qquad \textit{Radicand must be nonnegative.}$$
$$x - 3 + 3 \geq 0 + 3 \quad \textit{Add 3 to both sides.}$$
$$x \geq 3$$

From the graph of f, we see that the minimum point is $(3, 5)$, so the values of y are greater than or equal to 5. Therefore, the range is the set of numbers y where $y \geq 5$.

Performing Operations with Square Root Functions

In Example 4, we will use two square root functions to form a sum function, a difference function, a product function, and a quotient function.

▶ **Example 4** Performing Operations with Square Root Functions

Let $f(x) = 2\sqrt{x} - 3$ and $g(x) = 5\sqrt{x} + 4$. For each of the following functions, find an equation of the function.

1. $f + g$ **2.** $f - g$ **3.** $f \cdot g$ **4.** $\dfrac{f}{g}$

Solution

1. $(f + g)(x) = f(x) + g(x) = \left(2\sqrt{x} - 3\right) + \left(5\sqrt{x} + 4\right)$ *Substitute for f(x) and g(x).*
$$= 7\sqrt{x} + 1 \qquad \textit{Combine like radicals.}$$

2. $(f - g)(x) = f(x) - g(x) = \left(2\sqrt{x} - 3\right) - \left(5\sqrt{x} + 4\right)$ *Substitute for f(x) and g(x).*
$$= 2\sqrt{x} - 3 - 5\sqrt{x} - 4 \qquad \textit{Subtract.}$$
$$= -3\sqrt{x} - 7 \qquad \textit{Combine like radicals.}$$

3. $(f \cdot g)(x) = f(x)g(x) = \left(2\sqrt{x} - 3\right)\left(5\sqrt{x} + 4\right)$ *Substitute for f(x) and g(x).*
$$= 2\sqrt{x} \cdot 5\sqrt{x} + 2\sqrt{x} \cdot 4 - 3 \cdot 5\sqrt{x} - 12 \quad \textit{Multiply pairs of terms.}$$
$$= 10x + 8\sqrt{x} - 15\sqrt{x} - 12 \qquad \textit{Simplify.}$$
$$= 10x - 7\sqrt{x} - 12 \qquad \textit{Combine like radicals.}$$

Figure 22 Verify the work

4. $\left(\dfrac{f}{g}\right)(x) = \dfrac{f(x)}{g(x)} = \dfrac{2\sqrt{x}-3}{5\sqrt{x}+4}$ *Substitute for $f(x)$ and $g(x)$.*

$= \dfrac{2\sqrt{x}-3}{5\sqrt{x}+4} \cdot \dfrac{5\sqrt{x}-4}{5\sqrt{x}-4}$ *Rationalize denominator.*

$= \dfrac{2\sqrt{x}\cdot 5\sqrt{x} - 2\sqrt{x}\cdot 4 - 3\cdot 5\sqrt{x} + 12}{\left(5\sqrt{x}\right)^2 - 4^2}$ *Multiply numerators; multiply denominators.*

$= \dfrac{10x - 8\sqrt{x} - 15\sqrt{x} + 12}{5^2\left(\sqrt{x}\right)^2 - 4^2}$ *Simplify.*

$= \dfrac{10x - 23\sqrt{x} + 12}{25x - 16}$ *Simplify.*

We verify our work by comparing graphing calculator tables for $y = \dfrac{2\sqrt{x}-3}{5\sqrt{x}+4}$ and $y = \dfrac{10x - 23\sqrt{x} + 12}{25x - 16}$ for $x > 0$ and $x \neq \dfrac{16}{25}$ (see Fig. 22).

Group Exploration

Translating and reflecting the absolute value function

1. Complete Table 11 for the absolute value function $y = |x|$. For example, $|-2| = 2$, $|0| = 0$, and $|3| = 3$. To review absolute value, see Section A.3.

Table 11 Values of the Function $y = |x|$

x	y
-3	
-2	
-1	
1	
2	
3	

2. Sketch a graph of $y = |x|$. Use a graphing calculator to verify your graph. To enter $|x|$, press $\boxed{\text{MATH}}\,\boxed{\triangleright}\,\mathbf{1}$ $\boxed{\text{X,T,}\Theta,n}\,\boxed{)}$.

3. Translate and/or reflect the graph of $y = |x|$ to sketch the graph of the given function. Use a graphing calculator to verify your sketch.
  a. $y = |x| - 2$ **b.** $y = |x - 4|$
  c. $y = -|x + 3|$ **d.** $y = -|x - 2| + 5$

4. Sketch the graph of the given function.
  a. $y = 2|x|$ **b.** $y = -3|x|$

5. Describe the graphical significance of a, h, and k for a function of the form $y = a|x - h| + k$, where $a \neq 0$.

Homework 9.4

For extra help ▶ **MyMathLab**®   Watch the videos in MyMathLab   Download the MyDashboard App

Graph the function by hand. Use a graphing calculator to verify your sketch.

1. $y = 2\sqrt{x}$

2. $y = -3\sqrt{x}$

3. $y = -\sqrt{x}$

4. $y = -\dfrac{1}{2}\sqrt{x}$

5. $y = \sqrt{x} + 3$

6. $y = \sqrt{x} - 5$

7. $y = 2\sqrt{x} - 5$

8. $y = 3\sqrt{x} - 2$

9. $y = -3\sqrt{x} + 4$

10. $y = -2\sqrt{x} + 1$

11. $y = \sqrt{x} - 2$

12. $y = \sqrt{x} - 5$

13. $y = -\sqrt{x} + 2$

14. $y = -2\sqrt{x} + 5$

15. $y = \dfrac{1}{2}\sqrt{x} - 4$

16. $y = \dfrac{1}{4}\sqrt{x} - 1$

17. $y = \sqrt{x} + 3 + 2$

18. $y = \sqrt{x} + 1 + 3$

19. $y = -2\sqrt{x} + 3 - 4$

20. $y = -3\sqrt{x} + 2 - 1$

21. $y = 4\sqrt{x} - 1 - 3$

22. $y = 2\sqrt{x} - 6 - 2$

23. $\sqrt{x} + y = 4$

24. $2\sqrt{x} - y = 3$

25. $2y - 6\sqrt{x} = 8$

26. $3y - 6\sqrt{x} = 9$

Graph the function by hand. Use a graphing calculator to verify your sketch. Also, find the domain and range of the function.

27. $y = -2\sqrt{x}$

28. $y = 3\sqrt{x}$

29. $y = \sqrt{x} + 2$

30. $y = \sqrt{x} - 6$

31. $y = \sqrt{x + 2}$

32. $y = \sqrt{x} - 1$

33. $y = \sqrt{x - 5} - 3$

34. $y = \sqrt{x + 1} + 2$

35. $y = 2\sqrt{x + 5} + 1$

36. $y = 3\sqrt{x - 3} - 6$

37. $y = -\sqrt{x - 2} + 4$

38. $y = -2\sqrt{x + 4} - 2$

39. Recall that we can describe some or all of the input–output pairs of a function by means of an equation, a graph, a table, or words. Let $f(x) = 2\sqrt{x - 3}$.

  a. Describe five input–output pairs of f by using a table.
  b. Describe the input–output pairs of f by using a graph.
  c. Describe the input–output pairs of f by using words.

40. Recall that we can describe some or all of the input–output pairs of a function by means of an equation, a graph, a table, or words. Let $g(x) = -\sqrt{x + 4}$.

  a. Describe five input–output pairs of g by using a table.
  b. Describe the input–output pairs of g by using a graph.
  c. Describe the input–output pairs of g by using words.

Evaluate the function $f(x) = 7\sqrt{x} - 3$ at the indicated value of x. Assume $c \geq 0$.

41. $f(4)$

42. $f(0)$

43. $f(9c)$

44. $f(4c)$

For $f(x) = 5\sqrt{x} - 9$ and $g(x) = 4\sqrt{x} + 1$, find an equation of the given function.

45. $f + g$

46. $f - g$

47. $f \cdot g$

48. $\dfrac{f}{g}$

For $f(x) = 2\sqrt{x} - 3\sqrt{5}$ and $g(x) = 2\sqrt{x} + 3\sqrt{5}$, find an equation of the given function.

49. $f - g$

50. $f + g$

51. $\dfrac{f}{g}$

52. $f \cdot g$

For $f(x) = \sqrt{x + 1} - 2$ and $g(x) = \sqrt{x + 1} + 2$, find an equation of the given function.

53. $f + g$

54. $f - g$

55. $f \cdot g$

56. $\dfrac{f}{g}$

57. The percentages of e-mail that is spam are shown in Table 12 for various years.

Table 12 Percentages of E-Mail That Is Spam

Year	Percent
1999	21
2002	56
2004	68
2006	80
2008	81
2010	85

Source: *IronPort*

Let $f(t)$ be the percentage of e-mail that is spam at t years since 1999. A reasonable model is $f(t) = 20.4\sqrt{t} + 21$.

  a. Use a graphing calculator to draw the graph of the model and, in the same viewing window, the scattergram of the data. Does the model fit the data well?

  b. Estimate the percentage of e-mail that was spam in 2005. Did you perform interpolation or extrapolation? Explain.

  c. Predict the percentage of e-mail that will be spam in 2013. Did you perform interpolation or extrapolation? Explain.

58. The global airline industry's revenues from fees not included in fares are shown in Table 13 for various years.

Table 13 Global Airline Industry's Revenues from Fees Not Included in Fares

Year	Revenue (billions of dollars)
2007	2.5
2008	10.3
2009	13.5
2010	21.5
2011	22.6

Source: *IdeaWorks and Amadeus*

Let $f(t)$ be the global airline industry's annual revenue (in billions of dollars) from fees not included in fares at t years since 2007. A reasonable model is $f(t) = 10\sqrt{t} + 2.5$.

  a. Use a graphing calculator to draw the graph of the model and, in the same viewing window, the scattergram of the data. Does the model fit the data well?

  b. Estimate the global airline industry's revenue from fees not included in fares in 2010. Is your result an underestimate or an overestimate? Did you perform interpolation or extrapolation? Explain.

  c. Predict the global airline industry's revenue from fees not included in fares in 2018. Did you perform interpolation or extrapolation? Explain.

For Exercises 59–66, refer to Fig. 23.

59. Estimate $f(-6)$.

60. Estimate $f(-2)$.

61. Estimate $f(0)$.

62. Estimate $f(5)$.

63. Estimate x when $f(x) = 0$.

64. Estimate x when $f(x) = 2$.

65. Estimate x when $f(x) = 3$.

66. Estimate x when $f(x) = 4$.

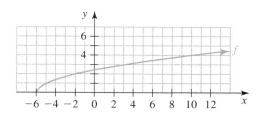

Figure 23 Exercises 59–66

Concepts

67. Figure 24 shows four functions of the form $y = a\sqrt{x - h} + k$. For each, describe the signs of the constants a, h, and k.

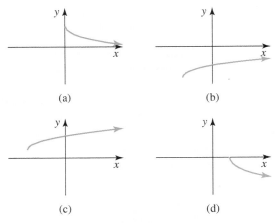

(a)   (b)

(c)   (d)

Figure 24 Exercise 67

68. For each part, copy the graph of $f(x) = a\sqrt{x - h} + k$ as shown in Fig. 25. On the same coordinate system, use the graph of f to sketch the graph of the given function. Label each graph.
a. $g(x) = a\sqrt{x - h} + 2k$
b. $h(x) = a\sqrt{x - 2h} + k$
c. $k(x) = -a\sqrt{x - h} + k$
d. $r(x) = 2a\sqrt{x + h} - k$

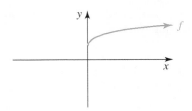

Figure 25 Exercise 68

69. Use a graphing calculator to graph a family of square root curves similar to the one in Fig. 26. List the equations of your square root curves.

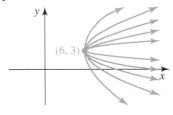

(0, 2)

Figure 26 A family of square root curves— Exercise 69

70. Use a graphing calculator to graph a family of square root curves similar to the one in Fig. 27. List the equations of your square root curves.

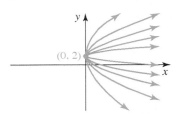

(6, 3)

Figure 27 Another family of square root curves—Exercise 70

71. For what values of a, h, and k for the square root function $f(x) = a\sqrt{x - h} + k$, where $a \neq 0$, is there a point on the graph of f that is higher than all other points on the graph? (Recall that this point is the maximum point.) For what values of a, h, and k does f have a minimum point? Describe the maximum or minimum point in terms of a, h, and k.

72. Solve the system
$$y = 2\sqrt{x - 3} + 1$$
$$y = -2\sqrt{x - 3} + 1$$

73. Use ZStandard followed by ZSquare to draw the graphs of $f(x) = 2\sqrt{x + 3} + 2$ and $g(x) = -2\sqrt{x + 3} + 2$ on the same coordinate system. Consider the combined graph as the graph of a single relation. What do you notice about the graph? Is the relation described by this graph a function? Explain.

74. Find two functions that have the same domain and range as the function $f(x) = \sqrt{x + 7} - 2$.

75. Explain why the graphs of $f(x) = -a\sqrt{x}$ and $g(x) = a\sqrt{x}$ are reflections of each other across the x-axis.

76. Let k be a positive constant. To graph the function $g(x) = \sqrt{x} + k$, we translate the graph of $f(x) = \sqrt{x}$ up by k units. Explain why this makes sense.

77. Describe how to graph the function $g(x) = a\sqrt{x - h} + k$, where $a \neq 0$, given the graph of $f(x) = \sqrt{x}$.

78. Compare the process of graphing a square root function of the form $f(x) = a\sqrt{x - h} + k$, where $a \neq 0$, with that of graphing a quadratic function of the form $g(x) = a(x - h)^2 + k$. How are the processes similar? different?

Related Review

Graph the function by hand.

79. $2x - 5y = 20$

80. $y = -2(x - 4)^2 + 3$

81. $y = 2\sqrt{x + 3} - 4$

82. $y = -3\sqrt{x - 1} + 3$

83. $y = 8\left(\dfrac{1}{2}\right)^x$

84. $y = 3x^2 - 12x + 9$

For $f(x) = \sqrt{3x + 2} - 7$ and $g(x) = 4x + 5$, find an equation of the given composite function.

85. $f \circ g$ **86.** $g \circ f$

For $f(x) = \sqrt{x + 3}$ and $g(x) = x^2 + 2$, find an equation of the given composite function.

87. $f \circ g$ **88.** $g \circ f$

Expressions, Equations, Functions, and Graphs

Perform the indicated instruction. Then use words such as linear, quadratic, cubic, exponential, logarithmic, rational, radical, polynomial, degree, function, one variable, *and* two variables *to describe the expression, equation, or system.*

89. Factor $6x^2 - 5x - 6$.

90. Find the product $(3\sqrt{x} - 5)(2\sqrt{x} + 4)$.

91. Let $f(x) = 3x^2 - 2x + 4$. Find x when $f(x) = 6$.

92. Graph $f(x) = -2\sqrt{x - 3} + 1$ by hand.

93. Find an equation of a parabola that contains the points $(1, 4)$, $(3, 14)$, and $(4, 25)$.

94. Graph $f(x) = -2(x - 3)^2 + 1$.

▼ 9.5 Solving Radical Equations

Objectives

» Solve radical equations.

» Find the *x*-intercept of the graph of a square root function.

» Use a radical model to make predictions about the independent variable.

In Sections 9.1–9.3, we worked with radical *expressions*. In this section, we solve radical *equations*. A **radical equation in one variable** is an equation in one variable that contains a radical with the variable in the radicand. Here are some examples of a radical equation in one variable:

$$\sqrt{x} = 5 \qquad \sqrt[3]{7x - 3} = 2 \qquad \sqrt{x - 2} = x - 4 \qquad \sqrt{x + 3} - \sqrt{2x - 4} = 6$$

We begin by solving square root equations in one variable.

Solving Square Root Equations in One Variable

Consider the square root equation

$$\sqrt{x} = 3$$

If *x* is nonnegative, then $\left(\sqrt{x}\right)^2 = x$. To get the left side of the equation $\sqrt{x} = 3$ to be *x*, we square both sides:

$$\left(\sqrt{x}\right)^2 = 3^2$$
$$x = 9$$

So, the solution is 9. This checks out, because $\sqrt{9} = 3$.

▶ **Squaring Property of Equality**

If *A* and *B* are expressions, then all solutions of the equation $A = B$ are *among* the solutions of the equation $A^2 = B^2$. That is, the solutions of an equation are among the solutions of the equation obtained by squaring both sides.

Recall from Section 8.5 that if we clear a rational equation of fractions and arrive at a value of *x* that is an excluded value, then we call that result an extraneous solution. In general, if a proposed solution of any type of equation is *not* a solution, we call it an **extraneous solution.**

Squaring both sides of an equation can introduce extraneous solutions. Consider the simple equation $x = 5$, whose only solution is 5. Here we square both sides of $x = 5$ and solve by using the square root property (Section 7.3):

$$
\begin{array}{ll}
x = 5 & \textit{The only solution is 5.} \\
x^2 = 5^2 & \textit{Square both sides.} \\
x^2 = 25 & \textit{$5^2 = 25$} \\
x = \pm\sqrt{25} & \textit{Square root property} \\
x = \pm 5 & \textit{$\sqrt{25} = 5$}
\end{array}
$$

Squaring both sides of the equation $x = 5$ introduced the extraneous solution -5 (which is *not* a solution of the original equation).

▶ **Checking Proposed Solutions**

Because squaring both sides of a square root equation may introduce extraneous solutions, it is essential to check that each proposed solution satisfies the original equation.

▶ **Example 1**   Solving a Square Root Equation

Solve the equation $2\sqrt{x} + 5 = 13$.

Solution

First, we isolate $\sqrt{x}$ (get $\sqrt{x}$ alone) on one side of the equation:

$$2\sqrt{x} + 5 = 13 \qquad \textit{Original equation}$$
$$2\sqrt{x} = 8 \qquad \textit{Subtract 5 from both sides.}$$
$$\sqrt{x} = 4 \qquad \textit{Divide both sides by 2.}$$
$$\left(\sqrt{x}\right)^2 = 4^2 \qquad \textit{Square both sides.}$$
$$x = 16 \qquad \left(\sqrt{x}\right)^2 = x \textit{ for } x \geq 0; 4^2 = 16$$

We check that 16 satisfies the original equation:

$$2\sqrt{x} + 5 = 13 \qquad \textit{Original equation}$$
$$2\sqrt{16} + 5 \stackrel{?}{=} 13 \qquad \textit{Substitute 16 for x.}$$
$$2 \cdot 4 + 5 \stackrel{?}{=} 13 \qquad \sqrt{16} = 4$$
$$13 \stackrel{?}{=} 13$$
$$\text{true}$$

So, the solution is 16.

▶

We see from Example 1 that, to solve a square root equation, we isolate a square root term on one side of the equation before we square both sides.

▶ **Example 2**   Solving a Square Root Equation

Solve $x = \sqrt{x - 1} + 3$.

Solution

$$x = \sqrt{x - 1} + 3 \qquad \textit{Original equation}$$
$$x - 3 = \sqrt{x - 1} \qquad \textit{Isolate radical.}$$
$$(x - 3)^2 = \left(\sqrt{x - 1}\right)^2 \qquad \textit{Square both sides.}$$
$$x^2 - 6x + 9 = x - 1 \qquad (A - B)^2 = A^2 - 2AB + B^2; \left(\sqrt{x}\right)^2 = x \textit{ for } x \geq 0$$
$$x^2 - 7x + 10 = 0 \qquad \textit{Write in } ax^2 + bx + c = 0 \textit{ form.}$$
$$(x - 2)(x - 5) = 0 \qquad \textit{Factor left side.}$$
$$x - 2 = 0 \quad \text{or} \quad x - 5 = 0 \qquad \textit{Zero factor property}$$
$$x = 2 \quad \text{or} \qquad x = 5$$

We check that 2 and 5 satisfy the original equation:

Check $x = 2$	**Check** $x = 5$
$x = \sqrt{x - 1} + 3$	$x = \sqrt{x - 1} + 3$
$2 \stackrel{?}{=} \sqrt{2 - 1} + 3$	$5 \stackrel{?}{=} \sqrt{5 - 1} + 3$
$2 \stackrel{?}{=} 4$	$5 \stackrel{?}{=} 5$
false	true

Since 2 does not satisfy the original equation, it is an extraneous solution. Therefore, the only solution is 5.

We use "intersect" on a graphing calculator to verify our work (see Fig. 28). The point $(5, 5)$ is the only point of intersection. This supports our conclusion that the only solution of the original equation is 5.

▶

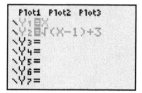

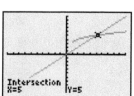

Figure 28 Verify the work

▶ **Example 3**   Solving a Square Root Equation

Solve $2\sqrt{x - 3} - \sqrt{x} = 0$.

Solution

First, we isolate $2\sqrt{x - 3}$; then we square both sides of the equation:

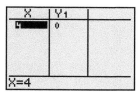

Figure 29 Verify that 4 is a solution

$$2\sqrt{x-3} - \sqrt{x} = 0 \quad \textit{Original equation}$$
$$2\sqrt{x-3} = \sqrt{x} \quad \textit{Isolate } 2\sqrt{x-3}.$$
$$\left(2\sqrt{x-3}\right)^2 = \left(\sqrt{x}\right)^2 \quad \textit{Square both sides.}$$
$$2^2\left(\sqrt{x-3}\right)^2 = \left(\sqrt{x}\right)^2 \quad (AB)^2 = A^2 B^2$$
$$4(x-3) = x \quad \left(\sqrt{x}\right)^2 = x \textit{ for } x \geq 0$$
$$4x - 12 = x \quad \textit{Distributive law}$$
$$3x = 12$$
$$x = 4$$

To verify that 4 is a solution, we enter the function $y = 2\sqrt{x-3} - \sqrt{x}$. Then we check that, for the input 4, the output is 0 (see Fig. 29).

In Example 3, after squaring both sides of $2\sqrt{x-3} = \sqrt{x}$, we simplified $\left(2\sqrt{x-3}\right)^2$:

$$\left(2\sqrt{x-3}\right)^2 = 2^2\left(\sqrt{x-3}\right)^2 = 4(x-3) \quad \textit{Correct}$$

WARNING   It is a common error to forget to square the coefficient 2 and write

$$\left(2\sqrt{x-3}\right)^2 = 2(x-3) \quad \textit{Incorrect}$$

Recall from Section 4.1 that when we simplify $(AB)^2$, we square both A and B:

$$(AB)^2 = A^2 B^2$$

If an equation contains two or more square root terms, we may need to use the squaring property of equality twice.

▶ **Example 4**   Solving a Square Root Equation

Solve $\sqrt{t-5} - \sqrt{t} = -1$.

Solution

First, we isolate the radical $\sqrt{t-5}$; then we square both sides of the equation:

$$\sqrt{t-5} - \sqrt{t} = -1 \quad \textit{Original equation}$$
$$\sqrt{t-5} = \sqrt{t} - 1 \quad \textit{Isolate radical } \sqrt{t-5}.$$
$$\left(\sqrt{t-5}\right)^2 = \left(\sqrt{t}-1\right)^2 \quad \textit{Square both sides.}$$
$$t - 5 = \left(\sqrt{t}\right)^2 - 2\sqrt{t} \cdot 1 + 1^2 \quad \begin{array}{l}\left(\sqrt{x}\right)^2 = x \textit{ for } x \geq 0; \\ (A-B)^2 = A^2 - 2AB + B^2\end{array}$$
$$t - 5 = t - 2\sqrt{t} + 1 \quad \left(\sqrt{x}\right)^2 = x \textit{ for } x \geq 0$$

Next, we isolate the radical $\sqrt{t}$ and square both sides:

$$2\sqrt{t} = t + 1 - t + 5 \quad \textit{Isolate } 2\sqrt{t}.$$
$$2\sqrt{t} = 6 \quad \textit{Combine like terms.}$$
$$\sqrt{t} = 3 \quad \textit{Divide both sides by 2.}$$
$$\left(\sqrt{t}\right)^2 = 3^2 \quad \textit{Square both sides.}$$
$$t = 9 \quad \left(\sqrt{x}\right)^2 = x \textit{ for } x \geq 0$$

Now we check that 9 satisfies the original equation:

$$\sqrt{t-5} - \sqrt{t} = -1 \quad \textit{Original equation}$$
$$\sqrt{9-5} - \sqrt{9} \overset{?}{=} -1 \quad \textit{Substitute 9 for t.}$$
$$2 - 3 \overset{?}{=} -1$$
$$-1 \overset{?}{=} -1$$
$$\text{true}$$

So, the solution is 9.

> **Solving a Square Root Equation in One Variable**
>
> To solve a square root equation in one variable,
>
> 1. Isolate a square root term on one side of the equation.
> 2. Square both sides.
> 3. Repeat steps 1 and 2 until no square root terms remain.
> 4. Solve the new equation.
> 5. Check that each proposed solution satisfies the original equation.

▶ **Example 5** Solving a Square Root Equation

Solve $\sqrt{2x + 1} - \sqrt{x + 2} = 1$.

Solution

$$\sqrt{2x + 1} - \sqrt{x + 2} = 1 \qquad \textit{Original equation}$$

$$\sqrt{2x + 1} = \sqrt{x + 2} + 1 \qquad \textit{Isolate radical } \sqrt{2x + 1}.$$

$$\left(\sqrt{2x + 1}\right)^2 = \left(\sqrt{x + 2} + 1\right)^2 \qquad \textit{Square both sides.}$$

$$2x + 1 = \left(\sqrt{x + 2}\right)^2 + 2\sqrt{x + 2} \cdot 1 + 1^2 \qquad \begin{array}{l}\left(\sqrt{x}\right)^2 = x \textit{ for } x \geq 0, \\ (A + B)^2 = A^2 + 2AB + B^2\end{array}$$

$$2x + 1 = x + 2 + 2\sqrt{x + 2} + 1 \qquad \left(\sqrt{x}\right)^2 = x \textit{ for } x \geq 0$$

$$x - 2 = 2\sqrt{x + 2} \qquad \textit{Isolate radical } 2\sqrt{x + 2}.$$

$$(x - 2)^2 = \left(2\sqrt{x + 2}\right)^2 \qquad \textit{Square both sides.}$$

$$x^2 - 4x + 4 = 4(x + 2) \qquad \begin{array}{l}(A - B)^2 = A^2 - 2AB + B^2; \\ (bc)^n = b^n c^n\end{array}$$

$$x^2 - 4x + 4 = 4x + 8 \qquad \textit{Distributive law}$$

$$x^2 - 8x - 4 = 0 \qquad \textit{Write in } ax^2 + bx + c = 0 \textit{ form.}$$

$$x = \frac{-(-8) \pm \sqrt{(-8)^2 - 4(1)(-4)}}{2(1)} \qquad \begin{array}{l}\textit{Substitute } a = 1, b = -8, \\ c = -4 \textit{ into quadratic formula.}\end{array}$$

$$= \frac{8 \pm \sqrt{80}}{2} \qquad \textit{Simplify.}$$

$$= \frac{8 \pm 4\sqrt{5}}{2} \qquad \sqrt{80} = \sqrt{16 \cdot 5} = 4\sqrt{5}$$

$$= \frac{2\left(4 \pm 2\sqrt{5}\right)}{2} \qquad \textit{Factor out 2.}$$

$$= 4 \pm 2\sqrt{5} \qquad \textit{Simplify.}$$

So, $x = 4 - 2\sqrt{5} \approx -0.47$ or $x = 4 + 2\sqrt{5} \approx 8.47$. We check that the approximations of the solutions approximately satisfy the original equation $\sqrt{2x + 1} - \sqrt{x + 2} = 1$:

Check $x \approx -0.47$	**Check $x \approx 8.47$**
$\sqrt{2(-0.47) + 1} - \sqrt{-0.47 + 2} \approx -0.9920$	$\sqrt{2(8.47) + 1} - \sqrt{8.47 + 2} \approx 0.9998$
not close to 1	close to 1

So, the only solution is $4 + 2\sqrt{5}$.

Now we store $4 - 2\sqrt{5}$ for the variable "X" in a graphing calculator and perform a similar, but more precise, check. We do the same for $4 + 2\sqrt{5}$ (see Fig. 30).

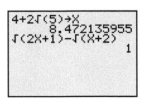

Figure 30 Verify that $4 - 2\sqrt{5}$ is an extraneous solution and $4 + 2\sqrt{5}$ is a solution

In Example 5, we simplified the right-hand side of the equation

$$\left(\sqrt{2x + 1}\right)^2 = \left(\sqrt{x + 2} + 1\right)^2$$

by using the property for the square of a sum, $(A + B)^2 = A^2 + 2AB + B^2$:

$$\left(\sqrt{x + 2} + 1\right)^2 = \left(\sqrt{x + 2}\right)^2 + 2\sqrt{x + 2} \cdot 1 + 1^2 \qquad \textit{Correct}$$

WARNING   Remember that, in general, $(A + B)^2$ is *not* equal to $A^2 + B^2$, so it is incorrect to say that

$$\left(\sqrt{x + 2} + 1\right)^2 = \left(\sqrt{x + 2}\right)^2 + 1^2 \quad \textit{Incorrect}$$

▶ **Example 6** | Solving a General Square Root Equation

Solve the equation $F = \dfrac{1}{2L}\sqrt{\dfrac{T}{p}}$ for p. Assume the constants have values for which the equation has exactly one real-number solution.

Solution

First, we square both sides of the equation:

$$F = \dfrac{1}{2L}\sqrt{\dfrac{T}{p}} \qquad \textit{Original equation}$$

$$F^2 = \left(\dfrac{1}{2L}\sqrt{\dfrac{T}{p}}\right)^2 \qquad \textit{Square both sides.}$$

$$F^2 = \left(\dfrac{1}{2L}\right)^2\left(\sqrt{\dfrac{T}{p}}\right)^2 \qquad (AB)^2 = A^2B^2$$

$$F^2 = \dfrac{1}{4L^2}\cdot\dfrac{T}{p} \qquad \left(\dfrac{1}{2L}\right)^2 = \dfrac{1^2}{(2L)^2} = \dfrac{1}{2^2L^2} = \dfrac{1}{4L^2};\ \left(\sqrt{x}\right)^2 = x \text{ for } x \geq 0.$$

$$F^2 = \dfrac{T}{4L^2p} \qquad \textit{Multiply numerators; multiply denominators.}$$

$$F^2\cdot p = \dfrac{T}{4L^2p}\cdot p \qquad \textit{Multiply both sides by p.}$$

$$F^2p = \dfrac{T}{4L^2} \qquad \textit{Simplify.}$$

$$\dfrac{1}{F^2}\cdot F^2p = \dfrac{1}{F^2}\cdot\dfrac{T}{4L^2} \qquad \textit{Multiply both sides by } \dfrac{1}{F^2}.$$

$$p = \dfrac{T}{4F^2L^2} \qquad \textit{Simplify; multiply numerators; multiply denominators.}$$

◀

The equation $\sqrt{x + 8} = x^2 - 3x - 4$ would be very difficult to solve by using properties such as the squaring property of equality. In Example 7, we will use graphing to find approximate solutions of the equation.

▶ **Example 7** | Using Graphing to Solve a Square Root Equation in One Variable

Use graphing to solve $\sqrt{x + 8} = x^2 - 3x - 4$.

Solution

We use "intersect" on a graphing calculator to find the solutions of the system

$$y = \sqrt{x + 8}$$
$$y = x^2 - 3x - 4$$

See Fig. 31.

The approximate solutions of the system are $(-1.47, 2.56)$ and $(4.63, 3.55)$. The x-coordinates of these ordered pairs, -1.47 and 4.63, are the approximate solutions of the equation $\sqrt{x + 8} = x^2 - 3x - 4$.

◀

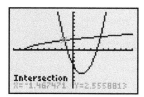

Intersection
X=-1.467471 Y=2.5558813

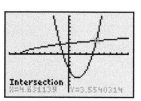

Intersection
X=4.631139 Y=3.5540314

Figure 31 Solve the system

Finding x-Intercepts of the Graph of a Square Root Function

To find all x-intercepts of the graph of a square root equation in x and y, we substitute 0 for y and solve for x.

▶ **Example 8** Finding the *x*-Intercept of a Square Root Function

Find the *x*-intercepts of the graph of $f(x) = \sqrt{3x - 4} - \sqrt{x + 2}$.

Solution

We substitute 0 for $f(x)$ and solve for *x*:

$$\sqrt{3x - 4} - \sqrt{x + 2} = 0 \qquad \text{\textit{Substitute 0 for} f(x).}$$
$$\sqrt{3x - 4} = \sqrt{x + 2} \qquad \text{\textit{Isolate at least one radical.}}$$
$$\left(\sqrt{3x - 4}\right)^2 = \left(\sqrt{x + 2}\right)^2 \qquad \text{\textit{Square both sides.}}$$
$$3x - 4 = x + 2 \qquad \left(\sqrt{x}\right)^2 = x \text{ \textit{for} } x \geq 0$$
$$2x = 6$$
$$x = 3$$

We check that 3 satisfies the equation $\sqrt{3x - 4} - \sqrt{x + 2} = 0$:

$$\sqrt{3x - 4} - \sqrt{x + 2} = 0 \qquad \text{\textit{Original equation}}$$
$$\sqrt{3(3) - 4} - \sqrt{3 + 2} \stackrel{?}{=} 0 \qquad \text{\textit{Substitute 3 for x.}}$$
$$\sqrt{5} - \sqrt{5} \stackrel{?}{=} 0$$
$$0 \stackrel{?}{=} 0$$
$$\text{true}$$

The *x*-intercept is $(3, 0)$. We use "zero" on a graphing calculator to verify our work (see Fig. 32).

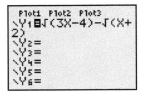

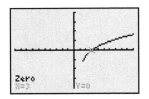

Figure 32 Verify the work

Solving Radical Equations

So far, we have solved square root equations in one variable. We can solve other types of radical equations in one variable in a similar way.

> ▶ **Power Property of Equality**
>
> If A and B are expressions and n is a counting number greater than 1, then all solutions of the equation $A = B$ are *among* the solutions of the equation $A^n = B^n$. That is, the solutions of an equation are among the solutions of the equation obtained by raising both sides to the *n*th power.

▶ **Example 9** Solving a Radical Equation

Solve $\sqrt[3]{2w - 4} + 7 = 9$.

Solution

We isolate $\sqrt[3]{2w - 4}$ on one side of the equation:

$$\sqrt[3]{2w - 4} + 7 = 9 \qquad \text{\textit{Original equation}}$$
$$\sqrt[3]{2w - 4} = 2 \qquad \text{\textit{Subtract 7 from both sides.}}$$

From the power property for radicals (Section 9.2), $\left(\sqrt[3]{2w - 4}\right)^3 = 2w - 4$. To get the left side of the equation $\sqrt[3]{2w - 4} = 2$ to be $2w - 4$, we cube both sides:

$$\left(\sqrt[3]{2w - 4}\right)^3 = 2^3 \qquad \text{\textit{Cube both sides.}}$$
$$2w - 4 = 8 \qquad \left(\sqrt[3]{x}\right)^3 = x$$
$$2w = 12$$
$$w = 6$$

We check that 6 satisfies the original equation:

$$\sqrt[3]{2w - 4} + 7 = 9 \quad \textit{Original equation}$$
$$\sqrt[3]{2(6) - 4} + 7 \stackrel{?}{=} 9 \quad \textit{Substitute 6 for w.}$$
$$\sqrt[3]{8} + 7 \stackrel{?}{=} 9$$
$$2 + 7 \stackrel{?}{=} 9 \quad \sqrt[3]{8} = 2$$
$$9 \stackrel{?}{=} 9$$
$$\text{true}$$

So, the solution is 6.

▶

It is only when we raise both sides of an equation to an *even* power that we might introduce extraneous solutions. However, no matter what type of equation we are solving, it is a good idea to check that any results satisfy the original equation to make sure the work is correct.

Using a Radical Model to Make Predictions about the Independent Variable

Now that we have discussed how to solve radical equations in one variable, we can use radical models to make predictions about the independent variable.

▶ **Example 10**   Using a Radical Model to Make Predictions

In Example 10 of Section 9.1, we worked with the model $f(a) = 1.5\sqrt{a} + 4$, where $f(a)$ is the percentage of foundations with assets of a million dollars that compensate all of their board members (see Table 14). Estimate the assets of foundations of which 25% of the foundations compensate all of their board members.

Table 14 Percentages of Foundations That Compensate All of Their Board Members

Asset Group (millions of dollars)	Asset Used to Represent Asset Group (millions of dollars)	Percent
0–5	2.5	4
5–10	7.5	8
10–25	17.5	10
25–50	37.5	15
50–100	75	20
100–250	175	21
250–500	375	32

Source: *The New York Times*

Solution

We substitute 25 for $f(a)$ and solve for a:

$$25 = 1.5\sqrt{a} + 4 \quad \textit{Substitute 25 for } f(a).$$
$$21 = 1.5\sqrt{a} \quad \textit{Subtract 4 from both sides.}$$
$$14 = \sqrt{a} \quad \textit{Divide both sides by 1.5.}$$
$$14^2 = \left(\sqrt{a}\right)^2 \quad \textit{Square both sides.}$$
$$a = 196$$

The model estimates that 25% of foundations with assets of $196 million compensate all of their board members.

▶

◢◣ Group Exploration
Extraneous solutions

1. Solve the equation $\sqrt{3x - 2} + 2 = x$. Record each step of your work carefully.

2. In Problem 1, you found that 1 is an extraneous solution and that 6 is the only solution. Now substitute 1 for x in each step you recorded in Problem 1. Which of the equations are satisfied by 1?

3. What does it mean to say that 1 is an extraneous solution? Why do we sometimes get extraneous solutions when we solve square root equations but not when we solve linear, exponential, or quadratic equations?

Homework 9.5

For extra help ▶ MyMathLab°   Watch the videos in MyMathLab   Download the MyDashboard App

Solve.

1. $\sqrt{x} = 5$

2. $\sqrt{x} = 8$

3. $\sqrt{x} = -2$

4. $\sqrt{x} = -7$

5. $\sqrt[3]{t} = -2$

6. $\sqrt[4]{w} = -3$

7. $3\sqrt{x} - 1 = 5$

8. $5\sqrt{x} + 2 = 37$

9. $\sqrt{x - 1} = 2$

10. $\sqrt{x - 5} = 3$

11. $\sqrt[4]{r + 2} = 2$

12. $\sqrt[3]{b + 7} = 3$

13. $\sqrt{5x - 7} + 7 = 3$

14. $\sqrt{15 + x} + 8 = 2$

15. $\sqrt[3]{2x - 5} + 3 = 7$

16. $\sqrt[4]{3x - 1} + 5 = 8$

17. $2 - 10\sqrt{6x + 3} = -98$

18. $7 - 8\sqrt{2x - 1} = -17$

19. $\sqrt{3k + 1} = \sqrt{2k + 6}$

20. $\sqrt{10m - 3} = \sqrt{6m + 2}$

21. $\sqrt[4]{6x - 3} = \sqrt[4]{2x + 17}$

22. $\sqrt[3]{5x - 8} = \sqrt[3]{3x + 6}$

23. $2\sqrt{1 - x} - \sqrt{2x + 5} = 0$

24. $2\sqrt{x - 1} - \sqrt{3x - 1} = 0$

25. $\sqrt{3w + 3} = w - 5$

26. $\sqrt{t + 10} = t - 2$

27. $\sqrt{12x + 13} + 2 = 3x$

28. $\sqrt{x + 2} - x = 2$

29. $2 + \sqrt{10 - x} = -x$

30. $1 + \sqrt{2x + 5} = 2x$

31. $\sqrt{r^2 - 5r + 1} = r - 3$

32. $\sqrt{k^2 + 2k} = k + 5$

33. $\sqrt{x - 1} = \sqrt{5 - x}$

34. $3 = \sqrt{6 + x} + \sqrt{x}$

35. $\sqrt{x} - \sqrt{2x} = -1$

36. $\sqrt{x} = \sqrt{3x} - 2$

37. $\sqrt{x - 3} + \sqrt{x + 5} = 4$

38. $\sqrt{x + 6} - \sqrt{x - 2} = 2$

39. $\sqrt{2p - 1} + \sqrt{3p - 2} = 2$

40. $\sqrt{3t - 1} - \sqrt{4t + 1} = -1$

41. $\sqrt{\sqrt{x} - 2} = 3$

42. $\sqrt{\sqrt{x} + 1} = 1$

43. $\dfrac{1}{\sqrt{x + 2}} = 3 - \sqrt{x + 2}$

44. $\dfrac{1}{\sqrt{x - 5}} = 2 - \sqrt{x - 5}$

Find an approximate solution of the equation. Round your result to the second decimal place.

45. $5.2\sqrt{x} - 2.8 = 13.9$

46. $4.7\sqrt{x} + 3.1 = 46.9$

47. $1.52 - 4.91\sqrt{3.18x - 7.14} = -0.69$

48. $-7.93 = 5.61 - 3.79\sqrt{4.42 - 9.87x}$

Solve for the specified variable. Assume the constants have values for which the equation has exactly one real-number solution.

49. $S = \sqrt{gd}$, for d

50. $r = 30d^2\sqrt{P}$, for P

51. $d = \sqrt{\dfrac{3h}{2}}$, for h

52. $T = \sqrt{\dfrac{2d}{g}}$, for d

53. $v = \sqrt{\dfrac{2GM}{R}}$, for R

54. $S = 2\pi\sqrt{\dfrac{L}{32}}$, for L

Use "intersect" on a graphing calculator to solve the equation. Round any solutions to the second decimal place.

55. $\sqrt{x + 1} = 4 - \sqrt{x + 3}$

56. $\sqrt{x + 6} = 6 - \sqrt{x + 4}$

57. $\sqrt{x + 3} = x^2 - 4x - 2$

58. $\sqrt{x + 7} = x^2 - 2x - 7$

For Exercises 59–64, estimate all solutions of the equation or system by referring to the graphs shown in Fig. 33. Round results or coordinates of results to the first decimal place.

59. $\sqrt{x + 5} = x^2 - 2x - 4$

60. $\sqrt{x + 5} = -2x - 5$

61. $\sqrt{x + 5} = 1$

62. $\sqrt{x + 5} = 2$

63. $y = \sqrt{x + 5}$
$y = -2x - 5$

64. $y = \sqrt{x + 5}$
$y = x^2 - 2x - 4$

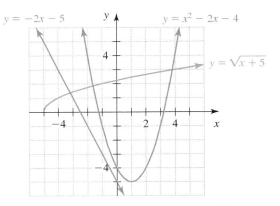

Figure 33 Exercises 59–64

Find all x-intercepts. Use a graphing calculator to verify your work.

65. $h(x) = 3\sqrt{-3x + 4} - 15$

66. $k(x) = 2\sqrt{4x + 1} - 22$

67. $f(x) = \sqrt{3x - 2} - \sqrt{x + 8}$

68. $g(x) = \sqrt{2x + 5} - \sqrt{4x + 1}$

69. $h(x) = 2\sqrt{x + 4} + 3\sqrt{x - 5}$

70. $k(x) = 3\sqrt{x - 1} + 5\sqrt{x - 4}$

Let $f(x) = 3\sqrt{x} - 7$.

71. Find x when $f(x) = -1$.   **72.** Find x when $f(x) = -8$.

For Exercises 73 and 74, let $f(x) = -2\sqrt{x - 4} + 5$.

73. Find x when $f(x) = -3$.   **74.** Find x when $f(x) = 1$.

75. In Exercise 57 of Homework 9.4, you worked with the model $f(t) = 20.4\sqrt{t} + 21$, where $f(t)$ is the percentage of e-mail that is spam at t years since 1999 (see Table 15).

Table 15 Percentages of E-Mail That Is Spam

Year	Percent
1999	21
2002	56
2004	68
2006	80
2008	81
2010	85

Source: *IronPort*

a. Find $f(4)$. What does it mean in this situation?

b. Find t when $f(t) = 95$. What does it mean in this situation?

c. Predict when all e-mails will be spam.

d. In 2011, corporate employees received an average of 72 e-mails per day (Source: *Radicati Group*). Estimate the average daily *number* of e-mails received by corporate employees that were spam in 2011.

e. A corporation loses about $1250 in productivity per employee per year due to employees reading and deleting spam (Source: *Alinean*). Assuming employees work 50 weeks per year, use your result in part (d) to estimate the number of cents lost in productivity *per e-mail*.

76. In Exercise 58 of Homework 9.4, you worked with the model $f(t) = 10\sqrt{t} + 2.5$, where $f(t)$ is the global airline industry's revenue (in billions of dollars) from fees not included in fares at t years since 2007 (see Table 16).

Table 16 Global Airline Industry's Revenues from Fees Not Included in Fares

Year	Revenue (billions of dollars)
2007	2.5
2008	10.3
2009	13.5
2010	21.5
2011	22.6

Source: *IdeaWorks and Amadeus*

a. Find $f(10)$. What does it mean in this situation?

b. Find t when $f(t) = 37$. What does it mean in this situation?

c. The global airline industry's total revenue from fares and fees was $598 billion in 2011. Find the ratio of $598 billion to $22.6 billion, which is the revenue from fees not included in fares in 2011 (see Table 16). Then use that ratio to help you estimate the total revenue from fares and fees in 2012. Describe any assumptions you have made.

77. For the academic year 2005–2006, tuition at Princeton Day School ranged from $19,200 to $23,600 by grade (kindergarten through 8th grade). In addition, the school charges for supplies and field-trip expenses (see Table 17).

Table 17 Charges for Supplies and Field Trips at Princeton Day School

Grade	Per-Student Charge for Supplies and Field Trips (dollars)
kindergarten	260
1	310
3	365
5	410
6	425
7	425

Source: *Princeton Day School*

Let $f(n)$ be the per-student charge (in dollars) for supplies and field trips for nth grade; kindergarten is represented by $n = 0$. A model of the situation is $f(n) = 257\sqrt[4]{n+1}$.

a. Use a graphing calculator to draw the graph of the model and, in the same viewing window, the scattergram of the data. Does the model fit the data well?

b. Estimate the per-student charge for supplies and field trips for 2nd grade. The actual charge is $365. Is your result an underestimate or an overestimate?

c. Estimate for what grade the per-student charge for supplies and field trips is $385.

d. The actual per-student charge for 4th grade is $450. By referring to the data shown in Table 17, explain why this charge is surprising.

78. The percentages of registered voters who voted in 2008 are shown in Table 18 for various household income groups.

Table 18 Percentages of Registered Voters Who Voted in 2008, by Household Income Groups

Income Group ($1000s)	Income Used to Represent Income Group ($1000s)	Percent
0–9.999	5.0	41.3
10–14.999	12.5	41.2
15–19.999	17.5	44.3
20–29.999	25.0	48.0
30–39.999	35.0	54.4
40–49.999	45.0	58.2
50–74.999	62.5	65.9
75–99.999	87.5	72.6
100–149.999	125.0	74.9

Source: *U.S. Census Bureau*

Let $f(d)$ be the percentage of registered voters with a household income of d thousand dollars who voted in 2008. A model of the situation is $f(d) = 4.2\sqrt{d} + 30$.

a. Use a graphing calculator to draw the graph of the model and, in the same viewing window, the scattergram of the data. Does the model fit the data well?

b. Estimate the percentage of registered voters with a household income of $38 thousand who voted in 2008.

c. Estimate at which household income 60% of registered voters voted in 2008.

d. Is f an increasing function, decreasing function, or neither? What does that mean in this situation?

Concepts

79. A student tries to solve $\sqrt{x^2 + 4x + 5} = x + 3$:

$$\sqrt{x^2 + 4x + 5} = x + 3$$
$$\left(\sqrt{x^2 + 4x + 5}\right)^2 = (x + 3)^2$$
$$x^2 + 4x + 5 = x^2 + 9$$
$$4x = 4$$
$$x = 1$$

Describe any errors. Then solve the equation correctly.

80. A student tries to solve $\sqrt{x - 2} = x - 4$:

$$\sqrt{x - 2} = x - 4$$
$$\left(\sqrt{x - 2}\right)^2 = (x - 4)^2$$
$$x - 2 = x^2 - 8x + 16$$
$$0 = x^2 - 9x + 18$$
$$0 = (x - 3)(x - 6)$$
$$x - 3 = 0 \quad \text{or} \quad x - 6 = 0$$
$$x = 3 \quad \text{or} \quad x = 6$$

He says the solutions are 3 and 6. Is he correct? Explain.

81. Solve the system; then use "intersect" on a graphing calculator to verify your work:

$$y = 3\sqrt{x} - 4$$
$$y = -2\sqrt{x} + 6$$

82. Create a system of two square root equations that has $(4, 5)$ as its only solution. Verify your system graphically.

83. Find nonzero values of a, h, and k so the equation $\sqrt{x} = a\sqrt{x - h} + k$ has no real-number solutions. [**Hint:** Think about the graphs of $y = \sqrt{x}$ and $y = a\sqrt{x - h} + k$.]

84. For the equation $\sqrt{x} + 2 = 5$, why do we first subtract 2 from both sides, rather than first square both sides?

85. The first of the following statements is true, yet the last statement is false:

$$2x - x = x$$
$$(2x)^2 - x^2 = x^2$$
$$4x^2 - x^2 = x^2$$
$$3x^2 = x^2$$
$$3 = 1$$

Describe any errors.

86. Describe how to solve square root equations that contain one square root. Also, describe how to solve square root equations that contain two or more square roots.

Related Review

Solve or simplify, as appropriate.

87. $3\sqrt{x} + 4 - 7\sqrt{x} + 1$
88. $2\sqrt{x + 1} - 2 + 5\sqrt{x + 1} - 9 = 3$
89. $3\sqrt{x} + 4 - 7\sqrt{x} + 1 = -7$
90. $2\sqrt{x + 1} - 2 + 5\sqrt{x + 1} - 9$
91. $(\sqrt{p} + 3)(\sqrt{p} + 1) = 3$

92. $(\sqrt{m} - 2)(\sqrt{m} - 3)$
93. $(\sqrt{p} + 3)(\sqrt{p} + 1)$
94. $(\sqrt{m} - 2)(\sqrt{m} - 3) = 2$

Solve. Round any approximate solutions to the fourth decimal place.

95. $50 - 4(2)^x = -83$
96. $\dfrac{1}{x - 2} - \dfrac{2}{x + 3} = \dfrac{11}{x^2 + x - 6}$
97. $\sqrt{x + 3} - \sqrt{x - 2} = 1$
98. $3x^2 + 2x - 4 = 0$
99. $-3(2k - 5) + 1 = 2(4x + 3)$
100. $3b^4 - 29 = 83$
101. $\log_2(5t - 1) = 5$
102. $\log_2(2y + 1) - 2\log_2(y - 1) = 1$

Expressions, Equations, Functions, and Graphs

Perform the indicated instruction. Then use words such as linear, *quadratic, cubic, exponential, logarithmic, rational, radical, polynomial, degree, function, one variable, and* two variables *to describe the expression, equation, or system.*

103. Find the quotient $\dfrac{3x^2 - x - 10}{x^3 - x^2 - x + 1} \div \dfrac{3x^2 - 12}{2x^2 + x - 3}$.

104. Solve $\log_4(7x - 2) = 3$.

105. Find the sum $\dfrac{6}{b - 2} + \dfrac{3b}{b^2 - 7b + 10}$.

106. Solve $2(5)^t + 14 = 249$. Round any solutions to the fourth decimal place.

107. Solve $\dfrac{6}{x - 2} + \dfrac{3x}{x^2 - 7x + 10} = \dfrac{x}{x - 5}$.

108. Write $3\log_b(2x^2) + 2\log_b(3x^7)$ as a single logarithm.

▼ 9.6 Modeling with Square Root Functions

Objectives

» Find an equation of a square root curve that contains two given points.

» Find an equation of a square root model.

» Use a square root model to make estimates and predictions.

In this section, we will discuss how to find the equation of a square root function of the form $f(x) = a\sqrt{x} + b$ whose graph contains two given points. Then we will find a model of this form that describes an authentic situation and use the model to make estimates and predictions.

Finding a Square Root Function

Recall that the first step in finding an exponential function (Section 4.4) or a quadratic function (Section 7.6) is to substitute any given ordered pairs into a general equation of the function. We will do this same first step to find a square root function.

▶ **Example 1**   Finding an Equation of a Square Root Function

Find an equation of a square root curve that contains the points $(2, 3)$ and $(5, 7)$.

Solution

We substitute the ordered pairs $(2, 3)$ and $(5, 7)$ into the equation $f(x) = a\sqrt{x} + b$:

$$3 = a\sqrt{2} + b \quad \text{\small Substitute 2 for x and 3 for y.}$$
$$7 = a\sqrt{5} + b \quad \text{\small Substitute 5 for x and 7 for y.}$$

We then calculate approximate values for $\sqrt{2}$ and $\sqrt{5}$:

$$1.41a + b = 3 \quad \textit{Equation (1)}$$
$$2.24a + b = 7 \quad \textit{Equation (2)}$$

Next, we multiply both sides of equation (1) by -1:

$$-1.41a - b = -3 \quad \textit{Equation (3)}$$

To eliminate b, we add the left sides and add the right sides of equations (2) and (3) and solve for a:

$$
\begin{aligned}
2.24a + b &= 7 \\
\underline{-1.41a - b} &= \underline{-3} \\
0.83a + 0 &= 4 \\
0.83a &= 4 \quad C + 0 = C \\
a &= \frac{4}{0.83} \\
a &\approx 4.82
\end{aligned}
$$

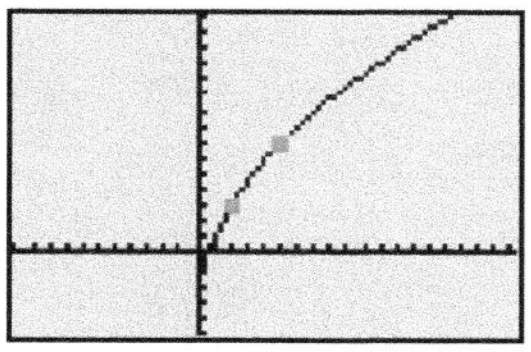

So, our equation has the form $f(x) = 4.82\sqrt{x} + b$. To find b, we substitute the ordered pair $(2, 3)$ into the equation $f(x) = 4.82\sqrt{x} + b$:

$$3 = 4.82\sqrt{2} + b \quad \textit{Substitute 2 for x and 3 for y.}$$
$$3 - 4.82\sqrt{2} = b \quad \textit{Isolate b.}$$
$$b \approx -3.82 \quad \textit{Compute.}$$

So, the equation is $f(x) = 4.82\sqrt{x} - 3.82$.

We use a graphing calculator to verify that the graph of f approximately contains the two given points (see Fig. 34).

Figure 34 Verify that the graph of $f(x) = 4.82\sqrt{x} - 3.82$ approximately contains the points $(2, 3)$ and $(5, 7)$

To find an equation of a square root curve that contains two given points, we substitute the points' ordered pairs into the equation $f(x) = a\sqrt{x} + b$ and get a system of two equations. We find values of a and b by solving the system by elimination or substitution.

> **Finding an Equation of a Square Root Curve**
>
> To find an equation of a square root curve that contains two given points,
>
> 1. Obtain a system of two linear equations in two variables by substituting the coordinates of both points into the general equation $y = a\sqrt{x} + b$.
> 2. Solve the system you found in step 1.
> 3. Substitute the values of a and b you found in step 2 into the equation $y = a\sqrt{x} + b$.

Using the *y*-Intercept and One Other Point to Find an Equation

For an equation of the form $y = a\sqrt{x} + b$, we can find the *y*-intercept by substituting 0 for x:

$$y = a\sqrt{0} + b = b$$

So, the *y*-intercept is $(0, b)$.

> **y-Intercept of the Graph of $y = a\sqrt{x} + b$**
>
> The graph of an equation of the form $y = a\sqrt{x} + b$ has *y*-intercept $(0, b)$.

For example, the graph of the equation $y = 3\sqrt{x} + 7$ has *y*-intercept $(0, 7)$.

The process of finding an equation of a square root function is easier if one of the two given points is the *y*-intercept, as we shall see in Example 2.

▶ **Example 2**   Finding an Equation when One Given Point Is the *y*-Intercept

Find an equation of a square root curve that contains the points $(0, 5)$ and $(6, 19)$.

Solution

Since the *y*-intercept of the curve is $(0, 5)$, we can find an equation of the form

$$y = a\sqrt{x} + 5$$

To find *a*, we substitute the ordered pair $(6, 19)$ in the equation $y = a\sqrt{x} + 5$:

$$19 = a\sqrt{6} + 5 \qquad \textit{Substitute 6 for x and 19 for y.}$$
$$14 = a\sqrt{6} \qquad \textit{Subtract 5 from both sides.}$$
$$\frac{14}{\sqrt{6}} = a \qquad \textit{Divide both sides by } \sqrt{6}.$$
$$a \approx 5.72 \qquad \textit{Compute.}$$

So, the equation is $f(x) = 5.72\sqrt{x} + 5$.

We use a graphing calculator table, as well as TRACE on a graphing calculator, to check that the graph of $f(x) = 5.72\sqrt{x} + 5$ approximately contains the points $(0, 5)$ and $(6, 19)$. See Fig. 35.

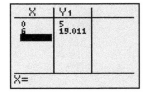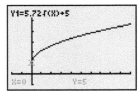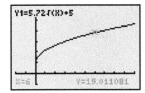

Figure 35 Verify the work

Finding a Square Root Model

Now that we have discussed how to find an equation of a square root function, we can find an equation of a square root model.

▶ **Example 3**   Finding an Equation of a Square Root Model

The percentages of American adults who watch cable television are shown in Table 19 for various income groups. Let $f(I)$ be the percentage of American adults with an annual income of *I* thousand dollars who watch cable television. Find an equation of *f*.

Table 19 Percentages of American Adults Who Watch Cable Television

Thousands of Dollars		
Annual Income Group	Income Used to Represent Income Group	Percent
0–9.999	5.0	55.9
10–19.999	15.0	62.3
20–29.999	25.0	67.8
30–34.999	32.5	72.2
35–39.999	37.5	74.2
40–49.999	45.0	77.2
50 or over	70.0	84.8

Source: *Mediamark Research, Inc.*

Solution

First, we use a graphing calculator to draw a scattergram of the data (see Fig. 36). It appears the data might be modeled well by a square root function or a quadratic function. To decide which model to use, we find an equation of both types of functions and compare the fit of each model.

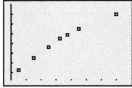

Figure 36 Cable television scattergram

For the square root model, we use a function of the form

$$f(I) = a\sqrt{I} + b$$

We use the data points $(5, 55.9)$ and $(70, 84.8)$ to find the values of a and b. To begin, we substitute the ordered pairs $(5, 55.9)$ and $(70, 84.8)$ in the equation $f(I) = a\sqrt{I} + b$:

$$55.9 = a\sqrt{5} + b \qquad \text{Substitute } (5, 55.9) \text{ in } f(I) = a\sqrt{I} + b.$$

$$84.8 = a\sqrt{70} + b \qquad \text{Substitute } (70, 84.8) \text{ in } f(I) = a\sqrt{I} + b.$$

We then calculate $\sqrt{5} \approx 2.24$ and $\sqrt{70} \approx 8.37$:

$$2.24a + b = 55.9 \qquad \text{Equation (1)}$$

$$8.37a + b = 84.8 \qquad \text{Equation (2)}$$

Next, we multiply both sides of equation (1) by -1:

$$-2.24a - b = -55.9 \qquad \text{Equation (3)}$$

To eliminate b, we add the left sides and add the right sides of equations (2) and (3) and solve for a:

$$8.37a + b = 84.8 \qquad \text{Equation (2)}$$
$$\underline{-2.24a - b = -55.9} \qquad \text{Equation (3)}$$
$$6.13a + 0 = 28.9 \qquad \text{Add left sides and add right sides; combine like terms.}$$
$$a = \frac{28.9}{6.13}$$
$$a \approx 4.71$$

So, our equation has the form $f(I) = 4.71\sqrt{I} + b$. To find b, we substitute the ordered pair $(5, 55.9)$ in the equation $f(I) = 4.71\sqrt{I} + b$:

$$55.9 = 4.71\sqrt{5} + b \qquad \text{Substitute } (5, 55.9) \text{ in } f(I) = 4.71\sqrt{I} + b.$$

$$55.9 - 4.71\sqrt{5} = b \qquad \text{Subtract } 4.71\sqrt{5} \text{ from both sides.}$$

$$45.37 \approx b \qquad \text{Compute.}$$

So, the square root model is $f(I) = 4.71\sqrt{I} + 45.37$.

We use a graphing calculator to find the quadratic regression equation:

$$f(I) = -0.0037I^2 + 0.72I + 52.36$$

Next, we use a graphing calculator to compare the fits of the two models (see Figs. 37 and 38).

The quadratic model appears to fit the data slightly better than the square root model. However, recall from Section 7.7 that we should also consider whether either model makes sense within the context of the situation. In this situation, it will help to consider what each model estimates for Americans with incomes well over $50 thousand. So, we Zoom Out and compare the graphs again (see Figs. 39 and 40).

The square root model estimates that the percentage of adults who watch cable television continues to increase as income increases, whereas the quadratic model estimates that the percentage of adults who watch cable television will decrease significantly as income increases, which is model breakdown, as a little research would show. Model breakdown also occurs for the square root model, because it estimates the percentage of adults who watch cable television is over 100% for very large incomes (over $135 thousand—as we can show, with work). But for incomes up to $135 thousand, the square root model is the better of the two models.

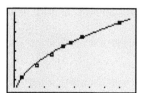

Figure 37 Square root model

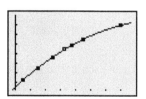

Figure 38 Quadratic model

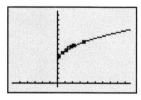

Figure 39 Square root model

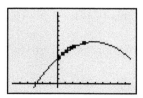

Figure 40 Quadratic model

> ### Finding an Equation of a Square Root Model
>
> To find an equation of a square root model, given some data,
>
> 1. Create a scattergram of the data.
> 2. Imagine a square root curve that comes close to the data points, and choose two points (not necessarily data points) that lie on or close to the square root curve.
> 3. Use the two points to find an equation of the square root curve.
> 4. Use a graphing calculator to verify that the graph of the equation comes close to the points of the scattergram.

Using a Square Root Model to Make Estimates and Predictions

Once we have found a square root model, we can use it to make estimates and predictions.

▶ Example 4 Using a Square Root Model to Make Predictions

In Example 3, we found the equation $f(I) = 4.71\sqrt{I} + 45.37$, where $f(I)$ is the percentage of American adults with an annual income of I thousand dollars who watch cable television. Let $p = f(I)$.

1. Find the p-intercept. What does it mean in this situation?
2. Estimate the percentage of adults with an annual income of $30 thousand who watch cable television.
3. At what level of income do 80% of Americans watch cable television?

Solution

1. To find the p-intercept, we find $f(0)$:
$$f(0) = 4.71\sqrt{0} + 45.37 = 45.37$$
The p-intercept is $(0, 45.37)$. The model estimates about 45.4% of adults with no income watch cable television.

2. We evaluate f at 30:
$$f(30) = 4.71\sqrt{30} + 45.37 = 71.17$$
About 71.2% of adults with an annual income of $30 thousand watch cable television, according to the model.

3. We substitute 80 for $f(I)$ in the equation $f(I) = 4.71\sqrt{I} + 45.37$ and solve for I:

$$80 = 4.71\sqrt{I} + 45.37 \qquad \text{Substitute 80 for } f(I).$$
$$34.63 = 4.71\sqrt{I} \qquad \text{Subtract 45.37 from both sides.}$$
$$\frac{34.63}{4.71} = \sqrt{I} \qquad \text{Divide both sides by 4.71.}$$
$$\left(\frac{34.63}{4.71}\right)^2 = \left(\sqrt{I}\right)^2 \qquad \text{Square both sides.}$$
$$I \approx 54.06 \qquad \text{Compute.}$$

The model estimates 80% of adults with an approximate income of $54.1 thousand watch cable television.

We use a graphing calculator table to verify our work in Problems 1–3 (see Fig. 41).

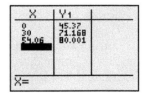

Figure 41 Verify the work

We close this section by incorporating square root modeling into the four-step modeling process.

> ### ▶ Four-Step Modeling Process
>
> To find a model and make estimates and predictions,
>
> 1. Create a scattergram of the data. Decide whether a line, an exponential curve, a parabola, a square root curve, or none of these comes close to the points.
> 2. Find an equation of your model.

3. Verify that your equation has a graph that comes close to the points in the scattergram. If it doesn't, check for calculation errors or use different points to find the equation. An alternative is to reconsider your choice of model in step 1.

4. Use your equation of the model to draw conclusions, make estimates, and/or make predictions.

 Group Exploration ────────────────────────────────

Looking ahead: Arithmetic sequences

A math tutor charges $25 per hour to tutor one student, plus $8 per hour for each additional student.

1. Let $f(n)$ be the amount of money (in dollars) the tutor will charge per hour to work with n students. Find an equation of f.

2. Evaluate f at each given value of n. Explain what each result means in this situation.
  a. $f(3.8)$ **b.** $f(-2)$ **c.** $f(0)$

3. On the basis of your results in Problem 2, determine a domain of the *model* f. [**Hint:** Which inputs make sense in this situation?]

4. On the basis of your domain of f, find the range of f. List the values of the range of f in this order: $f(1)$, $f(2)$, $f(3)$, $f(4)$, ... What do you notice about these numbers?

5. Sketch a graph of f, but plot only points whose n-coordinates are in the domain. [**Hint:** Your graph will look like a scattergram.]

▶ Tips for Success   **Create a Mind Map for the Final Exam**

In preparing for a final exam, consider how all the concepts you have learned are interconnected. One way to help yourself do this is to make a *mind map*. Put the main topic in the middle. Around it, attach concepts that relate to it, then concepts that relate to those concepts, and so on.

A portion of a mind map that describes this course is illustrated in Fig. 42. Many more "concept rectangles" could be added to it. You could make one mind map showing an overview of the course and several mind maps for the components of the overview mind map.

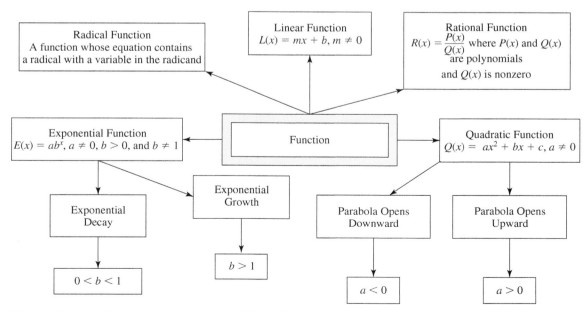

Figure 42 A portion of a mind map describing this course

Homework 9.6

Find an equation of a square root curve of the form $y = a\sqrt{x} + b$ that approximately contains the given points. Round the values of a and b to the second decimal place.

1. $(0, 3)$ and $(4, 5)$ **2.** $(0, 5)$ and $(4, 3)$

3. $(0, 2)$ and $(9, 6)$ **4.** $(0, 3)$ and $(1, 2)$

5. $(0, 4)$ and $(5, 7)$ **6.** $(0, 1)$ and $(2, 3)$

7. $(0, 9)$ and $(3, 2)$ **8.** $(0, 8)$ and $(6, 3)$

9. $(1, 2)$ and $(4, 3)$ **10.** $(4, 5)$ and $(9, 8)$

11. $(2, 4)$ and $(3, 5)$ **12.** $(5, 2)$ and $(7, 4)$

13. $(2, 6)$ and $(5, 4)$ **14.** $(3, 8)$ and $(6, 5)$

15. $(5, 7)$ and $(13, 21)$ **16.** $(3, 9)$ and $(15, 29)$

17. $(7, 31)$ and $(10, 6)$ **18.** $(6, 43)$ and $(14, 5)$

19. $(15, 3)$ and $(35, 18)$ **20.** $(17, 6)$ and $(26, 19)$

21. The numbers of American female troops in Iraq and Afghanistan are shown in Table 20 for various years.

Table 20 Numbers of American Female Troops in Iraq and Afghanistan

Year	Number of Female Troops (thousands)
2004	10
2005	15
2006	20
2007	20
2008	25
2009	25
2010	26

Source: *U.S. Army*

Let $n = f(t)$ be the number (in thousands) of American female troops in Iraq and Afghanistan at t years since 2004.
a. Find a square root equation of f.
b. What is the n-intercept? What does it mean in this situation?
c. Estimate when there were 28 thousand female troops in Iraq and Afghanistan.
d. By December 18, 2011, the United States had withdrawn all its troops from Iraq. Use the fact that there were 15 thousand American female troops in Afghanistan in 2012 to estimate the number of American female troops that would have been in Iraq in 2012 if the withdrawal had not occurred.

22. The percentages of U.S. households owning stocks are shown in Table 21 for various years. Let $p = f(t)$ be the percentage of U.S. households owning stocks at t years since 1983.
a. Find a square root equation of f.
b. What is the p-intercept? What does it mean in this situation?
c. Predict the percentage of U.S. households that will own stocks in 2017.
d. Predict when 58% of U.S. households will own stocks.

Table 21 Percentages of U.S. Households Owning Stocks

Year	Percent
1983	19
1989	32
1992	37
1995	40
1999	48
2002	50
2005	50
2008	52
2011	52

Sources: *ICI/SIA; Federal Reserve Board*

23. The average monthly bills for pay-TV are shown in Table 22 for various years.

Table 22 Average Monthly Bills for Pay-TV

Year	Average Monthly Bill (dollars)
2006	56.0
2007	63.8
2008	65.6
2009	68.0
2010	70.8
2011	72.8

Source: *IHS Screen Digest*

Let $M = f(t)$ be the average monthly bill (in dollars) for pay-TV in the year that is t years since 2006.
a. Find an equation of f.
b. What is the M-intercept? What does it mean in this situation?
c. Find $f(13)$. What does it mean in this situation?
d. Find t when $f(t) = 81$. What does it mean in this situation?
e. In 2011, there were 100.9 million subscribers to pay-TV (Source: *The NPD Group*). Assuming the number of subscribers does not change, predict the total *annual* revenue from *all* subscribers of pay-TV in 2017.

24. The total annual net incomes (in billions of dollars) of the top five oil companies are shown in Table 23 for various years.

Table 23 Total Annual Net Incomes of the Top Five Oil Companies

Year	Total Annual Net Income (billions of dollars)
2003	58.2
2004	82.4
2005	111.4
2006	119.6
2007	123.4

Source: *Evaluate Energy*

Let $I = f(t)$ be the total annual net income (in billions of dollars) of the top five oil companies at t years since 2003.

a. Find a square root equation of f.

b. Find the I-intercept. What does it mean in this situation?

c. Estimate when the total annual net income was $144 billion.

d. Estimate the total net income in 2010.

e. The actual total net income in 2010 was only $78 billion, due to lower oil prices and BP's Gulf oil spill, which significantly decreased the company's profits. Estimate how much total net income was lost in 2010 due to these events.

25. In Exercise 83 of Homework 9.1, you worked with the model $f(d) = \sqrt{9.8d}$, where $f(d)$ is the speed (in meters per second) of a tsunami in which the average water depth is d meters.

a. Before 1856, scientists believed the average depth of the Pacific Ocean was about 18,000 meters. If that were true, what would be the average speed of a tsunami in the Pacific Ocean?

b. In 1856, scientists used their knowledge of tsunamis to estimate the average depth of the Pacific Ocean. They estimated that the average speed of tsunamis in the Pacific Ocean was between 203 and 210 meters per second. Does this estimate suggest that the average depth of the Pacific Ocean is 18,000 meters? Explain.

c. Use the model to estimate between what two depths is the average depth of the Pacific Ocean.

d. Most current estimates of the average depth of the Pacific Ocean are close to 4280 meters. Is this estimate between the two depths you found in part (c)?

26. A study of children who were adopted after being in temporary foster care explored the relationship between the children's age when separated from their foster parents and the percentage of children showing problems immediately after the separation (see Table 24).

Table 24 Adopted Children Separated from Foster Parents

Age when Separated from Foster Parents (years)	Middle of Age Group (years)	Percent Showing Problems
<3	1.5	4
3–4	3.5	40
4–5	4.5	70
6–8	7.0	90
9	9.0	100

Source: The Immediate Impact of Separation: Reactions of Infants to a Change in Mother Figures, *by Yarrow and Goodwin*

Let $p = f(t)$ be the percentage of adopted children showing problems immediately after separation if they are separated from foster parents at age t years.

a. Find a square root equation of f.

b. Is f an increasing function, a decreasing function, or neither? What does that mean in this situation?

c. Estimate the percentage of adopted children who show problems if separated at age 10 years. Is this a reasonable estimate? If so, explain why. If not, explain why not and suggest a better value.

d. Sketch a qualitative graph that describes the relationship between t and p for *all* ages of adopted children.

27. Some students ran an experiment to explore the relationship between the time it takes a baseball to fall to the ground and the various heights from which it was dropped (see Table 25). Let $T = S(h)$ be the time (in seconds) it takes a baseball to fall to the ground when dropped from h feet above the ground.

Table 25 Drop Heights and Falling Times of a Baseball*

Drop Height (feet)	Falling Time (seconds)
0.00	0.00
3.28	0.53
13.10	0.96
26.30	1.40
39.40	1.70
52.50	1.94

Source: *J. Lehmann*

* Although a ball cannot be dropped from height zero feet, the data point $(0, 0)$ is included because drop heights near zero will correspond to falling times near zero.

a. Find a square root equation of S.

b. A linear model of the baseball drop data is given by $L(h) = 0.034h + 0.327$. A quadratic model is given by $Q(h) = -0.00058h^2 + 0.064h + 0.165$.

   i. Describe how well each of the functions S, L, and Q fits the data points in the scattergram.

   ii. Find $S(0)$, $L(0)$, and $Q(0)$. Which function models the baseball situation the best near $h = 0$? Explain.

   iii. Use Zoom Out and decide which function could not be a good model for the baseball situation when the drop heights are very large. Explain.

   iv. On the basis of your responses to parts (i)–(iii), determine which of S, L, or Q best models the baseball drop situation. Explain.

   v. An equation that is often used to model drop times is

$$T = \sqrt{\frac{2h}{g}},$$ where g is the constant 32.2 feet per second

squared. Find an approximate form $T = a\sqrt{h}$ of this equation so you can compare the model with S.

c. Suppose you wish to estimate the height of a sheer cliff. You drop a stone from the top of the cliff, and it takes 3 seconds to reach the foot of the cliff. Use S to estimate the height of the cliff.

d. Use S to estimate how long it would take for a baseball to reach the ground if it were to be dropped from the top of the Empire State Building, which is 1250 feet tall.

28. The percentages of ex-convicts who have been arrested for a new crime after being out of a state prison for various numbers of years are shown in Table 26.

Table 26 Ex-Convicts Who Have Been Arrested for a New Crime

Number of Years since Release	Percent
0	0
0.5	30
1	44
2	59
3	68

Source: *U.S. Department of Justice*

Let $p = S(t)$ be the percentage of convicts released from a state prison who are arrested for a new crime after being out of prison for t years.
a. Find a square root equation of S.
b. A quadratic model of the data is given by

$$Q(t) = -9.05t^2 + 48.09t + 3.47$$

   i. Describe how well both of the functions S and Q fit the data points in the scattergram.
   ii. Explain in terms of the situation why the model should be increasing for $t \geq 0$. Is function S or Q increasing for $t \geq 0$?
c. Use S to estimate the percentage of ex-convicts who have been arrested for a new crime after being out of prison for 4 years.
d. Use S to estimate after how many years since release all ex-convicts will have been arrested for a new crime.

29. A study of births among 1444 fertile couples recorded the birth order and claims by the parents that conception occurred despite the use of contraception (see Table 27). The percentage, for example, of first births that occurred despite contraception, according to the parents, was 37.6%.

Table 27 Percentages of Births Despite Contraception

Birth Order	Percentage of Conceptions Despite Contraception
1	37.6
2	54.3
3	66.5
4	73.0
5	84.1
6	81.2

Source: Social and Psychological Factors Affecting Fertility, *by Whelpton and Kiser*

Let $p = f(n)$ be the percentage of births of the nth-born child that occurred despite the use of contraception at the time of conception, as claimed by the parents.
a. Find a square root equation of f. [**Hint:** Use the points $(2, 54.3)$ and $(4, 73.0)$.]
b. Find $f(7)$. What does it mean in this situation?
c. Find n when $f(n) = 100$. What does your result mean in this situation?
d. Note that f is an increasing function. What does that mean in this situation? Form a theory to explain why this happens.

30. The numbers of McDonald's restaurants around the world are shown in Table 28 for various years.

Table 28 Numbers of McDonald's Restaurants

Year	Number of Restaurants (thousands)
1998	24.5
2000	27.9
2002	30.2
2004	30.5
2006	31.0
2008	32.0
2010	32.7
2011	33.5

Source: *McDonald's*

Let $n = f(t)$ be the number (in thousands) of McDonald's restaurants at t years since 1998.
a. Find an equation of f.
b. Predict the number of McDonald's restaurants in 2019.
c. There are 192 countries in the world. What will be the average number of McDonald's restaurants per country in 2019?
d. Predict when there will be 35 thousand McDonald's restaurants.

Concepts

Consider the scattergram of data and the graph of the model $f(t) = a\sqrt{t} + b$ in the indicated figure. For Exercises 31 and 32, sketch the graph of a square root model that describes the data better. Then explain how you would adjust the values of a and b of the original model to describe the data better.

31. See Fig. 43.

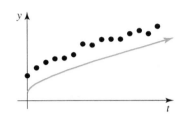

Figure 43 Exercise 31

32. See Fig. 44.

Figure 44 Exercise 32

33. Explain why the graph of an equation of the form $y = a\sqrt{x} + b$ has y-intercept $(0, b)$.

34. Describe how to find an equation of a square root function that contains two given points. How is this process different if one point is the y-intercept?

Related Review

35. The numbers of U.S. communities with cameras that photograph drivers who run red lights are shown in Table 29 for various years.

Table 29 Numbers of U.S. Communities with Red-Light Cameras

Year	Number of Communities with Red-Light Cameras
1999	19
2001	28
2003	74
2005	120
2007	243
2009	445
2010	501

Source: *Insurance Institute for Highway Safety*

Let $f(t)$ be the number of U.S. communities with red-light cameras at t years since 1990.

a. Use a graphing calculator to draw a scattergram to describe the data. By inspecting the scattergram alone, determine which two of the following functions *might* fit the data well: linear, exponential, quadratic, and square root.

b. Find equations of the two types of functions that you selected in part (a).

c. Compare how well each of your two models fits the data.

d. Which of your two models describes the situation better for years before 1999?

e. Use both of your models to predict when there will be 6000 U.S. communities with red-light cameras. Refer to the graphs of the two models to explain why your two results are so different.

f. **i.** Use the exponential model to find $f(15) - f(14)$. What does it mean in this situation? (Assume $f(t)$ is the number of communities with red-light cameras by the *end* of the year that is t years since 1990.)

   ii. Use the exponential model to find $f(27) - f(26)$. What does it mean in this situation?

   iii. In 2005, Redflex Traffic Systems sold $26 million worth of red-light cameras. Assuming Redflex continues to sell about 40% of the red-light cameras used in the United States, predict Redflex's revenue from sales of red-light cameras in 2017. Describe all the assumptions you have made. [**Hint:** Use the ratio of your result in part (ii) to your result in part (i).]

36. Annual revenues from portable media and MP3 players in the United States are shown in Table 30 for various years. Let $f(t)$ be the annual revenue (in billions of dollars) from portable media and MP3 players at t years since 2000.

a. Find an equation of f.

b. Estimate the revenue in 2011.

Table 30 Revenues from Portable Media and MP3 Players

Year	Revenue (billions of dollars)
2005	4.23
2006	5.56
2007	5.97
2008	5.84
2009	5.21
2010	4.73

Source: *Consumer Electronics Association*

c. Estimate when the annual revenue was $1.4 billion.

d. What are the t-intercepts? What do they mean in this situation?

e. For what values of t is there model breakdown for certain?

Expressions, Equations, Functions, and Graphs

Give an example of the following. Then solve, simplify, or graph, as appropriate.

37. rational equation in one variable

38. system of two linear equations in two variables

39. difference of two rational expressions

40. quadratic equation in one variable

41. square root equation in one variable

42. expression involving exponents

43. exponential function

44. difference of two logarithmic expressions with the same base

Taking it to the Lab

Pendulum Lab

Do you know what a *pendulum* is? You can construct a pendulum by tying one end of some thread to a washer and attaching the other end to a surface so that the washer is suspended and swings forward and backward freely.

The *period* of the pendulum is the amount of time it takes for the washer to swing forward *and* backward once. The period of a pendulum depends on the length of the thread. In this lab, you will discover the relationship between the period of a pendulum and the length of its thread.

Materials
You will need the following materials:

1. thread

2. scissors

3. a timing device

4. tape

5. a washer (or some other small, dense object that can be tied to the thread)

6. a meterstick

Preparation
Knot one end of the thread to the washer. Tape the other end of the thread to a surface well so that the washer is suspended and swings freely. The distance from the middle of the washer to the tape should be at least 100 centimeters.

Recording of Data
Record the distance from the middle of the washer to the tape. Then time how long it takes for the washer to swing back and forth four times. Divide this time by 4 to find the period of the pendulum. Repeat the procedure several times. Discard the times that are very different from most of the times, and average the remaining times.

Repeat the procedure for various lengths of thread. When the thread is quite short, time how long it takes for the washer to swing back and forth eight times and divide this time by 8 to find the period.

Analyzing the Data

1. Display your data in a table.

2. Let $f(L)$ be the period (in seconds) of the pendulum, where L is the length (in centimeters) of the thread. Use a graphing calculator to draw a scattergram of your data.

3. Find an equation of f.

4. Use a graphing calculator to graph your model and the scattergram in the same viewing window. Graph your model and the scattergram by hand. How well does f model the data?

5. Find all intercepts of your model, and describe what they mean in this situation.

6. Is f an increasing function, a decreasing function, or neither? What does that mean in this situation?

7. Use your model to estimate the period of the pendulum if the thread's length is 150 centimeters.

8. Use your model to estimate the length of the thread if the pendulum's period is 0.1 second.

9. Suppose that a big chunk of concrete attached to some thin, strong cable is suspended from the skydeck of the Willis Tower in Chicago. The skydeck is 1353 feet above Wacker Drive. Assume that the concrete, when at rest, almost touches the street. Estimate the period of this pendulum. (*Note:* You can use f to model the Willis Tower pendulum even though a concrete chunk weighs a lot more than a washer.)

10. What is the length of a pendulum that has a period of 1 minute?

Chapter Summary

Key Points of Chapter 9

Section 9.1   Simplifying Radical Expressions

Perfect nth power

If n is a counting number greater than 1, then each of the following is a **perfect nth power:**
- A number that has an nth root that is rational.
- A power x^k, where k is a multiple of n.

Product property for radicals

If $\sqrt[n]{a}$ and $\sqrt[n]{b}$ are defined, then $\sqrt[n]{ab} = \sqrt[n]{a}\sqrt[n]{b}$.

Simplified radical

A radical with index n is **simplified** when the radicand does not have any factors that are perfect nth powers (other than -1 or 1) and the index is as small as possible.

Selecting perfect nth-power factors

To select perfect nth-power factors of radicands,
- If the radicand has more than one numerical factor that is a perfect nth power, select the largest one.
- If the radicand has more than one factor that is a perfect nth power with the same variable base, select the one with the largest exponent.

Decreasing the index

If $\sqrt[n]{x}$ is defined and the fraction $\dfrac{m}{n}$ can be simplified, then we can decrease the index of $\sqrt[n]{x^m}$ by writing $\sqrt[n]{x^m} = x^{m/n}$ and simplifying the exponent $\dfrac{m}{n}$.

Simplifying a radical expression

To simplify a radical expression with index n,
1. Find perfect nth-power factors of the radicand.
2. Apply the product property for radicals.
3. Find the nth root of each perfect nth power.
4. Write the radical with as small an index as possible.

Power property for radicals

Let n be a counting number greater than 1:
- If n is even, then $\sqrt[n]{x^n} = |x|$.
- If n is odd, then $\sqrt[n]{x^n} = x$.

Radical function

A **radical function** is a function whose equation contains a radical with a variable in the radicand.

Square root function

A **square root function** is a radical function in which any radicals are square root radicals.

Section 9.1   Simplifying Radical Expressions (*Continued*)

Radical model	A **radical model** is a radical function, or its graph, that describes an authentic situation.
Square root model	A **square root model** is a square root function, or its graph, that describes an authentic situation.

Section 9.2   Adding, Subtracting, and Multiplying Radical Expressions

Like radicals

Radicals that have the same index and the same radicand are called **like radicals.**

Adding or subtracting like radicals

To add or subtract like radicals, we use the distributive law.

Power property for radicals

If $\sqrt[n]{x}$ is defined, then $\left(\sqrt[n]{x}\right)^n = x$.

Multiplying radicals that have the same index

To multiply two radicals that have the same index, we use the product property.

Multiplying two radicals that have different indexes but the same radicand

To multiply two radicals that have different indexes but the same radicand,
1. Write the radicals in exponential form.
2. Use exponential properties to simplify the expression involving exponents.
3. Write the simplified expression in radical form.

Simplifying a radical expression

To simplify a radical expression,
1. Perform any indicated multiplications.
2. Combine like radicals.
3. For any radical with index n, write the radicand as a product of one or more perfect nth powers and another expression that has no factors that are perfect nth powers. Then apply the product property for radicals.
4. Write any radicals with as small an index as possible.

Section 9.3   Rationalizing Denominators and Simplifying Quotients of Radical Expressions

Rationalizing the denominator of $\dfrac{A}{\sqrt[n]{x^m}}$

To rationalize the denominator of a radical expression of the form $\dfrac{A}{\sqrt[n]{x^m}}$, we multiply the expression by a fraction of the form $\dfrac{\sqrt[n]{x^k}}{\sqrt[n]{x^k}}$ so the radical in the denominator has a perfect nth-power radicand.

Quotient property for radicals

If $\sqrt[n]{a}$ and $\sqrt[n]{b}$ are defined and b is nonzero, then $\sqrt[n]{\dfrac{a}{b}} = \dfrac{\sqrt[n]{a}}{\sqrt[n]{b}}$.

Radical conjugates

We say the sum of two radicals and the difference of the same two radicals are **radical conjugates** of each other.

Rationalizing a denominator by using a radical conjugate

To rationalize the denominator of a square root expression if the denominator is a sum or difference involving radicals,
1. Determine the radical conjugate of the denominator.
2. Multiply the original fraction by the fraction $\dfrac{\text{conjugate}}{\text{conjugate}}$.
3. Find the product of the denominators by using $(A + B)(A - B) = A^2 - B^2$.

Section 9.4   Graphing and Combining Square Root Functions

Reflections across x-axis

The graphs of $f(x) = -a\sqrt{x}$ and $g(x) = a\sqrt{x}$ are reflections of each other across the x-axis.

Increasing or decreasing

If $a > 0$, then $g(x) = a\sqrt{x - h} + k$ is an increasing function and (h, k) is the minimum point. If $a < 0$, then g is a decreasing function and (h, k) is the maximum point.

Graph rises more quickly or more slowly

If $a > 1$, then the graph of $g(x) = a\sqrt{x - h} + k$ rises more quickly than the graph of $y = \sqrt{x - h} + k$. If $0 < a < 1$, then the graph rises more slowly.

Three-step method for graphing a square root function

To sketch the graph of $f(x) = a\sqrt{x - h} + k$, where $a \neq 0$,
1. Sketch the graph of $y = a\sqrt{x}$.
2. Translate the graph sketched in step 1 to the right by h units if $h > 0$ and to the left by $|h|$ units if $h < 0$.
3. Translate the graph sketched in step 2 up by k units if $k > 0$ and down by $|k|$ units if $k < 0$.

Section 9.5   Solving Radical Equations

Squaring property of equality If A and B are expressions, then all solutions of the equation $A = B$ are *among* the solutions of the equation $A^2 = B^2$. That is, the solutions of an equation are among the solutions of the equation obtained by squaring both sides.

Checking proposed solutions Because squaring both sides of a square root equation may introduce extraneous solutions, it is essential to check that each proposed solution satisfies the original equation.

Solving a square root equation in one variable To solve a square root equation in one variable,

1. Isolate a square root term on one side of the equation.
2. Square both sides.
3. Repeat steps 1 and 2 until no square root terms remain.
4. Solve the new equation.
5. Check that each proposed solution satisfies the original equation.

Power property of equality If A and B are expressions and n is a counting number greater than 1, then all solutions of the equation $A = B$ are *among* the solutions of the equation $A^n = B^n$. That is, the solutions of an equation are among the solutions of the equation obtained by raising both sides to the nth power.

Section 9.6   Modeling with Square Root Functions

Finding an equation of a square root curve To find an equation of a square root curve that contains two given points,

1. Obtain a system of two linear equations in two variables by substituting the coordinates of both points into the general equation $y = a\sqrt{x} + b$.
2. Solve the system you found in step 1.
3. Substitute the values of a and b you found in step 2 into the equation $y = a\sqrt{x} + b$.

y-Intercept of the graph of $y = a\sqrt{x} + b$ The graph of an equation of the form $y = a\sqrt{x} + b$ has y-intercept $(0, b)$.

Finding an equation of a square root model To find an equation of a square root model, given some data,

1. Create a scattergram of the data.
2. Imagine a square root curve that comes close to the data points, and choose two points (not necessarily data points) that lie on or close to the square root curve.
3. Use the two points to find an equation of the square root curve.
4. Use a graphing calculator to verify that the graph of the equation comes close to the points of the scattergram.

Four-step modeling process To find a model and make estimates and predictions,

1. Create a scattergram of the data. Decide whether a line, an exponential curve, a parabola, a square root curve, or none of these comes close to the points.
2. Find an equation of your model.
3. Verify that your equation has a graph that comes close to the points in the scattergram. If it doesn't, check for calculation errors or use different points to find the equation. An alternative is to reconsider your choice of model in step 1.
4. Use your equation of the model to draw conclusions, make estimates, and/or make predictions.

Chapter 9 Review Exercises

If the expression is in exponential form, then write it in radical form. If it is in radical form, then write it in exponential form.

1. $x^{3/7}$ **2.** $\sqrt[5]{(3k + 4)^7}$

Simplify. Assume each variable is nonnegative.

3. $\sqrt{8x^6}$ **4.** $\sqrt{18x^7y^{10}}$

5. $\sqrt[8]{x^6}$ **6.** $\sqrt[3]{24x^{10}y^{24}}$

7. $\sqrt[5]{(6x + 11)^{27}}$ **8.** $5\sqrt{20x} - 2\sqrt{45x} + 7\sqrt{5x}$

9. $b\sqrt[3]{16a^5b} + a\sqrt[3]{2a^2b^4}$

10. $5\left(4\sqrt{x} - \sqrt[3]{x}\right) - 2\sqrt[3]{x} + 8\sqrt{x}$

11. $3\sqrt{x}\left(\sqrt{x} - 7\right)$

12. $\left(4\sqrt{x} - 3\right)\left(2\sqrt{x} + 1\right)$

13. $\left(2\sqrt{a} - \sqrt{b}\right)\left(5\sqrt{a} + \sqrt{b}\right)$

14. $\left(5\sqrt{a} - 7\sqrt{b}\right)\left(5\sqrt{a} + 7\sqrt{b}\right)$

15. $\left(4\sqrt{x} + 3\right)^2$ **16.** $\left(2\sqrt[3]{x} - 5\right)^2$ **17.** $\sqrt[4]{x}\sqrt[3]{x}$

18. $\dfrac{\sqrt[4]{x}}{\sqrt[6]{x}}$ **19.** $\sqrt{\dfrac{3}{x}}$ **20.** $\dfrac{5t}{\sqrt[3]{t}}$

21. $\sqrt[5]{\dfrac{7y}{27x^2}}$ **22.** $\dfrac{\sqrt{a}}{\sqrt{a}-2\sqrt{b}}$ **23.** $\dfrac{5\sqrt{x}-4}{2\sqrt{x}+3}$

Graph the function by hand.

24. $y=-\sqrt{x-5}+3$

25. $y=2\sqrt{x+4}-1$

For $f(x)=3\sqrt{x}+5$ and $g(x)=2-4\sqrt{x}$, find an equation of the given function.

26. $f+g$ **27.** $f-g$ **28.** $f\cdot g$ **29.** $\dfrac{f}{g}$

For Exercises 30–34, solve.

30. $\sqrt{2x+1}+4=7$

31. $\sqrt{2p-4}-p=-2$

32. $\sqrt{x+6}=x$

33. $\sqrt{13x+4}=\sqrt{5x+20}$

34. $\sqrt{w+2}+\sqrt{w+9}=7$

35. Solve $3.57+2.99\sqrt{8.06x-6.83}=14.55$. Round your result to the second decimal place.

36. Solve $\sqrt{x+5}=x^2-3x-4$ by using "intersect" on a graphing calculator. Round any solutions to the second decimal place.

37. Find all x-intercepts of the graph of the square root function $f(x)=\sqrt{4x-7}-\sqrt{2x+1}$.

38. Consider the scattergram of data and the graph of the model $f(x)=a\sqrt{x}+b$ in Fig. 45. Draw a square root model that fits the data better. Explain how you would adjust the values of a and b of the original model to describe the data better.

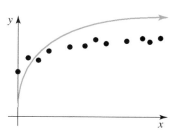

Figure 45 Exercise 38

For Exercises 39 and 40, find an equation of a square root curve of the form $y=a\sqrt{x}+b$ that approximately contains the given points. Round the values of a and b to the second decimal place.

39. $(0,3)$ and $(4,8)$ **40.** $(3,7)$ and $(5,4)$

41. Average credit card debts per household are shown in Table 31 for various years.

Table 31 Average Credit Card Debts per Household

Year	Average Credit Card Debt Per Household (thousands of dollars)
1992	3.8
1996	6.9
2000	8.3
2004	9.6
2008	10.7

Source: *CardTrak.com*

Let $D=f(t)$ be the average credit card debt (in thousands of dollars) per household at t years since 1992.

a. Find a square root equation of f.

b. Find the D-intercept. What does it mean in this situation?

c. Find $f(26)$. What does it mean in this situation?

d. Find t when $f(t)=13$. What does it mean in this situation?

Chapter 9 Test

Simplify. Assume $x\ge 0$.

1. $\sqrt{32x^9y^{12}}$ **2.** $\sqrt[3]{64x^{22}y^{14}}$

3. $\sqrt[4]{(2x+8)^{27}}$ **4.** $\dfrac{4\sqrt[3]{x}}{6\sqrt[5]{x}}$

5. $\dfrac{\sqrt{x}+1}{2\sqrt{x}-3}$ **6.** $4\sqrt{12x^3}-2x\sqrt{75x}+\sqrt{3x^3}$

7. $3\sqrt{x}(6\sqrt{x}-5)$ **8.** $(2+4\sqrt{x})(3-5\sqrt{x})$

9. $(3\sqrt{a}-5\sqrt{b})(3\sqrt{a}+5\sqrt{b})$

10. $(4\sqrt[5]{x}-3)^2$

11. Show that if n and k are counting numbers greater than 1 and $x>0$, then the statement

$$\dfrac{\sqrt[n]{x}}{\sqrt[k]{x}}=\sqrt[kn]{x^{k-n}}$$

is true.

12. Graph the function $y=-2\sqrt{x+3}+1$ by hand.

13. Let $f(x)=a\sqrt{x-h}+k$, where $a\ne 0$.

a. What must be true of a,h, and k for the graph of f to have an x-intercept? [**Hint:** Think graphically.]

b. Now assume the graph of f has an x-intercept. Find the x-intercept in terms of a,h, and k.

For $f(x)=7-3\sqrt{x}$ and $g(x)=4+5\sqrt{x}$, find an equation of the given function.

14. $f+g$ **15.** $f-g$ **16.** $f\cdot g$ **17.** $\dfrac{f}{g}$

Solve.

18. $2\sqrt{x}+3=13$ **19.** $3\sqrt{5x-4}=27$

20. $3-2\sqrt{x}+\sqrt{9-x}=0$

For Exercises 21 and 22, let $f(x)=6-4\sqrt{x+1}$.

21. Find $f(8)$.

22. Find a value of x such that $f(x)=-2$.

23. Find all x-intercepts of the graph of the square root function $f(x)=3\sqrt{2x-4}-2\sqrt{2x+1}$.

For Exercises 24 and 25, estimate all solutions of the equation by referring to the graphs shown in Fig. 46. Round results to the first decimal place.

24. $\sqrt{x + 4} = x^2 - 4x + 5$ **25.** $\sqrt{x + 4} = 1$

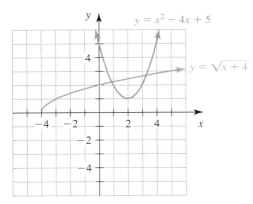

Figure 46
Exercises 24
and 25

26. Consider the scattergram of the data and the graph of the model $y = a\sqrt{x} + b$ sketched in Fig. 47. Draw a square root model that fits the data better; then explain how you would adjust the values of a and b of the original model to describe the data better.

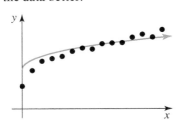

Figure 47 Exercise 26

27. Find an equation of a square root curve of the form $y = a\sqrt{x} + b$ that approximately contains the points $(2, 4)$ and $(5, 6)$.

28. The median heights of boys in the United States are listed in Table 32 for various ages, up to 5 years.

Table 32 Boys' Median Heights	
Age (months)	Height (inches)
0	20.5
6	27.0
12	30.8
18	32.9
24	35.0
36	37.5
48	40.8
60	43.4

Source: The Portable Pediatrician for Parents, *by Laura Walther Nathanson*

Let $h = f(t)$ be the median height (in inches) of boys who are t months of age.

a. Find an equation of f.
b. Estimate the median height of boys who are 6 years old.
c. Estimate the age at which the median height of boys is 3 feet.
d. Find the h-intercept. What does it mean in this situation?

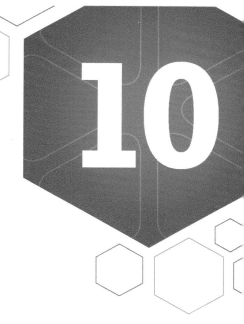

Sequences and Series

Did you know many organizations spend millions of dollars to try to influence decisions in government and politics? Members of Congress said the pharmaceutical industry was the fifth most effective special-interest group (Source: *National Journal*). See Table 1. In Exercise 35 of Homework 10.3, you will predict the total spending by the pharmaceutical industry on government and politics from 2000 through 2017.

In this chapter, we reexamine linear and exponential functions from a different perspective—that of lists of numbers called *sequences* and sums of numbers called *series*. We will use these ideas to help us model new situations. We will also discuss how to find sums of quantities efficiently, such as the total spending on pets from 2000 to 2018.

Table 1 Spending by the Pharmaceutical Industry on Government and Politics

Year	Spending (millions of dollars)
2002	14.3
2004	15.5
2006	18.1
2008	20.2
2010	21.7

Source: *Political Moneyline*

10.1 Arithmetic Sequences

Objectives

» Know the meaning of *sequence, term, term number,* and *arithmetic sequence.*

» Find a formula, term, or term number of an arithmetic sequence.

» Use an arithmetic sequence to make estimates and predictions.

In this section, we use lists of numbers to reexamine linear functions from a different perspective. We will also use these ideas to make estimates and predictions.

Definition of Arithmetic Sequence

Suppose a math tutor charges $23 per hour for one student, plus $6 per hour for each additional student. The tutor will take up to 10 students. We list the total charges (in dollars per hour) for 1 through 10 students in order:

$$23, 29, 35, 41, 47, 53, 59, 65, 71, 77$$

We call this list of numbers a sequence.

> ### Definition Sequence
>
> Any ordered list of numbers is called a **sequence.** Each number is a **term** of the sequence.

A sequence that has a last term, such as 77 in the math tutor sequence, is called a **finite sequence.** A sequence that does not have a last term is called an **infinite sequence.** For example, the sequence of odd numbers

$$1, 3, 5, 7, 9, \ldots$$

is an infinite sequence. The three dots mean the pattern of numbers continues without ending.

For the math tutor sequence, notice that the difference between any term and the preceding term is 6:

$$29 - 23 = 6, 35 - 29 = 6, 41 - 35 = 6, \ldots, 77 - 71 = 6$$

We call 6 the common difference of this sequence and say the sequence is arithmetic.

▶ Definition   **Arithmetic Sequence**

If the difference between any term of a sequence and the preceding term is a constant d for every such pair of terms, then the sequence is an **arithmetic sequence.** We call the constant d the **common difference.**

▶ Example 1   Identifying Arithmetic Sequences

Determine whether the sequence is arithmetic. If it is, find the common difference d.
1. 2, 6, 10, 14, 18, ...   **2.** 80, 77, 74, 71, 68, ...
3. 3, 6, 12, 24, 48, ...

Solution

1. The sequence is arithmetic, because it has a common difference of 4:

$$6 - 2 = 4, 10 - 6 = 4, 14 - 10 = 4, 18 - 14 = 4, \ldots$$

2. The sequence is arithmetic, because it has a common difference of -3:

$$77 - 80 = -3, 74 - 77 = -3, 71 - 74 = -3, 68 - 71 = -3, \ldots$$

3. The sequence is not arithmetic, because we can see from the first two differences that the sequence does not have a common difference:

$$6 - 3 = 3, 12 - 6 = 6$$

▶

We use the notation $a_1, a_2, a_3, \ldots$ to denote the terms of a sequence. We say that a_n is the **nth term** of the sequence and that its **term number** is n. For the math tutor sequence, we write

$$a_1 = 23, a_2 = 29, a_3 = 35, \ldots, a_{10} = 77$$

where a_n is the charge (in dollars per hour) for n students. For instance, the term 35 is the 3rd term, and its term number is 3.

Finding a Formula of an Arithmetic Sequence

Can we find a formula that describes the terms of an arithmetic sequence? Since the math tutor sequence has a common difference of 6, we add 6 to the first term, 23, to find the second term; we add 6 two times to 23 to find the third term; we add 6 three times to 23 to find the fourth term; and so on:

$$23 + 6 = 29, 23 + 6 + 6 = 35, 23 + 6 + 6 + 6 = 41, \ldots$$

In general, for an arithmetic sequence with common difference d, we have the terms

$$a_1, a_1 + d, a_1 + d + d, a_1 + d + d + d, \ldots$$

Simplifying, we have

$$a_1, a_1 + d, a_1 + 2d, a_1 + 3d, \ldots$$

We can use a pattern to find a formula that describes any term a_n of an arithmetic sequence:

$$a_1 = a_1$$
$$a_2 = a_1 + d \qquad \text{\textit{Add d once to the first term to get the second term.}}$$
$$a_3 = a_1 + 2d \qquad \text{\textit{Add d twice to the first term to get the third term.}}$$
$$a_4 = a_1 + 3d \qquad \text{\textit{Add d three times to the first term to get the fourth term.}}$$
$$\vdots$$
$$a_n = a_1 + (n-1)d \qquad \text{\textit{Add d a total of }} (n-1) \text{ \textit{times to the first term to get the nth term.}}$$

> **Formula That Describes the nth Term of an Arithmetic Sequence**
>
> If an arithmetic sequence $a_1, a_2, a_3, \ldots, a_n, \ldots$ has the common difference d, then
> $$a_n = a_1 + (n-1)d$$
> In words, the nth term of an arithmetic sequence is equal to the first term plus $n - 1$ times the common difference.

▶ **Example 2** Finding a Formula

Find a formula that describes the terms of the math tutor sequence.

Solution

To find a formula that describes the math tutor sequence 23, 29, 35, 41, 47,..., 77, we substitute $a_1 = 23$ and $d = 6$ in the formula $a_n = a_1 + (n-1)d$:

$$a_n = 23 + (n-1)(6) \qquad \text{\textit{Substitute 23 for } } a_1 \text{ \textit{and 6 for d.}}$$
$$= 23 + 6n - 6 \qquad \text{\textit{Distributive law}}$$
$$= 6n + 17$$

▶

The tutor equation $a_n = 6n + 17$ describes a linear function whose inputs are only the numbers of students $1, 2, 3, \ldots, 10$ and whose outputs are only the dollars-per-hour charges $23, 29, 35, \ldots, 77$. For instance,

$$a_1 = 6(1) + 17 = 23$$
$$a_2 = 6(2) + 17 = 29$$
$$a_3 = 6(3) + 17 = 35$$
$$a_{10} = 6(10) + 17 = 77$$

We can verify our formula by entering $y = 6x + 17$ in a graphing calculator and checking that the inputs $1, 2, 3, \ldots, 10$ give the outputs $23, 29, 35, \ldots, 77$ (see Fig. 1).

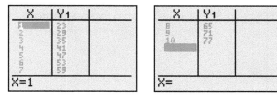

Figure 1 Verify the formula $a_n = 6n + 17$

We can also sketch a graph of the math tutor sequence. The graph consists of the 10 input–output pairs $(1, 23), (2, 29), (3, 35), \ldots, (10, 77)$. For $a_n = 6n + 17$, the coefficient of the independent variable n is 6, so the points lie on an increasing line with slope 6 (see Fig. 2).

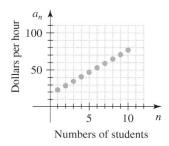

Figure 2 Math tutor sequence

Finding a Term or a Term Number of an Arithmetic Sequence

For an arithmetic sequence, if we know the values of three of the four variables $a_1, a_n, n,$ and d, we can find the value of the fourth variable from the formula $a_n = a_1 + (n - 1)d$.

Because the formula $a_n = a_1 + (n - 1)d$ is valid for arithmetic sequences only, we must first check that a sequence is arithmetic before we use the formula.

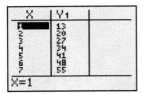

Figure 3 Verify the work

▶ **Example 3** Finding a Term

Find the 25th term of the sequence 13, 20, 27, 34, 41, ...

Solution

The sequence has a common difference $(d = 7)$, so the sequence is arithmetic. We substitute $a_1 = 13, n = 25$, and $d = 7$ in the formula $a_n = a_1 + (n - 1)d$:

$$a_{25} = 13 + (25 - 1)(7) \quad \textit{Substitute 13 for } a_1, \textit{ 25 for n, and 7 for d.}$$
$$= 13 + 24(7)$$
$$= 181$$

So, the 25th term is $a_{25} = 181$. To verify our work, we enter $y = 13 + (x - 1)(7)$ in a graphing calculator; we check that the first five terms of the sequence are 13, 20, 27, 34, and 41 and that the 25th term is 181 (see Fig. 3).

▶ **Example 4** Finding a Term Number

The number 23 is a term in the sequence 155, 151, 147, 143, 139, ... What is its term number?

Solution

The sequence has a common difference $(d = -4)$, so the sequence is arithmetic. We substitute $a_1 = 155, d = -4$, and $a_n = 23$ in the formula $a_n = a_1 + (n - 1)d$ and solve for n:

$$23 = 155 + (n - 1)(-4) \quad \textit{Substitute 155 for } a_1, -4 \textit{ for d, and 23 for } a_n.$$
$$23 = 155 - 4n + 4 \qquad \textit{Distributive law}$$
$$4n = 136 \qquad\qquad\quad \textit{Isolate 4n.}$$
$$n = 34$$

So, 23 is the 34th term. In symbols, $a_{34} = 23$. We can use a graphing calculator table to verify our work.

▶ **Example 5** Modeling with an Arithmetic Sequence

A person's salary is \$25,000 in the first year. It will increase by \$750 each year. Let a_n be the salary (in dollars) in the nth year.

1. Find a formula that describes a_n.
2. What will be the salary in the 32nd year?
3. In what year will the salary be \$40,000?

Solution

1. The salary sequence has a common difference of 750, so the sequence is arithmetic. We substitute $a_1 = 25,000$ and $d = 750$ in the formula $a_n = a_1 + (n - 1)d$:

$$a_n = 25,000 + (n - 1)(750) \quad \textit{Substitute 25,000 for } a_1 \textit{ and 750 for d.}$$
$$= 25,000 + 750n - 750 \qquad \textit{Distributive law}$$
$$= 750n + 24,250$$

The formula is $a_n = 750n + 24,250$. We can verify our work with a graphing calculator table by checking that $a_1 = 25,000$ and that the common difference is 750.

2. To find the salary in the 32nd year, we substitute $n = 32$ in the formula $a_n = 750n + 24{,}250$:

$$a_{32} = 750(32) + 24{,}250 = 48{,}250$$

The salary will be $48,250 in the 32nd year.

3. To determine when the salary will be $40,000, we substitute $a_n = 40{,}000$ in the formula $a_n = 750n + 24{,}250$ and solve for n:

$$40{,}000 = 750n + 24{,}250 \quad \textit{Substitute 40,000 for } a_n.$$
$$15{,}750 = 750n$$
$$21 = n \qquad\qquad \textit{Divide.}$$

The salary will be $40,000 in the 21st year.

Connection Between a Linear Function and an Arithmetic Sequence

We close this section by noticing a connection between a linear function and an arithmetic sequence. Note that the math tutor formula $a_n = 6n + 17$ describes a linear function whose graph has a slope of 6, which is the common difference of the sequence. If we let $f(n)$ be the tutor's charge (in dollars per hour) for n students, then

$$f(n) = 6n + 17$$

and the sequence $23, 29, 35, 41, 47, \ldots, 77$ is given by

$$f(1), f(2), f(3), \ldots, f(10)$$

> **Connection Between a Linear Function and an Arithmetic Sequence**
>
> If f is a linear function of the form $f(x) = mx + b$, then
> $$f(1), f(2), f(3), \ldots$$
> is an arithmetic sequence with common difference equal to the slope m.

> **Example 6**   Identifying an Arithmetic Sequence
>
> Let $f(x) = -5x + 38$. Is the sequence $f(1), f(2), f(3), \ldots$ arithmetic? Explain.

Solution

Since f is a linear function whose graph has a slope of -5, the sequence $f(1)$, $f(2)$, $f(3), \ldots$ must be an arithmetic sequence with common difference -5. By computing the outputs, we see that the sequence is $33, 28, 23, 18, 13, \ldots$.

We know from the slope addition property (Section 1.4) that if the inputs of a linear function increase by 1, the outputs change by the value of the slope. In terms of the slope addition property, it makes sense that the slope of the graph of a linear function and the common difference of the corresponding arithmetic sequence are equal.

Homework 10.1

For extra help ▶ **MyMathLab®**   Watch the videos in MyMathLab   Download the MyDashboard App

Check whether the sequence is arithmetic. If so, find the common difference d.

1. $3, 11, 19, 27, 35, \ldots$

2. $40, 38, 36, 34, 32, \ldots$

3. $1, 5, 7, 11, 13, \ldots$

4. $9, 2, -4, -9, -13, \ldots$

5. $-20, -13, -6, 1, 8, \ldots$

6. $-2, -5, -8, -11, -14, \ldots$

7. $4, 44, 444, 4444, 44{,}444, \ldots$

8. $1, 1, 2, 2, 3, 3, \ldots$

Using a_n notation, find a formula of the sequence. Use a graphing calculator table to verify your result.

9. $5, 11, 17, 23, 29, \ldots$

10. $7, 11, 15, 19, 23, \ldots$

11. $-4, -15, -26, -37, -48, \ldots$

12. $-3, -7, -11, -15, -19, \ldots$

13. $100, 94, 88, 82, 76, \ldots$

14. $72, 69, 66, 63, 60, \ldots$

15. $1, 3, 5, 7, 9, \ldots$

16. $1, 2, 3, 4, 5, \ldots$

Find the indicated term of the sequence. Verify your result with a graphing calculator table.

17. 37th term of $5, 8, 11, 14, 17, \ldots$

18. 52nd term of $4, 19, 34, 49, 64, \ldots$

19. 45th term of $200, 191, 182, 173, 164, \ldots$

20. 21st term of $83, 79, 75, 71, 67, \ldots$

21. a_{96} of $4.1, 5.7, 7.3, 8.9, 10.5, \ldots$

22. a_{31} of $23.8, 21.5, 19.2, 16.9, 14.6, \ldots$

23. a_{400} of $1, 2, 3, 4, 5, \ldots$

24. a_{235} of $-2, -4, -6, -8, -10, \ldots$

Find the term number n of the last term of the finite sequence. Verify your result with a graphing calculator table.

25. $3, 8, 13, 18, 23, \ldots, 533$

26. $4, 10, 16, 22, 28, \ldots, 1426$

27. $7, 15, 23, 31, 39, \ldots, 695$

28. $10, 19, 28, 37, 46, \ldots, 415$

29. $-27, -19, -11, -3, 5, \ldots, 2469$

30. $-11, -5, 1, 7, 13, \ldots, 409$

31. $29, 25, 21, 17, 13, \ldots, -14{,}251$

32. $35, 32, 29, 26, 23, \ldots, -703$

33. $-8, -13, -18, -23, -28, \ldots, -493$

34. $-27, -39, -51, -63, -75, \ldots, -999$

35. Is 2537 a term in the sequence $8, 15, 22, 29, 36, \ldots$? Explain.

36. Is 3901 a term in the sequence $5, 14, 23, 32, 41, \ldots$? Explain.

37. Find an equation of a function f such that $f(1), f(2), f(3), f(4), f(5), \ldots$ is the sequence $8, 17, 26, 35, 44, \ldots$.

38. Find an equation of a function g such that $g(1), g(2), g(3), g(4), g(5), \ldots$ is the sequence $75, 65, 55, 45, 35, \ldots$.

39. A person's starting salary is $27,500. Each year, he receives an $800 raise.
   a. Let a_n be the person's salary (in dollars) for the nth year. Find a formula that describes a_n.
   b. What will be his salary for the 22nd year?
   c. In what year will his salary first exceed $50,000?

40. A person's starting salary is $30,700. At the end of each of the first 9 years, she will get a $950 raise. After that, she will get an $1150 raise at the end of each year. What will be her salary for the 17th year?

41. A math instructor estimates that it takes an average of 10 minutes per student to grade students' quizzes and tests each week. She also spends a total of 35 hours per week in classroom activities, holding office hours, planning for classes, and attending committee meetings. Let a_n be the number of hours that the instructor works per week when n students are enrolled in her courses.
   a. Find a formula that describes a_n.
   b. Find the values of $a_1, a_2, a_3,$ and a_4. What do these four terms mean in this situation?
   c. If the instructor has 130 students, how many hours does she work per week?

d. What is the greatest number of students the instructor can have without having to work over 60 hours per week?

42. A full bottle of household glass cleaner holds 22 fluid ounces. It takes about 500 squeezes of the bottle's trigger to use all the cleaner.
   a. Let a_n be the number of ounces of cleaner remaining in the bottle after the trigger has been squeezed n times. Find a formula that describes a_n.
   b. Find $a_1, a_2, a_3,$ and a_4. What do these four terms mean in this situation?
   c. Assume it takes about 7 squeezes of the trigger to clean one side of a 4×3-foot window. If the bottle starts out full, how much liquid would remain in it after both sides of the 4×3-foot windows have been cleaned in a building that has 32 such windows?

43. The underground rock band Little Muddy spends $50 to send postcards announcing its latest gig at a club. Three bands are playing that night. Each band gets 30% of the money collected from a cover charge of $6 per person. Let a_n be Little Muddy's profit (in dollars) if n people pay the cover charge.
   a. Find a formula that describes a_n.
   b. If the band's profit is $256, how many people paid the cover charge?
   c. The club's maximum capacity is 200 people. Assume 18 people are on the guest list, 11 people are in the three bands, 6 people work for the club, and all of these people get in free. What is the greatest profit Little Muddy can earn, assuming no one leaves the club until closing time?
   d. For what values of n will Little Muddy lose money?

44. The main library in San Francisco has a five-story-high glass sculpture created in 1996 by Nayland Blake. It looks like a star constellation made up of white lights. Each light is actually an illuminated disk displaying the name of an author etched into the glass. The sculpture originally had 160 names, but Blake left room for 200 more names, 5 to be added each year.

   Let a_n be the number of names in the sculpture in the nth year, where 1996 is the first year. So, $a_1 = 160$, $a_2 = 165$, $a_3 = 170$, and so on.
   a. Find a formula that describes a_n.
   b. Predict the number of names there will be in the 33rd year (2028).
   c. Graph by hand the library sculpture sequence.

45. The pharmaceutical industry's spending on government and politics is shown in Table 2 for various years.

Table 2 Spending by the Pharmaceutical Industry on Government and Politics

Year	Spending (millions of dollars)
2002	14.3
2004	15.5
2006	18.1
2008	20.2
2010	21.7

Source: *Political Moneyline*

Let $f(t)$ be the pharmaceutical industry's spending (in millions of dollars) on government and politics in the year that is t years since 2000.
 a. Find an equation of f.
 b. Use a graphing calculator table to find the values of the sequence $f(13), f(14), f(15), f(16), f(17)$. What do they mean in this situation?
 c. Predict in which year the pharmaceutical industry's spending on government and politics will be $30 million.

46. The number of Chihuahuas in Los Angeles city and county shelters has more than doubled since 2006 (see Table 3).

Table 3 Numbers of Chihuahuas in Los Angeles City and County Shelters

Year	Number of Chihuahuas (thousands)
2006	6
2007	7
2008	10
2009	12
2010	14
2011	16

Source: *Los Angeles Animal Services*

Let $f(t)$ be the number (in thousands) of Chihuahuas in Los Angeles city and county shelters at t years since 2000.
 a. Find an equation of f.
 b. Use a graphing calculator table to find the values of the sequence $f(14), f(15), f(16), f(17), f(18)$. What do they mean in this situation?
 c. Despite large demand for Chihuahuas in the rest of the country, about a third of Chihuahuas in Los Angeles city and county shelters are euthanized (Source: *Los Angeles Animal Services*). Estimate the number of Chihuahuas euthanized in 2012.

47. Postage for a large envelope depends on its weight. In 2012, the cost to mail a large envelope weighing 1 ounce or less was $0.90. The postage increased by $0.20 for each additional ounce through 13 total ounces.
 a. Let a_n be the postage (in dollars) for a large envelope that weighs n ounces. Find a formula that describes a_n.
 b. Find the postage for a large envelope that weighs 13 ounces.
 c. Postage for a 1-pound large envelope sent by priority mail is $6.30 (there is no first-class service for this weight). Is this a better deal than the postage that would be required by your formula? (There are 16 ounces in 1 pound.)
 d. Postage from Boston to Chicago for a 5-pound package is $14.55. According to your formula, how much would the postage be?

Concepts

48. Describe an arithmetic sequence. Also, given the first few terms of an arithmetic sequence, explain how to find
 • A term with a known term number.
 • The term number of a known term.
 (See page 4 for guidelines on writing a good response.)

49. If $a_{41} = 500$ and $a_{81} = 500$ are terms of an arithmetic sequence, find a_{990}.

50. If $a_{12} = 12$ and $a_{78} = 78$ are terms of an arithmetic sequence, find a_{103}.

51. Let $f(x) = 4x - 2$. Is the sequence $f(1), f(2), f(3), \ldots$ arithmetic? Explain.

52. Let $f(x) = -5x + 1$. Is the sequence $f(1), f(2), f(3), \ldots$ arithmetic? Explain.

53. Let $f(x) = x^2$. Is the sequence $f(1), f(2), f(3), \ldots$ arithmetic? Explain.

54. Let $f(x) = \sqrt{x}$. Is the sequence $f(1), f(2), f(3), \ldots$ arithmetic? Explain.

55. A student tries to find a_{54} of the sequence 2, 7, 11, 16, 20, 25, 29, 34, 38, …:

$$a_{54} = 2 + (54 - 1)(5)$$
$$= 2 + 53(5)$$
$$= 267$$

Is the student's work correct? Explain.

56. An arithmetic sequence is described by $a_n = 3n + 7$. A student concludes that the first term is 7 and that the common difference is 3. What would you tell the student?

Related Review

57. a. Find the common difference of the arithmetic sequence 5, 7, 9, 11, 13, ….
 b. Find the slope of the line that contains the points $(1, 5)$, $(2, 7)$, $(3, 9)$, $(4, 11)$, and $(5, 13)$.
 c. Compare your results in parts (a) and (b). Explain.

58. a. Using a_n notation, find a formula of the sequence 20, 17, 14, 11, 8, ….
 b. Find an equation of the line that contains the points $(2, 17)$ and $(5, 8)$.
 c. Compare your results in parts (a) and (b). Explain.

Expressions, Equations, Functions, and Graphs

Perform the indicated instruction. Then use words such as linear, quadratic, cubic, exponential, logarithmic, rational, radical, polynomial, degree, function, one variable, *and* two variables *to describe the expression, equation, or system.*

59. Solve $2\sqrt{x + 3} - 1 = 5$.

60. Find the product $(4x - 5)(4x + 5)$.

61. Graph $f(x) = 2\sqrt{x + 3} - 1$ by hand.

62. Factor $9x^2 - 49$.

63. Find the product $(4\sqrt{x} - 5)(3\sqrt{x} - 2)$.

64. Solve $100x^2 + 81 = 0$.

▼ 10.2 Geometric Sequences

Objectives

» Know the meaning of *geometric sequence*.

» Find a formula, term, or term number of a geometric sequence.

» Use a geometric sequence to make estimates and predictions.

In Section 10.1, we worked with arithmetic sequences. In this section, we will study another type of sequence: the geometric sequence.

Definition of Geometric Sequence

Consider the sequence

$$3, 6, 12, 24, 48, \ldots$$

Notice that the *ratio* of any term to its preceding term is 2:

$$\frac{6}{3} = 2, \frac{12}{6} = 2, \frac{24}{12} = 2, \frac{48}{24} = 2, \ldots$$

We call 2 the common ratio, and we call the sequence a geometric sequence.

▶ Definition   **Geometric sequence**

If the ratio of any term of a sequence to the preceding term is a constant r for every such pair of terms, then the sequence is a **geometric sequence.** We call the constant r the **common ratio.**

▶ Example 1   Identifying Geometric Sequences

Determine whether the sequence is geometric. If so, find the common ratio r.

1. $2, 6, 18, 54, 162, \ldots$ 2. $4, 8, 24, 48, 240, \ldots$
3. $32, 16, 8, 4, 2, \ldots$

Solution

1. The sequence is geometric, because it has a common ratio of 3:

$$\frac{6}{2} = 3, \frac{18}{6} = 3, \frac{54}{18} = 3, \frac{162}{54} = 3, \ldots$$

2. The sequence is not geometric, because we can see from the first two ratios that it does not have a common ratio:

$$\frac{8}{4} = 2, \frac{24}{8} = 3$$

3. The sequence is geometric, because it has a common ratio of $\frac{1}{2}$:

$$\frac{16}{32} = \frac{1}{2}, \frac{8}{16} = \frac{1}{2}, \frac{4}{8} = \frac{1}{2}, \frac{2}{4} = \frac{1}{2}, \ldots$$

Finding a Formula of a Geometric Sequence

Can we find a general formula that describes the terms of a geometric sequence? Earlier, we determined that the geometric sequence 3, 6, 12, 24, 48, … has the common ratio 2. This means we multiply the first term, 3, by 2 to find the second term; we multiply 3 by 2 two times to find the third term; we multiply 3 by 2 three times to find the fourth term; and so on:

$$3 \cdot 2 = 6, 3 \cdot 2 \cdot 2 = 12, 3 \cdot 2 \cdot 2 \cdot 2 = 24, \ldots$$

In general, for a geometric sequence with common ratio r, we have the terms

$$a_1, a_1 \cdot r, a_1 \cdot r \cdot r, a_1 \cdot r \cdot r \cdot r, \ldots$$

Using exponents, we have

$$a_1, a_1 r, a_1 r^2, a_1 r^3, \ldots$$

We can use a pattern to find a formula that describes any term a_n of a geometric sequence:

$$a_1 = a_1$$

$a_2 = a_1 r$ *Multiply a_1 by r once to get the second term.*

$a_3 = a_1 r^2$ *Multiply a_1 by r twice to get the third term.*

$a_4 = a_1 r^3$ *Multiply a_1 by r three times to get the fourth term.*

$$\vdots$$

$a_n = a_1 r^{n-1}$ *Multiply a_1 by r a total of $(n-1)$ times to get the nth term.*

▶ Formula That Describes the nth Term of a Geometric Sequence

If a geometric sequence $a_1, a_2, a_3, \ldots, a_n, \ldots$ has the common ratio r, then

$$a_n = a_1 r^{n-1}$$

In words, the nth term of a geometric sequence is equal to the first term times the $(n-1)$th power of r.

▶ Example 2   Finding a Formula

Find a formula that describes the terms of the sequence $12, 36, 108, 324, 972, \ldots$.

Solution

The sequence has a common ratio ($r = 3$), so the sequence is geometric. We substitute $a_1 = 12$ and $r = 3$ in the formula $a_n = a_1 r^{n-1}$:

$$a_n = 12(3)^{n-1}$$

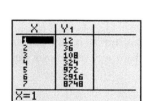

Figure 4 Verify the formula $a_n = 12(3)^{n-1}$

We verify our formula by entering $y = 12(3)^{x-1}$ in a graphing calculator and checking that the first five terms are $12, 36, 108, 324$, and 972 (see Fig. 4).

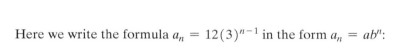

Here we write the formula $a_n = 12(3)^{n-1}$ in the form $a_n = ab^n$:

$$a_n = 12(3)^{n-1} \quad \text{\textit{Original formula}}$$
$$= 12(3)^n (3)^{-1} \quad b^{m+n} = b^m b^n$$
$$= \frac{12(3)^n}{3} \quad b^{-n} = \frac{1}{b^n}$$
$$= 4(3)^n \quad \text{\textit{Simplify.}}$$

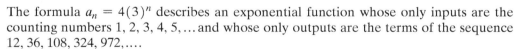

The formula $a_n = 4(3)^n$ describes an exponential function whose only inputs are the counting numbers $1, 2, 3, 4, 5, \ldots$ and whose only outputs are the terms of the sequence $12, 36, 108, 324, 972, \ldots$.

Figure 5 The first five terms of the sequence 12, 36, 108, 324, 972,...

In Fig. 5, we sketch a graph of the first five terms of the sequence $12, 36, 108, 324, 972, \ldots$. For $a_n = 4(3)^n$, the base 3 is greater than 1, so the points lie on an *increasing* exponential curve.

Finding a Term or a Term Number of a Geometric Sequence

For a geometric sequence, if we know values of three of the four variables a_1, a_n, n, and r, we can find the value of the fourth variable by using the formula $a_n = a_1 r^{n-1}$.

▶ Example 3   Finding a Term

Find the 12th term of the sequence $160, 80, 40, 20, 10, \ldots$.

Solution

The sequence has a common ratio $\left(r = \dfrac{1}{2} \right)$, so the sequence is geometric. We substitute $a_1 = 160, n = 12$, and $r = \dfrac{1}{2}$ in the formula $a_n = a_1 r^{n-1}$:

$$a_{12} = 160\left(\frac{1}{2}\right)^{12-1} \qquad \textit{Substitute 160 for } a_1, \textit{ 12 for n, and } \tfrac{1}{2} \textit{ for r.}$$

$$= 160\left(\frac{1}{2}\right)^{11} \qquad \textit{Subtract.}$$

$$= 160\left(\frac{1}{2^{11}}\right) \qquad \left(\frac{a}{b}\right)^n = \frac{a^n}{b^n}$$

$$= \frac{160}{2^{11}} \qquad \textit{Multiply numerators; multiply denominators.}$$

$$= 0.078125 \qquad \textit{Divide.}$$

We enter $y = 160\left(\dfrac{1}{2}\right)^{x-1}$ in a graphing calculator and check that the first five terms are 160, 80, 40, 20, and 10 and that the 12th term is 0.078125 (see Fig. 6). The entry across from $x = 12$ has been rounded. However, the bottom entry of the table displays the exact value $a_{12} = 0.078125$.

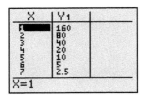

Figure 6 Verify the work

In working with a sequence, we must first determine whether it is arithmetic, geometric, or neither. An arithmetic sequence has a common difference, whereas a geometric sequence has a common ratio.

▶ **Example 4**   Finding a Term Number

The number 1,572,864 is a term in the sequence 6, 24, 96, 384, 1536,…. What is its term number?

Solution

The sequence has a common ratio ($r = 4$), so the sequence is geometric. We substitute $a_1 = 6, a_n = 1{,}572{,}864$, and $r = 4$ in the formula $a_n = a_1 r^{n-1}$ and solve for n:

$$1{,}572{,}864 = 6(4)^{n-1} \qquad \textit{Substitute 6 for } a_1, \textit{ 1,572,864 for } a_n, \textit{ and 4 for r.}$$

$$262{,}144 = 4^{n-1} \qquad \textit{Divide both sides by 6.}$$

$$\log(262{,}144) = \log(4^{n-1}) \qquad \textit{Take the logarithm of both sides.}$$

$$\log(262{,}144) = (n-1)\log(4) \qquad \textit{Power property: } \log_b(x)^p = p\log_b(x)$$

$$\frac{\log(262{,}144)}{\log(4)} = n - 1 \qquad \textit{Divide both sides by log(4).}$$

$$\frac{\log(262{,}144)}{\log(4)} + 1 = n \qquad \textit{Add 1 to both sides.}$$

$$10 = n \qquad \textit{Compute.}$$

So, 1,572,864 is the 10th term. We can use a graphing calculator table to verify our work.

▶ **Example 5**   Modeling with a Geometric Sequence

A person's salary is $25,000 in the first year. It will increase by 3% each year. Let a_n be the salary (in dollars) in the nth year.

1. Find a formula that describes a_n.
2. Predict the salary in the 32nd year.

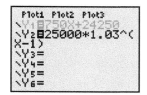

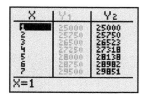

Figure 7 Verify the comparison of the two scenarios

3. Compare the result from Problem 2 with the result from Section 10.1, Example 5, Problem 2, where we assumed the salary increases by a constant $750 each year.

Solution

1. The salary in the second year is 103% of $25,000, or $25,000(1.03) = 25,750$ dollars. Each year, the salary is equal to 1.03 times the salary in the preceding year. So, a_n is a geometric sequence with the common ratio 1.03. We substitute $a_1 = 25,000$ and $r = 1.03$ in the formula $a_n = a_1 r^{n-1}$:

$$a_n = 25,000(1.03)^{n-1}$$

2. To find the salary in the 32nd year, we substitute $n = 32$ in the formula $a_n = 25,000(1.03)^{n-1}$:

$$a_{32} = 25,000(1.03)^{32-1} \approx 62,502.01$$

The salary will be $62,502.01 in the 32nd year.

3. First, we note that 3% of $25,000 is $750, so the first raise is the same in both scenarios. In Example 5 of Section 10.1, we found that if the salary increases by $750 each year, the salary in the 32nd year will be $48,250, considerably less than the salary of $62,502.01 from receiving 3% raises each year.

We can verify our salary comparison by entering the constant-raise formula $a_n = 750n + 24,250$ and the percentage-raise formula $a_n = 25,000(1.03)^{n-1}$ in a graphing calculator and comparing tables (see Fig. 7).

Connection Between an Exponential Function and a Geometric Sequence

Now we write the geometric sequence $a_n = 25,000(1.03)^{n-1}$ of Example 5 in the form $a_n = ab^n$:

$$
\begin{aligned}
a_n &= 25,000(1.03)^{n-1} && \text{\textit{Original formula}}\\
&= 25,000(1.03)^n(1.03)^{-1} && b^{m+n} = b^m b^n\\
&= \frac{25,000(1.03)^n}{1.03} && b^{-n} = \frac{1}{b^n}\\
&= \frac{25,000}{1.03}(1.03)^n && \text{\textit{Write right-hand side in }} ab^n \text{\textit{ form.}}
\end{aligned}
$$

Notice that the base of the exponential function $a_n = \dfrac{25,000}{1.03}(1.03)^n$ is 1.03, which is also the common ratio of the geometric sequence. If we let $f(n)$ be the person's salary (in dollars) in the nth year, then

$$f(n) = \frac{25,000}{1.03}(1.03)^n$$

and the geometric sequence of the salary is

$$f(1), f(2), f(3), \ldots$$

▶ **Connection Between an Exponential Function and a Geometric Sequence**

If f is an exponential function of the form $f(x) = ab^x$, then

$$f(1), f(2), f(3), \ldots$$

is a geometric sequence with common ratio equal to the base b of f.

Example 6   Identifying a Geometric Sequence

Let $f(x) = 4(3)^x$. Is the sequence $f(1), f(2), f(3), \ldots$ geometric? Explain.

Solution

Since f is an exponential function with base 3, the sequence $f(1), f(2), f(3), \ldots$ must be a geometric sequence with common ratio 3. By computing the outputs, we see that the sequence is $12, 36, 108, 324, 972, \ldots$.

▶

Recall from Section 4.3 that the base multiplier property for exponential functions states that if the value of the independent variable increases by 1, then the value of the dependent variable is multiplied by the base of the exponential function. If we think in terms of the base multiplier property, it makes sense that the base of an exponential function is equal to the common ratio of the corresponding geometric sequence.

 # Homework 10.2

For extra help ▶   MyMathLab°   Watch the videos in MyMathLab   Download the MyDashboard App

Check whether the sequence is arithmetic, geometric, or neither. If the sequence is geometric, find the common ratio r. If the sequence is arithmetic, find the common difference d.

1. $4, 28, 196, 1372, 9604, \ldots$

2. $0.08, 0.8, 8, 80, 800, \ldots$

3. $13, 6, -1, -8, -15, \ldots$

4. $3, 7, 11, 15, 19, \ldots$

5. $3, 4, 6, 9, 13, \ldots$

6. $62, 57, 54, 42, 39, \ldots$

7. $200, 40, 8, \dfrac{8}{5}, \dfrac{8}{25}, \ldots$

8. $96, 48, 24, 12, 6, \ldots$

Find a formula of the sequence. Use a_n notation. Use a graphing calculator table to verify your formula.

9. $3, 6, 12, 24, 48, \ldots$

10. $4, 20, 100, 500, 2500, \ldots$

11. $800, 200, 50, 12.5, 3.125, \ldots$

12. $162, 54, 18, 6, 2, \ldots$

13. $100, 50, 25, 12.5, 6.25, \ldots$

14. $1250, 250, 50, 10, 2, \ldots$

15. $1, 4, 16, 64, 256, \ldots$

16. $5, 15, 45, 135, 405, \ldots$

Find the indicated term of the sequence. Write the result in scientific notation $N \times 10^k$, with N rounded to the fourth decimal place. Use a graphing calculator table to verify your result.

17. 34th term of $4, 20, 100, 500, 2500, \ldots$

18. 103rd term of $2, 8, 32, 128, 512, \ldots$

19. 27th term of $80, 40, 20, 10, 5, \ldots$

20. 25th term of $36, 12, 4, \dfrac{4}{3}, \dfrac{4}{9}, \ldots$

21. a_{23} of $8, 16, 32, 64, 128, \ldots$

22. a_{60} of $1, \dfrac{3}{2}, \dfrac{9}{4}, \dfrac{27}{8}, \dfrac{81}{16}, \ldots$

Find the term number n of the last term of the finite sequence. Verify your result with a graphing calculator.

23. $240, 120, 60, 30, 15, \ldots, 0.46875$

24. $80, 20, 5, 1.25, 0.3125, \ldots, 0.01953125$

25. $0.00224, 0.0112, 0.056, 0.28, 1.4, \ldots, 109,375$

26. $0.046875, 0.09375, 0.1875, 0.375, 0.75, \ldots, 192$

The given number is a term in the sequence that follows. Find the term number of that term. Use a graphing calculator table to verify your result.

27. $3,407,872;\quad 13, 26, 52, 104, 208, \ldots$

28. $2,470,629;\quad 3, 21, 147, 1029, 7203, \ldots$

29. $28,697,814;\quad 2, 6, 18, 54, 162, \ldots$

30. $25,165,824;\quad 6, 24, 96, 384, 1536, \ldots$

31. Find an equation of a function f such that $f(1), f(2), f(3), f(4), f(5), \ldots$ is the sequence $8, 24, 72, 216, 648, \ldots$.

32. Find an equation of a function g such that $g(1), g(2), g(3), g(4), g(5), \ldots$ is the sequence $48, 24, 12, 6, 3, \ldots$.

33. Is $9,238,946$ a term in the sequence $13, 26, 52, 104, 208, \ldots$? Explain.

34. Is $1,240,029$ a term in the sequence $7, 21, 63, 189, 567, \ldots$? Explain.

35. Assume a person's salary is \$27,000 in the first year and the salary increases by 4% each year.

    a. Let a_n be the salary (in dollars) in the nth year. Find a formula that describes a_n.

    b. What will be the person's salary in the 10th year?

    c. In what year will the salary first exceed \$50,000?

36. A person's salary is \$24,000 in the first year.

    a. If the salary increases by \$960 each year, calculate the salary in the 2nd year and in the 30th year.

    b. If the salary increases by 4% each year, calculate the salary in the 2nd year and in the 30th year.

c. Compare your results for parts (a) and (b). Explain why the salaries are the same in the 2nd year but different in the 30th year.

37. Your ancestors one generation back are your natural parents. Your ancestors two generations back are your natural grandparents. Let a_n be the number of ancestors that you had in the nth generation back.
   a. List the first five terms of the sequence a_n.
   b. Find a formula that describes a_n.
   c. Use your formula to find the number of ancestors in the 8th generation back.
   d. Use your formula to find the number of ancestors in the 35th generation back. Explain why model breakdown has occurred. Describe any assumptions you made.

38. A rubber ball is dropped. The height of the ball is measured from the floor to the bottom of the ball. The ball's maximum height after one bounce is 4 feet. The ball's maximum height after the second bounce is 70% of 4 feet, or 2.8 feet. This pattern continues; that is, the maximum height after each bounce is 70% of the maximum height of the preceding bounce. Let a_n be the maximum height (in feet) of the ball after the nth bounce.
   a. Find a formula that describes a_n.
   b. Predict the ball's maximum height after the 5th bounce.
   c. For which bounce does the ball reach at least half a foot for the last time?
   d. Graph by hand the first five terms of the bouncing-ball sequence.
   e. Does model breakdown occur? Explain.

39. The *origination volume* of some loans is the total amount of money originally borrowed. The origination volumes of federal student loans are shown in Table 4 for various years.

Table 4 Federal Student Loan Origination Volume

Year	Origination Volume (billions of dollars)
2005	55.8
2006	58.9
2007	64.4
2008	75.8
2009	94.5
2010	104.3

Source: *President's 2012 Budget*

Let $f(t)$ be the origination volume (in billions of dollars) of federal student loans in the year that is t years since 2000.
   a. Find an exponential equation of f.
   b. Use a graphing calculator table to find the values of the sequence $f(11), f(12), f(13), f(14), f(15)$. What do they mean in this situation?
   c. Predict in which year the origination volume of federal student loans will be $250 billion.

40. The numbers of Iraq and Afghanistan War veterans who are homeless or at risk of becoming homeless are shown in Table 5 for various years.

Table 5 Numbers of Iraq and Afghanistan War Veterans Who Are Homeless or at Risk of Becoming Homeless

Year	Number (thousands)
2006	1
2007	2
2008	4
2009	7
2010	13
2011	20

Source: *Department of Veterans Affairs*

Let $f(t)$ be the number (in thousands) of Iraq and Afghanistan War veterans who are homeless or at risk of becoming homeless at t years since 2000.
   a. Find an exponential equation of f.
   b. Use a graphing calculator table to find the values of the sequence $f(12), f(13), f(14), f(15), f(16)$. What do they mean in this situation?
   c. Predict when there will be 840 thousand Iraq and Afghanistan War veterans who are homeless or at risk of becoming homeless.

41. Suppose a rumor is spreading on campus that students will not have to take any final exams this semester. On the first day, 5 students hear the rumor. Each person who hears the rumor tells it, approximately 24 hours later, to exactly 3 students who have not yet heard it. Let a_n be the number of students who hear the rumor on the nth day.
   a. Find a formula that describes a_n.
   b. How many students will hear the rumor on the 5th day?
   c. Use your formula to predict the number of students who will hear the rumor on the 11th day. Has model breakdown occurred? Explain.
   d. To find your formula, you made some assumptions about the way the rumor would spread. Describe each assumption, and discuss whether you think it is reasonable.

Concepts

42. Describe a geometric sequence. Also, given the first few terms of a geometric sequence, explain how to find
   • A term with a known term number.
   • The term number of a known term.

For f, is the sequence $f(1)$, $f(2)$, $f(3)$, ... *arithmetic, geometric, or neither? Explain.*

43. $f(x) = 2(5)^x$

44. $f(x) = 8\left(\frac{1}{2}\right)^x$

45. $f(x) = 7x - 3$

46. $f(x) = 3x^2$

47. A student tries to find a_{17} for the sequence $2, 6, 10, 14, 18, \ldots$:

$$a_n = a_1 r^{n-1}$$
$$a_{17} = 2(3)^{17-1}$$
$$= 2(3)^{16}$$
$$= 86{,}093{,}442$$

Describe any errors. Then find the term correctly.

48. A geometric sequence is described by the formula $a_n = 4(6)^n$. A student concludes that the first term is 4 and the common ratio is 6. What would you tell the student?

Related Review

49. a. Find the common ratio of the geometric sequence 7, 14, 28, 56, 112, ...
   b. Find the base b of the exponential function $y = ab^x$ that contains the points $(1, 7)$, $(2, 14)$, $(3, 28)$, $(4, 56)$, and $(5, 112)$.
   c. Compare your results in parts (a) and (b). Explain why this happened.

50. a. Find a formula of the sequence 486, 162, 54, 18, 6, ... Write your result in the form $a_n = cb^n$. [**Hint:** $b^{n-1} = b^n b^{-1}$]
   b. Find an equation of the exponential curve that contains the points $(3, 54)$ and $(5, 6)$.
   c. Compare your results in parts (a) and (b). Explain why this happened.

Find a formula of the sequence. Use a_n notation.

51. 14, 19, 24, 29, 34, ...
52. 57, 49, 41, 33, 25, ...
53. 448, 224, 112, 56, 28, ...
54. 4, 12, 36, 108, 324, ...

Find the indicated term of the sequence.

55. a_9 of 2, 10, 50, 250, 1250, ...
56. a_{10} of 3200, 640, 128, 25.6, 5.12, ...

57. a_{99} of 17, 12, 7, 2, −3, ...
58. a_{96} of 9.5, 12.9, 16.3, 19.7, 23.1, ...

Find the term number n of the last term of the finite sequence.

59. 4, 7, 10, 13, 16, ... , 367
60. 88, 81, 74, 67, 60, ... , −801
61. 8192, 2048, 512, 128, 32, ... , 0.0078125
62. 5, 15, 45, 135, 405, ... , 2,657,205

Expressions, Equations, Functions, and Graphs

Perform the indicated instruction. Then use words such as linear, quadratic, cubic, exponential, logarithmic, rational, radical, polynomial, degree, function, one variable, *and* two variables *to describe the expression, equation, or system.*

63. Solve $-3(4)^x = -44$. Round any solutions to the fourth decimal place.

64. Solve: $2x - 7y = 14$
$$y = \frac{2}{7}x - 2$$

65. Graph $f(x) = -3(4)^x$ by hand.
66. Graph $2x - 7y = 14$ by hand.
67. Write $2\log_b(5x^3) - 3\log_b(2x^7)$ as a single logarithm.

68. Find the inverse of $f(x) = \frac{2}{7}x - 2$.

▼ 10.3 Arithmetic Series

Objectives

» Know the meaning of *arithmetic series.*

» Evaluate the sum of an arithmetic series.

» Use arithmetic series to make estimates and predictions.

So far in this chapter, we have worked with arithmetic sequences and geometric sequences. In the next two sections, we will discuss sums that are related to these sequences.

Definition of Arithmetic Series

Suppose a person's salary is $23,000 in the first year and increases by $2000 each year. Here we use an arithmetic sequence to describe the salaries (in thousands of dollars) for the first 32 years:

$$23, 25, 27, \ldots, 81, 83, 85$$

To find the *total* earnings (in thousands of dollars) during the first 32 years, we find the sum

$$23 + 25 + 27 + \cdots + 81 + 83 + 85$$

We call this sum an arithmetic series.

▶ Definition   **Arithmetic series**

If the sequence $a_1, a_2, a_3, \ldots, a_n$ is an arithmetic sequence, then the sum $a_1 + a_2 + a_3 + \cdots + a_n$ is an **arithmetic series.** We say a_i is the **ith term** of the series and its **term number** is i.

For example, for the series $23 + 25 + 27 + \cdots + 81 + 83 + 85$, the number 27 is the third term and its term number is 3. We use the notation S_n to represent the sum of the first n terms of an arithmetic sequence:

$$S_n = a_1 + a_2 + a_3 + \cdots + a_n$$

Finding the Sum of an Arithmetic Series

Next, we find the total earnings, S_{32} (in thousands of dollars), for 32 years, where

$$S_{32} = 23 + 25 + 27 + \cdots + 81 + 83 + 85$$

We find the sum in a way that suggests a general formula of S_n for any arithmetic series.

To find the sum, we write the equation for S_{32} twice, the second time with the terms in reverse order. Then we add the left-hand sides and add the right-hand sides of the two equations:

$$\begin{array}{rcccccccccccccc}
S_{32} &=& 23 &+& 25 &+& 27 &+& \cdots &+& 81 &+& 83 &+& 85 \\
S_{32} &=& 85 &+& 83 &+& 81 &+& \cdots &+& 27 &+& 25 &+& 23 \\
\hline
2S_{32} &=& 108 &+& 108 &+& 108 &+& \cdots &+& 108 &+& 108 &+& 108
\end{array}$$

On the right-hand side of the last equation, the number 108 appears 32 times, so the sum equals $32(108)$:

$$2S_{32} = 32(108) \quad \textit{Equation (1)}$$

$$S_{32} = \frac{32(108)}{2} \quad \textit{Equation (2)}$$

$$S_{32} = 1728 \quad \textit{Equation (3)}$$

The total earnings for 32 years will be $1,728,000.

Notice that 108 is the sum of the first and last terms of the series:

$$108 = 23 + 85$$

So, we can write equation (2) as

$$S_{32} = \frac{32(23 + 85)}{2}$$

Our process and result suggest we can find S_n for any arithmetic series by first multiplying the sum of the first and last terms, $a_1 + a_n$, by the number of terms n and dividing the product by 2.

▶ Formula for Sum of an Arithmetic Series

If $S_n = a_1 + a_2 + a_3 + \cdots + a_n$ is an arithmetic series, then

$$S_n = \frac{n(a_1 + a_n)}{2}$$

We derive the formula $S_n = \dfrac{n(a_1 + a_n)}{2}$ at the end of this section.

To evaluate the sum $S_n = a_1 + a_2 + a_3 + \cdots + a_n$, we must first check that the sequence $a_1, a_2, a_3, \ldots, a_n$ is arithmetic before we use the formula $S_n = \dfrac{n(a_1 + a_n)}{2}$.

▶ Example 1   Evaluating Sums

1. Evaluate S_{50}, where $S_{50} = 3 + 7 + 11 + 15 + 19 + \cdots + 199$.
2. Evaluate S_{80}, where $S_{80} = 60 + 53 + 46 + 39 + 32 + \cdots + (-493)$.

Solution

1. The sequence 3, 7, 11, 15, 19, ..., 199 is arithmetic with common difference $d = 4$. We substitute $n = 50$, $a_1 = 3$, and $a_n = 199$ in the equation $S_n = \dfrac{n(a_1 + a_n)}{2}$:

$$S_{50} = \frac{50(3 + 199)}{2} = 5050$$

2. The sequence 60, 53, 46, 39, 32, ..., -493 is arithmetic with common difference $d = -7$. We substitute $n = 80$, $a_1 = 60$, and $a_n = -493$ in the equation $S_n = \dfrac{n(a_1 + a_n)}{2}$:

$$S_{80} = \frac{80(60 + (-493))}{2} = -17,320$$

In evaluating S_n for an arithmetic series, we sometimes must use the formula $a_n = a_1 + (n - 1)d$ to find n, a_1, or a_n before we can use the formula $S_n = \dfrac{n(a_1 + a_n)}{2}$.

▶ **Example 2**   Evaluating a Sum

Evaluate S_{43}, where $S_{43} = 150 + 147 + 144 + 141 + 138 + \cdots + a_{43}$.

Solution

The sequence 150, 147, 144, 141, 138, ..., a_{43} is arithmetic with common difference $d = -3$. Although we know that $a_1 = 150$ and $n = 43$, we must first find a_{43} before we can use the formula $S_n = \dfrac{n(a_1 + a_n)}{2}$. We find a_{43} by substituting $a_1 = 150$, $n = 43$, and $d = -3$ in the equation $a_n = a_1 + (n - 1)d$:

$$a_{43} = 150 + (43 - 1)(-3) = 24$$

Next, we substitute $n = 43$, $a_1 = 150$, and $a_n = 24$ in the equation $S_n = \dfrac{n(a_1 + a_n)}{2}$:

$$S_{43} = \frac{43(150 + 24)}{2} = 3741$$

▶ **Example 3**   Evaluating a Sum

Evaluate the sum $2 + 8 + 14 + 20 + 26 + \cdots + 338$.

Solution

The sequence 2, 8, 14, 20, 26, ..., 338 is arithmetic with common difference $d = 6$. Although we know that $a_1 = 2$ and $a_n = 338$, we must first find n before we can use the formula $S_n = \dfrac{n(a_1 + a_n)}{2}$. We find n by substituting $a_1 = 2$, $a_n = 338$, and $d = 6$ in the equation $a_n = a_1 + (n - 1)d$:

$$338 = 2 + (n - 1)6 \qquad \text{Substitute 2 for } a_1, \text{ 338 for } a_n, \text{ and 6 for } d.$$
$$336 = (n - 1)6 \qquad \text{Subtract 2 from both sides.}$$
$$56 = n - 1 \qquad \text{Divide both sides by 6.}$$
$$57 = n$$

Now we substitute $n = 57$, $a_1 = 2$, and $a_n = 338$ in the equation $S_n = \dfrac{n(a_1 + a_n)}{2}$:

$$S_{57} = \frac{57(2 + 338)}{2} = 9690$$

> **Example 4** Modeling with an Arithmetic Series

A person's salary is \$30,000 in the first year and increases by \$1200 each year. Find the person's total earnings for the first 25 years.

Solution

Let a_n be the person's salary (in dollars) in the nth year. The salary sequence a_1, a_2, $a_3, \ldots, a_n$ is arithmetic with common difference 1200. First, we find the salary in the 25th year by substituting $a_1 = 30{,}000, n = 25$, and $d = 1200$ in the equation $a_n = a_1 + (n - 1)d$:

$$a_{25} = 30{,}000 + (25 - 1)(1200) = 58{,}800$$

Next, we find S_{25} by substituting $n = 25, a_1 = 30{,}000$, and $a_n = 58{,}800$ in the equation $S_n = \dfrac{n(a_1 + a_n)}{2}$:

$$S_{25} = \frac{25(30{,}000 + 58{,}800)}{2} = 1{,}110{,}000$$

The total earnings for 25 years will be \$1,110,000.

▶

How do we derive the formula $S_n = \dfrac{n(a_1 + a_n)}{2}$? To begin, consider an arithmetic series:

$$S_n = a_1 + a_2 + a_3 + \cdots + a_n$$

Since the series is arithmetic, each term of the series is found by adding d (the common difference) to the preceding term. This means a_2 is found by adding d to a_1, so $a_2 = a_1 + d$. Also, a_3 is found by adding d twice to a_1, so $a_3 = a_1 + 2d$. The pattern continues, so the series can be expressed as

$$S_n = a_1 + (a_1 + d) + (a_1 + 2d) + \cdots + a_n$$

If we list backward from a_n, we find the term before a_n by subtracting d, so the term before a_n is $a_n - d$. Likewise, the term before that is $a_n - 2d$. This means the series can be expressed as

$$S_n = a_1 + (a_1 + d) + (a_1 + 2d) + \cdots + (a_n - 2d) + (a_n - d) + a_n$$

Now, just as we did at the start of the section, we write the equation that describes S_n twice, the second time with the terms in reverse order. Then we add the left-hand sides and add the right-hand sides of the two equations:

$$
\begin{array}{rll}
S_n = & a_1 & + (a_1 + d) + (a_1 + 2d) + \cdots + (a_n - 2d) + (a_n - d) + \quad a_n \\
S_n = & a_n & + (a_n - d) + (a_n - 2d) + \cdots + (a_1 + 2d) + (a_1 + d) + \quad a_1 \\
\hline
2S_n = & (a_1 + a_n) & + (a_1 + a_n) + (a_1 + a_n) + \cdots + (a_1 + a_n) + (a_1 + a_n) + (a_1 + a_n)
\end{array}
$$

Notice that the expression $a_1 + a_n$ appears n times on the right-hand side of the last equation. Thus, the sum on the right-hand side is $n(a_1 + a_n)$. We have

$$2S_n = n(a_1 + a_n)$$

$$S_n = \frac{n(a_1 + a_n)}{2} \qquad \textit{Divide both sides by 2.}$$

This is the formula we set out to derive, that of the sum of an arithmetic series.

Homework 10.3

Evaluate the sum of the arithmetic series with the given values of a_1, a_n, *and* n.

1. $a_1 = 2$, $a_n = 447$, and $n = 90$

2. $a_1 = 7$, $a_n = 187$, and $n = 61$

3. $a_1 = 13$, $a_n = 548$, and $n = 108$

4. $a_1 = 38$, $a_n = 605$, and $n = 82$

5. $a_1 = 37$, $a_n = -1099$, and $n = 72$

6. $a_1 = 208$, $a_n = -386$, and $n = 67$

Evaluate the sum of the series.

7. $S_{74} = 5 + 13 + 21 + 29 + 37 + \cdots + 589$

8. $S_{59} = 14 + 17 + 20 + 23 + 26 + \cdots + 188$

9. $S_{101} = 93 + 89 + 85 + 81 + 77 + \cdots + (-307)$

10. $S_{45} = 131 + 129 + 127 + 125 + 123 + \cdots + 43$

11. $S_{117} = 4 + 4 + 4 + 4 + 4 + \cdots + 4$

12. $S_{46} = -6 + (-6) + (-6) + (-6) + (-6) + \cdots + (-6)$

13. $S_{125} = 3 + 13 + 23 + 33 + 43 + \cdots + a_{125}$

14. $S_{125} = 4 + 14 + 24 + 34 + 44 + \cdots + a_{125}$

15. $S_{81} = 8 + 19 + 30 + 41 + 52 + \cdots + a_{81}$

16. $S_{87} = 11 + 17 + 23 + 29 + 35 + \cdots + a_{87}$

17. $(-15) + (-28) + (-41) + (-54) + (-67) + \cdots + a_{152}$

18. $(-23) + (-26) + (-29) + (-32) + (-35) + \cdots + a_{85}$

19. $(-40) + (-37) + (-34) + (-31) + (-28) + \cdots + a_{137}$

20. $(-29) + (-24) + (-19) + (-14) + (-9) + \cdots + a_{214}$

21. $19 + 25 + 31 + 37 + 43 + \cdots + 247$

22. $14 + 26 + 38 + 50 + 62 + \cdots + 794$

23. $900 + 892 + 884 + 876 + 868 + \cdots + (-900)$

24. $207 + 203 + 199 + 195 + 191 + \cdots + 3$

25. $4 + 7 + 10 + 13 + 16 + \cdots + 340$

26. $1 + 3 + 5 + 7 + 9 + \cdots + 10{,}001$

27. $1 + 2 + 3 + 4 + 5 + \cdots + 10{,}000$

28. $2 + 3 + 4 + 5 + 6 + \cdots + 10{,}001$

29. A first-year salary is $28,500. Each year there is a raise of $1100.
  a. Find the salary in the 28th year of work.
  b. Find the total earnings for 28 years of work.

30. A first-year salary is $35,100. Each year there is a raise of $1400.
  a. Find the salary in the 30th year of work.
  b. Find the total earnings for 30 years of work.

31. Two companies have made you job offers. Company A offers a first-year salary of $35,000 with a $700 raise at the end of each year. Company B offers a first-year salary of $27,000 with a $1500 raise at the end of each year. At which company would your total earnings over 20 years be greater? By how much?

32. Two companies have made you job offers. Company A offers a first-year salary of $24,500 with a $1700 raise at the end of each year. Company B offers a first-year salary of $33,200 with a $600 raise at the end of each year. At which company would your total earnings over 20 years be greater? By how much?

33. An auditorium has 30 rows of seats. There are 20 seats in the front row, 24 in the second row, 28 in the third row, and so on. In other words, each row has four more seats than the row in front of it.
  a. How many seats are in the back row?
  b. How many seats are in the auditorium?

34. An auditorium has 50 rows of seats. There are 16 seats in the front row, 18 in the second row, 20 in the third row, and so on. In other words, each row has two more seats than the row in front of it.
  a. How many seats are in the auditorium?
  b. If a ticket costs $20 for a seat in the first 10 rows and $15 for a seat in the remaining rows, what is the revenue for a sellout performance?
  c. If 2900 people buy tickets for one performance, describe all possibilities for the revenue from the performance.

35. In Exercise 45 of Homework 10.1, you found the model $f(t) = 0.98t + 12.11$, where $f(t)$ is the pharmaceutical industry's spending (in millions of dollars) on government and politics in the year that is t years since 2000 (see Table 6).

Table 6 Spending by the Pharmaceutical Industry on Government and Politics

Year	Spending (millions of dollars)
2002	14.3
2004	15.5
2006	18.1
2008	20.2
2010	21.7

Source: *Political Moneyline*

  a. Use f to estimate the pharmaceutical industry's spending on government and politics in 2000.
  b. Predict the pharmaceutical industry's spending on government and politics in 2017.
  c. Predict the pharmaceutical industry's total spending on government and politics from 2000 through 2017. [**Hint:** When finding the sum, think carefully about the value of n.]

36. The median revenues from Division I-A athletic departments are shown in Table 7 for various years.

Table 7 Median Annual Revenues from Division I-A Athletic Departments

Year	Median Annual Revenue (millions of dollars)
2005	32
2006	36
2007	38
2008	41
2009	46
2010	49
2011	52

Source: *NCAA Division I Revenues and Expense Report*

Let $f(t)$ be the median annual revenue (in millions of dollars) at t years since 2000.
 a. Find an equation of f.
 b. Find $f(0)$. What does it mean in this situation?
 c. Find $f(18)$. What does it mean in this situation?
 d. Find $f(0) + f(1) + f(2) + \cdots + f(18)$. What does it mean in this situation? [**Hint:** When finding the sum, think carefully about the value of n.]

37. A first-year salary is $24,800. Each year there is a raise of $1200.

 a. What will be the total amount of money earned in 26 years?
 b. What would have been the total amount of money earned in 26 years if there were no raises? How much less is this result than your result in part (a)?
 c. What is the mean amount of money earned per year for the 26 years? For which of the 26 years will this mean be greater than the actual amount of money earned? For which years will this mean be less than the actual amount of money earned?
 d. Assume, for each of the 26 years, *taxable income* is equal to salary minus $4250. Assume also the federal income tax rate is 15.016% on the first $25,000 of taxable income and 17.04% on the remaining taxable income. Estimate the total amount paid in federal income tax for the 26 years.

Concepts

38. Describe an arithmetic series. Also, explain how to evaluate the sum of an arithmetic series $S_n = a_1 + a_2 + a_3 + \cdots + a_n$ if you know a_1, a_n, and the common difference d of the arithmetic sequence $a_1, a_2, a_3, \ldots, a_n$.

*For Exercises 39–42, let S_n be the sum of an arithmetic series. For the given conditions, determine whether S_n is positive or negative. Explain. [**Hint:** Try experimenting with specific values of a_1, d, and n that meet the stated conditions. Then explain why your answer makes sense for any values that meet those conditions.]*

39. $a_1 > 0$, $d > 0$, and n is any counting number
40. $a_1 < 0$, $d < 0$, and n is any counting number

41. $a_1 = -20$, $d = 8$, and n is a very large counting number
42. $a_1 = 10$, $d = -4$, and n is a very large counting number
43. If $f(x) = 7x - 1$, is the series

$$f(1) + f(2) + f(3) + \cdots + f(100)$$

arithmetic? Explain.

44. If $g(x) = 4(3)^x$, is the series

$$g(1) + g(2) + g(3) + \cdots + g(50)$$

arithmetic? Explain.

Related Review

For each of the following, if it is a sequence, find the 15th term; if it is a series, find the sum.

45. $8, 24, 40, 56, 72, \ldots$
46. $8, 24, 72, 216, 648, \ldots$
47. $8 + 24 + 40 + 56 + 72 + \cdots + a_{15}$
48. $8 + (-8) + (-24) + (-40) + (-56) + \cdots + a_{15}$

Expressions, Equations, Functions, and Graphs

Perform the indicated instruction. Then use words such as linear, quadratic, cubic, exponential, logarithmic, rational, radical, polynomial, degree, function, one variable, *and* two variables *to describe the expression, equation, or system.*

49. Find the sum $\dfrac{x-5}{x^2-9} + \dfrac{x+3}{x^2-8x+15}$.
50. Solve $3x(x-2) = 5(x-1)$.
51. Find the product $\dfrac{x-5}{x^2-9} \cdot \dfrac{x+3}{x^2-8x+15}$.
52. Factor $8x^3 + 12x^2 - 2x - 3$.
53. Solve $\dfrac{x-5}{x^2-9} + \dfrac{x+3}{x^2-8x+15} = \dfrac{2}{x-5}$.
54. Find an equation of a parabola that contains the points $(2,7)$, $(4,15)$, and $(5,22)$.

▼ 10.4 Geometric Series

Objectives

» Know the meaning of *geometric series*.

» Evaluate the sum of a geometric series.

» Use geometric series to make estimates and predictions.

In Section 10.3, we worked with arithmetic series. In this section, we will discuss another type of series: the geometric series.

Definition of Geometric Series

Consider the geometric sequence

$$3, 6, 12, 24, 48, \ldots, 1536$$

We call the sum

$$3 + 6 + 12 + 24 + 48 + \cdots + 1536$$

a geometric series.

▶ **Definition   Geometric series**

If the sequence $a_1, a_2, a_3, \ldots, a_n$ is a geometric sequence, then the sum $a_1 + a_2 + a_3 + \cdots + a_n$ is a **geometric series.** We say a_i is the **ith term** of the series and its **term number** is i.

Finding the Sum of a Geometric Series

Can we derive a general formula that describes the sum of a geometric series $S_n = a_1 + a_2 + a_3 + \cdots + a_n$? In Section 10.2, we described the terms of a geometric sequence $a_1, a_2, a_3, \ldots, a_n$ in terms of a_1 and r:

$$a_1 = a_1$$
$$a_2 = a_1 r$$
$$a_3 = a_1 r^2$$
$$a_4 = a_1 r^3$$
$$\vdots$$
$$a_n = a_1 r^{n-1}$$

In each case, the exponent of r is one less than the term number. So, we can express the series $S_n = a_1 + a_2 + a_3 + \cdots + a_n$ as

$$S_n = a_1 + a_1 r + a_1 r^2 + \cdots + a_1 r^{n-1}$$

If we list the terms backward from $a_1 r^{n-1}$, we find that the term before $a_1 r^{n-1}$ will have an exponent of r that is one less than $n-1$. So, the term before $a_1 r^{n-1}$ is $a_1 r^{n-2}$. Similarly, the term before that is $a_1 r^{n-3}$. This means the series can be expressed as

$$S_n = a_1 + a_1 r + a_1 r^2 + \cdots + a_1 r^{n-3} + a_1 r^{n-2} + a_1 r^{n-1} \qquad \textit{Equation (1)}$$

We multiply both sides of this equation by r to obtain

$$rS_n = a_1 r + a_1 r^2 + a_1 r^3 + \cdots + a_1 r^{n-2} + a_1 r^{n-1} + a_1 r^n \qquad \textit{Equation (2)}$$

Next, we multiply both sides of equation (2) by -1, add the left-hand sides, and add the right-hand sides of the resulting equation and equation (1):

$$\begin{aligned} S_n &= a_1 + a_1 r + a_1 r^2 + \cdots + a_1 r^{n-2} + a_1 r^{n-1} \\ -rS_n &= \quad\ \ -a_1 r - a_1 r^2 - \cdots - a_1 r^{n-2} - a_1 r^{n-1} - a_1 r^n \\ \hline S_n - rS_n &= a_1 + 0 + 0 + \cdots + 0 + 0 - a_1 r^n \end{aligned}$$

We can simplify both sides of the last equation:

$$S_n - rS_n = a_1 - a_1 r^n$$

We now factor out S_n from the left-hand side and a_1 from the right-hand side:

$$S_n(1 - r) = a_1(1 - r^n) \qquad \textit{Factor both sides.}$$

$$S_n = \frac{a_1(1 - r^n)}{1 - r}, \quad r \neq 1 \qquad \textit{Divide both sides by } 1 - r.$$

▶ **Formula for Sum of a Geometric Series**

If $S_n = a_1 + a_2 + a_3 + \cdots + a_n$ is a geometric series with common ratio $r \neq 1$, then

$$S_n = \frac{a_1(1 - r^n)}{1 - r}.$$

To find the sum $S_n = a_1 + a_2 + a_3 + \cdots + a_n$, we must first determine whether the series is arithmetic, geometric, or neither. If the series is arithmetic, we use $S_n = \dfrac{n(a_1 + a_n)}{2}$. If the series is geometric with common ratio $r \neq 1$, we use $S_n = \dfrac{a_1(1 - r^n)}{1 - r}$.

▶ **Example 1**   Evaluating Sums

Evaluate the sum of the series. Round the result to the fourth decimal place.

1. $S_{15} = 4 + 12 + 36 + 108 + 324 + \cdots + a_{15}$
2. $S_{13} = 486 + 162 + 54 + 18 + 6 + \cdots + a_{13}$

Solution

1. The sequence 4, 12, 36, 108, 324, ..., a_{15} is geometric with common ratio $r = 3$. We substitute $a_1 = 4$, $r = 3$, and $n = 15$ in the equation $S_n = \dfrac{a_1\left(1 - r^n\right)}{1 - r}$:

$$S_{15} = \frac{4\left(1 - 3^{15}\right)}{1 - 3} = 28{,}697{,}812$$

2. The sequence 486, 162, 54, 18, 6, ..., a_{13} is geometric with common ratio $r = \dfrac{1}{3}$. We substitute $a_1 = 486$, $r = \dfrac{1}{3}$, and $n = 13$ in the equation $S_n = \dfrac{a_1\left(1 - r^n\right)}{1 - r}$:

$$S_{13} = \frac{486\left(1 - \left(\dfrac{1}{3}\right)^{13}\right)}{1 - \dfrac{1}{3}} \approx 728.9995$$

▶

In evaluating S_n for a geometric series with common ratio $r \neq 1$, we sometimes must use the formula $a_n = a_1 r^{n-1}$ to find a_1, r, or n before we can use the formula $S_n = \dfrac{a_1(1 - r^n)}{1 - r}$.

▶ **Example 2**   Evaluating a Sum

Evaluate the sum of the series $24{,}576 + 12{,}288 + 6144 + 3072 + 1536 + \cdots + 3$.

Solution

The sequence 24,576, 12,288, 6144, 3072, 1536, ..., 3 is geometric with common ratio $r = \dfrac{1}{2}$. First, we find the term number n of the last term, 3; then we find S_n. To find n, we substitute $a_1 = 24{,}576$, $a_n = 3$, and $r = \dfrac{1}{2}$ in the equation $a_n = a_1 r^{n-1}$ and solve for n:

$$3 = 24{,}576\left(\frac{1}{2}\right)^{n-1} \qquad \text{Substitute 24,576 for } a_1, \text{ 3 for } a_n, \text{ and } \tfrac{1}{2} \text{ for } r.$$

$$\frac{3}{24{,}576} = \left(\frac{1}{2}\right)^{n-1} \qquad \text{Divide both sides by 24,576.}$$

$$\log\left(\frac{3}{24{,}576}\right) = \log\left(\frac{1}{2}\right)^{n-1} \qquad \text{Take the logarithm of both sides.}$$

$$\log\left(\frac{3}{24{,}576}\right) = (n - 1)\log\left(\frac{1}{2}\right) \qquad \text{Power property: } \log_b(x)^p = p\log_b(x)$$

$$\frac{\log\left(\dfrac{3}{24{,}576}\right)}{\log\left(\dfrac{1}{2}\right)} = n - 1 \qquad \text{Divide both sides by } \log\left(\tfrac{1}{2}\right).$$

$$\frac{\log\left(\dfrac{3}{24{,}576}\right)}{\log\left(\dfrac{1}{2}\right)} + 1 = n \qquad \text{Add 1 to both sides.}$$

$$14 = n \qquad \text{Compute.}$$

Next, we substitute $a_1 = 24{,}576$, $r = \dfrac{1}{2}$, and $n = 14$ in the equation $S_n = \dfrac{a_1\left(1 - r^n\right)}{1 - r}$:

$$S_{14} = \frac{24{,}576\left(1 - \left(\frac{1}{2}\right)^{14}\right)}{1 - \dfrac{1}{2}} = 49{,}149$$

▶ **Example 3** Modeling with a Geometric Series

A person's salary is \$30,000 in the first year and increases by 4% at the end of each year.

1. Calculate the person's total earnings for the first 25 years.
2. Compare the result from Problem 1 with the result from Example 4 of Section 10.3, where we assumed the person's salary increases by a constant \$1200 each year.

Solution

1. Let a_n be the person's salary (in dollars) in the nth year. Since the salary in each year is 104% of the salary in the previous year, the sequence $a_1, a_2, a_3, \ldots, a_n$ is geometric with common ratio 1.04. To find the total earnings, we substitute $a_1 = 30{,}000$, $r = 1.04$, and $n = 25$ in the equation $S_n = \dfrac{a_1\left(1 - r^n\right)}{1 - r}$:

$$S_{25} = \frac{30{,}000\left(1 - 1.04^{25}\right)}{1 - 1.04} \approx 1{,}249{,}377.25$$

So, the total earnings will be about \$1,249,377.25.

2. First, note that 4% of \$30,000 is \$1200, so the first raise is the same in both scenarios. In Example 4 of Section 10.3, we found that if the person receives constant raises of \$1200, the total earnings will be \$1,110,000 in 25 years, which is \$139,377.25 less than the total earnings of \$1,249,377.25 from earning 4% raises each year.

Homework 10.4

For extra help ▶ **MyMathLab®**   ▦ Watch the videos in MyMathLab   ☁ Download the MyDashboard App

Evaluate the sum of the geometric series with the given values of a_1, r, and n. Round any approximate results to the fourth decimal place.

1. $a_1 = 5$, $r = 2$, and $n = 13$
2. $a_1 = 6$, $r = 3$, and $n = 9$
3. $a_1 = 6$, $r = 1.3$, and $n = 12$
4. $a_1 = 10$, $r = 1.5$, and $n = 15$
5. $a_1 = 13$, $r = 0.8$, and $n = 13$
6. $a_1 = 9$, $r = 0.7$, and $n = 12$
7. $a_1 = 2.3$, $r = 0.9$, and $n = 10$
8. $a_1 = 4$, $r = 0.6$, and $n = 11$

Find the sum of the series. Round any approximate results to the fourth decimal place.

9. $2 + 10 + 50 + 250 + 1250 + \cdots + a_{13}$
10. $1 + 2 + 4 + 8 + 16 + \cdots + a_{18}$
11. $600 + 180 + 54 + 16.2 + 4.86 + \cdots + a_{11}$
12. $625 + 500 + 400 + 320 + 256 + \cdots + a_{12}$
13. $3 + 2 + \dfrac{4}{3} + \dfrac{8}{9} + \dfrac{16}{27} + \cdots + a_{10}$

14. $10 + 6 + \dfrac{18}{5} + \dfrac{54}{25} + \dfrac{162}{125} + \cdots + a_{12}$
15. $1 + 4 + 16 + 64 + 256 + \cdots + 67{,}108{,}864$
16. $7 + 21 + 63 + 189 + 567 + \cdots + 33{,}480{,}783$
17. $5 + 6 + 7.2 + 8.64 + 10.368 + \cdots + 21.4990848$
18. $800 + 1120 + 1568 + 2195.2 + 3073.28 + \cdots + 11{,}806.312448$
19. $10{,}000 + 5000 + 2500 + 1250 + 625 + \cdots + 4.8828125$
20. $2500 + 2000 + 1600 + 1280 + 1024 + \cdots + 335.54432$
21. $S_{100} = 1 + 1 + 1 + 1 + 1 + \cdots + 1$
22. $3 + 30 + 300 + 3000 + 30{,}000 + \cdots + 3{,}000{,}000{,}000{,}000$
23. $324 + 108 + 36 + 12 + 4 + \cdots + \dfrac{4}{729}$
24. $80 + 40 + 20 + 10 + 5 + \cdots + \dfrac{5}{1024}$
25. A person's starting salary is \$23,500. Each year, the salary increases by 4%. What will be the person's total earnings after 20 years of work?

26. A person's first-year salary is $32,000. The salary increases by 3% each year. What will be the person's total earnings after 30 years of work?

27. Two companies make you job offers. Company A offers a first-year salary of $26,000 and a 5% raise at the end of each year. Company B offers a first-year salary of $31,000 and a 3% raise at the end of each year. At which company would your total earnings for 30 years be greater? By how much?

28. Two companies are bidding against each other to hire you. Company A offers a first-year salary of $25,000, a 4% raise at the end of each year, and a $500 bonus at the end of each year. (The 4% raise is based on the salary, not on the bonus.) Company B offers a first-year salary of $30,000 and a 3% raise at the end of each year. At which company would your total earnings for 26 years be greater? By how much?

29. In Exercise 37 of Homework 10.2, you found the (greatest possible) number of ancestors a person has in the nth generation back. Find the total number of ancestors a person has through 10 generations back.

30. Suppose a rumor is spreading in the United States that chlorine in swimming pools causes skin cancer. On the first day, 4 people hear the rumor. Approximately 24 hours after hearing the rumor, each person who hears it tells it to exactly 5 people who have not yet heard it.
a. How many people will have heard the rumor after 10 days?
b. After how many days will everyone in the United States have heard the rumor? Assume the U.S. population is 315 million.
c. To model the spread of the chlorine-causes-cancer rumor, you made some assumptions about the way the rumor would spread. Describe each assumption, and discuss whether you think it is reasonable.

31. An entrepreneur writes letters to 8 people (the first round of letters), explaining she has found a way for herself and many other people to get rich. On each letter, she has written her name and address. She asks each of the 8 people to send her $5 and to add their name and address below hers, so each letter will now have two names on it. The entrepreneur also instructs each of the 8 people to send the list of two names, together with the instructions, to 8 more people (the second round). Then all these people should send her $5, add their names and addresses to the list, send the list of three names to 8 more people (the third round), and so on. Each person who receives a letter is instructed to send $5 to the name at the top of the list. When there are 10 people on the list, the next person should send $5 to the name at the top of the list, scratch that name off the list, and add his or her name to the bottom of the list. The instructions include a warning that something terrible will happen to those who do not send the money as well as the eight letters. (These letters are called *chain letters* and are illegal.)

Assume the letters of any one round are received at approximately the same time and no one receives more than one letter.
a. In which round would the entrepreneur's name be taken off the list? How much money could she receive?
b. By which round would everyone in the world (about 7.0 billion people) have received a letter?
c. How many people will receive money from the chain letters? How much will each of them receive? [**Hint:** With 7.0 billion people, there would be only $35 billion to go around.]

32. Suppose you win a contest and choose between two award plans. If you choose plan A, you will receive $100,000 per day for 30 days. If you choose plan B, you will receive 1 cent the first day, 2 cents the second day, 4 cents the third day, and so on (each day you receive twice as much as you did on the preceding day) for 30 days. Which plan would you choose? Explain your reasoning.

33. The name Nevaeh has made the fastest climb in U.S. girls' names in more than a century (see Table 8). "Nevaeh" is "Heaven" spelled backward.

Table 8 Numbers of Nevaehs Born

Year	Number of Nevaehs Born
2001	1191
2002	1692
2003	2287
2004	3156
2005	4457
2006	5922
2007	6784

Source: *Social Security Administration*

a. Find an exponential equation of f.
b. Find $f(1)$. What does it mean in this situation?
c. Find $f(17)$. What does it mean in this situation?
d. Find $f(1) + f(2) + f(3) + \cdots + f(17)$. What does it mean in this situation?

34. Prior to CDs and cassettes, popular recordings were sold on *eight-track* tape cartridges. In 1980, 89.5 million eight-track cartridges were sold. After that year, sales dropped off sharply due to consumers' preference for cassettes over eight-tracks. (Sound recordings are no longer made on eight-tracks.) The numbers of eight-track cartridges (in millions) sold are listed in Table 9 for various years.

Table 9 Eight-Track Cartridge Sales

Year	Sales (millions)
1980	89.5
1981	32.0
1982	20.0
1983	10.0
1984	5.0
1985	1.5

Source: *Recording Industry Association of America*

a. Let $f(t)$ be the number of eight-track cartridges (in millions) sold in the year that is t years since 1980. Find an exponential equation of f.
b. Find $f(0)$. What does it mean in this situation?
c. Use the formula for the sum of a geometric series to find
$$f(0) + f(1) + f(2) + f(3) + f(4) + f(5)$$
[**Hint:** Think carefully about the value of n.]
d. Compare your result from part (c) with the actual total.
e. Predict the total number of eight-track cartridges that would have been sold from 1980 through 2018. Explain why this total is not much more than your total found in part (c).

Concepts

*For Exercises 35 and 36, let S_n be the sum of a geometric series. For the given conditions, determine whether S_n is positive or negative. Explain. [**Hint:** Try experimenting with specific values of a_1, r, and n that meet the conditions stated. Then explain why your response makes sense for any values that meet those conditions.]*

35. $a_1 > 0, r > 0$, and n is a counting number

36. $a_1 < 0, r > 0$, and n is a counting number

37. If $f(x) = 7 - x$, is the series

$$f(1) + f(2) + f(3) + \cdots + f(30)$$

arithmetic, geometric, or neither? Explain.

38. If $f(x) = 2(4)^x$, is the series

$$f(1) + f(2) + f(3) + \cdots + f(70)$$

arithmetic, geometric, or neither? Explain.

39. a. Find the sum

$$5 + 10 + 20 + 40 + 80 + \cdots + 2560$$

b. Solve the equation

$$a_n = a_1 r^{n-1}$$

for n.

c. Use the equation you found in part (b) to help you make a substitution for n in the equation

$$S_n = \frac{a_1(1 - r^n)}{1 - r}$$

d. Use the equation you found in part (c) to find the sum

$$5 + 10 + 20 + 40 + 80 + \cdots + 2560$$

e. Compare the methods you used in parts (a) and (d) to find the sum

$$5 + 10 + 20 + 40 + 80 + \cdots + 2560$$

Which method do you prefer? Explain.

40. Describe a geometric series. Also, explain how to evaluate the sum of a geometric series

$$S_n = a_1 + a_2 + a_3 + \cdots + a_n$$

if you know a_1, a_n, and the common ratio r of the geometric sequence

$$a_1, a_2, a_3, \ldots, a_n$$

Related Review

Find the sum of the series. Round any approximate results to the fourth decimal place.

41. $3 + 9 + 15 + 21 + 27 + \cdots + 351$

42. $351 + 347 + 343 + 339 + 335 + \cdots + 103$

43. $10 + 9 + 8.1 + 7.29 + 6.561 + \cdots + 3.486784401$

44. $7 + 28 + 112 + 448 + 1792 + \cdots + 469{,}762{,}048$

Expressions, Equations, Functions, and Graphs

For each of the following, give an example and then solve, simplify, or graph, as appropriate.

45. quadratic function   **46.** square root function

47. quotient of two rational expressions

48. linear function

49. quadratic equation in one variable

50. product of two radical expressions

51. exponential function

52. rational equation in one variable

53. system of two linear equations in two variables

54. exponential equation in one variable

 # Taking it to the Lab

Bouncing Ball Lab

In this lab, you will analyze the heights reached by a bouncing ball. The heights represent the distance from the floor to the bottom of the ball.

Check with your instructor whether you should collect your own data or use the data listed in Table 10. In this table, $f(n)$ is the maximum height (in centimeters) reached by a ball after n bounces.

Table 10 Maximum Heights of a Bouncing Ball

Number of Bounces	Maximum Height (centimeters)
1	72.930
2	48.673
3	33.745
5	18.379
6	11.301
7	10.805

Source: *J. Lehmann*

Materials

If you are going to perform your own experiment, you will need the following materials:

1. a rubber ball

2. a Texas Instruments CBL unit

3. a TI-83, TI-84, TI-86, or TI-Nspire graphing calculator

4. a Vernier motion detector

5. (optional) a Texas Instruments CBR unit (to be used in place of the CBL unit and motion detector)

If you don't have items 2, 4, and/or 5, another option is to use a video camera to tape the bouncing ball. You can make a background indicating heights in large print so you can estimate the heights by watching the video recording and using "pause" on your video player.

Preparation

First, find a level surface for bouncing the ball. For the experimenting, it is ideal for the ball to bounce almost straight up and down at least seven times. Attach the motion detector to a fixed object so the motion detector is above where the ball will bounce, facing directly downward (see Fig. 8). If you have a low ceiling, you can tape the motion detector to it.

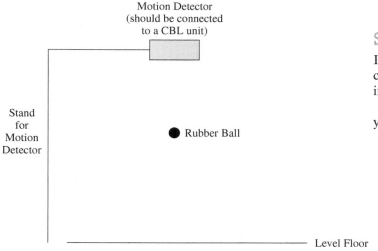

Figure 8 Equipment setup

Recording of Data
Use the CBL unit and motion detector to measure the maximum height (in centimeters) of the ball after each bounce. It is ideal to measure the heights reached by the ball for at least seven bounces.

Analyzing the Data
1. Let $f(n)$ be the maximum height (in centimeters) of the ball after n bounces. Display your data in a table or use the data in Table 10.

2. Recall that we have defined the ball's "height" to be the distance from the floor to the bottom of the ball. If you measured the distance from the floor to the top of the ball, adjust your data accordingly. (The data in Table 10 have already been adjusted.)

3. Find a quadratic and an exponential equation of f. Which model fits the data better? Which model is likely to make better predictions? Decide which equation of f you will use for the rest of this lab.

4. Is the sequence $f(1), f(2), f(3), f(4), \ldots, f(7)$ arithmetic, geometric, or neither? Explain.

5. If you performed your own experiment, you may skip this question. If you are using the data from Table 10, notice that no information is given for the maximum height between the 4th and 5th bounces. That's because the motion detector malfunctioned. Use your equation of f to estimate the maximum height reached after the 4th bounce.

6. Use your equation of f to estimate the height of the ball after the 8th bounce.

7. After which bounces will the ball reach a height of at least 1 foot?

8. Use your equation of f to estimate the height reached by the ball after the 30th bounce.

9. If your function f is an exponential function, then describe what the base means in this situation.

Stacked Cups Lab

In this lab, you will compare the height of a stack of plastic cups (one placed inside the next) with the number of cups in the stack.

Check with your instructor whether you should collect your own data or use the data listed in Table 11.

Table 11 Heights of Stacks of Cups

Number of Cups in Stack	Height of Stack (centimeters)
1	12.00
2	14.75
3	17.50
4	20.25
5	23.00

Source: *J. Lehmann*

Materials
If you are going to perform your own experiment, you will need the following materials:
1. Some plastic cups that can be stacked
2. A ruler

Recording of Data
Measure (in centimeters) the height of one cup. Then measure the heights of stacks of two, three, four, and five cups.

Analyzing the Data
1. Display your data in a table, or use the data in Table 11.

2. Let $h = f(n)$ be the height (in centimeters) of n cups. Find an equation of f.

3. Use f to estimate the height of a stack of 70 cups.

4. Find the h-intercept. What does it mean in this situation?

5. Find the slope. What does it mean in this situation?

6. Sketch a graph of your model. Sketch only the portion for which your model makes reasonably good estimates.

7. Suppose that $f(n) = 0.3n + 20$ for a different set of cups.
   a. What does this equation tell you about the cups?
   b. What is the arithmetic sequence that corresponds to f?

Chapter Summary

Key Points of Chapter 10

Section 10.1   Arithmetic Sequences

Sequence	Any ordered list of numbers is called a **sequence.** Each number is a **term** of the sequence.
Arithmetic sequence	If the difference between any term of a sequence and the preceding term is a constant d for every such pair of terms, then the sequence is an **arithmetic sequence.** We call the constant d the **common difference.**
Formula that describes the nth term of an arithmetic sequence	If an arithmetic sequence $a_1, a_2, a_3, \ldots, a_n, \ldots$ has the common difference d, then $a_n = a_1 + (n-1)d$.
Check that a sequence is arithmetic	Because the formula $a_n = a_1 + (n-1)d$ is valid for arithmetic sequences only, we must first check that a sequence is arithmetic before we use the formula.
Connection between a linear function and an arithmetic sequence	If f is a linear function of the form $f(x) = mx + b$, then $f(1), f(2), f(3), \ldots$ is an arithmetic sequence with common difference equal to the slope m.

Section 10.2   Geometric Sequences

Geometric sequence	If the ratio of any term of a sequence to the preceding term is a constant r for every such pair of terms, then the sequence is a **geometric sequence.** We call the constant r the **common ratio.**
Formula that describes the nth term of a geometric sequence	If a geometric sequence $a_1, a_2, a_3, \ldots, a_n, \ldots$ has the common ratio r, then $a_n = a_1 r^{n-1}$.
Check that a sequence is geometric	In working with a sequence, we must first determine whether it is arithmetic, geometric, or neither. An arithmetic sequence has a common difference, whereas a geometric sequence has a common ratio.
Connection between an exponential function and a geometric sequence	If f is an exponential function of the form $f(x) = ab^x$, then $f(1), f(2), f(3), \ldots$ is a geometric sequence with common ratio equal to the base b of f.

Section 10.3   Arithmetic Series

Arithmetic series	If the sequence $a_1, a_2, a_3, \ldots, a_n$ is an arithmetic sequence, then the sum $a_1 + a_2 + a_3 + \cdots + a_n$ is an **arithmetic series.** We say a_i is the **ith term** of the series and its **term number** is i.
Formula for sum of an arithmetic series	If $S_n = a_1 + a_2 + a_3 + \cdots + a_n$ is an arithmetic series, then $S_n = \dfrac{n(a_1 + a_n)}{2}$.
Check that a series is arithmetic	To evaluate the sum $S_n = a_1 + a_2 + a_3 + \cdots + a_n$, we must first check that the sequence $a_1, a_2, a_3, \ldots, a_n$ is arithmetic before we use the formula $S_n = \dfrac{n(a_1 + a_n)}{2}$.
Using a combination of formulas	In evaluating S_n for an arithmetic series, we sometimes must use the formula $a_n = a_1 + (n-1)d$ to find n, a_1, or a_n before we can use the formula $S_n = \dfrac{n(a_1 + a_n)}{2}$.

Section 10.4   Geometric Series

Geometric series

If the sequence $a_1, a_2, a_3, \ldots, a_n$ is a geometric sequence, then the sum $a_1 + a_2 + a_3 + \cdots + a_n$ is a **geometric series.** We say a_i is the ***i*th term** of the series and its **term number** is i.

Formula for sum of a geometric series

If $S_n = a_1 + a_2 + a_3 + \cdots + a_n$ is a geometric series with common ratio $r \neq 1$, then

$$S_n = \frac{a_1(1 - r^n)}{1 - r}.$$

Check that a series is geometric

To find the sum $S_n = a_1 + a_2 + a_3 + \cdots + a_n$, we must first determine whether the series is arithmetic, geometric, or neither. If the series is arithmetic, we use $S_n = \frac{n(a_1 + a_n)}{2}$. If the series is geometric with common ratio $r \neq 1$, we use $S_n = \frac{a_1(1 - r^n)}{1 - r}$.

Using a combination of formulas

In evaluating S_n for a geometric series with common ratio $r \neq 1$, we sometimes must use the formula $a_n = a_1 r^{n-1}$ to find $a_1, r,$ or n before we can use the formula $S_n = \frac{a_1(1 - r^n)}{1 - r}$.

Chapter 10 Review Exercises

Determine whether the following is an arithmetic sequence, an arithmetic series, a geometric sequence, a geometric series, or none of these types of sequences or series.

1. $160, 40, 10, 2.5, 0.625, \ldots$

2. $13 + 24 + 35 + 46 + 57 + \cdots + 299$

3. $101, 95, 89, 83, 77, \ldots$

4. $7 + \dfrac{7}{5} + \dfrac{7}{25} + \dfrac{7}{125} + \dfrac{7}{625} + \cdots + \dfrac{7}{390,625}$

Using a_n notation, find a formula of the sequence.

5. $2, 6, 18, 54, 162, \ldots$

6. $9, 4, -1, -6, -11, \ldots$

7. $200, 100, 50, 25, 12.5, \ldots$

8. $3.2, 5.9, 8.6, 11.3, 14, \ldots$

Find the indicated term of the sequence. Find the exact value, or write the result in scientific notation $N \times 10^k$ with N rounded to the fourth decimal place.

9. 47th term of $6, 12, 24, 48, 96, \ldots$

10. 9th term of $768, 192, 48, 12, 3, \ldots$

11. 98th term of $87, 84, 81, 78, 75, \ldots$

12. 87th term of $2.3, 4.9, 7.5, 10.1, 12.7, \ldots$

Find the term number of the last term in the finite sequence.

13. $7, 11, 15, 19, 23, \ldots, 2023$

14. $501, 493, 485, 477, 469, \ldots, -107$

15. The number $470,715,894,135$ is a term in the sequence $5, 15, 45, 135, 405, \ldots$. What is its term number?

16. If $a_5 = 52$ and $a_9 = 36$ are terms of an arithmetic sequence, find a_{69}.

17. Find the sum of the first 43 terms of an arithmetic series with $a_1 = 52$ and $a_{43} = -200$.

18. Find the sum of the first 22 terms of a geometric series with $a_1 = 4$, $r = 1.7$, and $n = 22$. Round your result to the fourth decimal place.

For Exercises 19–22, evaluate the sum of the series.

19. $3 + 6 + 12 + 24 + 48 + \cdots + 1,610,612,736$

20. $30 + 36 + 42 + 48 + 54 + \cdots + 1200$

21. $11 + 7 + 3 + (-1) + (-5) + \cdots + a_{33}$

22. $531,441 + 177,147 + 59,049 + 19,683 + 6561 + \cdots + a_{13}$

23. If $f(x) = 4(5)^x$, is $f(1) + f(2) + f(3) + \cdots + f(80)$ an arithmetic sequence, an arithmetic series, a geometric sequence, or a geometric series? Explain.

24. If $f(x) = -9x + 40$, is $f(1), f(2), f(3), \ldots, f(80)$ an arithmetic sequence, an arithmetic series, a geometric sequence, or a geometric series? Explain.

25. Two companies have made you job offers. Company A offers a first-year salary of $28,000 with a 4% raise at the end of each year. Company B offers a first-year salary of $34,000 with a constant raise of $1500 each year.
    a. What would be the salary in the 25th year at company A? at company B?
    b. What would be the total earnings for 25 years of work at company A? at company B?
    c. Explain how it is possible for the salary in the 25th year to be greater at company A than at company B, yet the total earnings for 25 years to be greater at company B than at company A.

26. Levels of spending (in billions of dollars) on pets in the United States are shown in Table 12 for various years.

Table 12 Levels of Spending on Pets in the United States

Year	Spending on Pets (billions of dollars)
2002	29.5
2004	34.4
2006	38.5
2008	43.2
2010	48.4
2011	51.0

Source: *American Pet Products Manufacturers Association*

Let $f(t)$ be the spending (in billions of dollars) on pets in the United States in the year that is t years since 2000.
  a. Find a linear equation of f.
  b. Find the slope of the graph of f. What does it mean in this situation?
  c. Use f to predict the spending on pets in 2018.
  d. Use f to estimate the total spending on pets from 2000 through 2018.

Chapter 10 Test

Determine whether the following is an arithmetic sequence, an arithmetic series, a geometric sequence, a geometric series, or none of these types of sequences or series.

1. $3, 6, 12, 24, 48, \ldots$

2. $20, 19, 17, 14, 10, \ldots$

3. $7 + 35 + 175 + 875 + 4375 + \cdots + 546{,}875$

4. $69 + 61 + 53 + 45 + 37 + \cdots + 5$

Using a_n notation, find a formula of the sequence.

5. $31, 25, 19, 13, 7, \ldots$

6. $6, 24, 96, 384, 1536, \ldots$

7. Find the 87th term of the sequence $4, 7, 10, 13, 16, \ldots$.

8. Find the 16th term of the sequence $6144, 3072, 1536, 768, 384, \ldots$.

Find the term number of the last term of the finite sequence.

9. $-27, -23, -19, -15, -11, \ldots, 1789$

10. $200, 220, 242, 266.2, 292.82, \ldots, 428.717762$

Evaluate the sum of the series. Round any approximate results to the fourth decimal place, or write such results in scientific notation $N \times 10^k$ with N rounded to the fourth decimal place.

11. $27 + 9 + 3 + 1 + \dfrac{1}{3} + \cdots + a_{20}$

12. $4 + 8 + 16 + 32 + 64 + \cdots + 2{,}147{,}483{,}648$

13. $50 + 46 + 42 + 38 + 34 + \cdots + (-78)$

14. $19 + 33 + 47 + 61 + 75 + \cdots + a_{400}$

15. Evaluate the sum of the series [**Hint:** Begin by writing the series as a sum of two series]:

$$(7 + 2) + \left(7 \cdot 2 + 2^2\right) + \left(7 \cdot 3 + 2^3\right) + \left(7 \cdot 4 + 2^4\right)$$
$$+ \left(7 \cdot 5 + 2^5\right) + \cdots + \left(7 \cdot 20 + 2^{20}\right)$$

16. Let $f(x) = 3x^2 + 1$. Is $f(1) + f(2) + f(3) + \cdots + f(100)$ an arithmetic sequence, an arithmetic series, a geometric sequence, a geometric series, or none of these types of sequences or series? Explain.

17. Let S_n be the sum of an arithmetic series. Determine whether S_n is positive or negative if $a_1 = 10$, $d = -3$, and n is a very large counting number. Explain.

18. Online retail sales are shown in Table 13 for various years. Let $f(t)$ be the online retail sales (in billions of dollars) in the year that is t years since 2000.

Table 13 Online Retail Sales

Year	Online Retail Sales (billions of dollars)
2002	42
2004	67
2006	102
2008	130
2010	142
2011	162

Source: *Forrester*

  a. Find a linear equation of f.
  b. Find $f(1)$. What does it mean in this situation?
  c. Find $f(18)$. What does it mean in this situation?
  d. Find $f(1) + f(2) + f(3) + \cdots + f(18)$. What does it mean in this situation?

19. Assume a person's salary is \$32 thousand for the first year and increases by 3% each year.
  a. Let a_n be the person's salary (in thousands of dollars) in the nth year. Find a formula that describes a_n.
  b. When will the salary first exceed \$40 thousand?
  c. What will the salary be in the 25th year?
  d. What will the total earnings be for the first 25 years?

Cumulative Review of Chapters 1–10

Solve. All solutions are real numbers.

1. $6x^2 + 13x = 5$

2. $\log_3(4x - 7) = 4$

3. $(t + 3)(t - 4) = 5$

4. $\dfrac{1}{w^2 - w - 6} - \dfrac{w}{w + 2} = \dfrac{w - 2}{w - 3}$

5. $5(3x - 2)^2 + 7 = 17$

6. $\log_6(3x) + \log_6(x - 1) = 1$

7. $20 - 4x = 7(2x + 9)$ **8.** $\sqrt{x + 1} - \sqrt{2x - 5} = 1$

For Exercises 9–11, solve. All solutions are real numbers. Round any results to the fourth decimal place.

9. $2b^7 - 3 = 51$ **10.** $6(3)^x - 5 = 52$

11. $5e^x = 98$

12. Solve $3x^2 - 5x + 1 = 0$ by completing the square.

13. Find all complex-number solutions of $2x^2 = 4x - 3$.

For Exercises 14–16, solve the system.

14. $2x + 4y = 0$ **15.** $y = 3x + 9$
    $5x + 3y = 7$ $4x + 2y = -2$

16. $2x - 3y + 4z = 19$
    $5x + y - 5z = -6$
    $3x - y + 2z = 13$

17. Solve the inequality $5 - 2(3x - 5) + 1 \geq 2 - 4x$. Describe the solution set as an inequality, in interval notation, and in a graph.

Simplify. Assume any variable is positive.

18. $\left(3b^{-2}c^{-3}\right)^4\left(6b^{-5}c^2\right)^2$ **19.** $\dfrac{8b^{1/2}c^{-4/3}}{10b^{3/4}c^{-7/3}}$

20. $3y\sqrt{8x^3} - 2x\sqrt{18xy^2}$ **21.** $\sqrt{12x^7y^{14}}$

22. $\sqrt[3]{\dfrac{4}{x}}$ **23.** $\dfrac{3\sqrt{x} - \sqrt{y}}{2\sqrt{x} + \sqrt{y}}$

Simplify. Write your result as a single logarithm with a coefficient of 1.

24. $2\ln\left(x^4\right) + 3\ln\left(x^9\right)$ **25.** $4\log_b\left(x^5\right) - 5\log_b(2x)$

For Exercises 26–28, perform the indicated operation.

26. $(3a - 5b)^2$ **27.** $\left(3\sqrt{k} - 4\right)\left(2\sqrt{k} + 7\right)$

28. $\left(2x^2 - x + 3\right)\left(x^2 + 2x - 1\right)$

29. Perform long division: $\dfrac{9x^3 - 9x^2 + 14x - 13}{3x - 2}$.

For Exercises 30–33, perform the indicated operation.

30. $\dfrac{x^3 - 27}{2x^2 - 3x + 1} \div \dfrac{2x^3 + 6x^2 + 18x}{4x^2 - 1}$

31. $\dfrac{3x}{x^2 - 10x + 25} - \dfrac{x + 2}{x^2 - 7x + 10}$

32. $\dfrac{4x - x^2}{6x^2 + 10x - 4} \cdot \dfrac{7 - 21x}{x^2 - 8x + 16}$

33. $\dfrac{1}{x^2 + 12x + 27} + \dfrac{x + 2}{x^3 + x^2 - 9x - 9}$

34. Simplify $\dfrac{\dfrac{x + 2}{x^2 - 64}}{\dfrac{x^2 + 4x + 4}{3x + 24}}$.

35. Write $f(x) = -3(x + 3)^2 - 7$ in standard form.

36. For $f(x) = 2x^2 - 4x + 3$ and $g(x) = x - 2$, find an equation of $f \circ g$.

Factor.

37. $4x^3 - 8x^2 - 25x + 50$ **38.** $2x^3 - 4x^2 - 30x$

39. $6w^2 + 2wy - 20y^2$ **40.** $100p^2 - 1$

For Exercises 41–45, refer to Fig. 9.

41. Find $f(2)$.

42. Find x when $f(x) = 3$.

43. Find an equation of f.

44. Find the domain of f.

45. Find the range of f.

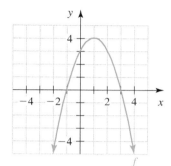

Figure 9 Exercises 41–45

For Exercises 46–50, graph the equation by hand.

46. $y = -3(x - 4)^2 + 3$ **47.** $y = 2\sqrt{x + 5} - 4$

48. $y = 15\left(\dfrac{1}{3}\right)^x$ **49.** $y = 2x^2 + 5x - 1$

50. $2x(x - 3) + y = 5(x + 1)$

51. Find an equation of the line that contains the points $(-3, 2)$ and $(2, -5)$.

52. Find an approximate equation $y = ab^x$ of an exponential curve that contains the points $(3, 95)$ and $(6, 12)$. Round the values of a and b to the second decimal place.

53. Find an equation of a parabola that contains the points $(2, 1)$, $(3, 6)$, and $(4, 15)$.

54. Find an approximate equation of a square root curve $y = a\sqrt{x} + b$ that contains the points $(2, 5)$ and $(6, 17)$. Round the values of a and b to the second decimal place.

55. Let f be the linear function, g be the exponential function, and h be a quadratic function whose graphs contain the points $(0, 2)$ and $(1, 4)$.
  a. Find possible equations of $f, g,$ and h.
  b. Use a graphing calculator to draw the graphs of $f, g,$ and h in the same viewing window.

Find the logarithm.

56. $\log_3(81)$ **57.** $\log_b\left(\sqrt{b}\right)$

For Exercises 58 and 59, find the inverse of the function.

58. $g(x) = \log_2(x)$ **59.** $f(x) = -4x - 7$

60. Find the domain of $f(x) = \dfrac{x - 3}{x^2 - 2x - 35}$.

61. Find the 10th term of the sequence $2, 8, 32, 128, 512, \ldots$.

62. Find the term number of the last term of the finite sequence $-86, -82, -78, -74, -70, \ldots, 170$.

For Exercises 63 and 64, find the sum of the series.

63. $98{,}304 + 49{,}152 + 24{,}576 + 12{,}288 + 6144 + \cdots + 3$

64. $11 + 14 + 17 + 20 + 23 + \cdots + 182$

65. A chemist wants to mix a 15% acid solution and a 30% acid solution to make a 25% acid solution. How many liters of each solution must be mixed to make 6 liters of the 25% solution?

66. The numbers of slot machines and video poker machines are shown in Table 14 for various years.

Table 14 Numbers of Slot Machines and Video Poker Machines

Year	Number of Slot Machines and Video Poker Machines (in thousands)
2001	561
2003	618
2005	689
2007	730
2008	770

Source: *Datamonitor's Productscan Online*

Let $n = f(t)$ be the number (in thousands) of slot machines and video poker machines at t years since 2000.
  a. Find an equation of f.
  b. Find an equation of f^{-1}.
  c. Find $f(18)$. What does it mean in this situation?
  d. Find $f^{-1}(1100)$. What does it mean in this situation?
  e. Find the slope of the graph of f. What does it mean in this situation?

67. In 2011, the two most populous nations were China and India, with populations of 1.347 billion and 1.210 billion, respectively. India is expected to surpass China as the most populous nation within the next 50 years. The population of India in 1980 was 0.687 billion.
  a. First, assume India's population is growing linearly. Let $L(t)$ be India's population (in billions) at t years since 1980. Find an equation of L.
  b. Now assume India's population is growing exponentially. Let $E(t)$ be India's population (in billions) at t years since 1980. Find an equation of E.
  c. Find $L(70)$ and $E(70)$. What do they mean in terms of India's population?
  d. Find $(E - L)(70)$. What does this result mean in terms of India's population? To get an idea of the size of your result, compare it with 0.439, a prediction of the U.S. population (in billions) in 2050 (Source: *U.S. Census Bureau*).
  e. The U.S. Census Bureau predicts China's population will reach 1.424 billion in 2050. Use first L and then E to predict when India's population will reach that level. Compare your results.

68. The sales of U.S. Irish whiskey are shown in Table 15 for various years. Let $f(t)$ be annual U.S. Irish whiskey sales (in millions of 9-liter cases) at t years since 2000.
  a. Find an exponential equation of f and a quadratic equation of f. Compare how well the two models fit the data.
  b. If sales have generally increased, which of the two models describes the situation better for years before 2005?

Table 15 U.S. Irish Whiskey Sales

Year	Sales (millions of 9-liter cases)
2005	0.6
2006	0.7
2007	0.8
2008	1.0
2009	1.1
2010	1.4

Source: *Distilled Spirits Council of the United States*

  c. Use the exponential model to predict when the annual sales will be 5 million 9-liter cases.
  d. Use the quadratic model to predict when the annual sales will be 5 million 9-liter cases.
  e. Explain why the year predicted in part (d) is later than the year you predicted in part (c).

69. Average annual per-person expenditures on books and all forms of recreation in the United States are shown in Table 16 for various years.

Table 16 Average per-Person Expenditures on Books and All Forms of Recreation

Year	Average per-Person Expenditure (dollars)	
	Books	All Forms of Recreation
2000	146	1863
2002	139	2079
2004	130	2218
2006	117	2376
2008	116	2835
2009	110	2693

Source: *U.S. Bureau of Labor Statistics*

  a. Let $B(t)$ be the average annual per-person expenditure (in dollars) on books at t years since 2000. Find a linear equation of B.
  b. Let $R(t)$ be the average annual per-person expenditure (in dollars) on all forms of recreation at t years since 2000. Find a linear equation of R.
  c. Let $P(t)$ be the percentage of total recreational expenditures that consist of book purchases in the year that is t years since 2000. Find an equation of P.
  d. Use the window settings in Fig. 10 to graph P. Is P increasing, decreasing, or neither for values of t between 0 and 20? What does that mean in this situation?

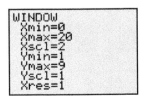

Figure 10 Window settings for Exercise 69d

  e. Predict when 2% of recreational expenditures will consist of book purchases.

Additional Topics

11.1 Absolute Value: Equations and Inequalities

Objectives

» Know the meaning of *absolute value* in terms of the number line.

» Know the meaning of *absolute value function*, *absolute value equation in one variable*, and *absolute value inequality in one variable*.

» Solve absolute value equations and absolute value inequalities.

In this section, we will work with *absolute value functions*. We will also solve equations and inequalities that have absolute values.

Absolute Value

We begin by defining the absolute value of a number.

▶ **Definition** **Absolute value**

The **absolute value** of a number a, written $|a|$, is the distance from a to 0 on the number line.

For example, $|-6| = 6$, because -6 is a distance of 6 units from 0 (see Fig. 1). Also, $|6| = 6$, because 6 is a distance of 6 units from 0 (see Fig. 1).

Figure 1 Both the numbers −6 and 6 are a distance of 6 units from 0

Two more examples are $|-3.7| = 3.7$ and $|95| = 95$. Since the absolute value of a number is the *distance* from that number to 0, **the absolute value of any number is nonnegative.**

Absolute Value Function

An **absolute value function** is a function whose equation contains the absolute value of a variable expression. Here are some examples of absolute value functions:

$$f(x) = |x| \qquad g(x) = |5x - 3| + 4 \qquad h(x) = \left|\frac{3x - 7}{2}\right|$$

▶ **Example 1** Graphing an Absolute Value Function

Graph $f(x) = |x|$.

Solution

First, we list some input–output pairs of f in Table 1. Then we plot the corresponding points and sketch a "V"-shaped curve through them (see Fig. 2).

Table 1 Input–Output Pairs of $f(x) = |x|$

x	$f(x)$
−3	3
−2	2
−1	1
0	0
1	1
2	2
3	3

We use ZStandard followed by ZSquare to verify our graph (see Fig. 3). To enter $|x|$, press $\boxed{\text{MATH}}\;\boxed{\triangleright}\;\mathbf{1}\;\boxed{\text{X,T,}\Theta,n}\;\boxed{)}$.

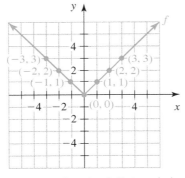

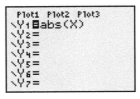
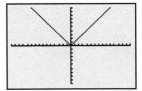

Figure 2 Graph of $f(x) = |x|$ **Figure 3** Verify the work

Solving Absolute Value Equations in One Variable

We will now solve some equations in *one* variable that contain absolute values. An **absolute value equation in one variable** is an equation in one variable that contains the absolute value of a variable expression. Here are some examples:

$$|x| = 3 \qquad |3x - 7| + 8 = 2 \qquad |4x - 5| = |3 - x| \qquad \left|\frac{2x}{3} - \frac{1}{2}\right| = \frac{5}{6}$$

To solve the absolute value equation $|x| = 4$, we must determine all numbers that are a distance of 4 units from 0. There are two such numbers: -4 and 4. So, the statements $|x| = 4$ and $x = \pm 4$ are equivalent statements.

Absolute Value Property for Equations

For an expression A and a positive constant k, the equation $|A| = k$ is equivalent to

$$A = -k \text{ or } A = k$$

▶ **Example 2**   Solving an Absolute Value Equation

Solve $|2x + 1| = 11$.

Solution

In $|2x + 1| = 11$, the expression $2x + 1$ represents numbers that are a distance of 11 from 0. These are the numbers -11 and 11:

$$\begin{array}{lcl} 2x + 1 = -11 & \text{or} & 2x + 1 = 11 \quad \textit{Absolute value property for equations}\\ 2x = -12 & \text{or} & 2x = 10 \\ x = -6 & \text{or} & x = 5 \end{array}$$

We check that both -6 and 5 satisfy the original equation:

$$\begin{array}{ll} \textbf{\textit{Check x = -6}} & \textbf{\textit{Check x = 5}} \\ |2x + 1| = 11 & |2x + 1| = 11 \\ |2(-6) + 1| \overset{?}{=} 11 & |2(5) + 1| \overset{?}{=} 11 \\ |-11| \overset{?}{=} 11 & |11| \overset{?}{=} 11 \\ 11 \overset{?}{=} 11 & 11 \overset{?}{=} 11 \\ \text{true} & \text{true} \end{array}$$

▶ **Example 3**   Solving an Absolute Value Equation

Solve $2|x| - 3 = 5$.

Solution

We isolate $|x|$ on one side of the equation; then we use the absolute value property for equations:

$$2|x| - 3 = 5 \qquad \textit{Original equation}$$
$$2|x| = 8 \qquad \textit{Add 3 to both sides.}$$
$$|x| = 4 \qquad \textit{Divide both sides by 2.}$$
$$x = \pm 4 \qquad \textit{Absolute value property for equations}$$

We use "intersect" on a graphing calculator to verify our work (see Fig. 4).

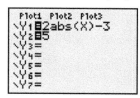 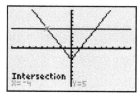 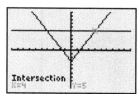

Figure 4 Verify the work

▶ **Example 4**   Solving Absolute Value Equations

Solve.

1. $|4p + 12| = 0$ **2.** $|2x - 8| = -3$

Solution

1. In $|4p + 12| = 0$, the expression $4p + 12$ represents the one number that is a distance of 0 units from 0. This is the number 0:

$$4p + 12 = 0$$
$$4p = -12$$
$$p = -3$$

2. Since $|2x - 8|$ is nonnegative, the solution set of $|2x - 8| = -3$ is the empty set.

The graphical check in Fig. 5 shows that the graphs of $y = |2x - 8|$ and $y = -3$ do not intersect. This means the solution set of the equation $|2x - 8| = -3$ is the empty set, which checks.

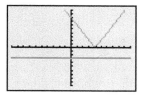

Figure 5 Verify the work

If $|a| = |b|$, what can we say about the numbers a and b? Since the absolute value of a number is its distance from 0, this means that a and b are the same distance from 0 on the number line. So, the numbers must be opposites of each other ($a = -b$) or equal to each other ($a = b$).

▶ **Solving an Equation of the Form $|A| = |B|$**

For expressions A and B, the equation $|A| = |B|$ is equivalent to

$$A = -B \text{ or } A = B$$

For example, $|x| = |3|$ is equivalent to $x = -3$ or $x = 3$. This makes sense, because the only solutions of $|x| = 3$ are ± 3.

▶ **Example 5**   Solving an Absolute Value Equation

Solve $|6x - 2| = |4x + 5|$.

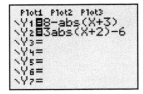

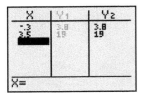

Figure 6 Verify the work

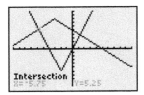

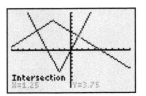

Figure 7 Solve the system

Solution

$$|6x - 2| = |4x + 5|$$ *Original equation*

$6x - 2 = -(4x + 5)$ or $6x - 2 = 4x + 5$ *If $|A| = |B|$, then $A = -B$ or $A = B$.*

$6x - 2 = -4x - 5$ or $6x - 2 = 4x + 5$ *Simplify right-hand side of equation./*

$10x - 2 = -5$ or $2x - 2 = 5$ *Add 4x to both sides./Subtract 4x*

$10x = -3$ or $2x = 7$ *from both sides.*

$x = -\dfrac{3}{10}$ or $x = \dfrac{7}{2}$

We use a graphing calculator table to verify that $-\dfrac{3}{10} = -0.3$ and $\dfrac{7}{2} = 3.5$ are solutions (see Fig. 6).

▶ **Example 6**   Using Graphing to Solve an Equation in One Variable

Use graphing to solve $8 - |x + 3| = 3|x + 2| - 6$.

Solution

We use "intersect" on a graphing calculator to find the solutions of the system

$$y = 8 - |x + 3|$$
$$y = 3|x + 2| - 6$$

See Fig. 7.

The solutions of the system are $(-5.75, 5.25)$ and $(1.25, 3.75)$. The x-coordinates of these ordered pairs, -5.75 and 1.25, are the solutions of $8 - |x + 3| = 3|x + 2| - 6$.

▶

Solving Absolute Value Inequalities in One Variable

We now turn our attention from solving *equations* to solving *inequalities*. An **absolute value inequality in one variable** is an inequality in one variable that contains the absolute value of a variable expression. Here are some absolute value inequalities in one variable:

$$|x| < 5 \qquad 3|x| - 7 \le 2 \qquad |4x + 1| > 6 \qquad \left|\dfrac{8x - 5}{3}\right| \ge 2$$

To solve the absolute value inequality $|x| < 3$, we find all numbers whose distance from 0 is less than 3 units. So, the solutions of $|x| < 3$ are all the numbers between -3 and 3 (see Fig. 8). The solution set is the set of numbers x where $-3 < x < 3$. In interval notation (Section 3.5), the solution set is $(-3, 3)$.

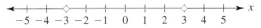

Figure 8 Graph of numbers whose distance from 0 is less than 3 units

The solution set of an absolute value inequality is sometimes best described as the union of two sets. If A and B are sets, then the **union of A and B,** denoted $A \cup B$, is the set of all members of A together with all members of B. So, $(-\infty, 1) \cup (3, \infty)$ is the set of numbers less than 1 together with numbers greater than 3.

To solve $|x| > 3$, we find all numbers whose distance from 0 is more than 3 units. So, the solutions of $|x| > 3$ are all numbers that are either less than -3 *or* greater than 3 (see Fig. 9). The solution set is the set of numbers x where $x < -3$ or $x > 3$ or, in interval notation, $(-\infty, -3) \cup (3, \infty)$.

Figure 9 Graph of numbers whose distance from 0 is more than 3 units

> **Absolute Value Property for Inequalities**

For an expression A and a positive constant k,

- The inequality $|A| < k$ is equivalent to $-k < A < k$.
- The inequality $|A| > k$ is equivalent to $A < -k$ or $A > k$.

▶ **Example 7**   Solving an Absolute Value Inequality

Solve $|2x - 3| \leq 9$. Describe the solution set as an inequality, in interval notation, and in a graph.

Solution

In $|2x - 3| \leq 9$, the expression $2x - 3$ represents numbers whose distance from 0 is less than or equal to 9. Such a number is between -9 and 9, inclusive:

$$-9 \leq 2x - 3 \leq 9$$

Next, we solve the inequality $-9 \leq 2x - 3 \leq 9$:

$$
\begin{aligned}
-9 &\leq 2x - 3 \leq 9 && \textit{Original inequality} \\
-9 + 3 &\leq 2x - 3 + 3 \leq 9 + 3 && \textit{Add 3 to all parts.} \\
-6 &\leq 2x \leq 12 && \textit{Add.} \\
-3 &\leq x \leq 6 && \textit{Divide all parts by 2.}
\end{aligned}
$$

So, the solution set is the set of numbers x where $-3 \leq x \leq 6$ or, in interval notation, $[-3, 6]$. We graph the solution set in Fig. 10.

Figure 10 Graph of $-3 \leq x \leq 6$

To verify our result, we check that, for inputs between -3 and 6, inclusive, the outputs of $y = |2x - 3|$ are less than or equal to 9 (see Fig. 11).

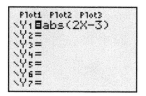

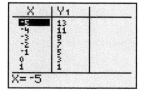

Figure 11 Verify the work

▶ **Example 8**   Solving an Absolute Value Inequality

Solve $|3t + 4| > 12$. Describe the solution set as an inequality, in a graph, and in interval notation.

Solution

For $|3t + 4| > 12$, the expression $3t + 4$ represents numbers whose distance is more than 12 units from 0. These numbers are less than -12 or greater than 12:

$$
\begin{aligned}
3t + 4 &< -12 && \text{or} && 3t + 4 > 12 \\
3t &< -16 && \text{or} && 3t > 8 && \textit{Subtract 4 from both sides.} \\
t &< -\frac{16}{3} && \text{or} && t > \frac{8}{3} && \textit{Divide both sides by 3.}
\end{aligned}
$$

We can graph the solution set on a number line (see Fig. 12), or we can describe the solution set in interval notation as $\left(-\infty, -\dfrac{16}{3}\right) \cup \left(\dfrac{8}{3}, \infty\right)$.

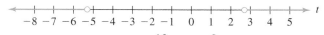

Figure 12 Graph of $t < -\dfrac{16}{3}$ or $t > \dfrac{8}{3}$

Recall from Section 3.5 that when we multiply or divide both sides of an inequality by a negative number, we reverse the inequality symbol.

▶ **Example 9**   Solving an Absolute Value Inequality

Solve $7 - |x + 2| > 3$. Describe the solution set as an inequality, in a graph, and in interval notation.

Solution

To begin, we isolate $|x + 2|$ on the left-hand side of the inequality:

$$7 - |x + 2| > 3 \quad \textit{Original inequality}$$
$$-|x + 2| > -4 \quad \textit{Subtract 7 from both sides.}$$
$$|x + 2| < 4 \quad \textit{Multiply both sides by } -1; \textit{ reverse inequality symbol.}$$

So, $x + 2$ represents numbers whose distance is less than 4 units from 0. These numbers are between -4 and 4:

$$-4 < x + 2 < 4$$
$$-4 - 2 < x + 2 - 2 < 4 - 2 \quad \textit{Subtract 2 from all three parts.}$$
$$-6 < x < 2$$

We can graph the solution set on a number line (see Fig. 13), or we can describe the solution set in interval notation as $(-6, 2)$.

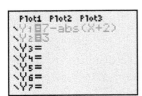
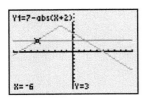

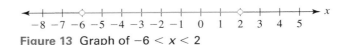

Figure 13 Graph of $-6 < x < 2$

To verify our work, we check that the graph of $y = 7 - |x + 2|$ is above the horizontal line $y = 3$ for values of x between -6 and 2 (see Fig. 14).

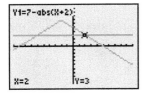

Figure 14 Verify the work

▶ **Example 10**   Solving Absolute Value Inequalities

Solve.

1. $|7x - 10| \le -2$ 2. $|5x - 8| > -1$

Solution

1. Since $|7x - 10|$ is nonnegative, the inequality $|7x - 10| \le -2$ has an empty-set solution.
2. Since $|5x - 8|$ is nonnegative for *any* real number x, the solution set of $|5x - 8| > -1$ is the set of all real numbers or, in interval notation, $(-\infty, \infty)$.

▲◢◣**Group Exploration** ————————————————————————————————
◣◢◤   Graphical meaning of $|a - b|$

In this exploration, you will explore the graphical meaning of $|a - b|$.

1. Plot the points 1 and 6 on a number line. What is the distance between 1 and 6? Compare your result with $|1 - 6|$ and with $|6 - 1|$.

2. Plot the points -2 and 3 on a number line. What is the distance between -2 and 3? Compare your result with $|(-2) - 3|$ and with $|3 - (-2)|$.

3. Find the distance between -7 and -3, and compare your result with $|(-7) - (-3)|$ and with $|(-3) - (-7)|$.

4. Describe the graphical meaning of $|a - b|$.

5. Solve the equation. Then find the distance between 5 and each solution. Explain why your result makes sense in terms of the graphical meaning of $|x - 5|$.

    a. $|x - 5| = 1$

    b. $|x - 5| = 2$

    c. $|x - 5| = 3$

6. Solve the equation or inequality and graph the solutions. Explain why your result makes sense in terms of the graphical meaning of $|x - 4|$.

    a. $|x - 4| = 3$ [**Hint:** For the graph, plot the two solutions.]

    b. $|x - 4| < 3$

    c. $|x - 4| > 3$

Key Points of Section 11.1

Absolute value	The **absolute value** of a number a, written $|a|$, is the distance from a to 0 on the number line.
Absolute value is nonnegative	The absolute value of any number is nonnegative.
Absolute value function	An **absolute value function** is a function whose equation contains the absolute value of a variable expression.
Absolute value equation	An **absolute value equation in one variable** is an equation in one variable that contains the absolute value of a variable expression.
Absolute value property for equations	For an expression A and a positive constant k, the equation $|A| = k$ is equivalent to $A = -k$ or $A = k$.
Solving an equation of the form $|A| = |B|$	For expressions A and B, the equation $|A| = |B|$ is equivalent to $A = -B$ or $A = B$.
Absolute value inequality	An **absolute value inequality in one variable** is an inequality in one variable that contains the absolute value of a variable expression.
Absolute value property for inequalities	For an expression A and a positive constant k, • The inequality $|A| < k$ is equivalent to $-k < A < k$. • The inequality $|A| > k$ is equivalent to $A < -k$ or $A > k$.

Homework 11.1

For extra help ▶ **MyMathLab®** Watch the videos in MyMathLab   Download the MyDashboard App

Solve. Use a graphing calculator table or graph to verify your work.

1. $|x| = 7$

2. $|x| = 4$

3. $|x| = -3$

4. $|x| = -1$

5. $5|p| - 3 = 15$

6. $-7|w| + 6 = 4$

7. $|x + 2| = 5$

8. $|x - 3| = 8$

9. $|x - 5| = 0$

10. $|x + 1| = 0$

11. $|3t - 1| = 11$

12. $|6k + 4| = 7$

13. $|2x + 9| = -6$

14. $|5x - 1| = -3$

15. $|4x| + 1 = 9$

16. $|6x| - 5 = 7$

17. $2|a + 5| = 8$

18. $-3|m - 4| = -15$

19. $|2x - 5| - 4 = -3$

20. $|5x + 3| - 2 = 5$

21. $|4x - 5| = |3x + 2|$

22. $|3x + 7| = |2x - 1|$

23. $|5w + 1| = |3 - w|$

24. $|2p - 4| = |5 - p|$

25. $\left|\dfrac{4x + 3}{2}\right| = 5$

26. $\left|\dfrac{3x - 5}{6}\right| = 2$

27. $\left|\dfrac{1}{2}x - \dfrac{5}{3}\right| = \dfrac{7}{6}$

28. $\left|\dfrac{3}{4}x + \dfrac{7}{2}\right| = \dfrac{1}{3}$

29. $\left|\dfrac{2}{3}k + \dfrac{4}{9}\right| = \left|\dfrac{5}{6}k - \dfrac{1}{3}\right|$

30. $\left|\dfrac{5}{6}t - \dfrac{3}{4}\right| = \left|\dfrac{1}{4}t + \dfrac{3}{2}\right|$

Solve. Round any solutions to the second decimal place.

31. $4.7|x| - 3.9 = 8.8$

32. $1.9|x| + 4.1 = 12.8$

33. $|2.1x + 5.8| - 9.7 = 10.2$

34. $|3.6x - 2.1| + 2.8 = 9.4$

Solve by using "intersect" on a graphing calculator. Round any solutions to the second decimal place.

35. $|x| - 3 = 7 - |x + 1|$

36. $|x| - 1 = 8 - |x - 3|$

37. $|x + 4| + 3 = 9 - 2|x + 5|$

38. $2|x - 2| + 1 = 6 - |x - 3|$

For Exercises 39–42, use the graphs shown in Fig. 15 to solve the given equation or system.

39. $1 - |x| = -3$

40. $|x + 1| - 4 = 0$

41. $|x + 1| - 4 = 1 - |x|$

42. $y = |x + 1| - 4$
$y = 1 - |x|$

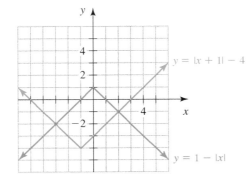

Figure 15 Exercises 39–42

Let $f(x) = 2|x| - 11$.

43. Find $f(-5)$.

44. Find $f(-3)$.

45. Find x, where $f(x) = -5$.

46. Find x, where $f(x) = -3$.

Let $f(x) = |4x + 7| - 9$.

47. Find $f(-3)$.

48. Find $f(-5)$.

49. Find x, where $f(x) = -3$.

50. Find x, where $f(x) = -5$.

Solve. Describe the solution set as an inequality, in a graph, and in interval notation.

51. $|x| < 4$

52. $|x| \le 1$

53. $|x| \ge 3$

54. $|x| > 2$

55. $|r| < -3$

56. $|m| > -5$

57. $|x| > 0$

58. $|x| \le 0$

59. $|x - 6| \ge 7$

60. $|x + 1| > 3$

61. $|2x + 5| < 15$

62. $|3x - 4| \le 25$

63. $|7x + 15| > -4$

64. $|2x - 1| \ge -2$

65. $|0.25t - 1.3| \ge 1.1$

66. $|0.8w - 3.1| < 2.9$

67. $2|x| - 5 > 3$

68. $3|x| - 1 \ge 11$

69. $2 - 5|p| \le -8$

70. $10 - 4|b| < -2$

71. $7 - |x + 3| \le 2$

72. $5 - |x - 2| < 4$

73. $\left|\dfrac{x + 4}{3}\right| \ge 2$

74. $\left|\dfrac{x - 1}{2}\right| > 4$

75. $\left|\dfrac{2x}{5} + \dfrac{3}{2}\right| \le \dfrac{9}{20}$

76. $\left|\dfrac{5x}{3} - \dfrac{1}{4}\right| > \dfrac{7}{12}$

Concepts

77. Assume $m \ne 0$ and the equation $|mx + b| + c = k$ has at least one solution for x. Solve the equation for x.

78. What must be true of the constants m, b, c, and k if the equation $|mx + b| + c = k$ has exactly one solution?

79. A student tries to solve the equation $|x - 5| = 7$:

$$|x - 5| = 7$$
$$x + 5 = 7$$
$$x = 2$$

Describe any errors. Then solve the equation correctly.

80. A student tries to solve the equation $|x + 6| = -3$:

$$|x + 6| = -3$$
$$x + 6 = 3 \quad \text{or} \quad x + 6 = -3$$
$$x = -3 \quad \text{or} \qquad x = -9$$

Describe any errors. Then solve the equation correctly.

81. A student tries to solve the inequality $|x + 3| < 10$:

$$|x + 3| < 10$$
$$x + 3 < -10 \quad \text{or} \quad x + 3 < 10$$
$$x < -13 \quad \text{or} \qquad x < 7$$

Describe any errors. Then solve the inequality correctly.

82. A student tries to solve the inequality $|x + 2| < 7$:

$$|x + 2| < 7$$
$$x + 2 < 7$$
$$x < 5$$

Describe any errors. Then solve the inequality correctly.

83. **a.** Solve $|2x + 3| = 13$.   **b.** Solve $|2x + 3| < 13$.
    c. Solve $|2x + 3| > 13$.
    d. Graph the solutions in parts (a), (b), and (c) on the same number line. Use three colors to identify the different solutions. Make some observations about the solutions. Explain these observations.

84. List three numbers that satisfy the inequality $-2|3x - 4| < -4$.

85. The inequality $|x| < 3$ is equivalent to $-3 < x < 3$. Graph the equations $y = |x|$ and $y = 3$ on the same coordinate system to help explain.

86. The inequality $|x| > 2$ is equivalent to $x < -2$ or $x > 2$. Graph the equations $y = |x|$ and $y = 2$ to help explain.

87. Is the statement "$|a + b| = |a| + |b|$ for all real numbers a and b" true or false? Explain. [**Hint:** Try substituting a positive number for a and a negative number for b.]

88. Explain how to solve an inequality of the form $|mx + b| + c < k$, where $m \ne 0$. (See page 4 for guidelines on writing a good response.)

Related Review

Solve. Round any approximate solutions to the fourth decimal place.

89. $|x - 5| = 4$

90. $|x^2 - 5| = 4$

91. $|2^y - 5| = 4$

92. $|\sqrt{w} - 5| = 4$

93. $\left|\dfrac{2x + 3}{x - 2} - 5\right| = 4$

94. $|\log_4(x) - 5| = 4$

Solve. Describe the solution set as an inequality, in a graph, and in interval notation.

95. $3(2x) - 5 \le 7$

96. $2(2x - 3) > 6$

97. $3|2x| - 5 \le 7$

98. $2|2x - 3| > 6$

Expressions, Equations, Functions, and Graphs

Perform the indicated instruction. Then use words such as absolute value, linear, quadratic, cubic, exponential, logarithmic, rational, radical, polynomial, degree, function, one variable, and two variables to describe the expression, equation, or system.

99. Graph $y = 3(x - 2) + 1$ by hand.

100. Factor $4x^3 - 20x^2 + 24x$.

101. Solve $3|x - 2| + 1 = 7$.

102. Solve $4x^3 - 20x^2 + 24x = 0$.

103. Find an equation of a line that contains the points $(-4, 2)$ and $(5, -3)$.

104. Find the product $(2x - 6)(3x^2 + 4x - 2)$.

Section 11.1 Quiz

Solve.

1. $3|t| - 4 = 11$

2. $5|6r - 5| = 15$

3. $|7x + 1| = -3$

4. $|5x - 2| = |3x + 6|$

5. $\left| \dfrac{3}{4}x - \dfrac{1}{2} \right| = \dfrac{7}{8}$

6. Is the statement "$|a - b| = |a| - |b|$ for all real numbers a and b" true or false? Explain.

Solve. Describe the solution set as an inequality, in a graph, and in interval notation.

7. $3|k| - 4 \geq 2$

8. $|4c - 8| > 12$

9. $7|3x - 2| \leq 42$

10. $|x - 5| < -7$

▼ 11.2 Performing Operations with Complex Numbers

Objective

» Perform operations with complex numbers.

Recall from Section 7.3 that the *imaginary unit i* is the number whose square is -1. That is,

$$i^2 = -1 \quad \text{and} \quad i = \sqrt{-1}$$

If b is a nonzero real number, then an expression of the form bi is a *pure imaginary number*. A *complex number* is a number of the form $a + bi$, where a and b are real numbers. An *imaginary number* is a number $a + bi$, where a and b are real numbers and $b \neq 0$.

Finally, recall from Section 7.3 that if p is a positive real number, then $\sqrt{-p} = i\sqrt{p}$. For example, $\sqrt{-25} = i\sqrt{25} = 5i$.

In this section, we will perform operations with complex numbers.

Adding, Subtracting, and Multiplying Complex Numbers

Since $i = \sqrt{-1}$, **we perform operations with complex numbers in much the same way as we do with radical expressions.** For example,

$$\left(2 + 3\sqrt{7}\right) + \left(1 + 5\sqrt{7}\right) = 3 + 8\sqrt{7} \quad \text{\textit{Add two radical expressions.}}$$
$$(2 + 3i) + (1 + 5i) = 3 + 8i \quad \text{\textit{Add two complex numbers.}}$$

If a radicand is a negative real number, we first write the radical in terms of i before performing any operations:

$$\sqrt{-1}\sqrt{-1} = i \cdot i = i^2 = -1 \quad \text{\textit{Correct}}$$
$$\sqrt{-1}\sqrt{-1} = \sqrt{-1 \cdot -1} = \sqrt{1} = 1 \quad \text{\textit{Incorrect}}$$

So, there is no product property $\sqrt{a}\sqrt{b} = \sqrt{ab}$ when a and b are both negative. To find $\sqrt{-2}\sqrt{-3}$, we first write each radical in terms of i:

$$\sqrt{-2}\sqrt{-3} = i\sqrt{2} \cdot i\sqrt{3} = i^2\sqrt{6} = -\sqrt{6}$$

When we use an operation to combine two complex numbers, we write the result in the form $a + bi$, where a and b are in lowest terms.

▶ **Example 1** Performing Operations with Complex Numbers

Perform the indicated operation. Simplify the result.

1. $(5 + 9i) + (3 - 2i)$

2. $\left(3 - \sqrt{-36}\right) - \left(2 - \sqrt{-16}\right)$

3. $4i \cdot 6i$

4. $\sqrt{-4}\sqrt{-9}$

Solution

1. $(5 + 9i) + (3 - 2i) = 5 + 3 + 9i - 2i$ *Rearrange terms.*

$= 8 + 7i$ *Write in $a + bi$ form.*

2. $\left(3 - \sqrt{-36}\right) - \left(2 - \sqrt{-16}\right) = \left(3 - i\sqrt{36}\right) - \left(2 - i\sqrt{16}\right)$ *Write in terms of i.*

$= (3 - 6i) - (2 - 4i)$ *$\sqrt{36} = 6$, $\sqrt{16} = 4$*

$= 3 - 6i - 2 + 4i$ *Distributive law*

$= 3 - 2 - 6i + 4i$ *Rearrange terms.*

$= 1 - 2i$ *Write in $a + bi$ form.*

3. $4i \cdot 6i = 24i^2$ *Simplify.*

$= 24(-1)$ *$i^2 = -1$*

$= -24$

4. $\sqrt{-4}\sqrt{-9} = i\sqrt{4} \cdot i\sqrt{9}$ *Write in terms of i.*

$= 2i \cdot 3i$ *$\sqrt{4} = 2$, $\sqrt{9} = 3$*

$= 6i^2$ *Simplify.*

$= 6(-1)$ *$i^2 = -1$*

$= -6$

▶ **Example 2**   Performing Operations with Complex Numbers

Perform the indicated operations. Simplify the result.

1. $9 - 4i(2 - 7i)$ **2.** $(2 + 5i)(3 - 7i)$ **3.** $(3 - 5i)^2$

Solution

1. $9 - 4i(2 - 7i) = 9 - 8i + 28i^2$ *Distributive law*

$= 9 - 8i + 28(-1)$ *$i^2 = -1$*

$= 9 - 8i - 28$ *Multiply.*

$= -19 - 8i$

2. $(2 + 5i)(3 - 7i) = 2 \cdot 3 - 2 \cdot 7i + 5i \cdot 3 - 5i \cdot 7i$ *Multiply pairs of terms.*

$= 6 - 14i + 15i - 35i^2$ *Simplify.*

$= 6 + i - 35(-1)$ *Simplify; $i^2 = -1$*

$= 6 + i + 35$ *Multiply.*

$= 41 + i$

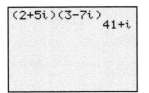

Figure 16 Verify that $(2 + 5i)(3 - 7i) = 41 + i$

We use a graphing calculator to verify our work (see Fig. 16). Press ⟨2nd⟩ ⟨·⟩ to enter the imaginary unit i.

3. $(3 - 5i)^2 = 3^2 - 2(3)(5i) + (5i)^2$ *$(A - B)^2 = A^2 - 2AB + B^2$*

$= 9 - 30i + 25i^2$ *$(bc)^n = b^n c^n$*

$= 9 - 30i + 25(-1)$ *$i^2 = -1$*

$= 9 - 30i - 25$ *Multiply.*

$= -16 - 30i$

Recall from Section 9.3 that we call radical expressions such as $7 + \sqrt{3}$ and $7 - \sqrt{3}$ radical conjugates of each other. Similarly, we call the complex numbers $7 + 3i$ and $7 - 3i$ complex conjugates of each other.

▶ **Definition** **Complex conjugate**

The complex numbers $a + bi$ and $a - bi$ are called **complex conjugates** of each other.

For example, the complex conjugate of $2 - 8i$ is $2 + 8i$. The complex conjugate of $6i$ is $-6i$.

▶ **Example 3** Finding the Product of Two Complex Conjugates

Find the product $(4 + 7i)(4 - 7i)$.

Solution

$$
\begin{aligned}
(4 + 7i)(4 - 7i) &= 4^2 - (7i)^2 &\quad (A + B)(A - B) = A^2 - B^2 \\
&= 16 - 7^2 i^2 &\quad (bc)^n = b^n c^n \\
&= 16 - 49(-1) &\quad i^2 = -1 \\
&= 65
\end{aligned}
$$

Dividing Complex Numbers

We **simplify** a quotient of two complex numbers by removing i from the denominator of the quotient. In Example 3, we found that the product of two particular complex conjugates is a real number. In general, **the product of *any* two complex conjugates is a real number.** We can use this generalization to remove i from the denominator of a quotient of two complex numbers.

▶ **Example 4** Simplifying the Quotient of Two Complex Numbers

Simplify $\dfrac{5}{2 + 3i}$.

Solution

Since the product of the complex conjugates $2 + 3i$ and $2 - 3i$ is a real number, we can remove i from the denominator of $\dfrac{5}{2 + 3i}$ by multiplying the quotient by $\dfrac{2 - 3i}{2 - 3i}$:

$$
\begin{aligned}
\frac{5}{2 + 3i} &= \frac{5}{2 + 3i} \cdot \frac{2 - 3i}{2 - 3i} &\quad \text{The conjugate of } 2 + 3i \text{ is } 2 - 3i. \\
&= \frac{10 - 15i}{4 - 9i^2} &\quad \text{Distributive law; } (A + B)(A - B) = (A^2 - B^2) \\
&= \frac{10 - 15i}{4 - 9(-1)} &\quad i^2 = -1 \\
&= \frac{10 - 15i}{13} &\quad \text{Simplify.} \\
&= \frac{10}{13} - \frac{15}{13}i &\quad \text{Write in } a + bi \text{ form.}
\end{aligned}
$$

To simplify the quotient of two complex numbers, we multiply the quotient by $\dfrac{\text{complex conjugate of the denominator}}{\text{complex conjugate of the denominator}}$. Notice that this process is similar to the way we rationalize the denominator of a radical expression such as $\dfrac{5}{2 + 3\sqrt{7}}$.

▶ **Example 5**   Simplifying the Quotient of Two Complex Numbers

Simplify $\dfrac{2 + 4i}{3 - 5i}$.

Solution

$$\dfrac{2 + 4i}{3 - 5i} = \dfrac{2 + 4i}{3 - 5i} \cdot \dfrac{3 + 5i}{3 + 5i} \qquad \textit{The conjugate of } 3 - 5i \textit{ is } 3 + 5i.$$

$$= \dfrac{(2 + 4i)(3 + 5i)}{(3 - 5i)(3 + 5i)} \qquad \textit{Multiply numerators; multiply denominators.}$$

$$= \dfrac{6 + 10i + 12i + 20i^2}{9 - 25i^2} \qquad \begin{array}{l}\textit{Multiply pairs of terms;}\\ (A - B)(A + B) = A^2 - B^2\end{array}$$

$$= \dfrac{6 + 22i + 20(-1)}{9 - 25(-1)} \qquad \textit{Simplify; } i^2 = -1$$

$$= \dfrac{-14 + 22i}{34} \qquad \textit{Simplify.}$$

$$= -\dfrac{14}{34} + \dfrac{22}{34}i \qquad \textit{Write in } a + bi \textit{ form.}$$

$$= -\dfrac{7}{17} + \dfrac{11}{17}i \qquad \textit{Simplify.}$$

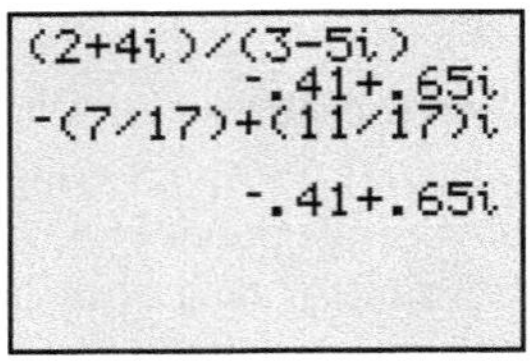

We use a graphing calculator to verify our work (see Fig. 17). Here we set the float to 2, so the numbers in the result are rounded to the second decimal place.

```
(2+4i)/(3-5i)
           -.41+.65i
-(7/17)+(11/17)i
           -.41+.65i
```

Figure 17 Verify the work

When the denominator of a fraction is a pure imaginary number, the easiest way to remove i from the denominator is to multiply the fraction by $\dfrac{i}{i}$.

▶ **Example 6**   Simplifying the Quotient of Two Complex Numbers

Simplify $\dfrac{2 - 5i}{3i}$.

Solution

Since the denominator $3i$ is a pure imaginary number, we can remove i from the denominator by multiplying by $\dfrac{i}{i}$:

$$\dfrac{2 - 5i}{3i} = \dfrac{2 - 5i}{3i} \cdot \dfrac{i}{i} \qquad \textit{Multiply by } \dfrac{i}{i}.$$

$$= \dfrac{2i - 5i^2}{3i^2} \qquad \textit{Multiply numerators; multiply denominators.}$$

$$= \dfrac{2i - 5(-1)}{3(-1)} \qquad i^2 = -1$$

$$= \dfrac{5 + 2i}{-3} \qquad \textit{Multiply.}$$

$$= -\dfrac{5}{3} - \dfrac{2}{3}i \qquad \textit{Write in } a + bi \textit{ form.}$$

Group Exploration
Finding powers of i

1. Find the indicated power of i. Verify your work with a graphing calculator.
   a. i^2
   b. i^3 [**Hint:** $i^3 = i^2 \cdot i$]
   c. i^4 [**Hint:** $i^4 = i^3 \cdot i$]
   d. i^5

2. Continue finding powers of i, such as i^6, i^7, i^8,..., until you see a pattern in your results. Describe the pattern.

3. Find the indicated power of i. Verify your result with a graphing calculator.
   a. i^{23}
   b. i^{41}
   c. i^{102}
   d. i^{400}

Key Points of Section 11.2

Performing operations with complex numbers	We perform operations with complex numbers in much the same way as we do with radical expressions.
First write radicals in terms of i	If a radicand is a negative real number, we first write the radical in terms of i before performing any operations.
Complex conjugate	The complex numbers $a + bi$ and $a - bi$ are called **complex conjugates** of each other.
Simplify a quotient	We **simplify** a quotient of two complex numbers by removing i from the denominator of the quotient.
Product of complex conjugates	The product of *any* two complex conjugates is a real number.
Simplifying the quotient of two complex numbers	To simplify the quotient of two complex numbers, we multiply the quotient by $\dfrac{\text{complex conjugate of the denominator}}{\text{complex conjugate of the denominator}}$.
Multiplying by $\dfrac{i}{i}$	When the denominator of a fraction is a pure imaginary number, the easiest way to remove i from the denominator is to multiply the fraction by $\dfrac{i}{i}$.

Homework 11.2

For extra help ▶ **MyMathLab®** ⊞ Watch the videos in MyMathLab   ● Download the MyDashboard App

Perform the indicated operation. If your result is an imaginary number, write it in $a + bi$ form. Use a graphing calculator to verify your work when possible.

1. $(4 - 7i) + (3 + 10i)$
2. $(15 - 2i) + (6 + 17i)$
3. $(5 - \sqrt{-9}) + (2 - \sqrt{-25})$
4. $(7 - \sqrt{-4}) + (9 - \sqrt{-36})$
5. $(6 - 5i) - (2 - 13i)$
6. $(9 - 4i) - (8 - 2i)$
7. $(6 - \sqrt{-49}) - (1 + \sqrt{-81})$
8. $(3 - \sqrt{-1}) - (3 + \sqrt{-64})$
9. $2i \cdot 9i$
10. $4i \cdot 6i$
11. $-10i(-5i)$
12. $-7i(4i)$
13. $\sqrt{-4}\sqrt{-25}$
14. $\sqrt{-49}\sqrt{-16}$
15. $\sqrt{-3}\sqrt{-5}$
16. $\sqrt{-2}\sqrt{-11}$
17. $(8i)^2$
18. $(-4i)^2$
19. $5i(3 - 2i)$
20. $6i(1 + 3i)$
21. $20 - 3i(2 - 7i)$
22. $2 + 4i(3 - 8i)$
23. $(2 + 5i)(3 + 4i)$
24. $(7 + 3i)(10 + 2i)$
25. $(3 - 6i)(5 + 2i)$
26. $(4 - 3i)(2 + 7i)$
27. $(-6 + 4i)(-2 + 7i)$
28. $(-5 + 7i)(-3 + 2i)$
29. $(5 + 4i)(5 - 4i)$
30. $(8 + 3i)(8 - 3i)$
31. $(2 - 9i)(2 + 9i)$
32. $(3 - 7i)(3 + 7i)$
33. $(1 + i)(1 - i)$
34. $(3 + i)(3 - i)$

35. $(2 + 7i)^2$
36. $(6 + 3i)^2$
37. $(4 - 5i)^2$
38. $(7 - 4i)^2$
39. $(-4 + 3i)^2$
40. $(-5 + 2i)^2$

41. $\dfrac{3}{2 + 5i}$
42. $\dfrac{4}{4 + 3i}$
43. $\dfrac{3i}{7 - 2i}$
44. $\dfrac{2i}{3 - 8i}$
45. $\dfrac{2 + 3i}{7 + i}$
46. $\dfrac{5 + 8i}{3 + i}$
47. $\dfrac{3 + 4i}{3 - 4i}$
48. $\dfrac{4 - 7i}{4 + 7i}$
49. $\dfrac{3 - 5i}{2 - 9i}$
50. $\dfrac{4 - 3i}{1 - 5i}$
51. $\dfrac{5 + 7i}{4i}$
52. $\dfrac{2 + 8i}{3i}$
53. $\dfrac{7}{5i}$
54. $\dfrac{3}{2i}$

Concepts

55. Two students try to find the product $\sqrt{-2}\sqrt{-8}$:

Student 1's work	**Student 2's work**
$\sqrt{-2}\sqrt{-8} = \sqrt{-2(-8)}$	$\sqrt{-2}\sqrt{-8} = i\sqrt{2} \cdot i\sqrt{8}$
$= \sqrt{16}$	$= i^2\sqrt{16}$
$= 4$	$= -4$

Did one, both, or neither student find the product correctly? Explain.

56. A student tries to find the product $(3 + i)(3 - i)$:

$$
\begin{aligned}
(3 + i)(3 - i) &= 3^2 - i^2 \\
&= 9 - 1 \\
&= 8
\end{aligned}
$$

Describe any errors. Then find the product correctly.

57. Find nonzero real-number values of a, b, c, and d such that the sum $(a + bi) + (c + di)$
a. is an imaginary number (not pure).
b. is a real number.
c. is a pure imaginary number.

58. Find nonzero real-number values of a, b, c, and d such that the product $(a + bi)(c + di)$
a. is an imaginary number (not pure).
b. is a real number.
c. is a pure imaginary number.

59. If a radicand is a negative number, explain why it is important we first write the radical in terms of i before performing any operations.

60. Give an example of a quadratic equation in which $3i$ and $-3i$ are solutions.

61. The square of a real number is a nonnegative real number. What can you say about the square of a pure imaginary number? Explain.

62. Describe how to multiply two complex numbers. Describe how to simplify the quotient of two complex numbers.

Related Review

Simplify. If your result is an imaginary number, write it in a + bi form.

63. $\dfrac{4}{3 + 2\sqrt{x}}$

64. $\dfrac{7 + 4\sqrt{x}}{2 - 5\sqrt{x}}$

65. $\dfrac{4}{3 + 2i}$

66. $\dfrac{7 + 4i}{2 - 5i}$

Find all complex-number solutions of the equation.

67. $3x^2 - 2x + 3 = 0$

68. $x^2 - 2x + 5 = 0$

69. $5x^2 - 4x = -1$

70. $4x^2 - x = -2$

71. $(p - 3)(2p + 1) = -10$

72. $(b + 1)(b + 2) = b$

73. $x(3x - 2) = 2 + 2(x - 3)$

74. $5 - 2(x - 4) = -2x(x - 2)$

75. $(5w + 3)^2 = -20$

76. $(4m - 7)^2 = -18$

Expressions, Equations, Functions, and Graphs

Perform the indicated instruction. Then use words such as linear, quadratic, cubic, exponential, logarithmic, rational, radical, polynomial, degree, function, imaginary number, one variable, *and* two variables *to describe the expression, equation, or system.*

77. Solve $4x^2 - 2x + 3 = 0$.

78. Simplify $2\sqrt{20x^3} - 3x\sqrt{45x} + 4x\sqrt{24}$.

79. Factor $10x^2 - 19x + 6$.

80. Simplify $\dfrac{2\sqrt{x} - 5}{3\sqrt{x} + 4}$.

81. Find the product $(3i - 7)(4i + 6)$.

82. Solve $4\sqrt{3x - 1} - 3 = 5$.

Section 11.2 Quiz

Perform the indicated operations. If your result is an imaginary number, write it in a + bi form.

1. $(6 - 2i) + (3 - 4i)$

2. $(3 + 7i) - (8 - 2i)$

3. $-4i \cdot 3i$

4. $\sqrt{-2}\sqrt{-7}$

5. $(5 - 3i)(7 + i)$

6. $(4 - 3i)^2$

7. $(8 + 5i)(8 - 5i)$

8. $\dfrac{3 + 2i}{5 - 4i}$

9. $\dfrac{5 - 7i}{6i}$

10. True or false? A complex number times a pure imaginary number must be an imaginary number. Explain.

▼ 11.3 Pythagorean Theorem, Distance Formula, and Circles

Objectives

» Use the Pythagorean theorem to find the length of a side of a right triangle.

» Use the Pythagorean theorem to make estimates about authentic situations.

» Use the distance formula to find the distance between two points.

» Find or graph the equation of a circle.

In this section, we will discuss a special type of triangle called a *right triangle* and a useful formula relating to right triangles: the Pythagorean theorem. We will also find the distance between two points. Finally, we will find and graph equations of circles.

Pythagorean Theorem

We begin by working with an important type of triangle called a *right triangle*. An angle of 90° is called a *right angle*. If one angle of a triangle measures 90°, the triangle is a **right triangle** (see Fig. 18). The side opposite the right angle is the triangle's longest side. We call that side the **hypotenuse,** and we call the two shorter sides the **legs.**

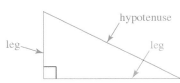

Figure 18 A right triangle

The **Pythagorean theorem** describes the relationship between the lengths of the legs and the length of the hypotenuse of a right triangle.

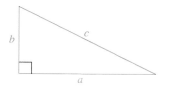

Figure 19 The Pythagorean theorem: $a^2 + b^2 = c^2$

> **Pythagorean Theorem**
>
> If a and b are the lengths of the legs of a right triangle and c is the length of the hypotenuse, then
>
> $$a^2 + b^2 = c^2$$
>
> In words, the sum of the squares of the lengths of the legs is equal to the square of the length of the hypotenuse (see Fig. 19).

If we know the lengths of two of the three sides of a right triangle, how can we use the Pythagorean theorem to find the length of the third side?

▶ **Example 1**   Finding the Length of a Side of a Right Triangle

The lengths of two sides of a right triangle are given. Find the length of the third side.

1.

6
8

2.

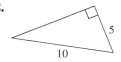

5
10

Solution

1. Since the lengths of the legs are given, we are to find the length of the hypotenuse. We substitute $a = 6$ and $b = 8$ into the equation $c^2 = a^2 + b^2$ and solve for c:

$$c^2 = 6^2 + 8^2 \quad \text{\textit{Substitute 6 for a and 8 for b.}}$$
$$c^2 = 36 + 64 \quad \text{\textit{Simplify.}}$$
$$c^2 = 100$$
$$c = 10 \qquad \text{\textit{c is nonnegative.}}$$

The length of the hypotenuse is 10 units.

2. The length of the hypotenuse is 10 units, and the length of one of the legs is 5 units. We substitute $a = 5$ and $c = 10$ into the equation $a^2 + b^2 = c^2$ and solve for b:

$$5^2 + b^2 = 10^2 \quad \text{\textit{Substitute 5 for a and 10 for c.}}$$
$$25 + b^2 = 100 \quad \text{\textit{Simplify.}}$$
$$b^2 = 75 \quad \text{\textit{Subtract 25 from both sides.}}$$
$$b = \sqrt{75} \quad \text{\textit{b is nonnegative.}}$$
$$b = 5\sqrt{3} \quad \text{\textit{$\sqrt{75} = \sqrt{25 \cdot 3} = 5\sqrt{3}$}}$$

The length of the other leg is $5\sqrt{3}$ units (about 8.66 units).

Using the Pythagorean Theorem to Make Estimates about Authentic Situations

The Pythagorean theorem is used in numerous fields, including architecture, physics, engineering, graphic design, mathematics, surveying, chemistry, and aeronautics.

▶ **Example 2**   Using the Pythagorean Theorem to Find a Distance

A surveyor wants to estimate the distance (in miles) across a lake from point A to point B as shown in Fig. 20. Find that distance.

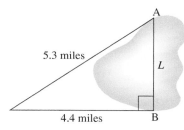

5.3 miles
4.4 miles
A
L
B

Figure 20 Surveying a lake

Solution

We define L to be the distance (in miles) between points A and B (see Fig. 20). The triangle is a right triangle in which the hypotenuse has length 5.3 miles and one of its legs has length 4.4 miles. We use the Pythagorean theorem to find L:

$$4.4^2 + L^2 = 5.3^2 \qquad \textit{Pythagorean theorem}$$
$$19.36 + L^2 = 28.09 \qquad \textit{Find the squares.}$$
$$L^2 = 8.73 \qquad \textit{Subtract 19.36 from both sides.}$$
$$L = \sqrt{8.73} \qquad \textit{L is nonnegative.}$$
$$L \approx 3.0 \qquad \textit{Compute.}$$

So, the distance across the lake between points A and B is approximately 3.0 miles.

Distance Between Two Points

We can use the Pythagorean theorem to find a formula for the distance between two points in a coordinate system. Let (x_1, y_1) and (x_2, y_2) represent two points, where $x_2 > x_1$ and $y_2 > y_1$ (see Fig. 21). We let d be the distance between the two points.

Notice that the triangle shown in Fig. 21 is a right triangle with hypotenuse of length d and legs of lengths $x_2 - x_1$ and $y_2 - y_1$. We apply the Pythagorean theorem:

$$d^2 = (x_2 - x_1)^2 + (y_2 - y_1)^2$$
$$d = \sqrt{(x_2 - x_1)^2 + (y_2 - y_1)^2} \qquad \textit{d is nonnegative.}$$

Although we assumed $x_2 > x_1$ and $y_2 > y_1$ to find the *distance formula*, it can be shown that the formula gives the correct distance between *any* two points.

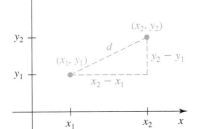

Figure 21 Find the distance between points (x_1, y_1) and (x_2, y_2)

▶ **Distance Formula**

The distance d between points (x_1, y_1) and (x_2, y_2) is given by the **distance formula:**

$$d = \sqrt{(x_2 - x_1)^2 + (y_2 - y_1)^2}$$

▶ **Example 3**   Finding the Distance Between Two Points

Find the distance between $(-2, 5)$ and $(3, -1)$.

Solution

We substitute $x_1 = -2, y_1 = 5, x_2 = 3$, and $y_2 = -1$ into the distance formula:

$$d = \sqrt{(3 - (-2))^2 + (-1 - 5)^2} \qquad \textit{Substitute into distance formula.}$$
$$= \sqrt{5^2 + (-6)^2} \qquad \textit{Subtract.}$$
$$= \sqrt{61} \qquad \textit{Simplify.}$$

The distance between $(-2, 5)$ and $(3, -1)$ is $\sqrt{61}$ units (about 7.81 units).

Equation of a Circle

We can use the distance formula to find an equation whose graph is a circle. To see how, we first state the definition of a circle in terms of its *center* and *radius*.

Figure 22 Circle with center C and radius r

▶ **Definition   Circle**

A **circle** with **center** point C and **radius** r, where $r > 0$, is the set of all points in a plane that are r units from point C in that plane (see Fig. 22).

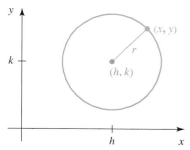

Figure 23 Circle with center (h, k) and radius r

Now we find an equation of a circle with center (h, k) and radius r (see Fig. 23). If (x, y) is a point on the circle, then the distance between (x, y) and (h, k) is the radius r:

$$\sqrt{(x - h)^2 + (y - k)^2} = r \quad \textit{Distance formula}$$

Squaring both sides of the equation gives

$$(x - h)^2 + (y - k)^2 = r^2$$

▶ **Equation of a Circle**

If a circle has center (h, k) and radius r, then an equation of the circle is

$$(x - h)^2 + (y - k)^2 = r^2$$

The graph of an equation of this form with $r > 0$ is a circle with center (h, k) and radius r.

▶ **Example 4** Finding an Equation of a Circle

Find an equation of the circle with the given center and radius.

1. Center $(0, 0)$, radius 3   **2.** Center $(2, -5)$, radius $\sqrt{13}$

Solution

1. We substitute $h = 0, k = 0$, and $r = 3$ in $(x - h)^2 + (y - k)^2 = r^2$:

$$(x - 0)^2 + (y - 0)^2 = 3^2 \quad \textit{Substitute 0 for h, 0 for k, and 3 for r.}$$
$$x^2 + y^2 = 9 \quad \textit{Simplify.}$$

2. We substitute $h = 2, k = -5$, and $r = \sqrt{13}$ in $(x - h)^2 + (y - k)^2 = r^2$:

$$(x - 2)^2 + (y - (-5))^2 = (\sqrt{13})^2 \quad \textit{Substitute 2 for h, -5 for k, and $\sqrt{13}$ for r.}$$
$$(x - 2)^2 + (y + 5)^2 = 13 \quad \textit{Simplify.}$$

The equation of a circle centered at the origin $(0, 0)$ with radius r is

$$(x - 0)^2 + (y - 0)^2 = r^2$$
$$x^2 + y^2 = r^2$$

▶ **Equation of a Circle Centered at the Origin**

If a circle has center $(0, 0)$ and radius r, then an equation of the circle is

$$x^2 + y^2 = r^2$$

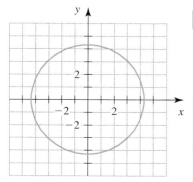

Figure 24 Graph of $x^2 + y^2 = 19$

▶ **Example 5** Finding the Center and Radius of a Circle

Determine the center and radius of the circle. Also, sketch the circle.

1. $x^2 + y^2 = 19$ **2.** $(x + 5)^2 + (y - 3)^2 = 4$

Solution

1. The equation has the form $x^2 + y^2 = r^2$. Thus, the circle is centered at the origin $(0, 0)$, and we have

$$r^2 = 19$$
$$r = \sqrt{19} \quad \textit{r is positive.}$$

So, the radius is $\sqrt{19} \approx 4.36$. We sketch the circle in Fig. 24.

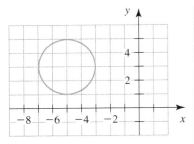

Figure 25 Graph of
$(x + 5)^2 + (y - 3)^2 = 4$

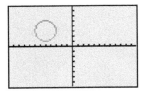

Figure 26 Use ZStandard, then
ZInteger, and then Zoom In

2. We write $(x + 5)^2 + (y - 3)^2 = 4$ in the form $(x - h)^2 + (y - k)^2 = r^2$:

$$(x - (-5))^2 + (y - 3)^2 = 2^2$$

Here $h = -5, k = 3$, and $r = 2$. So, the circle has center $(-5, 3)$ and radius 2. We sketch the circle in Fig. 25.

To use a graphing calculator to draw the circle $(x + 5)^2 + (y - 3)^2 = 4$, we first isolate y:

$(x + 5)^2 + (y - 3)^2 = 4$	*Original equation*
$(y - 3)^2 = 4 - (x + 5)^2$	*Subtract $(x + 5)^2$ from both sides.*
$y - 3 = \pm\sqrt{4 - (x + 5)^2}$	*Square root property*
$y = 3 \pm \sqrt{4 - (x + 5)^2}$	*Add 3 to both sides.*

Then we enter $y = 3 - \sqrt{4 - (x + 5)^2}$ and $y = 3 + \sqrt{4 - (x + 5)^2}$ and draw the graphs of both functions on the same coordinate system (see Fig. 26).

Group Exploration

Pythagorean theorem and its converse

For this exploration, you will need a ruler, scissors, and paper. It will help to have a tool for drawing right angles, such as a protractor or graph paper, although a corner of a piece of paper will suffice. For each triangle, assume c is the length of (one of) the *longest* side(s) and a and b are the lengths of the other sides.

1. Sketch three right triangles of different sizes. Measure the sides and show that, for each right triangle, $a^2 + b^2 = c^2$.

2. Now sketch three triangles of different sizes that are *not* right triangles. For these triangles, check whether $a^2 + b^2 = c^2$.

3. Sketch a triangle that has an angle close, but not equal, to $90°$. Check whether $a^2 + b^2 \approx c^2$. If you cannot

show this for your triangle, repeat the problem with a triangle that has an angle even closer to $90°$.

4. If $a = 3, b = 5$, and $c = \sqrt{34}$, then $a^2 + b^2 = c^2$. Cut three thin strips of paper that are about 3, 5, and $\sqrt{34}$ inches in length. Form a triangle with the three strips of paper. Is the triangle a right triangle?

5. Find values of a, b, and c, other than the ones in Problem 4, such that $a^2 + b^2 = c^2$. Then repeat Problem 4 with your values.

6. Find three more values of a, b, and c such that $a^2 + b^2 = c^2$. Then repeat Problem 4 with your values.

7. Summarize at least three concepts addressed in this exploration.

Key Points of Section 11.3

Pythagorean theorem	If a and b are the lengths of the legs of a right triangle and c is the length of the hypotenuse, then $a^2 + b^2 = c^2$.
Distance formula	The distance d between points (x_1, y_1) and (x_2, y_2) is given by the **distance formula:** $d = \sqrt{(x_2 - x_1)^2 + (y_2 - y_1)^2}.$
Definition of a circle	A **circle** with **center** point C and **radius** r, where $r > 0$, is the set of all points in a plane that are r units from point C in that plane.
Equation of a circle	If a circle has center (h, k) and radius r, then an equation of the circle is $$(x - h)^2 + (y - k)^2 = r^2$$ The graph of an equation of this form with $r > 0$ is a circle with center (h, k) and radius r.
Equation of a circle centered at the origin	If a circle has center $(0, 0)$ and radius r, then an equation of the circle is $x^2 + y^2 = r^2$.

Homework 11.3

Let a and b be the lengths of the legs of a right triangle, and let c be the length of the hypotenuse. Values of two of the three lengths are given. Find the third length.

1. $a = 5$ and $b = 12$ **2.** $a = 9$ and $b = 12$

3. $a = 4$ and $b = 5$ **4.** $a = 2$ and $b = 7$

5. $a = 3$ and $c = 8$ **6.** $a = 2$ and $c = 9$

7. $b = 5$ and $c = 7$ **8.** $b = 4$ and $c = 10$

9. $a = \sqrt{2}$ and $b = \sqrt{5}$ **10.** $a = \sqrt{3}$ and $b = \sqrt{11}$

For Exercises 11–14, the lengths of two sides of a right triangle are given. Find the length of the third side.

11. See Fig. 27.   **12.** See Fig. 28.

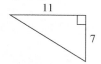

Figure 27 Exercise 11

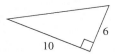

Figure 28 Exercise 12

13. See Fig. 29.   **14.** See Fig. 30.

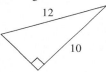

Figure 29 Exercise 13

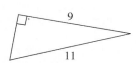

Figure 30 Exercise 14

15. The bottom of a ladder is 5 feet from the base of the building against which the ladder leans. How long must the ladder be so that its top will reach a window that is 20 feet above the ground?

16. The bottom of a ladder is 4 feet from the base of the building against which the ladder leans. How long must the ladder be so that its top will reach a window that is 13 feet above the ground?

17. The size of a rectangular television screen is usually described as the length of a diagonal. If a 20-inch screen has a height of 13 inches, what is the screen's width?

18. The size of a rectangular television screen is usually described as the length of a diagonal. If a 25-inch screen has a height of 14 inches, what is the screen's width?

19. A surveyor wants to estimate the distance (in miles) across a lake from point A to point B as shown in Fig. 31. Find that distance.

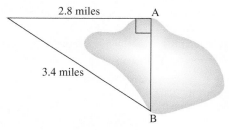

Figure 31 Exercise 19

20. A surveyor wants to estimate the distance (in miles) across a lake from point A to point B as shown in Fig. 32. Find that distance.

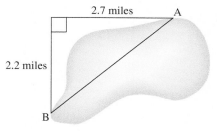

Figure 32 Exercise 20

21. Los Angeles is about 465 miles almost directly south of Reno, Nevada, and is almost directly west of Albuquerque, New Mexico. The distance between Albuquerque and Reno is about 964 miles. What would be the total distance of a trip from Los Angeles to Reno to Albuquerque to Los Angeles?

22. Salt Lake City, Utah, is about 498 miles almost directly south of Helena, Montana, and is almost directly west of Omaha, Nebraska. The distance between Omaha and Helena is about 1144 miles. What would be the total distance of a trip from Salt Lake City to Omaha to Helena to Salt Lake City?

Find the distance between the two given points.

23. $(2, 9)$ and $(8, 1)$ **24.** $(3, 2)$ and $(7, 5)$

25. $(-3, 5)$ and $(4, 2)$ **26.** $(-3, 4)$ and $(2, 7)$

27. $(-6, -3)$ and $(-4, 1)$ **28.** $(-7, 2)$ and $(-5, -6)$

29. $(-4, -5)$ and $(-8, -9)$ **30.** $(-5, -4)$ and $(-2, -7)$

Find the distance between the two given points. Round your result to the second decimal place.

31. $(2.1, 8.9)$ and $(5.6, 1.7)$

32. $(3.2, 7.1)$ and $(6.6, 8.4)$

33. $(-2.18, -5.74)$ and $(3.44, 6.29)$

34. $(-6.41, 1.12)$ and $(2.89, -3.55)$

Find an equation of the circle with the given center and radius.

35. Center $(0, 0)$, radius 7

36. Center $(0, 0)$, radius 10

37. Center $(0, 0)$, radius 6.7

38. Center $(0, 0)$, radius 2.3

39. Center $(5, 3)$, radius 2

40. Center $(4, 7)$, radius 5

41. Center $(-2, 1)$, radius 4

42. Center $(3, -4)$, radius 6

43. Center $(-7, -3)$, radius $\sqrt{3}$

44. Center $(-6, -1)$, radius $\sqrt{2}$

Find the center and radius of the circle. Graph the equation by hand.

45. $x^2 + y^2 = 25$ **46.** $x^2 + y^2 = 9$

47. $x^2 + y^2 = 8$ **48.** $x^2 + y^2 = 17$

49. $(x - 3)^2 + (y - 5)^2 = 16$ **50.** $(x - 2)^2 + (y - 4)^2 = 4$

51. $(x + 6)^2 + (y - 1)^2 = 7$ **52.** $(x - 5)^2 + (y + 2)^2 = 3$

53. $(x + 3)^2 + (y + 2)^2 = 1$ **54.** $(x + 1)^2 + (y + 1)^2 = 1$

55. Find an equation of the circle shown in Fig. 33.

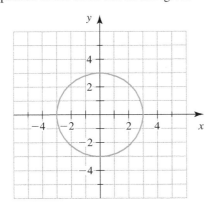

Figure 33 Exercise 55

56. Find an equation of the circle shown in Fig. 34.

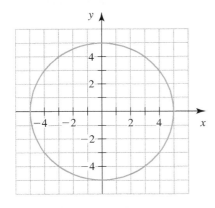

Figure 34 Exercise 56

57. Find an equation of the circle shown in Fig. 35.

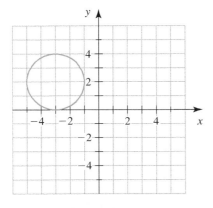

Figure 35 Exercise 57

58. Find an equation of the circle shown in Fig. 36.

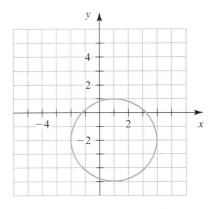

Figure 36 Exercise 58

Concepts

59. A circle with center $(3, 2)$ contains the point $(5, 6)$. Find an equation of the circle.

60. A circle with center $(-4, 3)$ contains the point $(2, -1)$. Find an equation of the circle.

61. Find equations of two distinct circles that contain the point $(5, 3)$. Sketch the two circles by hand in the same coordinate system.

62. Show with a sketch that there are many circles that contain the points $(2, 1)$ and $(4, 6)$. Which of these circles has the smallest radius? What is an equation of this circle?

63. The Rule of Four can be applied to relations as well as functions. So, we can describe some or all of the input–output pairs of a relation by means of an equation, a graph, a table, or words.
 a. Describe the input–output pairs of $x^2 + y^2 = 16$ by using a graph.
 b. Describe eight input–output pairs of $x^2 + y^2 = 16$ by using a table. Round approximate inputs and outputs to the second decimal place.
 c. Describe the input–output pairs of $x^2 + y^2 = 16$ by using words.

64. The Rule of Four can be applied to relations as well as functions. So, we can describe some or all of the input–output pairs of a relation by means of an equation, a graph, a table, or words.
 a. Describe the input–output pairs of $(x + 1)^2 + (y - 3)^2 = 9$ by using a graph.
 b. Describe eight input–output pairs of $(x + 1)^2 + (y - 3)^2 = 9$ by using a table. Round approximate inputs and outputs to the second decimal place.
 c. Describe the input–output pairs of $(x + 1)^2 + (y - 3)^2 = 9$ by using words.

65. Give the coordinates of five points that are a distance of 4 units from the point $(3, 2)$.

66. Give the coordinates of five points that are a distance of 1 unit from the point $(-4, 1)$.

67. Is the relation $x^2 + y^2 = 49$ a function? Explain.

68. Is the relation $(x - 4)^2 + (y + 2)^2 = 16$ a function? Explain.

69. a. For $y = \sqrt{25 - x^2}$, explain why $y \geq 0$ for real-number values of y.
 b. Graph the function $y = \sqrt{25 - x^2}$ by hand. [**Hint:** Square both sides of the equation.] Use a graphing calculator to verify your graph.

70. a. For $y = \sqrt{9 - (x - 5)^2}$, explain why $y \geq 0$ for real-number values of y.

b. Graph the function $y = \sqrt{9 - (x - 5)^2}$ by hand. [**Hint:** Square both sides of the equation.] Use a graphing calculator to verify your graph.

71. If the lengths of the legs of a right triangle are equal, we call the triangle an *isosceles right triangle*.

a. Sketch an example of an isosceles right triangle.

b. Show that the length of the hypotenuse of an isosceles right triangle is $\sqrt{2}$ times the length of either leg of the triangle. [**Hint:** Let $a = k$ and $b = k$, and apply the Pythagorean theorem.]

c. If the length of a leg of an isosceles right triangle is 3 units, what is the length of the hypotenuse?

d. If the length of the hypotenuse of an isosceles right triangle is 5 units, what is the length of each leg?

72. Explain how to graph by hand an equation of the form $(x - h)^2 + (y - k)^2 = r$, where $r > 0$.

Related Review

Sketch the graph.

73. $x + y = 4$ **74.** $x^2 + y = 4$ **75.** $x^2 + y^2 = 4$

76. $x^{1/2} + y = 4$ **77.** $2^x + y = 0$ **78.** $\left(\dfrac{1}{2}\right)^x + y = 0$

Expressions, Equations, Functions, and Graphs

Perform the indicated instruction. Then use words such as linear, quadratic, cubic, exponential, logarithmic, rational, radical, polynomial, degree, function, one variable, *and* two variables *to describe the expression, equation, or system.*

79. Graph $f(x) = 2(x - 4)^2 - 3$ by hand.

80. Find the domain of $f(x) = \dfrac{x + 7}{27x^3 + 18x^2 - 12x - 8}$.

81. Factor $6x^2 - 16x + 8$.

82. Find the difference $\dfrac{3x + 5}{x^2 + 5x - 14} - \dfrac{2x}{x^2 - 4x - 21}$.

83. Solve $x(5x - 3) = 3(x + 1)$.

84. Solve $\dfrac{x + 5}{x} - \dfrac{2}{3x^2} = 7$.

Section 11.3 Quiz

1. The length of a leg of a right triangle is 4 inches, and the length of the hypotenuse is 8 inches. Find the length of the other leg.

2. The size of a rectangular television screen is usually described as the length of a diagonal. If a 19-inch screen has a width of 16 inches, what is the screen's height?

Find the distance between the two given points.

3. $(-2, -5)$ and $(3, -1)$ **4.** $(-3, 2)$ and $(-7, -2)$

Find an equation of the circle with the given center and radius.

5. Center $(-3, 2)$, radius 6   **6.** Center $(0, 0)$, radius 2.8

Find the center and radius of the circle. Graph the equation by hand.

7. $x^2 + y^2 = 12$ **8.** $(x + 4)^2 + (y - 3)^2 = 25$

9. Find an equation of a circle that has center $(2, -1)$ and contains the point $(4, 7)$.

10. Find equations of two circles that contain the point $(0, 0)$. Sketch the two circles in the same coordinate system.

▼ 11.4 Ellipses and Hyperbolas

Objective

» Graph equations of ellipses and hyperbolas.

In this text, we work with four types of curves that are cross sections of cones: circles, *ellipses*, parabolas, and *hyperbolas* (see Fig. 37).

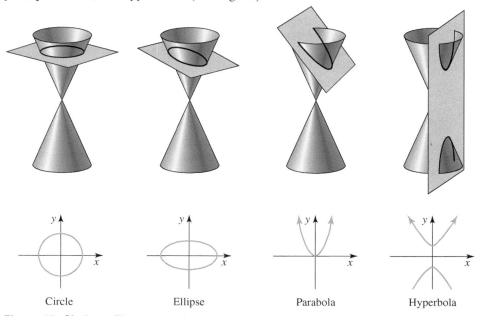

Figure 37 Circles, ellipses, parabolas, and hyperbolas are cross sections of cones

In Chapters 6 and 7, we worked with parabolas. In Section 11.3, we studied circles. In this section, we first discuss ellipses; then we discuss hyperbolas.

Graphing Ellipses

To begin our study of ellipses, we sketch a graph of

$$\frac{x^2}{25} + \frac{y^2}{9} = 1$$

First, we find the y-intercepts by substituting 0 for x and solving for y:

$$\frac{0^2}{25} + \frac{y^2}{9} = 1 \qquad \text{Substitute 0 for x.}$$

$$\frac{y^2}{9} = 1 \qquad \text{Simplify.}$$

$$y^2 = 9 \qquad \text{Multiply both sides by 9.}$$

$$y = \pm 3 \qquad \text{Square root property}$$

So, the y-intercepts are $(0, -3)$ and $(0, 3)$.

Then we find the x-intercepts by substituting 0 for y and solving for x:

$$\frac{x^2}{25} + \frac{0^2}{9} = 1 \qquad \text{Substitute 0 for y.}$$

$$\frac{x^2}{25} = 1 \qquad \text{Simplify.}$$

$$x^2 = 25 \qquad \text{Multiply both sides by 25.}$$

$$x = \pm 5 \qquad \text{Square root property}$$

So, the x-intercepts are $(-5, 0)$ and $(5, 0)$.

All of the points on the graph of the relation have x-coordinates between -5 and 5, inclusive. To see why, we isolate the term $\frac{y^2}{9}$ in the equation $\frac{x^2}{25} + \frac{y^2}{9} = 1$:

$$\frac{y^2}{9} = 1 - \frac{x^2}{25}$$

Table 2 Solutions of

$$\frac{x^2}{25} + \frac{y^2}{9} = 1$$

x	y
−4	±1.8
−3	±2.4
−2	±2.75
−1	±2.94
0	±3
1	±2.94
2	±2.75
3	±2.4
4	±1.8

Note that $\frac{y^2}{9}$ is nonnegative, so

$$1 - \frac{x^2}{25} \geq 0 \qquad 1 - \frac{x^2}{25} \text{ is nonnegative.}$$

$$-\frac{x^2}{25} \geq -1 \qquad \text{Subtract 1 from both sides.}$$

$$x^2 \leq 25 \qquad \text{Multiply both sides by } -25; \text{ reverse inequality symbol.}$$

As we set out to show, $x^2 \leq 25$ implies that x is between -5 and 5, inclusive.

Next, we find points on the graph where x is $-4, -3, -2, \ldots, 4$ (see Table 2) and plot these points as well as the intercepts (see Fig. 38).

Finally, we sketch a curve through the points we've plotted (see Fig. 39). The graph is an ellipse.

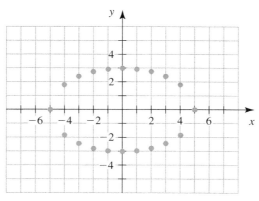

Figure 38 Plot the points

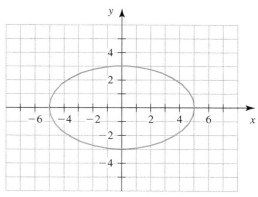

Figure 39 Graph of $\dfrac{x^2}{25} + \dfrac{y^2}{9} = 1$

▶ **Equation of an Ellipse**

An equation that can be put into the form

$$\frac{x^2}{a^2} + \frac{y^2}{b^2} = 1, \qquad \text{where } a > 0 \text{ and } b > 0$$

has an **ellipse** as its graph.

Intercepts of an Ellipse

There is an easier way to sketch the graph of an equation in the form $\dfrac{x^2}{a^2} + \dfrac{y^2}{b^2} = 1,$ where $a > 0$ and $b > 0$. We begin by finding the x-intercepts:

$$\frac{x^2}{a^2} + \frac{0^2}{b^2} = 1 \qquad \textit{Substitute 0 for y.}$$

$$\frac{x^2}{a^2} = 1 \qquad \textit{Simplify.}$$

$$x^2 = a^2 \qquad \textit{Multiply both sides by } a^2.$$

$$x = \pm\sqrt{a^2} \qquad \textit{Square root property}$$

$$x = \pm a \qquad \sqrt{a^2} = a, \textit{where } a \geq 0$$

So, the x-intercepts are $(-a, 0)$ and $(a, 0)$.

The y-intercepts are $(0, -b)$ and $(0, b)$. You will show this in Exercise 59.

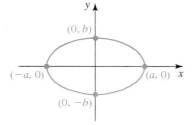

Figure 40 Intercepts of the ellipse $\dfrac{x^2}{a^2} + \dfrac{y^2}{b^2} = 1$

▶ **Intercepts of an Ellipse**

The ellipse described by

$$\frac{x^2}{a^2} + \frac{y^2}{b^2} = 1$$

has x-intercepts $(-a, 0)$ and $(a, 0)$ and y-intercepts $(0, -b)$ and $(0, b)$. See Fig. 40.

▶ **Example 1**   Sketching the Graph of an Ellipse

Sketch the graph of $9x^2 + 4y^2 = 36$.

Solution

First, we divide both sides of the equation $9x^2 + 4y^2 = 36$ by 36 so that the right-hand side of the equation is 1:

$$\frac{9x^2}{36} + \frac{4y^2}{36} = \frac{36}{36} \qquad \textit{Divide both sides by 36.}$$

$$\frac{x^2}{4} + \frac{y^2}{9} = 1 \qquad \textit{Simplify.}$$

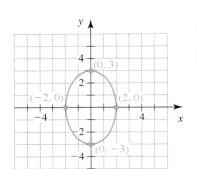

Figure 41 Graph of
$9x^2 + 4y^2 = 36$

The equation is of the form $\frac{x^2}{a^2} + \frac{y^2}{b^2} = 1$, where $a > 0$ and $b > 0$, with $a^2 = 4$ and $b^2 = 9$. Since $a^2 = 4$, we have $a = 2$. So, the x-intercepts are $(-2, 0)$ and $(2, 0)$. Because $b^2 = 9$, we have $b = 3$. So, the y-intercepts are $(0, -3)$ and $(0, 3)$. We plot the intercepts and sketch an ellipse that contains them (see Fig. 41).

To use a graphing calculator to draw the ellipse $9x^2 + 4y^2 = 36$, we begin by isolating y:

$$9x^2 + 4y^2 = 36 \qquad \textit{Original equation}$$

$$4y^2 = 36 - 9x^2 \qquad \textit{Subtract } 9x^2 \textit{ from both sides.}$$

$$y^2 = \frac{36 - 9x^2}{4} \qquad \textit{Divide both sides by 4.}$$

$$y = \pm\sqrt{\frac{36 - 9x^2}{4}} \qquad \textit{Square root property}$$

$$y = \pm\sqrt{\frac{9(4 - x^2)}{4}} \qquad \textit{Factor.}$$

$$y = \pm\frac{3}{2}\sqrt{4 - x^2} \qquad \textit{Simplify.}$$

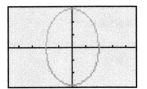

Figure 42 Graph of
$9x^2 + 4y^2 = 36$, using
ZDecimal

Then we enter the functions $y = \frac{3}{2}\sqrt{4 - x^2}$ and $y = -\frac{3}{2}\sqrt{4 - x^2}$ (or $Y_2 = -Y_1$) and graph both functions in the same coordinate system (see Fig. 42).

▶

Graphing Hyperbolas

We now turn our attention to sketching graphs of hyperbolas. The general equation of a hyperbola is similar to the general equation of an ellipse, except that the left side of the equation is a difference rather than a sum.

▶ **Equations of a Hyperbola**

An equation that can be put into one of the following forms has a **hyperbola** as its graph:

• An equation that can be put into the form

$$\frac{x^2}{a^2} - \frac{y^2}{b^2} = 1, \qquad \text{where } a > 0 \text{ and } b > 0$$

is a hyperbola with x-intercepts $(-a, 0)$ and $(a, 0)$. See Fig. 43. There are no y-intercepts.

• An equation that can be put into the form

$$\frac{y^2}{b^2} - \frac{x^2}{a^2} = 1, \qquad \text{where } a > 0 \text{ and } b > 0$$

is a hyperbola with y-intercepts $(0, -b)$ and $(0, b)$. See Fig. 44. There are no x-intercepts.

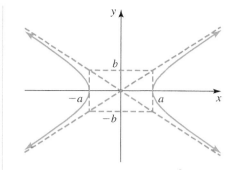

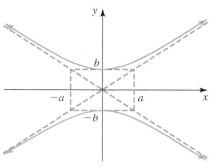

Figure 43 Graph of $\dfrac{x^2}{a^2} - \dfrac{y^2}{b^2} = 1$

Figure 44 Graph of $\dfrac{y^2}{b^2} - \dfrac{x^2}{a^2} = 1$

Each *pair* of curves in Figs. 43 and 44 is a hyperbola. Each curve is a *branch*. The red dashes are *not* parts of the hyperbola; they are simply tools to guide us in sketching the branches. The dashed rectangles are centered at the origin and stretch *a* units in both directions horizontally and *b* units in both directions vertically. Through their opposite corners, we draw the dashed lines that are *inclined asymptotes*. The branches of the hyperbolas approach the inclined asymptotes as $|x|$ gets large.

▶ **Graphing Hyperbolas**

To sketch a hyperbola on the basis of its equation,

1. Sketch a dashed rectangle whose sides are parallel to the axes and contain the points $(-a, 0), (a, 0), (0, -b),$ and $(0, b)$.
2. Sketch two dashed lines (the inclined asymptotes) that contain the diagonals of the rectangle.
3. Plot the intercepts of the hyperbola.
4. Sketch the branches to contain the intercepts and get closer to the asymptotes as $|x|$ gets large.

▶ **Example 2**   Sketching the Graph of a Hyperbola

Sketch the graph of $\dfrac{y^2}{4} - \dfrac{x^2}{9} = 1$.

Solution

Since the equation is of the form $\dfrac{y^2}{b^2} - \dfrac{x^2}{a^2} = 1$, where $a > 0$ and $b > 0$, we have $a^2 = 9$ and $b^2 = 4$. So, $a = 3$ and $b = 2$. We sketch a dashed rectangle that contains the points $(-3, 0), (3, 0), (0, -2),$ and $(0, 2)$; then we sketch the inclined asymptotes (see Fig. 45).

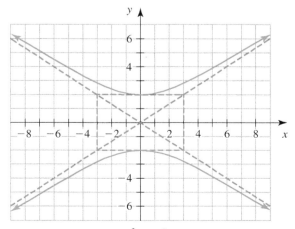

Figure 45 Graph of $\dfrac{y^2}{4} - \dfrac{x^2}{9} = 1$

Since the equation is of the form $\dfrac{y^2}{b^2} - \dfrac{x^2}{a^2} = 1$ (with $\dfrac{y^2}{b^2}$ first), the graph has y-intercepts at $(0, -2)$ and $(0, 2)$ and there are no x-intercepts. The branches contain the y-intercepts and approach the inclined asymptotes for large $|x|$.

▶ **Example 3**   Sketching the Graph of a Hyperbola

Sketch the graph of $4x^2 - 25y^2 = 100$.

Solution

We divide both sides of the equation by 100 so the right-hand side of the equation is equal to 1:

$$4x^2 - 25y^2 = 100 \qquad \textit{Original equation}$$

$$\frac{4x^2}{100} - \frac{25y^2}{100} = \frac{100}{100} \qquad \textit{Divide both sides by 100.}$$

$$\frac{x^2}{25} - \frac{y^2}{4} = 1 \qquad \textit{Simplify.}$$

The equation is of the form $\dfrac{x^2}{a^2} - \dfrac{y^2}{b^2} = 1$, where $a > 0, b > 0, a^2 = 25$, and $b^2 = 4$. So, $a = 5$ and $b = 2$. We sketch the dashed rectangle that contains $(-5, 0)$, $(5, 0)$, $(0, -2)$, and $(0, 2)$ and then sketch the inclined asymptotes (see Fig. 46).

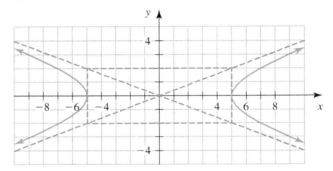

Figure 46 Graph of $4x^2 - 25y^2 = 100$

Since the equation is in $\dfrac{x^2}{a^2} - \dfrac{y^2}{b^2} = 1$ form (with $\dfrac{x^2}{a^2}$ first), the graph has x-intercepts at $(-5, 0)$ and $(5, 0)$ and there are no y-intercepts. The branches contain the intercepts and approach the inclined asymptotes for large $|x|$.

To use a graphing calculator to draw a graph of $4x^2 - 25y^2 = 100$, we begin by isolating y:

$$4x^2 - 25y^2 = 100 \qquad \textit{Original equation}$$

$$4x^2 - 100 = 25y^2 \qquad \textit{Isolate } 25y^2.$$

$$\frac{4x^2 - 100}{25} = y^2 \qquad \textit{Divide both sides by 25.}$$

$$y = \pm \sqrt{\frac{4x^2 - 100}{25}} \qquad \textit{Square root property}$$

$$y = \pm \sqrt{\frac{4\left(x^2 - 25\right)}{25}} \qquad \textit{Factor.}$$

$$y = \pm \frac{2}{5}\sqrt{x^2 - 25} \qquad \textit{Simplify.}$$

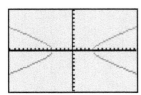

Figure 47 Use ZStandard followed by ZSquare to graph $4x^2 - 25y^2 = 100$

Then we enter the functions $y = \dfrac{2}{5}\sqrt{x^2 - 25}$ and $y = -\dfrac{2}{5}\sqrt{x^2 - 25}$ (or $Y_2 = -Y_1$) and draw the graphs in the same coordinate system (see Fig. 47).

▶

 Group Exploration

Graphical significance of *a* and *b* for ellipses and hyperbolas

1. Sketch two ellipses that
   a. intersect in four points.
   b. intersect in two points.
   c. intersect in no points.

2. Write and graph equations to correspond to each of your sketches in Problem 1.

3. Sketch an ellipse and a hyperbola that
   a. intersect in four points.
   b. intersect in two points.
   c. intersect in no points.

4. Write and graph equations to correspond to each of your sketches in Problem 3.

5. Sketch two hyperbolas that
   a. intersect in four points.
   b. intersect in two points.
   c. have no intersection points.

6. Write and graph equations to correspond to each of your sketches in Problem 5.

Key Points of Section 11.4

Throughout these Key Points, assume *a* and *b* are positive.

Equation of an ellipse An equation that can be put into the form $\dfrac{x^2}{a^2} + \dfrac{y^2}{b^2} = 1$ has an **ellipse** as its graph.

Intercepts of an ellipse The ellipse described by $\dfrac{x^2}{a^2} + \dfrac{y^2}{b^2} = 1$ has *x*-intercepts $(-a, 0)$ and $(a, 0)$ and *y*-intercepts $(0, -b)$ and $(0, b)$.

Equations of a hyperbola An equation that can be put into one of the following forms has a **hyperbola** as its graph:

- An equation that can be put into the form $\dfrac{x^2}{a^2} - \dfrac{y^2}{b^2} = 1$ is a hyperbola with *x*-intercepts $(-a, 0)$ and $(a, 0)$. There are no *y*-intercepts.

- An equation that can be put into the form $\dfrac{y^2}{b^2} - \dfrac{x^2}{a^2} = 1$ is a hyperbola with *y*-intercepts $(0, -b)$ and $(0, b)$. There are no *x*-intercepts.

Graphing hyperbolas To sketch a hyperbola on the basis of its equation,

1. Sketch a dashed rectangle whose sides are parallel to the axes and contain the points $(-a, 0), (a, 0), (0, -b)$, and $(0, b)$.

2. Sketch two dashed lines (the inclined asymptotes) that contain the diagonals of the rectangle.

3. Plot the intercepts of the hyperbola.

4. Sketch the branches to contain the intercepts and get closer to the asymptotes as $|x|$ gets large.

 Homework 11.4

For extra help ▶ **MyMathLab®**   Watch the videos in MyMathLab Download the MyDashboard App

For Exercises 1–16, graph the equation by hand.

1. $\dfrac{x^2}{36} + \dfrac{y^2}{9} = 1$ 2. $\dfrac{x^2}{49} + \dfrac{y^2}{16} = 1$ 3. $\dfrac{x^2}{4} + \dfrac{y^2}{36} = 1$

4. $\dfrac{x^2}{9} + \dfrac{y^2}{64} = 1$ 5. $\dfrac{x^2}{100} + \dfrac{y^2}{16} = 1$ 6. $\dfrac{x^2}{81} + \dfrac{y^2}{25} = 1$

7. $25x^2 + 4y^2 = 100$ 8. $4x^2 + 16y^2 = 64$

9. $9x^2 + 100y^2 = 900$ 10. $16x^2 + 25y^2 = 400$

11. $x^2 + y^2 = 36$ 12. $2x^2 + 2y^2 = 50$

13. $x^2 + 25y^2 = 25$ 14. $64x^2 + y^2 = 64$

15. $5x^2 + 16y^2 = 80$ 16. $22x^2 + 4y^2 = 88$

17. Find an equation of the ellipse shown in Fig. 48.

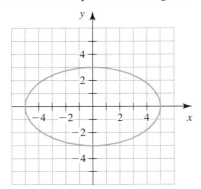

Figure 48 Exercise 17

18. Find an equation of the ellipse shown in Fig. 49.

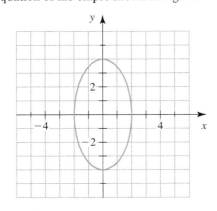

Figure 49 Exercise 18

Graph the equation by hand.

19. $\dfrac{x^2}{16} - \dfrac{y^2}{4} = 1$ **20.** $\dfrac{y^2}{25} - \dfrac{x^2}{9} = 1$

21. $\dfrac{y^2}{16} - \dfrac{x^2}{25} = 1$ **22.** $\dfrac{x^2}{49} - \dfrac{y^2}{16} = 1$

23. $\dfrac{x^2}{25} - \dfrac{y^2}{81} = 1$ **24.** $\dfrac{x^2}{64} - \dfrac{y^2}{9} = 1$

25. $16x^2 - 4y^2 = 64$ **26.** $25x^2 - 16y^2 = 400$

27. $x^2 - 9y^2 = 9$ **28.** $y^2 - 4x^2 = 4$

29. $y^2 - x^2 = 4$ **30.** $4x^2 - 4y^2 = 36$

31. $16y^2 - x^2 = 16$ **32.** $25x^2 - y^2 = 25$

33. $25x^2 - 7y^2 = 175$ **34.** $30x^2 - 9y^2 = 270$

For Exercises 35–52, graph the equation by hand.

35. $\dfrac{x^2}{64} + \dfrac{y^2}{4} = 1$ **36.** $\dfrac{x^2}{49} + \dfrac{y^2}{100} = 1$

37. $x^2 - y^2 = 1$ **38.** $x^2 - y^2 = 9$

39. $81x^2 + 49y^2 = 3969$ **40.** $4x^2 + 36y^2 = 144$

41. $x^2 + y^2 = 1$ **42.** $x^2 + y^2 = 49$

43. $9y^2 - 4x^2 = 144$ **44.** $4x^2 - 25y^2 = 100$

45. $\dfrac{x^2}{25} - \dfrac{y^2}{25} = 1$ **46.** $\dfrac{x^2}{9} - \dfrac{y^2}{25} = 1$

47. $x^2 + y^2 = 16$ **48.** $5x^2 + 5y^2 = 45$

49. $9x^2 + 16y^2 = 144$ **50.** $4x^2 + 9y^2 = 36$

51. $\dfrac{x^2}{16} + \dfrac{y^2}{16} = 1$ **52.** $\dfrac{x^2}{36} + \dfrac{y^2}{36} = 1$

Concepts

53. a. Graph the equation $\dfrac{x^2}{c} + \dfrac{y^2}{d} = 1$ by hand for the given values of the constants c and d.
  i. $c = 4$ and $d = 16$.   **ii.** $c = 4$ and $d = -16$.
  iii. $c = -4$ and $d = 16$.   **iv.** $c = 4$ and $d = 4$.
  b. In terms of the values of c and d, discuss whether the graph of the equation $\dfrac{x^2}{c} + \dfrac{y^2}{d} = 1$ is a circle, an ellipse, a hyperbola with x-intercepts, or a hyperbola with y-intercepts.

54. Graph by hand the following equations in the same coordinate system.
  a. $\dfrac{x^2}{36} + \dfrac{y^2}{9} = 1$ **b.** $\dfrac{x^2}{36} - \dfrac{y^2}{9} = 1$ **c.** $\dfrac{y^2}{9} - \dfrac{x^2}{36} = 1$

55. The Rule of Four can be applied to relations as well as functions. So, we can describe some or all of the input–output pairs of a relation by means of an equation, a graph, a table, or words.
  a. Describe the input–output pairs of $4x^2 + 25y^2 = 100$ by using a graph.
  b. Describe eight input–output pairs of $4x^2 + 25y^2 = 100$ by using a table. Round approximate inputs and outputs to the second decimal place.
  c. Describe the input–output pairs of $4x^2 + 25y^2 = 100$ by using words.

56. The Rule of Four can be applied to relations as well as functions. So, we can describe some or all of the input–output pairs of a relation by means of an equation, a graph, a table, or words.
  a. Describe the input–output pairs of $x^2 - 4y^2 = 4$ by using a graph.
  b. Describe six input–output pairs of $x^2 - 4y^2 = 4$ by using a table. Round approximate inputs and outputs to the second decimal place.
  c. Describe the input–output pairs of $x^2 - 4y^2 = 4$ by using words.

57. a. For $y = \dfrac{5}{2}\sqrt{4 - x^2}$, explain why $y \geq 0$ for real-number values of y.
  b. Graph the function $y = \dfrac{5}{2}\sqrt{4 - x^2}$ by hand. [**Hint:** Square both sides of the equation.] Use a graphing calculator to verify your graph.

58. a. For $y = \dfrac{2}{3}\sqrt{x^2 - 9}$, explain why $y \geq 0$ for real-number values of y.
  b. Graph the function $y = \dfrac{2}{3}\sqrt{x^2 - 9}$ by hand. Use a graphing calculator to verify your graph. [**Hint:** Square both sides of the equation.]

59. Show that the y-intercepts of the graph of $\dfrac{x^2}{a^2} + \dfrac{y^2}{b^2} = 1$ are the points $(0, -b)$ and $(0, b)$.

60. Assume $a > 0$ and $b < 0$. Show that the graph of $\dfrac{x^2}{a^2} - \dfrac{y^2}{b^2} = 1$ has no y-intercepts.

61. Is the graph of the equation $x^2 + y^2 = r^2$ with $r > 0$ a circle, an ellipse, both, or neither? Explain. [**Hint:** Is it possible to write the equation in the form $\dfrac{x^2}{a^2} + \dfrac{y^2}{b^2} = 1$?]

62. Find equations of five ellipses that do not intersect each other. Sketch the five ellipses in the same coordinate system.

63. Assume $a > 0$ and $b > 0$. Describe how to graph by hand an equation of the form $\dfrac{x^2}{a^2} + \dfrac{y^2}{b^2} = 1$.

64. Describe how to graph by hand an equation of the form $\dfrac{x^2}{a^2} - \dfrac{y^2}{b^2} = 1$.

Related Review

65. a. Graph by hand the equations $x^2 + y^2 = 1$ and $(x - 3)^2 + (y - 2)^2 = 1$ in the same coordinate system. How can the graph of $x^2 + y^2 = 1$ be translated to get the graph of $(x - 3)^2 + (y - 2)^2 = 1$?
b. Graph by hand the equations $x^2 + y^2 = 1$ and $(x + 3)^2 + (y + 2)^2 = 1$ in the same coordinate system. How can the graph of $x^2 + y^2 = 1$ be translated to get the graph of $(x + 3)^2 + (y + 2)^2 = 1$?
c. Explain how you can translate the graph of an equation of the form $x^2 + y^2 = r^2$ to get the graph of $(x - h)^2 + (y - k)^2 = r^2$, where h, k, and r are constants and $r > 0$.
d. Graph $4x^2 + 25y^2 = 100$ by hand. Then translate your graph to get the graph of $4(x + 2)^2 + 25(y - 5)^2 = 100$.
e. Graph $4x^2 - 25y^2 = 100$ by hand. Then translate your graph to get the graph of $4(x + 2)^2 - 25(y - 5)^2 = 100$.

For Exercises 66–70, graph the equation by hand.

66. $3x - 2y = 8$

67. $y = \log_2(x)$

68. $y = -2(x - 4)^2 + 6$

69. $y = 3\sqrt{x + 5} - 4$

70. $y = -2(3)^x$

71. Is the relation $\dfrac{x^2}{4} + \dfrac{y^2}{81} = 1$ a function? Explain.

72. Is the relation $\dfrac{x^2}{9} - \dfrac{y^2}{81} = 1$ a function? Explain.

Expressions, Equations, Functions, and Graphs

Perform the indicated instruction. Then use words such as linear, *quadratic, cubic, exponential, logarithmic, rational, radical, polynomial, degree, function, one variable, and two variables to describe the expression, equation, or system.*

73. Graph $y = 2x^2 - 8x + 3$ by hand.

74. Solve $\log_3\left(7x^3\right) = 5$. Round any solutions to the fourth decimal place.

75. Solve $2x^2 - 8x + 3 = 0$.

76. Graph $f(x) = \log_3(x)$ by hand.

77. Find the product $-5x(2x - 1)(3x - 1)$.

78. Write $4\log_b\left(2x^2\right) - 3\log_b\left(4x^5\right)$ as a single logarithm.

Section 11.4 Quiz

For Exercises 1–8, graph the equation by hand.

1. $\dfrac{x^2}{9} + \dfrac{y^2}{25} = 1$

2. $\dfrac{y^2}{49} - \dfrac{x^2}{9} = 1$

3. $4x^2 - y^2 = 16$

4. $16x^2 + 3y^2 = 48$

5. $x^2 - 9y^2 = 81$

6. $4y^2 - 4x^2 = 16$

7. $\dfrac{x^2}{5} + \dfrac{y^2}{14} = 1$

8. $\dfrac{x^2}{8} + \dfrac{y^2}{3} = 1$

9. Is the relation $\dfrac{x^2}{9} - \dfrac{y^2}{4} = 1$ a function? Explain.

10. Find equations of three distinct ellipses that all contain the points $(0, 3)$ and $(0, -3)$.

▼11.5 Solving Nonlinear Systems of Equations

Objectives

» Know the meaning of a *nonlinear system.*

» Solve nonlinear systems by graphing, substitution, or elimination.

In this section, we will solve nonlinear systems. A **nonlinear system of equations** is a system of equations in which *at least* one of the equations is not linear. Here is an example of a nonlinear system:

$$x^2 + y^2 = 4$$
$$y = x^2$$

The graph of $x^2 + y^2 = 4$ is a circle, and the graph of $y = x^2$ is a parabola. Just as with solutions of linear systems, a *solution* of a nonlinear system is an ordered pair that satisfies *all* of the equations in the system. The *solution set* of a nonlinear system is the set of all solutions of the system.

When solving nonlinear systems in this text, we find only solutions that have real-number coordinates.

Solving a Nonlinear System by Graphing and by Substitution

Just as we solve linear systems, we can solve a nonlinear system by graphing. **The solution set of a system of nonlinear equations can be found by locating the intersection of the graphs of *all* of the equations.**

We can also solve some nonlinear systems by substitution.

▶ **Example 1**   Solving a Nonlinear System

Solve the system

$$y = x^2 - 5$$
$$y = -x + 1$$

by graphing and by substitution.

Solution

The graph of $y = x^2 - 5$ is a parabola, and the graph of $y = -x + 1$ is a line. We sketch graphs of both equations in the same coordinate system (see Fig. 50).

The graphs appear to intersect at $(-3, 4)$ and $(2, -1)$. The two intersection points are the solutions of the system.

Next, we solve the system

$$y = x^2 - 5$$
$$y = -x + 1$$

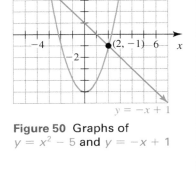

Figure 50 Graphs of $y = x^2 - 5$ and $y = -x + 1$

by substitution. To begin, we substitute $x^2 - 5$ for y in the equation $y = -x + 1$ and solve for x:

$$
\begin{aligned}
x^2 - 5 &= -x + 1 && \textit{Substitute } x^2 - 5 \textit{ for } y. \\
x^2 + x - 6 &= 0 && \textit{Write in } ax^2 + bx + c = 0 \textit{ form.} \\
(x + 3)(x - 2) &= 0 && \textit{Factor left side.} \\
x + 3 = 0 \quad &\text{or} \quad x - 2 = 0 && \textit{Zero factor property} \\
x = -3 \quad &\text{or} \quad x = 2
\end{aligned}
$$

We substitute $x = -3$ and $x = 2$ into the equation $y = -x + 1$ to find the corresponding values of y:

$$
\begin{array}{ll}
y = -(-3) + 1 & y = -2 + 1 \\
\quad = 4 & \quad = -1
\end{array}
$$

So, $(-3, 4)$ and $(2, -1)$ are the solutions of the system.

We can check that $(-3, 4)$ and $(2, -1)$ satisfy both equations in the original system. However, the fact that we have solved the system in two different ways and gotten the same result is itself a check of our work.

We could also solve the nonlinear system in Example 1 by using "intersect" on a graphing calculator (see Fig. 51).

Solving a Nonlinear System by Elimination

We can solve some nonlinear systems by elimination.

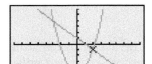

Figure 51 Verify that $(-3, 4)$ and $(2, -1)$ are solutions

▶ **Example 2**   Solving a Nonlinear System

Solve the system

$$x^2 + y^2 = 9$$
$$9x^2 + 4y^2 = 36$$

by graphing and by elimination.

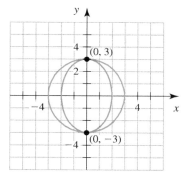

Figure 52 Graphs of
$x^2 + y^2 = 9$ and
$9x^2 + 4y^2 = 36$

Solution

The graph of $x^2 + y^2 = 9$ is a circle, and the graph of $9x^2 + 4y^2 = 36$ is an ellipse. We sketch the graphs in the same coordinate system (see Fig. 52). (We sketched the ellipse $9x^2 + 4y^2 = 36$ in Example 1 of Section 11.4.)

The intersection points appear to be $(0, -3)$ and $(0, 3)$. These points are the solutions of the system.

Now we solve the system

$$x^2 + y^2 = 9 \qquad \textit{Equation (1)}$$
$$9x^2 + 4y^2 = 36 \qquad \textit{Equation (2)}$$

by elimination. First, we multiply both sides of equation (1) by -4, yielding the system

$$-4x^2 - 4y^2 = -36 \quad \textit{Multiply both sides of equation (1) by} -4.$$
$$9x^2 + 4y^2 = 36 \qquad \textit{Equation (2)}$$

Next, we add the left-hand sides and add the right-hand sides of the equations and solve for x:

$$\begin{array}{r} -4x^2 - 4y^2 = -36 \\ \underline{9x^2 + 4y^2 = 36} \\ 5x^2 + 0 \;\;= 0 \end{array}$$

$$5x^2 = 0 \qquad \textit{a + 0 = a}$$
$$x^2 = 0 \qquad \textit{Divide both sides by 5.}$$
$$x = 0 \qquad \textit{Square root property}$$

Then we substitute 0 for x in equation (1) and solve for y:

$$0^2 + y^2 = 9 \qquad \textit{Substitute 0 for x.}$$
$$y^2 = 9 \qquad \textit{Simplify.}$$
$$y = \pm 3 \qquad \textit{Square root property}$$

The solutions are $(0, -3)$ and $(0, 3)$. We got the same result when we solved the system by graphing.

▶

If it is reasonable to do so, we first graph the equations of a nonlinear system to determine the number of solutions and to find approximate coordinates of the solutions. Then we solve the system by substitution or elimination.

▶ **Example 3**   Solving a Nonlinear System

Solve the system

$$x^2 + y^2 = 25$$
$$-4x^2 + 9y^2 = 36$$

by graphing and by elimination. Round coordinates of any solutions to the second decimal place.

Solution

The graph of $x^2 + y^2 = 25$ is a circle, and the graph of $-4x^2 + 9y^2 = 36$ is a hyperbola. We sketch both graphs in the same coordinate system (see Fig. 53). (If we divide both sides of $-4x^2 + 9y^2 = 36$ by 36, we have $-\dfrac{x^2}{9} + \dfrac{y^2}{4} = 1$. We sketched the graph of this equation in Example 2 of Section 11.4.)

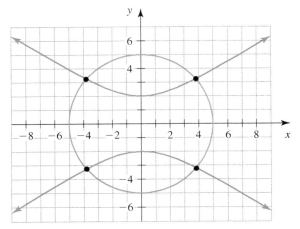

Figure 53 Graphs of $x^2 + y^2 = 25$ and $-4x^2 + 9y^2 = 36$

The graphs suggest there are four solutions: $(-3.8, -3.2)$, $(-3.8, 3.2)$, $(3.8, -3.2)$, and $(3.8, 3.2)$.

Now we solve the system

$$x^2 + y^2 = 25 \quad \textit{Equation (1)}$$
$$-4x^2 + 9y^2 = 36 \quad \textit{Equation (2)}$$

by elimination. First, we multiply both sides of equation (1) by 4, yielding the system

$$4x^2 + 4y^2 = 100 \quad \textit{Multiply both sides by 4.}$$
$$-4x^2 + 9y^2 = 36 \quad \textit{Equation (2)}$$

Next, we add the left-hand sides and add the right-hand sides of the equations and solve for y:

$$4x^2 + 4y^2 = 100$$
$$\underline{-4x^2 + 9y^2 = 36}$$
$$0 + 13y^2 = 136$$
$$13y^2 = 136 \qquad 0 + a = a$$
$$y^2 = \frac{136}{13} \qquad \textit{Divide both sides by 13.}$$
$$y = \pm\sqrt{\frac{136}{13}} \qquad \textit{Square root property}$$
$$y \approx \pm 3.234 \qquad \textit{Compute.}$$

Then we substitute -3.234 and 3.234 for y in equation (1) and solve for x:

$$x^2 + (-3.234)^2 = 25 \qquad\qquad x^2 + 3.234^2 = 25$$
$$x^2 + 3.234^2 = 25 \qquad\qquad x^2 = 25 - 3.234^2$$
$$x^2 = 25 - 3.234^2 \qquad\qquad x = \pm\sqrt{25 - 3.234^2}$$
$$x = \pm\sqrt{25 - 3.234^2} \qquad\qquad x \approx \pm 3.81$$
$$x \approx \pm 3.81$$

So, the four approximate solutions are $(-3.81, -3.23)$, $(-3.81, 3.23)$, $(3.81, -3.23)$, and $(3.81, 3.23)$, which agrees with what we found graphically.

Group Exploration
Using graphs to find the number of solutions

For each problem, think graphically. It is not necessary to solve the systems in Problems 2 and 4. Assume a, b, and r are positive constants.

1. If $r < a$ and $r < b$, explain why there are no solutions with real-number coordinates for the following system:
$$x^2 + y^2 = r^2$$
$$\frac{x^2}{a^2} + \frac{y^2}{b^2} = 1$$

2. If $a < r < b$, explain why the following system has four solutions:
$$x^2 + y^2 = r^2$$
$$\frac{x^2}{a^2} + \frac{y^2}{b^2} = 1$$

3. If $a < r < b$, explain why there are no solutions with real-number coordinates for the following system:
$$x^2 + y^2 = r^2$$
$$\frac{y^2}{b^2} - \frac{x^2}{a^2} = 1$$

4. If $a < r < b$, explain why the following system has four solutions:
$$x^2 + y^2 = r^2$$
$$\frac{x^2}{a^2} - \frac{y^2}{b^2} = 1$$

Key Points of Section 11.5

Nonlinear system of equations	A **nonlinear system of equations** is a system of equations in which *at least* one of the equations is not linear.
Solution set of a nonlinear system	The solution set of a system of nonlinear equations can be found by locating the intersection of the graphs of *all* of the equations.
First graph a nonlinear system	If it is reasonable to do so, we first graph the equations of a nonlinear system to determine the number of solutions and to find approximate coordinates of the solutions. Then we solve the system by substitution or elimination.

Homework 11.5

For extra help ▶ MyMathLab®   Watch the videos in MyMathLab   Download the MyDashboard App

Solve the system by graphing the equations by hand. Also, solve the system by substitution or elimination.

1. $x^2 + y^2 = 25$
   $4x^2 + 25y^2 = 100$

2. $x^2 + y^2 = 4$
   $4x^2 + 16y^2 = 64$

3. $y = x^2 + 1$
   $y = -x + 3$

4. $y = x^2 - 3$
   $y = 2x$

5. $y = x^2 - 2$
   $y = -x^2 + 6$

6. $y = 2x^2 - 8$
   $y = x^2 + 1$

7. $x^2 + y^2 = 49$
   $x^2 + y^2 = 16$

8. $4x^2 + 9y^2 = 36$
   $9x^2 + 25y^2 = 225$

9. $x^2 + y^2 = 25$
   $y = -x - 1$

10. $x^2 + y^2 = 36$
    $y = x + 6$

11. $y^2 - x^2 = 16$
    $y + x^2 = 4$

12. $y^2 - 4x^2 = 4$
    $4x^2 + y^2 = 4$

13. $25x^2 - 9y^2 = 225$
    $4x^2 + 9y^2 = 36$

14. $y^2 - x^2 = 9$
    $4x^2 + 100y^2 = 400$

15. $9x^2 + y^2 = 9$
    $y = 3x + 3$

16. $x^2 - y^2 = 16$
    $y = -x + 1$

17. $4x^2 + 9y^2 = 36$
    $16x^2 + 25y^2 = 225$

18. $16x^2 + 9y^2 = 144$
    $x^2 + 4y^2 = 4$

19. $y = \sqrt{x} - 3$
    $y = -x - 1$

20. $y = \sqrt{x} + 1$
    $y = -\sqrt{x} + 5$

21. $y = 2x^2 - 5$
    $y = x^2 - 2$

22. $y = -3x^2 + 7$
    $y = -x^2 + 3$

Solve the system by graphing the equations by hand. Also, solve the system by substitution or elimination. Round the coordinates of your solution(s) to the second decimal place.

23. $25y^2 - 4x^2 = 100$
   $9x^2 + y^2 = 9$

24. $16x^2 - 4y^2 = 64$
   $x^2 + 16y^2 = 16$

25. $25x^2 + 9y^2 = 225$
   $x^2 + y^2 = 16$

26. $36x^2 + 4y^2 = 144$
   $x^2 + y^2 = 9$

Solve the system by substitution or elimination. Check that any results satisfy both equations.

27. $9x^2 + y^2 = 85$
   $2x^2 - 3y^2 = 6$

28. $x^2 - 6y = 34$
   $x^2 + y^2 = 25$

29. $x^2 + 4y^2 = 25$
   $y = -x + 5$

30. $x^2 + 9y^2 = 13$
   $y = x - 1$

31. $y = x^2 - 3x + 2$
   $y = 2x - 4$

32. $y = 2x^2 - 5x - 11$
   $y = x^2 - 3x + 4$

Solve the system of three equations by graphing the equations by hand. Check that any results satisfy each equation.

33. $x^2 + y^2 = 25$
   $4x^2 - 25y^2 = 100$
   $4x^2 + 25y^2 = 100$

34. $x^2 + y^2 = 1$
   $9x^2 + y^2 = 9$
   $y = x + 1$

Concepts

35. Create a nonlinear system of two equations in two variables whose solutions are $(-4, 0)$ and $(4, 0)$.

36. Create a nonlinear system of two equations in two variables whose solutions are $(0, -3)$ and $(0, 3)$.

37. Consider the system
$$y = x^2$$
$$y = -x^2 + c$$
For what values of c does the system have
   a. two solutions?
   b. one solution?
   c. no solutions?

38. Consider the system
$$y = ax^2$$
$$y = x^2 + 3$$
For what values of a does the system have
   a. two solutions?
   b. one solution?
   c. no solutions?

39. Find values of c and d such that $(1, 4)$ is a solution of the system
$$2x^2 + cy^2 = 82$$
$$y = x^2 + dx + 5$$

40. Find values of c and d such that $(2, -5)$ is a solution of the system
$$y = cx^2 - 4x^2 - 5$$
$$y = dx - 13$$

41. Explain how to solve a nonlinear system.

42. In your own words, describe a linear system and a nonlinear system. Also, compare the numbers of possible solutions for both types of systems.

Related Review

Solve the system by substitution or elimination.

43. $y = 2^x$
$$y = 4\left(\frac{1}{2}\right)^x$$
   [**Hint:** $4 = 2^2$ and $\frac{1}{2} = 2^{-1}$]

44. $y = \log_2(x + 1) + 2$
   $y = \log_2(3x + 13) - 1$

Expressions, Equations, Functions, and Graphs

For each description that follows, give an example. Then solve, simplify, or graph, as appropriate.

45. linear function

46. quotient of two radical expressions

47. rational equation in one variable

48. system of two linear equations in two variables

49. exponential function

50. square root function

51. quadratic function

52. difference of two rational expressions

53. quadratic equation in one variable

54. logarithmic equation in one variable

Section 11.5 Quiz

For Exercises 1–4, solve the system.

1. $9x^2 + y^2 = 81$
   $x^2 + y^2 = 9$

2. $y = x^2 - 2$
   $y = -2x + 1$

3. $y = x^2 + 3$
   $y = x^2 - 6x + 9$

4. $25x^2 - 4y^2 = 100$
   $9x^2 + y^2 = 9$

5. Solve the system of three equations by graphing the equations by hand:
$$x^2 - y^2 = 16$$
$$x^2 + y^2 = 16$$
$$y = (x + 4)^2$$

6. Create a nonlinear system of two equations whose solution is $(0, 5)$.

Reviewing Prerequisite Material

In this appendix, we review skills you will need to work with the text. Review these skills before you begin Section 1.2. The answers to exercises in this appendix are located at the end of the Answers to Odd-Numbered Exercises.

▼A.1 Plotting Points

How do we plot points? To start, we draw a horizontal number line called the x-axis and a vertical number line called the y-axis (see Fig. 1). We refer to such a pair of axes as a **coordinate system.** The **origin** is the intersection point of the axes.

Next, we plot the ordered pair $(5, 4)$. To do so, we start at the origin, look 5 units to the right and 4 units up, and draw a dot (see Fig. 2). The points $(-4, 2)$, $(-5, -3)$, and $(3, -4)$ have also been plotted in Fig. 2.

Plot the given points in a coordinate system.

1. $(2, 4)$ **2.** $(-3, 1)$ **3.** $(4, -2)$ **4.** $(-4, -3)$

5. $(-2, -1)$ **6.** $(0, 1)$ **7.** $(-2, 0)$ **8.** $(0, 0)$

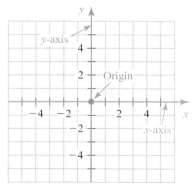

Figure 1 Coordinate system

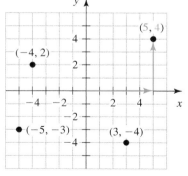

Figure 2 Plotting the points $(5, 4)$, $(-4, 2)$, $(-5, -3)$, and $(3, -4)$

▼A.2 Identifying Types of Numbers

The **counting numbers** are the numbers 1, 2, 3, 4, 5, …. The three dots before the period at the end of the sentence mean the pattern of the numbers shown continues without ending. In this case, the pattern continues with 6, 7, 8, and so on.

The **integers** are the numbers

$$\ldots, -3, -2, -1, 0, 1, 2, 3, \ldots$$

The three dots on both sides mean the pattern of the numbers shown continues without ending in both directions. In this case, the pattern continues with $-4, -5, -6$, and so on, and with $4, 5, 6$, and so on.

The **rational numbers** are the numbers that can be written in the form $\dfrac{n}{d}$, where n and d are integers and d is nonzero. Here are some examples of rational numbers:

$$\frac{2}{3} \qquad \frac{-9}{5} \qquad 6 = \frac{6}{1}$$

A rational number can be written as a decimal number that either terminates or repeats:

$$\underbrace{\frac{5}{8} = 0.625}_{\text{terminates}} \qquad \underbrace{\frac{2}{11} = 0.18181818\ldots}_{\text{repeats}}$$

An **irrational** number is a number that can be represented on the number line but is *not* rational. The number $\sqrt{5}$ is the number greater than zero that we multiply by itself to get 5. The number $\sqrt{5}$ is an irrational number. Here are some more examples of irrational numbers:

$$\sqrt{2} \qquad \sqrt{7} \qquad \pi$$

An irrational number can be written as a decimal number that neither terminates nor repeats.

The **real numbers** are all of the numbers represented on the number line. Here are some real numbers:

$$5 \qquad \frac{8}{3} \qquad -7.28 \qquad \pi \qquad 6 \qquad -\frac{9}{7} \qquad 0$$

Consider the following numbers:

$$\frac{2}{9} \qquad 4 \qquad -7.19 \qquad 0 \qquad -2 \qquad \sqrt{17} \qquad 85$$

Which of these numbers are the given type of number?

1. Counting numbers   **2.** Integers   **3.** Rational numbers

4. Irrational numbers   **5.** Real numbers

▼A.3 Absolute Value

The absolute value of a number a, written $|a|$, is the distance from a to 0 on the number line. So, $|-5| = 5$, because -5 is a distance of 5 units from 0, and $|5| = 5$, because 5 is a distance of 5 units from 0 (see Fig. 3).

Figure 3 Both numbers -5 and 5 are a distance of 5 units from 0

Here are two more examples:

$$\left|\frac{2}{3}\right| = \frac{2}{3} \qquad \text{and} \qquad |-2.89| = 2.89$$

Compute.

1. $|-3|$ **2.** $|4.69|$ **3.** $|0|$ **4.** $|-\pi|$

▼A.4 Performing Operations with Real Numbers

In this section, we will review how to multiply, divide, add, and subtract real numbers.

Do you recall how to multiply and divide real numbers? Here are some examples to refresh your memory:

$$2(-5) = -10 \qquad -2(-5) = 10 \qquad \frac{-10}{5} = -2 \qquad \frac{-10}{-5} = 2$$

In general,

- The product or quotient of two numbers with the same sign is positive.
- The product or quotient of two numbers with different signs is negative.

Do you recall how to add real numbers? Here are some examples:

$$2 + 5 = 7 \qquad -2 + (-5) = -7 \qquad -2 + 5 = 3 \qquad 2 + (-5) = -3$$

When you add real numbers, it helps to think in terms of the number line. To find $-2 + (-5)$, imagine moving 2 units to the left of 0, then 5 more units to the left. Figure 4 illustrates $-2 + (-5) = -7$.

Figure 4 Illustration of $-2 + (-5) = -7$

To find $2 + (-5)$, imagine moving 2 units to the right of 0, then 5 units to the left of 2. Figure 5 illustrates $2 + (-5) = -3$.

Figure 5 Illustration of $2 + (-5) = -3$

Do you recall how to subtract real numbers? Here are some examples:

$$10 - 2 = 10 + (-2) = 8$$
$$10 - (-2) = 10 + [-(-2)] = 10 + 2 = 12$$

In general, subtracting a number is the same as adding the opposite of that number. In symbols, we write $x - y = x + (-y)$.

Compute.

1. $-3(7)$ **2.** $5(-6)$ **3.** $-9(-4)$ **4.** $-8(-2)$

5. $-(-4)$ **6.** $-(-(-9))$ **7.** $\dfrac{8}{-2}$ **8.** $\dfrac{-6}{-2}$

[**Hint:** $-(-4) = (-1)(-4)$]

9. $-3 + (-5)$ **10.** $-6 + (-7)$ **11.** $2 + (-8)$ **12.** $-7 + 3$

13. $-1 + 6$ **14.** $8 + (-3)$ **15.** $-4 + (-6)$ **16.** $-2 + (-3)$

17. $3 - 7$ **18.** $2 - 8$ **19.** $5 - (-3)$ **20.** $9 - (-4)$

21. $-4 - 9$ **22.** $-2 - 4$ **23.** $-1 - (-1)$ **24.** $-10 - (-6)$

▼ A.5 Exponents

We can use a special notation to describe repeated multiplications. For example, $2^4 = 2 \cdot 2 \cdot 2 \cdot 2 = 16$. In general, for any counting number n,

$$b^n = \underbrace{b \cdot b \cdot b \cdot \ldots \cdot b}_{n \text{ factors of } b}$$

We refer to b^n as the **power,** the **nth power of b,** or **b raised to the nth power.** We call b the **base** and n the **exponent.** When we calculate a power, we say we have performed an **exponentiation.** Here we perform some exponentiations:

$$4^3 = 4 \cdot 4 \cdot 4 = 64 \qquad 2^5 = 2 \cdot 2 \cdot 2 \cdot 2 \cdot 2 = 32$$
$$(-3)^4 = (-3) \cdot (-3) \cdot (-3) \cdot (-3) = 81 \qquad -3^4 = -(3 \cdot 3 \cdot 3 \cdot 3) = -81$$

Perform the indicated exponentiation.

1. 7^2 　　　　**2.** 9^2 　　　　**3.** 6^3 　　　　**4.** 5^4

5. $(-2)^4$ 　　　**6.** $(-3)^3$ 　　　**7.** -2^4 　　　**8.** -3^3

▼ A.6 Order of Operations

In this section, we will review the order in which we perform operations:

1. First, perform operations within parentheses or other grouping symbols, starting with the innermost group.

2. Then perform exponentiations.

3. Next, perform multiplications and divisions, going from left to right.

4. Last, perform additions and subtractions, going from left to right.

For example, here's how to perform the operations in $5 - 8 \div (7 - 5)^2 + 2 \cdot 3$:

$$\begin{aligned}
5 - 8 \div (7 - 5)^2 + 2 \cdot 3 &= 5 - 8 \div (2)^2 + 2 \cdot 3 \qquad &\text{Work within parentheses first.} \\
&= 5 - 8 \div 4 + 2 \cdot 3 \qquad &\text{Perform exponentiation: } 2^2 = 4. \\
&= 5 - 2 + 2 \cdot 3 \qquad &\text{Divide, because the division is} \\
& &\text{to the left of the multiplication.} \\
&= 5 - 2 + 6 \qquad &\text{Multiply before adding or subtracting.} \\
&= 3 + 6 \qquad &\text{Subtract, because the subtraction} \\
& &\text{is to the left of the addition.} \\
&= 9 \qquad &\text{Add.}
\end{aligned}$$

Perform the operations.

1. $3 + 5 \cdot 2$ 　　　　**2.** $2(8) - 4$ 　　　　**3.** $2 + 10 \div (-5)$

4. $14 \div (-2) - 1$ 　　　**5.** $2(1 - 3) + 4 \cdot 2$ 　　　**6.** $10(2 - 7) + 5 \cdot 4$

7. $(5 - 9)(4 + 2) \div 8 + 2$ 　　　　**8.** $(3 + 5)(2 - 6) \div 4 + 1$

9. $4(3)^2$ 　　　　　　　　**10.** $-3(2)^3$

11. $-3^2 + (-3)^2 - (-3)^2$ 　　　　**12.** $2^3 - (-2)^3 + (-2)^3$

13. $5 - 4^2 + (-8) \div (-2)$ 　　　　**14.** $2^3 - 10 \div (-5) + 1$

15. $6 - (3 - 1)^3 + 8$ 　　　　**16.** $10 - (9 - 6)^3 + 5$

▼A.7 Constants, Variables, Expressions, and Equations

A **variable** is a symbol that represents a quantity that can vary. For example, we can define T to be the temperature (in degrees Fahrenheit) at the top of the Empire State Building. As time passes, the temperature will change. So, T is a variable.

A **constant** is a symbol that represents a specific number (a quantity that does *not* vary). For example, $8, 0, -3.5$, and π are constants.

An **expression** is a constant, a variable, or a combination of constants, variables, operation symbols, and grouping symbols, such as parentheses. Here are some examples of expressions:

$$2\pi x - 3y \qquad ax^2 + bx + c \qquad 7 \qquad x^3 - 8 \qquad x \qquad (x - 5)^2 + 8x$$

We **evaluate an expression** by substituting a number for each variable in the expression and calculating the result. If a variable appears more than once in the expression, the same number is substituted for that variable each time.

An **equation** consists of an equality sign "=" with expressions on both sides. Here are some examples of equations:

$$2\pi x + 3y = k \qquad ax^2 + bx + c = 0 \qquad 7 = y(y - 4) \qquad x^3 - 8 = x^2 + 1 \qquad x = 1$$

Identify each of the following as an expression or an equation.

1. $y = mx + b$

2. $3x^2 - 5x + 4 = 8$

3. $2x - 5\pi + 1$

4. $x^3 - 8$

▼A.8 Distributive Law

Here we review the **distributive law:**

$$a(b + c) = ab + ac$$

For example, $4(x + 5) = 4x + 4 \cdot 5 = 4x + 20$. Also,

$$a(b - c) = ab - ac$$
$$(a + b)c = ac + bc$$
$$(a - b)c = ac - bc$$

For example, $(2x - 7)(3) = 2x \cdot 3 - 7 \cdot 3 = 6x - 21$.

Apply the distributive law.

1. $2(x + 4)$

2. $4(x + 7)$

3. $6(2t - 3)$

4. $5(4w - 6)$

5. $(x + 8)(-3)$

6. $(x + 5)(-4)$

7. $(2x - 9)(-5)$

8. $(3x - 1)(-6)$

9. $2.8(p + 4.1)$

10. $-5.2(b + 3.9)$

▼A.9 Combining Like Terms

A **term** is a constant, a variable, or a product of a constant and one or more variables raised to powers. Terms include $7, y, 4x$, and $9y^2$. **Like terms** are either constant terms or variable terms that contain the same variable(s) raised to the same power(s). For example, the terms $3x^2y^5$ and $8x^2y^5$ are like terms, because both terms have an x with the exponent 2 and a y with the exponent 5. (We discuss terms and like terms in Section 6.1.)

We can use the distributive law to add the like terms $3x$ and $5x$:

$$3x + 5x = (3 + 5)x = 8x$$

Notice that we can find $3x + 5x$ in one step by adding the *coefficients*, 3 and 5:

$$3x + 5x = 8x$$
$$3 + 5 = 8$$

We call this process *combining like terms*. Similarly, we can combine like terms to find $9x - 4x$ by adding the coefficients, 9 and -4:

$$9x - 4x = 5x$$
$$9 + (-4) = 5$$

If terms are not like terms, we say they are **unlike terms**. For example, $4x$ and $7y$ are unlike terms, because the expressions contain different variables. We can't add the coefficients in $4x + 7y$, because there is no helpful way to use the distributive law for unlike terms.

Here we simplify the expression $5x + 9 - 8y + 3x - 2y$ by combining like terms:

$$5x + 9 - 8y + 3x - 2y = 5x + 3x - 8y - 2y + 9 \quad \text{Rearrange terms.}$$
$$= 8x - 10y + 9 \qquad\qquad \text{Combine like terms.}$$

When possible, apply the distributive law and combine like terms.

1. $4x + 3x$

2. $7x - 2x$

3. $5x - 9y - 3x + 2y$

4. $8x - 4y - 6x + 5y$

5. $7a - 4 + b - 9a - 3b + 2$

6. $4t - 2w + 5 + t - 1 - 8w$

7. $4(2x + 3) + 5(4x - 1)$

8. $5(3x + 2) + 2(3x + 6)$

9. $2(5x - y) - 3(4x + y)$

10. $3(4x - y) - 5(2x + y)$

11. $10 - (3m - 2n) + 4m - 7n$

12. $6 - (6a - 3b) - 5b + 2a$

▼ A.10 Solving Linear Equations in One Variable

We say an equation is an **equation in one variable** if its expressions have exactly one variable. Here are some examples of equations in one variable:

$$3x = 21 \qquad 2x^3 - 1 = 5x^2 + x \qquad 5(2x - 7) + 3 = 18 \qquad x^2 - 2x - 8 = 0$$

A number is a **solution** of an equation in one variable if the equation becomes a true statement when the number is substituted for the variable. We say the number **satisfies** the equation.

The **solution set** of an equation is the set of all solutions of the equation. We **solve** the equation by finding its solution set.

In this section, we will solve linear equations in one variable. A **linear equation in one variable** is an equation that can be put into the form $mx + b = 0$, where m and b are constants and $m \neq 0$. Here we solve $5(x - 2) = 3x + 4$, a linear equation in one variable:

$$5(x - 2) = 3x + 4 \qquad\qquad \text{Original equation}$$
$$5x - 10 = 3x + 4 \qquad\qquad \text{Distributive law}$$
$$5x - 10 - 3x = 3x + 4 - 3x \quad \text{Subtract } 3x \text{ from both sides.}$$
$$2x - 10 = 4 \qquad\qquad \text{Combine like terms.}$$
$$2x - 10 + 10 = 4 + 10 \qquad\qquad \text{Add 10 to both sides.}$$
$$2x = 14 \qquad\qquad a + o = a$$
$$\frac{2x}{2} = \frac{14}{2} \qquad\qquad \text{Divide both sides by 2.}$$
$$x = 7 \qquad\qquad \text{Simplify.}$$

We check that the original equation becomes a true statement if 7 is substituted for x:

$$5(x - 2) = 3x + 4 \qquad \textit{Original equation}$$
$$5(7 - 2) \overset{?}{=} 3(7) + 4 \qquad \textit{Substitute 7 for x.}$$
$$5(5) \overset{?}{=} 21 + 4 \qquad \textit{Subtract; multiply.}$$
$$25 \overset{?}{=} 25 \qquad \textit{Multiply; add.}$$
$$\text{true}$$

So, the solution of the equation is 7.

If an equation contains fractions, it is often helpful to multiply both sides of the equation by the *least common denominator* (*LCD*) of the fractions. To illustrate, we solve $\dfrac{5}{6}x - \dfrac{1}{2} = \dfrac{9}{4}$.

To find the LCD of the three fractions in this equation, we list the multiples of 6, the multiples of 2, and the multiples of 4:

Multiples of 6:   6, 12, 18, 24, 30, 36, 42,...
Multiples of 2:   2, 4, 6, 8, 10, 12, 14, 16, 18, 20, 22, 24, 26, 28, 30, 32, 34, 36,...
Multiples of 4:   4, 8, 12, 16, 20, 24, 28, 32, 36, 40,...

Common multiples of 6, 2, and 4 are

$$12, 24, 36,...$$

Notice that 12 is the least (lowest) number in the list. We call it the least common multiple of 6, 2, and 4. The **least common multiple** (**LCM**) of a group of numbers is the smallest number that is a multiple of *all* of the numbers in the group.

Next, we multiply both sides of $\dfrac{5}{6}x - \dfrac{1}{2} = \dfrac{9}{4}$ by the LCD, 12:

$$\frac{5}{6}x - \frac{1}{2} = \frac{9}{4} \qquad \textit{Original equation}$$
$$12\left(\frac{5}{6}x - \frac{1}{2}\right) = 12 \cdot \frac{9}{4} \qquad \textit{Multiply both sides by LCD, 12.}$$
$$12 \cdot \frac{5}{6}x - 12 \cdot \frac{1}{2} = 12 \cdot \frac{9}{4} \qquad \textit{Distributive law}$$
$$10x - 6 = 27 \qquad \textit{Simplify.}$$
$$10x = 33 \qquad \textit{Add 6 to both sides.}$$
$$x = \frac{33}{10} \qquad \textit{Divide both sides by 10.}$$

Since $\dfrac{33}{10} = 3.3$, we can use a calculator to check that the original equation becomes a true statement if 3.3 is substituted for x.

Solve.

1. $x + 5 = 9$

2. $x - 3 = 4$

3. $4x = 12$

4. $-3x = 21$

5. $5(w - 3) = 13$

6. $-2(k - 4) = 5$

7. $2x + 5 = 6x - 3$

8. $4x - 7 = 9x + 3$

9. $5 - 4(2x - 3) = 13$

10. $7 - 2(3x + 5) = 19$

11. $\dfrac{2}{3}t + \dfrac{1}{4} = \dfrac{5}{12}$

12. $\dfrac{5}{9}w + \dfrac{1}{2} = \dfrac{7}{6}$

13. $\dfrac{5}{2}x - \dfrac{7}{4} = \dfrac{3}{8}x$

14. $\dfrac{5}{3}x - \dfrac{7}{2} = \dfrac{11}{6}x$

▼ **A.11** Solving Equations in Two or More Variables

In this section, we will review how to solve *equations in two or more variables*. For example, we solve the equation $5x + 3y = 15$ for y:

$$5x + 3y = 15 \qquad \textit{Original equation}$$
$$5x + 3y - 5x = 15 - 5x \qquad \textit{Subtract 5x from both sides.}$$
$$3y = 15 - 5x \qquad \textit{Combine like terms.}$$
$$3y = -5x + 15 \qquad \textit{Rearrange terms on right-hand side.}$$
$$\frac{3y}{3} = \frac{-5x}{3} + \frac{15}{3} \qquad \textit{Divide both sides by 3.}$$
$$y = -\frac{5}{3}x + 5 \qquad \textit{Simplify.}$$

Here we solve $a(mx + b) = k$ for x:

$$\overbrace{a(mx + b)} = k \qquad \textit{Original equation}$$
$$amx + ab = k \qquad \textit{Distributive law}$$
$$amx + ab - ab = k - ab \qquad \textit{Subtract ab from both sides.}$$
$$amx = k - ab \qquad \textit{Combine like terms.}$$
$$\frac{amx}{am} = \frac{k - ab}{am} \qquad \textit{Divide both sides by am.}$$
$$x = \frac{k - ab}{am} \qquad \textit{Simplify left-hand side.}$$

As yet another example, we solve $-\frac{1}{4}x + \frac{7}{10}y = \frac{3}{5}$ for y. To find the LCD of the three fractions in this equation, we list the multiples of 4, the multiples of 10, and the multiples of 5:

Multiples of 4:   4, 8, 12, 16, 20, 24, 28, ...
Multiples of 10:   10, 20, 30, 40, 50, 60, 70, ...
Multiples of 5:   5, 10, 15, 20, 25, 30, 35, ...

The LCD is 20. Next, we multiply both sides of $-\frac{1}{4}x + \frac{7}{10}y = \frac{3}{5}$ by the LCD, 20:

$$-\frac{1}{4}x + \frac{7}{10}y = \frac{3}{5} \qquad \textit{Original equation}$$
$$20\left(-\frac{1}{4}x + \frac{7}{10}y\right) = 20 \cdot \frac{3}{5} \qquad \textit{Multiply both sides by LCD, 20.}$$
$$20\left(-\frac{1}{4}x\right) + 20\left(\frac{7}{10}y\right) = 20 \cdot \frac{3}{5} \qquad \textit{Distributive law}$$
$$-5x + 14y = 12 \qquad \textit{Simplify.}$$
$$-5x + 14y + 5x = 12 + 5x \qquad \textit{Add 5x to both sides.}$$
$$14y = 5x + 12 \qquad \textit{Combine like terms; rearrange terms.}$$
$$\frac{14y}{14} = \frac{5x}{14} + \frac{12}{14} \qquad \textit{Divide both sides by 14.}$$
$$y = \frac{5}{14}x + \frac{6}{7} \qquad \textit{Simplify.}$$

Solve for the specified variable.

1. $2x + y = 8$, for y 　　　　　　　**2.** $3x - y = 5$, for y

3. $3x - 5y = 15$, for x 　　　　　　**4.** $3x - 5y = 15$, for y

5. $ax - by = c$, for y

6. $ax - by = c$, for x

7. $-4x + 3y = 2x + 9$, for x

8. $-4x + 3y = 2x + 9$, for y

9. $\frac{1}{2}x - \frac{3}{4}y = \frac{5}{8}$, for y

10. $\frac{3}{4}x - \frac{2}{3}y = \frac{1}{4}$, for y

11. $\frac{x}{a} - \frac{y}{a} = 1$, for x

12. $\frac{x}{a} - \frac{y}{a} = 1$, for y

▼ A.12 Equivalent Expressions and Equivalent Equations

By the distributive law, we have $2(x + 3) = 2x + 6$. In Table 1, we show that the expressions $2(x + 3)$ and $2x + 6$ attain equal values when we substitute 0, 1, 2, 3, and 4 for x.

Table 1 Substituting Values for x in $2(x + 3)$ and $2x + 6$

x	$2(x + 3)$	$2x + 6$
0	$2(0 + 3) = 6$	$2(0) + 6 = 6$
1	$2(1 + 3) = 8$	$2(1) + 6 = 8$
2	$2(2 + 3) = 10$	$2(2) + 6 = 10$
3	$2(3 + 3) = 12$	$2(3) + 6 = 12$
4	$2(4 + 3) = 14$	$2(4) + 6 = 14$

It turns out $2(x + 3)$ and $2x + 6$ have equal values when *any* number is substituted for x. We say $2(x + 3)$ and $2x + 6$ are equivalent expressions. In general, two or more expressions are **equivalent expressions** if, when each variable is evaluated for *any* real number (for which all the expressions are defined), they give equal results.

As another example, consider the expression $2x + 4x + 3$. By combining like terms, we have $2x + 4x + 3 = 6x + 3$. The expressions $2x + 4x + 3$ and $6x + 3$ are equivalent expressions.

We **simplify** an expression such as $2(x - 5) + 4x + 1$ by applying the distributive law to remove parentheses, combining like terms, and/or performing as many operations with numbers as possible. The result is a **simplified expression** that is equivalent to the original expression.

Now we turn our attention to *equivalent equations*. To solve the equation $x + 3 = 7$, we write

$$x + 3 = 7 \qquad \textit{Original equation}$$
$$x + 3 - 3 = 7 - 3 \qquad \textit{Subtract 3 from both sides.}$$
$$x = 4 \qquad \textit{Combine like terms.}$$

Each of the equations $x + 3 = 7$, $x + 3 - 3 = 7 - 3$, and $x = 4$ has 4 as its only solution. So, the three equations have the same solution set. Equations that have the same solution set are called **equivalent equations.**

It is important to know the difference between simplifying an expression and solving an equation. To *simplify an expression,* we find a simpler *equivalent expression.* To *solve an equation*, we find any numbers that *satisfy the equation.*

Determine whether the pair are two equivalent expressions, two equivalent equations, or neither. Explain.

1. $5(x - 4)$ and $5x - 20$

2. $x + 8 = 0$ and $x = -8$

3. $4x - 3x + 8$ and $-12x + 8$

4. $3(x + 1) + 7$ and $3x + 8$

5. $4(x + 2)$ and $4x + 8 = 0$

6. $-3(2x - 5)$ and $-6x + 15$

7. $3x + 1 = 16$ and $3x = 15$

8. $2(x - 3) + 5 = 25$ and $2x = 23$

9. $-3(x - 4) = -18$ and $x = 2$

10. $3x + 4x - 2$ and $2x + x - 2 + 5x$

Answers to Odd-Numbered Exercises

Answers to most discussion exercises and to exercises in which answers may vary have been omitted.

Chapter 1

Homework 1.1 **1. a.** (d) **b.** (c) **c.** (a) **d.** (b) **3.** N independent, T dependent **5.** F independent, T dependent
7. L independent, T dependent **9.** I independent, P dependent **11.** r independent, n dependent

13. **15.** **17.** **19.**

21. **23.** **25.** **27.**

29. **31.** **33.** **35.**

37. Answers may vary. **39. a–d.** Answers may vary.

Homework 1.2

1. **3.** **5.** **7.** **9.** **11.**

13. **15.** **17.** **19.** **21.** **23.**

25. **27.** **29.** **31.** **33.**

35. a. 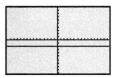 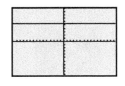 **b.** The graph is a horizontal line with y-intercept $(0, b)$.

37.   **39.**   **41.** 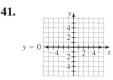 $y = 0$ **43.** 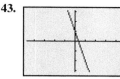 **45.**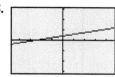

47. 2 **49.** $-\dfrac{2}{3}$ **51.** $\dfrac{4}{11}$ **53.** -17 **55.** $\dfrac{13}{3}$ **57.** $\dfrac{17}{16}$ **59.** 8.80 **61.** $L = \dfrac{P - 2W}{2}$ **63.** $y = \dfrac{c - ax}{b}$ **65.** x-intercept: $(-5, 0)$; y-intercept: $(0, 10)$ **67.** x-intercept: $(6, 0)$; y-intercept: $(0, 4)$ **69.** x-intercept: $(0, 0)$; y-intercept: $(0, 0)$ **71.** no x-intercept; y-intercept: $(0, 3)$ **73.** x-intercept: $\left(-\dfrac{b}{m}, 0\right)$; y-intercept: $(0, b)$ **75.** x-intercept: $\left(\dfrac{c}{ab}, 0\right)$; y-intercept: $\left(0, \dfrac{c}{a}\right)$ **77.** x-intercept: $\left(-\dfrac{bd}{a}, 0\right)$; y-intercept: $\left(0, \dfrac{d}{c}\right)$ **79.** x-intercept: $(a, 0)$; y-intercept: $(0, b)$ **81.** Answers may vary. **83.** $y = -3$ **85.** 3 **87.** -2.5 **89.** 6 **91.** -2

93. -5 **95. a.** 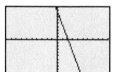   **b.** $(0, 800)$; when the person began releasing air from the balloon, his altitude was 800 feet. **c.** $(4, 0)$; after air had been released for 4 minutes, the balloon reached the ground.

97. a. 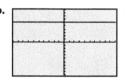 yes **b.** yes **c.** Answers may vary; yes. **99.** -9 **101.** B, C, and F

103. $(1, 3)$ **105.** Answers may vary. **107.** Answers may vary.

Homework 1.3 **1.** road A **3.** ski run A **5.** 2; increasing **7.** $-\dfrac{2}{3}$; decreasing **9.** -2; decreasing **11.** $-\dfrac{1}{3}$; decreasing **13.** $\dfrac{2}{3}$; increasing **15.** 4; increasing **17.** 1; increasing **19.** 0; horizontal **21.** undefined slope; vertical **23.** $\dfrac{2}{5}$; increasing **25.** -1.04; decreasing **27.** 1.28; increasing **29.** $-\dfrac{2}{5}$ **31.** parallel **33.** neither **35.** perpendicular **37.** neither **39.** perpendicular **41.** no

43.   **45.**   **47.**   **49.**   **51. a.** positive **b.** negative **c.** zero **d.** undefined **53.** Answers may vary. The line with slope 3 is steeper.

Answers may vary. Answers may vary. Answers may vary. Answers may vary.

55.   **57.**   **59.**   **61.**

Answers may vary. Answers may vary. Answers may vary. Answers may vary.

63. Interchange the numerator and denominator; $\dfrac{3}{2}$. **65.** $(1, 4), (4, 13), (5, 16)$—but answers may vary.

67. a. i.   **ii.** 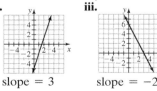 **iii.** **b.** The slope is equal to the coefficient of x.

slope $= 2$ slope $= 3$ slope $= -2$

69. a. 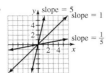 **b.** 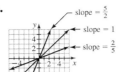 **c.** 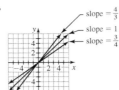 **d.** For $m \neq 0$, the lines $y = mx$ and $y = \dfrac{1}{m}x$ are mirror reflections of each other across the line $y = x$.

e. 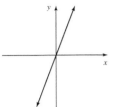   **71.** yes; yes; answers may vary.   **73.** Answers may vary.

Homework 1.4

1. slope: 6; y-intercept: $(0, 1)$ **3.** slope: -2; y-intercept: $(0, 7)$ **5.** slope: $\dfrac{5}{4}$; y-intercept: $(0, -2)$ **7.** slope: $-\dfrac{3}{7}$; y-intercept: $(0, 2)$

9. slope: $-\dfrac{5}{3}$; y-intercept: $(0, -1)$ **11.** slope: -1; y-intercept: $(0, 5)$ **13.** slope: $\dfrac{7}{2}$; y-intercept: $(0, 5)$ **15.** slope: $\dfrac{1}{2}$; y-intercept: $\left(0, -\dfrac{3}{2}\right)$

17. slope: $\dfrac{2}{3}$; y-intercept: $(0, -1)$ **19.** slope: $\dfrac{2}{3}$; y-intercept: $(0, 2)$ **21.** slope: $-\dfrac{1}{2}$; y-intercept: $(0, 1)$ **23.** slope: 4; y-intercept: $(0, 0)$

25. slope: -1.5; y-intercept: $(0, 3)$ **27.** slope: 1; y-intercept: $(0, 0)$ **29.** slope: 0; y-intercept: $(0, 4)$ **31.** slope: 0; y-intercept: $(0, -2)$

33. slope: $\dfrac{a}{b}$; y-intercept: $\left(0, -\dfrac{c}{b}\right)$ **35.** slope: $\dfrac{b}{a}$; y-intercept: $\left(0, -\dfrac{bd}{a}\right)$ **37.** slope: $\dfrac{1}{a}$; y-intercept: $(0, -b)$ **39.** slope: 1;

y-intercept: $\left(0, -\dfrac{d}{a}\right)$ **41.** slope: -1; y-intercept: $(0, a)$ **43.** set 1: a line comes close to every point; set 2: a line with slope -0.3 passes through every point; set 3: no line comes close to every point; set 4: a line with slope -10 passes through every point.

45.

x	y	x	y	x	y	x	y
1	12	23	69	1	47	30	15
2	15	24	53	2	41	31	24
3	18	25	37	3	35	32	33
4	21	26	21	4	29	33	42
5	24	27	5	5	23	34	51
6	27	28	-11	6	17	35	60

47. parallel   **49.** neither   **51.** parallel   **53.** perpendicular   **55.** parallel   **57.** perpendicular   **59. a.** y values, from top: 18, 15, 12, 9, 6, 3, 0   **b.** The amount of gas is decreasing by 3 gallons per hour. The slope is -3.   **c.** 20 miles per gallon   **61. a.** y values, from top: 26, 28, 30, 32, 34   **b.** Her salary is increasing by \$2 thousand per year. The slope is 2.   **63. a.** m: negative; b: positive   **b.** m: positive; b: negative   **c.** m: 0; b: negative   **d.** m: negative; b: 0   **65.** $y = -2x + 3$ **67.** Answers may vary.   **69.** Answers may vary.

71. a. 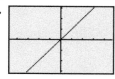   **b.** 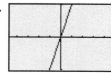   **c.**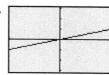

d. The graph appears steeper in part (b) than in part (a). The graph appears less steep in part (c) than in part (a).   **e.** no; no; the line will always appear to be increasing and will always pass through the origin and lie in quadrants I and III, but we may make it appear to have any steepness.   **73.** $y = 2x - 3$ **75. a.**   **b.** $y = 5x - 7$ **77. a.**    **b.** $y = -\dfrac{3}{8}x + \dfrac{27}{4}$

79. a. 0; 0; 0   **b.** 0   **81.** no; answers may vary.   **83.** Answers may vary.   **85.** Answers may vary.

Homework 1.5

1. $y = 3x - 13$; increasing   **3.** $y = -2x - 3$; decreasing   **5.** $y = \dfrac{3}{5}x - 5$; increasing   **7.** $y = -\dfrac{1}{6}x - \dfrac{8}{3}$; decreasing   **9.** $y = -\dfrac{5}{2}x - \dfrac{23}{2}$; decreasing   **11.** $y = 2$; horizontal   **13.** $x = 3$; vertical   **15.** $y = 1.6x + 0.44$ **17.** $y = -3.24x - 15.18$

19. $y = x + 1$ **21.** $y = -2x + 2$ **23.** $y = -2x - 22$ **25.** $y = x$ **27.** $y = \dfrac{4}{5}x - \dfrac{3}{5}$ **29.** $y = -\dfrac{7}{6}x - \dfrac{8}{3}$ **31.** $y = \dfrac{5}{2}x + \dfrac{11}{2}$

33. $y = 5$ **35.** $x = -3$ **37.** $y = 0.49x - 1.41$ **39.** $y = 0.46x - 3.47$ **41.** $y = 3x - 7$ **43.** $y = -2x + 2$ **45.** $y = \dfrac{1}{2}x - 1$

47. $y = \dfrac{3}{4}x + \dfrac{7}{4}$ **49.** $y = \dfrac{1}{6}x - \dfrac{3}{2}$ **51.** $y = 3$ **53.** $x = -5$ **55.** $y = -\dfrac{1}{2}x + \dfrac{19}{2}$ **57.** $y = \dfrac{1}{3}x + \dfrac{22}{3}$ **59.** $y = \dfrac{5}{2}x + 2$

61. $y = -\dfrac{5}{4}x + \dfrac{31}{2}$ **63.** $y = -\dfrac{3}{2}x - \dfrac{11}{2}$ **65.** $y = 3$ **67.** $x = 2$ **69.** $y = -2x + 19$ **71.** $y = \dfrac{1}{3}x - \dfrac{2}{3}$ **73.** $y = -\dfrac{3}{2}x + \dfrac{15}{2}$

75. a. yes; answers may vary.   **b.** yes; answers may vary.   **c.** no; answers may vary.   **d.** yes; $y = 0$ **77.** yes; $y = -2x + 7$
79. a–c. Answers may vary.   **81. a.** Answers may vary.   **b.** Answers may vary.   **c.** Answers may vary.   **d.** no   **83.** Answers may vary.   **85.** Answers may vary.   **87.** Answers may vary.

Homework 1.6

1. relations 2 and 3   **3.** no   **5.** yes   **7.** yes   **9.** no   **11.** no   **13.** yes   **15.** yes   **17.** yes   **19.** yes   **21.** no   **23.** yes   **25.** yes; the graph will pass the vertical line test.   **27.** no; the graph will not pass the vertical line test.
29. a. Answers may vary.   **b.** 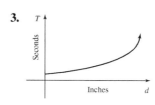   **c.** For each input–output pair, the output is 2 less than 3 times the input.

31. domain: $-4 \le x \le 5$; range: $-2 \le y \le 3$ **33.** domain: $-5 \le x \le 4$; range: $-2 \le y \le 3$ **35.** domain: $-4 \le x \le 4$; range: $-2 \le y \le 2$ **37.** domain: $0 \le x \le 4$; range: $0 \le y \le 2$ **39.** domain: all real numbers; range: $y \le 4$ **41.** domain: $x \ge 0$; range: $y \ge 0$
43. yes   **45.** no   **47.** Answers may vary.   **49.** Answers may vary. No; an input of $x = 2$ gives two different outputs.   **51.** Answers may vary.   **53.** Answers may vary.   **55.** nonvertical lines; answers may vary.   **57.** no; no input corresponds to two different outputs, so the definition of a function is not violated.

Chapter 1 Review

1. n independent, t dependent   **2.** 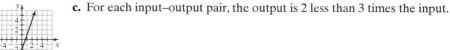   **3.**   **4.** $-\dfrac{11}{3}$ **5.** -11 **6.** $\dfrac{ac + d}{a}$

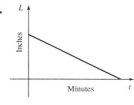

7. x-intercept: $\left(\dfrac{17}{3}, 0\right)$; y-intercept: $\left(0, -\dfrac{17}{5}\right)$ **8.** x-intercept: $\left(-\dfrac{b}{a}, 0\right)$; y-intercept: $\left(0, \dfrac{b}{c}\right)$ **9.** -4 **10.** $-\dfrac{2}{3}$ **11.** -4

12. -1 **13.** $-\dfrac{3}{5}$; decreasing **14.** $\dfrac{1}{2}$; increasing **15.** undefined; vertical **16.** -1.30; decreasing

17.   **18.**   **19.**   **20.** 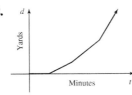 **21.**   **22.**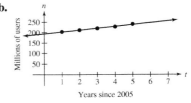

23. slope: 1; y-intercept: $\left(0, -\dfrac{c}{a}\right)$ **24.** neither **25.** parallel **26.** $y = -4x - 5$ **27.** $y = -\dfrac{2}{3}x - \dfrac{2}{3}$ **28.** $y = \dfrac{8}{5}x + \dfrac{14}{5}$

29. $y = -\dfrac{4}{3}x + \dfrac{2}{3}$ **30.** $x = 3$ **31.** $y = 0.39x - 7.37$ **32.** line 1: $y = -2x$; line 2: $y = 2x + 2$; line 3: $y = -3$ **33.** y values, from top: $20, 16, 12, 8, 4, 0$ **34.** $y = 0.5x + 3$ **35. a.** B, C, F **b.** C, E **c.** C **d.** A, D **36.** $y = 3x + 11$ **37.** yes; $y = 0$
38. relations 1 and 3 **39.** no **40.** yes **41.** no **42.** no **43.** domain: all real numbers; range: $y \le 4$

Chapter 1 Test

1. w independent; v dependent **2.**   **3.** Answers may vary. **4.** $\dfrac{4}{5}$

5. line 1: $y = -\dfrac{5}{2}x + 10$; line 2: $y = \dfrac{2}{3}x + 2$; line 3: $x = -3$ **6. a.** k **b.** b **7.** ski run A **8.** y values, from top: $25, 29, 33, 37, 41, 45$

9. 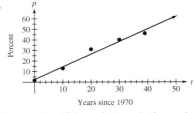 **10.** **11.** $-\dfrac{5}{4}$ **12.** $(-1, 10), (8, 4), (11, 2)$; answers may vary. **13.** $y = -\dfrac{3}{7}x + \dfrac{29}{7}$ **14.** $y = -\dfrac{12}{5}x - \dfrac{1}{5}$

15. no; $y = -2x + 1$ **16.** $y = -\dfrac{5}{3}x + \dfrac{17}{3}$ **17.** x-intercept: $\left(\dfrac{3}{2}, 0\right)$; y-intercept: $(0, -3)$ **18. a.** Answers may vary. **b.**

c. For each input–output pair, the output is 4 less than twice the input. **19.** Answers may vary. **20.** no **21.** yes
22. domain: $-3 \le x \le 5$; range: $-3 \le y \le 4$; yes

Chapter 2

Homework 2.1

1. a–b. 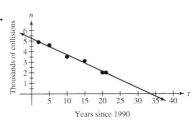 **c.** 60% **d.** 1985 **3. a–b.**

c. 2.6 thousand collisions; interpolation **d.** 2017; extrapolation **e.** $(0, 5.3)$; there were 5.3 thousand collisions in 1990.

f. $(34, 0)$; there will be no collisions in 2024; model breakdown has likely occurred. **5. a–b.**

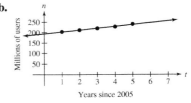

c. (0, 194); there were 194 million Internet users in 2005; extrapolation.   **d.** 9 million users per year   **e.** 2019; extrapolation; model breakdown has likely occurred.   **7. a–b.**

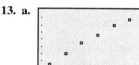

c. 27 years   **d.** (0, 85); 85% of newborns believe
marriages between same-sex couples should be recognized by the law as valid; model breakdown has occurred.
e. (117, 0); no 117-year-old Americans believe marriages
between same-sex couples should be recognized by law
as valid; model breakdown has occurred.

9. a–b.

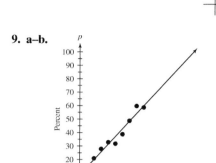

c. 100%   **d.**

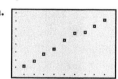

e. 69 percentage points; answers may
vary.

11. a. (2, 0); the profit was 0 dollars in 2004.   **b.** (0, −68); the profit was −68 million dollars in 2002.   **13.** Answers may vary.
15. Answers may vary.   **17.** Answers may vary.

Homework 2.2   **1.** $n = 34.9t − 291.9$ **3.** $p = −99.67t + 1609.67$ **5.** $p = 1.67t − 0.67$ **7.** $L = 1.96a + 15.21$
9. $y = 2.5x − 2.7$; answers may vary.   **11. a.**

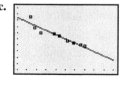

b. $p = 0.76t − 42.04$; answers may vary.

c.

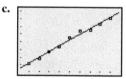

13. a.

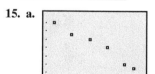

b. $p = 12.74n + 4.40$; answers may vary.   **c.**

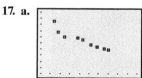

15. a.

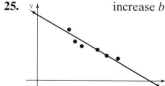

b. $p = −1.19t + 64.86$; answers may vary.   **c.**

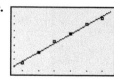

17. a.

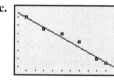

b. $r = −0.27t + 70.45$; answers may vary.   **c.**

19. a.

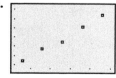

b. yes; 42.62 seconds; 2003

c. yes; after 2003   **21. a.**

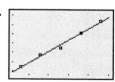

b. $p = 2.48x − 23.64$; answers may vary.   **c.**

23. student B

25.

increase b **27.** Answers may vary.

Homework 2.3 **1.** 26 **3.** 0 **5.** $6a + 8$ **7.** -2 **9.** 33 **11.** $\dfrac{1}{6}$ **13.** $\dfrac{3a-13}{5a-13}$ **15.** -16 **17.** -3 **19.** -4 **21.** $-20a - 7$

23. $-2a - 7$ **25.** $-4a - 23$ **27.** $-4a + 4h - 7$ **29.** $\dfrac{1}{3}$ **31.** $\dfrac{3}{2}$ **33.** $\dfrac{7-a}{3}$ **35.** 118.31 **37.** 14.10 **39.** 4 **41.** 1, 3 **43.** 4 **45.** $\dfrac{7}{6}$

47. 6 **49.** -3 **51.** 4.5 **53.** all real numbers **55.** 1 **57.** $-4 \le x \le 5$ **59.** -3 **61.** $-5 \le x \le 4$ **63.** x-intercept: $\left(\dfrac{8}{5}, 0\right)$;

y-intercept: $(0, -8)$ **65.** x-intercept: $(0, 0)$; y-intercept: $(0, 0)$ **67.** no x-intercept; y-intercept: $(0, 5)$ **69.** x-intercept: $(6, 0)$;

y-intercept: $(0, -3)$ **71.** x-intercept: $(17.52, 0)$; y-intercept: $(0, -45.21)$ **73. a.** Answers may vary. **b.** 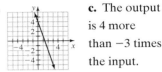 **c.** The output is 4 more than -3 times the input.

75. a. $f(t) = 0.76t - 42.04$ **b.** 47.6; in 2018, 47.6% of births will be outside marriage. **c.** 117.16; in 2017, 47% of births will be outside marriage. **d.** 2087; model breakdown has likely occurred. **e.** 31.7%; -0.7 percentage point **77. a.** $f(t) = -1.19t + 64.86$
b. 31.54; in 2018, baseball will be the favorite sport of about 32% of Americans. **c.** 30.97; in 2021, baseball will be the favorite sport of 28% of Americans. **d.** $(0, 64.86)$; in 1990, baseball was the favorite sport of about 65% of Americans. **e.** $(54.50, 0)$; in 2045, baseball will not be the favorite sport of any Americans; model breakdown has likely occurred. **79. a.** $f(n) = 12.74n + 4.40$ **b.** $(0, 4.40)$; the price of renting skis for 0 days is $4.40; model breakdown has occurred. **c.** $93.58 **d.** 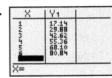 12.74; equal to slope of the graph of f; the price increases by $12.74 for each additional day.

e. 17.14, 14.94, 14.21, 13.84, 13.62, 13.47; 13.47; the cost per day is lowest for a 6-day package ($13.47 per day). **f.** The cost increase for each additional day is less than the $13 charge per day; the cost per day for the 6-day package is more than the $13 charge per day.
81. a. 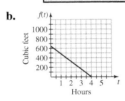 **b.** $f(t) = 24.07t + 423.92$; yes **c.** 689 million; 67 million boardings **d.** $5.7 billion
83. a. $f(C) = 1.8C + 32$ **b.** 75.2°F **c.** 17.78°C **d.** -459.67°F **85. a.** $f(x) = 2.48x - 23.64$
b. 50 points **c.** less than 10 points **d.** 30 students; no **e.** 83 students **87.** $13.7 thousand
89. 2018 **91. a.** $4.7 billion **b.** 2021 **93.** 218 points **95. a.** $f(t) = -160t + 640$
b. **c.** domain: $0 \le t \le 4$; range: $0 \le f(t) \le 640$ **97.** The student should substitute 5 for $f(x)$, not x; 3
99. a. 12; 20; 32; yes **b.** 4; 9; 25; no **c.** 3; 4; 5; no **d.** no **101.** Answers may vary. **103.** input: 3; output: 5; answers may vary.

Homework 2.4 **1.** about 1.77 shredder models per year **3.** -3 million trips per year **5.** about -4.58 executions per year
7. $98 per credit hour **9. a.** yes; 70; the student is traveling 70 miles per hour. **b.** $d = 70t$ **11. a.** yes; 5.3; the number of house-holds that pay bills online has increased by 5.3 million per year. **b.** $(0, 66)$; in 2010, 66 million households paid bills online.
c. $n = 5.3t + 66$ **d.** The units of the expressions on both sides of the equation are millions of households. **e.** 97.8 million households
13. a. -0.7; the unemployment rate has decreased by 0.7 percentage point per year. **b.** $g(t) = -0.7t + 7.8$ **c.** 2015; earlier
d. 4.3% **e.** $(11.14, 0)$; no one will be unemployed in 2023; model breakdown has occurred. **15. a.** 45; textbook rental costs $45 per course. **b.** $f(n) = 45n + 15.50$ **c.** The units of the expressions on both sides of the equation are dollars. **d.** 195.5; the cost of an ID plus textbook rental for 4 courses is $195.50. **e.** 5; a student who pays $240.50 for an ID and textbook rental is taking 5 courses.
17. a. -0.05; the car uses 0.05 gallon of gas per mile. **b.** $g(x) = -0.05x + 15.3$ **c.** $(306, 0)$; after she has driven 306 miles, the tank will be empty. **d.** domain: $0 \le x \le 306$; range: $0 \le g(x) \le 15.3$ **e.** 286 miles **19. a.** $s = 33.3t + 400$, where s is the sales (in millions of gallons) in the year that is t years since 2012; answers may vary. **b.** The units for both of the expressions s and $33.3t + 400$ are millions of gallons; answers may vary. **c.** 33.3; sales are increasing by 33.3 million gallons per year; answers may vary. **d.** 2018; 2.1 gallons
21. a. $c = 2d + 5.75$, where c is cab fare (in dollars) for traveling d miles; answers may vary. **b.** 13 miles **23.** 2014; yes
25. 870 minutes **27.** 1.82; the average salary increases by $1820 per year. **29.** -0.27; the record time for the women's 400-meter run decreased by 0.27 second per year. **31.** 1.8; for each 1° temperature increase on the Celsius scale, the Fahrenheit temperature rises by 1.8°. **33. a.** $f(t) = -0.36t + 70.29$ **b.** -0.36; the percentage of the world's population that lives in rural areas has decreased by 0.36 percentage point per year. **c.** 3.4 billion **d.** 2017 **e.** $(195.25, 0)$; in 2145, none of the world's population will live in rural areas;

model breakdown has likely occurred.   **35. a.** no; a line doesn't lie near all the points.   **b.** 0 billion barrels per year; if the data could be modeled exactly by a linear function, an average rate of change of 0 would mean that oil production did not change from year to year in the period 1992–2007. But there *were* changes; so, the data cannot be modeled exactly by a linear function for this period.   **c.** yes; $U(t) = -0.059t + 2.76$ **d.** -0.059 billion barrels per year.   **e.** 2018   **37. a.** $f(a) = -0.99a + 29.85$ **b.** -0.99; for each thousand-foot increase in altitude, the pressure decreases by 0.99 inch of mercury.   **c. i.** -1.01 inches of mercury per thousand feet; close to -0.99 **ii.** -0.98 inch of mercury per thousand feet; close to -0.99 **iii.** -0.99 inch of mercury per thousand feet; equal to slope   **d.** 15.55 inches of mercury   **39. a.**

t	0	1	2	3	4	5
$f(t)$	0	500	1000	1500	1900	2300

b.   **c.** no   **d.** Answers may vary.

41. $-\dfrac{5}{3}$; the revenue is decreasing by about \$1.67 million per year.   **43.** $\dfrac{5}{4}$; the price increases \$1.25 per ingredient.

45. 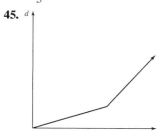   **47.** 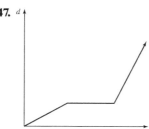   **49.** Answers may vary.   **51.** Answers may vary.

Chapter 2 Review

1. 20   **2.** 20   **3.** $\dfrac{3}{4}$ **4.** -9 **5.** $-10a - 33$ **6.** $-\dfrac{9}{2}$ **7.** $-\dfrac{7}{6}$ **8.** $\dfrac{a + 4}{2}$ **9.** 0   **10.** 1   **11.** 3.6   **12.** -2 **13.** 2   **14.** 4

15. $-5 \le x \le 6$ **16.** $-2 \le y \le 4$ **17.** 1   **18.** 4   **19.** 4   **20.** 1   **21.** x-intercept: $\left(\dfrac{3}{7}, 0\right)$; y-intercept: $(0, 3)$ **22.** x-intercept: none; y-intercept: $(0, 4)$ **23.** x-intercept: $\left(\dfrac{7}{2}, 0\right)$; y-intercept: $(0, 2)$ **24.** x-intercept: $(30.57, 0)$; y-intercept: $(0, -8.32)$

25. Increase the slope and lower the y-intercept.   **26. a.** $f(t) = -1.8t + 13$ **b.** -1.8; the car uses 1.8 gallons of gas per hour.   **c.** $(0, 13)$; he started the trip with 13 gallons in the tank.   **d.** The units of the expressions on both sides of the equation are gallons.   **e.** $(7.2, 0)$; the tank will be empty after 7.2 hours of driving at 65 miles per hour.   **f.** domain: $0 \le t \le 7.2$; range: $0 \le A \le 13$ **27. a.** 37; the median compensation is increasing by \$37 thousand per year.   **b.** $C(t) = 37t + 870$ **c.** 1166; the median compensation will be \$1166 thousand (\$1.166 million) in 2018.   **d.** 3.51; the median compensation will be \$1000 thousand (\$1 million) in 2014.   **28.** -0.53 million vehicles per year (-530 thousand vehicles per year)   **29.** \$29,052; overestimate; answers may vary.   **30. a.** $f(t) = 2.02t + 32.32$ **b.** 2.02; each year, the IRS standard mileage rate for businesses has increased by about 2.0 cents per mile.   **c.** $(0, 32.32)$; in 2000, the standard mileage rate was about 32.3 cents per mile.   **d.** 2018   **e.** \$8375   **f.** 54.5 is the average of 50.5 and 58.5.   **31. a.** $f(t) = -2.11t + 39.02$ **b.** -2.11; the percentage of Americans who think the First Amendment goes too far in the rights it guarantees decreases by 2.11 percentage points per year.   **c.** 2017   **d.** 22.14; in 2008, 22% of Americans thought the First Amendment went too far in the rights it guarantees.   **e.** 14.70; in 2015, 8% of Americans will think the First Amendment goes too far in the rights it guarantees.   **f.** $(18.49, 0)$; in 2018, no Americans will think the First Amendment goes too far in the rights it guarantees; model breakdown has occurred.

Chapter 2 Test

1. -2 **2.** 0   **3.** -1 **4.** -2.7 **5.** -6 **6.** -3 **7.** 3   **8.** 4.5   **9.** $-6 \le x \le 6$ **10.** $-3 \le y \le 1$ **11.** 19   **12.** $-4a + 27$ **13.** $\dfrac{5}{4}$ **14.** $-\dfrac{a - 7}{4}$ or $\dfrac{7 - a}{4}$ **15.** x-intercept: $\left(\dfrac{7}{3}, 0\right)$; y-intercept: $(0, -7)$ **16.** x-intercept: $(0, 0)$; y-intercept: $(0, 0)$ **17.** x-intercept: $(24, 0)$; y-intercept: $(0, -8)$ **18. a.** $f(a) = 6.81a - 52.32$ **b.** 6.81; the percentage of teenagers who have driver's licenses increases by 6.81 percentage points per year of age.   **c.** $(7.68, 0)$; no 8-year-olds have driver's licenses.   **d.** 90.7%   **e.** 22 years; model breakdown has likely occurred.   **19. a.** $f(t) = 0.26t + 0.53$ **b.** 0.26; The number of farmers markets is increasing by 0.26 thousand (260) markets per year.   **c.** 2.61; in 1998, there were about 2.6 thousand farmers markets.   **d.** 28.73; in 2019, there will be 8 thousand farmers markets.

e. $(-2.04, 0)$; in 1988, there were no farmers markets; model breakdown has occurred.   **20.** \$832.5 million   **21. a.** yes; 1.7; the number of states with ethanol plants is increasing by about 1.7 states per year.   **b.** $(0, 29)$; 29 states had ethanol plants in 2012. **c.** $f(t) = 1.7t + 29$ **d.** 39 states   **e.** 2024   **22.**

Chapter 3

Homework 3.1   **1.** $(1, 4)$ **3.** $(-6, 6)$ **5.** $(2, 3)$ **7.** $(4, 4)$ **9.** $(0, 5)$ **11.** all points on the line $y = -2x + 3$; dependent system **13.** empty set; inconsistent system   **15.** $(4, 2)$ **17.** $(-1.12, -3.69)$ **19.** $(-1.61, 2.04)$ **21.** all points on the line $y = 2x - 1$; dependent system   **23.** empty set; inconsistent system   **25.** $(3.33, 1.33)$ **27. a.** 37.07 seconds; 34.24 seconds; -0.98 second; -0.67 second   **b.** The absolute value of the slope of W is greater than the absolute value of the slope of M; the women's winning times are decreasing at a faster rate than the men's winning times.   **c.** Answers may vary.   **d.** 2167; 13.02 seconds; model breakdown has likely occurred.   **29. a.** $C(t) = -2.7t + 53.1$; $W(t) = 2.5t + 21.5$ **b.** 2006; 37%   **c.** 71%   **31. a.** $I(t) = 2.3t + 47.6$; $B(t) = 6.83t + 1.4$ **b.** 2010   **c.** Answers may vary.   **33.** $(-1.9, -2.8)$ **35.** $(10, -1)$ **37.** $(3, -4)$ **39.** $(3.5, 19.5)$ **41.** 0   **43.** 5   **45.** -1 **47. a.** B and E   **b.** E and F   **c.** E   **d.** A, C, and D   **49. a–c.** Answers may vary.   **51.** $(2, 3)$ **53.** Answers may vary.   **55.** The ordered pair $(1, 2)$ does not satisfy the equation $y = -2x + 9$, so $(1, 2)$ is not a solution of the system; $(2, 5)$ **57.** Answers may vary.

Homework 3.2   **1.** $(7, 2)$ **3.** $(-5, -3)$ **5.** $(3, -4)$ **7.** $(0, 0)$ **9.** $(-3, -7)$ **11.** $(2, 1)$ **13.** $(-1, 2)$ **15.** $(4, -3)$ **17.** $(4, -7)$ **19.** $(2, 3)$ **21.** $(-1, 4)$ **23.** $(1, -2)$ **25.** $(-4, 3)$ **27.** $(-2, 3)$ **29.** $(-2, 3)$ **31.** $(-3, -4)$ **33.** $(3, -2)$ **35.** $(2, 1)$ **37.** $(5, 4)$ **39.** $(-2, 3)$ **41.** empty set; inconsistent system   **43.** $(1, -2)$ **45.** all points on the line $4x - 5y = 3$; dependent system

47. empty set; inconsistent system   **49.** $(3, -2)$ **51.** $(-3, 1)$ **53.** all points on the line $y = \frac{1}{2}x + 3$; dependent system   **55.** $(3, 2)$ **57.** $(1, 2)$ **59.** $(2.77, -1.15)$ **61.** $(-4.11, 8.01)$ **63.** -3 **65.** 1   **67.** -5 **69.** 4   **71.** 1   **73.** $(-2, 1)$ **75.** 1.57   **77.** -2.42

79. -1.58 **81.** 5   **83.** 3   **85.** $(1, 2.8)$ **87.** $\left(\frac{47}{10}, \frac{109}{5} \right)$ **89.** $(2, 5)$ **91. a.** $(3, 1)$ **b.** $(3, 1)$ **c.** They are the same.   **93.** The lines are not parallel; $(200, 403)$ **95.** A: $(0, 0)$; B: $(0, 3)$; C: $(3, 9)$; D: $(6, 8)$; E: $\left(\frac{36}{5}, \frac{22}{5} \right)$; F: $(5, 0)$ **97. a.** $\left(\frac{cp - bd}{ap - bk}, \frac{ad - ck}{ap - bk} \right)$, assuming that $ap - bk \neq 0$ **b.** $\left(\frac{14}{11}, -\frac{4}{11} \right)$ **99.** Answers may vary.   **101.** Answers may vary.

Homework 3.3   **1.** 2167; 13.02 seconds; model breakdown has likely occurred.   **3. a.** 2.30; 6.83; the percentage of households that have Internet access is increasing by 2.30 percentage points per year; the percentage of households that have broadband Internet access is increasing by 6.83 percentage points per year.   **b.** Answers may vary.   **c.** 2010   **5. a.** $M(t) = -0.28t + 50.87$; $S(t) = 0.82t - 32.00$ **b.** 1975; 29.8 gallons per person   **c.**

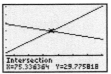

d. Answers may vary.   **e.** Answers may vary. **7. a.** $K(a) = 0.014a - 0.75$; $M(a) = -0.028a + 1.66$ **b.** 57 years; 0.1 point

c.

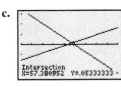

9. a. 1997   **b.** The competition heated up because the two newspapers had approximately equal circulations.   **c.** 147 thousand bonus issues   **d.** 688 thousand newspapers   **e.** overestimate; answers may vary.   **11. a.** $F(t) = -1414t + 14{,}290$; $D(t) = -3740t + 30{,}450$ **b.** 2019; \$4466

c.

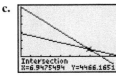

13. a. $N(t) = 91t$; $W(t) = 87t + 20$ **b.** For each equation, the units of the expressions on both sides of the equation are dollars.   **c.** 5 weeks; \$455

d.

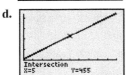

e. Weight Watchers   **15.** 2023; 35.3%   **17. a.** $H(t) = 1.31t + 24.5$; $C(t) = 0.99t + 28.9$ **b.** 2014; \$42.5 thousand

c.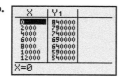

d. $46.25 thousand; overestimate; answers may vary.
19. 2013; 17.9%   **21. a–b.**

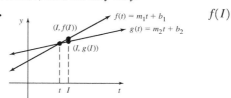

Homework 3.4   **1.** 3800 tickets at $27, 1200 tickets at $40   **3.** 128 of album *Plans,* 708 of album *Codes and Keys*   **5.** $25 for balcony seats, $40 for main-level seats   **7.** 1500 part-time students, 4500 full-time students   **9. a.** $f(x) = -25x + 1,500,000$

b. [graph] -25; the more $50 tickets are sold (so, the fewer $75 tickets are sold), the lower the total revenue will be (by $25 for each additional $50 ticket sold).   **c.** 1,100,000; if 16,000 $50 tickets are sold (and 4000 $75 tickets are sold), the total revenue will be $1,100,000.   **d.** 17,000 $50 tickets, 3000 $75 tickets

11. a. $f(x) = -25x + 840,000$ **b.** 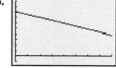 See second column of table. If the number of $45 tickets sold is 0, 2000, 4000, 6000, 8000, 10,000, or 12,000, the total revenue will be $840,000, $790,000, $740,000, $690,000, $640,000, $590,000, or $540,000, respectively.   **c.** The total revenue will be between $540,000 and $840,000, inclusive.

d. 9500 $45 tickets, 2500 $70 tickets   **13. a.** $f(x) = 134x + 1936$ **b.** 134; if the prices of all tickets are increased by $1, the total revenue increases by $134.   **c.** coach: $91; first class: $333   **15.** $12,000 in American Funds New Perspective F; $3000 in Oppenheimer Global Y   **17.** $6000 in GMO Growth III; $2500 in Gartmore Destinations Mod Agg Svc   **19.** $4000 in Lord Abbett Developing Growth B; $2000 in Bridgeway Micro-Cap Limited   **21.** $4500 in Dreyfus Premier Worldwide Growth R; $1500 in Oppenheimer Global Opportunities Y   **23. a.** $f(x) = -0.0523x + 810$ **b.** [graph] -0.0523; for each additional $1 invested in the CD (so, $1 less invested in the mutual fund), the total interest decreases by 5.23 cents.   **c.** CD: $7839.39; mutual fund: $2160.61

25. a. $f(x) = -0.0695x + 850.5$ **b.** 815.75; if $500 is invested in the CD (and $8500 in the mutual fund), the total interest will be $815.75.   **c.** 5043.17; if $5043.17 is invested in the CD (and $3956.83 in the mutual fund), the total interest will be $500.   **d.** 155.5; if $10,000 is invested in the CD, the total interest will be $155.50; model breakdown has occurred, because only $9000 is being invested.
27. a. $f(x) = -0.101x + 928$ **b.** The total interest will be between $120 and $675.50, inclusive.   **c.** $5227.72 should be invested in the CD and $2772.28 in the mutual fund.   **29. a.** $f(x) = -0.0615x + 540$ **b.** (0, 540); if all of the $6000 is invested in the mutual fund, the total interest will be $540.   **c.** (8780.49, 0); if $8780.49 is invested in the CD, the revenue will be $0; model breakdown has occurred, because only $6000 is being invested.   **d.** -0.0615; if $1 more is invested in the CD (and $1 less in the mutual fund), the total interest will decrease by 6.15 cents.   **31.** 4 ounces of 10% solution, 6 ounces of 30% solution   **33.** 1 gallon of 5% solution, 2 gallons of 20% solution   **35.** 4 cups of 10% solution, 2 cups of 25% solution   **37.** 4 liters of 25% solution, 1 liter of water
39. 20%   **41.** Answers may vary; $x = 42, y = 72$ **43.** Answers may vary; $x = 1500, y = 500$

Homework 3.5

1.

In Words	Inequality	Graph	Interval Notation
Numbers greater than 3	$x > 3$	[graph: open circle at 3]	$(3, \infty)$
Numbers less than or equal to -4	$x \le -4$	[graph: closed circle at -4]	$(-\infty, -4]$
Numbers less than 5	$x < 5$	[graph: open circle at 5]	$(-\infty, 5)$
Numbers greater than or equal to -1	$x \ge -1$	[graph: closed circle at -1]	$[-1, \infty)$

3. $x \geq 3$; $[3, \infty)$; 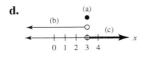 x **5.** $x \leq -3$; $(-\infty, -3]$; x **7.** $w < 2$; $(-\infty, 2)$; w

9. $x < 1$; $(-\infty, 1)$; x **11.** $x \leq 5.6$; $(-\infty, 5.6]$; x

13. $b < -5$; $(-\infty, -5)$; b **15.** $x < \dfrac{5}{3}$; $\left(-\infty, \dfrac{5}{3}\right)$; x

17. $a < -2.3$; $(-\infty, -2.3)$; a **19.** $x \geq 23$; $[23, \infty)$; x

21. $r \leq 2$; $(-\infty, 2]$; r **23.** $x < -6$; $(-\infty, -6)$; x

25. $t \geq -\dfrac{22}{9}$; $\left[-\dfrac{22}{9}, \infty\right)$; t **27.** $x \leq -\dfrac{7}{12}$; $\left(-\infty, -\dfrac{7}{12}\right]$; x

29. $c \geq -31$; $[-31, \infty)$; c **31.** $x < -5$; $(-\infty, -5)$; x

33. $1 < x < 5$; $(1, 5)$; x **35.** $-5 \leq x \leq 6$; $[-5, 6]$; x

37. $-3 \leq x < 5$; $[-3, 5)$; x **39.** $3 < x \leq \dfrac{11}{2}$; $\left(3, \dfrac{11}{2}\right]$; x

41. years before 2019   **43. a.** $U(d) = 0.69d + 19.95$; $P(d) = 0.39d + 29.95$ **b.** for miles driven less than 33.33 miles   **45.** years after 2015   **47. a.** $D(t) = 0.34t + 0.56$; $C(t) = -1.52t + 10.57$ **b.** after 2010   **c.** -1.18; the total revenue from downloaded music and music CDs is decreasing by \$1.18 billion per year.   **49. a.** 4.0 years   **b.** for birth years after 2062   **c. i.** younger man   **ii.** birth years 1986 and thereafter   **51.** When dividing by 3, do not reverse the inequality symbol; $x > -2$ **53. a, b.** Answers may vary.
55. Answers may vary.   **57. a.** $x = 3$ **b.** $x < 3$ **c.** $x > 3$

d.   **e.** 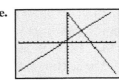 $f(x) < g(x)$ when $x < 3$; $f(x) = g(x)$ when $x = 3$; $f(x) > g(x)$ when $x > 3$.
59. no   **61.** no   **63.** $x < 2.8$ **65.** Answers may vary.   **67.** Answers may vary.

Homework 3.6

1. 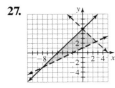   **3.**   **5.** 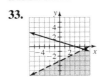   **7.**   **9.**   **11.**   **13.**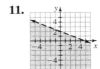

15. 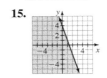   **17.**   **19.**   **21.**   **23.**   **25.**

27.   **29.**   **31.**   **33.**   **35.**   **37.**

39. a. $B(t) = 0.196t + 70.00$; $T(t) = 0.167t + 51.73$ **b.** The system consists of the inequalities $L \leq 0.196t + 70.00$, $L \geq 0.167t + 51.73$, $t \geq 0$, and $t \leq 40$.

c.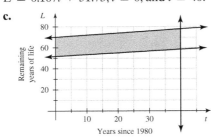

Remaining years of life — Years since 1980

d. between 57.6 years and 76.9 years   **41. a.** $B(w) = 0.44w + 84.21$; $I(w) = 0.44w + 89.21$ **b.** The system consists of the inequalities $L \geq 0.44w + 84.21$, $L \leq 0.44w + 89.21$, $w \geq 130$, and $w \leq 150$.

c. 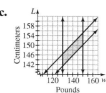   **d.** from 145.81 centimeters to 150.81 centimeters   **43.** The graph is the region above the line $2x - 3y = 6$.

45. Answers may vary.   **47.**   **49. a. i.**   **ii.**   **iii.**

iv.   **v.**   **b.** Answers may vary.   **51.** Answers may vary.

Chapter 3 Review

1. $(4, -5)$ **2.** $(3, 2)$ **3.** $(-3, 2)$ **4.** empty set; inconsistent system   **5.** all points on the line $-4x - 5y = 3$; dependent system
6. $(1.2, -2.86)$ **7.** $(0, 0)$ **8.** $(2, -3)$ **9.** $(10, 3)$ **10.** $(2, -1)$ **11.** $(5, -1)$ **12. a–c.** Answers may vary.   **13.** 1   **14.** -5
15. $(0.4, 15.1), (2.6, 21.9)$ **16.** $a = 19, b = 18$ **17.** A: $(0, 0)$; B: $(0, 4)$; C: $(2, 10)$; D: $(5, 8)$; E: $(6, 4)$; F: $\left(\dfrac{14}{3}, 0\right)$ **18.** empty set
19. $x \le 7; (-\infty, 7]$; ⟵———•——→ x **20.** $a \le 2.8; (-\infty, 2.8]$; ⟵———•——→ a
               0   7   0   2.8
21. $x \le -\dfrac{7}{16}; \left(-\infty, -\dfrac{7}{16}\right]$; ⟵•———+———→ x **22.** $x < -\dfrac{29}{2}; \left(-\infty, -\dfrac{29}{2}\right)$; ⟵—+○——+——→ x
             $-\frac{7}{16}$ 0 -15 -14 0
23. $-2 \le x < 3; [-2, 3)$; ⟵•———○——→ x **24. a, b.** Answers may vary.   **25.** When dividing both sides of the inequality by -3,
             -2 0   3
reverse the inequality symbol; $x \ge -2$ **26.** 1   **27.** -5 **28.** -2 **29.** $x > -2$ **30.** Answers may vary.
31.   **32.**   **33.**   **34.**   **35.**   **36.**   **37.**

38. Answers may vary.   **39. a.** $L(t) = -4.23t + 113.20; W(t) = 4.28t - 15.94$ **b.** $-4.23; 4.28$; the percentage of households with phone landlines is decreasing by 4.23 percentage points per year; the percentage of households with only wireless phones is increasing by 4.28 percentage points per year.   **c.** 2015; 49.0%   **d.** Some households do not have phones.   **e.** $t > 15.18$; the percentage of households with phone landlines will be less than the percentage of households with only wireless phones after 2015.
40. a. $w(t) = -0.58t + 31.57; p(t) = -0.37t + 20.76$ **b.** 2021; 1.7   **41. a.** $R(d) = 0.22d + 75; U(d) = 0.69d + 29.95$
b. 95.85 miles; $96.09   **c.** for miles driven over 95.85 miles   **42.** 2019   **43.** 13,500 tickets at $55; 6500 tickets at $70
44. a. $f(x) = -0.062x + 1040$ **b.** 1004.35; if $575 is invested in Hartford Global Leaders Y (and $7425 in Mutual Discovery Z), the total interest will be $1004.35.   **c.** 7500; if $7500 is invested in Hartford Global Leaders Y (and $500 in Mutual Discovery Z), the total interest will be $575.

Chapter 3 Test

1. $(1, 2)$ **2.** all points on the line $2x - 5y = 3$; dependent   **3.** empty set; inconsistent system   **4.** $(5, -8)$ **5.** $(-2, 4)$
6. Answers may vary.   **7.** $(3, 1)$ **8.** $m = 5, b \ne -13$ **9.** $x \le -\dfrac{12}{13}; \left(-\infty, -\dfrac{12}{13}\right]$; ⟵•——+——→ x
                           -1 0
10. $x > \dfrac{23}{2}; \left(\dfrac{23}{2}, \infty\right)$; ⟵—+○+——→ x **11.** $t < 0.8; (-\infty, 0.8)$; ⟵——+○+——→ t
               11   12   0   1
12. $w \ge \dfrac{2}{41}; \left[\dfrac{2}{41}, \infty\right)$; ⟵——•————→ w **13.** $x > 13$ **14.** 3   **15.** -4 **16.** 2   **17.** $x \le 2$ **18.** -1.44 **19. a, b.** Answers may vary.
              $\frac{2}{41}$
20.   **21.**   **22.**   **23. a.** $w(t) = -0.73t + 98.28; s(t) = -0.94t + 90.78$ **b.** 1934; 124.4 feet
                                   c. 54.5 feet   **24. a.** $A(t) = 0.8t - 1; B(t) = -0.47t + 6.97$ **b.** 2006; 4.0 billion   **c.** years before 2006   **d.** -0.47; the revenue of Borders decreased by $0.47 billion (470 million) per year; answers may vary.
25. 4 gallons of 10% solution, 6 gallons of 20% solution

26. a. $f(x) = -15x + 500,000$ **b.** -15; the more \$35 tickets are sold (so, the fewer \$50 tickets are sold), the lower the total revenue will be (by \$15 for each additional \$35 ticket sold).   **c.** 7300 \$35 tickets, 2700 \$50 tickets

Cumulative Review, Chapters 1–3

1.

2.   **3.**   **4.** $-\dfrac{3}{7}$ **5.** $y = -\dfrac{3}{5}x - \dfrac{9}{5}$ **6.** $y = \dfrac{5}{3}x + \dfrac{19}{3}$

7. $y = -\dfrac{5}{2}x - \dfrac{19}{2}$ **8.** Answers may vary.

9.

x	$f(x)$	x	$g(x)$	x	$h(x)$	x	$k(x)$
0	97	4	-22	1	23	10	-28
1	84	5	-9	2	14	11	-25
2	71	6	4	3	5	12	-22
3	58	7	17	4	-4	13	-19
4	45	8	30	5	-13	14	-16
5	32	9	43	6	-22	15	-13

10. 32   **11.** 8   **12.** 13   **13.** $\dfrac{32}{9}$ **14.** $\left(\dfrac{14}{3}, 0\right)$ **15.** $(0, 7)$

16. 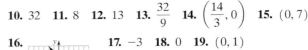   **17.** -3 **18.** 0   **19.** $(0, 1)$

20. $f(x) = \dfrac{2}{3}x + 1$ **21.** -3 **22.** $x \le -3$

23. $-\dfrac{20}{9}$ **24.** $\dfrac{3}{5}$ **25.** $b = cd + k$ **26.** x-intercept: $\left(-\dfrac{2}{5}, 0\right)$; y-intercept: $\left(0, \dfrac{2}{3}\right)$ **27.** $-5 \le x \le 5$ **28.** $-2 \le y \le 3$

29. yes   **30.** $(2, -3)$ **31.** all points on the line $y = \dfrac{3}{7}x - 2$ **32.** -2 **33.** 6   **34.** $(2, -2)$

35. $x \le \dfrac{10}{11}$; $\left(-\infty, \dfrac{10}{11}\right]$; 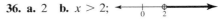   **36. a.** 2   **b.** $x > 2$; 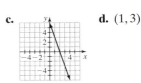   **c.** 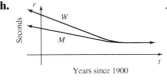   **d.** $(1, 3)$

37. a–f. Answers may vary.   **38. a.** $f(t) = -2.37t + 35.17$ **b.** 25.69; in the year 2004, about 25.7 thousand foreign children were adopted by American families.   **c.** 13.15; in the year 2013, 4 thousand foreign children will be adopted by American families. **d.** -2.37; each year there is a decrease of 2.37 thousand foreign children adopted by American families.   **e.** $(14.84, 0)$; in 2015, American families will not adopt any foreign children; model breakdown has likely occurred.   **39. a.** $f(t) = -9t + 82$ **b.** -9; each year 9 fewer bicyclists younger than 16 are hit and killed by motor vehicles.   **c.** $(0, 82)$; in the year 2009, 82 bicyclists younger than 16 were hit and killed by motor vehicles.   **d.** $(9.11, 0)$; in 2018, no bicyclists younger than 16 will be hit and killed by motor vehicles; model breakdown has likely occurred.   **e.** years after 2018   **40. a.** $H(t) = 2.2t + 86.8$; $L(t) = 3.2t + 95.9$ **b.** 2.2; 3.2; the DSI of Home Depot is increasing by 2.2 days per year; the DSI of Lowes is increasing by 3.2 days per year; negative slope; answers may vary.   **c.** 2001; 66.8 days **d.** $t > -9.1$; the DSI of Home Depot has been less than the DSI of Lowes after 2001.   **41. a.** $W(t) = -0.064t + 27.00$; $M(t) = -0.026t + 21.86$ **b.** $W(118) = 19.45$; $M(118) = 18.79$; in 2018, the women's record time will be 19.45 seconds and the men's record time will be 18.79 seconds.   **c.** The absolute value of W's slope is greater than the absolute value of M's slope. Women's record times are decreasing at a greater rate than men's record times.   **d.** Answers may vary.   **e.** 2035; 18.34 seconds   **f.** $t < 135$; women's record times are greater than men's record times for years before 2035.   **g.** W: $(421.88, 0)$; M: $(840.77, 0)$; the women's record time will be 0 seconds in 2322, and the men's record time will be 0 seconds in 2741; model breakdown has occurred.

h.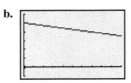

Answers may vary.   **42.** \$5000 in UBS Global Equity Y, \$2500 in Fidelity Worldwide

Chapter 4

Homework 4.1   **1.** $\frac{1}{2}$ **3.** 1   **5.** -16 **7.** 16   **9.** 64   **11.** $\frac{5}{6}$ **13.** 49   **15.** 1   **17.** 1   **19.** $\frac{1}{b^2}$ **21.** $-\frac{14}{b^8}$ **23.** $\frac{72}{b}$ **25.** $108b^{12}c^{22}$

27. $\frac{3}{b^{10}c^2}$ **29.** $\frac{32b^{26}}{9c^2}$ **31.** $\frac{1}{b^{25}}$ **33.** $\frac{2}{5b^3}$ **35.** $-\frac{6}{7b^{10}}$ **37.** $-\frac{1}{3bc^5}$ **39.** $-\frac{1}{4b^{10}c^{14}}$ **41.** $\frac{3b^5}{c^{13}}$ **43.** $\frac{54b^{18}}{c^7}$ **45.** $\frac{b^8c^7}{32}$ **47.** $\frac{36b^6}{49c^{12}}$

49. $\frac{81c^8}{b^{24}}$ **51.** 1   **53.** $\frac{1}{bc}$ **55.** $b + c$ **57.** b^{7n} **59.** b^{5n-4} **61.** 54   **63.** $\frac{2}{81}$ **65.** $16(4^a)$ **67.** 16^a

69. a.

x	$f(x)$	x	$f(x)$
-3	$\frac{1}{8}$	1	2
-2	$\frac{1}{4}$	2	4
-1	$\frac{1}{2}$	3	8
0	1	4	16

b.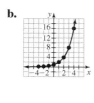

c. 1.4   **71.** 396.5   **73.** 0.239   **75.** 520   **77.** 0.00009113
79. -0.000652 **81.** 900,000   **83.** -8 **85.** 5.426×10^7
87. 2.3587×10^4 **89.** 9.8×10^{-4} **91.** 3.46×10^{-5}
93. -4.2215×10^4 **95.** -2.44×10^{-3} **97.** $0.0000063; 0.00013;$
$3,200,000; 64,000,000$ **99.** $3,600,000,000$ years   **101.** 0.000000063
mole per liter   **103.** 1.008×10^7 gallons   **105.** 4.7×10^{-7} meter

107. a.  exponential function   **b.** 21.7 thousand pairs   **c.** 10.3 thousand pairs; answers may vary.
109. Student B was correct; student A should have 5 in the denominator, not -5
in the numerator.   **111.** The 3 should stay in the numerator; $\frac{3c^4}{b^2d^7}$

113. -2^2, which is -4; $2(-1)$, which is -2; $\left(\frac{1}{2}\right)^2$, which is $\frac{1}{4}$; $2^{-1} = \frac{1}{2}$ (tie); $\left(\frac{1}{2}\right)^{-1}$, which is 2; $(-2)^2 = (2)^2$, which are 4 (tie)

115. a. $1; 1; 1; 1; 1; 1$ **b.** $0; 0; 0; 0; 0; 0$ **c.** Answers may vary.   **117.** Answers may vary.   **119.** 6   **121.** 8   **123.** $(-5, -14)$; a linear system in two variables   **125.** -5; a linear equation in one variable

Homework 4.2   **1.** 4   **3.** 10   **5.** 7   **7.** 5   **9.** 16   **11.** 27   **13.** 4   **15.** 32   **17.** $\frac{1}{3}$ **19.** $-\frac{1}{6}$ **21.** $\frac{1}{32}$ **23.** $\frac{1}{81}$ **25.** 2   **27.** 24

29. 49   **31.** 27   **33.** 12   **35.** $\frac{4}{3}$ **37.** -16

39.

x	$f(x)$	x	$f(x)$
$-\frac{3}{4}$	$\frac{1}{8}$	$\frac{1}{4}$	2
$-\frac{1}{2}$	$\frac{1}{4}$	$\frac{1}{2}$	4
$-\frac{1}{4}$	$\frac{1}{2}$	$\frac{3}{4}$	8
0	1	1	16

41. b^2 **43.** $\frac{1}{b^2}$ **45.** $2b^2$ **47.** $\frac{4}{5b^4c^7}$ **49.** $\frac{b}{c^2}$ **51.** $5bcd$ **53.** $3b^6c^2$ **55.** $\frac{c^2}{b^4}$ **57.** $\frac{5c^3}{3b^4}$

59. $2b^{29/35}$ **61.** $b^{7/12}$ **63.** $3b^{29/6}$ **65.** $\frac{8}{b^{1/5}}$ **67.** $\frac{2b^{49/12}}{27c^{5/4}}$ **69.** $b^2 + b$

71. a. 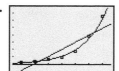 exponential function   **b.** 107,416 megawatts   **c.** 2016

73. Answers may vary.   **75.** The student did not compute $36^{1/2}$ correctly; $6x^{18}$ **77.** Answers may vary.

79. a. $(-9)^{1/2}, (-81)^{1/4}, (-1)^{1/6}$ **b.** b is negative and n is even.   **81.** Answers may vary.   **83.** $\frac{8}{3}$ **85.** 2   **87.** $-\frac{8}{3}$ **89.** $\frac{1}{2}$

91. 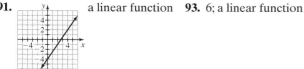 a linear function   **93.** 6; a linear function

Homework 4.3

1. 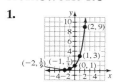   **3.**   **5.**   **7.**   **9.**   **11.**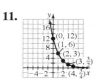

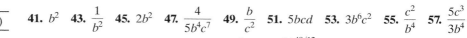

13. **15.** **17.** **19.** **21.**

domain: all real numbers; range: $y > 0$　　domain: all real numbers; range: $y < 0$

23. a. Answers may vary.　**b.** 　**c.** For each input–output pair, the output is 4 times 2 raised to the power equal to the input.

25.

x	$f(x)$	$g(x)$	$h(x)$	$k(x)$
0	162	3	2	800
1	54	12	10	400
2	18	48	50	200
3	6	192	250	100
4	2	768	1250	50

27.

x	$f(x)$	$g(x)$	$h(x)$	$k(x)$
0	5	160	162	3
1	10	80	54	12
2	20	40	18	48
3	40	20	6	192
4	80	10	2	768

29. 8　**31.** 1　**33.** -2　**35.** 0　**37.** 24
39. 96　**41.** 0　**43.** 3

45. a. 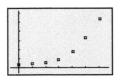 exponential function　**b.** 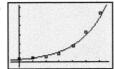 yes　**c.** \$35.92　**d.** 2026　**47.** no x-intercept; y-intercept: $(0, 1)$　**49.** no x-intercept; y-intercept: $(0, 3)$　**51.** 13

53. $\dfrac{13}{36}$　**55.** 1　**57.** 0　**59.** $f(x) = g(x)$

61. $f(x) = g(x)$　**63.** $f(x) = g(x)$　**65.** $f(x) = g(x)$　**67.** $f(x) = g(x)$　**69.** $f(x) = g(x)$　**71. a.** $a < 0, b > 1$
b. $a > 0, b > 1$　**c.** $a > 0, 0 < b < 1$　**d.** $a < 0, 0 < b < 1$　**73.** Answers may vary.　**75.** $f(x) = 3(2)^x$　**77.** Answers may vary.
79. a. for f: $(0, 100)$; for g: $(0, 5)$　**b.** For f, as the value of x increases by 1, the value of $f(x)$ is multiplied by 2. For g, as the value of x increases by 1, the value of $g(x)$ is multiplied by 3.　**c.** The outputs of g will eventually be much greater.
d. 　**81. a.** no　**b.** no　**83.** Answers may vary.　**85.** Answers may vary.
87. 　**89.** 　**91.** x-intercept: $(-2, 0)$; y-intercept: $(0, 8)$
93. f might be linear; g might be exponential; h might be exponential; k is neither linear nor exponential.
95. an exponential function　**97.** 24; an exponential function

Homework 4.4　**1.** $f(x) = 4(2)^x, g(x) = 36\left(\dfrac{1}{3}\right)^x, h(x) = 5(10)^x, k(x) = 250\left(\dfrac{1}{5}\right)^x$　**3.** $f(x) = 100\left(\dfrac{1}{2}\right)^x,$
$g(x) = -50x + 100, h(x) = 4x + 2, k(x) = 2(3)^x$　**5.** ± 4　**7.** 3　**9.** 2　**11.** ± 0.81　**13.** 2.28　**15.** ± 1.51　**17.** 2.22　**19.** ± 3
21. 1.74　**23.** $(d - c)^{1/n}$　**25.** $\left(\dfrac{c + d}{a}\right)^{1/n}$　**27.** $d^{1/(m-n)}$　**29.** $\left(\dfrac{d - c}{a}\right)^{1/(m-n)}$　**31.** $y = 4(2)^x$　**33.** $y = 3(2.02)^x$　**35.** $y = 87(0.74)^x$
37. $y = 5.5(3.67)^x$　**39.** $y = 7.4(0.56)^x$　**41.** $y = 39.18(0.85)^x$　**43.** $y = 1.33(3)^x$　**45.** $y = 1.19(1.50)^x$　**47.** $y = 1170.33(0.88)^x$
49. $y = 37.05(0.74)^x$　**51.** $y = 0.072(1.57)^x$　**53.** $y = 146.91(0.71)^x$　**55.** $y = 4\left(\dfrac{1}{2}\right)^x$　**57.** $y = 1.26(1.58)^x$　**59.** $(0, 6)$
61. a. i. yes; answers may vary.　**ii.** no; answers may vary.　**b.** no; answers may vary.　**63.** Answers may vary.　**65.** b^5
67. 2.38　**69.** $\dfrac{4b^4}{3}$　**71.** ± 0.75　**73.** $L(x) = 4x + 2; E(x) = 2(3)^x$　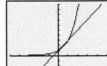　**75.** could be linear or exponential

77. a. $L: (0, 100)$; $E: (0, 3)$ **b.** $L(x)$ increases by 2; $E(x)$ is multiplied by 2.   **c.** $E(x)$ will eventually dominate over $L(x)$.

d.

X	Y₁	Y₂
0	100	3
1	102	6
2	104	12
3	106	24
4	108	48
5	110	96
6	112	192

79. an exponential function   **81.** $\frac{3}{8}$; an exponential function

Homework 4.5

1. a. $f(t) = 40(3)^t$ **b.** 2,361,960 people   **c.** 573,956,280 people; model breakdown has occurred, because this number exceeds the U.S. population.   **3. a.** $f(t) = 30(2)^t$ **b.** 1920 trillion (1.92 quadrillion) web pages   **c.** 121 million miles
5. a. $f(t) = 8.3(2.08)^t$ **b.** $(0, 8.3)$; in 2010, the market share of eBooks was 8.3%.   **c.** 2.08; each year, the market share is 2.08 times that of the previous year.   **d.** 74.7%; $3.74 billion   **7. a.** $D(t) = 2.5(1.5)^t$ **b.** $S(t) = 1.71(2.2)^t$ **c.** $(0.99, 3.74)$; in 2008, the subscribers who got TiVo through DIRECTV equaled the number of stand-alone TiVo subscribers, 3.74 million subscribers.   **9. a.** $f(t) = 3000(1.08)^t$
b. 1.08; the account balance increases by 8% per year.   **c.** 3000; the initial amount invested was $3000.   **d.** $9516.51

11. a. $f(t) = 4000(2)^{t/6}$ or $f(t) = 4000(1.1225)^t$ **b.** $40,317.47   **13.** $8749.97   **15. a.** $g(t) = 984\left(\frac{1}{2}\right)^t$ **b.** $(0, 984)$; in 2011, 984 new copies of the textbook were sold.   **c.** 123; in 2014, 123 new copies of the textbook will be sold.   **d.** 1 year   **17. a.** $f(t) = 100\left(\frac{1}{2}\right)^{t/1600}$
or $f(t) = 100(0.999567)^t$ **b.** 95.76%   **c.** 25%; 3200 years is two half-lives; so, half of 100% is 50%, and half of that is 25%.

19. a. $f(t) = 100\left(\frac{1}{2}\right)^{t/7.56}$ or $f(t) = 100(0.9124)^t$ **b.** 75.95%   **c.** 32.7 days   **21.** 15.87 milligrams   **23.** 190 million users

25. $263   **27. a.**  exponential function   **b.** $f(t) = 1.21(1.0161)^t$ **c.** 7.011; the world population in 2010 was 7.011 billion people; interpolation; answers may vary.   **d.** 7.967; the world population in 2018 will be 7.967 billion people; extrapolation; answers may vary.

29. a. $f(t) = 100.84(1.41)^t$ **b.** 41% growth per year   **c.** 48,930 stores; no; answers may vary.   **d.** 2000   **31. a.** $g(t) = 0.66(1.096)^t$
b. 0.66; at $t = 0$ (a newborn), the faculty member pays $0.66; model breakdown has occurred.   **c.** 1.096; the rate increases by 9.6% each year of age.   **d.** 16.33; a 35-year-old faculty member must pay $16.33 per month.   **e.** men   **33. a.** right-hand column: 1.36, 1.36, 1.33, 1.34, 1.33, 1.36, 1.35   **b.** They are approximately equal.   **c.** exponential function; answers may vary.   **d.** $f(t) = 3.94(1.03)^t$
e. right-hand column: 1.27, 1.26, 1.25, 1.21   **f.** no; answers may vary.   **g.** 2788.4 million (2.7884 billion) people; 2474.5 million (2.4745 billion) people   **35. a.** $f(t) = 18.47(0.95)^t$ **b.** 0.05 death per million people per year   **c.** 17 lightning deaths   **d.** 170 injuries
e. $g(t) = 50.68(0.992)^t$ **f.** The base of f is $b = 0.95$, which means the lightning fatality rate is decreasing by 5% per year, but the base of g is 0.992, which means the percentage of Americans who live in rural areas is decreasing by only 0.8%, so migration of Americans from rural areas to urban ones can't be the only reason the lightning fatality rate is decreasing.   **37. a.** 10 years   **b.** 6.25%

39. Decrease b.   **41.** Answers may vary.   **43.** Answers may vary.   **45. a.** $C(t) = 800(1.03)^t$
b. $S(t) = 24t + 800$ **c.** $C(1) = 824$; $C(2) = 848.72$; $S(1) = 824$; $S(2) = 848$; answers may vary   **d.** 1444.89, 1280; compound interest gives a larger balance than simple interest does.

47. a. linear function   **b.** $f(t) = 0.16t - 0.44$ **c.** $2.28 trillion   **d.** 2032   **49.** Answers may vary.
51. Answers may vary.   **53.** Answers may vary.

Chapter 4 Review

1. 32   **2.** $\frac{bc^9}{4}$ **3.** $\frac{8c^6}{9b^{23}}$ **4.** $\frac{b}{c}$ **5.** 16   **6.** $\frac{1}{8}$ **7.** $\frac{1}{b^{5/3}}$ **8.** $\frac{2b^{11}}{125c^7}$ **9.** $2b^2c$ **10.** $\frac{b^{1/6}}{c^{7/4}}$ **11.** b^{6n+2} **12.** $b^{n/6}$ **13.** $3^{2x} = \left(3^2\right)^x = 9^x$

14. $\frac{3}{25}$ **15.** $36(6^a)$ **16.** 7   **17.** $\frac{2}{27}$ **18.** 44,487,000   **19.** 0.0000385   **20.** 5.4×10^7 **21.** -8.97×10^{-3} **22.**

23.   domain: all real numbers; range: $y < 0$ **24.**   domain: all real numbers; range: $y > 0$ **25.** 1.84   **26.** ± 2

27. ± 1.61 **28.** f is linear, $f(x) = -4x + 34$; g is exponential, $g(x) = \dfrac{5}{3}(3)^x$; h is neither; k is exponential, $k(x) = 192\left(\dfrac{1}{2}\right)^x$.

29. 18   **30.** 5   **31.** $y = 2(1.08)^x$ **32.** $y = 62.11(0.78)^x$

33. 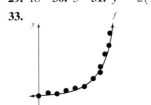   Increase a and decrease b.   **34. a.** $f(t) = 2000(1.07)^t$ **b.** \$2805.10   **35. a.** $g(t) = 17(2)^t$

b. \$4,352,000   **36. a.** $f(t) = 100\left(\dfrac{1}{2}\right)^{t/5730}$ or $f(t) = 100(0.999879)^t$

b. 98.8%   **37.** 15.9 million homes

38. a.   exponential function   **b.** $f(t) = 233.91(1.17)^t$ **c.** 233.91; the price of one ounce of gold was about \$234 in 2000.   **d.** 1.17; the price of one ounce of gold is growing exponentially by 17% per year.   **e.** 3948.16; the price of one ounce of gold will be about \$3948 in 2018.   **39. a.** $f(t) = 0.011(2.43)^t$ **b.** 143%   **c.** 39,509 thousand (39.509 million) users   **d.** 2019; model breakdown has occurred.

Chapter 4 Test

1. 4   **2.** $-\dfrac{1}{16}$ **3.** $8b^9 c^{24}$ **4.** 1   **5.** $b^{1/6}$ **6.** $\dfrac{5b}{7c^5}$ **7.** $\dfrac{4b^4}{c^{14}}$ **8.** $\dfrac{250b^{14}}{7c^6}$ **9.** $8^{x/3} 2^{x+3} = \left(2^3\right)^{x/3} 2^{x+3} = 2^x 2^{x+3} = 2^{2x+3} = 2^{2x} 2^3 = 8(2^2)^x = 8(4)^x$ **10.** $\dfrac{1}{16}$ **11.** $\dfrac{1}{8}$ **12.** domain: all real numbers; range: $y < 0$ **13.** domain: all real numbers; range $y > 0$

14. Answers may vary.   **15.** $f(t) = 160\left(\dfrac{1}{2}\right)^t$ **16.** ± 1.72 **17.** $y = 70(0.81)^x$ **18.** $y = 0.91(1.77)^x$ **19.** 6   **20.** 1

21. $f(x) = 6\left(\dfrac{1}{2}\right)^x$ **22. a.** $f(t) = 400(3)^t$ **b.** 291,600; there will be 291,600 leaves on the tree six weeks after March 1.

c. approximately 2.58×10^{27}; one year after March 1, there will be about 2.58×10^{27} leaves on the tree; model breakdown has occurred.   **23. a.** $f(t) = 0.27(1.16)^t$ **b.** 1.16; the number of fraud complaints by consumers is increasing by 16% per year.   **c.** 0.27; there were 0.27 million (270 thousand) fraud complaints by consumers in 2000.   **d.** 3.9 million complaints   **e.** 1.5%

Chapter 5

Homework 5.1   **1.** 2   **3.** 0   **5.** 4   **7.**

x	$(f \circ g)(x)$
0	2
1	1
2	4
3	0
4	3

9. 7   **11.** 5   **13.** 8   **15.**

x	$(g \circ f)(x)$
5	9
6	7
7	8
8	5
9	6

17. a. 1   **b.** 21

19. a. 16   **b.** 2   **21. a.** 54   **b.** 67   **23. a.** $\dfrac{5}{13}$ **b.** 13   **25. a.** $(f \circ g)(x) = 2x + 4$ **b.** $(g \circ f)(x) = 2x + 8$ **c.** 10   **d.** 14

27. a. $(f \circ g)(x) = 6x - 19$ **b.** $(g \circ f)(x) = 6x - 18$ **c.** -1 **d.** 0   **29. a.** $(f \circ g)(x) = 2^{x+2}$ **b.** $(g \circ f)(x) = 2^x + 2$ **c.** 32   **d.** 10   **31. a.** $(f \circ g)(x) = (x - 1)^4$ **b.** $(g \circ f)(x) = x^4 - 1$ **c.** 16   **d.** 80   **33.** 1   **35.** 1   **37.** -2 **39.** $(0, 0.5)$ **41.** 8   **43.** 2   **45.** 2

47. $f(x) = 5^x$; $g(x) = x - 9$; answers may vary   **49.** $f(x) = x + 6$; $g(x) = 2^x$; answers may vary   **51.** $f(x) = x^2$; $g(x) = 5x - 2$;

answers may vary   **53.** $f(x) = \dfrac{1}{x}$; $g(x) = 3x - 7$; answers may vary   **55.** Americans will eat 9.8 billion pounds of french fries in

2019.   **57.** The revenue will be \$2.3 million if the price of the album is \$8.99.

59. a. $f(y) = 3y; g(x) = 12x$ **b.** $(g \circ f)(y) = 36y$ **c.** 180; there are 180 inches in 5 yards. **61. a.** $f(M) = 60M; g(H) = 60H$

b. $(f \circ g)(H) = 3600H$ **c.** 10,800; there are 10,800 seconds in 3 hours. **63. a.** $f(d) = \dfrac{d}{25}; g(x) = 4.25x$ **b.** $(g \circ f)(d) = 0.17d$

c. 51; for a 300-mile trip, the cost of gasoline is \$51. **65. a.** Answers may vary. **b.** $h(t) = (g \circ f)(t)$; answers may vary.

c. $h(t) = -0.76t + 142.04$ **d.** 53.12; about 53.1% of births will be from married couples in 2017. **e.** 118.47; 52% of births will be

from married couples in 2018. **67. a.** Answers may vary. **b.** $h(t) = (M \circ D)(t)$; answers may vary. **c.** $h(t) = 340t + 560$ **d.** 220;

in 2004, the revenue from downloaded music was \$220 million. **e.** $(-1.65, 0)$; there was no revenue from downloaded music in 2003;

the t-intercept of the graph of h is the same as the t-intercept of the graph of D; answers may vary. **69. a.** $h(C) = (g \circ f)(C)$; answers

may vary. **b.** $h(C) = 7.74C - 34.4$ **c.** 144 chirps per minute **d.** 30°C **71.** The student found the product of $x + 8$ and $x + 5$,

which is incorrect; $(f \circ g)(x) = x + 13$ **73.** The student substituted $4x - 2$ for x in $g(x) = -7x + 3$, which is incorrect;

$(f \circ g)(x) = -28x + 10$ **75. a.** 4 **b.** 26 **c.** no **77. a.** 9 **b.** $(f \circ g)(x) = 12x - 15$ **c.** 9; the result is equal to the one in part (a).

79. a. $(f \circ f)(x) = 4x$ **b.** $(f \circ (f \circ f))(x) = 8x$ **c.** $(f \circ (f \circ (f \circ f)))(x) = 16x$ **d.** $\underbrace{(f \circ (f \circ (f \circ \cdots \circ f) \cdots))}_{n \text{ functions}}(x) = 2^n x$

81. Answers may vary. **83. a.** Each input x of f has exactly one output $f(x)$, because f is a function, and each input $f(x)$ of g has

exactly one output $g(f(x))$, because g is a function. **b.** domain: set A; range: set C **85.** exponential function

87. linear function

Homework 5.2 **1.** 4 **3.** 6 **5.** 5 **7.**

x	$f^{-1}(x)$
2	6
4	5
6	4
8	3
10	2

9. 6 **11.** 6 **13.** 1 **15.**

x	$g^{-1}(x)$
2	1
6	2
18	3
54	4
162	5
486	6

17. 4 **19.** fourth column:
6, 5, 4, 3, 2, and 1
21. Answers may vary.
23. 24 **25.** 0

27. 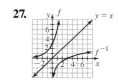 **29.** 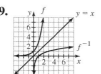 **31.** 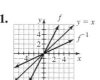 **33.** 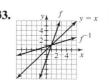 **35.** 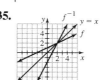 **37.**

39. 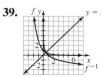 **41.** 3 **43.** 1 **45.** 0 **47.** 1 **49.** 3 **51.** **53. a.** $f^{-1}(p) = 1.32p + 55.32$ **b.** 33.96; in 2000,

about 34.0% of births were outside marriage. **c.** 187.32; in 2087, 100% of births will be outside marriage; model breakdown has likely occurred.

d. 1.32; the percentage of births outside marriage increases by 1 percentage point every 1.32 years.

55. a. 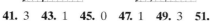 linear function **b.** $f(t) = 3.07t + 14.07$ **c.** $f^{-1}(p) = 0.33p - 4.58$ **d.** 2018 **e.** 2018
f. They are the same.

57. a. linear function **b.** $f(a) = 2.17a + 581.49$ **c.** $f^{-1}(c) = 0.46c - 267.97$ **d.** 43 years **e.** 114 years
f. 0.46; the credit score increases by 1 unit for each age increase of 0.46 year. **59.** $f^{-1}(x) = x - 8$

61. $f^{-1}(x) = -\dfrac{1}{4}x$ **63.** $f^{-1}(x) = 7x$ **65.** $f^{-1}(x) = -\dfrac{1}{6}x - \dfrac{1}{3}$ **67.** $f^{-1}(x) = 2.5x + 19.75$

69. $f^{-1}(x) = \dfrac{3}{7}x - \dfrac{3}{7}$ **71.** $f^{-1}(x) = -\dfrac{6}{5}x - \dfrac{18}{5}$ **73.** $f^{-1}(x) = \dfrac{5}{6}x + \dfrac{1}{3}$ **75.** $f^{-1}(x) = -\dfrac{1}{8}x - \dfrac{1}{8}$ **77.** $f^{-1}(x) = x$ **79.** $f^{-1}(x) = x^{\frac{1}{3}}$

81. a. $(f^{-1} \circ f)(x) = f^{-1}(f(x)) = f^{-1}(x + 7) = x + 7 - 7 = x$　**b.** $(f \circ f^{-1})(x) = f(f^{-1}(x)) = f(x - 7) = x - 7 + 7 = x$

83. a. $(f^{-1} \circ f)(x) = f^{-1}(f(x)) = f^{-1}(2x - 5) = \dfrac{1}{2}(2x - 5) + \dfrac{5}{2} = \dfrac{1}{2} \cdot 2x - \dfrac{1}{2} \cdot 5 + \dfrac{5}{2} = x - \dfrac{5}{2} + \dfrac{5}{2} = x$

b. $(f \circ f^{-1})(x) = f(f^{-1}(x)) = f\left(\dfrac{1}{2}x + \dfrac{5}{2}\right) = 2\left(\dfrac{1}{2}x + \dfrac{5}{2}\right) - 5 = 2 \cdot \dfrac{1}{2}x + 2 \cdot \dfrac{5}{2} - 5 = x + 5 - 5 = x$

85. a. $(f^{-1} \circ f)(x) = f^{-1}(f(x)) = f^{-1}\left(\dfrac{3}{4}x - 2\right) = \dfrac{4}{3}\left(\dfrac{3}{4}x - 2\right) + \dfrac{8}{3} = \dfrac{4}{3} \cdot \dfrac{3}{4}x - \dfrac{4}{3} \cdot 2 + \dfrac{8}{3} = x - \dfrac{8}{3} + \dfrac{8}{3} = x$

b. $(f \circ f^{-1})(x) = f(f^{-1}(x)) = f\left(\dfrac{4}{3}x + \dfrac{8}{3}\right) = \dfrac{3}{4}\left(\dfrac{4}{3}x + \dfrac{8}{3}\right) - 2 = \dfrac{3}{4} \cdot \dfrac{4}{3}x + \dfrac{3}{4} \cdot \dfrac{8}{3} - 2 = x + 2 - 2 = x$

87. a. $f^{-1}(x) = \dfrac{1}{5}x + \dfrac{9}{5}$　**b.** 11　**c.** $\dfrac{13}{5}$　**89. a.** $f^{-1}(x) = \dfrac{1}{3}x + \dfrac{5}{3}$　**b.** Answers may vary.　**c.**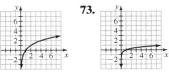

d. For each input–output pair, the output variable is $\dfrac{5}{3}$ more than $\dfrac{1}{3}$ the input variable.　**91.** no; answers may vary.　**93.** Answers may

vary.　**95.** Answers may vary.　**97.** no; no; answers may vary.　**99. a.** $f^{-1}(x) = \dfrac{1}{m}x - \dfrac{b}{m}$　**b.** Answers may vary.　**101. a.** $(4, 5)$

b. $f^{-1}(x) = \dfrac{1}{2}x + \dfrac{3}{2}$　**c.** $g^{-1}(x) = 2x - 6$　**d.** $(5, 4)$　**e.** The coordinates are interchanged; answers may vary.

103. $(5, 1)$; a linear system in two variables　**105.** 　a linear equation in two variables (or a linear function)

Homework 5.3

1. 2　**3.** 3　**5.** 4　**7.** 3　**9.** 2　**11.** -1　**13.** -3　**15.** -4　**17.** 0　**19.** 1　**21.** $\dfrac{1}{2}$　**23.** $\dfrac{1}{3}$　**25.** $\dfrac{1}{2}$　**27.** $\dfrac{1}{4}$　**29.** 2

31. 0　**33.** 1　**35.** 4　**37.** -5　**39.** $\dfrac{1}{2}$　**41.** 0　**43.** $f^{-1}(x) = \log_3(x)$　**45.** $h^{-1}(x) = \log(x)$　**47.** $f^{-1}(x) = 5^x$　**49.** $h^{-1}(x) = 10^x$

51. 4　**53.** 1　**55.** 1　**57.** 27　**59.** 3　**61.** $0; \log_3(1)$　**63.** 6　**65.** 8　**67.** 7　**69.** 3　**71.**　**73.**

75. 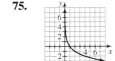　**77. a.** Answers may vary.　**b.**　**c.** For each input–output pair, the output variable is the logarithm, base 5, of the input variable.　**79. a.** 2　**b.** 2　**c.** Answers may vary.

81. a. 9.2　**b.** 7.8　**c.** 25.4　**83.** $0, 20, 40, 60, 80, 100, 120$

85. (a)　**87.** (d)　**89.** $\log_2(7)$; because 2 is less than 3, 2 requires a larger exponent to get 7 than 3 does.　**91.** Answers may vary.

93. a.

x	$f(x)$	$g(x)$	$h(x)$
1	0	2	2
2	1	4	4
4	2	8	16
8	3	16	256
16	4	32	65,536

b. $h; g$

95. a. $(f^{-1} \circ f)(x) = f^{-1}(f(x)) = f^{-1}(3^x + 5) = \log_3(3^x + 5 - 5) = \log_3(3^x) = x$
b. $(f \circ f^{-1})(x) = f(f^{-1}(x)) = f(\log_3(x - 5)) = 3^{\log_3(x-5)} + 5 = x - 5 + 5 = x$

97. a. $(f^{-1} \circ f)(x) = f^{-1}(f(x)) = f^{-1}(5 \cdot 2^x - 6) = \log_2\left(\dfrac{5 \cdot 2^x - 6 + 6}{5}\right) = \log_2\left(\dfrac{5 \cdot 2^x}{5}\right) = \log_2(2^x) = x$

b. $(f \circ f^{-1})(x) = f(f^{-1}(x)) = f\left(\log_2\left(\dfrac{x + 6}{5}\right)\right) = 5(2)^{\log_2\left(\frac{x+6}{5}\right)} - 6 = 5 \cdot \dfrac{x + 6}{5} - 6 = x + 6 - 6 = x$

99. $y = 0.58(2.05)^x$; an exponential function or an exponential equation in two variables　**101.** $\dfrac{8b^{7/15}}{c^{1/2}}$; an expression in two variables that involves exponents

Homework 5.4   **1.** $3^5 = 243$ **3.** $10^2 = 100$ **5.** $b^c = a$ **7.** $10^n = m$ **9.** $\log_5(125) = 3$ **11.** $\log(1000) = 3$ **13.** $\log_y(x) = w$

15. $\log(q) = p$ **17.** 16   **19.** $\dfrac{1}{100}$ **21.** 1   **23.** 81   **25.** $\dfrac{69}{2}$ **27.** 3   **29.** 6561   **31.** 3.3019   **33.** 7   **35.** 2   **37.** 1.7411   **39.** 1.5850

41. 2   **43.** 4.8738   **45.** 3.8278   **47.** -0.2281 **49.** 3.4850   **51.** 0.8644   **53.** no real-number solution   **55.** 64   **57.** 3.5130   **59.** 2.3587

61. 10   **63.** 1.6975   **65.** 1   **67.** 0, 3.7   **69.** 2   **71.** 1.2122   **73.** 1.3618   **75.** 5.4723   **77.** 2   **79.** 5   **81.** $(3, 1.5)$ **83.** $\dfrac{\log\left(\dfrac{c}{a}\right)}{\log(b)}$

85. $\dfrac{\log(d - c)}{\log(b)}$ **87.** $\dfrac{\log\left(\dfrac{d + c}{a}\right)}{\log(b)}$ **89.** $\dfrac{\log\left(\dfrac{c + d}{a}\right) - p\log(b)}{\log(b)}$ **91.** $\log\left[3(8)^x\right] \neq x\log\left[3(8)\right]; 0.4075$ **93.** 256   **95.** 0.7925   **97.** 3

99. 32   **101. a.** no   **b.** no   **c.** no   **d.** no   **103. a.** the part of the line $y = 1$ where $x > 0$ **b.** We cannot take the logarithm of a

negative number.   **c.** $f(x) = \log(x^3) - 3\log(x) + 1 = 3\log(x) - 3\log(x) + 1 = 1$; answers may vary.   **105.** Answers may vary; no.

107. $\dfrac{29}{5}$ **109.** ± 1.7508 **111.** $\dfrac{16}{11}$ **113.** $\dfrac{1}{32}$; a logarithmic equation in one variable   **115.** 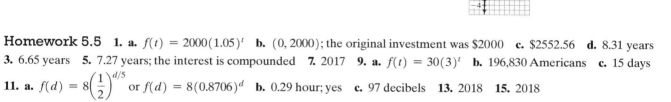 a logarithmic function

Homework 5.5   **1. a.** $f(t) = 2000(1.05)^t$ **b.** $(0, 2000)$; the original investment was \$2000   **c.** \$2552.56   **d.** 8.31 years
3. 6.65 years   **5.** 7.27 years; the interest is compounded   **7.** 2017   **9. a.** $f(t) = 30(3)^t$ **b.** 196,830 Americans   **c.** 15 days

11. a. $f(d) = 8\left(\dfrac{1}{2}\right)^{d/5}$ or $f(d) = 8(0.8706)^d$ **b.** 0.29 hour; yes   **c.** 97 decibels   **13.** 2018   **15.** 2018

17. a. 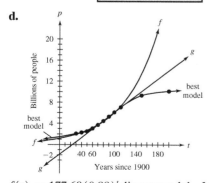 exponential function   **b.** $f(t) = 0.25(3.30)^t$ **c.** 3.30; the number of Twitter employees is growing exponentially by 230% per year.   **d.** 11,603 employees   **e.** 2017

19. a. exponential function   **b.** $f(t) = 2726(0.75)^t$ **c.** 0.049 thousand cases, or 49 cases   **d.** 2032   **e.** 2.41 years

21. a. 2028   **b.** linear function; $g(t) = 0.080t - 1.92$ **c.** 2040; after; answers may vary.

d.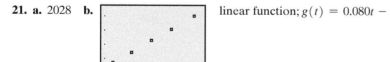

23. a. $f(t) = 0.00067(1.12)^t$ **b.** 1.12; the percentage of seniors with severe memory impairment increases by 12% for each additional year of age.   **c.** 1.9%   **d.** 85 years
e. no; answers may vary.   **25. a.** $E(s) = 0.36(1.0036)^s$; $R(s) = 0.037(1.0049)^s$ **b.** 60%; 39%
c. 1373 points; 1475 points   **d.** 102 points   **e.** $(1757.58, 199.19)$; students who score 1758 points have the same chance (199%) of being selected by early decision as by regular decision; model

breakdown has occurred.   **27. a.** $f(t) = 100\left(\dfrac{1}{2}\right)^{t/3.25}$ or $f(t) = 100(0.8079)^t$ **b.** 65.28%

c. 26.0 days   **29.** 11,641 years ago   **31. a.** 5730 years old   **b.** 11,460 years old   **c.** 19,035

years old   **33.** 1329 years   **35.** 24.14 years   **37. a.** linear: $f(t) = -5.51t + 122.84$; exponential:
$f(t) = 177.69(0.88)^t$; linear model   **b.** 14 days   **c.** -5.51; the weight of the soap decreases by 5.51 grams per day   **d.** 22 days; yes;

answers may vary.   **39.** $-\dfrac{5}{8b^{1/40}}$; an expression in one variable that involves exponents   **41.** 2.2132; an exponential equation in one
variable

Homework 5.6　**1.** $\log_b(3x^2)$　**3.** $\log_b(4x)$　**5.** $\log_b(5t^5)$　**7.** $\log_b\left(\dfrac{3}{x^3}\right)$　**9.** $\log_b(9x^{11})$　**11.** $\log_b\left(\dfrac{8m^{12}}{3}\right)$　**13.** 2.0412　**15.** 10.6667

17. 1.5275　**19.** 1.5849　**21.** 1.2011　**23.** 3.2702　**25.** 1.7712　**27.** 0.5804　**29.** -2.0431　**31.** 1.6204　**33.** 2.6031　**35.** $-2.6876, 1.6964$

37. $\log_7(x)$　**39.** $\log_s(r)$　**41.** 1.1402　**43.** 0.8368　**45.** all three students　**47.** $\log_b(b^2) = \log_b(b^6) - \log_b(b^4) = 2 = \log_b\left(\dfrac{b^6}{b^4}\right)$

49. $\log_b(x) - \log_b(x) = \log_b\left(\dfrac{x}{x}\right) = \log_b(1)$; hence, $\log_b(1) = 0$　**51. a.** $\log_2(x^8)$　**b.** 1.8340　**c, d.** Answers may vary.

53. $\log_2(x^7)$　**55.** 1.4860　**57.** 8.6535　**59.** $\log_9\left(\dfrac{x^3}{8}\right)$　**61.** $\dfrac{6b^{13}}{c^{1/12}}$　**63.** $\log_b(72x^{23})$　**65.** $(2, -1)$　**67.** $(8, 5)$　**69.** all points on the

line $y = \dfrac{2}{3}x - 2$; dependent linear system of equations in two variables　**71.** 　a linear equation in two variables (or a linear function)

Homework 5.7　**1.** 4.0037　**3.** -0.6931　**5.** 4　**7.** 1　**9.** -1　**11.** 3　**13.** 7　**15.** 7.3891　**17.** 15.0855　**19.** 1.8383　**21.** 0.9061

23. 1.2777　**25.** 1.9811　**27.** 3.4541　**29.** 1.9458　**31.** 3.3673　**33.** $\ln(12x^5)$　**35.** $\ln(5x)$　**37.** $\ln(8w^{11})$　**39.** $\ln\left(\dfrac{27}{x}\right)$　**41.** $\ln(8k^4)$

43. 4.2661　**45.** 37.1033　**47.** 2.0654　**49.** 0.6036　**51.** 1.3066　**53.** 1.2377　**55.** $-1.6856, 7.0194$　**57.** 20　**59.** 0.1353　**61.** $\dfrac{\ln\left(\dfrac{c}{a}\right)}{b}$, or

$\dfrac{\ln(c) - \ln(a)}{b}$　**63. a.** 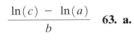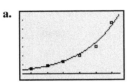　**b.** $(0, 29.89)$; there were about 30 laser incidents involving aircraft in 2000.　**c.** 2017　**d.** 65,976　**65. a.** $207°$ F　**b.** 3.66 minutes　**c.** $70°$ F　**67. a.** 20.91 feet　**b.** 20.32; the cable's height 4 feet to the left of the right pole is 20.32 feet.　**c.** 20 feet　**69.** both students; answers may vary.

71. $3\ln(x) = \ln(x^7) - \ln(x^4) = \ln(x^3)$　**73.** Answers may vary.　**75. a. i.** 3.6960　**ii.** 3.6960　**iii.** They are the same.　**b. i.** Answers may vary.　**ii.** Answers may vary.　**iii.** They are the same.　**c.** Answers may vary.　**77.** $\ln(x^5)$　**79.** 2.2255

81. 1.3863　**83.** $\dfrac{13}{11}$　**85.** ± 2　**87.** Answers may vary.　**89.** Answers may vary.　**91.** Answers may vary.

Chapter 5 Review

1. 3　**2.** 0　**3.** 3　**4.** 0　**5.** 3　**6.** 1　**7.**

x	$(f \circ g)(x)$
0	0
1	3
2	4
3	1
4	2

8. a. $(f \circ g)(x) = -20x + 33$　**b.** $(g \circ f)(x) = -20x + 15$　**c.** -27

d. -45　**9. a.** $(f \circ g)(x) = 4(2)^{2x-4}$　**b.** $(g \circ f)(x) = 8(2)^x - 4$　**c.** 16　**d.** 60　**10. a.** $(f \circ g)(x) = \log_3(x + 6)$
b. $(g \circ f)(x) = \log_3(x) + 6$　**c.** 2　**d.** 7　**11.** $f(x) = e^x; g(x) = x - 5$; answers may vary　**12. a.** $f(n) = 8n; g(d) = 0.06d$
b. $g(f(n)) = 0.48n$　**c.** 3.36; the sales tax on the purchase of 7 books is \$3.36.　**13.** 　**14.** 　**15. a.**

linear function　**b.** $f(t) = 1.21t + 2.86$　**c.** 24.64; there will be about 25 million background checks in 2018.　**d.** 12.51; in 2013, there were about 18 million background checks.　**e.** $C(n) = 15n$　**f.** $h(t) = (C \circ f)(t)$; answers may vary.
g. $h(t) = 18.15t + 42.9$　**h.** 351.45; in 2017, the total cost of background checks will be about \$351 million.　**16. a.** $f^{-1}(x) = \dfrac{1}{3}x$

b. $(f^{-1} \circ f)(x) = f^{-1}(f(x)) = f^{-1}(3x) = \frac{1}{3} \cdot 3x = x$ **c.** $(f \circ f^{-1})(x) = f(f^{-1}(x)) = f\left(\frac{1}{3}x\right) = 3\left(\frac{1}{3}x\right) = x$

17. a. $f^{-1}(x) = \frac{6}{5}x + \frac{12}{5}$ **b.** $(f^{-1} \circ f)(x) = f^{-1}(f(x)) = f^{-1}\left(\frac{5}{6}x - 2\right) = \frac{6}{5}\left(\frac{5}{6}x - 2\right) + \frac{12}{5} =$

$\frac{6}{5} \cdot \frac{5}{6}x - \frac{6}{5} \cdot 2 + \frac{12}{5} = x - \frac{12}{5} + \frac{12}{5} = x$ **c.** $(f \circ f^{-1})(x) = f(f^{-1}(x)) = f\left(\frac{6}{5}x + \frac{12}{5}\right) = \frac{5}{6}\left(\frac{6}{5}x + \frac{12}{5}\right) - 2 =$

$\frac{5}{6} \cdot \frac{6}{5}x + \frac{5}{6} \cdot \frac{12}{5} - 2 = x + 2 - 2 = x$ **18.** 2   **19.** 5   **20.** −2   **21.** −3   **22.** $\frac{1}{3}$ **23.** 1.7712   **24.** 1.6094   **25.** 7

26. $h^{-1}(x) = \log_3(x)$ **27.** $h^{-1}(x) = 10^x$ **28.**   **29.** $\log_d(k) = x$ **30.** $y^r = w$ **31.** 2.3219   **32.** $\frac{1}{81}$ **33.** 0.4310

34. 2.0886   **35.** 4   **36.** 2.8333   **37.** 1.6507

38. 4   **39.** 0   **40.** $(4, 2)$ **41.** 81   **42.** 2.9299   **43.** 1.6309   **44.** 729   **45. a.** $f(t) = 8000(1.05)^t$ **b.** \$12,410.63
c. 14.2 years   **46. a.** $f(t) = 30(4)^t$ **b.** 30,720 leaves   **c.** 5.9 weeks after April 1   **47. a.** $f(t) = 0.12(1.083)^t$ **b.** $(0, 0.12)$; the
national health spending in 1970 was 0.12 trillion (120 billion) dollars.   **c.** 8.3% per year   **d.** 6.0 trillion dollars   **e.** 2017
48. a. $f(n) = 9.33(1.31)^n$ **b.** 1.31; for each additional cassette, the length increases by 31%.   **c.** 9.33; the initial length of the rubber
band was 9.33 inches.   **d.** 80.92 inches; answers may vary.   **e.** 10 cassettes; yes   **49.** 14.5 years   **50.** $\log_b(3p)$ **51.** $\log_b\left(72x^5\right)$
52. $\log_b\left(\frac{1}{x^2}\right)$ **53.** $\log_y(w)$ **54.** $\log_b\left(b^5\right) - \log_b\left(b^2\right) = 3 = \log_b\left(b^3\right) = \log_b\left(\frac{b^5}{b^2}\right)$ **55.** 3   **56.** 8.4853   **57.** $\ln\left(256x^5\right)$ **58.** $\ln(2m)$
59. 2.9312   **60.** 7.3891   **61.** 2.8479

Chapter 5 Test

1. a. $(f \circ g)(x) = 6x - 11$ **b.** $(g \circ f)(x) = 6x + 3$ **c.** 1   **d.** 15   **2. a.** $(f \circ g)(x) = 3^{x-4}$ **b.** $(g \circ f)(x) = 3^x - 4$ **c.** $\frac{1}{9}$
d. 5   **3.** 2   **4.** 5   **5.** 2   **6.**   **7.**   **8. a.** $f(t) = 3.75t + 44.21$ **b.** \$85.46   **c.** $f^{-1}(p) = 0.27p - 11.79$
d. 2018   **e.** $S(d) = 0.065d$ **f.** $h(t) = (S \circ f)(t)$; answers may vary.
g. $h(t) = 0.24t + 2.87$ **h.** 6.95; in 2017, the sales tax on an adult
one-day ticket will be \$6.95.

9. $g^{-1}(x) = \frac{5}{2}x + \frac{9}{2}$ **10.** 4   **11.** −3   **12.** 1.1833   **13.** −1   **14.** $\frac{1}{2}$ **15.** −2   **16.** $h^{-1}(x) = \log_4(x)$ **17.** $f^{-1}(x) = 5^x$ **18.** $\log_s(w) = k$
19. $c^d = a$ **20.** 2.6591   **21.** 2.4150   **22.** −0.6964   **23.** 1.67   **24. a.** $f(t) = 682.95(1.071)^t$ **b.** $(0, 682.95)$; the tuition in 1950 was
about \$683.   **c.** 7.1% per year   **d.** \$67,652   **e.** 2019   **25.** 2050 years old   **26.** $\log_b(5x^4)$ **27.** $\log_b(2)$ **28.** 11.0227   **29.** 4.4413
30. $\ln\left(25w^{20}\right)$ **31.** 1.4319   **32.** 4.0427

Cumulative Review Chapters 1–5

1. 0.5087   **2.** 86   **3.** 1.3538   **4.** 1.2528   **5.** ±0.7811   **6.** $\frac{7}{10}$ **7.** 1   **8.** 2   **9.** $(-1, 2)$ **10.** $(2, 4)$

11. $x \geq \frac{9}{10}; \left[\frac{9}{10}, \infty\right)$;   **12.** $\frac{1600c^4}{b^{23}}$ **13.** $\frac{4b^{5/6}}{3c^{5/4}}$ **14.** $\log_b\left(\frac{x^{26}}{49}\right)$ **15.** $\ln\left(p^{26}\right)$ **16.** $f(x) = 5(3)^x$

17. $g(x) = 3x + 25$ **18.** −7   **19.** 40   **20.** 40   **21.** 0   **22.** 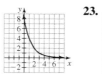   **23.** 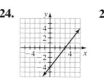   **24.**   **25.**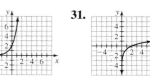

26. $y = -\frac{10}{9}x + \frac{23}{9}$ **27.** $y = 347.56(0.63)^x$ **28. a.** 29   **b.** $(g \circ f)(x) = 2^{x-3}$ **29.** $\frac{2}{81}$ **30.**   **31.**

32. 2.6053   **33.** −4   **34.** $\dfrac{1}{7}$ **35.** 2.0633   **36.** 3   **37.** 4   **38.** $f(x) = 2(2)^x$, or $f(x) = (2)^{x+1}$ **39.** 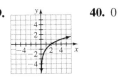   **40.** 0

41. $f^{-1}(x) = \dfrac{7}{2}x + \dfrac{21}{2}$ **42.** $g^{-1}(x) = \log_8(x)$ **43.** Answers may vary.   **44. a.** f:(0, 2); g:(0, 2)   **b.** As x increases by 1, $f(x)$

increases by 3 and $g(x)$ is multiplied by 3.   **c.** g **d.**   **45. a.** $f(x) = \dfrac{5}{3}x - \dfrac{11}{3}$ **b.** $g(x) = 0.81(1.39)^x$

c. 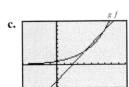   **46. a.** $f(2) = 6; g(2) = 9$ **b.** $f^{-1}(x) = \dfrac{1}{3}x; g^{-1}(x) = \log_3(x)$ **c.** $f^{-1}(81) = 27; g^{-1}(81) = 4$

47. a. $U(x) = 0.69x + 19.95; B(x) = 0.45x + 29.95$ **b.** 0.69, 0.45; U-Haul charges \$0.69 per additional
mile, and Budget charges \$0.45 per additional mile.   **c.** 41.67 miles   **d.** $x < 41.67$; below 41.67 miles,
U-Haul charges less than Budget.   **48.** 10,500 tickets at \$43, 4500 tickets at \$60   **49. a.** $f(t) = 9.0(1.14)^t$
b. (0, 9.0); in 2010, the revenue was \$9.0 billion.   **c.** 1.14; the revenue is growing exponentially by 14% per year.   **d.** 2018
50. a. $f(t) = 76.58(0.97)^t$ **b.** (0, 76.58); there were 76,580 tuberculosis cases in 1950.   **c.** 3%; the number of tuberculosis cases
decreases by 3% per year.   **d.** 58.22; there were 58,220 tuberculosis cases in 1959.   **e.** 70.29; there will be 9 thousand tuberculosis
cases in 2020.   **f.** 22.76 years   **51. a.** $f(t) = 0.53t - 0.17$ **b.** 0.53; the number of women who place in the top 100 is increasing by
0.53 woman per year, on average.   **c.** (0.32, 0); no women placed in the top 100 in 1980.   **d.** 17 women   **e.** $f^{-1}(n) = 1.89n + 0.32$
f. 38.12; in 2018, 20 women will place in the top 100.   **g.** $h(t) = -0.53t + 100.17$ **h.** 80.56; in 2017, 81 men will place in the top 100.

Chapter 6

Homework 6.1   **1.** quadratic (second-degree) polynomial in one variable   **3.** cubic (third-degree) polynomial in one variable
5. seventh-degree polynomial in two variables   **7.** $4x^2 + x$ **9.** $-12x^3 + 2x^2 - 5x + 5$ **11.** $-5a^4b^2 - 5ab^3$ **13.** $2x^4 - 3x^3y + xy^3$
15. $9x^2 - 3x - 9$ **17.** $3x^3 - 6x^2 + 4x - 1$ **19.** $11a^2 - 3ab - 5b^2$ **21.** $2m^4p + 2m^3p^2 - 8mp^3$ **23.** $-7x^2 + 9x - 11$
25. $13x^3 - 3x^2 - x + 5$ **27.** $10m^2 + 10mp - p^2$ **29.** $a^3b - 10a^2b^2 + 8ab^3 - b^3$ **31.** −30   **33.** 79   **35.** 3   **37.** 42   **39.** −8   **41.** 3
43. −1   **45.** −1,3   **47.** 1   **49.** 19   **51.** 3   **53.** 0,6   **55.** 3   **57. a.** 1,5   **b.** Answers may vary.
59. 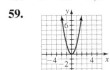   **61.**   **63.**   **65.**   **67.** $(f + g)(x) = 11x^2 + 3x + 7; 115$

69. $(f - h)(x) = 7x^2 + 2x + 17; 137$ **71.** $(f + g)(x) = 2x^3 - 3x^2 + x - 2; 4$ **73.** $(f - h)(x) = x^3 + 3x^2 - 6x + 1; 9$
75. a. $(M + S)(t) = 0.54t + 45.63$ **b.** gallons per person   **c.** 74.3; in 2003, 74.3 gallons of milk and soft drinks (combined)
were consumed per person.   **d.** $(M - S)(t) = -1.1t + 27.71$ **e.** −30.6; in 2003, 30.6 fewer gallons of milk than soft drinks
were consumed per person.   **77. a.** $R(s) = 2.2s$ **b.** $(R + B)(s) = 0.063s^2 + 2.2s$ **c.** feet   **d.** 99.79; if you are driving at
26 miles per hour, it will take about 100 feet to stop.   **e.** yes; she would need about 175 feet to stop.   **79.** Answers may vary;
$4x^2 + 4x + 2$ **81. a.** $(f - g)(x) = -2x + 5; (g - f)(x) = 2x - 5$ **b.** 1, −1; the answers are opposites.   **c.** −3,3; the answers
are opposites.   **d.** −9,9; the answers are opposites.   **e.** In general, $(f - g)(x) = -(g - f)(x)$.   **83.** Answers may vary.

85. Answers may vary.   **87.** (b)   **89.** (c)   **91.** (a)   **93.** $(f \circ g)(x) = 8x + 7; 31$ **95.** $(f - g)(x) = -2x - 8; -12$ **97.** $\dfrac{5b^4}{2c^4}$; an

expression in two variables involving exponents

99.   an exponential function (or an exponential equation in two variables)

Homework 6.2 **1.** $18x^6$ **3.** $-8a^5b^8$ **5.** $-30x^2 + 12x$ **7.** $20a^3b^2 - 35a^2b^3 + 15ab^4$ **9.** $x^2 + 9x + 18$ **11.** $15m^2 + 2m - 8$ **13.** $32x^2 - 20x + 3$ **15.** $3.91x^2 - 3.48x - 2.88$ **17.** $6a^2 + ab - 35b^2$ **19.** $20x^2 - 53xy + 18y^2$ **21.** $14a^4 - 29a^2b^2 - 15b^4$ **23.** $24x^4 - 54x^3 - 15x^2$ **25.** $5x^4 - 20x^3 + 15x^2 - 60x$ **27.** $12x^3 + 23x^2 + x - 6$ **29.** $a^3 + b^3$ **31.** $8x^3 - 10x^2y + 23xy^2 - 15y^3$ **33.** $x^4 + x^3 - 3x^2 + 7x - 6$ **35.** $2x^4 - 3x^3y - 3x^2y^2 + 7xy^3 - 3y^4$ **37.** $x^2 + 10x + 25$ **39.** $x^2 - 16x + 64$ **41.** $9x^2 + 30x + 25$ **43.** $6.76x^2 - 16.64x + 10.24$ **45.** $16a^2 + 24ab + 9b^2$ **47.** $4x^4 - 24x^2y^2 + 36y^4$ **49.** $-8x^3 - 40x^2 - 50x$ **51.** $x^2 - 16$ **53.** $9x^2 - 36$ **55.** $4r^2 - 64t^2$ **57.** $9r^2t^2 - 81w^2$ **59.** $64a^4 - 9b^4$ **61.** $x^4 - 16$ **63.** $81a^4 - 16b^4$ **65.** $25b^2 - 15b$ **67.** $c^2 + 5c + 4$ **69.** $b^2 - 9b + 18$ **71.** $4a - 2$ **73.** $h^2 + 2ah - 3h$ **75.** $f(x) = x^2 + 12x + 36$ **77.** $f(x) = 2x^2 + 12x + 19$ **79.** $f(x) = -3x^2 + 30x - 76$ **81.** $(f \cdot g)(x) = 6x^2 - 5x - 6; 33$ **83.** $(f \cdot h)(x) = 4x^3 - 14x^2 + 18x - 9; 3$ **85.** $(f \cdot f)(x) = 4x^2 - 12x + 9; 25$ **87.** $(f \cdot g)(x) = 20x^2 + 17x + 3; 6$ **89.** $(f \cdot h)(x) = 12x^3 - x^2 - 9x - 2; -84$ **91.** $(h \cdot h)(x) = 9x^4 - 6x^3 - 11x^2 + 4x + 4; 0$

93. a. 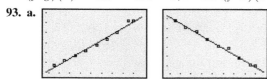 **b.** $(V \cdot A)(t) = -204.6t^2 + 58,959.6t + 496,824$ **c.** millions of dollars **d.** 1,939,579.8; in 2017, the total value of U.S. farmland will be $1,939,579.8 million, or about $1.94 trillion. **e.** increasing; between 1990 and 2017, the total value of U.S. farmland was increasing and will continue to increase every year; answers may vary.

95. a. 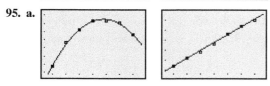 **b.** $(B \cdot N)(t) = -3.94t^3 + 141.124t^2 - 505.8t - 276$ **c.** millions of dollars per month **d.** 14,406; in 2014, the total monthly revenue from cell phones will be $14,406 million, or about $14.4 billion. **e.** increasing; between 2004 and 2010, the total monthly revenue from cell phones increased every year; answers may vary. **97.** The middle term, $16x$, is missing; $x^2 + 16x + 64$

99. a. 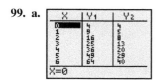 **b.** $x^2 + 4x + 4$ **c.**

101. The student performed subtraction instead of multiplication; $-14x^2$ **103.** $(2x - 5)(3x + 4) = 3x(2x - 2) - x - 20 = 6x^2 - 7x - 20 = (3x + 4)(2x - 5); 6x^2 + 7x - 20 = (3x - 4)(2x + 5)$ **105.** Answers may vary. **107.** $(g - h)(x) = -2x^2 + 7x - 6; -28$ **109.** $(h \cdot k)(x) = 2x^3 + 3x^2 - 8x + 3; 12$ **111.** $(f \circ g)(x) = 16x^2 - 40x + 25; 49$ **113.** $(h \circ k)(x) = 2x^2 + 9x + 10; 36$ **115.** $f(x) = 6x^2 - 17x + 5;$ quadratic **117.** $f(x) = -2x - 1;$ linear **119.** $\log_b(x^2 + 2x - 15)$ **121.** $\log_b(w^3 - 3w^2 - 9w + 27)$ **123.** $24x^3 + 4x^2 - 60x;$ a cubic polynomial in one variable **125.** $f(x) = -3x^2 + 24x - 43;$ a quadratic function

Homework 6.3 **1.** $3x^4 + 7x^2$ **3.** $2x^2 + 4x$ **5.** $4p^6 - p^3 + 3$ **7.** $-2x^3 + \dfrac{3}{8}x^2 + 3x$ **9.** $2x - 4 + \dfrac{7}{2x^2}$ **11.** $2k^2 + \dfrac{3}{2}k - \dfrac{3}{k}$ **13.** $x^3 + x^2y - y^3$ **15.** $5m^3 + \dfrac{3}{2}mr + 2r^2$ **17.** $-3x^3y^2 - \dfrac{9}{2}x^2 + \dfrac{2x}{y}$ **19.** $3x + 2$ **21.** $4x - 2$ **23.** $2p + 5 + \dfrac{2}{3p + 2}$ **25.** $2x - 4 - \dfrac{3}{2x + 5}$ **27.** $2x - 1 + \dfrac{2}{5x - 1}$ **29.** $5m + 3 - \dfrac{3}{4m - 2}$ **31.** $2x^2 + 3x + 3 + \dfrac{4}{2x + 3}$ **33.** $4p^2 - 2p + 3 - \dfrac{2}{3p - 4}$ **35.** $x - 3 + \dfrac{16}{x + 3}$ **37.** $4x^2 + 10x + 25$ **39.** $x^2 - 3x - 1 + \dfrac{6}{3x - 1}$ **41.** $3x - 4 - \dfrac{4}{x^2 + 3}$ **43.** $2y + 3 - \dfrac{1}{3y^2 - 2}$ **45.** $3x^2 - 4x + 2$ **47.** $-x^2 + 5 + \dfrac{3}{x + 4}$ **49.** $3k - 4 - \dfrac{3}{k - 1}$ **51.** $2x^2 - x + 3 - \dfrac{2}{x - 5}$ **53.** $3x^2 - x + 4 - \dfrac{2}{x + 4}$ **55.** The student did not divide $7x$ by $2x^2$; $3 + \dfrac{7}{2x}$ **57.** The student did not change the signs before adding; $2x + 4$ **59.** Answers may vary; $4x^2 + 2x - 3 + \dfrac{6}{x - 3}$ **61.** Answers may vary. **63.** $2x^2 - 11x + 19$ **65.** Answers may vary. **67.** Answers may vary. **69.** Answers may vary. **71.** $18x^3 - 15x^2 - 4x + 4$ **73.** $6x^2 - 4x$ **75.** $2x + 1$ **77.** $9x^2 - 12x + 4$ **79.** $(1, -3);$ system of linear equations in two variables **81.** 0.9366

Homework 6.4 **1.** $(x + 7)(x + 4)$ **3.** $(x - 2)(x - 6)$ **5.** $(r - 8)(r + 4)$ **7.** $(x + 7)(x - 2)$ **9.** prime **11.** $(x + 5)^2$ **13.** $(t - 9)^2$ **15.** $(x + 5)(x - 1)$ **17.** $(a + 10b)(a + 2b)$ **19.** $(w - 4y)(w - y)$ **21.** $(p - 4q)(p + 7q)$ **23.** prime **25.** $(p - 8q)(p + 2q)$ **27.** $3(x + 7)$ **29.** $4x(4x - 3)$ **31.** $9y^3(y^2 + 2)$ **33.** $3ab(1 - 4a)$ **35.** $6a^2b^2(3a^2 + 2b)$ **37.** $-7x^2y(2x^3 - 9y)$ **39.** $2(x + 3)^2$ **41.** $3(x - 3)(x + 2)$ **43.** $5(k + 5)(k - 2)$ **45.** $-4(x - 3)^2$ **47.** $-(x - 1)(x - 10)$ **49.** $3(w^2 - 9w - 20)$ **51.** $4x(x - 4)(x - 2)$

53. $a^2(a - 1)(a - 20)$ **55.** $5y(x + 8y)(x + y)$ **57.** $4x^2y(x - 5y)(x + 2y)$ **59.** $-2xy^2(x - 4y)^2$ **61.** The trinomial can be further factored; $2(x + 3)(x + 5)$ **63.** The GCF is $6x^2$; $6x^2(2x + 3)$ **65.** $(x - 3)(x + 6) = x^2 + 3x - 18 = (x + 6)(x - 3)$ **67. a.** $(x - 1)(x - 4)$ **b.** $(1, 0); (4, 0)$ **c.** Answers may vary.   **69.** Answers may vary.   **71.** $\pm 11, \pm 16, \pm 29$ **73.** Answers may vary.   **75.** $x^2 + 2x - 15$ **77.** $(k + 3)(k - 10)$ **79.** $49x^2 - 25$ **81.** $(9r + 7)(9r - 7)$ **83.** $(x + 7)(x - 4)$; a quadratic polynomial in one variable   **85.** $6w^3 + w^2 - 27w + 20$; a cubic polynomial in one variable

Homework 6.5
1. $(x + 3)(x^2 + 4)$ **3.** $(x - 4)(5x^2 + 3)$ **5.** $(2m - 5)(3m^2 + 1)$ **7.** $(2x + 5)(5x^2 - 1)$ **9.** $(x - 3y)(a - 2b)$ **11.** $(5x + 2y)(a^2 - b)$ **13.** $(3x + 5)(x + 2)$ **15.** $(2x + 5)(x - 3)$ **17.** $(5p - 1)(p - 4)$ **19.** $(2x + 3)(2x + 5)$ **21.** prime   **23.** $(3w - 1)^2$ **25.** $(5x - 3)(3x + 2)$ **27.** $(3x - 4)(2x - 3)$ **29.** $(16y + 3)(y - 2)$ **31.** $(5a + 3b)(2a + 3b)$ **33.** $(20x - 3y)(x + y)$ **35.** prime   **37.** $(2r - 5y)^2$ **39.** $2(3x - 2)(x + 5)$ **41.** $-3(4x + 3)(x - 1)$ **43.** $4x(2x - 3)(2x - 1)$ **45.** $2x^2(5x - 1)(3x + 1)$ **47.** $4t(3t + 2w)^2$ **49.** $10ab^2(2a + 7b)(a - 2b)$ **51.** $(x + 4)(x - 10)$ **53.** $(w - 2)(3w^2 + 5)$ **55.** $3x^2(x - 9y)(x + 2y)$ **57.** prime   **59.** $(3x - 2)(2x - 5)$ **61.** $(x - 5y)(x + 6y)$ **63.** $-6r(r - 2)^2$ **65.** $2(6x - 5)(x + 1)$ **67.** $(x - 3y)(a^2 - 2b)$ **69.** prime   **71.** $2pt^2(5p - 4t)(p + 3t)$ **73.** The polynomial is not factored; $(x + 5)(x^2 - 3)$ **75.** The polynomial is not completely factored; $3(x - 5)(x + 2)$ **77.** $2(x - 2)(x - 6) = 2(x^2 - 8x + 12) = 2x^2 - 16x + 24 = (x - 2)(2x - 12) = 2(x - 4)^2 - 8 = (2x - 4)(x - 6)$ **79.** Answers may vary; $8(x + 2)(x + 3)$ **81.** $3x(2x + 3)(2x - 3)$ **83.** $-24p^2 - 22p + 30$ **85.** $(2x - 5)(x + 3)(x - 3)$ **87.** $6k^3 + 5k^2 + 5k + 12$ **89.** $-18x^3 + 60x^2 - 50x$; a cubic polynomial in one variable   **91.** $2x(2x - 5)^2$; a cubic polynomial in one variable

Homework 6.6
1. $(x + 5)(x - 5)$ **3.** $(a + 6)(a - 6)$ **5.** $(2x + 7)(2x - 7)$ **7.** prime   **9.** $(4p + 5t)(4p - 5t)$ **11.** $3(5x + 2)(5x - 2)$ **13.** $2ab(3a + 4b)(3a - 4b)$ **15.** $(4x^2 + 9)(2x + 3)(2x - 3)$ **17.** $(t^2 + w^2)(t + w)(t - w)$ **19.** $(x + 3)(x^2 - 3x + 9)$ **21.** $(x - 2)(x^2 + 2x + 4)$ **23.** $(m + 1)(m^2 - m + 1)$ **25.** $(2x + 3)(4x^2 - 6x + 9)$ **27.** $(5x - 2)(25x^2 + 10x + 4)$ **29.** $(3p + 2t)(9p^2 - 6pt + 4t^2)$ **31.** $(3x - 4y)(9x^2 + 12xy + 16y^2)$ **33.** $5(x + 2)(x^2 - 2x + 4)$ **35.** $2x(x - 3y)(x^2 + 3xy + 9y^2)$ **37.** $(k + 1)(k^2 - k + 1)(k - 1)(k^2 + k + 1)$ **39.** $(2x + y)(4x^2 - 2xy + y^2)(2x - y)(4x^2 + 2xy + y^2)$ **41.** $(a - 7b)(a + 4b)$ **43.** $2x(x - 2y)(x^2 + 2xy + 4y^2)$ **45.** $(x - 9)(x + 2)$ **47.** $4xy(x + 4y)(x - 6y)$ **49.** $-(k - 6)^2$ **51.** prime   **53.** $(x - 2)(x + 3)(x - 3)$ **55.** $3x^2(2x - 5)(x - 3)$ **57.** $2(4m + 7t)(4m - 7t)$ **59.** $(4x - 1)(2x + 3)$ **61.** $2y(2x - 5y)(3x + y)$ **63.** prime   **65.** $(5x + 3)(25x^2 - 15x + 9)$ **67.** $(p + 9)^2$ **69.** $(5x - 2)(2x + 1)(2x - 1)$ **71.** $(7x + 1)^2$ **73.** prime   **75.** $2y(w + 5y)(w^2 - 5wy + 25y^2)$ **77.** $-3x(x - 6)(x + 5)$ **79.** $3x(3x + 5)(3x - 5)$ **81.** $(9p^2 + 4q^2)(3p + 2q)(3p - 2q)$ **83.** The difference of cubes is $A^3 - B^3 = (A - B)(A^2 + AB + B^2)$; $(x - 2)(x^2 + 2x + 4)$ **85.** The polynomial $x^2 + 25$ is prime; $4(x^2 + 25)$ **87. a.** $(x + 2)(x - 2)$ **b.** $(-2, 0), (2, 0)$ **c.** Answers may vary.   **89.** $(A - B)(A^2 + AB + B^2) = A^3 + A^2B + AB^2 - A^2B - AB^2 - B^3 = A^3 - B^3$ **91.** Answers may vary.   **93.** $9x^2 - 49$ **95.** $(6p + 7)(6p - 7)$ **97.** $t^3 - 125$ **99.** $(3p + 1)(9p^2 - 3p + 1)$ **101.**

a linear equation in two variables (or a linear function)   **103.** $(2, -3)$; a system of linear equations in two variables

Homework 6.7
1. $-4, 7$ **3.** $-4, 3$ **5.** $3, 5$ **7.** -7 **9.** $-4, 6$ **11.** $\pm \dfrac{7}{5}$ **13.** $\dfrac{1}{3}, \dfrac{3}{2}$ **15.** $-6, 5$ **17.** $-1, 0, \dfrac{5}{2}$ **19.** $-2, 7$ **21.** $-2, 4$ **23.** 6 **25.** $\pm \dfrac{5}{4}$ **27.** $\pm 2, 0$ **29.** $0, 2$ **31.** $-5, \dfrac{1}{2}$ **33.** $-3, 0, 6$ **35.** $-\dfrac{2}{3}, 0, \dfrac{1}{2}$ **37.** $-\dfrac{5}{2}$ **39.** $-4, 6$ **41.** $-\dfrac{2}{3}, 1$ **43.** $\pm \dfrac{1}{5}$ **45.** $-10, 3$ **47.** $\pm 3, \dfrac{1}{2}$ **49.** $-3, \pm \dfrac{2}{3}$ **51.** $0, \dfrac{37}{3}$ **53.** $-6, 4$ **55.** $-3, -2, 8$ **57.** $(4, 0), (5, 0)$ **59.** $\left(-\dfrac{5}{6}, 0\right), \left(\dfrac{5}{6}, 0\right)$ **61.** $\left(-\dfrac{2}{3}, 0\right), (0, 0), \left(\dfrac{5}{4}, 0\right)$ **63.** $(-2, 0), (-1, 0), (1, 0)$ **65.** 0 **67.** $-4, 5$ **69.** $-5, 3$ **71.** -1 **73.** $-1, 2$ **75.** $\pm 1, 3$ **77.** $-1.24, 3.24$ **79.** $-0.81, 1.47, 3.34$ **81.** $-2, 4$ **83.** no real solution   **85. a.**  Q **b.** Q

c. $L: (0, 1301)$; $E: (0, 1325)$; $Q: (0, 1376)$; that of the quadratic model   **d.** 1980, 1992

87. a.  yes   **b.** 35; 7 years after being rated B2, 35% of companies default on their bonds.   **c.** 1, 21; 1 year and 21 years after being rated B2, 7% of companies default on their bonds; model breakdown has occurred for the estimate of 21 years.   **d.** (0, 0), (22, 0); no companies default 0 years and 22 years after being rated B2; model breakdown has occurred for the estimate of 22 years.

89. a. 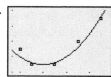 yes   **b.** (0, 28); in 2000, 28% of Americans thought that labor unions would become stronger.   **c.** 49%   **d.** 2016   **e.** The percentage of private-sector workers who are in a union decreased from 2007 to 2011.

91. a. 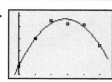 yes   **b.** 10,661 thousand (10.661 million) people   **c.** 2005, 2011   **d.** no; the model predicts attendance will continue to decrease.   **93.** width: 5 feet, length: 12 feet   **95.** width: 2 centimeters, length: 6 centimeters   **97.** 2 feet   **99.** 1 inch   **101.** Dividing both sides by x is not allowed if $x = 0$; $x = 0$ or $x = 1$ **103.** The student should have factored the left side of the equation; $x = -4$, $x = -3$, or $x = 3$

105. Answers may vary.   **107.** Answers may vary.   **109.** Answers may vary.   **111.** Answers may vary.   **113.** $(x + 2)(x + 3)$

115. $-2, -3$ **117.** $-2, -\dfrac{2}{3}, 0$ **119.** $p(3p + 2)(p + 2)$ **121.** $0, 2, 6$ **123.** ± 1.6660 **125.** 4.5969 **127.** -1 **129.** Answers may vary.

131. Answers may vary.   **133.** Answers may vary.

Chapter 6 Review

1. $-5x^3 - 3x^2 + 3x - 9$ **2.** $-3a^3b - 6a^2b^2 + 10ab^3$ **3.** 24   **4.** 9   **5.** 2, 4   **6.** $(f + g)(x) = x^3 - 2x^2 - 7x + 3$; -11
7. $(f - g)(x) = 5x^3 - 12x^2 - x + 1$; -239 **8.** $x^2 - 49$ **9.** $-40a^5b^6$ **10.** $8p^2 - 2pt - 45t^2$ **11.** $20x^3 - 23x^2 + 22x - 12$
12. $9x^2 + 42xy + 49y^2$ **13.** $36p^4 - 81t^6$ **14.** $-6r^3t^3 + 15r^2t^4 - 9rt^5$ **15.** $-36x^3 + 48x^2 - 16x$ **16.** $6m^4 + 7m^3p - 11m^2p^2 + 10mp^3 - 8p^4$
17. $a^2 - 10a + 24$ **18.** $6a + 3$ **19.** $f(x) = -2x^2 + 16x - 29$ **20.** $(f \cdot g)(x) = 6x^3 - 26x^2 + 37x - 21$; 18   **21.** $-2x^3 + \dfrac{2}{3}x - \dfrac{3}{x}$

22. $4w^2 + 3wp - 7p^2$ **23.** $4x - 5 - \dfrac{3}{2x + 1}$ **24.** $2x^2 - 4x + 3 + \dfrac{4}{3x - 2}$ **25.** $16b^2 + 12b + 9$ **26.** $2x^2 - 4x + 3 + \dfrac{5}{x - 3}$

27. $3y^2 - y - 4$ **28.** $x^2 - 2x + 6 - \dfrac{2}{x + 3}$ **29.** $(x + 5)(x - 5)$ **30.** $(x - 6)^2$ **31.** $(a + 9b)(a - 4b)$ **32.** $4a^3b^2(4a^2b - 5)$

33. prime   **34.** $(3w - 8y)(w + y)$ **35.** $(9t^2 + 4w^2)(3t + 2w)(3t - 2w)$ **36.** $2x^2(3x - 2)(x + 4)$ **37.** prime
38. $(x - 9)(x + 6)$ **39.** $2(y - 3)(y^2 + 3y + 9)$ **40.** $5t(r + 3t)^2$ **41.** $(x - 5y)(2a - 3b)$ **42.** $-4, 6$ **43.** $\pm \dfrac{3}{8}$ **44.** $-2, 0, \dfrac{5}{2}$
45. $-3, \pm 2$ **46.** $\dfrac{1}{3}, 2$ **47.** $0, \dfrac{3}{4}$ **48.** $\dfrac{3}{4}$ **49.** $(-3, 0), (0, 0), (2, 0)$ **50.** $-5, 1$ **51.** $-3, 1$ **52. a.** $(B + A)(t) = -4.71t^2 + 157.6t - 303$

b. thousands of bank tellers and ATMs   **c.** 884.56; in 2012, there were a total of about 885 thousand bank tellers and ATMs.
d. $(B - A)(t) = -0.13t^2 + 4t + 151$ **e.** 176.08; in 2012, there were about 176 thousand more bank tellers than ATMs.
53. a. 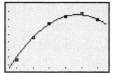 yes   **b.** 238 million prescriptions   **c.** 2015   **54.** width: 4 meters, length: 12 meters

Chapter 6 Test

1. $-a^3b - 5a^2b^2 + ab^3$ **2.** $(f - g)(x) = -2x^2 + 8x - 16$; -40 **3.** -3 **4.** no such value   **5.** 1   **6.** $-3, 5$
7. $-14x^3y^2 + 6x^2y^3 - 12xy^4$ **8.** $12x^2 - xy - 35y^2$ **9.** $6w^3 - 17w^2t + 13wt^2 - 20t^3$ **10.** $12x^3 + 36x^2 + 27x$
11. $6x^4 + 14x^3 - 9x^2 - 21x + 5$ **12.** $16x^4 - 81y^4$ **13.** $a^2 - 13a + 40$ **14.** $f(x) = -3x^2 - 24x - 55$

15. $(f \cdot g)(x) = 6x^3 - 19x^2 + 22x - 8$; 49   **16.** $\dfrac{2a^3}{b} - 3a^2 - 5ab$ **17.** $2x + 5 - \dfrac{3}{4x - 3}$ **18.** $4x^2 - 2x + 1 - \dfrac{2}{x + 3}$

19. $(x - 12)(x + 2)$ **20.** $2x(x - 3)^2$ **21.** $-2(8x - 3)(x + 2)$ **22.** $(3m + 8t)(3m - 8t)$ **23.** $2a^2b(4a - 3b)(2a - 3b)$

24. $2(3m + 4p)(9m^2 - 12mp + 16p^2)$ **25.** $\pm \dfrac{4}{5}$ **26.** $-2, 0, 5$ **27.** $1, \dfrac{11}{2}$ **28.** $\pm 3, -\dfrac{3}{2}$ **29.** $\dfrac{2}{3}, \dfrac{3}{2}$ **30.** $\left(\dfrac{2}{5}, 0\right), \left(\dfrac{3}{2}, 0\right)$ **31.** $-2.06, 2.19$

32. a. 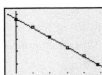   **b.** $(R \cdot P)(t) = -202.8t^2 + 748.8t + 1,006,176$ **c.** number of deaths
d. $367,387.2$; in 2018, there will be about $367,387$ deaths from heart disease.
e. decreasing; from 1965 to 2020, the number of deaths from heart disease
decreased and will continue decreasing; answers may vary.

33. a. 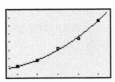   yes   **b.** 138; in 2017, the opium cultivation will be 138 thousand hectares.   **c.** $-2, 15$; the opium
cultivation was 100 thousand hectares in 1998 and the opium cultivation will be 100 thousand hectares
in 2015.   **34.** 2 inches

Chapter 7

Homework 7.1

1. $(0, 0)$ **3.** $(0, 0)$ **5.** $(0, 5)$ **7.** $(1, 0)$ **9.** $(-2, 0)$

11. $(-2, -6)$ **13.** $(1, 3)$ **15.** $(-6, -6)$ **17.** $(6, -2)$

19. $(2, 3)$ **21.** 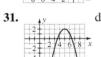   domain: all real numbers; range: $y \geq -4$

23.   domain: all real numbers; range: $y \leq -3$ **25.**   domain: all real numbers; range: $y \geq 0$

27.   domain: all real numbers; range: $y \geq 2$ **29.** 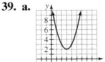   domain: all real numbers; range: $y \geq -4$

31. 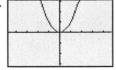   domain: all real numbers; range: $y \leq 2$ **33. a.** $f(t) = 2.25(t - 5.7)^2 + 265$ **b.** $(5.7, 265)$; in 1996, the U.S. Department
of Defense spent the least, $265 billion.   **c.** $605 billion   **d.** 11.6
35. a. $f(t) = -0.016(t - 52.3)^2 + 31$ **b.** $(52.3, 31)$; the largest percentage
of Americans who are obese, 31%, occurs at age 52 years.   **c.** 24%   **d.** $(8.28, 0)$,
$(96.32, 0)$; no 8-year-old Americans and no 96-year-old Americans are obese;
model breakdown has occurred.

37. a. 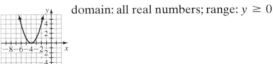   **b.** Answers may vary.   **c.** For each input–output pair, the output variable is 3 less than twice the square of the difference of the input variable and 1.   **39. a.** 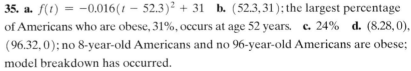   **b.** $2, 4$ **c.** 3   **d.** no such value   **41.** Answers may vary.
43. a. $a > 0, h < 0, k < 0$ **b.** $a < 0, h < 0, k > 0$
c. $a > 0, h > 0, k = 0$ **d.** $a < 0, h = 0, k < 0$
45. Answers may vary; functions are of the form
$f(x) = a(x + 5)^2 + 3$, where $a \neq 0$.   **47.** $f(x) = \frac{5}{8}(x - 5)^2 - 6$ **49.** $f(x) = -2.1(x + 7)^2 + 3.71$ **51.** yes; answers may
vary.   **53.** yes; answers may vary.   **55.** $(2, 5)$ **57. a.** 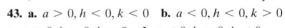   **b.**   Answers may vary.

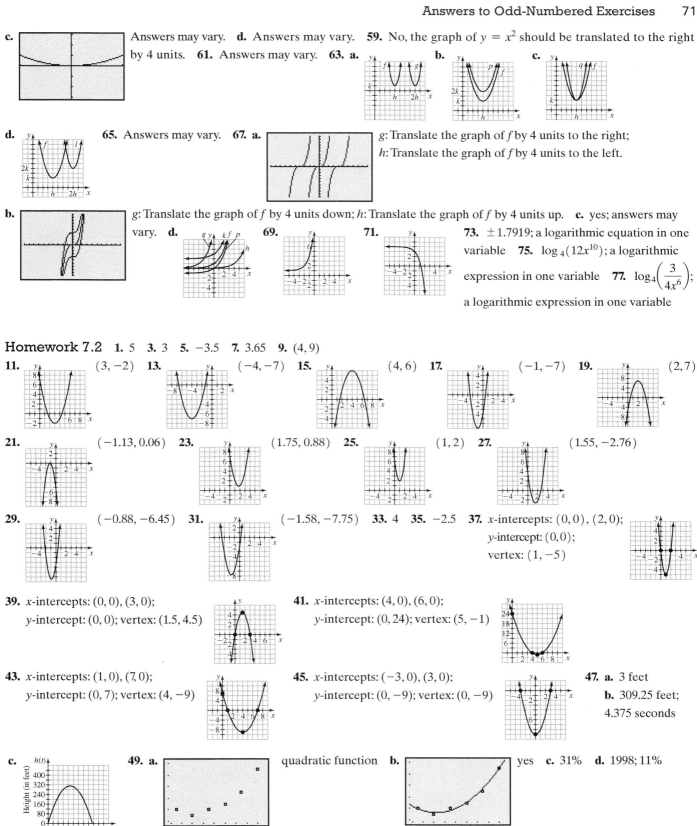

c. Answers may vary.   **d.** Answers may vary.   **59.** No, the graph of $y = x^2$ should be translated to the right by 4 units.   **61.** Answers may vary.   **63. a.**   **b.**   **c.**

d.   **65.** Answers may vary.   **67. a.** g: Translate the graph of f by 4 units to the right; h: Translate the graph of f by 4 units to the left.

b. g: Translate the graph of f by 4 units down; h: Translate the graph of f by 4 units up.   **c.** yes; answers may vary.   **d.**   **69.**   **71.**   **73.** ± 1.7919; a logarithmic equation in one variable   **75.** $\log_4(12x^{10})$; a logarithmic expression in one variable   **77.** $\log_4\left(\dfrac{3}{4x^6}\right)$; a logarithmic expression in one variable

Homework 7.2   **1.** 5   **3.** 3   **5.** -3.5 **7.** 3.65   **9.** $(4, 9)$

11. $(3, -2)$ **13.** $(-4, -7)$ **15.** $(4, 6)$ **17.** $(-1, -7)$ **19.** $(2, 7)$

21. $(-1.13, 0.06)$ **23.** $(1.75, 0.88)$ **25.** $(1, 2)$ **27.** $(1.55, -2.76)$

29. $(-0.88, -6.45)$ **31.** $(-1.58, -7.75)$ **33.** 4   **35.** -2.5 **37.** x-intercepts: $(0, 0)$, $(2, 0)$; y-intercept: $(0, 0)$; vertex: $(1, -5)$

39. x-intercepts: $(0, 0)$, $(3, 0)$; y-intercept: $(0, 0)$; vertex: $(1.5, 4.5)$

41. x-intercepts: $(4, 0)$, $(6, 0)$; y-intercept: $(0, 24)$; vertex: $(5, -1)$

43. x-intercepts: $(1, 0)$, $(7, 0)$; y-intercept: $(0, 7)$; vertex: $(4, -9)$

45. x-intercepts: $(-3, 0)$, $(3, 0)$; y-intercept: $(0, -9)$; vertex: $(0, -9)$

47. a. 3 feet   **b.** 309.25 feet; 4.375 seconds

c.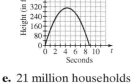

49. a.   quadratic function   **b.**   yes   **c.** 31%   **d.** 1998; 11%

e. 21 million households   **51. a.**   quadratic function   **b.**   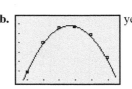   yes   **c.** $20.8 thousand

d. 46 years; $49.1 thousand   **53. a.** 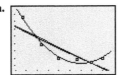 Q **b.** L **c.** 2022 **d.** 2001; 10.6 **e.** 150 professors   **55.** width: 20 feet, length: 20 feet; 400 square feet

57. width: 100 feet, length: 200 feet; 20,000 square feet   **59. a.** **b.** Answers may vary.   **c.** For each input–output pair, the output is 18 more than the difference between the square of the input and 10 times the input.   **61.** -1 **63.** -3 **65.** $-2, -4$ **67.** 3 **69. a.** -2 **b.** -2 **c.** yes

d. averaging x-coordinates of y-intercept and its symmetric point   **e.** averaging x-coordinates of y-intercept and its symmetric point   **f.** Answers may vary.   **71.** for f and k: $(3, 2)$; for g: $(2.7, 1.8)$; for h: $(3.3, 1.7)$ **73.** Answers may vary.   **75.** Answers may vary.

77. (graph)   **79.** (graph)   **81. a.** $a(x - h)^2 + k = a(x^2 - 2xh + h^2) + k = ax^2 - 2ahx + ah^2 + k = ax^2 - 2ahx + c$

b. x-coordinate of vertex: $-\dfrac{b}{2a} = -\dfrac{-2ah}{2a} = h$: y-coordinate: $f(h) = ah^2 - 2ah^2 + ah^2 + k = k$

83. $\dfrac{9c^6}{4b^6}$; an expression in two variables involving exponents   **85.** an exponential function   **87.** 4.19; an exponential equation in one variable

Homework 7.3   **1.** 13   **3.** $2\sqrt{3}$ **5.** $\dfrac{2}{3}$ **7.** $\dfrac{\sqrt{6}}{7}$ **9.** $\dfrac{5\sqrt{2}}{2}$ **11.** $\dfrac{3\sqrt{2}}{8}$ **13.** $\dfrac{\sqrt{6}}{2}$ **15.** $\dfrac{\sqrt{55}}{10}$ **17.** ± 5 **19.** $\pm\sqrt{3}$ **21.** $\pm 4\sqrt{2}$

23. $\pm\dfrac{\sqrt{15}}{5}$ **25.** $\pm\dfrac{\sqrt{42}}{3}$ **27.** $-4 \pm \sqrt{7}$ **29.** $5 \pm 3\sqrt{3}$ **31.** $-\dfrac{9}{8}, \dfrac{3}{8}$ **33.** $\dfrac{5}{9}$ **35.** $\dfrac{-3 \pm \sqrt{41}}{4}$ **37.** $\dfrac{7 \pm \sqrt{5}}{3}$ **39.** $6 \pm \sqrt{6}$

41. $\dfrac{-3 \pm \sqrt{21}}{3}$ **43.** $(-\sqrt{17}, 0), (\sqrt{17}, 0)$ **45.** $\left(\dfrac{6 - \sqrt{14}}{2}, 0\right), \left(\dfrac{6 + \sqrt{14}}{2}, 0\right)$ **47.** no x-intercepts   **49.** $6i$ **51.** $-3i\sqrt{5}$ **53.** $\dfrac{i\sqrt{5}}{7}$

55. $\dfrac{i\sqrt{65}}{5}$ **57.** $\pm 7i$ **59.** $\pm 3i\sqrt{2}$ **61.** $\pm i\sqrt{3}$ **63.** $-4 \pm 2i\sqrt{2}$ **65.** $\dfrac{5 \pm i\sqrt{3}}{4}$ **67.** $-3 \pm 2i$ **69. a.** $f(t) = -0.018(t - 19.9)^2 + 36.2$

b. 20.96; in 2019, about 21% of Americans will say they are "very happy."   **c.** $-7.18, 46.98$; in 1963, about 23% of Americans said they were "very happy," and in 2017, about 23% of Americans will say they are "very happy."   **d.** $(19.9, 36.2)$; the largest percentage of Americans who said they were "very happy," about 36%, occurred in 1990.   **71. a.** 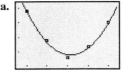 yes   **b.** $(9.15, 4.45)$; the smallest annual revenue from U.S. adult mattresses, about $4.5 billion, occurred in 2009.

c. $14.3 billion   **d.** 2015   **73.** 1.4, 4.2   **75.** 2, 4   **77.** $(1.1, -3.5), (4.7, -1.7)$ **79.** $\pm\sqrt{c^2 - b^2}$ **81.** $\pm\sqrt{rb - rp}$ **83.** $-b \pm \sqrt{k}$

85. $\dfrac{-a \pm \sqrt{c - b}}{p}$ **87.** There is still an x on the right-hand side; 5   **89. a.** $(3, 5)$ **b.** upward.   **c. i.** 2 **ii.** 1 **iii.** 0   **91. a.** $\pm\dfrac{7}{5}$

b. $\pm\dfrac{7}{5}$ **c.** They are the same.   **d.** Answers may vary.   **93. a.** yes; $-4 \pm \sqrt{5}$ **b.** no   **c.** no; answers may vary.   **95.** Answers may vary.   **97.** ± 2.2841 **99.** 8.4480   **101.** 0.7411   **103.** $(2w + 3)(w + 3)(w - 3)$; a cubic polynomial in one variable

105. $\pm 3, -\dfrac{3}{2}$; a cubic equation in one variable   **107.** $20w^3 + 15w^2 - 8w - 6$; a cubic polynomial in one variable

Homework 7.4   **1.** 36; $(x + 6)^2$ **3.** 49; $(x - 7)^2$ **5.** $\dfrac{49}{4}$; $\left(x + \dfrac{7}{2}\right)^2$ **7.** $\dfrac{9}{4}$; $\left(x - \dfrac{3}{2}\right)^2$ **9.** $\dfrac{1}{16}$; $\left(x + \dfrac{1}{4}\right)^2$ **11.** $\dfrac{4}{25}$; $\left(x - \dfrac{2}{5}\right)^2$

13. $-3 \pm \sqrt{10}$ **15.** $1 \pm 2\sqrt{5}$ **17.** $-2 \pm 2\sqrt{7}$ **19.** $\dfrac{7 \pm \sqrt{61}}{2}$ **21.** $\dfrac{-5 \pm \sqrt{41}}{2}$ **23.** $\dfrac{5 \pm \sqrt{33}}{4}$ **25.** $\dfrac{-4 \pm \sqrt{22}}{2}$

27. $\dfrac{1 \pm \sqrt{57}}{4}$ **29.** $\dfrac{-2 \pm \sqrt{19}}{3}$ **31.** $\dfrac{4 \pm \sqrt{10}}{6}$ **33.** $\dfrac{-1 \pm \sqrt{7}}{4}$ **35.** $-1 \pm i\sqrt{6}$ **37.** $3 \pm 2i\sqrt{2}$ **39.** $\dfrac{-3 \pm i\sqrt{7}}{2}$

41. $\dfrac{-1 \pm 2i\sqrt{5}}{3}$ **43.** $\dfrac{3 \pm i\sqrt{71}}{8}$ **45.** $\dfrac{-3 \pm i\sqrt{3}}{4}$ **47.** $(4 - \sqrt{13}, 0), (4 + \sqrt{13}, 0)$ **49.** $\left(\dfrac{5 - \sqrt{57}}{4}, 0\right), \left(\dfrac{5 + \sqrt{57}}{4}, 0\right)$

51. $(-5, 0)$ **53.** To complete the square, the leading coefficient must be 1; $\dfrac{-3 \pm \sqrt{13}}{4}$ **55. a.** no such real-number value

b. -3 **c.** $-3 \pm \sqrt{2}$ **57.** $1, 3$ **59.** $2, 3$ **61.** $(0, -0.5), (5, -8)$ **63. a.** $x^2 + 2kx + k^2$ **b.** $\left(\dfrac{2k}{2}\right)^2 = k^2$ **65.** Answers may vary.

67. Answers may vary. **69.** $(w - 5)^2$ **71.** $\left(x + \dfrac{5}{6}\right)^2$ **73.** an exponential function **75.** 3.17; an exponential function
77. 26.33; a logarithmic equation in one variable

Homework 7.5 **1.** $\dfrac{-5 \pm \sqrt{41}}{4}$ **3.** $\dfrac{3 \pm \sqrt{6}}{3}$ **5.** $2 \pm \sqrt{7}$ **7.** $1, \dfrac{3}{2}$ **9.** $\pm\dfrac{\sqrt{51}}{3}$ **11.** $-\dfrac{5}{2}, 0$ **13.** $\dfrac{5 \pm \sqrt{57}}{8}$

15. $\dfrac{1 \pm \sqrt{37}}{6}$ **17.** $-0.64, 3.14$ **19.** $-0.52, 3.02$ **21.** $-8.54, 0.02$ **23.** $\left(\dfrac{1 - \sqrt{57}}{4}, 0\right), \left(\dfrac{1 + \sqrt{57}}{4}, 0\right)$ **25.** no x-intercepts

27. $(-1 - \sqrt{6}, 0), (-1 + \sqrt{6}, 0)$ **29.** $\dfrac{3 \pm i\sqrt{23}}{2}$ **31.** $1 \pm 2i$ **33.** $4 \pm i\sqrt{2}$ **35.** $\dfrac{1 \pm i}{3}$ **37.** $\dfrac{2 \pm i\sqrt{11}}{3}$ **39.** $\pm 2\sqrt{5}$

41. $\dfrac{-15 \pm \sqrt{30}}{5}$ **43.** -6 **45.** $-\dfrac{5}{4}, 2$ **47.** $\dfrac{9 \pm \sqrt{89}}{4}$ **49.** $3 \pm 3\sqrt{2}$ **51.** $\pm\dfrac{7}{5}$ **53.** $\dfrac{-1 \pm \sqrt{3}}{2}$ **55.** $\pm\dfrac{5}{2}i$ **57.** $\dfrac{5 \pm i\sqrt{23}}{4}$

59. $6 \pm 4i\sqrt{3}$ **61.** $\dfrac{7 \pm i\sqrt{7}}{2}$ **63.** 2 real solutions **65.** 2 imaginary solutions **67.** 1 real solution **69. a.** 0 **b.** 1 **c.** 2

d. 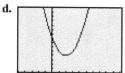 Answers may vary. **71.** $(1, 2), (5, 2); (3, -2)$;   **73. a.** 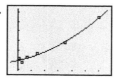 yes

b. \$47 billion **c.** 2015 **d.** 2010; 2010; 2009; 1 year **75. a.** yes **b.** 8.2% **c.** $-312.92, 112.92$; 10% of police officers are women in cities with populations of about -312.9 thousand (model breakdown) and about 112.9 thousand. **77. a.** 16 feet
b. 0.62 second, 2.63 seconds **c.** 3.33 seconds

79. $-2, 1.3$ **81.** ± 2.4 **83.** $(-3.4, -3.4), (2.0, -1.2)$ **85.** The equation is not in standard form; $\dfrac{-5 \pm \sqrt{33}}{4}$ **87.** The student did not simplify the result; $\dfrac{2 \pm \sqrt{14}}{5}$ **89. a.** $x = -\dfrac{b}{m}$ **b.** -3 **91.** The results are the same by all three methods: $-4, 5$ **93.** Answers may vary. **95.** $x^2 - 3x - 10$ **97.** $\dfrac{3 \pm \sqrt{61}}{2}$ **99.** $1, 3$ **101.** $-4x^2 + 16x - 13$ **103.** 2.1529 **105.** $\dfrac{2}{3}$ **107.** 3.3007

109. $(4x - 3)(2x - 3)$; a quadratic polynomial in one variable **111.** 77; a quadratic function **113.** $\dfrac{3}{4}, \dfrac{3}{2}$; a quadratic equation in one variable

Homework 7.6 **1.** $(1, -3, 2)$ **3.** $(-2, 15, 14)$ **5.** $(2, 4, -1)$ **7.** $(3, -3, 0)$ **9.** $(-2, 3, -1)$ **11.** $(2, 0, 1)$ **13.** $(3, 4, -1)$ **15.** $(-2, 4, 6)$
17. $y = x^2 + 2x + 3$ **19.** $y = -3x^2 + 7x + 5$ **21.** $y = 2x^2 - x - 4$ **23.** $y = x^2 + 2x - 6$ **25.** $y = -2x^2 + 7x + 4$
27. $y = 2x^2 - 8x + 3$ **29.** $y = -3x^2 + 8x + 4$ **31.** $y = 3x^2 + x - 1$ **33.** $y = x^2$ **35.** $y = 2x^2 - 6x + 4$ **37.** $y = x^2 - 9x + 22$
39. $y = -2x^2 + 20x - 42$ **41. a.** b–d. Answers may vary. **43.** Answers may vary. **45.** Answers may vary.
47. $L(x) = 18x - 41; E(x) = 3.18(1.60)^x$ **49.** linear function: $y = 2x + 2$; exponential function: $y = 2(2)^x$; quadratic function: answers may vary. **51.** $f(x) = x$; linear **53.** $y = 2(x - 5)^2 - 7$, or $y = 2x^2 - 20x + 43$

55. $x = \dfrac{5 \pm \sqrt{11}}{2}$; a quadratic equation in one variable   **57.** -5; a quadratic function   **59.** a quadratic function

Homework 7.7

1. a. quadratic   **b.** linear   **c.** exponential   **d.** none   **3.** by hand, using points $(14, 8.4)$, $(15, 13.6)$, and $(16, 20.1)$: $f(t) = 0.65t^2 - 13.65t + 72.10$; by regression: $f(t) = 0.52t^2 - 9.95t + 45.79$; 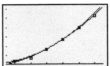 ; answers may vary.

5. a. $f(t) = 11.78t^2 - 29.02t + 320.92$ **b.** $2002, 2007$, and 2012; yes; answers may vary.   **7. a.** $f(t) = 0.0068t^2 - 0.13t + 6.49$
b. i. 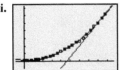 quadratic function   **ii.**  linear function   **iii.** Answers may vary.   **iv.** linear; answers

may vary.   **9. a.** $f(t) = 2.20t^2 - 31.65t + 115.51$; $g(t) = 6.11t - 42.75$ **b.** $(7.27, 1.69)$, $(9.89, 17.68)$; in 2007, the numbers of gigawatts of solar panels manufactured in China and installed in the world were both about 2 gigawatts; in 2010, the numbers of gigawatts of solar panels manufactured in China and installed in the world were both about 18 gigawatts.   **11.** A scattergram of the data does not suggest a quadratic relationship.   **13.** Answers may vary.   **15. a.** linear: $f(t) = 0.70t + 8.86$; exponential: $f(t) = 12.09(1.029)^t$; quadratic: $f(t) = 0.017t^2 - 0.08t + 14.94$; both the exponential model and the quadratic model fit the data well. The linear model does not.
b. exponential model   **17.** $(12, 6)$; a linear system in two variables   **19.** a linear function   **21.** $y = -\dfrac{5}{3}x - \dfrac{31}{3}$; a linear function

Homework 7.8

1. a. $(0, 15.43)$; in 1990, about 15% of households had outstanding student debt.   **b.** 18%; interpolation
c. 33%; extrapolation   **d.** 2019   **3. a.** $f(a) = -0.0313a^2 + 4.03a - 47.05$ **b.** $(12.98, 0)$, $(115.77, 0)$; 13-year-old householders and 116-year-old householders do not own a home.   **c.** $a < 12.98$ or $a > 115.77$; less than 12.98 years and more than 115.77 years
d. 64.4 years; 83%   **e.** 32.1 years, 96.7 years   **5. a.** 330.34; in 2018, the U.S. population will be about 330.3 million people.
b. $-210.44, 229.56$; in 1580, the U.S. population was 335 million (model breakdown has occurred); in 2020, the U.S. population will be 335 million people.   **c.** 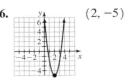   **d.** $t < 9.56$; years before 1800   **e.**

7. a. $f(t) = 0.88t^2 + 11.63t - 85.63$ **b.** 2005   **c.** $755.12, 811.63$; 56.51; yes   **d.** Answers may vary.   **9.** $2007, 2010$
11. a. $f(t) = -0.081t^2 - 2.06t + 72.85$; $g(t) = 3.80t + 10.11$ **b.** 1999; no; 2000   **c.** $h(t) = 100 - (f + g)(t)$
d. $h(t) = 0.081t^2 - 1.74t + 17.04$ **e.** 10.87; in 2007, about 10.9% of registered voters used voting methods other than punch cards, lever machines, or optical scan or other modern electronic systems.   **13.** 25 people   **15.** 70 people   **17.** width: 40 feet; length: 40 feet; 1600 square feet   **19.** Answers may vary.   **21.** Answers may vary.   **23. a.** $L(t) = 12.90t - 88.74$; $E(t) = 1.42(1.28)^t$; $Q(t) = 1.23t^2 - 18.18t + 65.79$; the linear model does not fit the data well; the quadratic model fits the data well; the exponential model fits the data the best.   **b.** exponential   **c.** 2024   **d.** 2073   **e.** Answers may vary.   **25.** Answers may vary.   **27.** Answers may vary.   **29.** Answers may vary.   **31.** Answers may vary.

Chapter 7 Review

1.   **2.**   **3.**   **4.**   **5.** $a < 0, h < 0, k > 0$ **6.** $(2, -5)$

7. 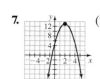 $(2, 13)$ **8.** $(1.43, -6.25)$ **9.** $6\sqrt{2}$ **10.** $\dfrac{7}{10}$ **11.** $\dfrac{1 \pm \sqrt{7}}{3}$ **12.** $\pm\dfrac{\sqrt{35}}{5}$ **13.** $\dfrac{15 \pm \sqrt{15}}{5}$ **14.** $3 \pm 2\sqrt{5}$

15. $\dfrac{-5 \pm \sqrt{57}}{4}$ **16.** $2 \pm \sqrt{3}$ **17.** $\dfrac{3 \pm \sqrt{19}}{5}$ **18.** $\pm\dfrac{2\sqrt{35}}{7}$ **19.** $\dfrac{1 \pm \sqrt{5}}{2}$

20. $\pm\dfrac{7}{5}$ **21.** $\dfrac{3 \pm \sqrt{57}}{12}$ **22.** $-1.18, 3.07$ **23.** $-3.05, 1.41$ **24.** $\dfrac{-8 \pm 3i\sqrt{2}}{2}$

25. $\dfrac{2 \pm i\sqrt{10}}{2}$ **26.** $-3 \pm \sqrt{13}$ **27.** $\dfrac{-3 \pm \sqrt{57}}{4}$ **28.** $\left(\dfrac{-1 - \sqrt{7}}{3}, 0\right), \left(\dfrac{-1 + \sqrt{7}}{3}, 0\right)$ **29.** no x-intercepts   **30.** $-2, 4$ **31.** 2

imaginary solutions   **32. a.** no such value   **b.** 1   **c.** $\dfrac{3 \pm \sqrt{3}}{3}$ **d.** Answers may vary.   **33.** $-0.6, 1$ **34.** $-3, 5$ **35.** $(-2.0, -1.3)$,

$(5.4, -3.8)$ **36.** $(1, 2, 3)$ **37.** $(1, -3, 2)$ **38.** $y = 2x^2 - x + 3$ **39.** $y = -2x^2 + 3x + 5$ **40.** linear: $y = -2x + 4$; exponential:

$y = 4\left(\dfrac{1}{2}\right)^x$; quadratic: answers may vary.   **41.** $y = x^2 - 5x + 7$ **42. a.** 159.25 feet; 3.125 seconds   **b.** 6.25 seconds

c. 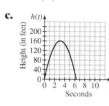   **43.** width: 45 feet, length: 90 feet; 4050 square feet   **44. a.** $f(t) = -0.33t^2 + 7.06t + 0.19$ **b.** $(10.70, 37.95)$; the largest percentage of military personnel who had done more than one tour of duty, about 38%, occurred in 2011.   **c.** $2009, 2012$ **d.** 31%   **45. a.** $f(t) = -0.027t^2 - 0.59t + 54.54$; $g(t) = 2.35t - 13.16$ **b.** 2010; 33%

Chapter 7 Test

1.   **2.** $a > 0, h > 0, k = 0$ **3.** Answers may vary.   **4.** $(-1, 5)$ **5. a.** $(-2, 0), (4, 0)$ **b.** $(1, -9)$

c.   **6.** $4\sqrt{2}$ **7.** $\dfrac{2\sqrt{15}}{15}$ **8.** $-2, 5$ **9.** $\pm\dfrac{5\sqrt{6}}{3}$ **10.** $\dfrac{6 \pm \sqrt{6}}{2}$ **11.** $\dfrac{3 \pm \sqrt{89}}{10}$ **12.** $-1 \pm \sqrt{22}$ **13.** $\dfrac{-3 \pm \sqrt{3}}{2}$

14. $\dfrac{3 \pm 2\sqrt{3}}{3}$ **15.** $-1.93, 0.34$ **16.** $\dfrac{3 \pm i\sqrt{6}}{3}$ **17.** $-4 \pm 2i\sqrt{3}$ **18.** $4 \pm 3\sqrt{2}$ **19.** $\dfrac{-3 \pm \sqrt{73}}{4}$ **20.** $\left(\dfrac{4 - \sqrt{13}}{3}, 0\right)$,

$\left(\dfrac{4 + \sqrt{13}}{3}, 0\right)$ **21.** x-intercepts: $(1.42, 0), (4.58, 0)$; vertex: $(3, 5)$;   **22.** ± 1 **23.** $y = x^2 + 2x + 1$, or $y = (x + 1)^2$ **24.** $y = 2(x - 5)^2 + 3$, or $y = 2x^2 - 20x + 53$ **25. a.** 0   **b.** 1   **c.** 2   **26.** $(4, -8, 10)$ **27.** $(-1, -2, 4)$ **28.** 2.5 seconds; 103 feet   **29. a.** $f(t) = -0.028t^2 + 2.54t - 15.92$

b. 35.91; about 36% of 31-year-old Americans feel that they are taking a great risk by entering personal information in a pop-up ad.   **c.** 25.82, 64.89; 31% of 26-year-old and 31% of 65-year-old Americans feel that they are taking a great risk.   **d.** $(6.77, 0), (83.94, 0)$; no 7-year-old or 84-year-old Americans feel that they are taking a great risk; model breakdown has likely occurred for the estimate about 84-year-old Americans.   **e.** $(45.36, 41.68)$; the age at which the maximum percentage, about 42%, of Americans feel that they are taking a great risk is 45 years.   **30.** 80 people

Cumulative Review of Chapters 1–7

1. $\pm\dfrac{7}{9}$ **2.** 13   **3.** $\dfrac{1 \pm \sqrt{21}}{5}$ **4.** $-\dfrac{5}{2}, \dfrac{4}{3}$ **5.** $-1, 3$ **6.** $-\dfrac{11}{2}$ **7.** $\dfrac{1}{7}, 1$ **8.** 2.1057   **9.** ± 1.5807 **10.** 2.4962   **11.** 2.8394   **12.** 2.8904

13. 1.8661   **14.** $\dfrac{3 \pm i}{2}$ **15.** $\dfrac{-3 \pm \sqrt{57}}{4}$ **16.** $(2, 5)$ **17.** $(-3, -4)$ **18.** $(-2, 1, 2)$

19. $x < -\frac{1}{12}; \left(-\infty, -\frac{1}{12}\right);$ 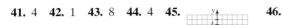   **20.** $\frac{648b^8}{c^{23}}$ **21.** $\frac{27b^{36}}{64c^6}$ **22.** $\log_b\left(\frac{64}{x^9}\right)$ **23.** $\ln\left(x^{31}\right)$ **24.** $9x^2 - 24xy + 16y^2$

25. $25p^2 - 49q^2$ **26.** $-3x^6 + 15x^4 - 24x^3 + 120x$ **27.** $x^4 + x^3 - 21x^2 - x + 20$ **28.** $f(x) = -2x^2 + 20x - 47$

29. $(f + g)(x) = 5x^2 - 8x + 2; 6$ **30.** $(f - g)(x) = -x^2 + 2x + 6; -9$ **31.** $(g \cdot h)(x) = 12x^3 - 26x^2 + 2x + 4; -36$

32. $(g \cdot k)(x) = 3x^2 - 23x + 40; 0$ **33.** $3x^2 - x + 2 - \frac{4}{2x - 3}$ **34.** $2x^2 - 3x - 2 - \frac{1}{x + 4}$ **35.** $\left(m^2 + 4n^2\right)(m + 2n)(m - 2n)$

36. $x(x - 5)(x - 8)$ **37.** $(4p - 3q)(2p + 7q)$ **38.** $(x + 4)(x + 3)(x - 3)$ **39.** $f(x) = -3x + 20$ **40.** $g(x) = \frac{4}{3}(3)^x$

41. 4   **42.** 1   **43.** 8   **44.** 4   **45.**   **46.**   **47.**   **48.**   **49.**

50.   **51.** domain: $-3 \le x \le 5$; range: $-2 \le y \le 4$; yes   **52.** $y = -\frac{4}{3}x + \frac{10}{3}$ **53.** $y = 12.77(1.45)^x$

54. $y = x^2 + 2x - 4$ **55. a.** $f(x) = 3x + 3; g(x) = 3(2)^x; h(x) = 3x^2 + 3$ (answers may vary)

b.   **56.** $2, 4$ **57.** $(1, 0), (5, 0)$ **58.** 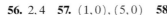   **59.** 4   **60.** -2 **61.** (graph)

62.   a. $f^{-1}(x) = \log_3(x)$ **b.** $\left(f^{-1} \circ f\right)(x) = f^{-1}(f(x)) = f^{-1}\left(3^x\right) = \log_3\left(3^x\right) = x$ **c.** $\left(f \circ f^{-1}\right)(x) = f(f^{-1}(x)) = f(\log_3(x)) =$

$3^{\log_3(x)} = x$ **63.   a.** $f^{-1}(x) = \frac{5}{2}x - \frac{5}{2}$ **b.** $\left(f^{-1} \circ f\right)(x) = f^{-1}(f(x)) = f^{-1}\left(\frac{2}{5}x + 1\right) = \frac{5}{2}\left(\frac{2}{5}x + 1\right) - \frac{5}{2} = \frac{5}{2} \cdot \frac{2}{5}x + \frac{5}{2} \cdot 1 - \frac{5}{2} = x$

c. $\left(f \circ f^{-1}\right)(x) = f(f^{-1}(x)) = f\left(\frac{5}{2}x - \frac{5}{2}\right) = \frac{2}{5}\left(\frac{5}{2}x - \frac{5}{2}\right) + 1 = \frac{2}{5} \cdot \frac{5}{2}x - \frac{2}{5} \cdot \frac{5}{2} + 1 = x - 1 + 1 = x$ **64.** \$9500 at 6%, \$2500

at 11%   **65.** 2017   **66.   a.** $L(t) = 0.42t + 0.72; E(t) = 1.09(1.17)^t; Q(t) = 0.03t^2 + 0.12t + 1.12$; the linear model fits the
data fairly well; the exponential and quadratic models both fit the data quite well.   **b.** $(-2, 1)$; the admission rate was the lowest,
1 admission per 100,000 people, in 1998.   **c.** exponential model; answers may vary.   **d.** 2018   **e.** 2022   **f.** Answers may vary.
67. a. $f(t) = -0.69t + 31.67$ **b.** 6.14; in 2017, about 6% of union members will work in manufacturing.   **c.** 38.65; in 2019, 5% of
union members will work in manufacturing.   **d.** $f^{-1}(p) = -1.45p + 45.90$ **e.** -99.1; in 1881, 100% of union members worked in
manufacturing; model breakdown has occurred.   **f.** $(45.90, 0)$; in 2026, no union members will be working in manufacturing; model
breakdown has likely occurred.   **g.** $t \le -99.1, t > 45.90$ **68. a.** $f(t) = 0.36t + 6.48; g(t) = 0.18t + 9.16$ **b.** 12.6; 12.22; in 2017,
the average age of light trucks will be 12.6 years; in 2017, the average age of passenger cars will be about 12.2 years.   **c.** 2015; 11.8
years   **d.** after 2015   **e.** $(f - g)(t) = 0.18t - 2.68; 0.56$; in 2018 the average age of light trucks will be 0.56 year more than the
average age of passenger cars.   **f.** 12.68; answers may vary.

Chapter 8

Homework 8.1   1. $0, -\frac{3}{5},$ undefined   **3.** $\frac{9}{2}, 8, \frac{19}{26}$ **5.** all real numbers except 0   **7.** all real numbers   **9.** all real numbers except -3

11. all real numbers except $-\frac{1}{2}$ **13.** all real numbers except -2 and 5   **15.** all real numbers except $\pm\frac{5}{2}$ **17.** all real numbers

19. all real numbers except $-\frac{3}{2}$ and 5   **21.** all real numbers   **23.** all real numbers except $\frac{1 \pm \sqrt{22}}{3}$ **25.** all real numbers except $\pm\frac{3}{2}$

and 2   **27.** $f(x) = \frac{4x^3}{3}$ **29.** $f(x) = \frac{4}{5}$ **31.** $f(x) = \frac{x + 5}{x - 9}$ **33.** $f(x) = \frac{x + 7}{x - 7}$ **35.** $f(x) = \frac{4x + 5}{2x - 3}$ **37.** $f(x) = -1$

39. $f(x) = -\frac{2}{3}$ **41.** $f(x) = -\frac{6}{x + 3}$ **43.** $f(x) = -\frac{x + 7}{x + 2}$ **45.** $f(x) = \frac{3x(x + 4)}{x - 3}$ **47.** $f(x) = \frac{x - 4}{(2x + 3)(2x - 3)}$

49. $f(x) = \dfrac{x^2 - 2x + 4}{x - 2}$ **51.** $f(x) = \dfrac{x + 3}{9x^2 + 6x + 4}$ **53.** $\dfrac{x - 3y}{x}$ **55.** $\dfrac{2a - b}{a - 3b}$ **57.** $\dfrac{p^2 + pq + q^2}{p + q}$ **59.** $\dfrac{f}{g}(x) = \dfrac{x + 4}{x - 6}; -\dfrac{7}{3}$

61. $\dfrac{h}{f}(x) = \dfrac{3x + 5}{x - 2}; \dfrac{17}{2}$ **63.** $\dfrac{f}{h}(x) = \dfrac{x^2}{3x + 1}; -\dfrac{4}{5}$ **65.** $\dfrac{k}{g}(x) = \dfrac{9x^2 - 3x + 1}{2x(3x + 1)}; \dfrac{13}{4}$ **67. a.** $P(t) = \dfrac{-103t^2 + 2509t - 10{,}588}{0.0068t^2 + 2.71t + 277.9};$

answers may vary.   **b.** 15.1%; 14.9%; overestimate   **c.** 9.9; in August of 2016, 9.9% of Americans will participate in SNAP.

69. a. $R(t) = 0.0048t^2 + 0.14t + 2.95$ **b.** $E(t) = 0.015t^2 + 0.055t + 6.05$ **c.** $P(t) = \dfrac{0.48t^2 + 14t + 295}{0.015t^2 + 0.055t + 6.05}$ **d.** 51.4%

e. $(12.73, 60.02)$; the largest percentage of voter-eligible Latinos who were registered, about 60.0%, occurred in 1993.   **f.** decreasing; the number of Latinos who are eligible to vote has been growing at a faster rate than the number of Latinos who are registered to vote.   **71.** Answers may vary.   **73.** domain: $-3, -2, -1, 0, 1, 2, 3$; range: $50.4, 25.2, 16.8, 12.6, 10.08, 8.4, 7.2$ **75.** no; answers may vary.

77. $\dfrac{17}{14}, \dfrac{5}{2}$; the work is incorrect; answers may vary.   **79. a.** 8.4; the drive takes 8.4 hours at a constant speed of 50 mph.   **b.** 7.64, 7, 6.46, 6

c. decreasing; answers may vary.   **81.** Answers may vary.   **83.** all real numbers   **85.** all real numbers   **87. a.** $x + 2$ **b.** $x + 2$

c. Answers may vary.   **89.** all real numbers except -3 and 7; a rational function   **91.** $-\dfrac{5}{3}, -2, 2$; a cubic equation in one variable

93. $(2x - 5)(4x^2 + 10x + 25)$; a cubic polynomial in one variable

Homework 8.2   1. $\dfrac{10}{x^2}$ **3.** $\dfrac{21x^2}{5}$ **5.** $\dfrac{3}{8p^5}$ **7.** $\dfrac{6}{25x^2}$ **9.** $\dfrac{a^2b^3}{6}$ **11.** $\dfrac{8x^3}{5y^4}$ **13.** $\dfrac{2(r + 7)}{r - 3}$ **15.** $\dfrac{2(x + 1)}{x - 3}$ **17.** $-\dfrac{8}{3}$

19. $\dfrac{2(k - 4)(k - 1)}{k + 6}$ **21.** $\dfrac{a(a + 2b)}{3b}$ **23.** $\dfrac{x - 5}{3(x + 5)(x + 1)}$ **25.** $-\dfrac{t - 4}{(t + 1)(t + 4)}$ **27.** $\dfrac{2(x - 5)(2x + 3)}{(x + 4)(x + 2)}$

29. $\dfrac{8}{(x - 6)(3x - 4)}$ **31.** $\dfrac{3x + 4}{(x + 2)(x + 3)}$ **33.** $-\dfrac{(3m + 2)(m - 3)}{(m + 3)(2m + 7)}$ **35.** $\dfrac{(x + 4)(x - 1)}{(x + 3)(x + 6)}$ **37.** $\dfrac{(p + 6t)(p + 3t)}{(p - 3t)(p - 5t)}$

39. $\dfrac{(x + y)(x - 3y)}{y(2x + 3y)}$ **41.** $\dfrac{3(x - 3)(x - 8)}{4x(x - 5)(x + 8)}$ **43.** $\dfrac{3(w + 2)(2w + 3)}{2w(3w - 1)(w - 5)}$ **45.** $\dfrac{x - 1}{(x - 2)(x + 5)}$ **47.** $\dfrac{1}{x - 1}$

49. $\dfrac{(k - 3)(k^2 + 2k + 4)}{(k + 2)(k^2 - 3k + 9)}$ **51.** $(2x - 3)(x + 2)$ **53.** $\dfrac{(a + 2b)}{(a^2 - ab + b^2)}$ **55.** $(f \cdot g)(x) = \dfrac{(x - 8)^2}{(x - 5)^2}; 4$

57. $\left(\dfrac{g}{f}\right)(x) = \dfrac{(x + 8)^2}{(x + 2)^2}; \dfrac{25}{9}$ **59.** $\left(\dfrac{f}{g}\right)(x) = -\dfrac{(x + 1)^2}{(x - 7)^2}; -\dfrac{25}{9}$ **61.** $\dfrac{25}{2x^6(x - 12)}$ **63.** $-\dfrac{36}{k^4}$ **65.** 1   **67.** 5.32 feet

69. 56.76 liters   **71.** 101.88 milligrams   **73.** 5.45 gallons per day   **75.** 98.27 feet per second   **77.** Answers may vary; $\dfrac{(x - 2)(x - 5)}{(x + 8)^2}$

79. a. 1   **b.** $\dfrac{1}{x}$ **c.** 1   **d.** $\dfrac{1}{x}$ **e.** 1 if n is odd, $\dfrac{1}{x}$ if n is even   **81.** Answers may vary.   **83.** $(f \cdot g)(x) = 16^x; \left(\dfrac{f}{g}\right)(x) = 4^x$

85. $(f \cdot g)(x) = 36(12)^x; \left(\dfrac{f}{g}\right)(x) = 4(3)^x$ **87. a.** 90 inches   **b. i.** $f(w) = 12w; g(x) = 3x$ **ii.** $(f \circ g)(x) = 36x$ **iii.** 90; the width

is 90 inches; the two results are equal.   **89.** $\log_b\left(\dfrac{16x^2}{9}\right)$; a logarithmic expression in one variable   **91.** 5.3723; a logarithmic equation

in one variable   **93.** 2.1893; an exponential equation in one variable

Homework 8.3   1. $\dfrac{7}{x}$ **3.** $\dfrac{1}{x - 3}$ **5.** $\dfrac{2m}{m - 1}$ **7.** $\dfrac{x + 5}{x + 7}$ **9.** $\dfrac{2(1 - 2x^4)}{x^6}$ **11.** $\dfrac{25x^2 + 18}{60x^6}$ **13.** $\dfrac{21b^2 - 10a}{12a^2b^3}$ **15.** $\dfrac{7x - 2}{(x - 2)(x + 1)}$

17. $\dfrac{2(x + 9)}{(x - 6)(x - 1)(x + 4)}$ **19.** $\dfrac{19t + 87}{15(t - 2)(t + 3)}$ **21.** $\dfrac{8x + 25}{x(x - 5)(x + 5)}$ **23.** $\dfrac{5x + 1}{(x - 4)(x - 3)(x + 3)}$ **25.** $\dfrac{3k - 1}{k + 1}$

27. $\dfrac{2x}{x + 1}$ **29.** $\dfrac{12}{x - 6}$ **31.** $\dfrac{1}{2(x + 3)}$ **33.** $\dfrac{4c^2 + 13c - 1}{(2c - 7)(2c + 7)}$ **35.** $\dfrac{a^2 + ab + 2b^2}{b(a + b)(a - b)}$ **37.** $\dfrac{x - 2}{(x + 2)(x + 4)}$ **39.** $\dfrac{2x^2 + 2x + 5}{(x - 1)(x + 2)}$

41. $-\dfrac{16}{(y - 3)(y + 5)}$ **43.** $\dfrac{x^2 + 4x + 30}{(x - 2)(x - 5)(x + 5)}$ **45.** $\dfrac{2x^2 + 5x - 1}{(x - 4)(x + 1)(x + 3)^2}$ **47.** $\dfrac{4}{c - 2}$ **49.** $\dfrac{x^2 - 15x - 21}{(2x + 5)^2(3x + 1)}$

51. $\dfrac{11x^2 - x + 3}{(x + 2)^2(3x - 1)}$ **53.** $\dfrac{3p^2 + 7pq - 8q^2}{(p - 6q)(p + 3q)(p + 4q)}$ **55.** $\dfrac{x^2 + x + 8}{6x(x - 4)(x + 2)}$ **57.** $\dfrac{5}{2(x + 2)}$ **59.** $\dfrac{-t + 16}{(t + 1)(t + 5)}$

61. $(f + g)(x) = \dfrac{2x^2 - 25}{(x - 4)(x - 3)}$ **63.** $(g - f)(x) = -\dfrac{7}{(x - 4)(x - 3)}$ **65.** $(f - g)(x) = \dfrac{-x^2 + 6x - 2}{3(x - 4)(x + 2)}$ **67.** First fraction

should be multiplied by $\dfrac{x + 2}{x + 2}$, second fraction by $\dfrac{x + 1}{x + 1}$; $\dfrac{5x + 7}{(x + 1)(x + 2)}$ **69.** Numerator should be $9x - (5x + 1) = 9x - 5x - 1$

$= 4x - 1$; $\dfrac{4x - 1}{x - 3}$ **71.** Answers may vary.   **73.** $(f + g)(x) = 8x^2 - 11x - 2$; $(f - g)(x) = 4x^2 + 3x + 8$ **75.** $(f + g)(x) = -5^x$;

$(f - g)(x) = (5)^{x+1}$ **77.** $\dfrac{2(2x^2 + 8x + 5)}{(x + 2)^2}$ **79.** $\dfrac{5(x + 2)}{3(x + 1)}$

81. 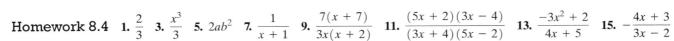   an exponential function   **83.** ± 1.9061; a fourth-degree polynomial equation in one variable

85. $y = 1718.87(0.38)^x$; an exponential function

Homework 8.4   **1.** $\dfrac{2}{3}$ **3.** $\dfrac{x^3}{3}$ **5.** $2ab^2$ **7.** $\dfrac{1}{x + 1}$ **9.** $\dfrac{7(x + 7)}{3x(x + 2)}$ **11.** $\dfrac{(5x + 2)(3x - 4)}{(3x + 4)(5x - 2)}$ **13.** $\dfrac{-3x^2 + 2}{4x + 5}$ **15.** $-\dfrac{4x + 3}{3x - 2}$

17. $\dfrac{3(8x^3 - 5)}{18x^3 - 1}$ **19.** $a(a + b)$ **21.** $\dfrac{x - 3}{x}$ **23.** $\dfrac{x - 9}{x + 6}$ **25.** $\dfrac{p^2 - 4p + 2}{p^2 - 4p - 3}$ **27.** $-\dfrac{1}{x(x + 3)}$ **29.** $-\dfrac{3}{a(a + b)(a - b)}$

31. $-\dfrac{2(x + 1)}{x^2(x + 2)^2}$ **33.** $-\dfrac{(x + 3)(x + 4)(3x + 10)}{x(x + 2)}$ **35.** $\dfrac{(x + 6)(x - 5)}{(x + 4)(x + 3)}$ **37.** $\left(\dfrac{f}{g}\right)(x) = \dfrac{5(x - 1)}{4(x - 3)}$ **39.** $\left(\dfrac{f}{g}\right)(x) = \dfrac{x - 2}{3}$

41. $\left(\dfrac{f}{g}\right)(x) = \dfrac{x^2 + 12x + 25}{x^2 - 7x + 25}$ **43.** The reciprocal of $\left(\dfrac{1}{x} + \dfrac{1}{2}\right)$ is not $\left(\dfrac{x}{1} + \dfrac{2}{1}\right)$; $\dfrac{2x^2}{x + 2}$ **45.** $-\dfrac{2(5x - 6)}{3x + 4}$; answers may vary.

47. $6 \cdot \dfrac{1}{3} = 2$; yes   **49.** Answers may vary.   **51.** $\dfrac{4x^5}{3y^3}$ **53.** $-\dfrac{x + 1}{x - 1}$ **55.** $\dfrac{2b^3 - 1}{b(3b^2 - 4)}$ **57.** $(f \circ g)(x) = \dfrac{3x - 2}{2x - 3}$ **59. a.** $H_e = \dfrac{H_p H_b}{H_p + H_b}$

b. 76.6 days   **61.** $\dfrac{2(x^2 + 2x + 10)}{(x - 6)(x + 4)(x - 2)}$; a rational expression in one variable   **63.** $\dfrac{1}{(x - 6)^2}$; a rational expression in one variable

65. all real numbers except -4 and 6; a rational function

Homework 8.5   **1.** 5   **3.** 2   **5.** empty set   **7.** $-\dfrac{29}{2}$ **9.** 4   **11.** empty set   **13.** -2 **15.** empty set   **17.** -8 **19.** -1

21. $\dfrac{-1 \pm \sqrt{13}}{3}$ **23.** $-10, 3$ **25.** $\dfrac{-3 \pm \sqrt{17}}{2}$ **27.** -1 **29.** 1   **31.** empty set   **33.** 1   **35.** $\dfrac{4 \pm \sqrt{22}}{2}$ **37.** $\dfrac{5 \pm \sqrt{89}}{2}$

39. $\dfrac{5 \pm i\sqrt{7}}{8}$ **41.** $\dfrac{17 \pm i\sqrt{11}}{6}$ **43.** $\dfrac{-3 \pm i\sqrt{47}}{4}$ **45.** $\dfrac{23}{4}$ **47.** $-4 \pm \sqrt{15}$ **49.** $\left(-\dfrac{7}{5}, 0\right)$ **51.** $r = \dfrac{mv^2}{F}$ **53.** $M = -\dfrac{r^2 F}{mG}$

55. $t = \dfrac{A - P}{rP}$ **57.** 2021   **59. a.** $E(t) = 0.13t + 1.14$ **b.** $C(t) = 0.59t + 4.47$ **c.** $P(t) = \dfrac{13t + 114}{0.59t + 4.47}$ **d.** 23.10; in 2017, 23.1%

of the total cost of health insurance will be paid by employees.   **e.** 19.63; employees will pay 23% of the total cost of health insurance
in 2020.   **f.** decreasing; the percentage of the total cost of health insurance that employees pay is decreasing; the rate of change of the
amount of money employers pay for employees' health insurance is greater than the rate of change of the amount of money employees
pay for health insurance.   **61.** 4.2   **63.** 3.3   **65.** $(-0.6, -1.9)$ **67.** $a = -6, b = -3$ **69.** Answers may vary.   **71.** Answers may vary.

73. Answers may vary.   **75.** $\dfrac{2(3x + 1)}{x(x + 1)}$ **77.** $-\dfrac{1}{3}$ **79.** $-\dfrac{15}{2}$ **81.** $\dfrac{10x - 1}{(x - 3)(x + 2)(x - 2)}$ **83.** $\pm 2, \dfrac{1}{2}$ **85.** 2.8433   **87.** $\dfrac{23}{13}$

89.   a quadratic function (or a quadratic equation in two variables)   **91.** $-5, 1$; a quadratic equation in one variable

93. $-2x^2 - 8x - 5$; a quadratic polynomial in
one variable

Homework 8.6   **1. a.** $C(n) = 350n + 1250$ **b.** $M(n) = \dfrac{350n + 1250}{n}$ **c.** \$391.67   **d.** 25 students   **3. a.** $T(n) = 50n + 500$

b. $M(n) = \dfrac{50n + 500}{n}$ **c.** 51.85; if 270 people attend, the mean cost per person is \$51.85.   **d.** 50; if 50 people attend, the mean cost per person is $60.   **e.** second column: 55, 52.5, 51.67, 51.25, 51   **f.** 50; If tens of thousands of people attend the reunion, the mean cost per person would be a few cents above $50; model breakdown has occurred.   **5. a.** $C(n) = 7000n + 90,000$ **b.** $B(n) = \dfrac{7000n + 90,000}{n}$

c. $P(n) = \dfrac{9000n + 90,000}{n}$ **d.** 11,250; if 40 cars are produced and sold each day, the price should be $11,250 per car for the profit to be $2000 per car.   **e.** 9000; if very many cars are produced and sold, a price set a few cents more than $9000 ensures a profit of $2000 per car.   **7. a.** $I(t) = 441.53t + 3852.97$ **b.** $M(t) = \dfrac{441.53t + 3852.97}{0.0013t + 0.093}$ **c.** The units of the expressions on both sides of the equation are dollars per household.   **d.** 2018   **e.** increasing; between 1995 and 2020, the mean annual income per household is increasing.

9. a. $R(t) = 464.8t + 2795.2$ **b.** $A(t) = \dfrac{464.8t + 2795.2}{0.026t^2 - 0.2t + 14.61}$ **c.** $537.85   **d.** 2020   **11. a.** $M(t) = 16.98t + 395.66$;

$E(t) = -29.87t + 1369.89$ **b.** $(M + E)(t) = -12.89t + 1765.55$; the inputs of $M + E$ are the number of years since 1980, and the outputs are the total number of daily newspapers.   **c.** $P(t) = \dfrac{1698t + 39,566}{-12.89t + 1765.55}$ **d.** 77.37; in 2016, about 77.4% of dailies will be morning newspapers.   **e.** 37.26; in 2017, 80% of dailies will be morning newspapers.   **13. a.** $W(t) = 0.31t^2 + 6.93t + 456.43$;

$M(t) = 0.33t^2 - 2.96t + 482.26$ **b.** $(W + M)(t) = 0.64t^2 + 3.97t + 938.69$; the inputs of $W + M$ are the number of years since 1980, and the outputs are the total number (in thousands) of people who have earned a bachelor's degree.

c. $P(t) = \dfrac{33t^2 - 296t + 48,226}{0.64t^2 + 3.97t + 938.69}$ **d.** 2013   **e.** decreasing; the number of bachelor's degrees earned has been increasing at a faster rate for women than for men.   **15.** 1.42 hours   **17. a.** $T(a) = \dfrac{85}{a + 70} + \dfrac{53}{a + 65}$ or $T(a) = \dfrac{138a + 9235}{(a + 65)(a + 70)}$ **b.** 1.89 hours

c. 8.67 mph   **19. a.** $T(a) = \dfrac{83}{a + 70} + \dfrac{37}{a + 65}$ or $T(a) = \dfrac{120a + 7985}{(a + 65)(a + 70)}$ **b.** 1.75, 1.53; the trip will take 1.75 hours at the speed limit and 1.53 hours at 10 mph over the speed limit.   **c.** 0.22; the trip will take 0.22 hour less at 10 mph over the speed limit than it would at the speed limit.   **d.** −66.61, 6.61; the trip will take 1.6 hours at 66.61 mph below the speed limit (model breakdown) and

1.6 hours at 6.61 mph over the speed limit.   **21. a.** $T(a) = \dfrac{285a + 19,130}{(a + 70)(a + 65)}$ **b.** 3.66 hours   **23. a.** Answers may vary.

b. Answers may vary.   **25. a.** $L(t) = 0.53t - 12.22$; $E(t) = 0.43(1.056)^t$; $Q(t) = 0.01t^2 - 0.47t + 6.10$; both the exponential and quadratic models fit the data well. The linear model does not.   **b.** Answers may vary; well.   **c.** 75 years   **d.** 1.056; the percentage of Americans who have shingles increases by 5.6% with each year a person ages.   **e.** 21.6%   **27.** $(3x - 2)(5x + 2)(5x - 2)$;

a cubic polynomial in one variable   **29.** $\pm\dfrac{2}{5}, \dfrac{2}{3}$; a cubic equation in one variable   **31.** $3x^4 + 5x^3 - 15x^2 - 5x + 12$; a fourth-degree polynomial in one variable

Homework 8.7   **1.** $I = kt$ **3.** $w = \dfrac{k}{x + 4}$ **5.** w varies inversely as r.   **7.** T varies directly as the square root of w.   **9.** $c = 4u$

11. $w = \dfrac{12}{\sqrt{t}}$ **13.** 27   **15.** 6   **17.** ± 4 **19.** $\dfrac{31}{7}$ **21.** It increases.   **23.** It decreases.   **25.** It increases.   **27.** less   **29.** Too many cooks spoil the broth.   **31.** $1344   **33.** 96 newtons   **35.** 186.1 feet   **37.** 3.5 meters   **39. a.** $F = \dfrac{5}{12}w$ **b.** 62.5 pounds   **c.** The variation constant should increase, because more force would be needed to move the sofa.   **41. a.** $T = 0.000906d$ **b.** 4415 feet   **c.** The time it takes to hear thunder increases by 0.000906 second for each 1 foot from the lightning strike.   **d.** no; the number of seconds divided by 5 is approximately the number of miles to the strike.   **43. a.** $f(d) = \dfrac{3200}{d^2}$ **b.** 128 pounds   **c.** 56,569 miles   **d.** 0.056 pound; yes; the astronaut would weigh much more than 0.056 pound due to the Moon's gravitational field.   **e.** Answers may vary.

45. a.   **b.** $F = \dfrac{2805.21}{L}$; yes   **c.** The frequency varies inversely as the effective length.   **d.** 370.1 hertz

e. Answers may vary.

47. a. 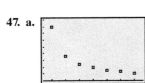   **b.** $f(d) = \dfrac{148.86}{d}$ **c.** The apparent height varies inversely as the distance.   **d.** As the distance increases, the apparent height decreases.   **e.** 1.5 inches   **f.** 148.9 inches

49. a. $T = k\sqrt{L}$ **b.** $k = \dfrac{T}{\sqrt{L}}$ **c.** third column: 0.2236, 0.1992, 0.2272, 0.2236, 0.2260, 0.2193, 0.2236, 0.2259, 0.2169, 0.2145; 0.22; average all values in third column.   **d.** $T = 0.22\sqrt{L}$ **e.** 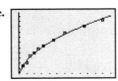   yes   **f.** 2.51 seconds   **51.** $f(L) = 5L; 5$

53. $f(n) = \dfrac{2}{n}; 2$ **55.** $f(r) = 2\pi r; 2\pi$ **57. a.** yes   **b.** no   **c.** Answers may vary.   **59.** false   **61.** false   **63.** yes; $\dfrac{1}{k}$ **65.** The students defined the variables x and y differently; 1 mile is approximately equal to 1.61 kilometers; 1 kilometer is approximately equal to 0.62 mile.
67. a. yes   **b.** not necessarily; answers may vary.   **69.** 62; the typist can type 62 words per minute.   **71.** Answers may vary.
73. Answers may vary.   **75.** Answers may vary.   **77.** Answers may vary.

Chapter 8 Review

1. $-3; \dfrac{7}{3}$ **2.** all real numbers except $\pm\dfrac{7}{2}$ **3.** all real numbers except $-\dfrac{7}{3}$ and $\dfrac{5}{4}$ **4.** all real numbers except -2 and $\pm\dfrac{1}{3}$ **5.** $\dfrac{3}{x-2}$

6. $-\dfrac{x+4}{2x(x-4)}$ **7.** $\dfrac{1}{x^2 - 2x + 4}$ **8.** $\dfrac{2a - 5b}{a - b}$ **9.** $\dfrac{f}{g}(x) = \dfrac{x+7}{x(x+3)}; -\dfrac{5}{2}$ **10.** $\dfrac{5}{4}$ **11.** $-\dfrac{2x(x+7)^2}{5(x+3)}$ **12.** $\dfrac{p + 5t}{t}$ **13.** $\dfrac{x-1}{4(x+1)}$

14. $\dfrac{4x}{x+4}$ **15.** $\dfrac{(x+3)(2x-3)}{x-3}$ **16.** $-\dfrac{2}{w-2}$ **17.** $\dfrac{(x+5)(x-2)}{x(x+1)(x-1)(2x-5)}$ **18.** $\dfrac{2(x^2 + x + 4)}{(x-2)^2(x+2)}$ **19.** $-\dfrac{1}{4(k+1)}$

20. $-\dfrac{(x-3)(3x+8)}{2(x+5)(x-5)(x-2)}$ **21.** $\dfrac{2(m^2 + 4mn + 10n^2)}{(m+6n)(m+2n)(m-5n)}$ **22.** $\dfrac{x-3}{x(x-5)}$ **23.** $(f \cdot g)(x) = \dfrac{(x-2)(x+1)}{(x+2)^2}$

24. $\left(\dfrac{f}{g}\right)(x) = \dfrac{(x-2)(x+1)}{(x+3)^2}$ **25.** $(f + g)(x) = \dfrac{2x^2 + 5x + 7}{(x+2)(x+3)}$ **26.** $(f - g)(x) = -\dfrac{7x + 11}{(x+2)(x+3)}$ **27.** minimum length:

109.36 yards; maximum length: 120.30 yards   **28.** 2.13 cups per minute   **29.** $\dfrac{1}{(x-3)(x+2)}$ **30.** $-\dfrac{4(x-2)}{3x^3}$ **31.** empty set

32. $-8, 1$ **33.** $\dfrac{-5 \pm \sqrt{73}}{6}$ **34.** $-3 \pm 3\sqrt{3}$ **35.** $\dfrac{5 \pm i}{2}$ **36.** $\left(\dfrac{5}{3}, 0\right)$ **37.** $r = \dfrac{S - a}{S}$ **38.** H varies directly as u squared.

39. w varies inversely as the common logarithm of t.   **40.** $y = \dfrac{2}{7}\sqrt{x}$ **41.** $B = \dfrac{72}{r^3}$ **42.** 4.14 inches   **43. a.** $m = kr^3$ **b.** $k = \dfrac{m}{r^3}$

c. third column: 17.1, 17.01, 17.02, 16.99, 16.99, 16.99; 17.02; average all of the values in the third column.   **d.** $m = 17.02r^3$
e.   yes   **f.** 207.1 grams

44. a. $C(n) = 40n + 600$ **b.** $M(n) = \dfrac{40n + 600}{n}$ **c.** 42.22; when 270 people use the room, the mean cost per person is $42.22.
d. 60; when the mean cost per person is $50, 60 people are using the room.   **45. a.** $(C + R)(t) = 0.19t + 184.17$; the inputs of $C + R$ are the number of years since 1970, and the outputs of $C + R$ are the total average annual per-person consumptions of chicken and red meat.   **b.** $P(t) = \dfrac{113t + 3929}{0.19t + 184.17}$ **c.** 44.6%; 44.7%; underestimate   **d.** 47.85; in 2017, about 47.9% of chicken and red meat consumed will be chicken.   **e.** 2021   **46. a.** $T(a) = \dfrac{75}{a + 50} + \dfrac{40}{a + 65}$ **b.** 1.94; when the student drives 5 mph above the speed limits, the driving time is about 1.9 hours.   **c.** 3.1 mph over the speed limits

Chapter 8 Test

1. all real numbers except $-\dfrac{5}{2}$ and $\dfrac{2}{3}$ **2.** all real numbers except ± 6 **3.** all real numbers   **4.** Answers may vary.

5. $f(x) = -\dfrac{3}{x-3}$ **6.** $f(x) = \dfrac{3x+1}{2x(3x-1)}$ **7.** $\dfrac{x-2}{9x^3}$ **8.** $\dfrac{p(p+2t)}{(p+3t)(p-t)}$ **9.** $\dfrac{-9x^2-4x+24}{2x(x-2)(x+4)}$

10. $\dfrac{x^2+13x+7}{(x+3)(x-3)(x+8)}$ **11.** $\dfrac{15(x+2)}{x(x^2-3x+5)}$ **12.** $(f-g)(x) = \dfrac{6(2x-1)}{(x-5)(x+4)}; \dfrac{3}{10}$ **13.** 1.33 grams

14. $\dfrac{(5x+2)(x-1)}{x(3x-7)}$ **15.** empty set   **16.** 5   **17.** $2 \pm \sqrt{6}$ **18.** 0   **19.** undefined   **20.** $-2, 5$ **21.** $W = \dfrac{3}{49}t^2$ **22.** $y = \dfrac{40}{\sqrt{x}}$

23. a. $C(n) = 200n + 10{,}000$ **b.** $B(n) = \dfrac{200n+10{,}000}{n}$ **c.** $P(n) = \dfrac{350n+10{,}000}{n}$ **d.** 450; if the manufacturer makes and sells 100 bikes in a month, the price should be \$450 per bike to make a profit of \$150 per bike.   **24. a.** $T(a) = \dfrac{400}{a+70} + \dfrac{920}{a+75}$

b. 16.83; when she drives 5 mph above the speed limits, the trip takes about 16.8 hours.   **c.** $-71.58, 4.23$; when the trip takes 17 hours, she is driving 71.58 mph below the speed limits (model breakdown) or 4.23 mph above the speed limits.   **25. a.** $g(L) = \dfrac{3200}{L^2}$

b. 88.89 hertz   **c.** 4 cm   **d.** decreasing; the longer the prongs, the lower is the frequency.   **26. a.** $C(t) = -0.0027t^2 + 0.073t + 0.68$

b. $P(t) = 1000t + 9000$ **c.** $M(t) = \dfrac{1000t+9000}{-0.0027t^2+0.073t+0.68}$ **d.** 22,793 patients per center   **e.** 2015

Chapter 9

Homework 9.1   **1.** $\sqrt[5]{x^2}$ **3.** $x^{3/4}$ **5.** $w^{1/2}$ **7.** $\sqrt{(2x+9)^3}$ **9.** $(3k+2)^{4/7}$ **11.** $5\sqrt{2}$ **13.** x^4 **15.** $6x^3$ **17.** $ab^6\sqrt{5}$ **19.** $x^4\sqrt{x}$
21. $2x^2\sqrt{6x}$ **23.** $4xy^4\sqrt{5x}$ **25.** $10ab^2\sqrt{2ab}$ **27.** $(2x+5)^4$ **29.** $(6t+3)^2\sqrt{6t+3}$ **31.** 3   **33.** x **35.** $2x$ **37.** $-2x^4$ **39.** $3a^3b^7$
41. $x^2\sqrt[6]{x^5}$ **43.** $-5a^5b^4\sqrt[3]{a^2}$ **45.** $2x^7y\sqrt[5]{2x^4y^2}$ **47.** $6xy$ **49.** $3x+6$ **51.** $(4p+7)^4$ **53.** $(2x+9)^5\sqrt[6]{2x+9}$ **55.** $\sqrt[4]{x^3}$
57. $\sqrt[3]{x^2}$ **59.** $\sqrt[6]{(2m+7)^5}$ **61.** $x^2\sqrt[3]{x}$ **63.** $\sqrt{3}$ **65.** $\sqrt[12]{p}$ **67.** $\sqrt[5]{4x^4}$ **69.** $\sqrt[8]{ab}$ **71.** -2 **73.** 2   **75.** $-\sqrt[3]{19}$ **77.** 9
79.

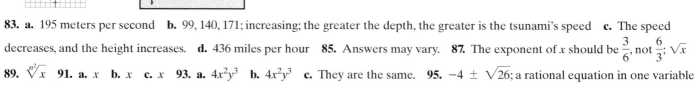

81. a. yes   **b.** 30°F   **c.** 129°F   **d.** 18 minutes

83. a. 195 meters per second   **b.** 99, 140, 171; increasing; the greater the depth, the greater is the tsunami's speed   **c.** The speed decreases, and the height increases.   **d.** 436 miles per hour   **85.** Answers may vary.   **87.** The exponent of x should be $\dfrac{3}{6}$, not $\dfrac{6}{3}$; $\sqrt{x}$
89. $\sqrt[n^2]{x}$ **91. a.** x **b.** x **c.** x **93. a.** $4x^2y^3$ **b.** $4x^2y^3$ **c.** They are the same.   **95.** $-4 \pm \sqrt{26}$; a rational equation in one variable
97. $-\dfrac{x^2-13x+2}{(x+3)^2(x-2)}$; a rational expression in one variable   **99.** all real numbers except -3 and 2; a rational function

Homework 9.2   **1.** $9\sqrt{x}$ **3.** $-4\sqrt[3]{5x^2y}$ **5.** $10\sqrt{5a} - 4\sqrt{3b}$ **7.** $-4 - 2\sqrt[3]{x} + 2\sqrt{x}$ **9.** $3\sqrt[3]{x-1} - 2\sqrt{x-1}$ **11.** $2.6\sqrt[4]{x}$
13. $25 - 4\sqrt{x}$ **15.** 14   **17.** $7\sqrt{3b}$ **19.** $13x^2\sqrt{2x}$ **21.** $4x\sqrt{x}$ **23.** $7x$ **25.** $7ab\sqrt{3b}$ **27.** $x\sqrt[3]{x^2}$ **29.** $-x^2y^2\sqrt[4]{x^3}$ **31.** $6x$
33. $-8x\sqrt{15}$ **35.** $14t - 2t\sqrt{14}$ **37.** $10x + 38\sqrt{x} + 24$ **39.** $8x - 4\sqrt{5x} + 2\sqrt{3x} - \sqrt{15}$ **41.** $5a - 9\sqrt{ab} - 2b$ **43.** $1 - w$
45. $49x^2 - 5$ **47.** $4a - b$ **49.** $36x + 60\sqrt{x} + 25$ **51.** $16x - 8\sqrt{5x} + 5$ **53.** $a + 4\sqrt{ab} + 4b$ **55.** $2x + 6\sqrt{2x-5} + 4$
57. $\sqrt[10]{x^7}$ **59.** $x\sqrt[5]{x^2}$ **61.** $-5\sqrt[3]{2m^3} + 20\sqrt{m}$ **63.** $\sqrt[3]{x^2} + 2\sqrt[3]{x} + 1$ **65.** $\sqrt{k} - 2\sqrt[12]{k^7} + \sqrt[3]{k^2}$ **67.** $6\sqrt[6]{x^5} + 2\sqrt{x} - 18\sqrt[3]{x} - 6$
69. $9\sqrt{x} - 25$ **71. a.** increases; answers may vary.   **b. i.** $75, 300, 675, 1200, 1875$, all in gallons per minute   **ii.** 1875 gallons per minute; 18 gallons per minute   **iii.** 75 gallons per minute; 1.35%   **c.** yes; 616 gallons per minute   **73.** The middle term is missing; $x^2 + 2x\sqrt{7} + 7$ **75.** The radicand should not be multiplied by 7; $14\sqrt{3}$ **77.** $\sqrt[6]{x}$ **79. a.** $\sqrt[20]{x^9}$ **b.** $\sqrt[kn]{x^{k+n}}$ **c.** $\sqrt[20]{x^9}$; they are the same.
d. $\sqrt[21]{x^{10}}$ **81. a. i.** true   **ii.** false   **iii.** true   **iv.** false   **v.** true   **vi.** false   **b.** Answers may vary.   **83.** Answers may vary.
85. $-2\sqrt{x}$ **87.** $-15x$ **89.** $\log_b\left(\dfrac{x-5}{x-8}\right)$; a logarithmic expression in one variable   **91.** $\dfrac{20}{13}$; a logarithmic equation in one variable
93. 0.7211; an exponential equation in one variable

Homework 9.3 **1.** $\dfrac{8\sqrt{x}}{x}$ **3.** $\dfrac{3\sqrt{5p}}{5p}$ **5.** $\dfrac{2\sqrt{2x}}{3x}$ **7.** $\dfrac{5\sqrt{2k}}{2k}$ **9.** $\dfrac{2\sqrt{x}}{x}$ **11.** $\dfrac{\sqrt{14}}{2}$ **13.** $\dfrac{\sqrt{2xy}}{x}$ **15.** $\dfrac{\sqrt{3xy}}{6y}$ **17.** $\dfrac{3\sqrt{x}-4}{x-4}$

19. $\dfrac{a\sqrt{6ab}}{3b}$ **21.** $\dfrac{2\sqrt[3]{25}}{5}$ **23.** $\dfrac{5\sqrt[3]{2}}{2}$ **25.** $\dfrac{4\sqrt[3]{x^2}}{5x}$ **27.** $\dfrac{3\sqrt[3]{4x}}{x}$ **29.** $\dfrac{7\sqrt[4]{4t}}{2}$ **31.** $\dfrac{\sqrt[6]{x^5}}{x}$ **33.** $\dfrac{\sqrt[5]{2x^2}}{x}$ **35.** $\dfrac{\sqrt[6]{6x}}{3x}$ **37.** $\dfrac{\sqrt[5]{24wxy^3}}{2xy}$

39. $\dfrac{5-\sqrt{3}}{22}$ **41.** $\dfrac{\sqrt{7}-\sqrt{3}}{2}$ **43.** $\dfrac{3\sqrt{r}+7}{9r-49}$ **45.** $\dfrac{x+\sqrt{x}}{x-1}$ **47.** $\dfrac{12x+3\sqrt{5x}}{16x-5}$ **49.** $\dfrac{x+y\sqrt{x}}{x-y^2}$ **51.** $\dfrac{x-10\sqrt{x}+25}{x-25}$

53. $\dfrac{6x+13\sqrt{x}-5}{9x-1}$ **55.** $\dfrac{18x+6\sqrt{7x}+3\sqrt{5x}+\sqrt{35}}{9x-7}$ **57.** $\dfrac{x-2\sqrt{xy}+y}{x-y}$ **59.** $\sqrt{x+1}+\sqrt{x}$ **61. a.** $f(h)=\dfrac{\sqrt{6h}}{2}$

b. 47 miles **c.** 212 miles **63. a.** Answers may vary. **b.** $\dfrac{\sqrt[4]{8}}{2}$ meter; 0.841 meter **65.** student 1; answers may vary.

67. Answers may vary; $\dfrac{5\sqrt[3]{x^2}}{x}$ **69.** $\dfrac{x}{3\sqrt{x}}$ **71.** $\dfrac{1}{\sqrt{x+2}+\sqrt{x}}$ **73.** $\dfrac{2x-7\sqrt{x}+3}{4x-1}$ **75.** $3\sqrt{10}$ **77.** Answers may vary.

79. a. $(A+B)(A^2-AB+B^2)$ **b.** A^3+B^3; answers may vary. **c.** x^3+8; answers may vary. **d.** $x+2$; answers may vary.

e. $\dfrac{\sqrt[3]{x^2}-\sqrt[3]{2x}+\sqrt[3]{4}}{x+2}$ **81.** $15x^3-22x^2+3x+4$; a cubic (or third-degree) polynomial in one variable **83.** $24(x-5)(x^2+5x+25)$;

a cubic (or third-degree) polynomial in one variable **85.** $\dfrac{2\pm\sqrt{14}}{5}$; a quadratic equation in one variable

Homework 9.4 **1.**   **3.**   **5.**   **7.**   **9.**

11.   **13.** 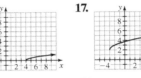 **15.**   **17.**   **19.**   **21.**

23.   **25.**   **27.**   **29.**   **31.**   **33.**

domain: $x\ge 0$; domain: $x\ge -2$; domain: $x\ge 0$; domain: $x\ge 5$;
range: $y\le 0$ range: $y\ge 0$ range: $y\ge 2$ range: $y\ge -3$

35.   **37.**   **39. a.** Answers may vary. **b.**   **c.** For each input–output pair, the output variable is equal to 2 times the square root of 3 less than the input variable.

domain: $x\ge -5$; domain: $x\ge 2$;
range: $y\ge 1$ range: $y\le 4$

41. 11 **43.** $21\sqrt{c}-3$ **45.** $(f+g)(x)=9\sqrt{x}-8$ **47.** $(f\cdot g)(x)=20x-31\sqrt{x}-9$ **49.** $(f-g)(x)=-6\sqrt{5}$

51. $\dfrac{f}{g}(x)=\dfrac{4x-12\sqrt{5x}+45}{4x-45}$ **53.** $(f+g)(x)=2\sqrt{x+1}$ **55.** $(f\cdot g)(x)=x-3$ **57. a.** 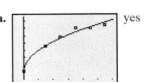 yes

b. 71%; interpolation **c.** 97%; extrapolation **59.** 0 **61.** 2.4 **63.** -6 **65.** 3 **67. a.** $a<0, h=0, k>0$
b. $a>0, h<0, k<0$ **c.** $a>0, h<0, k>0$ **d.** $a<0, h>0, k=0$ **69.** Answers may vary. **71.** If $a<0, f$ has a maximum point, (h,k). If $a>0, f$ has a minimum point, (h,k).

73. 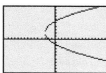 It is a parabola; no   **75.** Answers may vary.   **77.** Answers may vary.   **79.**

81. 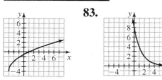   **83.**    **85.** $(f \circ g)(x) = \sqrt{12x + 17} - 7$ **87.** $(f \circ g)(x) = \sqrt{x^2 + 5}$ **89.** $(3x + 2)(2x - 3)$; a quadratic (or second-degree) polynomial in one variable

91. $\dfrac{1 \pm \sqrt{7}}{3}$; a quadratic function   **93.** $y = 2x^2 - 3x + 5$; a quadratic function

Homework 9.5   1. 25   **3.** empty set   **5.** -8 **7.** 4   **9.** 5   **11.** 14   **13.** empty set   **15.** $\dfrac{69}{2}$ **17.** $\dfrac{97}{6}$ **19.** 5   **21.** 5   **23.** $-\dfrac{1}{6}$

25. 11   **27.** 3   **29.** -6 **31.** 8   **33.** 4   **35.** $3 + 2\sqrt{2}$ **37.** 4   **39.** 1   **41.** 121   **43.** $\dfrac{3 \pm 3\sqrt{5}}{2}$ **45.** 10.31   **47.** 2.31   **49.** $d = \dfrac{S^2}{g}$

51. $h = \dfrac{2d^2}{3}$ **53.** $R = \dfrac{2GM}{v^2}$ **55.** 2.06   **57.** $-0.74, 4.97$ **59.** $-1.6, 3.8$ **61.** -4 **63.** $(-3.2, 1.4)$ **65.** $(-7, 0)$ **67.** $(5, 0)$

69. no x-intercepts   **71.** 4   **73.** 20   **75. a.** 61.8; in 2003, 62% of e-mails were spam.   **b.** 13.16; in 2012, 95% of e-mails were spam.   **c.** 2014; model breakdown has occurred.   **d.** 66 e-mails   **e.** 8 cents   **77. a.** 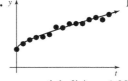 yes   **b.** $338; underestimate   **c.** 4th grade

d. The table seems to indicate that the function is increasing, so we would expect the per-student charge to be between $365 and $410.   **79.** Answers may vary; -2 **81.** $(4, 2)$ **83.** Answers may vary.   **85.** Answers may vary.   **87.** $-4\sqrt{x} + 5$ **89.** 9

91. 0   **93.** $p + 4\sqrt{p} + 3$ **95.** 5.0553   **97.** 6   **99.** $\dfrac{5}{7}$ **101.** $\dfrac{33}{5}$ **103.** $\dfrac{(3x + 5)(2x + 3)}{3(x + 1)(x - 1)(x + 2)}$; a rational expression in one variable   **105.** $\dfrac{3(3b - 10)}{(b - 2)(b - 5)}$; a rational expression in one variable   **107.** 6; a rational equation in one variable

Homework 9.6   1. $y = \sqrt{x} + 3$ **3.** $y = 1.33\sqrt{x} + 2$ **5.** $y = 1.34\sqrt{x} + 4$ **7.** $y = -4.04\sqrt{x} + 9$ **9.** $y = \sqrt{x} + 1$
11. $y = 3.15\sqrt{x} - 0.45$ **13.** $y = -2.43\sqrt{x} + 9.44$ **15.** $y = 10.22\sqrt{x} - 15.86$ **17.** $y = -48.40\sqrt{x} + 159.06$ **19.** $y = 7.34\sqrt{x} - 25.43$
21. a. $f(t) = 6.6\sqrt{t} + 10$ **b.** $(0, 10)$; there were 10 thousand American female troops in 2004.   **c.** 2011   **d.** 14 thousand American female troops   **23. a.** $f(t) = 7.3\sqrt{t} + 56$ **b.** $(0, 56)$; the average monthly bill for pay-TV was $56 in 2006.   **c.** 82.32; the average monthly bill for pay-TV will be about $82.32 in 2019.   **d.** 11.73; the average monthly bill for pay-TV will be $81 in 2018.   **e.** $97.1 billion
25. a. 420 meters per second   **b.** no; answers may vary.   **c.** between 4205 meters and 4500 meters, inclusive   **d.** yes
27. a. $S(h) = 0.27\sqrt{h}$ **b. i.** S fits the data points quite well; Q fits the data fairly well; L does not come close to the data points.
ii. $0, 0.327, 0.165$; S **iii.** Q; answers may vary.   **iv.** S; answers may vary.   **v.** $T = 0.25\sqrt{h}$; answers may vary.   **c.** 123.46 feet
d. 9.55 seconds   **29. a.** $f(n) = 31.92\sqrt{n} + 9.15$ **b.** 93.60; 93.6% of 7th births occurred despite contraception.
c. 8.10; all 8th births occurred despite contraception; model breakdown has likely occurred.   **d.** The higher the birth order, the higher is the percentage of births that occurred despite contraception; answers may vary.   **31.** 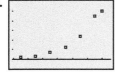 Increase b.

33. Answers may vary.   **35. a.** exponential and quadratic   **b.** exponential: $f(t) = 1.09(1.37)^t$; quadratic: $f(t) = 5.17t^2 - 105.43t + 556$ **c.** Both fit the data well.   **d.** exponential
e. exponential: 2017; quadratic: 2034; answers may vary.

f. i. 33.09; About 33 communities installed red-light cameras in 2005.   **ii.** 1446.65; About 1447 communities will install red-light cameras in 2017.   **iii.** $1137 million ($1.137 billion); we have assumed that the price of a red-light camera in 2017 will be equal to the price of one in 2005 and that the average number of red-light cameras sold per community in 2005 is equal to the average number of red-light cameras sold per community in 2017.   **37.** Answers may vary.   **39.** Answers may vary.   **41.** Answers may vary.   **43.** Answers may vary.

Chapter 9 Review

1. $\sqrt[8]{x^3}$ **2.** $(3k+4)^{7/5}$ **3.** $2x^3\sqrt{2}$ **4.** $3x^3y^5\sqrt{2x}$ **5.** $\sqrt[4]{x^3}$ **6.** $2x^3y^8\sqrt[3]{3x}$ **7.** $(6x+11)^5\sqrt[5]{(6x+11)^2}$ **8.** $11\sqrt{5x}$ **9.** $3ab\sqrt[3]{2a^2b}$

10. $28\sqrt{x} - 7\sqrt[3]{x}$ **11.** $3x - 21\sqrt{x}$ **12.** $8x - 2\sqrt{x} - 3$ **13.** $10a - 3\sqrt{ab} - b$ **14.** $25a - 49b$ **15.** $16x + 24\sqrt{x} + 9$

16. $4\sqrt[3]{x^2} - 20\sqrt[3]{x} + 25$ **17.** $\sqrt[28]{x^{11}}$ **18.** $\sqrt[12]{x}$ **19.** $\dfrac{\sqrt{3x}}{x}$ **20.** $5\sqrt[3]{t^2}$ **21.** $\dfrac{\sqrt[5]{63x^3y}}{3x}$ **22.** $\dfrac{a + 2\sqrt{ab}}{a - 4b}$ **23.** $\dfrac{10x - 23\sqrt{x} + 12}{4x - 9}$

24.   **25.**   **26.** $(f + g)(x) = -\sqrt{x} + 7$ **27.** $(f - g)(x) = 7\sqrt{x} + 3$

28. $(f \cdot g)(x) = -12x - 14\sqrt{x} + 10$ **29.** $\left(\dfrac{f}{q}\right)(x) = \dfrac{6x + 13\sqrt{x} + 5}{2 - 8x}$ **30.** 4   **31.** 2, 4   **32.** 9   **33.** 2   **34.** 7   **35.** 2.52

36. $-1.36, 4.56$ **37.** $(4, 0)$ **38.** [graph] Decrease a, increase b.   **39.** $y = 2.5\sqrt{x} + 3$ **40.** $y = -5.95\sqrt{x} + 17.31$

41. a. $f(t) = 1.67\sqrt{t} + 3.8$ **b.** $(0, 3.8)$; in 1992, the average credit card debt per household was $3.8 thousand.   **c.** 12.32; in 2018, the average credit card debt per household will be about $12.3 thousand.   **d.** 30.35; the average credit card debt per household will be $13 thousand in 2022.

Chapter 9 Test

1. $4x^4y^6\sqrt{2x}$ **2.** $4x^7y^4\sqrt[3]{xy^2}$ **3.** $(2x + 8)^6\sqrt[4]{(2x + 8)^3}$ **4.** $\dfrac{2\sqrt[15]{x^2}}{3}$ **5.** $\dfrac{2x + 5\sqrt{x} + 3}{4x - 9}$ **6.** $-x\sqrt{3x}$ **7.** $18x - 15\sqrt{x}$

8. $-20x + 2\sqrt{x} + 6$ **9.** $9a - 25b$ **10.** $16\sqrt[5]{x^2} - 24\sqrt[5]{x} + 9$ **11.** Answers may vary.   **12.**

13. a. $a < 0$ and $k \geq 0$, or $a > 0$ and $k \leq 0$ **b.** $\left(\dfrac{k^2 + a^2h}{a^2}, 0\right)$ **14.** $(f + g)(x) = 2\sqrt{x} + 11$ **15.** $(f - g)(x) = -8\sqrt{x} + 3$

16. $(f \cdot g)(x) = -15x + 23\sqrt{x} + 28$ **17.** $\left(\dfrac{f}{g}\right)(x) = \dfrac{15x - 47\sqrt{x} + 28}{-25x + 16}$ **18.** 25   **19.** 17   **20.** $\dfrac{144}{25}$ **21.** -6 **22.** 3

23. $(4, 0)$ **24.** $0.9, 3.3$ **25.** -3 **26.** [graph] Increase a, decrease b.   **27.** $y = 2.43\sqrt{x} + 0.56$

28. a. $f(t) = 2.90\sqrt{t} + 20.5$ **b.** 45.1 inches   **c.** 29 months   **d.** $(0, 20.50)$; the median height of boys at birth is 20.5 inches.

Chapter 10

Homework 10.1   **1.** arithmetic; $d = 8$ **3.** not arithmetic   **5.** arithmetic; $d = 7$ **7.** not arithmetic   **9.** $a_n = 6n - 1$

11. $a_n = -11n + 7$ **13.** $a_n = -6n + 106$ **15.** $a_n = 2n - 1$ **17.** 113   **19.** -196 **21.** 156.1   **23.** 400   **25.** 107   **27.** 87   **29.** 313

31. 3571   **33.** 98   **35.** no; answers may vary.   **37.** $f(n) = 9n - 1$ **39. a.** $a_n = 800n + 26,700$ **b.** $44,300   **c.** 30th year

41. a. $a_n = \dfrac{1}{6}n + 35$ **b.** 35.17, 35.33, 35.50, 35.67; they represent the number of hours the instructor would work if she had 1, 2, 3, or 4 students, respectively. **c.** 56.67 hours per week **d.** 150 students **43. a.** $a_n = 1.8n - 50$ **b.** 170 people **c.** $247 **d.** integers between 0 and 27, inclusive **45. a.** $f(t) = 0.98t + 12.11$ **b.** 24.85, 25.83, 26.81, 27.79, 28.77; from 2013 through 2017, the pharmaceutical industry spent (in millions of dollars) about 24.9, 25.8, 26.8, 27.8, 28.8, respectively, on government and politics. **c.** 2018 **47. a.** $a_n = 0.2n + 0.7$ **b.** $3.30 **c.** no **d.** $16.70 **49.** 500 **51.** yes; answers may vary. **53.** no; answers may vary. **55.** no; answers may vary. **57. a.** 2 **b.** 2 **c.** They are the same; answers may vary. **59.** 6; a radical equation in one variable **61.** a radical function **63.** $12x - 23\sqrt{x} + 10$; a radical expression in one variable

Homework 10.2

1. geometric; $r = 7$ **3.** arithmetic; $d = -7$ **5.** neither **7.** geometric; $r = \dfrac{1}{5}$ **9.** $a_n = 3(2)^{n-1}$ **11.** $a_n = 800\left(\dfrac{1}{4}\right)^{n-1}$ **13.** $a_n = 100\left(\dfrac{1}{2}\right)^{n-1}$ **15.** $a_n = 4^{n-1}$ **17.** 4.6566×10^{23} **19.** 1.1921×10^{-6} **21.** 3.3554×10^{7} **23.** 10 **25.** 12 **27.** 19 **29.** 16 **31.** $f(n) = 8(3)^{n-1}$ **33.** no; answers may vary. **35. a.** $a_n = 27{,}000(1.04)^{n-1}$ **b.** $38,429.42 **c.** 17th year **37. a.** 2, 4, 8, 16, 32 **b.** $a_n = 2^n$ **c.** 256 ancestors **d.** 34.36 billion ancestors; answers may vary. **39. a.** $f(t) = 26.81(1.144)^t$ **b.** 117.76, 134.71, 154.11, 176.30, 201.69; from 2011 through 2015, the federal student loan origination volumes (in billions of dollars) will be about 117.8, 134.7, 154.1, 176.3, 201.7, respectively. **c.** 2017 **41. a.** $a_n = 5(3)^{n-1}$ **b.** 405 students **c.** 295,245 students; yes; answers may vary. **d.** Answers may vary. **43.** geometric **45.** arithmetic **47.** The sequence is arithmetic, not geometric; 66 **49. a.** 2 **b.** 2 **c.** They are the same; answers may vary. **51.** $a_n = 5n + 9$ **53.** $a_n = 448\left(\dfrac{1}{2}\right)^{n-1}$ **55.** 781,250 **57.** −473 **59.** 122 **61.** 11 **63.** 1.9372; an exponential equation in one variable **65.** an exponential function **67.** $\log_b\left(\dfrac{25}{8x^{15}}\right)$; a logarithmic expression in one variable

Homework 10.3

1. 20,205 **3.** 30,294 **5.** −38,232 **7.** 21,978 **9.** −10,807 **11.** 468 **13.** 77,875 **15.** 36,288 **17.** −151,468 **19.** 22,468 **21.** 5187 **23.** 0 **25.** 19,436 **27.** 50,005,000 **29. a.** $58,200 **b.** $1,213,800 **31.** A; $8000 **33. a.** 136 seats **b.** 2340 seats **35. a.** $12.1 million **b.** $28.8 million **c.** $368.1 million **37. a.** $1,034,800 **b.** $644,800; $390,000 **c.** $39,800; years 1 through 13; years 14 through 26 **d.** $144,559 **39.** positive **41.** positive **43.** yes; answers may vary. **45.** 232 **47.** 1800 **49.** $\dfrac{2\left(x^2 - 2x + 17\right)}{(x + 3)(x - 3)(x - 5)}$; a rational expression in one variable **51.** $\dfrac{1}{(x - 3)^2}$; a rational expression in one variable **53.** 13; a rational equation in one variable

Homework 10.4

1. 40,955 **3.** 445.9617 **5.** 61.4266 **7.** 14.9804 **9.** 610,351,562 **11.** 857.1413 **13.** 8.8439 **15.** 89,478,485 **17.** 103.9945 **19.** 19,995.1172 **21.** 100 **23.** 485.9973 **25.** $699,784.85 **27.** A; $252,572.15 **29.** 2046 ancestors **31. a.** 11th round; approximately $6.14 billion **b.** There will be 10 full rounds and part of an 11th round. **c.** nine people; the entrepreneur will get approximately $6.14 billion; the other eight people will get an average of $3.61 billion. **33. a.** $f(t) = 927.46(1.35)^t$ **b.** 1252.07; 1252 Nevaehs were born in 2001. **c.** 152,394.49; 152,394 Nevaehs will be born in 2017. **d.** 584,229.49; 584,229 Nevaehs will be born from 2001 to 2017, inclusive. **35.** positive **37.** arithmetic **39. a.** 5115 **b.** $n = \dfrac{\log\left(\dfrac{a_n r}{a_1}\right)}{\log(r)}$ **c.** $S_n = \dfrac{a_1\left(1 - r^{\log(a_n r/a_1)/\log(r)}\right)}{1 - r}$ **d.** 5115 **e.** Answers may vary. **41.** 10,443 **43.** 68.6189 **45.** Answers may vary. **47.** Answers may vary. **49.** Answers may vary. **51.** Answers may vary. **53.** Answers may vary.

Chapter 10 Review

1. geometric sequence **2.** arithmetic series **3.** arithmetic sequence **4.** geometric series **5.** $a_n = 2(3)^{n-1}$ **6.** $a_n = -5n + 14$ **7.** $a_n = 200\left(\dfrac{1}{2}\right)^{n-1}$ **8.** $a_n = 2.7n + 0.5$ **9.** 4.2221×10^{14} **10.** 1.1719×10^{-2} **11.** −204 **12.** 225.9 **13.** 505 **14.** 77 **15.** 24

16. -204 **17.** -3182 **18.** $671,173.0723$ **19.** $3,221,225,469$ **20.** $120,540$ **21.** -1749 **22.** $797,161$ **23.** geometric series
24. arithmetic sequence   **25. a.** $\$71,772.52; \$70,000$ **b.** $\$1,166,085.43; \$1,300,000$ **c.** Answers may vary.   **26. a.** $f(t) = 2.37t + 24.65$
b. 2.37; the spending on pets in the United States increased by \$2.37 billion per year.   **c.** \$67.3 billion   **d.** \$873.6 billion

Chapter 10 Test

1. geometric sequence   **2.** none   **3.** geometric series   **4.** arithmetic series   **5.** $a_n = -6n + 37$ **6.** $a_n = 6(4)^{n-1}$ **7.** 262
8. 0.1875 **9.** 455 **10.** 9 **11.** 40.5000 **12.** 4.2950×10^9 **13.** -462 **14.** 1.1248×10^6 **15.** $2,098,620$ **16.** none   **17.** negative
18. a. $f(t) = 13.13t + 17.81$ **b.** 30.94; in 2001, online retail sales were about \$31 billion.   **c.** 254.15; in 2018, online retail sales will
be about \$254 billion.   **d.** 2565.81; total online retail sales from 2001 through 2018 will be about \$2566 billion, or about \$2.6 trillion.
19. a. $a_n = 32(1.03)^{n-1}$ **b.** 9th year   **c.** \$65,049.41   **d.** \$1,166,696.46

Cumulative Review of Chapters 1–10

1. $-\dfrac{5}{2}, \dfrac{1}{3}$ **2.** 22 **3.** $\dfrac{1 \pm \sqrt{69}}{2}$ **4.** $-1, \dfrac{5}{2}$ **5.** $\dfrac{2 \pm \sqrt{2}}{3}$ **6.** 2 **7.** $-\dfrac{43}{18}$ **8.** 3 **9.** 1.6013 **10.** 2.0492 **11.** 2.9755 **12.** $\dfrac{5 \pm \sqrt{13}}{6}$

13. $\dfrac{2 \pm i\sqrt{2}}{2}$ **14.** $(2, -1)$ **15.** $(-2, 3)$ **16.** $(2, -1, 3)$ **17.** $x \le 7; (-\infty, 7]$; 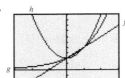   **18.** $\dfrac{2916}{b^{18}c^8}$ **19.** $\dfrac{4c}{5b^{1/4}}$ **20.** 0

21. $2x^3y^7\sqrt{3x}$ **22.** $\dfrac{\sqrt[3]{4x^2}}{x}$ **23.** $\dfrac{6x - 5\sqrt{xy} + y}{4x - y}$ **24.** $\ln(x^{35})$ **25.** $\log_b\left(\dfrac{x^{15}}{32}\right)$ **26.** $9a^2 - 30ab + 25b^2$ **27.** $6k + 13\sqrt{k} - 28$

28. $2x^4 + 3x^3 - x^2 + 7x - 3$ **29.** $3x^2 - x + 4 - \dfrac{5}{3x - 2}$ **30.** $\dfrac{(2x + 1)(x - 3)}{2x(x - 1)}$ **31.** $\dfrac{2x^2 - 3x + 10}{(x - 5)^2(x - 2)}$ **32.** $\dfrac{7x}{2(x - 4)(x + 2)}$

33. $\dfrac{2x^2 + 9x + 15}{(x - 3)(x + 1)(x + 3)(x + 9)}$ **34.** $\dfrac{3}{(x - 8)(x + 2)}$ **35.** $f(x) = -3x^2 - 18x - 34$ **36.** $(f \circ g)(x) = 2x^2 - 12x + 19$
37. $(x - 2)(2x - 5)(2x + 5)$ **38.** $2x(x - 5)(x + 3)$ **39.** $2(3w - 5y)(w + 2y)$ **40.** $(10p + 1)(10p - 1)$ **41.** 3 **42.** $0, 2$
43. $f(x) = -x^2 + 2x + 3$ **44.** all real numbers   **45.** $y \le 4$

46.   **47.**   **48.**   **49.**   **50.**

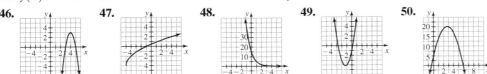

51. $y = -\dfrac{7}{5}x - \dfrac{11}{5}$ **52.** $y = 752.08(0.50)^x$ **53.** $y = 2x^2 - 5x + 3$ **54.** $y = 11.59\sqrt{x} - 11.39$ **55. a.** $f(x) = 2x + 2$;

$g(x) = 2(2)^x; h(x) = 2x^2 + 2$; answers may vary for h.   **b.**

56. 4 **57.** $\dfrac{1}{2}$ **58.** $g^{-1}(x) = 2^x$

59. $f^{-1}(x) = -\dfrac{1}{4}x - \dfrac{7}{4}$ **60.** all real numbers

except -5 and 7 **61.** $524,288$ **62.** 65

63. $196,605$ **64.** 5597 **65.** 2 liters of the 15% acid solution, 4 liters of the 30% acid solution   **66. a.** $f(t) = 29.38t + 532.59$
b. $f^{-1}(n) = 0.034n - 18.13$ **c.** 1061.4; there will be about 1061 thousand slot machines and video poker machines in 2018.
d. 19.27; there will be 1100 thousand (1.1 million) slot machines and video poker machines in 2019.   **e.** 29.38; the number of slot
machines and video poker machines is increasing by 29.38 thousand machines per year.   **67. a.** $L(t) = 0.0169t + 0.687$
b. $E(t) = 0.687(1.0184)^t$ **c.** $1.870; 2.462$; in 2050, India's population will be 1.870 billion according to the linear model and 2.462 billion
according to the exponential model.   **d.** 0.592; the difference in India's population in 2050 between the models is 592 million, which is
greater than the predicted U.S. population of 439 million for 2050.   **e.** linear: 2024; exponential: 2020; answers may vary.
68. a. exponential: $f(t) = 0.26(1.18)^t$; quadratic: $f(t) = 0.0179t^2 - 0.114t + 0.73$; both models fit the data well.
b. exponential   **c.** 2018   **d.** 2019   **e.** Answers may vary.   **69. a.** $B(t) = -4.04t + 145.85$ **b.** $R(t) = 102.36t + 1849.25$

c. $P(t) = \dfrac{-404t + 14,585}{102.36t + 1849.25}$ **d.** 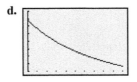   decreasing; between 2000 and 2020, the percentage of total recreational
expenditures that consists of book purchases is decreasing.
e. 2018

Chapter 11

Homework 11.1   **1.** ± 7 **3.** empty set **5.** $\pm \dfrac{18}{5}$ **7.** $-7, 3$ **9.** 5   **11.** $-\dfrac{10}{3}, 4$ **13.** empty set   **15.** $\pm$

21. $\dfrac{3}{7}, 7$ **23.** $-1, \dfrac{1}{3}$ **25.** $-\dfrac{13}{4}, \dfrac{7}{4}$ **27.** $1, \dfrac{17}{3}$ **29.** $-\dfrac{2}{27}, \dfrac{14}{3}$ **31.** ± 2.70 **33.** $-12.24, 6.71$ **35.** $-5.5, 4.5$ **37.**

41. $-3, 2$ **43.** -1 **45.** ± 3 **47.** -4 **49.** $\dfrac{3}{\;}, -\dfrac{1}{4}$ **51.** $-4 < x < 4$; x; $(-4, 4)$ **53.** $x \leq$

x; $(-\infty, -3] \cup [3, \infty)$ empty set   **57.** $x < 0$ or $x > 0$; x; $(-\infty, 0) \cup (0, \infty)$

59. $x \leq -1$ or $x \geq 13$; x; $\infty, -1] \cup [13, \infty)$ **61.** $-10 < x < 5$; x; $(-10,$

63. The set of real numbers; x; $\infty, \infty)$ **65.** $t \leq 0.8$ or $t \geq 9.6$; t; $(-\infty, 0.8] \cup$

67. $x < -4$ or $x > 4$; x; $(, -4) \cup (4, \infty)$ **69.** $p \leq -2$ or $p \geq 2$; p; $(-\infty,$
71. $x \leq -8$ or $x \geq 2$; x; $(-\infty,] \cup [2, \infty)$ **73.** $x \leq -10$ or $x \geq 2$; x; $(-\infty, -10] \cup$

75. $-\dfrac{39}{8} \leq x \leq -\dfrac{21}{8}$; x; $\left[\dfrac{9}{\;}, -\dfrac{21}{8}\right]$ **77.** $x = \dfrac{-b \pm (k - c)}{m}$ **79.** Answers may vary; $-2, 12$

81. Answers may vary; $-13 < x < 7$ **83.** **a.** $-\{$ **b.** $-8 < x < 5$ **c.** $x < -8$ or $x > 5$ **d.**   **85.** A
ma

87. false; answers may vary.   **89.** 1, 9   **91.** 0, 3.16 **93.** $-5, 3$ **95.** $x \leq 2$; x; $(-\infty, 2]$ **97.** $-2 \leq x \leq 2$;
x; $[-2, 2]$ **99.** near function   **101.** 0, 4; an absolute value equation in one variable

103. $y = -\dfrac{5}{9}x - \dfrac{2}{9}$; a linear equation in two vari

11.1 Quiz   **1.** ± 5 **2.** $\dfrac{1}{3}, \dfrac{4}{3}$ **3.** empty set   **4** **5.** $-\dfrac{1}{2}, \dfrac{11}{6}$ **6.** false; answers may vary.   **7.** $k \leq -2$ or $k \geq 2$;

k; $(-\infty, -2] \cup [2, \infty)$ **8.** c or $c > 5$; c; $(-\infty, -1) \cup (5, \infty)$
9. $-\dfrac{4}{3} \leq x \leq \dfrac{8}{3}$; x; $\left[-\dfrac{4}{3}, \dfrac{8}{3}\right]$ npty set

Homework 11.2   **1.** $7 + 3i$ **3.** $7 - 8i$ **5.** **7.** $5 - 16i$ **9.** -18 **11.** -50 **13.** -10 **15.** $-\sqrt{15}$ **17.** -64
19. $10 + 15i$ **21.** $-1 - 6i$ **23.** $-14 + 23i$ **25.** $4i$ **27.** $-16 - 50i$ **29.** 41   **31.** 85   **33.** 2   **35.** $-45 + 28i$ **37.** $-9 - 40i$
39. $7 - 24i$ **41.** $\dfrac{6}{29} - \dfrac{15}{29}i$ **43.** $\dfrac{-6}{53} + \dfrac{21}{53}i$ **45.** i **47.** $-\dfrac{7}{25} + \dfrac{24}{25}i$ **49.** $\dfrac{3}{5} + \dfrac{1}{5}i$ **51.** $\dfrac{7}{4} - \dfrac{5}{4}i$ **53.** $-\dfrac{7}{5}i$ **55.** Student 2's

work is correct; answers may vary.   **57. a–c.** Answ ary.   **59.** Answers may vary.   **61.** The result will be a negative real number;

answers may vary.   **63.** $\dfrac{12 - 8\sqrt{x}}{9 - 4x}$ **65.** $\dfrac{12}{13} - \dfrac{8 \pm 2i\sqrt{2}}{13 \cdot 3}$ **69.** $\dfrac{2 \pm i}{5}$ **71.** $\dfrac{5 \pm i\sqrt{31}}{4}$ **73.** $\dfrac{2 \pm 2i\sqrt{2}}{3}$

75. $\dfrac{-3 \pm 2i\sqrt{5}}{5}$ **77.** $\dfrac{1 \pm i\sqrt{11}}{4}$; a quadratic equ e variable   **79.** $(5x - 2)(2x - 3)$; a quadratic (or second-degree)

polynomial in one variable   **81.** $-54 - 10i$; an ima mber

11.2 Quiz   **1.** $9 - 6i$ **2.** $-5 + 9i$ **3.** 12   **4.** $-38 - 16i$ **6.** $7 - 24i$ **7.** 89   **8.** $\dfrac{7}{41} + \dfrac{22}{41}i$ **9.** $-\dfrac{7}{6} - \dfrac{5}{6}i$ **10.** false;
answers may vary.

Homework 11.3   **1.** $c = 13$ **3.** $c = \sqrt{41}$ **5.**   **7.** $a = 2\sqrt{6}$ **9.** $c = \sqrt{7}$ **11.** $\sqrt{170}$ **13.** $2\sqrt{11}$
15. $5\sqrt{17}$ feet ≈ 20.6 feet   **17.** $\sqrt{231}$ inches ≈ 15 **19.** 1.9 miles   **21.** 2273.4 miles   **23.** 10   **25.** $\sqrt{58}$ **27.** $2\sqrt{5}$ **29.** $4\sqrt{2}$
31. 8.01   **33.** 13.28   **35.** $x^2 + y^2 = 49$ **37.** $x^2 + y^2$ **39.** $(x - 5)^2 + (y - 3)^2 = 4$ **41.** $(x + 2)^2 + (y - 1)^2 = 16$

734

47. $(0,0), 2\sqrt{2}$

9. $(3,5), 4$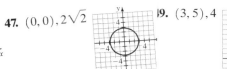

43. $(x +$

$3, -2), 1$

55. $x^2 + y^2 = 9$ **57.** $(x + 3)^2 + (y - 2)^2 = 4$

51.

. Answers may vary. **63. a.**

b. Arers may vary. **c.** The sum of the squares of

,wers may vary. **67.** no; answers may vary. **69. a.** Aers may vary. **b.**

o. Answers may vary. **c.** $3\sqrt{2}$ **d.** $\dfrac{5\sqrt{2}}{2}$ **73.**   **75.** 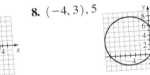 **77.**

. quadratic function **81.** $2(3x - 2)(x - 2)$; a quadratic (or seccegree) polynomial in one variable

$\dfrac{3 \pm 2\sqrt{6}}{5}$; a quadratic equation in one variable

.3 Quiz **1.** $4\sqrt{3}$ inches ≈ 6.9 inches **2.** $\sqrt{105}$ inches ≈ 10.2 inches **3. 4.** $4\sqrt{2}$ **5.** $(x + 3)^2 + (y - 2)^2 = 36$

. $x^2 + y^2 = 7.84$ **7.** $(0,0), 2\sqrt{3}$

8. $(-4, 3), 5$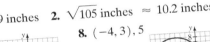

$(2)^2 + (y + 1)^2 = 68$ **10.** Answers may vary.

Homework 11.4

1.   **3.**   **5.**   **7.** 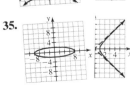 **9.**   **11.**   **13.**

15. 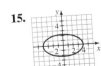 **17.** $\dfrac{x^2}{25} + \dfrac{y^2}{9} = 1$ **19.**  **21.**   **25.**   **27.**

29.  **31.** 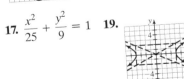 **33.**   **35.**   **39.**   **41.**

43. 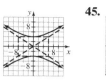   **45.**   **47.**   **49.**   **51.**   **53. a. i.**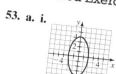

ii.   **iii.** 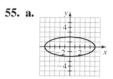 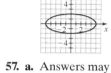   **iv.**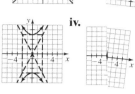

b. circle if $c = d$, both positive; ellipse if $c \neq d$, both positive; hyperbola with x-intercepts if $c > 0$ and $d < 0$; hyperbola with y-intercepts if $c < 0$ and $d > 0$

55. a. 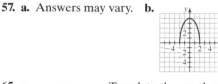   **b.** Answers may vary. Four times the square of x plus 25 times the square of y equals 100.

57. a. Answers may vary.   **b.** 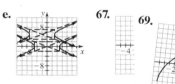 Answers may vary.   **61.** both a circle and an ellipse   **63.** Answers may vary.

65. a. Translate the graph of $= 1$ by 3 units to the right and 2 units up.

b. Translate the graph of x^2 by 3 units to the left and 2 units down. by h units to the right if h $|h|$ units to the left if $h < 0$, then by k units up if $k > 0$ or by $|k|$ units down $k < 0$.   **c.** Translate the graph of $x^2 + y^2 = r^2$

d.   **e.**   **67.**   **69.** 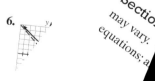   **71.** no; answers may vary.

73. a quadratic function   **75.** $\overline{!0}$; a quadratic equation in one variable

77. $-30x^3 + 25x^2 - 5x$; a cubic (or third-deg l in one variable

11.4 Quiz

1.   **2.**   **3.**   **5.**   **6.**

8.   **9.** no; answers may vary.   vary.

Homework 11.5   **1.** $(-5, 0), (5, 0)$ **3.**
11. $(-3, -5), (0, 4), (3, -5)$ **13.** $(-3, 0), ($ $(-2, 2), (2, 2)$
23. $(-0.74, -2.02), (-0.74, 2.02), (0.74, -2.0$ $(0, 3)$ **17.** en
   $(-2.25, -3.31)$,

9.
Se
Sect
7. $x =$
Section
may vary.
equations: a

27. $(-3, -2), (-3, 2), (3, -2), (3, 2)$ **29.** $(3, 2), (5, 0)$ **31.** $(3, 2), (2, 0)$ **33.** $(-5, 0, (5, 0)$ **35.** Answers may vary.
37. a. $c > 0$ **b.** $c = 0$ **c.** $c < 0$ **39.** $c = 5, d = -2$ **41.** Answers may vary. **43.** $(1!)$ **45.** Answers may vary.
47. Answers may vary. **49.** Answers may vary. **51.** Answers may vary. **53.** Answers may vary. **5.** $(-4$ **6.** Answers may vary.

11.5 Quiz **1.** $(-3, 0), (3, 0)$ **2.** $(-3, 7), (1, -1)$ **3.** $(1, 4)$ **4.** empty set

Appendix A

Section A.1 **1–8.**

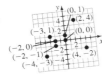

Section A.2 **1.** $4, 85$ **2.** $4, 0, -2, 85$ **3.** $\frac{2}{9}, 4, -7.19, 0, -2, 85$ **4.** $\sqrt{17}$ **5.** $\frac{2}{9}, 4, -, -2, \sqrt{17}, 85$

Section A.3 **1.** 3 **2.** 4.69 **3.** 0 **4.** π

Section A.4 **1.** -21 **2.** -30 **3.** 36 **4.** 16 **5.** 4 **6.** -9 **7.** -4 **8.** 3 **9.** -8 13 **11.** -6 **12.** -4 **13.** 5 **14.** 5
15. -10 **16.** -5 **17.** -4 **18.** -6 **19.** 8 **20.** 13 **21.** -13 **22.** -6 **23.** 0 **24.**

Section A.5 **1.** 49 **2.** 81 **3.** 216 **4.** 625 **5.** 16 **6.** -27 **7.** -16 **8.** -27

Section A.6 **1.** 13 **2.** 12 **3.** 0 **4.** -8 **5.** 4 **6.** -30 **7.** -1 **8.** -7 **9.** 36 **11.** -9 **12.** 8 **13.** -7 **14.** 11
15. 6 **16.** -12

Section A.7 **1.** equation **2.** equation **3.** expression **4.** expression

Section A.8 **1.** $2x + 8$ **2.** $4x + 28$ **3.** $12t - 18$ **4.** $20w - 30$ **5.** $-3x - 2$ $- 20$ **7.** $-10x + 45$ **8.** $-18x + 6$
9. $2.8p + 11.48$ **10.** $-5.2b - 20.28$

Section A.9 **1.** $7x$ **2.** $5x$ **3.** $2x - 7y$ **4.** $2x + y$ **5.** $-2a - 2b - 2$ **6.** $5t$ **7.** $28x + 7$ **8.** $21x + 22$
$-2x - 5y$ **10.** $2x - 8y$ **11.** $m - 5n + 10$ **12.** $-4a - 2b + 6$

Section A.10 **1.** 4 **2.** 7 **3.** 3 **4.** -7 **5.** $\frac{28}{5}$ **6.** $\frac{3}{2}$ **7.** 2 **8.** -2 **9.** $\frac{1}{2}$ $1\frac{1}{4}$ **12.** $\frac{6}{5}$ **13.** $\frac{14}{17}$ **14.** -21

Section A.11 **1.** $y = -2x + 8$ **2.** $y = 3x - 5$ **3.** $x = \frac{5}{3}y + 5$ **4.** $y = \frac{3}{5}$ $\frac{ax - c}{b}$ **6.** $x = \frac{by + c}{a}$
$\frac{1}{}y - \frac{3}{2}$ **8.** $y = 2x + 3$ **9.** $y = \frac{2}{3}x - \frac{5}{6}$ **10.** $y = \frac{9}{8}x - \frac{3}{8}$ **11.** $x = y$ $x - a$

A.12 **1.** equivalent expressions; answers may vary. **2.** equivalent ers may vary. **3.** neither; answers
4. neither; answers may vary. **5.** neither; answers may vary. **6.** eqions; answers may vary. **7.** equivalent
nswers may vary. **8.** neither; answers may vary. **9.** neither; answe· neither; answers may vary.

Index

absolute value, defined, 647
absolute value equation
  absolute value property for, 648
  of form $|A| = |B|$, 649–50
  in one variable, 648–50
    definition of, 648
    graphing to solve for, 650
  solving, 648–50
absolute value function
  definition of, 647
  graphing, 647–48
  translating and reflecting, 590
absolute value inequalities
  absolute value property for, 651
  in one variable, 650
  solving, 651–52
absolute value property
  for equations, 648
  for inequalities, 651
addition
  of complex numbers, 655–57
  of polynomials, 318
  of radical expressions, 571–72
    combining like radicals, 571
    using distributive law, 571
  of rational expressions,
    499–503, 507
    with common denominator,
      499–500
    with different denominators,
      500–502
    sum function, finding, 502–3
approximately exponentially
  related variables, 224
approximate solutions, quadratic
  formula and, 434
area of rectangular objects, 375–76
arithmetic sequences, 617–23
  common difference in, 618
  definition of, 617, 618
  formula of, finding, 618–19
  identifying, 618, 621
  linear functions and, 621
  modeling with, 620–21
  nth term of, formula that
    describes, 619
  term number of, 620
arithmetic series, 630–35
  definition of, 630
  ith term of, 630
  modeling with, 633
  sum of, 631–32
    evaluating, 631–32
    finding, 631
    formula for, 631
  term number of, 630
average rate of change, 92–93
axis of symmetry of parabola, 320

base
  e, 299, 303
  of exponent, 186
  of exponential function, 192, 269

of exponential model, 227
of logarithm, solving for,
  269, 275
logarithmic and exponential
  functions with same, 269
base multiplier property, 207–8
  to find exponential functions,
    216–17, 220
  to find exponential models,
    224–25
  to graph exponential functions,
    207–8
bi form, 420
binomial conjugates, 331–32
binomials
  binomial conjugates, 331–32
  definition of, 327
  dividing, by using long division,
    339–42
  factoring special, 362–68
  multiplying two binomials, 328
  special, 362–68
    difference of two squares,
      362–63
    factoring difference of two
      sixth powers, 365
    factoring strategy, 365–66
    sum or difference of two
      cubes, 363–65
    square of, 329–31
Boyle's law, 544

Cade, Eileen, 211
center of circle, finding, 663–64
change-of-base property, 295–96
circle
  center of, finding, 663–64
  definition of, 662
  equation of, 662–64
  radius of, finding, 663–64
Climate Change Lab, 104–10,
  175–77, 382–83, 467–70,
  553–54
coefficient
  factoring when leading coef-
    ficient is negative, 353
  term in polynomials, 317
common difference in arithmetic
  sequences, 618
common ratio of geometric
  sequences, 624
commutative law of multiplication, 331, 347
completely factoring polynomial,
  351–52
completing the square to solve
  quadratic equations, 425–31
  form $ax^2 + bx + c = 0$,
    427–29
  form $x^2 + bx + c = 0$,
    426–27
  imaginary-number solutions
    in, 429

perfect-square trinomials,
  425–26
  steps in, 428
complex conjugates
  complex numbers and, 657
  product of two, finding, 657
complex numbers, 655–60
  adding, subtracting, and multi-
    plying, 655–57
  complex conjugates and, 657
  definition of, 420, 655
  dividing, 657–59
  in quadratic equations,
    419–20
  simplifying quotient of, 657–58
complex rational expressions
  definition of, 510
  simplifying, 510–18
    by multiplying by $\dfrac{LCD}{LCD}$,
    512–15
    by writing as quotient of
      two rational expressions,
      510–12
composite functions, 244–54
  definition of, 244–45
  equations of
    to evaluate functions, 246
    finding, 246–48
  evaluating, 246, 247–48
    using equations of functions,
      246
    using graphs, 248–49
    using tables, 246
  to model authentic situation,
    249–50
  tables used to evaluate, 246
concepts
  describing, 4
  responding to a general
    question about, 4–5
conjugates
  binomial, 331–32
  radical, 581–83
constant rate of change, 92, 94–97
constants
  direct variation, ratios used to
    find, 546–47
  inverse variation, products
    used to find, 547
converse of Pythagorean
  theorem, 664
converting units of quantities,
  495–96
coordinates, 7
counting-number powers, 316
cube root in rational
  exponents, 199
cubes
cubes in powers, 187
cubic equations in one variable,
  372–74
  definition of, 372

factoring, 373
  finding x-intercepts of graph
    of cubic function,
    373–74
  solution set of, 374
cubic function, 321
  definition of, 321
  graphs of, 321
curves
  decreasing, 3
  exponential, 3
  increasing, 3
  intercept of, 3
  linear, 2

decreasing curves, 3
decreasing property, 208
  of exponential functions,
    graphing, 208
degree
  of polynomial, 317
  of term, 317
denominators
  in addition of rational
    expressions
    with common, 499–500
    with different, 500–502
  negative exponents in, 189
  of radical expressions,
    rationalizing, 579
    by using radical conjugates,
      581–83
  of radical expressions,
    simplifying, 415–16
  in subtraction of rational
    expressions
    with common, 503–4
    with different, 504–6
dependent linear system,
  119–20, 121
  substitution used to solve,
    130–31
dependent variables
  definition of, 2
  in qualitative graphs, 2–3
difference, sign of, 322
difference function, 321–23
  definition of, 321
  finding, 321–22
  modeling with, 322–23
  to solve a system, 323
  in subtraction of rational
    expressions, 506–7
direct variation, 539–42
  changes in values for, 540
  constants, ratios used to find,
    546–47
  definition of, 539
  model,
  using o
  variable
    exp
discrimina

distance
  Pythagorean theorem used to
    find, 661–62
  between two points, 662
distance formula, 662
distance-speed-time applications,
  531–33
distributive law
  in addition of radical
    expressions, 571
  in graphs of linear equations, 10
division
  of complex numbers, 657–59
  of polynomials, 338–45
    binomials using long
      division, 339–42
    with missing terms, 341–42
    monomials, 338–39
  of rational expressions, 493–95
  synthetic, 342–44
domain
  definition of, 43
  of exponential function, 210
  graphs used to find, 48
  input in, 43–45
  of linear models, 85
  of logarithmic functions, 268
  of quadratic functions, 394–96
  of rational functions, 480–82
    finding, 481–82
    property for, 481
    vertical asymptotes and,
      484–85, 487
  x-coordinate in, 48

e, base, 299, 303
elimination to solve systems of
  linear equations, 127–30,
  676–78
  adding left and right sides of
    two equations, 127
  steps in, 128
  system with fractions, 129–30
ellipses, 667–70, 673–75
  equation of, 669
  graphing, 668–69, 670
  intercepts of, 669–70
  significance of a and b for, 673
equality property, 276
equations
  absolute value property for, 648
  of circle, 662–64
  of ellipses, 669
  functions described by, 44–45, 46
  graphs of, 8
  of horizontal lines, 13
  of hyperbolas, 670–71
  linear regression, 72
  of parabolas, 446
    steps in, 447
    using points that are not
      y-intercepts, 446–47
    using y-intercept and two
      other points, 447–48
  of quadratic models, 396, 450–51
  satisfying, 7
  solution of, 7
  solution set of, 7
  square root model, finding,
    604–6

of vertical lines, 13
y-intercept and one other point
  used to find, 603–4
equations in one variable
  absolute value equation, 648–50
  absolute value inequalities, 650
  cubic equations, 372–74
  exponential, 275, 278–79
  logarithmic, 274–75
  polynomial equations, 374
  quadratic equations, 368–69
  rational equations, 518–21
  square root equations, 593–97
  systems of linear equations,
    131–32, 133
  using graphs, 279, 296
equations in three variables,
  442–50
  definition of, 443
  solution of, 443
  solving, 443–45
equations in two variables
  direct variation equations,
    539–42
  inverse variation equations,
    542–46
  linear equations, 8, 13
  systems of linear equations,
    116–20
equations of linear models
  finding, 69–77
    by data described in words,
      69–70
    by data displayed in tables,
      70–73
    by good points, 73–74
    steps in, 72
  to make predictions, 81–82,
    84–85
  rate of change used to find,
    95–96
  unit analysis of, 96–98
errors in modeling data, 63, 65, 72
estimates
  linear models used to make,
    60–61
  Pythagorean theorem used to
    make, 661–62
  square root model used to
    make, 606–7
excluded value of rational
  expression, 482
exponential curves, 3. *See also*
  exponential functions
  approximately exponentially
    related variables on, 224
  defined, 206
  equation of, finding
    in exponential model, 228–29
    points whose x-coordinates
      are consecutive integers,
      216–17
    points whose x-coordinates
      are not consecutive
      integers, 219–20
  exponentially related variables
    on, 224
  family of, 211
  types of, 210
exponential decay, 208

exponential equations in one
  variable, 275, 278–79
exponential form
  equation in, 274–75
  expression in, 562
  writing radical expressions
    in, 562
exponential functions
  base of, 192
  definition of, 192
  domain of, 210
  equations of, finding, 216–23
    comparing methods of, 221
    dividing left sides and right
      sides of two equations, 219
    of form $ab^n = k$ for a,
      217–19
    of form $b^n = k$ for b, 218
    using base multiplier
      property, 216–17
    using two points, 219–21
  evaluating, 192, 200
  geometric sequences and, 627
  graphing, 206–16 (*See also*
    exponential curves)
    with $0 < b < 1$, 206–7
    with $b > 1$, 206
    base multiplier property,
      207–8
    to find values, 210
    increasing or decreasing
      property, 208
    intercepts, 208–9
    reflection property, 209–10
  vs. linear functions, 192, 217
  and logarithmic function with
    same base, 269
  to model data (*See* exponential
    models)
  range of, 210
  x-axis as horizontal asymptote
    in, 209–10
exponential growth, 208
exponential/logarithmic forms
  property, 274–75
exponentially related variables, 224
exponential models, 224–30
  with base e to make estimates
    and predictions, 303
  base multiplier property used
    to find, 224–25
  base of, 227
  data described in words used to
    find, 227
  data displayed in tables used to
    find, 228–29
  defined, 224
  four-step modeling process
    used to find, 229
  half-life applications used to
    find, 225–27
  inverse of, finding, 286
  vs. linear models, 229
exponential/natural logarithmic
  forms property, 299
exponential regression, 229
exponential regression curve, 229
exponential regression
  equation, 229
exponentiation, 186–87

exponents
  definition of, 186–87
  general equations involving,
    218–19
  negative, 189–90
  one-variable equations
    involving, 217–18, 279
  properties of, 187–88, 190, 195
  rational, 199–205
  scientific notation and, 192–95
  simplifying expressions involv-
    ing, 188–89, 190–92
  zero as, 189
extraneous solutions
  to rational equations in one
    variable, 518
  to square root equations in one
    variable, 593, 599
extrapolation, 63

factored polynomial, defined, 346
factoring
  perfect-square trinomials, 425–26
  polynomial equations, 368–81
    area of rectangular objects,
      375–76
    connection between
      x-intercepts and solutions,
      369–70
    cubic equations in one
      variable, 372–74
    in one variable, solving by
      graphing, 374
    quadratic equations, 369–72
    quadratic function to model
      a situation, 374–75
    zero factor property, 368
  polynomials, 346–81
    binomials, 362–68
    completely factoring
      polynomial, 351–52
    definition of, 346
    factored polynomial,
      defined, 346
    with four terms by grouping,
      355–56
    vs. multiplying, 346
    strategy for, 365–66
    trinomials, 346–60
finite sequences, 617
five-step problem-solving
  method, 144
formula, defined, 18
four-step modeling process
  to find equation of inverse that
    is not a model, 260
  to find exponential models, 229
  to find quadratic models, 453
  to graph logarithmic
    function, 270
  to make predictions, 82, 606–7
fractions
  graphs of linear equations
    containing, 10
  quadratic equations containing,
    371–72
  rationalizing denominator of,
    415–16
  systems of linear equations
    with, solving, 129–30

frequency, 213
function notation, 78–84, 332
    definition of, 81
    equation used to find output
        and input, 79–80
    evaluating functions, 78–79
    to find intercepts, 83–84
    graph used to find values, 80
    models used with, 81–82
    table used to find output and
        input, 79
functions, 43–53
    definition of, 43, 44
    domain and, 43
        graphs used to find, 48
    equations describing, 44–45, 46
    evaluating, 78–79
    graphs describing, 45–46
    input in, 43–45
    linear, 46–47
    linear regression, 72
    output in, 43–45
    parabola used to find values
        of, 320
    range and, 43
        graphs used to find, 48
    relation and, 43–44, 45
    Rule of Four for, 47–48
    of sum, 297
    table describing, 45
    vertical line test and, 45, 48–49
    x-intercepts of, 353

geometric sequences, 624–30
    common ratio of, 624
    definition of, 624
    exponential functions and, 627
    formula of, finding, 624–25
    identifying, 624, 628
    modeling with, 626–27
    nth term of, formula that
        describes, 625
    term number of, finding, 625–26
geometric series, 635–40
    definition of, 635
    ith term of, 635
    modeling with, 638
    sum of, 636–38
        evaluating, 636–38
        finding, 636
        formula for, 636
    term number of, 635
grade, 18
graphing calculators
    exponential regression on, 229
    linear regression feature on, 72
    TRACE on, 11, 36, 82
    ZDecimal on, 8, 10, 29
    ZSquare on, 9, 10, 11, 27, 39
    ZStandard on, 9, 10, 11, 13, 27, 39
graphs/graphing
    of $|a - b|$, meaning of, 652–53
    absolute value function, 647–48
    authentic situations described
        with, 58–59
    of cubic function, 321
        finding x-intercepts of,
        373–74
    decreasing property of
        exponential functions, 208

definition of, 8
domain found with, 48
ellipses, 668–69, 670
of equations, 8
of exponential functions, 206–16
    with $0 < b < 1$, 206–7
    with $b > 1$, 206
    base multiplier property,
        207–8
    family of exponential
        curves, 211
    increasing or decreasing
        property, 208
    intercepts, 208–9
    reflection property, 209–10
to find domain, 48
to find range, 48
functions described by, 45–46
of hyperbolas, 670–72
of linear equations, 7–16
    containing fractions, 10
    distributive law in, 10
    horizontal line, 13
    intercepts of, 10–12
    slope in, 28–30
    in slope-intercept form, 9, 13
    solving with, 117–18
    in two variables, 8, 13
    using slope, 28–30
    vertical lines, 12–13
nonlinear system of equations
    solved by, 676, 679
parabolas, 319–20
    axis of symmetry of, 320
    drawing families of, 397
    equation of, finding, 446–48
    to find values of a
        function, 320
    maximum point of, 320
    minimum point of, 320
    vertex of, 320
    x-intercepts of, 418, 434
polynomial equations in one
    variable solved by, 374
of quadratic functions, 319–20
    (See also parabolas)
    comparing methods of, 409
    form $f(x) = ax^2$, 391–92
    form $f(x) = ax^2 + bx$
        $+ c = 0$, 403
    form $f(x) = ax^2 + bx + c$
        whose graph has vertex
        (h, k), 407
    form $f(x) = a(x - h)^2 + k$,
        394
    in standard form, 401–13
    in vertex form, 390–401
qualitative, 1–6
    definition of, 1
    dependent variables in, 2–3
    independent variables in,
        2–3
    reading, 1–3
    sketching, 3–5
square root equations in one
    variable solved by, 597
square root functions, 586–89
    minimum/maximum point
        of, 587
    three-step method for, 588

translating horizontally,
    586–88
system of inequalities solved
    by, 170–71
systems of linear equations
    solved by, 115–25
    intersection point of, 116
    to make predictions, 115–16
    in one variable, 131–32, 133
    in two variables, 117–19
translating, 392–94
    horizontally, 392–93, 586–88
    vertically, 392
greatest common factor (GCF)
    definition of, 351
    of polynomial, 350–51
        factoring out GCF, then
            factoring by trial and
            error, 358
        factoring out opposite of
            GCF of polynomial, 352–53
        finding GCF then factoring
            by grouping, 360
    grouping, factoring by, 355–56, 360

half-life
    to date archeological artifacts
        and fossils, 285
    definition of, 225
    to find exponential models,
        225–27
horizontal asymptote, 209–10
horizontal axis, 2
horizontal distance, 17–18
horizontal lines, 13
hyperbolas, 667, 670–75
    equation of, 670–71
    graphing, 670–72
    significance of a and b for, 673
hypotenuse, 660

i (imaginary unit), 420
    powers of, 659
imaginary number, 420
imaginary-number solutions,
    429, 435
imaginary unit i, 420
    powers of, 659
inconsistent linear system, 119, 121
    substitution used to solve, 130
increasing curves, 3
increasing property, 208
    of exponential functions,
        graphing, 208
independent variables
    defining, linear models and,
        64–65
    definition of, 2
    in qualitative graphs, 2–3
    radical model to make
        predictions about, 599
    rational models used to make
        predictions about, 522–23
index
    definition of, 561
    multiplying two radicals with
        same/different, 575
    of radical expressions, 561
inequality symbols, 48
infinite sequences, 617

input
    definition of, 43
    equation used to find, 79–80
    in function, 43–45
    of quadratic functions,
        finding, 372
    in Rule of Four, 47–48
    table used to find, 79
    value of rational equations in
        one variable, 520–21
intercepts. See also slope-intercept
        form ($y = mx + b$)
    of curves, 3
    definition of, 3
    of ellipses, 669–70
    of exponential functions,
        graphing, 208–9
    function notation used to find,
        83–84
    in graphs of linear equations,
        10–12
    of linear models, 62–64
    to sketch graphs, 11
interest problems, 147–49
    function model used to model,
        148–49
    interest from investment, 147
    solving, 147–48
interpolation, 63
interval, defined, 159
interval notation, 159–60
inverse functions, 255–66
    definition of, 255–57
    equation of inverse of model,
        finding, 259–60
        three-step process for, 260
    equation of inverse that is not
        a model, finding, 260–61
        four-step process for, 260
    equivalent statements in, 255
    evaluating, 256–57
    finding, 269
    graphing, 257–58
    input-output values of,
        finding, 257
    invertible functions in, 261–62
    one-to-one functions in, 262
    property of, 256
    reflection property of, 257, 258
inverses
    of exponential model,
        finding, 286
    logarithmic and exponential
        functions as inverses of
        each other, 269
inverse variation, 542–46
    changes in values for, 542
    definition of, 542
    model, 544–46
    using one point to find, 543
    variable varying inversely as an
        expression, 545–46
invertible functions
    composing with inverse,
        261–62
    one-to-one function as, 262
ith term of series
    in arithmetic series, 630
    definition of, 630
    in geometric series, 635

law of cooling, Newton's, 303
legs of triangle, 660
like terms in polynomials
    combining, 317–18
    definition of, 317
linear curves, 2
linear equations. *See also* systems
        of linear equations
    finding, 35–43
        parallel to a given line, 38
        perpendicular to a given line,
            38–39
        point-slope form in, 35, 39–40
        selecting points to use for, 40
        slope and point in, 36
        slope-intercept form in, 35–39
        two points in, 36–37
    graphs of, 7–16
        containing fractions, 10
        distributive law in, 10
        horizontal line, 13
        intercepts of, 10–12
        slope in, 28–30
        in slope-intercept form, 9, 13
        in two variables, 8, 13
        vertical lines, 12–13
    solution set of, graphing, 117–18
    in three variables, 442–50
        definition of, 442
        solutions of, 442–43
        solving system of, 443–45
    in two variables, 13
linear functions, 46–47. *See also*
        functions
    arithmetic sequences and, 621
    composition of two, 250
    vs. exponential functions,
        192, 217
    in modeling data, 61
linear inequalities in one variable,
        155–66
    addition property of
        inequalities, 156
    definition of, 158
    estimates and predictions made
        with, 162–63
    models used to compare
        quantities, 155–56, 162–63
    multiplication property of
        inequalities, 156–57
    solving, 157–61
linear inequalities in two
        variables, 167–75
    graph of, 167–70
    systems of, 170–71
        estimates made with, 171–73
        graphing solution set of,
            170–71
        modeling with, 171–73
        solution of, meaning of, 173
linear models. *See also* equations
        of linear models
    breakdown in, 62–64
    defining independent variable
        and, 64–65
    definition of, 60
    domain of, finding, 85
    vs. exponential models, 229
    extrapolation with, 63
    intercepts of, 62–64

interpolation with, 63
lines used in, 60–61
modifying, 64
predictions and estimates made
    by using, 60–61
range of, finding, 85
unit analysis of, 96–98
linear regression, 72
linear regression equation, 72
linear regression function, 72
linear systems
    comparing types of, 121
    dependent system, solving,
        119–20, 121
    inconsistent system, solving,
        119, 121
    one-solution system, solving,
        120, 121
    solution set of, 117–20
    table of solutions of equations
        for, 120
lines used in modeling data, 58–69
    intercepts of models and model
        breakdown, 62–64
    linear functions, 61
    linear models, 60–61
    scattergrams, 58–59
logarithmic equations, solving,
        294–95, 300–302
    for base of logarithm, 275
    in one variable, 274–75
    using exponential/logarithmic
        forms property, 274–75,
        300–301
    using power, product, and
        quotient properties,
        294–95, 302
logarithmic expression,
        simplifying, 302
logarithmic form, equation in,
        274–75
logarithmic functions, 267–315
    definition of, 267–68
    domain of, 268
    evaluating
        composite function, 246,
            247–48
        inverse function, 256–57
    and exponential functions with
        same base, 269
    graphing, 270
    properties of, 268–69, 274–79
logarithms
    common, 267
    definition of, 267–68
    finding, 267–68
    to model authentic situations,
        270–72, 282–92
    natural, 299–306
    properties of, 274–82, 292–99
        change-of-base property,
            295–96
        comparing, 297
        equality, 276
        exponential/logarithmic
            forms property, 274–75
        natural logarithms, 268–69
        power property, 275–79
        product property, 292–93
        quotient property, 293–94

to simplify logarithmic
    expression, 302

maximum point
    in graphing square root
        functions, 587
    of parabola, 320
maximum value
    definition of, 406
    modeling with quadratic
        function to find, 458–60
    of revenue, 461–62
    standard form of quadratic
        function to find, 406–9
mean
    computing, 527
    modeling, 526–29
minimum point
    in graphing square root
        functions, 587
    of parabola, 320
minimum value
    definition of, 406
    modeling with quadratic
        function to find, 458–60
    standard form of quadratic
        function to find, 406–9
missing terms
    division of polynomials with,
        341–42
    in synthetic division of
        polynomials, 343–44
mixture problems, solving, 149–51
model breakdown, 62–64
modeling, 58–114. *See also* linear
        models
    with arithmetic sequences,
        620–21
    with arithmetic series, 633
    with difference function, 322–23
    errors in, identifying types
        of, 65
    function notation in, 78–84
        equation used to find output
            and input, 79–80
        evaluating functions, 78–79
        to find intercepts, 83–84
        graph used to find values, 80
        models used with, 81–82
        table used to find output and
            input, 79
    with geometric sequences,
        626–27
    with geometric series, 638
    lines used in, 58–69
        intercepts of models and
            model breakdown, 62–64
        linear functions, 61
        linear models, 60–61
        scattergrams, 58–59
    predictions in, 84–85
    with product function to model
        a situation, 333–34
    with quadratic functions, 438,
        457–67
        differences of quantities, 462
        to find maximum value,
            458–62
        to find minimum value,
            458–60

making predictions with,
    457–58
    with system of quadratic
        equation and another
        equation, 460
    rate of change in, 92–104
        calculating, 92–94
        to find equation of linear
            model, 95–96
        to perform analysis of linear
            model, 96–97
        slope as, 94–95, 98
        two variables that are
            linearly related, 97–98
    with rational functions, 526–38
        distance-speed-time applica-
            tions, 531–33
        mean of quantity, 526–29
        percentage of quantity, 530–31
    with sum function, 322–23
    with systems of linear
        equations, 136–43
        predictions made with, 137–39
        rate of change used to find
            system for modeling,
            138–39
        table of data used to find
            system for modeling,
            136–38
models. *See also* linear models
    defined, 60
    function, to model interest
        problems, 148–49
monomials
    definition of, 316, 327
    dividing, 338–39
    multiplying
        monomial and polynomial,
            327–28
        two monomials, 327
multiplication
    commutative law of, 331, 347
    of complex numbers, 655–57
    of polynomials, 327–37
        binomial conjugates, 331–32
        binomials, 328–31
        vs. factoring, 346
        monomials, 327–28
        trinomials, 346
        two polynomials, 328–29
    of radical expressions, 572–76
    of rational expressions, 491–92
    of two radicals with same/
        different index, 575

natural logarithms, 299–306
    definition of, 299–300
    finding, 300
    properties of, 268–69
        exponential/natural
            logarithmic forms
            property, 299
        to simplify expressions, 302
        to solve equations,
            300–302
negative exponents, 189–90
    definition of, 189
    in denominator, 189
negative self-talk, 41
Newton's law of cooling, 303

nonlinear system of equations, 675–80
  definition of, 675
  elimination used to solve, 676–78
  graphing used to solve, 676, 679
  substitution used to solve, 676
nth term of sequences
  of arithmetic sequence, formula that describes, 619
  definition of, 618
  of geometric sequence, formula that describes, 625

one-solution linear system, 120, 121
one-variable equations involving exponents, 217–18, 279
ordered pairs
  definition of, 7
  satisfying two given equations, 117
ordered triple, 442
output
  definition of, 43
  equation used to find, 79–80
  in function, 43–45
  of quadratic functions, finding, 372
  in Rule of Four, 47–48
  table used to find, 79

parabolas, 319–20
  axis of symmetry of, 320
  drawing families of, 397
  equation of, finding, 446–48
    steps in, 447
    using points that are not y-intercepts, 446–47
    using y-intercept and two other points, 447–48
  to find values of a function, 320
  maximum point of, 320
  minimum point of, 320
  vertex of, 320
  x-intercepts of, 418, 434
parallel lines
  definition of, 21
  slope of, 21–22
percentage formula, 486–87
perfect cube, 562
perfect nth power, 562, 563
perfect square, defined, 414
perfect square trinomial, 330–31
perfect-square trinomial property, 425
perfect-square trinomials, 425–26
  in completing the square, 425–26
  factoring, 425–26
perpendicular lines
  definition of, 22
  slope of, 22
point-slope form, 35, 39–40
polynomial equations, 368–81
  area of rectangular objects, 375–76
  connection between x-intercepts and solutions, 369–70
  cubic equations in one variable, 372–74
  in one variable, solving by graphing, 374
  quadratic equations, 369–72

quadratic function to model a situation, 374–75
  zero factor property, 368
polynomial functions, 316–89
  cubic functions, 321
  definition of, 319
  difference function, 321–23
  function notation, 332
  product function, 332–34
  quadratic functions, 319–20
  sum function, 321–23
polynomials, 316–89
  adding, 318
  binomial conjugates, multiplying, 331–32
  binomials
    factoring, 362–68
    square of, multiplying, 329–31
  coefficient of term in, 317
  definition of, 316
  degree of, 317
  describing, 317
  dividing, 338–45
  factoring, 346–81
    binomials, 362–68
    completely, 351–52
    $vs.$ multiplying, 346
    polynomial with four terms by grouping, 355–56
    strategy, 365–66
    trinomials, 346–60
  like terms in, 317–18
  monomials
    multiplying, 327
    multiplying monomial and polynomial, 327–28
  multiplying, 327–37
    binomial conjugates, 331–32
    monomial and polynomial, 327–28
    monomials, 327
    square of binomial, 329–31
    two polynomials, 328–29
  in one variable, 316–17
    degree of a term in, 317
    descending order of, 316
  subtracting, 318–19
  trinomials, factoring, 346–60
  unlike terms in, 317
power property, 275–79
  comparing with other statements, 279
  of equality, 598
  with exponential models to make estimates, 284–85
  with exponential models to make predictions, 282–84
  for radicals, 566, 573, 575
  to solve logarithmic equations, 294–95, 302
powers
  calculating, 186–87
  counting-number, 316
  cubes in, 187
  definition of, 186
  of i, 659
  perfect nth, 562, 563
  raising a power to, 187, 190, 201
  raising a product to, 187, 190, 201
  raising a quotient to, 187, 190, 201

real-number, 206
  squares in, 187
predictions
  about independent variable, rational models to make, 522–23
  data described in words to make, 84–85
  equation of linear models to make, 81–82
  four-step modeling process to make, 82
  linear models to make, 60–61, 115–16
  modeling with quadratic functions to make, 457–58
  rational models to make, 486–87
  solving a system to make, 137–39
  square root model to make, 568, 606–7
  systems of linear equations to make, 137–39
prime polynomials, 349–50
  definition of, 349
  identifying, 349–50
principal square root, 199
procedures
  describing, 4
  responding to question about, 4–5
product function, 332–34
  definition of, 332
  finding, 333
  using to model a situation, 333–34
product function in multiplying rational expressions, 492
product property
  for exponents, 187, 190, 201
  of logarithms, 292–93
  for radicals, 563, 575
  to simplify square roots, 414
  to solve logarithmic equations, 294–95
  for square roots, 413
products used to find inverse variation constants, 547
pure imaginary number, 420
Pythagorean theorem, 660–67. See also right triangle
  converse of, 664
  definition of, 661
  to find distance, 661–62
  to make estimates about authentic situations, 661–62

quadratic equations, 369–72
  completing the square to solve, 425–31
    of form $ax^2 + bx + c = 0$, 427–29
    of form $x^2 + bx + c = 0$, 426–27
    imaginary-number solutions in, 429
    perfect-square trinomials, 425–26
    steps in, 428
  containing fractions, 371–72

finding x-intercepts of quadratic function, 369
methods used to solve
  comparing, 438
  determining, 436–37
  in one variable, 368–69
  definition of, 368
  factoring, 373
  solution set of, 370
  quadratic formula used to solve, 431–42
    approximate solutions, 434
    definition of, 432
    finding, 431–32
    imaginary-number solutions, 435
    quadratic equations solved with, 431–42
    real-number solutions, 435–36
    x-intercepts, finding, 434
  of quadratic function, finding, 376
  square root property used to solve, 413–24
    of form $(px + q)^2 = k$, 417–18
    of form $a(x - h)^2 + k = p$, 422
    of form $x^2 = k$, where $k < 0$, 421
    of form $x^2 = k$, where $k \geq 0$, 416–17
quadratic formula
  approximate solutions, 434
  definition of, 432
  finding, 431–32
  imaginary-number solutions, 435
  quadratic equations solved with, 431–42
  real-number solutions, 435–36
  x-intercepts, finding, 434
quadratic functions, 319–20, 390–478
  definition of, 319
  domain of, 394–96
  evaluating, 319, 332
  finding, 442–50
  finding equations of, 376
  finding input and output of, 372
  finding x-intercepts of, 369
  graphs of, 319–20 (See also parabolas)
  comparing methods of, 409
  form $f(x) = ax^2$, 391–92
  form $f(x) = ax^2 + bx + c = 0$, 403
  form $f(x) = ax^2 + bx + c$ whose graph has vertex (h, k), 407
  form $f(x) = a(x - h)^2 + k$, 394
  in standard form, 401–13
  in vertex form, 390–401
  to model a situation, 374–75
  modeling with, 438, ⸍ ⁻⁷
  differences of qu
  to find maximu⸍ 458–62
  to find minim⸍ 458–60

quadratic functions (*continued*)
  making predictions with,
    457–58
    with system of quadratic
      equation and another
      equation, 460
  range of, 394–96
  in standard form, 319, 332
  in vertex form, 391–92
  vertex of, 394
  writing, in standard form, 332
quadratic models, 450–57
  choosing points to find, 453
  defined, 374
  equation of, 396, 450–51
  four-step modeling process, 453
  making predictions with,
    418–19, 457–58
  selecting, 452–53
  in standard form, 450–51
  in vertex form, 396–97
quadratic regression curve, 451
quadratic regression equation, 451
qualitative graphs, 1–6
  definition of, 1
  dependent variables in, 2–3
  independent variables in, 2–3
  reading, 1–3
  sketching, 3–5
quantity
  mean of, modeling, 526–29
  modeling with quadratic
    functions to find
    differences of, 462
  percentage of
    modeling, 530–31
    rational models used to
      describe, 486–87
  units of, converting, 495–96
quotient function, 485–86, 494
  definition of, 485
  in dividing rational
    expressions, 494
  finding by multiplying by $\dfrac{LCD}{LCD}$,
    512–15

quotient property
  for exponents, 187, 190, 201
  for radicals, 580–81
  for simplifying radical expres-
    sions, 581
  to solve logarithmic equations,
    294–95, 302
  for square roots, 415

radical conjugates
  definition of, 581
  denominators rationalized
    with, 581–83
radical equations, 593–602. *See
  also* square root equations
  in one variable, solving
  in one variable, 593
  solving, 598–99
radical expressions
  adding, 571–72
  definition of, 561
  in exponential form,
    writing, 562
  ¹ex of, 561

multiplying, 572–76
  performing operations with, 571
  radical, 561
  in radical form, writing, 562
  radical sign in, 561
  radicand in, 561
  rationalizing denominator of,
    415–16
  rationalizing denominators
    of, 579
    by using radical conjugates,
      581–83
  simplifying, 414–16, 562–70,
    573–76
    square of radical expression
      with two terms, 574
    steps in, 566, 576
    by using quotient
      property, 581
  subtracting, 572
radical form, writing radical
  expressions in, 562
radical functions, 561–616
  absolute value function, 590
  adding radical expressions,
    571–72
  definition of, 567
  multiplying radical expressions,
    572–76
  simplifying, 561–70
  square root functions, 586–90
    definition of, 567
    graphing, 567, 586–89
    modeling with, 602–11
    performing operations with,
      589–90
  subtracting radical expressions,
    571–72
radical model, 567–68
  definition of, 567
  predictions made by using, 568
    about independent
      variable, 599
radicals
  combining like, 571
  definition of, 561
  evaluating, 562
  power property for, 566, 573,
    575
  product property for, 563, 575
  quotient property for, 580–81
  with same index,
    multiplying, 575
  simplified, 563
radical sign, 561
radicand, 561, 575
radius of circle, finding, 663–64
range
  definition of, 43
  of exponential function, 210
  graphs used to find, 48
  of linear models, finding, 85
  output in, 43–45
  of quadratic functions,
    394–96
  y-coordinate in, 48
rate of change, 92–104
  average, 92–93
  calculating, 92–94
  constant, 92, 94–97

to find equation of linear
    model, 95–96
  finding, 93–94
  formula for, 93
  increasing and decreasing
    quantities in, 93–94
  to perform analysis of linear
    model, 96–97
  slope as, 94–95, 98
  systems of linear equations
    used in, 138–39
  two variables that are linearly
    related, 97–98
rational equations, 518–27
  in one variable, 518–21
    definition of, 518
    extraneous solutions to, 518
    finding input value, 520–21
    solving, 518–20
  solving formulas involving
    rational expressions, 521
  solving *vs.* simplifying rational
    expressions, 522, 523
rational exponents, 199–205
  cube root in, 199
  definitions of, 199, 200
  principal square root in, 199
  properties of, 201
  simplifying expressions involv-
    ing, 199–200, 201–2
rational expressions
  adding, 499–503, 507
  combining three, 494–95
  complex, simplifying, 510–18
  to convert units of quantities,
    495–96
  definition of, 479–80
  dividing, 493–95
  excluded value of, 482
  in lowest terms, 483
  multiplying, 491–92
  rational equations to solve
    formulas involving, 521
  simplifying, 482–84
    right-hand side of equation,
      483–85
    vs. solving rational equations,
      522, 523
    steps in, 483
  solving formulas involving, 521
  subtracting, 503–7
rational functions, 479–560
  domain of, 480–82
    finding, 481–82
    property for, 481
    vertical asymptotes and,
      484–85, 487
  evaluating, 480
  meaning of, 479–80
  modeling with, 526–38
    distance-speed-time
      applications, 531–33
    mean of quantity, 526–29
    percentage of quantity, 530–31
    percentage formula in, 486–87
    quotient function in, 485–86, 494
    rational models in, 486–87
  rationalizing denominators
    of radical expressions,
      415–16, 579

by using radical conjugates,
    581–83
rational models, 486–87
  definition of, 486
  to make predictions about
    independent variable,
      522–23
  percentage of quantity
    described by, 486–87
ratios
  definition of, 92
  to find direct variation
    constants, 546–47
  in rate of change, 92–98
reading qualitative graphs, 1–3
real-number powers, 206
real-number solutions, 435–36
reciprocal, 493
rectangular objects, area of,
    375–76
reference amplitude, 270
reflection, defined, 210
reflection property, 209–10
regression line, 72
Richter numbers, 270, 271
right triangle, 660–61
  finding length of side of, 661
  hypotenuse of, 660
  legs of, 660–61
rise, 18–21, 23
r percent interest compounded
    annually, 225
run, 18–21, 23

satisfy, definition of, 7
scattergrams
  defined, 59
  in modeling data, 58–59
scientific notation, 192–95
  converting from standard
    decimal notation to,
      194–95
  converting to standard decimal
    notation, 193–94
  defined, 193
sequences. *See also* series
  arithmetic, 617–23
    common difference in, 618
    definition of, 617, 618
    formula of, finding, 618–19
    identifying, 618, 621
    linear functions and, 621
    modeling with, 620–21
    nth term of, formula that
      describes, 619
    term number of, 620
  finite, 617
  geometric, 624–30
    common ratio of, 624
    definition of, 624
    exponential functions
      and, 627
    formula of, finding, 624–25
    identifying, 624, 628
    modeling with, 626–27
    nth term of, formula that
      describes, 625
    term number of, finding,
      625–26
  infinite, 617

nth term
    of arithmetic sequence,
        formula that describes, 619
    definition of, 618
    of geometric sequence,
        formula that describes, 625
    term number of
        in arithmetic sequence,
            finding, 620
        definition of, 618
        in geometric sequence,
            finding, 625–26
series. *See also* sequences
    arithmetic, 630–35
        definition of, 630
        *i*th term of, 630
        modeling with, 633
        sum of, 631–32
        term number of, 630
    geometric, 635–40
        definition of, 635
        *i*th term of, 635
        modeling with, 638
        sum of, 636–38
        term number of, 635
    *i*th term of
        in arithmetic series, 630
        definition of, 630
        in geometric series, 635
    term number of
        in arithmetic series, 630
        definition of, 630
        in geometric series, 635
sign of difference, 322
simplifying
    complex rational expressions,
        510–18
    by multiplying by $\dfrac{\text{LCD}}{\text{LCD}}$, 512–15
        by writing as quotient of
            two rational expressions,
            510–12
    expressions involving
        exponents, 188–89, 190–92
        rational exponents, 199–200,
            201–2
        symbols used in, 191
    logarithmic expression, 302
    quotient of complex numbers,
        657–58
    radical expressions, 414–16,
        562–70, 573–76
        square of radical expression
            with two terms, 574
        steps in, 566, 576
        by using quotient property, 581
    radical functions, 561–70
    radicals, 563
    rational expressions, 482–84
        right-hand side of equation,
            483–85
        vs. solving rational equations,
            522, 523
        steps in, 483
    square of binomial, 329–31
sketching qualitative graphs, 3–5
slope, 17–35
    being vague in describing, 98
    comparing steepness of two
        objects, 17–18

of decreasing lines, 19–20
definition of, 18
formula for, 18–19, 86
in graphs of linear equations,
    28–30
of horizontal lines, 20, 21
of increasing lines, 19–20
of line, finding, 18–20, 26–27
of linear equation of form
    $y = mx + b$, 27–28
of nonvertical lines, 18
of parallel lines, 21–22
of perpendicular lines, 22
as rate of change, 94–95, 98
slope addition property for,
    30–31
of two lines, 20
various, drawing lines with, 31
vertical change property for,
    27–28
of vertical lines, 21
slope formula, 18–19
slope-intercept form
    $(y = mx + b)$
    definition of, 28
    graphs of equations in, 9, 13
    linear equations of, 35–39
    in linear functions, 46–47, 48
solution
    definition of, 7
    of equations, 7
    of linear equations in three
        variables, 442–43
    of linear inequalities in one
        variable, 157–61
    of linear inequalities in two
        variables, 173
    ordered triple as, 442
    of system of linear equations in
        three variables, 443
solution set
    of cubic equation in one vari-
        able, 374
    definition of, 7
    of equations, 7
    of inequality
        interval notation used to
            describe, 159–60
        meaning of, 163
    of linear equations, graphing,
        117–20
    of quadratic equation in one
        variable, 370
    of system of inequalities,
        graphing, 170–71
square of binomial, 329–31
    difference of two squares,
        362–63
    simplifying, 330–31
square root curve, 588. *See also*
        square root functions
    equation of, finding, 603
square root equations in one
        variable, solving, 593–97
    extraneous solutions to,
        593, 599
    general equation, 597
    by graphing, 597
    proposed solutions to,
        checking, 593

squaring property of equality
    in, 593
    steps in, 596
square root functions, 586–90
    equation of, finding, 602–3
    graphing, 586–89
        minimum/maximum point
            of, 587
        three-step method for, 588
        translating horizontally,
            586–88
    performing operations with,
        589–90
    x-intercepts of, 597–98
square root model
    definition of, 568
    equation of, finding, 604–6
    to make estimates, 606–7
    to make predictions, 568, 606–7
square root property
    definition of, 416
    to solve quadratic equations,
        413–24
        of form $(px + q)^2 = k$,
            417–18
        of form $a(x - h)^2 + k = p$,
            422
        of form $x^2 = k$, where $k < 0$,
            421
        of form $x^2 = k$, where $k \geq 0$,
            416–17
square roots
    of negative number, 420
    product property for, 413
    quotient property for, 415
    in rational exponents, 199
    simplifying expressions with,
        414–16
squares in powers, 187
squaring property of equality, 593
standard decimal notation
    converting from scientific
        notation to, 193–94
    converting to scientific
        notation from, 194–95
standard form
    graphing quadratic functions
        in, 401–13
    to find minimum or
        maximum value, 406–9
    by using two symmetric
        points to find vertex,
        401–4
    by using vertex formula to
        find vertex, 404–6
    quadratic functions in, 319, 332
    quadratic models in, 450–51
steepness of two objects, 17–18
substitution in systems of linear
        equations, 125–27, 676
    dependent system, 130–31
    inconsistent system, 130
    steps in, 126
subtraction
    of complex numbers, 655–57
    of polynomials, 318–19
    of radical expressions, 571–72
    of rational expressions, 503–7
        with common denominator,
            503–4

difference function, finding,
    506–7
    with different denominators,
        504–6
    performing operations with
        three rational expressions,
        506
sum
    of arithmetic series, 631–32
        evaluating, 631–32
        finding, 631
        formula for, 631
    of geometric series, 636–38
        evaluating, 636–38
        finding, 636
        formula for, 636
sum function, 297, 321–23
    in addition of rational
        expressions, 502–3
    definition of, 321
    finding, 321–22
    modeling with, 322–23
symmetric points
    definition of, 401
    to find vertex, 401–4
synthetic division, 342–44
    definition of, 342
    performing, 342–43
        when there are missing
            terms, 343–44
systems, difference function used
        to solve, 323
systems of linear equations, 115–85
    dependent, substitution used to
        solve, 130–31
    elimination used to solve, 127–30
        adding left and right sides of
            two equations, 127
        steps in, 128
        system with fractions, 129–30
    five-step problem-solving
        method, 144
    graphs and tables used to solve,
        115–25
        intersection point of graphs
            of two models, 116
        solving system from table of
            solutions of equations, 120
        two linear models used to
            make predictions,
            115–16
    inconsistent, substitution used
        to solve, 130
    interest problems, 147–49
        function model used to
            model, 148–49
        interest from investment, 147
        solving, 147–48
    linear inequalities in one
        variable, 155–66
    linear inequalities in two
        variables, 167–75
    mixture problems, solving,
        149–51
    to model data, 136–43
        rate of change used to find
            system for modeling,
            138–39
        solving a system to make
            predictions, 137–39

systems of linear equations
(*continued*)
   table of data used to find
      system for modeling,
      136–38
   in one variable
      graphing used to solve,
         131–32, 133
      tables used to solve, 132
   predictions made from models
      of, 115–16
   substitution used to solve,
      125–27
      dependent system, 130–31
      inconsistent system, 130
      steps in, 126
   tables used to solve, 120
   techniques of solving,
      comparing, 133
   in two variables, 116–20
      comparing types of, 121
      defined, 116
      definition of, 116
      graphing used to solve, 117–19
      graphs used to solve, 117–19
      ordered pairs satisfying two
         given equations, 117
      solution set of, 117
      types of, 119–21
   value problems, 144–47
      function model used to
         model, 146–47
      solving, 144–46
systems of linear inequalities in
   two variables, 170–71
   estimates made with, 171–73
   graphing solution set of, 170–71
   modeling with, 171–73
   solution of, meaning of, 173

tables
   to find exponential models,
      228–29
   to find system for modeling,
      136–38
   functions described by, 45
   to solve system, 120
term number
   of sequences
      in arithmetic sequence,
         finding, 620
      definition of, 618
      in geometric sequence,
         finding, 625–26
   of series
      in arithmetic series, 630
      definition of, 630
      in geometric series, 635
terms
   coeffeicient of, 317
   degree of, in polynomial in one
      variable, 317
   dividing polynomials with,
      341–42
   like terms
      combining, 317–18
      definition of, 317

lowest, rational expressions
   in, 483
missing
   in division of polynomials,
      341–42
   in synthetic division, 343–44
   in synthetic division of
      polynomials, 343–44
unlike terms, 317
three-part inequalities in one
   variable, 161–62
three-step method
   for graphing quadratic function
      in vertex form, 393
   for graphing square root
      functions, 588
tips for success
   affirmations, 41
   ask questions, 221
   calm down during a test, 304
   choose time and place to
      study, 361
   complete assignment, 323
   complete exercises without
      help, 203
   create example, 448
   create mind map for final
      exam, 607
   cross-checks, 133
   desire and faith, 211–10
   form study group to prepare for
      final exam, 462
   form study team, 163
   get in touch with classmates, 65
   instructor's office hours,
      using, 23
   make changes, 196
   math journal, 87
   plan for final exam, 548
   practice exams, 50
   reread a problem, 397
   retake quizzes and exams, 584
   review material, 263
   review notes, 335
   scan test problems, 377
   show what you know, 230
   solve problems, 430
   stick with it, 487
   study in test environment, 99
   study time, 14
   study with classmate, 139
   take a break, 280
   take notes, 152
   use 3-by-5 cards, 568
   verify your work, 74
   visualize, 121
   write summary, 507
total-value formula, 144
TRACE on graphing calculator,
   11, 36
translating graphs, 392–94
   horizontally, 392–93, 586–88
   vertically, 392
triangle, right. *See* right triangle
trinomials
   completely factoring
      polynomial, 351–52

definition of, 327
   factored polynomial of, 347
factoring
   form $x^2 + bx + c$, 346–55
   GCF of polynomial, 350–51
   by grouping, 359–60
   vs. multiplying, 346
   perfect square trinomial,
      330–31
   prime polynomials, 349–50
   by trial and error, 356–58
   trinomials with negative
      constant terms, 347, 348–49
   trinomials with positive
      constant terms,
         346, 347, 348
   trinomial with two
      variables, 349

unit analysis
   definition of, 96
   of linear models, 96–98
unit ratio
   definition of, 92
   in rate of change, 92–98
units of quantities, converting,
   495–96
unlike terms in polynomials, 317

value problems, 144–47
   function model used to model,
      146–47
   solving, 144–46
variables
   approximately exponentially
      related, 224
   dependent
      in qualitative graphs, 2–3
   exponentially related, 224
   graphs of linear equations in
      two, 8, 13
   independent
      in qualitative graphs, 2–3
   linearly related
      approximately, 60
   rate of change and, 97–98
variation
   constants, 546–47
   direct, 539–42
   inverse, 542–46
vertex
   to find maximum or minimum
      value, 406–9
   of parabola, 320
   of quadratic functions, 394
   vertex formula to find, 404–6
   x-coordinate of, 402
vertex form
   graphing quadratic functions
      in, 390–401
   domain and range, 394–96
   of form $f(x) = ax^2$, 391–92
   reflecting graph across x-axis,
      391–92
   stretching graph
      vertically, 391
   three-step method of, 393
   translating graphs, 392–94

quadratic models in
   finding, 396–97
   making predictions with,
      418–19
vertex formula, 404–6
   definition of, 405
   to find vertex, 404–6
   to graph quadratic
      function, 406
vertical asymptotes, 484–85, 487
vertical axis, 2
vertical distance, 17–18
vertical lines, 12–13
vertical line test, 45, 48–49

words to find exponential
   models, 227

x-axis
   in graphing square root
      functions, 587
   as horizontal asymptote in
      exponential functions,
      209–10
   reflecting graph across, 391–92
x-coordinates, 7
   in domain, 48
   to find x-intercept of, 10–12
x-intercepts
   to find x-coordinate, 10–12
   of functions, factors of
      expression and, 353
   of parabolas, 418, 434
   quadratic formula in
      finding, 434
   of quadratic functions,
      finding, 369
   solutions and, connection
      between, 369
   of square root functions, 597–98

y-coordinates, 7
   to find y-intercept of, 10–12
   in range, 48
y-intercepts
   of exponential functions,
      graphing, 208–9
   in finding equation of
      parabolas, 446–48
      using points that are not y-
         intercepts, 446–47
      using y-intercept and two
         other points, 447–48
   to find linear equations, 28
   to find y-coordinate, 10–12
   to graph linear equations, 30
   and one other point used to
      find equations, 603–4
$y = mx + b$. *See* slope-intercept
   form ($y = mx + b$)

ZDecimal on graphing calculator,
   8, 10, 29
zero as exponent, 189
ZSquare on graphing calculator,
   9, 10, 11, 27, 39
ZStandard on graphing calculator, 9, 10, 11, 13, 27, 39